# HARLEY HAHN'S

## LIST OF 25 THINGS TO DO WHEN YOU SHOULD BE WORKING

**1) ART GALLERIES AND EXHIBITS: Art Museums and Exhibits**

Lose yourself in the world of art by visiting an online museum.

*(See page 29.)*

**2) BIZARRE: Death Clock**

See how long you have left to live, and watch the seconds tick away.

*(See page 59.)*

**3) CARS AND TRUCKS: Car and Truck Prices**

Get the lowdown on your dream car, and find out exactly what the *dealer* pays.

*(See page 92.)*

**4) COMICS: Daily Comics**

Read your favorite comic strip without having to buy the newspaper.

*(See page 106.)*

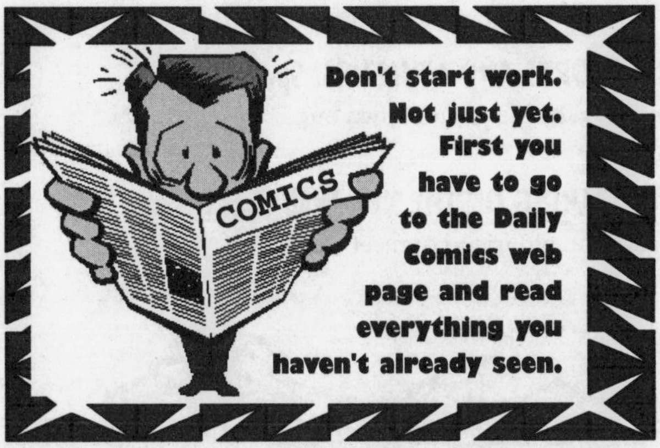
COMICS
Don't start work. Not just yet. First you have to go to the Daily Comics web page and read everything you haven't already seen.

**5) CONTESTS: Sweepstakes and Contests**

See if today is your lucky day. Enter a contest.

*(See page 151.)*

Today may be your lucky day, but there is only one way to find out. Connect to the Sweepstakes and Contests site, and see what destiny has in store for you.

**6) COOKING AND RECIPES: Virtual Kitchen**

Find a great recipe for your next dinner party.

*(See page 157.)*

**7) COOL, BUT USELESS: Paper Dolls**

Play dress-up with a Net doll.

*(See page 161.)*

**8) FASHION AND CLOTHING: Lumière**

Stay fashionable. Be current. Know your clothes.

*(See page 280.)*

**9) FUN: Diaries and Journals**

Peek into people's diaries.

*(See page 314.)*

**10) FUN: Electronic Postcards**

Send an electronic postcard to someone you love.

*(See page 314.)*

**11) GEOGRAPHY: Interactive World of Maps**

Find the location of anything, anywhere.

*(See page 350.)*

**12) HUMOR AND JOKES: Cruel Site of the Day**

Be irreverent: celebrate the peculiar and poke fun at the ordinary.

*(See page 413.)*

**13) INTERNET DEVICES, GIZMOS AND THINGAMAJIGS: Cameras on the Net**

Look at what's happening in the rest of the world.

*(See page 424.)*

Cameras
on the Net
Now, for a change, you get to be Big Brother. Use one of the cameras on the Net to see what someone else is doing.

**14) JOURNALISM AND MEDIA: Email the Media**

Speak out. Email a letter to the editor.

*(See page 443.)*

**Visit my web page at http://www.harley.com/**

**15) LITERATURE: COLLECTIONS: Electronic Books**

Read a book for free, right at your computer.

*(See page 488.)*

**16) MAGAZINES: Magazine Collections**

Read real articles from real magazines. (Really.)

*(See page 503.)*

***There is always something to read on the Net. Check the Magazine Collections and see what's new on the Internet newsstand.***

**17) MISCHIEF: Practical Jokes**

Don't get mad. Find out how to get even.

*(See page 539.)*

**18) MOVIES: Girls on Film**

See what the girls have to say about the movies.

*(See page 556.)*

## Girls on Film

Before you spend your time and money on a new movie, see what Lise, Sibyl, Andrea and Clare have to say about it: check with Girls on Film.

**19) NEWS: World News Sources**

Read the news *before* it gets into the newspaper.

*(See page 602.)*

**20) PEOPLE: FAMOUS AND INTERESTING: Celebrity Addresses**

Send email to your favorite celebrity.

*(See page 641.)*

**21) ROMANCE: Love Test**

Don't trust to chance. Take the love test and know for sure.

*(See page 721.)*

## *Love and Romance*

Where would we be without love and romance? Probably at home in front of the TV set. At least with romance we can be in front of the TV with someone to keep us company. As a Net person, you never need to worry about getting your share. There are lots of resources for the romantically inclined (and even for the romantically challenged).

But remember, even in a Harley Hahn book, "Romance" comes before "Sex".

**22) SOFTWARE: Cool Tool of the Day**

Try out a cool new program for free.

*(See page 751.)*

**23) SPORTS AND ATHLETICS: Sports News**

See how the big game turned out.

*(See page 771.)*

**24) TALKING ON THE NET: Web Chat Rooms**

Talk to an old friend or meet a new one.

*(See page 787.)*

Talk, joke, meet people, ask questions, flirt, give advice, make friends, argue, be intimate, show off, be serious, be goofy, pretend, tell the truth, listen, play games.

**Web chat rooms.**

**24 hours a day.**

**Free.**

**Now.**

**25) TELEVISION: TV Schedules**

Find out what's on TV anywhere in the world.

*(See page 801.)*

# HARLEY HAHN'S

# INTERNET & WEB YELLOW PAGES

## 1997 EDITION

## ABOUT THE AUTHOR

Harley Hahn is an internationally recognized writer, analyst and consultant. He is the author of eighteen books on various topics, including the best-selling *The Internet Complete Reference* and *The Internet Yellow Pages*, and the highly regarded *Assembler Inside & Out*. His Unix books include *Unix Unbound* and *Harley Hahn's Student Guide to Unix*.

Hahn has a degree in mathematics and computer science from the University of Waterloo, Canada; and a graduate degree in computer science from the University of California at San Diego. Before becoming a professional writer, he studied medicine at the University of Toronto Medical School.

Hahn enjoys writing computer books because "I get to sleep in, and I like telling people what to do."

Hahn does not live in a converted farmhouse in Connecticut with his wife, three children, and a Labrador retriever named Rolf. Nor does he commute frequently to New York.

His favorite pajamas are blue.

# HARLEY HAHN'S
# INTERNET & WEB YELLOW PAGES
## 1997 EDITION

**Harley Hahn**

**Osborne/McGraw-Hill**

Berkeley New York St. Louis San Francisco Auckland Bogotá Hamburg London
Madrid Mexico City Milan Montreal New Delhi Panama City Paris São Paulo
Singapore Sydney Tokyo Toronto

**HARLEY HAHN'S**

# INTERNET & WEB YELLOW PAGES

**1997 EDITION**

**OSBORNE/MCGRAW-HILL**
**2600 TENTH STREET**
**BERKELEY**
**CALIFORNIA 94710**
**U.S.A.**

This is not a commercial yellow pages book. Please do not write asking how you can buy an ad in this book. There are no commercial ads. In addition, please do not write us asking Harley to mention your new web site in the next edition. Thanks.

For information on translations or book distributors outside the U.S.A., or to arrange bulk purchase discounts for sales promotions, premiums, or fundraisers, please contact Osborne/**McGraw-Hill** at the above address.



1234567890 DOC 9987

ISBN 0-07-882258-0



**Publisher**
Brandon A. Nordin

**Editor-in-Chief**
Scott Rogers

**Project Editors**
Janet Walden
Heidi Poulin
Cynthia Douglas

**Copy Editor**
Lunaea Hougland

**Proofreader**
Pat Mannion

**Series Design**
Peter F. Hančík

**Computer Designer**
Peter F. Hančík

**Illustrator**
Leslee Bassin

**To Randy and Sheryl**

**and to Melissa and Anne.**

**—Harley Hahn**

# List of Categories

# Table of Contents

# Introduction

*An unspecified safe-location,*
*somewhere in the Third District, Western Region*
*December 14, 2052*

"Have you got it?"

"Yes, right here. Did anyone see you come?"

"No way. I changed autobots four times. Then I walked the rest of the way with an activated scan shield. If anyone was monitoring me I would have known."

"Wasn't that taking a chance? What if the MFS had picked up your rad reading?"

"Well, they didn't, because I'm here. Do you want the thing or not?"

"Yes, of course I do. Can I listen to it?"

"Sure. Let me plug it into an infoport. What are you going to do with an old datacube anyway? This thing must be over fifty years old."

"You don't know much about the Slicks do you?"

"Slicknets?"

"Same thing. Well, my friends and I are organizing an anti-MFS offensive to take back the Net. We are using a Slick which is completely unauthorized. If we get caught we'll be closed down in an hour. But we figure the main reason the MFS has so much control is because people don't really understand the Net. If they did, they wouldn't dare let the MFS get away with what they do."

"So what does this speech have to do with it?"

"Do you know what next week is?"

"No."

"It's the hundredth anniversary of the birth of Harley Hahn."

"Really?"

"Yes. But ever since the Reorganization, it's so hard to get old books that hardly anyone has actually ever seen a real Harley Hahn book. This speech is part of a talk Hahn gave at the UCLA School of Business in the spring of 1996. In the talk, Hahn explained the future of the Net and what he thought it would become. We—my friends and I—feel that if people were to hear the speech, they would have a feeling for what the Net could be without the MFS and, well... we're hoping to start a rebellion. That's why I asked you to break into the archives and steal this particular datacube."

"How could this be a real speech from 1996? Did someone record it?"

"No. It's a synjob. One of the students took notes. Just before the Information Decree, she hid them in a box where they were discovered a few years later. Someone reconstructed part of the speech and used a synspeak module with Hahn's voice. Go ahead, plug the thing in. I've never actually heard it myself. I know it's not the whole thing, but I'm not sure how much actually survived."

*"...evolution takes place in two ways. Biologically, cells evolve into more complex organisms, through fish, amphibians, reptiles and finally birds and mammals. However, as a species, human beings have stopped evolving biologically.*

*"But that doesn't mean evolution has stopped. Rather, once it reaches a certain point, evolution switches from being biological to being social. This started to happen to us about 25,000 years ago. However, it wasn't until post-Industrial Revolution information technology began to develop that our social evolution really became noticeable.*

*"With the telegraph, then the telephone, radio, television and satellites, the rate at which information flowed from one place to another became faster and faster.*

*"This ever-increasing information flow had an enormous influence on our social evolution as a species. The very fabric of our society began to change. And then we built the Net.*

*"What we now call the Net started as a small collection of computers connected together. But within ten years, that collection had grown to huge proportions and then, about the mid-1990s, something changed. Perhaps it was a critical mass of some type, but once enough people start getting connected, the thing that we now call the Net was formed.*

*"I want to be sure you understand this. The Net is not a computer network. It is nothing less than a being in its own right. The fact is, the Net is an independent lifeform. However, it is unlike any lifeform we have ever seen.*

*"The Net has four main components that combine in a way we still don't understand. These components are information, computers, connections and people.*

*"By information, I mean the vast amount of data that is available all over the Net. There is so much information on the Net that no one understands it. No one even understands how much information actually exists.*

*"The computers are of several types. You and I use computers to access the Net, but there are also a vast number of machines that*

*are working on their own to keep things running. Day and night, these computers, which are very much a part of the Net, work with only minimal help from us.*

*"The connections are the lines of transmission between all the computers. For example, when you use a computer to access the Net, your machine is connected to a host computer maintained by your Internet service provider. That machine is connected in a network which itself is connected to a larger part of the Net.*

*"Finally, a most important part of the Net is provided by the people who use it. Whenever you are connected, part of you merges with the Net itself. The Net can make use of part of your mind. When you design a web page or create a program to share on the Net, your efforts are part of the Net, even when you are not connected.*

*"The Net is a giant, amorphous organism that is always moving, creating, problem solving and organizing. In fact, I believe that the Net is involved in a great many activities that you and I don't understand. Perhaps we aren't capable of understanding what the Net is doing any more than a bee can understand the purpose of a beehive, or an ant can understand an ant hill.*

*"The point I want you to appreciate is that the Net, although it exists on its own, lives in cooperation with humans beings. Not with individual people, but with the human species as a whole.*

*"There are many people who are looking outward for signs of life elsewhere in the universe, life that is similar to the biological life here on Earth. Well, there is a type of life that is not biological, and the Net is the first example that I know of.*

*"I mean that literally. The Net is alive according to any definition of 'life' you wish to use. We helped create it, but now it's on its own. Human beings are not alone. We have the Net to help us, connect us, and—in the very best of ways—to use us.*

*"You know, we made a mistake. We assumed that life could only be biological. And, like the bees and ants, we didn't conceive of a lifeform that was a giant step larger than ourselves.*

*"In a way, we have also been blinded by our own biology. We assumed that if other life exists in the universe it would be like us, or at least similar enough to us to communicate. I feel it is far more likely that alien life will resemble the Net more than it resembles human beings. Indeed, there is no reason not to assume that the universe is populated by Net-like objects, each of which consists of information, computing machines, connections and a large number intelligent 'cells'.*

*"You have to wonder what compelled us to spend so much time and money in recent years to create the Net? My answer is that we are compelled to do so in order to fulfill our destiny. However, for what comes next, we must be part of a Net; individual human beings, even groups of humans, can only go so far.*

*"To me, it is clear that the Net is the next step in evolution. Moreover, if life is found elsewhere, I do not think it will be found by individual humans. The Net will grow until it becomes mature enough, and then it will reach out and find others of its kind.*

*"Whether or not we will realize when that happens, I do not know. We already do not understand most of what the Net does. However, what I can tell you is that the Net, by its nature, looks after humanity. The Net is our best friend: it connects our separate economies and social systems in such a way that war will soon be unlikely. I believe it won't be long before it just won't be economically feasible to do anything but cooperate with one another.*

*"All of this, of course, is on a grand level. In day-to-day events, I suppose human nature is not going to change. However, we are finally part of something larger than ourselves. And, as one cell to a group of cells, I can tell you that I like the experience. And, if you look around, you will see that just about everyone else does as well.*

*"In less than a hundred years, there will not be anyone alive who can remember a time before the Net. Long before then, life will be a lot different and—if I am correct—a lot better.*

*"We have finally begun to fulfill our biological destiny."*

## INTRODUCTION TO THE THIRD EDITION

At 10:30 AM, December 21, 2022, on my 70th birthday, I woke up and I Remembered. I spell the word "Remembered" with a capital "R" because the memory that returned to me was of great import.

It was thus:

On December 5, 1969 (sixteen days before my 17th birthday), the first wide area network connection among multiple computers was completed. The project was funded by the Advanced Research Projects Agency (ARPA), a part of the Department of Defense in what was then called the United States.

The planners at ARPA had decided to fund the development of a network that could connect distant computers. They wanted to design the system in such a way that, if part of the network were to be destroyed (say, by a nuclear bomb), the rest of the network would still work. The work began on September 25, 1968, with the first planning session at the Stanford Research Institute. A little over one year later, on November 21, 1969, the first two special-purpose communication computers, called IMPS (Interface Message Processors), were connected together. (IMP #1 was in Los Angeles at UCLA. IMP #2 was in Menlo Park, California, at the Stanford Research Institute.)

Two weeks later, on Thursday, December 5, four IMPs were connected to form the first wide area computer network in the history of mankind. In addition to the IMPs in Los Angeles and Menlo Park, there was one at U.C. Santa Barbara and one at the University of Utah.

In one moment, as a switch closed, electrical signals jumped from one computer to another, and the world was changed forever. These four computers formed the beginning of the Arpanet, which within a few years developed into the Internet, the ancestor of the Net.

The Net. A global communication organism spanning the Earth. In your time (the mid-1990s) the Net is still small. According to what I can remember, as you read this (somewhere around 1996 by my calculations) the Net has only several million computers and not much more than 20 million people. But within a decade, the Net will expand, and fragment, and expand some more until, well... I seem to be drifting from the main idea here.

The point is that, in late 1968, I heard about the beginning of the Arpanet on my birthday (December 21) and immediately had a feeling that this new computer "network" was something important. I was still in high school, but I was taking the first computer course ever offered in my area. (The teacher had studied "computers" for two months during the previous summer.)

As it happened, December 21 was not only my birthday, but the last day of school before the winter vacation and, that evening, some friends took me to a nightclub to celebrate. And it was there that I met The Great Mephisto.

The Great Mephisto was a stage hypnotist. I remember very little about him except that he had long black hair, a straggly beard, and talked in a strange, unidentifiable Eastern European accent. Indeed, I remember barely nothing at all about that night. Evidently, The Great Mephisto hypnotized me and left me with what he called a post-hypnotic suggestion. The idea was that I was to write a letter to myself, seal it in a secret place, and forget about it for exactly 54 years. On that same day, 54 years later, I was to remember the letter, find the place where it was hidden, take it out and read it.

And that is why, at 10:30 AM, on December 21, 2022, the day of my 70th birthday, I woke up, and I Remembered: I remembered writing the letter. I remembered where I hid it. (And I even remembered The Great Mephisto.)

Where did I hide the letter? I hid it in one of my old high school textbooks, which I had carefully preserved for so many years. (The book, by the way, was *Cours Moyen de Français*.) Imagine my excitement as I recalled events more than 50 years distant. Imagine my curiosity as, with trembling fingers, I retrieved the book from my personal storage area and opened it looking for the letter.

And imagine my amazement when I carefully opened the pages of 54-year-old paper and started to read about the Arpanet.

You see, for a reason I still can't explain, I had guessed that this new "computer network" was something important. And I had decided to write down some of the particulars (which is why, today, I am able to recall so many of the details).

As I read the letter today, it is, to my ancient and practiced eye, a study in immaturity and raw construction. However (and this is why I am telling you all of this), there was one thing I had anticipated correctly. I conjectured that if the new Arpanet were to become important, people would soon forget the events of the surrounding time and lose their historical perspective. To remedy this, I enclosed a summary of the important events of the day: what was happening in the news, and so forth.

Little did I realize how important all this would be. You see, ever since the Information Decree of 1999, the free access to information has been manipulated and controlled. Last year at this time, I was allowed to write a short note and send it through a Temporal Gateway to 1994. This, of course, was a highly unusual occurrence. At the time, I had the blessing of the Microsoft Friendship Society and the cooperation of the authorities.

Since then, the Slicknets have started to expand, and the Underground has become much better organized. In just 12 months, the strength of the MFS has begun to attenuate noticeably—something which I would not have believed when I wrote the first note.

Still, access to a Temporal Gateway is almost impossible to find and, to send this note to myself (in 1995), I had to break a lot of rules and bribe more than a few people to look the other way. I can't explain the details, because I need to hurry. I must get this into the transport chamber before it is too late. However, what I am trying to do is send this note to myself, back in late 1995, to print in one of my books.

I am doing this because I have come to realize why the MFS was able to grow so strong: instead of trying to control the flow of information (a more or less impossible task), they decided to control the *tools* people used to access the Net. And having done this, they were able to shape events so as to disconnect us from our past.

As odd as this sounds, by restricting our access to the details of recent history, the MFS was able to convince us that our likes, dislikes, preferences and antipathies were in harmony with their own. Although this may be hard for you to believe, very little of late twentieth-century life before 1998 was preserved. And, since then, the records have been changed so many times as to render them unreliable.

So, when a fortuitous concatenation of circumstances found me in procession of some historical details of the days of the original Arpanet, I felt compelled to write them down and do my best to transport them to a time before the Information Decree where they might be published. Although I can't take the time to explain it to you now, if you retain a understanding of what is important in your lifetime and how it connected to what everyone else is doing, the power of an organization like the MFS is greatly diminished.

I don't know if this message will ever make it back to late 1995, and I don't know if it will ever be published. But I do know that I have to try. So, at this point, I thank you for indulging an old man in his rambling, and I present some excerpts from the original letter I wrote myself, some 54 years to this very day.

*Harley Hahn*
*December 21, 2022*
*Third District, Western Region*

*...but perhaps the most important occurrence of recent time was the connection of four computers into a "network". I have heard of computers being connected (I think), but what makes this such an unusual experiment is the computers are far apart. I can't help but feel this is an important event. Of course, there probably won't be enough computers in the world to make much of a network, but, still, it's an intriguing idea...*

*...important to put this all in perspective. To do so, I will tell you a bit of what is going on right now. By the time you read this (that is, by the time I read this in 54 years), most of the details will probably have passed from memory.*

*The same day the four computers were connected into a network found the United States knee-deep in the Vietnam War. President Nixon says he cannot stop until we achieve "peace with honor". What a strange concept! A couple of weeks ago an army captain denied any knowledge or responsibility for last year's massacre in My Lai. Still, the Department of Defense (the same department that paid for connecting the four computers!) has admitted that someone slaughtered hundreds of Vietnamese civilians 19 months ago. No one really knows what happened, but peace with honor seems a long way off.*

*In the meantime, thousands of young men continue to die in the far-off steamy jungle, thousands of miles from home. Still, many of the countries in the world, especially the underdeveloped countries, are becoming Communist at an alarming rate, and I don't know what to make of it. The people at home are massively polarized. While the hawks adamantly support the war, the doves are protesting. About a month ago, 250,000 people protested in Washington, the largest anti-war demonstration ever in the U.S. capital. Vice President Agnew called the protesters "anarchists and ideological eunuchs". Referring to the liberal news people, Agnew said that "a spirit of national masochism prevails, encouraged by an effete corps of impudent snobs who characterize themselves as intellectuals." (Most everyone I know thinks he and Nixon are jerks. Still, they are the President and Vice President of the United States, and I guess they couldn't have gotten elected if they didn't have some intelligence and integrity.)*

*Speaking of protesters, hippies seem to be taking over the world (or at least the part of it that is under 30 years old). Four months ago, over 400,000 people traveled to Bethel, New York, for Woodstock: "four days of peace and music". Far out. I wish I could have gone. It seems that everything these days is sex, drugs and music. (I can't wait to get to college!)*

*And yet, something seems to be changing. On December 6, at a concert in Tracy, California—featuring the Rolling Stones, Jefferson Airplane and the Grateful Dead—some Hells Angels stabbed someone (while the Stones were singing "Sympathy for the Devil", actually).*

*In the Middle East, things are as bad as ever. On the same day the computers were being connected, Syria released two Israeli passengers from a plane that had been hijacked last August. In return, Israel had to trade 13 Arab prisoners. Three days later, the Israelis and the Syrians fought for an hour on the Golan Heights. And even within the Arab world, things are unsettled. Saudi Arabia is still fighting with South Yemen, and general confusion and misunderstanding are the rule rather than the exception. Interestingly enough, a few days ago the U.S. House of Representatives just passed the smallest foreign aid bill since World War II.*

*And what else? Well, one of my teachers was saying that the price of gold just dropped to $35 an ounce (although I don't understand what all the fuss is about). And there is something called "Women's Liberation" starting. I don't know a lot about it. Seems like a bunch of misfit women complaining. I guess nothing will come of it.*

*Anyway, that's all for now. I have to finish this letter and hide it.*

*But I can't get those computers out of my mind. I keep wondering if it means anything important. Maybe by the time I read this letter again, I'll know if I was right.*

*Harley Hahn*
*December 21, 1969*

## INTRODUCTION TO THE SECOND EDITION

If all this works out the way I hope, you will be reading this back in 1995. That is, I will receive this message from myself, sometime in late 1994, just in time to get it to the printer to be included in the second edition.

Wait a minute. Maybe I should take a moment to explain, because if you haven't heard of the Temporal Gateway—and how could you?—you probably haven't the foggiest idea what I am talking about.

Let me start from the beginning. I sent this message to myself from the year 2021, in order that it be included in the second edition of *The Internet Yellow Pages*. No, wait, that's not the beginning. I guess the beginning was in 2017, when T.L. Nipper figured out how to build the Temporal Gateway into the past.

No, wait, that's not really the beginning. The real beginning would be in the late 1990s when the Internet broke up into pieces and what came to be called the Net (or more formally, the People's Net) emerged as the organized successor to the free non-commercial information network.

Does that help? No, I guess this is all a hopeless muddle. You see, I did write some Internet books at one time, way back in the mid-1990s, but that was about 25 years ago and things have changed a lot. I am not sure how to explain it so you can understand. So many of the New Words don't even exist in 1995; I wouldn't even know where to start.

How about this: it happened that in 2017 a genius named T.L. Nipper figured out how to send information into the past. Like most people, I don't understand the details—I think it has something to do with neutrinos and tachyons—but the important thing is the process is only partially dependable and highly restricted by the MFS. Moreover, it takes an enormous amount of energy just to send a few characters.

To transmit this introduction, for example, consumed the equivalent of a month's energy allotment for the entire Western Region (what used to be California and parts of Nevada and Oregon). In fact, if it wasn't that the Governor of the Continental Fusion Project agreed to cooperate, I would never have been able to send this message at all.

Anyway, this all has to do with the 50th anniversary of what used to be called the Internet, and some researcher in the Information Division of the MFS discovered the date and thought it would be a good idea to send a message into the past—to celebrate, so to speak. (Ironically, no one really knows if it is exactly 50 years because, these days, such details are mostly forgotten. However, the MFS thinks it is close enough.)

I don't know how they did it and what strings they had to pull, but somehow they got the CFP to cooperate and they were able to set up a Temporal Gateway just long enough to send a message back to 1994. And since I was the author of some old-time Internet books, they asked me to write the message.

The deal was I could write anything I wanted, which would then be sent back 25 years into the past—November 1994, actually—to myself. And, if it all worked, the message from 2021 would suddenly appear in my electronic mailbox back in 1994. The intention is that I would send a message suitable for the introduction of one of my books.

The trouble is, once you send something, it generates what is called an "alternate reality", so that you don't get to see the results of what you send. Thus, I have no way of knowing whether or not this message got through. But if it did, and you are reading this in 1995, at least you will know that it worked.

So, having explained all of that, what do I want to tell you?

Well, to start, I should tell you that the Net is now considered to be the most significant invention of the 20th century. However, it wasn't until the early 2000s that it became apparent just how important the Net actually was. Unfortunately, the real nature of the Net had been completely misunderstood until this time, and just about nobody anticipated what would happen. In fact, until the Information Decree of 1999, most of what was on the Net was highly disorganized and left up to individual preference.

Perhaps another thing I should mention is what we now call the Net (in 2021) is really nothing like the old Internet, although there are a few similarities. We can access information just about anywhere we go, and the speed is so fast as to be unnoticeable. We can view and transmit with ease, and public access (to the Pubnet portion anyway) is universal.

The trouble is, everything is managed and organized and... well... boring. You see, in the olden days (as you are reading this), the Net was not really run by anyone and was poorly organized. Of course, this meant there were problems, but there was also an enormous amount of personal freedom. This freedom meant that anyone who knew how could create and broadcast information. As I write this, such facilities are completely unknown.*

The point is, you happen to be living at a time when you have enormous opportunity. The Net as you know it is not going to last all that long, but, while it does, you will have a chance to *participate* in way that never existed until the 1990s and certainly does not exist today.

If I remember correctly, back in 1995 you had just about total freedom to send out whatever information you wanted. I urge you to not lose sight of the importance of this capability. I keep thinking that if things had gone otherwise, we might not have had the Information Decree and the Microsoft Friendship Society might never have had... well, that's neither here nor there and, as the saying goes, you can't change the past.

I guess what I really want to tell you is the Net as you perceive it is a temporary resource, and you should enjoy and appreciate it while you can. If this message did get through, and you are really reading this in the second edition of *The Internet Yellow Pages*, I urge you buy the book and spend some time exploring. Nothing lasts forever, and some things end all too soon.

And, oh yes... have fun. Soon you will need a permit.

*Harley Hahn*
*December 21, 2021*
*Third District, Western Region*

---

* On the official Net, that is. There are rumors of underground Slicknets, but, like most people, I have never seen one.

## INTRODUCTION TO THE FIRST EDITION

This book will change the way you think about the world.

Even more important, this book will change the way you think about people and how we exist as a species.

How can this be? After all, this book is really just a large catalog, and what could be so important about a catalog?

Well, take a look at the list of categories, and you will see that virtually every important type of human activity is represented. Indeed, this book contains descriptions of thousands of separate items, grouped into well over 150 different categories.

The importance of all this is not so much in the details, but in the fact that it even exists at all. Not long ago, most of what you see in this book had not yet been created. A few years ago, none of it existed. But what does it all mean to *you*?...

Imagine yourself exploring. You walk for days through hot steamy jungles, you climb over rocky hills and through canyons; you drag yourself across an endless arid plain until, one day, you look at the horizon and see what looks like a city. As you approach, you see that it is not really a city, but—whatever it is—it is vast beyond description: more buildings, vehicles, works of art, and so on, than you have ever seen or even imagined.

You spend many hours exploring, always finding something new, something challenging, and something delightful. Being a stranger, you feel confused and you spend much of your time wandering haphazardly. Once in a while you see a bit of a pattern and, for an instant, you make some sense out of the immediate neighborhood. But for the most part, you wander from place to place in a cloud of distraction and fascination. What makes it all so frustrating is you get the feeling that everything you see is part of something very large you just can't understand.

One day, you happen upon a stranger who looks like he knows his way around; at least he seems familiar with the surroundings.

You ask him, how do you find your way?.

He shrugs. You'll get used to it.

But, you ask, why is this all here?

I don't know, he says, and he starts to wander away.

Wait, you call after him, where can I get a map?

No such thing, he answers over his shoulder.

But can't you help me at all?

He turns around and looks at you with a gleam in his eye and a funny half smile on his face. Clearly, he knows something that you don't. Something important.

This place, he gestures widely, is only a few years old. In fact, you could travel for days and almost everything you'd see would be less than a year old. You will see new places almost everywhere you look and, every so often, you will notice that old ones have disappeared. You turn around, and when you turn back it's changed—larger, more complicated, more... well, it's hard to explain. Like I said, you'll get used to it.

But don't be confused, he continues. The meaning in what you see is not about the structures or the vehicles. It's not about the art or the beauty, or pleasure or truth or good or bad. It's about people and what they have created. People working together and by themselves.

You will notice that wherever you go, you will never see another person (I know this to be a fact, and I have been here as long as anyone). However, you can talk to other people whenever you want, so you will never be lonely. No matter who you are, no matter how individual your desires and your preferences, there are people just like you here somewhere.

So where are you? Nobody really knows. The important thing is we are all here together. We are all connected. We all share. We all belong, especially those of us who have nowhere else to go. And the best thing is you can come here whenever you want. No one is ever turned away.

Personally, I don't really understand why this place is so important. Most of us just move around from place to place, doing whatever we feel like. Still, just be glad that you are here at all. As I say, most of this is only a few years old and you are among the first.

But wait, you say. You told me I would never actually see anyone. What about you? I can see you.

He looks at you for a long moment.

You only *think* you see me. I don't really exist. Anyway, for what it's worth, there is a map of sorts. Don't lose it and you can take it with you wherever you go.

He points behind you to a single piece of paper lying on the ground. You turn around to pick it up, and by the time you turn back he is gone. You look down. In the center of an otherwise blank piece of paper, is a big "X" and the words "You are here."

You stuff the paper into your pocket and start walking. After a few minutes, you turn around and gasp. Behind you is a large sign. It must have been there all the time, how could you have missed it? Okay, you say to yourself, I may not know where I am, or why I am here, or what anyone is really doing, but now at least, I know the name of this place. For the sign says:

**Welcome to the Net.**

# The Net and This Book

## WHAT DO YOU NEED TO KNOW TO USE THIS BOOK?

To use this book, you need to have access to the Net, and you need to know how to use the Net. I explain both these topics in another one of my books, *The Internet Complete Reference*. (The book is published by Osborne McGraw-Hill. Be sure to get the second edition. The ISBN is 0-07-882138-X.)

If you do not as yet have Net access, start with that book. Read Chapters 1, 2 and 3 for the basic concepts. If you do not already have a computer, Chapter 4 explains what you need and what to buy. Chapter 5 describes the rest of what you need to know about connecting to the Internet: what type of modem to get (or ISDN), and how to choose an Internet service provider.

Once you have Internet access, you need to master the skills necessary to use the Net. In practice, this means learning how to use the various types of Internet resources, all of which are different. The table at the bottom of this page shows the various resources. The chapter numbers show which part of *The Internet Complete Reference, Second edition*, explains that resource. For a quick introduction to all the resources, see Chapter 3.

People often ask, how much do I really need to learn? There are two answers—one bad and one good—to that question. The bad answer is:

> You do not need to know how to use everything. You only need to learn how to use the resources that you are interested in.

The good answer is a lot more realistic:

> You will likely become interested in all the resources, so you really do have to know how to use everything. You will miss out on a lot if all you know how to do is use your mouse to click on web pages.

## CENSORSHIP: OR, WHAT SHOULD I DO WHEN I AM OFFENDED?

I promise you, sooner or later, something on the Net will offend you. Indeed, since this book reflects much of what happens on the Net, something in this book will probably offend you.

The Net is the largest gathering of human beings ever, and one of the ground rules is that there is No One In Charge, which means that there is no censorship. This freedom is the prime reason that the Net has become so important and why there are so many diverse resources.

Still, some people have a little trouble getting used to such license. Eventually, we all come to realize that if we don't like something, we can ignore it. For example, if you are reading the articles in a Usenet discussion group, and you encounter one that you find particularly offensive, you can skip it. However, at the beginning, the temptation to complain is too strong for some people.

So someone complains... "Yes, I do believe in freedom of expression, but comparing the President of the United States to a retarded Nazi feminist minority member with AIDS is just too much and should not be allowed. After all,

| Chapter | Name | Description |
|---|---|---|
| 7,8 | Mail | send and receive messages |
| 9,10,11,12 | The Web | multi-linked information |
| 10 | Web Search Engines | search the Web |
| 13,14,15 | Usenet | vast system of discussion groups |
| 22 | Mailing Lists | discussions/information by mail |
| 23, 24 | Telnet (Remote Login) | connect to and use a remote host |
| 25, 26 | Talk Facilities | conversation |
| 27 | Internet Relay Chat (IRC) | conversation |
| 28 | Muds | multi-person imaginary environments |

Resources explained in *The Internet Complete Reference*, Second edition.

we must remember that using the Net is a privilege, not a right, and if people like you continue to pollute the network with ignorant, racist, dangerous opinions...blah, blah, blah..."

Well, now. Such a diatribe only goes to show that, as a Net user, the writer is still immature. I assure you, no one anywhere will pay the least bit of attention to a self-righteous pronouncement of what is right or wrong. So, should you ever run into such a complainer, remind him or her gently that the best part of the Net is its diversity, and that tolerance of other people's opinions and ways of thinking is a virtue.

Indeed, if there is one Internet Golden Rule, it is:

**Censor yourself, not others.**

Realistically, we all come to learn that we can't do anything about how other people use the Net, so there is no point even trying. The idea is to share and enjoy. If you don't like something, forget about it.

(And if you don't like something in this book, don't complain to me. Just rip out that page and throw it away.)

## ANSWERS TO FREQUENTLY ASKED QUESTIONS

To save you a bit of time, here are the answers to most the common questions people ask me.

(1) Do you have a Harley Hahn web page?

Yes. Take a look at **http://www.harley.com/**

(2) How can I advertise in this book?

You can't.

This is *not* a commercial directory like a telephone yellow pages book. I do my best to ensure that nothing gets in this book unless it is free to use. Thus, I do not take paid advertisements. All the "advertisements" in this book were written by me and are just for fun.

(3) My organization has just put up a new web page. How can I tell you about it, so you can put it in the book?

You can't.

I choose all the items in this book myself (with some help from my researchers).

(4) I am new to the Net and I don't know what to do. How do I access the resources in this book?

This book is a personal guide to Internet resources. It will *not* teach you how to use the Internet. If you are a new user, you need to spend a fair amount of time learning about the Net (sorry, but that's a fact), and the best suggestion I have is to use my book *The Internet Complete Reference.* (Make sure you get the second edition. The ISBN is 0-07-882138-X.)

Unless you already know something about using the Internet, don't expect to be able to start in right away. Still, don't be discouraged. The Net is a lot of fun and will well repay your effort.

(5) Do you mean that this book is filled with resources with no instructions on how to use them?

Yes. The instructions for how to use the Net well would fill an entire book. That is what *The Internet Complete Reference* is for. I wrote it as a companion to this book, so if you get both of them, they will work well together.

(6) But what about mailing lists?

Following this section, there is a description of how to subscribe and unsubscribe to mailing lists. It will show you the basics. For more information, see my other book.

(7) Nothing seems to work. Every item I try to access is not there. What is happening?

The Internet is always changing. By the time you get this book, a few of the items will be obsolete, and there is nothing anyone can do about it. However, virtually all the items should be fine. For each new edition, my researchers and I start from scratch and check each item in the book by hand.

If a few items don't seem to be there, that is to be expected. However, if *nothing* seems to work, you are doing something wrong. The best advice I can offer you is to get a friend to help you or ask your Internet service provider for assistance. Unless you happened to buy a particularly old copy of this book, most everything should work just fine. Before you get too frustrated, make sure you are doing everything correctly.

(8) I use the Net through a shell account on a Unix computer. How do I access the resources in this book?

Unix is a family of operating systems (master control programs) that run many of the computers on the Internet. If you access the Internet using a Unix computer, you will have what is called a "shell account".

If this is the case, you definitely must learn about Unix. The best way to start is with one my books, either *The Unix Companion* (ISBN 0-07-882149-5) published by Osborne McGraw-Hill, or *Harley Hahn's Student Guide to Unix, Second edition* (ISBN 0-07-025492-3) published by McGraw-Hill College Division. I wrote these books to work well with both *The Internet Complete Reference* and with this book.

## MAILING LISTS

A mailing list is a system by which a group of people can have a discussion via electronic mail. The idea is that a person can send a message to one central address. That message is then processed by a program which automatically sends a copy of the message to everyone on the list. Thus, once you join a mailing list, you will automatically receive copies of all the messages that anyone sends to the central address. These messages will be sent to your electronic mailbox.

When you join a mailing list, we say you "subscribe" to that list. To leave the list—that is, to stop receiving mail—you "unsubscribe". Although we use the words "subscribe" and "unsubscribe", there is no cost involved. You can join—and quit—as many mailing lists as you want for free. However, if you join too many, your mailbox will be flooded with so much mail, you won't have time to read it.

Subscribing and unsubscribing to a mailing list is easy. Each list has a special administrative address. All you have to do is send a message to that address saying that you want to subscribe or unsubscribe. A program (not a person) will read and process the message, and carry out your request.

There are three main types of mailing list systems. They are called Listserv, Listproc and Majordomo. Subscribing and unsubscribing with each is almost the same. The is only one small difference when you subscribe to a Majordomo list (which I will explain below).

Let's look at an example. In the "Animals and Pets" section of this book, you will see an item called "Horses" (page 13). One of the resources under this item is a mailing list. Here is the information:

**Listserv Mailing List:**
List Name: **equine-l**
Subscribe to: **listserv@psuvm.psu.edu**

What can we tell about this list?

First, we see that this is a Listserv mailing list, as opposed to Listproc or Majordomo.

Second, each mailing list has a name. The name of this list is **equine-l**.

Notice the two characters **-l** at the end of the name. In the olden days (before the Internet), it was necessary to know if an name belonged to a person or a mailing list. Thus, mailing lists were given names that ended with **-l**. The letter "l" (L) stands for "list". On some systems, this is still the custom. That is why this name, **equine-l**, ends with **-l**.

The third piece of information we see is the address to which we would send mail to subscribe. In this case, it is **listserv@psuvm.psu.edu**.

This is the address of the program that administers the list. When you send a message to this address, your message is not seen by a person. Everything is done automatically by the Listserv program. It will read your message, figure out what you want, and respond appropriately.

There are many commands you can send to a Listserv program (and the same goes for Listproc and Majordomo). I will describe four.

Before you subscribe to a mailing list, you should always send a request to the mailing list program asking for information about that list. This will help you make sure you really want to subscribe, as well as alert you to any special considerations about the list. To request such information, send an email message to the administrative (subscription) address. The subject of the message doesn't matter: it will be ignored. In the body (main part) of the message, put a single line consisting of the word **info** followed by the name of the list.

For example, in this case, you would send a message to:

**listserv@psuvm.psu.edu**

The subject of the message could be anything. In the body of the message, you would type the single line:

**info equine-l**

Now wait. You will receive a reply with some information. Sometimes this takes only a few minutes, sometimes longer. When you receive the reply, read the information and see if you still want to subscribe. (There will be a lot of technical information you can ignore.)

If you want to subscribe, send another one-line message to the same address. This message should have the word **subscribe**, followed by the name of the list, followed by your first and last names. You do not need to specify your email address. The program at the other end will pick it up automatically.

Let's say your name is Bartholomew Bunzlehammer. To subscribe to the **equine-l** mailing list, send a one-line message to the address:

**listserv@psuvm.psu.edu**

The subject of the message doesn't matter. In the body of the message, you type the single line:

**subscribe equine-l Bartholomew Bunzlehammer**

When the message is received, the Listserv program will automatically subscribe you to the list. From now on, any messages sent to the list will be sent to you as well.

Hint: For security reasons, some mailing list programs require you to confirm that you really want to join the list (just in case some friend has snuck over to your computer while you were away and sent in a subscription to a mailing list). If this is the case, you will be sent instructions on how to confirm. Usually, it is as simple as replying to a message and saying "ok".

You can unsubscribe to a mailing list at any time. Just send a one-line message to the administrative address with the word **unsubscribe**, followed by the name of the list. You do not need to include your name or your email address. In our example, you would send a message to the address:

**listserv@psuvm.psu.edu**

The subject of the message doesn't matter. In the body of the message, type the single line:

**unsubscribe equine-l**

For a Listproc mailing list, everything works exactly the same. For a Majordomo mailing list, there is only one difference: when you subscribe, you do not have to specify your first and last name.

The final command I want you to know about is **help**. Listserv, Listproc and Majordomo systems have more commands than **info**, **subscribe** and **unsubscribe**. To learn about these commands, send a one-line message to the administrative address with the single word **help**. For example, you can send a message to the address:

**listserv@psuvm.psu.edu**

The subject of the message doesn't matter. In the body of the message, type the single line:

**help**

Once you belong to a list, the question arises, how do you send messages to everyone on the list? You do not send messages to the administrative address: that is only for subscribing, unsubscribing and so on. Rather, you send messages to the list itself. The list's address consists of the name of the list, followed by the name of the computer.

In our example, the name of the list is **equine-l**. The name of the computer is **psuvm.psu.edu**. Thus, to send a message to the list itself (that is, to all the people on the list), you would mail to:

**equine-l@psuvm.psu.edu**

Each time you send a message to this address, it will be sent automatically to everyone on the list.

So remember, when you want to unsubscribe, do not send the unsubscribe message to this address. All administrative requests go to the administrative address (where they are handled automatically by a program).

For reference, the following table summarizes what I have explained in this section. Notice that—for the basic commands—all three systems work the same, except that when you subscribe to a Majordomo mailing list, you do not specify your first and last name.

## Subscribing and Unsubscribing to a Mailing List

To request information about a mailing list, or to subscribe or unsubscribe, send mail to the administrative (subscription) address for the list. These are the addresses given in this book. Here are three examples:

**listserv@psuvm.psu.edu**
**majordomo@massey.ac.nz**
**listproc@cornell.edu**

**Request Information About the List**

**info** *list*

**Request General Information**

**help**

**Subscribe to a List**

**subscribe** *list firstname lastname* (Listserv and Listproc)
**subscribe** *list* (Majordomo)

**Unsubscribe to a List**

**unsubscribe** *list*

# Acknowledgments

A great many people helped me with this book and, if you don't mind, I'd like to take a few minutes to thank these people by name and acknowledge their help. The question for you is, should you take the time to read all of this stuff? The answer is yes, and here are five reasons why:

(1) One day, you may be on a game show where you could win $10,000 just by answering questions like "Who is Harley Hahn's copy editor?"

(2) In case you ever encounter one of the people mentioned below, you will recognize their name and be able to ask for an autograph.

(3) If I ever have a contest in which I call people at random out of the phone book and award $1,000,000 to the first person I can find who had read the acknowledgments in this book, you will be ready.

(4) Your name might be in here. Wouldn't you be embarrassed if everyone came up and congratulated you on being mentioned in Harley's book, and you didn't know what they were talking about?

(5) Reading the acknowledgments is a polite thing to do, and your mother would be proud of you.

Still with me? Okay.

To start, we have Wendy Murdock, my Chief Researcher: a writer, researcher and artist whose skill, patience, dedication and hard work had a great deal to do with the quality of this book. Just between us, Wendy never stops amazing me; I still can't figure out how she can be so talented and accomplished. (And she's always in a good mood.)

Next I would like to thank Carrie Campbell, my Senior Researcher. In all the Internet, there is nothing that Carrie cannot find in 45 seconds. Carrie is not only an extraordinary researcher, she is a highly accomplished person, running her own Internet service provider business and maintaining some well-known and important web sites. Like Wendy, Carrie is nothing short of amazing. You should see what it is like when both of these Wonder Women work together in the same room. It's like watching Niagara Falls through the wrong end of a telescope: a huge amount of energy concentrated into a tiny area. Believe me, what Wendy and Carrie can do is very impressive (and I am hard to impress).

In addition to Wendy and Carrie, I had help from the following researchers (who can now consider themselves famous): Zbigniew Jurkowski (Canada), Johanna Newell (California), Martin Rivers (England), Eugene Katunin (Ukraine) and Kalyan Neelamraju (California).

For programming help, I thank James Brady, an expert in areas of computing that most people can't even spell. James worked many, many hours through nights and weekends to make sure that I had the best possible software. James is also an accomplished actor and writer.

Early software development was done by Kenn Nesbitt. Kenn is the well-known writer and programmer who founded Nesbitt software and created WebEdit (a program for creating web pages).

Next, I would like to thank my copy editor Lunaea Hougland. Lunaea's job is to read my work and make sure I haven't misplaced the punctuation or made any spelling mistakes. Lunaea also does a lot more: tasks that fall under the heading of quality control. This is a complex job which requires Lunaea to be kind, tactful, modest, clever, capable, selfless and sensitive (all of which she is) and to work long, inhumane hours (which she does). To make sure Lunaea's work is not in vain, everything is checked once it is set in pages by the proofreader Pat Mannion. Only when a page has been edited by Lunaea and made perfect by Pat is it printed.

On a more personal level, I thank Bill Rogers and Wendy Rogers for expert legal advice, and Don French for expert graphic design.

While researching this book I used an IBM PC running Windows 95, a Macintosh PowerPC and a Sun workstation. For software, I used Microsoft Access to maintain the database and Microsoft Word for word processing. For help with hardware and software, I would like to thank the following people.

At Rain (the Regional Alliance for Information Networking), Marcy Montgomery, Sylvia Tyndall and Timothy Tyndall provided me with Internet access.

For hardware resources, I thank the IBM PC Company (James Adkins, Joanie Miller, Terry Purucker, Brent Morris, Richard Rousseau, Eldrice Murphy, Kathy Minzenberger), Sun Microsystems (Laura Tong Sardina and Ranjini Mehdi) and Apple (Keri Walker, Tina Rodriguez, Doedy Hunter). For software, I thank Dawn Leonetti at Waggener-Edstrom (Microsoft public relations).

For telecommunications assistance I thank Kurt Albershardt for helping with my network and T1 line;

Patrick Linstruth and Chris Linstruth of Quantum Networking Solutions for help with domain names; and Mark Schildhauer of the National Ecology Center (U.C. Santa Barbara) for network configuration help.

Next we have my publisher, Osborne McGraw-Hill. There are two people who put in many hours working with me. First, Scott Rogers, the editor-in-chief, coordinated the logistics of producing the book. Scott has been associated with all four editions of this book. Janet Walden, a senior project editor, oversaw the many details that relate to getting the raw material processed, checking the page proofs, and generally making sure things get done.

Helping these two fine people we have Ann Sellers (Scott's editorial assistant), and Cynthia Douglas and Heidi Poulin (associate project editors).

On the production side of the fence, there are lots of people to thank. Deborah Wilson (director of manufacturing) runs the show. Marcela Hančík (production supervisor) manages everything.

The wonderful illustrations you see throughout the book were done by Leslee Bassin and Lance Ravella. Peter Hančík worked many, many hours laying out the pages (which is a difficult job in a book like this). Jani Beckwith and Roberta Steele generated the final page proofs (Roberta also helped with some of the page layout). The cover was created by Ted Mader Associates with help from Timm Sinclair, Osborne McGraw-Hill's art director.

With respect to marketing, I thank Kendal Andersen (marketing manager), Claudia Ramirez (international marketing), Polly Fusco (special sales), Anne Ellingsen and Susan Bergesen (publicity), Jodi Forrest and Daniela Dell'Orco (sales administration), and Alan Herrick (web manager).

Osborne McGraw-Hill is in Berkeley, California. The main part of McGraw-Hill is in New York. In particular, there are people in New York who work with international rights. These are the people who (along with Claudia Ramirez in Berkeley) work with the publishers around the world who translate and sell this book. For this help, I thank Peter Mellis (director of international rights) and Leslie Roxin (manager of international rights). Leslie also works with the publishers in Western Europe.

The rest of the world is ably assisted by Francesca Minerva (Eastern Europe), Gemma Farrell (Asia and the Pacific Rim), and Mary Murray and Gloria Escandar (Spain, Portugal and Latin America).

Finally, big thanks are in order for Barbara Yanucil (author relations specialist—isn't that a great title?) within the Royalties department in McGraw-Hill's New Jersey office. Barbara provides me with friendly, timely, competent help with respect to money.

After hearing about all of these people, you might be wondering, who runs the show? In Berkeley, the big boss is Brandon Nordin, the publisher of Osborne McGraw-Hill. If you take a survey and find out that everyone you know owns this book, look no further for someone to hold responsible: it's because of Brandon's marketing genius.

In New York, Ted Nardin, the Group Vice President of the McGraw-Hill Professional Book Group, supervises a lot of important stuff, including Osborne McGraw-Hill. Ted is helped by his wonderful assistant Monika Macezinskas.

The company that made the CD that comes with this book is Modern Age Books. The people at Modern Age worked hard to produce a high-quality CD. For all their good work, I thank Chris Williams (vice president of publishing services), Geoff Chappel (vice president of research and development), Amy Pedersen (program manager), Molly Yost (program manager), Steven Holden (engineer), Aaron Michal (engineer) and Jason Butterfield (page technician).

Finally, for extra-special delivery service (more important than you might think), I would like to thank the folks in my local DHL office: Danielle Ritchko, Sheila Burrows, Terry Chlentzos-Keramaris, Anna McConnell, Jason Cole and Kraig Williamson.

*—Harley Hahn*

# AGRICULTURE

## Aglinks

Farming doesn't have to be lonely business. Being out in the boonies won't keep you isolated if you can reach this great load of agricultural resources. This is just about all the information you will need if you are interested in any aspects of agriculture: Usenet groups, web resources, archives, mailing lists and other cool stuff are available.

**Web:**

**http://www.agpr.com/consulting/aglinks.html**

Man Does Not Live
By Cows Alone
There is a lot more to life than cows. True, they can be a lot of fun at birthday parties, and your pet cow does come in handy when you need a fourth for bridge. Still, the needs of the farming community stretch far beyond the bovine.
CHECK OUT Aglinks
a comprehensive guide to the Internet's agricultural resources, and make your life happy and complete.

## Agricultural Genome Information Server

A service provided by the U.S. Department of Agriculture, the Agricultural Genome information server presents genome information for agriculturally important organisms.

**Web:**

**http://probe.nalusda.gov**

## Agricultural Mailing List

Grassland husbandry, crop science, ecological simulation, crop production, tropical forestry, plant physiology, water management, irrigation, and anything else to do with agriculture.

**Listserv Mailing List:**

List Name: **agric-l**
Subscribe to: **listserv@uga.cc.uga.edu**

## Agricultural News

If you are out in the field all day, you don't have to feel entirely isolated and behind the times. When you turn off the tractor and have a little lunch, just fire up the lap top and check your email. If you are on the **agnews** mailing list you can get all sorts of agricultural news releases. Keep informed, no matter where in the world you are.

**Listserv Mailing List:**

List Name: **agnews**
Subscribe to: **listserv@vm.cc.purdue.edu**

## Agricultural Software

Check out Texas A&M's software catalog, peruse the U.S. Department of Agriculture Extension Service's collection of computer software or perform a search of specific software.

**Web:**

**http://www.gdb.org/Dan/softsearch/softsearch.html**

## Agriculture Network Information Center

In a time of agricultural need, it's always good to know you can find a specialist. The Agriculture Network Information Center (AgNIC) provides access to experts in various fields of agriculture as well as links to agricultural databases. Find out about conferences, meetings and seminars in your area. If you are going to be traveling, call ahead and arrange to take an agricultural expert to lunch.

**Web:**

**http://www.agnic.org/**

A B C D E F G H I J K L M N O P Q R S T U V W X Y Z

## Beekeeping

These beekeeping resources provide the novice and experienced apiarist alike with all the information relating to the art and science of beekeeping available through the Net. You'll find archived articles and newsletters, newsgroups, photos, FAQs, articles, links to web entomology servers, and other archives.

**Web:**

**http://weber.u.washington.edu/~jlks/bee.html**

**Usenet:**

**sci.agriculture.beekeeping**

**Listserv Mailing List:**

List Name: **bee-l**
Subscribe to: **listserv@uacsc2.albany.edu**

## Dairy Talk and General Discussion

The nice thing about cows is that they are useful for so many different things. Who would think that a simple thing like milking a cow could be developed into an entire industry? But there's a great deal more to milk than just squeezing an udder or two. Join professional educators and extension workers when they discuss problems and policies faced by dairy producers. Topics also cover educational tools such as visual aids, computer-aided support tools and outlines of educational programs.

**Listserv Mailing List:**

List Name: **dairy-l**
Subscribe to: **listserv@umdd.bitnet**

## Farm Journal Today

These days, people think you have go skydiving, bungee jumping, ice climbing or fire walking to get a thrill. How wrong can they get? On the Net, I can get a rush any time I want. Check out this site and you will see what I mean. This site offers several different agriculture magazines for your perusal. You can read articles from journals like Hogs Today, Beef Today, Dairy Today, Farm Journal and Top Producer. If you don't want to just read, you can hang with other agricultural thrill-seekers in chat rooms like "Farm Ladies Chat" or the "Monday Night Campfire".

**Web:**

**http://www.farmjournal.com/**

## Farming and Agriculture

It has been a long time since farmers were isolated tillers of the soil, living alone and working from dawn to dusk with little contact with the outside world. Today's modern farmer is as likely to have an Internet connection as a tractor. If you are a farmer or have an interest in agriculture, join the discussion, and stay in touch with your neighbors all over the world.

**Usenet:**

**alt.agriculture.fruit**
**alt.agriculture.misc**
**sci.agriculture**
**sci.agriculture.poultry**

### *Look What I Found on the Net...*

```
Newsgroup: alt.agriculture.misc
Subject: Sugar Production

> Can anyone tell me where to find sugar production by country?

Look in the yearbooks issued by United Nations organizations,
including the Food and Agriculture Organization's "Production
Yearbook".

Top sugar producers are usually India, Brazil, China (rising),
Russia, Cuba (falling), USA, Mexico, Pakistan, France, Colombia
and Australia, in that order.
```

## Forestry

The only thing bad about the forest is that there's no good waves to surf. Other than that, I really like the forest. Except for the bugs. But other than that, I like the forest. Except for the snakes, I mean. Other than that, I really do like the forest. If you are a big fan of forestry like I am, you have to check out the forestry resources on the Net. You can find software, databases, lists of conferences, mailing lists, research papers, journals, and links to other forestry stuff on the Net. And you don't even need any insect repellent.

**Web:**

**http://www.metla.fi/info/vlib/Forestry.html**

## Global Information and Early Warning System

The Global Information and Early Warning System (GIEWS) provides the food supply outlook for the world, including information on food crops and shortages, crop developments, and special reports and alerts.

**Web:**

**http://www.fao.org/WAICENT/faoinfo/economic/giews/english/giewse.htm**

## Grain Genes

I love bread. Sometimes when I'm not eating bread, I will go look at the grain genes web site. There I can see images of various grains and their gene diagrams. (It's good to know exactly what you are eating.) After I am finished looking at the pictures, I sometimes read the publications like the "Barley Genetics Newsletter" (barley is exceptional in a nice soup) or the annual wheat newsletters. At this site, you can also find autoradiogram images, information about the pathology and genetics of grains and other grain agronomy links.

**Web:**

**http://wheat.pw.usda.gov/graingenes.html**

## National Agricultural Library

The National Agricultural Library (NAL) is one of four national libraries in the United States. NAL is part of the U.S. Department of Agriculture's research service. Through this web page you may learn how to access ISIS, the library's public catalog, see part of the NAL's image collection that is online and get information on how to access other NAL resources.

**Web:**

**http://www.nalusda.gov/**

## National Genetic Resources Program

The USDA's National Genetic Resources Program (NGRP) provides germplasm information about plants, animals, microbes and insects, as well as links to other biological gopher resources around the world.

**Web:**

**http://www.ars-grin.gov/**

## Pesticide Action Network

The Pesticide Action Network North America (PANNA) is a nonprofit organization that promotes the use of ecologically sound agriculture practices in place of pesticides. If you are interested in a more environmentally friendly way of growing crops, check out the PANNA site. It has information about sustainable agriculture, pesticides and their effects on children, reports, publications, a searchable database of pesticides and pesticide alternatives, and links to related resources.

**Web:**

**http://www.panna.org/panna/**

## Poultry

If chicken is your business, hurry on over to this web site. It has pointers to poultry news and discussion lists, web links to cool things like Ostriches Online and the Bantam Club, avian research centers, poultry science departments and the National Poultry Museum. Break a wing.

**Web:**

**http://gallus.tamu.edu/1h/posc/dother.html**

A B C D E F G H I J K L M N O P Q R S T U V W X Y Z

## Precision Farming

I will admit I didn't anticipate information about farming to be interesting. However, after reading some documents about precision farming, I have changed my mind. Precision farming is the process of tailoring soil and crop management to fit the various conditions found in individual fields. Precision farming uses remote sensing, geographic information systems (GIS) and global positioning systems (GPS) to analyze field data to within inches. Using this system, farmers can adjust seeding rates, fertilizer and pesticide applications, make tillage adjustments and record yield data variations within each individual field. If you want to know more about this space age method of farming, check out this site, which has lots of good information, or join the mailing list and talk to other agricultural folk about precision farming.

**Web:**
**http://nespal.cpes.peachnet.edu/pf/**

**Listproc Mailing List:**
List Name: **precise-agri**
Subscribe to: **listproc@soils.umn.edu**

## Progressive Farmer Online

It's the '90s. If you are going to be a farmer, you should be a progressive farmer. Don't live in the past. Read this free online magazine that has news, weather, market information, feature articles, information about weed control, biotechnology and a forum where you can post messages for other agriculture buffs.

**Web:**
**http://pathfinder.com/PF/**

## Sustainable Agriculture Information

Access discussion group archives, pesticide education resources, information on rural skills, agronomy information, USDA statistics, and other great sustainable agriculture resources around the Net.

**Web:**
**http://pubweb.ucdavis.edu/documents/safs/pages.htm**
**http://www.koan.net/nexus/Permaculture/sust-ag-faq.html**

**Usenet:**
**alt.sustainable.agriculture**

### Can We Keep On Keeping On?

Traditional agriculture requires that we add a significant amount of substances and energy to the soil. For example, farmers routinely use chemical fertilizers, pesticides, soil conditioners, and so on.

The goal of sustainable agriculture is to depend as little as possible on external resources. The holy grail of sustainable agriculture is to create an agricultural system that is efficient and economically viable, while needing as little external support as possible.

In the long run, sustainable agriculture practices can benefit us all, conserving resources and saving money. However, to reach that goal, there will have to be a lot of experimentation, development and testing.

If you would like to follow the flow, check the sustainable agriculture resources on the Net. Maybe there is a way we can keep on keeping on without running out of resources.

## U.S.D.A. Economics and Statistics

The U.S. Department of Agriculture offers data sets and other information about crops, farm economics, food, international agriculture, livestock, rural affairs, specialty agriculture, and other items of agricultural and economic interest.

**Web:**
**http://usda.mannlib.cornell.edu/usda/usda.html**

## U.S.D.A. Extension Service

An informal educational system that links the education and research resources and activities of the USDA, many universities, and thousands of county administrative offices. These web and gopher servers provide links to information from the Extension Service of the USDA and other scientific agencies within the USDA.

**Web:**
**http://www.esusda.gov/**

## Weeds

Do you hate weeds? Like a pesky brother-in-law, weeds keep coming back, and nothing you can do will stop them. The best you can do is take a look at this web site created by the Weed Science Society of America. You can find out about herbicides, crop injury symptoms, herbicide manufacturers, chemical terminology, government regulations and more. It's nice to know someone has weeds down to a science. (Now if they can just get to work on brothers-in-law.)

**Web:**

**http://piked2.agn.uiuc.edu/wssa/**

## Women in Agriculture

In the country, it is certainly true that a woman's work is never done. Even after all the chores are done, the men are fed and the children tended to, there is still email to check. At least email is not without its rewards. This mailing list is for rural women and women involved in farming to talk about the various aspects of agriculture. Feel free to talk about any agricultural thing under the sun with other womenfolk around the world.

**Majordomo Mailing List:**

List Name: **agwomen-l**
Subscribe to: **majordomo@peg.apc.org**

## World Agricultural Information Center

The World Agriculture Information Center (WAICENT) was created by the Food and Agriculture Organization of the United Nations. WAICENT provides information on agriculture, fisheries, forestry, nutrition and rural development. Information is also available in languages other than English. This is just the thing when you have to pick up a quick present for a farm girl and you don't know what to get her.

**Web:**

**http://www.fao.org/WAICENT/waicent.htm**

# ANARCHY

## Anarchia

Here is a collection of resources related to anarchy. If you are a serious student of miscommunication and revolution, there are lots of resources for you, including discussion groups with other similarly inclined people.

**Web:**

**http://www.cybercity.dk/users/ccc4293/**

## Anarchism 101

There have been some scholarly individuals who supported anarchy. Anarchy is more than sitting around complaining about how terrible the government is. If you want to see what I mean, check out this collection of texts and documents about anarchy. You can read selected writings of Bakunin, Godwin, Hoffman, Thoreau, and more.

**Web:**

**http://astro.uchicago.edu/home/web/duvernoi/anarch.html**

## Anarchist Calendar

When you want to give a party, but you just don't have a good occasion to celebrate, check with the anarchist calendar on the Net. This site has a list of important anarchist happenings in history. Just find the anarchist event closest to the day you are giving the party, then call your caterer and tell him the theme of the gathering. Or you can read him the list of historical events and ask him which one goes best with frozen pigs-in-blankets.

**Web:**

**http://www.cs.utah.edu/~galt/anarcal.html**

**Want to waste some time? Try "Cool, But Useless".**

A B C D E F G H I J K L M N O P Q R S T U V W X Y Z

## Anarchist Feminism

Anarchy and feminism have been strolling hand in hand long before Hillary Clinton agreed to be ex-Princess Diana's financial planner for a straight percentage of the gross. If you would like to explore the roots of modern feminism, you need to look at the women who were not afraid to stand up and be counted at a time when even getting noticed could be hazardous to a lady's health. True, Hillary and Diana are honest-to-goodness folk heroes, but in my humble masculine opinion, they can't hold an intellectual candle to, say, Emma Goldman, the Russian-born American activist who was pro-birth control and anti-draft long before it was fashionable. Check the Net and see for yourself.

**Web:**

**http://www.geocities.com/Paris/2159/anrfem.html**

## Anarchist History and Education

Anarchy refers to a general lack of political order and authority. In this sense, the Net is worldwide anarchy in action: an anarchy that actually works. To really understand the Net, you need to understand anarchy, and to really understand anarchy, you need to know something about its history. Here is the place to start.

**Web:**

**http://www.teleport.com/~jwehling/AnarchistEducation.html**

## Anarchist Resources

After going through a three-hour corporate meeting, it's refreshing to look at a nice web site that can help you fantasize about throwing off the political ties that bind you. This site has lots of interesting resources that are related to anarchy and anarchists. It includes lists of newsgroups, archive sites, web pages, newsletters, mailing lists, publications, and more.

**Web:**

**http://www.duke.edu/~eagle/anarchy**

## History of Anarchy

Human society is a stew into which you throw all types of ingredients and cook for a long time, with no idea of how it is going to turn out. One of the most important ingredients in human history is anarchy. Every now and then, we need a few people to redefine the recipe of government and stir the stew.

Even a cursory glance at history will show you that what starts off as frank rebellion often ends up as the status quo. Thus, when we learn about the anarchy of the past, we are studying the seeds of our modern society.

Remember, those who do not understand the history of anarchy may find themselves repeating it with their own heads on the platter.

## Anarchy Archives

Here's an electronic library that provides zines and archives of an anarchist nature. If you are feeling a little rebellious, spend your lunch break reading the archives of an anarchist mailing list or have a taste of what is left over from the Sixties and read an anarchy zine. It makes a nice break from the real world.

**Web:**

**http://www.lglobal.com/TAO/**

## Anarchy FAQ

Anarchy comes in a variety of shapes and sizes with the one common belief that Government Is Bad. You can read more about the ins and outs of anarchy. This FAQ attempts to take all the ideas and philosophies and put them in a readable format. It explains anarchy from a critical point of view.

**Web:**

**http://digital.csionline.com/~lumber/anarchy/afaq.html**

## Anarchy for Anybody

If you've decided to become an anarchist and you just don't know where to start, try this web page. It has a page of anarchy-related quotes, a list of anarchy links, information about what anarchists believe in, a reading list, information on famous anarchists in history and much more.

**Web:**

**http://pubweb.acns.nwu.edu/~dtn307/anarchy.html**

## Anarchy History

The thing I like best about anarchy is that no one organizes it. Oh, people try, but anarchy seems to have a life of its own. If you like reading about the history of not following the rules, try this site. Learn about the people who did not feel like getting permission from Burger King just to have it their way: people like Noam Chomsky, Emma Goldman, William Godwin, Michael Bakunin and Max Stirner. Find out what the Haymarket massacre has in common with the Spanish Civil War, and see why, when push comes to anarchical shove, there's no business like show-em-how-it-really-ought-to-be-done business.

**Web:**

**http://www.miyazaki-mic.ac.jp/faculty/dward/Anarchist_Archives/archivehome.html**

**Need a pickup?**
**Try "Energy"**
**(or "Cars and Trucks").**

## Anarchy Talk and General Discussion

To some people, anarchy is society without government. To others, anarchy is life without television. Still, whether you are an armchair social critic or a couch potato with a plan to reform the world, you won't want to miss the discussion. Talk may be cheap, but good plans to reform the world the hard way are in short supply.

**Usenet:**

**alt.society.anarchy**

## History of the Black Flag

You may have noticed that when the political and fashionable hoi polloi congregate (say, at the opening of Congress or the annual Clinton, Arkansas, turkey drop) you never see a black flag. And you know why? Because a black flag is the symbol of anarchy, and if there is one thing the political and fashionable hoi polloi will not tolerate, it is anything that smacks of not following the rules. (Just ask any member of Congress or, for that matter, any turkey from Arkansas.) But how did the black flag come to have such a meaning? Read this article and find out.

**Web:**

**http://www.teleport.com/~jwehling/BlackFlag.html**

## Internet Anarchist University

Okay, so you are tired of everything being so predictable, and you want to learn more about mixing it up. But where can you go? If you go to a regular school, you will have to be politically correct just to stay in class. However, as a Net user, you have an option: the Internet Anarchist University, the only place of learning in the world where you get credit for being revolting.

**Web:**

**http://www.wam.umd.edu/~ctmunson/iau.html**

**The weather is always fine on the Net.**

## Siege of Paris

In 1870, Otto von Bismarck, the "Iron Chancellor", goaded the French into declaring war against Prussia (a German state). This was part of Bismark's plan to create a unified German Empire, and it worked. The French declared war—the Franco-Prussian War—and lost, after which Bismark was able to consolidate the German empire as an aggressive military force, leading to one or two minor military problems in the twentieth century. Once the war ended, Germany forced France to accept punitive and humiliating terms of surrender. Many of the working class citizens of Paris (such as writers of Internet books) were so upset at the new French government's acceptance of these terms that they forced out the National Assembly and formed a committee called the Commune of Paris to run the city. Led by the Commune of Paris, the citizens put up a brave and desperate struggle against government troops, but after a week of battles—called the Siege of Paris—the working class protesters lost. Afterward, there were massive reprisals in which tens of thousands of people were killed, putting a crimp in the French political scene for the next several years.

**Web:**

**http://www.library.nwu.edu/spec/siege/**

## Spunk Press

Spunk Press collects and distributes electronic literature with an emphasis on anarchism and related issues. Their home page offers a manifesto, a large catalog of anarchy articles as well as a list of anarchist resources.

**Web:**

**http://www.cwi.nl/cwi/people/Jack.Jansen/spunk/Spunk_Home.html**

**Web, web, web...**
**sleep, eat...**
**web, web, web...**

# ANIMALS AND PETS

## Animal Information Database

Created by Sea World and Busch Gardens, this web page is loaded with information, not only about aquatic animals, but also on a variety of terrestrial critters. Learn about manatee bodysurfing, hippos that sweat pink oil, and other interesting animal facts that will make you the life of any party.

**Web:**

**http://www.bev.net/education/SeaWorld/infobook.html**

### Animals R Us

You know, we don't really pay enough attention to our friends in the animal kingdom. Aside from Los Angeles, where lower invertebrates are routinely used to write television shows and movies, most of us are content to ignore our companions on Planet Earth. That's why I urge you to take some time and explore the **Animal Information Database**: a fund of useful knowledge.

You never really know when useful and important animal-oriented knowledge is going to make a difference in your life. For example, what do you do when your Uncle Louie surprises you by inviting himself over for dinner, and you are not sure what to feed him? Or say you pick a particularly strange-looking blind date, and you are interested in finding out if she might be dangerous. Not to worry, the Animal Information Database is ready and waiting for you, twenty-four hours a day.

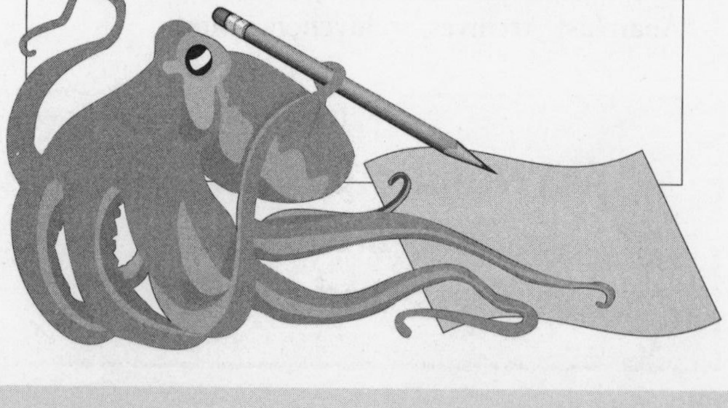

## Animal Rescue and Adoption

If you like pets, you will enjoy reading stories about rescuing animals. Moreover, you will find information about rescue organizations and animal shelters in the United States and abroad. If you have a pet, it would be a good idea to see what organizations exist in your area.

**Web:**

**http://petstation.com/central.html#TOP**
**http://pasture.ecn.purdue.edu/~laird/Dogs/Rescue/shelters.html**

## Animal Resources

Archives and FAQS about many different animals, including exotic birds and pets, cats, dogs, chinchillas, goats, sheep, cows, horses, and gerbils.

**Web:**

**http://netvet.wustl.edu/**

## Animal Talk and General Discussion

Animals are for more than eating or making into pets. Some are pretty or lovable, and some are to be admired for their skill in stalking and devouring small prey or unsuspecting pizza-delivery boys. On the Net there are several places you can go to participate in discussions of your favorite animal.

**Usenet:**

**alt.animals.badgers**
**alt.animals.bears**
**alt.animals.dolphins**
**alt.animals.felines.lions**
**alt.animals.felines.lynxes**
**alt.animals.felines.snowleopards**
**alt.animals.foxes**
**alt.animals.lampreys**
**alt.animals.raccoons**

**Why don't we do it on the Net?**

## Aquariums

What does it mean when your gourami is leaning thirty degrees to the right? He could be trying to steer, but that's probably not the case. Splash around with the rest of the ichthyophiles as they explore the true nature of tropical fish. Learn a wide variety of new things, like the best way to earthquake-proof your tanks, how to name your fish after famous Internet book writers, or what to feed your black piranha when all he really wants is you.

**Web:**

**http://www.actwin.com/fish**

**Usenet:**

**alt.aquaria**
**alt.aquaria.killies**
**alt.aquaria.marketplace**
**rec.aquaria**
**rec.aquaria.freshwater.cichlids**
**rec.aquaria.freshwater.goldfish**
**rec.aquaria.freshwater.misc**
**rec.aquaria.freshwater.plants**
**rec.aquaria.marine.misc**
**rec.aquaria.marine.reefs**
**rec.aquaria.marketplace**
**rec.aquaria.misc**
**rec.aquaria.tech**
**sci.aquaria**

**Listserv Mailing List:**

List Name: **aquarium**
Subscribe to: **listserv@emuvm1.cc.emory.edu**

## Bats

Bats are the only mammals capable of true flight. Their bodies are mouse-like, with forearms and special skinfolds that are adapted to act as wings. Bats are generally active at night. During the day, they hang around in groups, sleeping, eating pizza and watching daytime television. Most bats eat either fruit or insects. ("I'll have a large pizza, with ripe grapes and fly legs, hold the ant thoraxes.") However, out of 1000-2000 species of bats, there is one—the vampire bat of South America —that feeds exclusively on animal blood. Most other bats content themselves with flying around looking cool and getting in the hair of women, so they can watch them run around squeaking and looking silly. If you want even more authoritative information, check with the Net.

**Web:**

**http://ww.nyx.net/~jbuzbee/bat_house.html**

A B C D E F G H I J K L M N O P Q R S T U V W X Y Z

A B C D E F G H I J K L M N O P Q R S T U V W X Y Z

## Bird-Keeping

Bird magazines, books, terminology, buying guides, cage and toy reviews, diet and feeding information, training help, and other topics. The **dom_bird** mailing list is for keepers of domestic birds, while **exotic-l** is for lovers of exotic birds.

**Web:**

**http://www.cis.ohio-state.edu/hypertext/faq/usenet/birds-faq/pets/top.html**

**Usenet:**

**rec.pets.birds**

**Listserv Mailing List:**

List Name: **dom_bird**
Subscribe to: **listserv@plearn.edu.pl**

**Listserv Mailing List:**

List Name: **exotic-l**
Subscribe to: **listserv@plearn.edu.pl**

Cats Are People Too

I may be biased, seeing as I have the best cat in the entire world, but what could be better than a warm, fluffy bundle of feline affection sitting beside you as you work?

If you like cats, the Net is the place to be, with all the cat-related information you will ever need. My cat loves the Net so much, he often takes the laptop computer with him to bed. (I only wish he wouldn't get tuna all over the keyboard.)

## Bird-Watching

This is a hobby that can be as simple or as elaborate as you wish. Basic pieces of equipment are a lawn chair, a bird book, and a pair of binoculars—and some birds, of course. On the high end, you can use complicated camouflage, blinds, and camera equipment. No matter what your aim is, bird-watching is an endlessly fascinating pastime.

**Web:**

**http://compstat.wharton.upenn.edu:8001/~siler/birding.html**
**http://www.birder.com/**

**Usenet:**

**rec.birds**

## Cats

No doubt about it, cats are très cool. (And my cat, The Little Nipper, happens to be the coolest cat of all.) The Net abounds with cat information, and just about everything cat-wise is out there waiting for you. Cats are also involved in some of the most amazing coincidences in the world. For example, my chief researcher's mother's name is Kitty and—get this—mymaternal grandmother's name was Kitty. Farm out or what?

**Web:**

**http://www.zmall.com/pet_talk/cat-faqs/**

**Usenet:**

**rec.pets.cats**

**Majordomo Mailing List:**

List Name: **cats-l**
Subscribe to: **majordomo@stargame.org**

**Forget the sitter, check out the "Kids" section.**

## Dogs

The Net has some wonderful dog-oriented resources with frequently asked question lists, informative articles, poems about dogs, and technical information such as the Dog Genome Project. You can even learn the meaning of interesting terms like "flews" and "dewclaws." For discussion, there are some great Usenet groups.

**Web:**

**http://www.io.com/~wilf/dogs/**
**http://www.zmall.com/pet_talk/dog-faqs/**
**http://www.dog-e-zine.com/**

**Usenet:**

**rec.pets.dogs**
**rec.pets.dogs.activities**
**rec.pets.dogs.behavior**
**rec.pets.dogs.breeds**
**rec.pets.dogs.health**
**rec.pets.dogs.info**
**rec.pets.dogs.misc**
**rec.pets.dogs.rescue**

## Electronic Zoo

A compilation of animal-related Net resources: mailing lists, web sites, newsgroups, archives, databases, and much more. If you are an animal lover or a pet professional, you should definitely take time to visit this site.

**Web:**

**http://netvet.wustl.edu/e-zoo.htm**

**For some cool dreams, try sleeping with this book under your pillow.**

## Elephants

There are many misconceptions about elephants. For example, some people think that elephants never forget. Well, I can tell you that is just not true. When I was a graduate student, there was an elephant in my class, and he always forgot the formula for quadratic equations. (What a goober.) However, there are lots of interesting true facts about elephants. For example, an elephant that is sufficiently motivated can run as fast as 40 km/hour (25 miles/hour) for a short amount of time. And mother elephants carry their developing babies for a gestation period of 21 months. (Believe me, if you knew that getting pregnant meant having to carry a baby for 21 months, you too would find it handy to be able to run at 40 km/hour.) Want to know more? There's lots of elephant info, including pictures, waiting for you on the Net.

**Web:**

**http:/www.wineasy.se/elephant/**
**http://raptor.csc.flint.umich.edu/~mcdonald/**

## Exotic Pets

Do you have a fondness for exotic pets? Learn about special care for your special animals, including how to breed and feed them, recognize illnesses, and develop an awareness of safety. Discussion is not limited to reptiles (herpetology).

**Web:**

**http://fovea.retina.net/~gecko/herps**

**Usenet:**

**rec.pets.alligators**
**rec.pets.herp**

**IRC:**

**#herp**

## Felines

The feline family includes lions, tigers, leopards, jaguars, cougars, panthers, cheetahs, pumas, lynx, ocelots, as well as wild and domestic cats. Here is a lot of interesting information about felines, including pictures. The largest feline in the world, by the way, is the Siberian tiger. It can be up to 3.2 meters (almost 7½ feet) long. A Siberian tiger can kill a guar bull weighing as much as 1000 kilograms (over a ton). At the other end of the scale, my cat—The Little Nipper—can eat a small can of tuna at a single sitting (as long as someone else opens the can).

**Web:**

**http://evolution.bio.cornell.edu/efvs/**

## Ferrets

They are as playful as kittens, good-natured, energetic, and entertaining. Learn more about the suitability of ferrets as pets, get health information, and read ferret stories by owners and roommates of owners.

**Web:**
**http://www.optics.rochester.edu:8080/users/pgreene**

**Usenet:**
**alt.pets.ferrets**

**Listserv Mailing List:**
List Name: **ferret**
Subscribe to: **listserv@cunyvm.cuny.edu**

## Fleas and Ticks

Learn how to rid your pet or home of fleas and what to do about ticks. (The ol' gasoline trick probably isn't a very good idea anymore.)

**Web:**
**http://www.zmall.com/pet_talk/pet-faqs/fleas-ticks.html**

## Hamsters

Hamsters can be a lot of fun, and they are as cute as the dickens. When I was a kid I had a hamster named Hamlet. He used to stay up all night, running around inside a wheel in his cage. Aside from that, he was pretty easy to get along with. He never ate the last corndog; when we were watching TV, he didn't mind if I changed the channel to an old Dick Van Dyke rerun; and he always saved the comics for me to read before he started ripping them apart. If you would like to find out more about our pleasant little golden brown friends, here are some Net resources that are even more fun than running around inside a wheel.

**Web:**
**http://www.tela.bc.ca/hamster/**

**Usenet:**
**alt.pets.hamsters**

**The Net is immortal.**

### *Look What I Found on the Net...*

```
Newsgroup: alt.pets.hamsters
Subject: Do hamsters have nightmares?

>>> Do hamsters have nightmares?

>>> I was in my room this morning, when I suddenly heard a
>>> scream coming from my hamster's cage. (If you've ever heard
>>> a hamster scream, you know what I'm talking about). I
>>> jumped about 3 feet into the air! I thought he was dying,
>>> or in mortal agony or something! I ran over to his cage,
>>> popped open the top, popped open his house, and as soon as
>>> he saw me he stopped, then he crawled out into my hand.
>>> I held him for a few minutes, and he was fine, and he hasn't
>>> let out a peep since. Should I get him checked out, or has
>>> anyone else experienced a hamster with nightmares?

>> With humans, rapid eye movement is an indication of dream,
>> maybe hamsters have this too? Their eyes are large, so it
>> might be easy to observe.

> I like watching Li'l Hamster sleep, he seems to have a lot of
> Rapid Nose movement for a few minutes about half hour after he
> has been asleep, I am sure that they dream...

Until I read all of these "Do hamsters have nightmares?" I
hadn't really thought about it much. But after reading this,
I heard my hamster actually squeak in his sleep yesterday.
Thanks for the tip.
```

## Hedgehogs

Hedgehogs are cool. They are small, brown or yellow animals with spines on their back. When a hedgehog is threatened, it rolls itself into a small, spine-covered ball for protection (much like a porcupine). If you like these cute furry members of the family Erinaceidae, take a look at this hedgehog web site. After all, any animal that can give birth to a baby after only 37 days of gestation must have something on the ball.

**Web:**

**http://www.pci.on.ca/~macnamar/hedgehogs/**

## Horses

Why do so many young women love to ride horses? Well, I know, but I can't tell. What I can tell you is that this newsgroup is the place to meet horse lovers of all types for a general discussion of horses, riding, and all-around good, clean equestrian fun.

**Usenet:**

**rec.equestrian**

**Listserv Mailing List:**

List Name: **equine-l**
Subscribe to: **listserv@psuvm.psu.edu**

## Iguanas

An iguana is a large lizard, found in the tropical regions of the western hemisphere. Even in the dark, it is easy to tell an iguana from a cat or a dog, because iguanas have spiny projections along their backs. Here is information for every iguana lover or potential iguana lover about housing, feeding, health, reproduction, and so on.

**Web:**

**http://www.acmepet.com/reptile/veg_liz.html**

## Monkeys

I never had a pet monkey when I was growing up, but I did have a little sister. Of course, there are important differences. For example, many sisters do not live in tropical or semi-tropical climates. And monkeys do not tie up the telephone when you are waiting for an important call. If you need even more information, here's a good place to look.

**Web:**

**http://www.cdmnet.com/heather/**

## Penguins

Have you ever noticed how some people like penguins? I mean they *really* like penguins. If you are one of these people, here is some great information, including lots of pictures that you can copy for your own web page so people will know you like penguins. After all, penguins live in the Antarctic, so you probably will never get to see them in their natural habitat. But who needs a natural habitat when you have the Net?

**Web:**

**http://www.vni.net/~kwelch/penguins/**

## Pet-Keeping Dos and Don'ts

Before my brother was born, the doctor asked me what I hoped the baby would be. I said I wanted a pony. However, my mother knew I was too young to take care of a pony by myself, so she got me a brother instead. Pets can be a lot of fun, but we do have a responsibility to look after them. Here is a wealth of advice on how to select and care for a pet. For example, before you take a trip, make arrangements with your family or friends as to who should take care of your pet if you don't come back.

**Web:**

**http://petstation.com/do&dont.html**

## Pets General Discussion

If you have a pet, or want a pet, or happen to be cooking a pet for dinner, check with the general pet discussion group first. Share information and experiences on a range of topics, including exotic animals, nutrition, grooming, behavior, veterinary care and recipes.

**Usenet:**

**rec.pets**

**"Animals and Pets" are people too.**

## Plants Harmful to Animals

It sounds like a job for a professional politician, but truly, there are people who like to grow poisonous plants for a living. At least they do it for the common good. At this web site you can check out plants that are toxic to animals and humans. You can look up the plants by common name or by scientific name. There are also links to related sources. This is an important resource if you have kids or animals that chew on things they aren't supposed to chew on.

**Web:**

**http://www.grainger.uiuc.edu/vex/toxic/toxic.htm**

## Rabbits

Cuddly, soft, lovable little animals that you can dye pastel shades when Easter rolls around. Bunnies are not just for kids. They make great pets for everyone. Learn about how to care for a pet rabbit and get information about rabbit psychology and diseases that afflict bunnies. Non-bunny-lovers are not welcome unless you can mind your manners.

**Usenet:**

**alt.pets.rabbits**
**rec.pets.rabbits**

**Listserv Mailing List:**

List Name: **petbunny**
Subscribe to: **listserv@lsv.uky.edu**

**Over 95% of people check the "Trivia" section.**

## Rats

I once lived with someone who had a pet rat. One day she let it get away and it hid in the couch. Eventually, we were able to retrieve the rat, but the couch was never the same. Another time, she was playing with the rat by holding its tail. Much to her chagrin, the outside of the tail pulled off, leaving a raw, red inner core. Eventually, the rat healed, but the tail was never the same. As you can see, rats are pretty cool pets, and if your day-to-day existence is missing something or other, maybe you should get yourself a rat. If so, your life will never be the same.

**Web:**

**http://uptown.turnpike.net/~arturos/**

## Sharks

Okay, let's get the strange stuff out of the way. (1) Sharks don't have bones, they have cartilage. (2) There are 250 different species of sharks. (3) Fully grown sharks can range from cute pygmy sharks measuring only 60 cm (2 feet) up to large whale sharks stretching to 15 meters (50 feet). (4) The most feared shark is the white shark (called the "Great White Shark" in the movies). This animal can grow up to 6 meters (20 feet) and will attack and try to eat just about anything, even without provocation. (The huge whale shark, by the way, is much less dangerous, as it lives on microscopic plankton.) Although many people are afraid of sharks, it is more a testament to the movies than to common sense. I have been swimming in the ocean for years, and the closest I ever came to a shark was going snorkeling with my lawyer.

**Web:**

**http://www.ncf.carleton.ca/~bz050/HomePage.shark.html**
**http://www.oceanstar.com/shark/**
**http://ucmp1.berkeley.edu/Doug/shark.html**

**Listserv Mailing List:**

List Name: **shark-l**
Subscribe to: **listserv@utcvm.utc.edu**

### *Look What I Found on the Net...*

```
(from the message that describes the mailing list "petbunny")

...PetBunny is an open, unmoderated discussion list for owners
of pet rabbits. Things such as how to care for a pet rabbit,
rabbit diseases and rabbit psychology are likely to be
discussed. The list is NOT intended for rabbit bashing..
```

## Treatment of Animals

What goes on in the lives of animals that are not just pets? Develop awareness on the use and abuse of animals.

**Usenet:**

**talk.politics.animals**

## Veterinary Medicine

If you were always the one to bring home the bird with the broken wing or if you liked to wrap the dog up in gauze bandages, then maybe your calling is veterinary medicine. There is a wealth of information on the Net about animals and the veterinary field.

**Web:**

**http://vet.futurescan.com/**
**http://www.pathit.com/pathit/pathvet.htm**

**Listserv Mailing List:**

List Name: **vetmed-l**
Subscribe to: **listserv@uga.cc.uga.edu**

**Majordomo Mailing List:**

List Name: **vet-clin-sci-res**
Subscribe to: **majordomo@massey.ac.nz**

## Virtual Pet Cemetery

Finally, here is the perfect venue for you to publish "Ode to Wilhelmena, Marsupial Companion of my Youth". The Virtual Pet Cemetery is just the place to send an honorable epitaph for that favorite pet who, after handing in his dinner pail, has passed on to his final reward, beloved by all and sundry.

**Web:**

**http://www.lavamind.com/pet.html**

## Wildlife

Outside of downtown Los Angeles or the U.S. Republican National Convention, most people don't get a chance to see real wildlife in their native habitat. However, as a Net user, you can visit a virtual collection of various types of wildlife, including species that are extinct or endangered. This site is particularly suitable for children, especially those who are young enough to require protection against Republicans.

**Web:**

**http://www.olcommerce.com/terra/**

**Usenet:**

**rec.animals.wildlife**

## Wolves

There are three species of wolves: the gray or timber wolf, the red wolf, and the prairie wolf (coyote). Wolves collect in hierarchical packs and prey on both domestic and wild animals (sort of like tax return auditors). For more information, there are some great wolf-oriented resources on the Net. If you like to talk about wolves, there are Usenet groups in which you can participate.

**Web:**

**http://www.scs.unr.edu/~timb/desertm.html**

**Usenet:**

**alt.wolves**
**alt.wolves.hybrid**

# ARCHEOLOGY

## Aerial Archeology Journal

The Aerial Archeology Journal contains news and information relating to using aerial surveys and photography for archeological research. The next time you see a nondescript plane go by with someone pointing a camera at you, he may not be a spy for the CIA. It just may be a Ph.D. student working on his thesis about "Alexandria: The Shining Pearl of the Mediterranean, and Its Relation to Modern American Tract Housing."

**Web:**

**http://www.nmia.com/~jaybird/AANewsletter/**

## Ancient World Archeology

This site contains links to a large variety of archeological resources on the Net. If you are looking for specific information, this is a good place to start your search. If you have a few extra minutes, this is a wonderful place to find something interesting to investigate.

**Web:**

**http://atlantic.evsc.virginia.edu/julia/AW/subject/archaeo.html**

## Ancient World Archeology

**Do you want to make a lot of money? Here's a great investment.**

BEER
20th Century

Take a bunch of stuff from around the house—some old newspapers, a chipped cereal bowl, a few T-shirts with beer ads on them, an old car battery, and any other junk that you can spare—and put it all in a large, hermetically sealed box. Now all you have to do is wait.

After 2000 years or so, the items in your box will qualify as genuine archeological artifacts, and you will be able to sell them for a handsome profit.

If you would like to see what the Greeks, Romans and other ancient people put in ***their*** boxes, check out the Ancient World Archeology site.

## Archeology Talk and General Discussion

The study of archeology covers a huge amount of ground, which is why there are a great many archeology discussion groups on the Net. No matter what your interest or field of expertise, there is bound to be a group just for you. Follow the discussion over the Net, and you can work with people all over the world without having to venture more than a few feet from the fridge. Or, when you are out on a dig, you can take your laptop computer and cellular modem (paid for by a government grant) and keep up on what is happening, no matter how far you are from the trappings of civilization.

**Web:**

**http://www.duke.edu/web/jyounger/archlist.html**

## Archnet

I have a friend, Virginia (Ginny) Hatfield, who is an archeologist. She spends a lot of time running around the country digging up small pieces of whatnot and making esoteric discoveries. Myself, I prefer to stay at home with my cat and cruise the University of Connecticut's Archnet site. That way I can spend hours poring over all kinds of archeological resources without getting my hands dirty. Ginny may have more fun, but I'm a lot closer to the fridge.

**Web:**

**http://www.lib.uconn.edu/ArchNet/ArchNet.html**

## Biblical Archeology

People who study the Bible are especially interested in the archeological foundations of biblical writings. However, even for non-believers, the study of the archeology of biblical times can be rewarding, offering a glimpse into ancient societies that form the basis for much of modern Western civilization. Here is a well-organized collection of links relating to sites mentioned in the Bible. Aside from general resources, you will find links to maps, organizations, and information about ongoing excavations.

**Web:**

**http://www.lpl.arizona.edu/~kmeyers/archaeol/bib_arch.html**

## Classics and Mediterranean Archeology

Dedicated to information and other resources of interest to classicists and Mediterranean archeologists. Offers access to journals, texts, spatially referenced data as well as information on museum and library exhibits.

**Web:**

**http://rome.classics.lsa.umich.edu/**

## Cultural Site Etiquette

Archeology sites don't grow on trees (although trees do grow on some archeology sites). It is important, when you work on a site, to be able to investigate without damaging the site and the artifacts. Here is information about minimum impact techniques that every budding archeologist should understand before visiting a cultural or archeological site.

**Web:**

**http://www.nps.gov/care/arpa.htm**

## Egyptian Artifacts

You can be Indiana Jones without having to worry about sharp spikes being driven through your head or giant rolling rocks crushing you to death. Take a look at beautiful Egyptian artifacts at the Institute of Egyptian Art and Archaeology.

**Web:**

**http://www.memphis.edu/egypt/artifact.html**

## Mesoamerican Archeology

Experience the mystery and exotic qualities of old mesoamerican cultures by getting in on discussion of topics like pre-Columbian and pre-Mayan excavations and carbon dating of particular finds.

**Usenet:**

**sci.archaeology.mesoamerican**

## National Archeological Database

Throughout most of recorded history, people have had to dig around for official archeological data. Now, however, the National Archeological Database puts hard-to-find information at your virtual fingertips. Never again need you spend hours looking for documents such as the Notice of Inventory Completion for Native American Human Remains from Lake Winnepesauke, New Hampshire.

**Web:**

**http://www.cast.uark.edu/products/NADB/**

## Perseus Project

The Perseus Project contains a vast collection of information relating to art objects, archeological sites and buildings, vases, coins, and sculptures, including well over 10,000 pictures. My favorite part is the collection of ancient coins—information as well as pictures—because I like to collect coins myself. This is a great site for serious researchers. Information on all these artifacts, gathered from museums around the world, is collected and organized into a large, well-organized library.

**Web:**

**http://www.perseus.tufts.edu/art&arch.html**

## Treasure In Your Backyard?

How many people are passing up important --and perhaps valuable--Archeological treasures, right in their own backyard? This need never happen to you.

The National Archeological Database contains information on more investigations than you can shake a 500-year-old stick at. Connect to this bountiful resource and get the lowdown on what's low down.

## Rock Art

The oldest existing works of art we have are drawings and carvings on rocks. Such artifacts have been found on every continent and form an important body of archeological source material. Common rock art motifs include outlines of human hands, drawings of animals and hunting scenes, and pictures of daily activities. Here are a great many links to rock art Internet sites around the world.

**Web:**

**http://www.questorsys.com/rockart/links.htm**

## Roman Art and Archeology

The archeology of ancient Rome is a large, robust area of study, and this site has some great resources, including a large number of wonderful, well-organized essays and exhibits, as well as information and archives for related mailing lists. This is a great place for both research and browsing.

**Web:**
**http://www-personal.umich.edu/~pfoss/ROMARCH.html**

**Majordomo Mailing List:**
List Name: **romarch**
Subscribe to: **majordomo@rome.classics.lsa.umich.edu**

## Society for American Archeology

The Society for American Archeology is an international, professional organization for archeologists devoted to the study of North and South American archeology. This site is the place to look for information about membership, publications, meetings and lobbying the government. You can also find a nice list of educational programs in the United States, Canada and Latin America.

**Web:**
**http://www.saa.org/**

## Underwater Archeology

Not all archeology takes place on land. There is lots and lots of old and important stuff under the water. Here is an Internet site devoted to studying underwater archeology. You will find articles, discussion lists, information about shipwrecks, as well as links to other, related resources.

**Web:**
**http://fiat.gslis.utexas.edu/~trabourn/underwater.html**

Tired of the same old structures everywhere you look?
Try
Alternative Architecture
for new thinking about old ideas.

# ARCHITECTURE

## Aesthetic Architecture

This site has information about the aesthetic architecture movement of the late 19th and early 20th centuries. The works displayed at this site are from artists and architects who concentrated heavily on regional styles, hand craftsmanship and decorative detail. Represented movements include the Prairie School (Frank Lloyd Wright), Craftsman (Gustave Stickley) and other regional and international styles such as the Gothic revival.

**Web:**
**http://www.fswarchitects.com/links.html**

## Alternative Architecture

How boring our cities would be if architects only designed structures that looked like all the other structures. But wait, isn't that what they already do? Yes, indeed it is, and that is why our cities are so boring. If you are someone who likes to ask "What if...?" hang out with the people in the alternative architecture discussion group and find out what might be possible.

**Usenet:**
**alt.architecture.alternative**

## Architectural Reconstructions

Do you ever wonder what ancient ruins looked like before they were destroyed? If you have trouble imagining the architecture, you can take a look at some of the computer-modeled reconstructions of famous ancient buildings such as Hadrian's Bath and the Temple of Rameses III. This site has not only the pictures, but details about rebuilding by computer and other architectural explorations.

**Web:**
**http://archpropplan.auckland.ac.nz/misc/virtual_tour.html**

## Architectural Styles

When you have to go to one of those swanky, cultural, let's-show-off-who-we-are-and-what-we-do parties, it's good to have a few cocktail conversation topics prepared. Architecture is something good to talk about, because there will always be a building nearby. Before you head off to that party, read the information at this site. You'll find descriptions of various architectural styles and their influences. Before long, you will be able to name-drop with ease.

**Web:**

**http://www.escape.ca/~jmorgan/iadhp/arch.html**

## Architecture and Technology

Architecture, like many other arts, is now firmly wedded to modern technology. If you are an architect or interested in modern architecture, here are lots of resources related to architectural technology: CAD (computer aided design), online libraries, various types of computer programs, image manipulation, and more.

**Web:**

**http://www.students.uiuc.edu/~p-chen2/**

### *Look What I Found on the Net...*

```
(from the Web)

            AN ARCHITECTURAL MANIFESTO

Buckminister Fuller said that the average person doesn't give a
thought to the sophistication of the technology that allows him
to flush the toilet on the 104th floor and have it work...
I say, let's just cut holes in the floor and let the refuse fall
into the basement.

However, architectural critics pick nits with this design:

  "This design is a crock. Although cheap and effective in
   low buildings, random air currents blowing this way and
   that will inevitably cause the material descending from
   higher floors to splatter on the edges of the holes in the
   floors below."

I say, no problem, just make the holes on the lower floors
bigger.

Architectural critics still pick nits:

  "The hole in the first floor of a 104-story building would
   have to be at least 35 feet, 4 inches in diameter to be
   practical."

I say, so what, people will love 'em. What a conversation
piece... Imagine this: you're sitting in your living room,
eating toast points, drinking champagne before your maid serves
dinner, and you see a piece of refuse fall through the 35 foot hole
in the ceiling, silently descend the 12 feet to the 35 foot
4 inch hole in the floor, and vanish from sight. One of your
guests, remarks:

"Looked to be about 6.5 feet in from the edge, there.
I'd say it came from the 42nd floor..."
```

## Architecture Resource Center

When brain surgery is too involved and complicated and a game of frisbee is too much fun, try browsing some architecture resources on the Net as a way of spending your spare time. This site has information on computers and architecture, schools of architecture, links to architecture student pages, professional architects, discussion groups and links to related sites.

**Web:**
**http://www.u-net.com/~birchall/arch.htm**

## Architecture Talk and General Discussion

In my opinion, architects are some of the most talented, visionary, imaginative people in the world. Join the general architecture discussion group for all manner of architecture-oriented topics: building design, construction, architecture schools, materials, and so on. If they can build it, you can talk about it.

**Usenet:**
**alt.architecture**

## Athenian Architecture

If you can't tell your basic amphiprostyle structure from a peripteral layout, maybe it's time to brush up on your basic Greek architecture. Take a virtual tour of the architecture of Athens. Here you will see pictures of the Acropolis, the Library of Hadrian, the Arch of Hadrian, the Temple of Zeus, the Theater of Dionysius, and much more.

**Web:**
**http://www.indiana.edu/~kglowack/Athens/Athens.html**

**There's no such thing as too much bandwidth.**

## Cathedrals

The Gothic style of cathedrals was predominant in Europe from around 1150 to 1400. Gothic emerged in France and coincided with the rise of the monarchy as the central form of government. (Gothic cathedrals were not called gothic in their days of creation. The style was referred to as the "Modern" or "French" style. The term "Gothic" was coined in the 16th century by an Italian artist and historian named Giorgio Vasari. The expression was originally a negative term referring to the Goths who, Vasari felt, were responsible for ruining the classical artistry of the Roman empire. However, today the Gothic cathedral is admired as a breathtaking work of art.) This web page offers a tour of various cathedrals such as Notre Dame, Canterbury and Chartres.

**Web:**
**http://www.globalnet.net/elore/elore04.html**

## Classical Architecture of the Mediterranean

A huge database of classical architecture of the Mediterranean basin. Allows you to search for images from a specific country, century, type of work, site, and title of work.

**Web:**
**http://rubens.anu.edu.au/architecture_form.html**

## Gargoyles in New York City

Tired of driving down the streets of suburbia and looking at row after row of the same old house? Get a taste of some of the New York architecture by taking a monster tour of the city. This site has a virtual walking tour of New York City streets noted for creepy, cute or lurking stone monsters. The pictures are great and are accompanied by commentary.

**Web:**
**http://www.users.interport.net/~ameliaw/gargoyle.html**

## Images of Renaissance and Baroque Architecture

Images of Renaissance and Baroque architecture that show basic design and building principles of typical architecture of the time.

**Web:**

**http://www.lib.virginia.edu/dic/colls/arh102/**

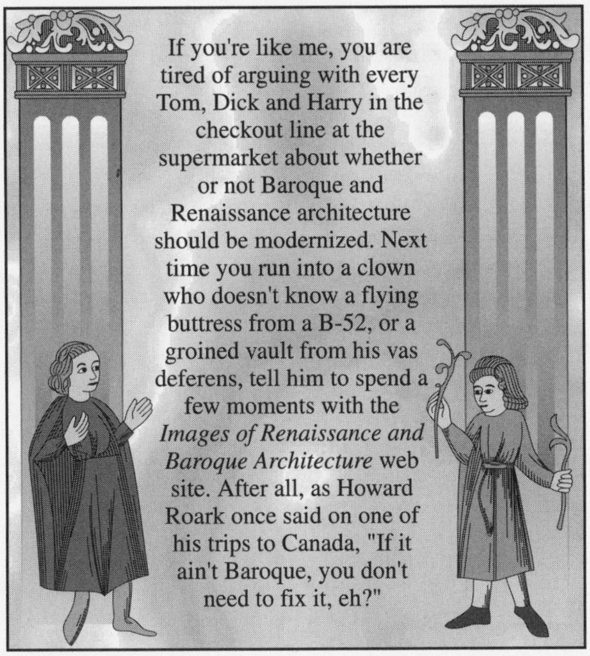
If you're like me, you are tired of arguing with every Tom, Dick and Harry in the checkout line at the supermarket about whether or not Baroque and Renaissance architecture should be modernized. Next time you run into a clown who doesn't know a flying buttress from a B-52, or a groined vault from his vas deferens, tell him to spend a few moments with the *Images of Renaissance and Baroque Architecture* web site. After all, as Howard Roark once said on one of his trips to Canada, "If it ain't Baroque, you don't need to fix it, eh?"

## Interior Design

It's a hard choice to make—should you be traditional with your home design or should you be quaintly archaic and put an outhouse in the backyard? Don't let these architectural dilemmas keep you up at night. Get together with other people who are interested in interior design as it relates to architecture.

**Usenet:**

**alt.architecture.int-design**

## Lighting

No more reading under the covers with a flashlight. Learn how to use color and light to create a unique and comfortably lit architectural environment. Read up on the color and temperature of light as well as the more technical and functional aspects of lighting.

**Usenet:**

**sci.engr.lighting**

## Wright, Frank Lloyd

Frank Lloyd Wright (1869-1959) was an American architect whose innovations later set standards in architecture. Wright invented the "prairie style" of home and believed in eliminating traditional room divisions in order to create a living space that was more in tune with the needs of the inhabitants. These web pages have lots of great information about Wright, along with pictures of his works.

**Web:**

**http://www.mcs.com/~tgiesler/flw_home.htm**
**http://selfpub.www.columbia.mo.us/~jmiller/wright1.html**
**http://www.geocities.com/CapitolHill/2317/flw.html**

# ART

## African Art

An enduring theme in African art is that ideas about life—both spiritual and worldly—can be portrayed through the rendering of human and animal images. Thus, masks, carvings, paintings and other works represent ideas and feelings. The African Art museum is a good place to look at African art and to start to appreciate its unique flavor.

**Web:**

**http://www.interlog.com/~csteele/orlist1.html**

## Age of Enlightenment Art

It's hard to believe that the Age of Enlightenment has nothing to do with the Internet beyond having its own web page. In this period, occurring between the death of Louis XIV and the rise to power of Napoleon Bonaparte, France experienced a few wonderful years of domestic growth and economic prosperity. The art of the time reflected this new age with its lightheartedness and childlike qualities. Read about the history and trends of the Age of Enlightenment and see paintings by artists such as Fragonard, David, Watteau, Boucher and many others.

**Web:**

**http://dmf.culture.fr/files/imaginary_exhibition.html**

## Art Criticism Forum

When it comes to art, everybody may know what they like, but not everybody's opinion is worthwhile. If you are serious about art, you may want to participate in an art criticism discussion. At least you can be sure there will always be one person who knows what he is talking about.

**Listserv Mailing List:**

List Name: **artcrit**
Subscribe to: **listserv@yorku.ca**

## Art History

Don't consign yourself to a life of blowing dust off old books. Immerse yourself in the sea of electronic resources that are available.

**Web:**

**http://www.hart.bbk.ac.uk/VirtualLibrary.html**

## Art History Information

The Getty Art History Information Program offers access to searchable databases. The image maps at this site are cleverly made to look like a Durer triptych that can be opened, so you can look inside. Fortunately, for those without graphical browsers or for those of you short on time, there is a text-only option as well.

**Web:**

**http://www.ahip.getty.edu/ahip/**

## Art History Server

This server offers a variety of image collections and small presentations, all of which deal in some way with art history. There are thousands of images of prints, largely from the 15th to the 19th century, as well as images of mainly classical architecture and architectural sculpture from around the Mediterranean.

**Web:**

**http://rubens.anu.edu.au/**

## Art Network for Integrated Media Applications

Links to many different resources relating to digital art, multimedia, the integration of art and technology, online arts and media publications, programs, tools and applications, and discussion groups.

**Web:**

**http://www.anima.wis.net/**

*Have you ever wondered what would happen if you mixed some sand in with finger paints?*
*So do the people at ANIMA (Art Network for Integrated Media Applications).*

## Art Nouveau

An overview of the Art Nouveau movement, a map of the major European centers of Art Nouveau, information on famous artists of the movement, what kind of art they created, and a section on architecture.

**Web:**

**http://www.loria.fr/AN/**

"Art Nouveau" is just another way of saying "New Art". (We just say it in French to make it more classy.) So take a look at the Internet's **Art Nouveau** overview, and soon you will be saying "Zut alors!" (French for "Way cool, Dude").

## Art Projects on the Internet

The Syracuse University Computer Graphics for the Arts server offers details and images from many projects, encouraging collaboration between artists across the Internet. It includes such projects as Digital Journeys, ChainArt, Search for the Lost Soul, as well as links to many more.

**Web:**
**http://ziris.syr.edu/**

## Art Sites

Don't spend time window shopping. Head straight to the supermarket of art sites. This collection of links to interesting traditional and contemporary art sites should keep you busy for many hours.

**Web:**
**http://bastille.gatech.edu/adam/art.html**

## Art Talk and General Discussion

This gathering on Usenet is a place for artists to talk about the art community, post announcements on new exhibits and gallery openings, rant about the politics of art and offer critical speculation on various works.

**Usenet:**
**alt.artcom**

LOOKING FOR AN ART JURY OF YOUR PEERS?

Try the **alt.artcom** discussion group. No need to waste your time hanging around a coffee house talking about the art world, when you can sit around your own house, drinking coffee and discussing the art world.

## Artistic Expression

A web page devoted to the free expression and distribution of artistic ideas. It is composed of and supports independent artists. Browse through a variety of resources: stories, images, poems, technical articles and photographs.

**Web:**
**http://www.knosso.com/NWHQ/**

### Freedom Art-Style

The best thing about Art is that everyone can do it (that is, everyone who is not too busy earning a living). The **Artistic Expression** web page is devoted to free expression and, as such, has my sincere gratitude and admiration.

After all, if it weren't for free expression, we would all have to pay just to voice an opinion. Pretty soon, only rich people would be able to speak their minds, while the rest of us would be reduced to writing letters-to-the-editor which we couldn't afford to mail.

So let's hear it for the artists: those brave philosophical warriors who are willing to say what's on their minds and let the intellectual chips fall where they may. Without the leaders of artistic expression and all of their followers, we might still be watching *Leave it to Beaver* or *Father Knows Best*, never dreaming that there was more to life than comfort and day-to-day satification.

A B C D E F G H I J K L M N O P Q R S T U V W X Y Z

## Artistic Melange

Find out about music, opera, and plays. Read reviews and interviews. If you've been looking for art in all the wrong places, you will definitely be able to find it here.

**Usenet:**

**rec.arts.misc**

## Artnet Magazine

Don't get left out of the cool art scene. No matter where on Earth you are—London, Cairo, or Fargo, North Dakota—you can keep up with the latest happenings in the art world. This art news magazine contains news, feature articles, art reviews, international reports about the art world, artist portfolios, art book reviews, fiction and lots more art-related stuff.

**Web:**

**http://www.artnet.com/magazine.html**

## ArtResources

A resource designed to be a storehouse of information about artists, museums, galleries, art publications, and art shows on the Net. Boasting thousands of listings, this site will keep you busier than a flea at a dog party.

**Web:**

**http://www.ftgi.com/**

## Ascii Art

There is no sense getting your hands dirty just to make art. Have a blast making cool pictures without ever having to throw down a dropcloth or stink up your room with brain-damaging chemicals. There are loads and loads of ascii art resources on the Net.

**Web:**

**http://gagme.wwa.com/~boba/scarecrow.html**

**Usenet:**

**alt.ascii-art**
**alt.binaries.pictures.ascii**
**rec.arts.ascii**

**Listserv Mailing List:**

List Name: **asciiart**
Subscribe to: **listserv@lsv.uky.edu**

## Basic Design in Art and Architecture

There is more to art and architecture than just expressing yourself. You have to do it in a way in which nobody gets killed. At least in architecture. (In the art world, you just call it performance art, and that makes it okay.) Participate in discussion relating to basic and applied design as it relates to both art and architecture.

**Listserv Mailing List:**

List Name: **design-l**
Subscribe to: **listserv@psuvm.psu.edu**

## Body Art

Pierced, tattooed, scarred, painted and more. These newsgroups are the place to talk about body art in all its forms. The **binaries** group will have pictures of various forms of body art.

**Usenet:**

**alt.binaries.pictures.bodyart**
**rec.arts.bodyart**

### I Too, You Too, We All Too for Tattoo

Only a humph-brained ignoramus would think that decorating your body by permanent disfigurement is foolish. After all, if God didn't want us to modify our outer covering in the name of Art, why did he give us safety pins (and needles and knives and paper shredders)?

Personally, I feel that the human body comes with only the minimum set of holes, and anyone who wants to add to the collection has a perfect right to do so. If cleanliness is next to godliness, then holiness must be next to . . . well, I'm not quite sure, but it must be something important.

So next time you have a few spare moments and it is not too close to mealtime, spend some time reading the Body Art discussion groups. I guarantee a fun time for all and more than a few ideas for how to decorate the neighbors' children next Christmas.

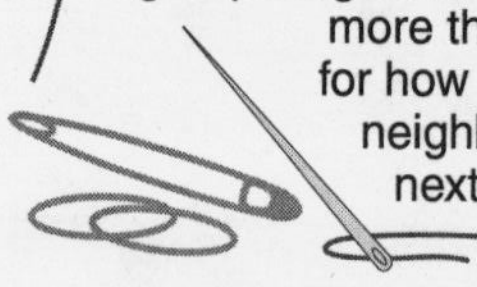

## Ceramic Arts

A mailing list of interest to folks into ceramic arts and pottery. Discuss any related subject you like, including aesthetic issues and concerns, grant information, and exhibition opportunities.

**Listserv Mailing List:**

List Name: **clayart**
Subscribe to: **listserv@lsv.uky.edu**

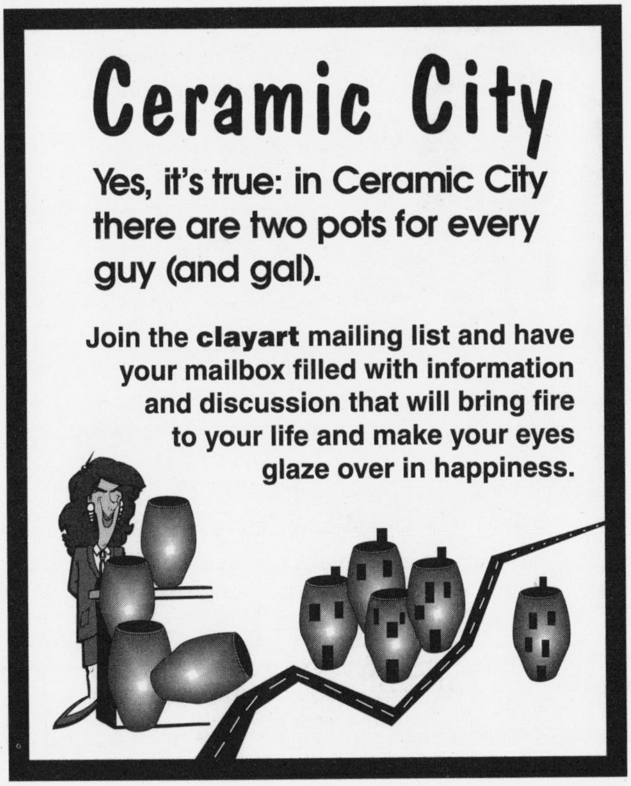
Ceramic City
Yes, it's true: in Ceramic City there are two pots for every guy (and gal).
Join the **clayart** mailing list and have your mailbox filled with information and discussion that will bring fire to your life and make your eyes glaze over in happiness.

## Contemporary Art Mailing List

Don't believe any rumors you might hear about art being dead. It's alive and well, and contemplating itself on this mailing list devoted to the discussion of issues relevant to contemporary art.

**Listserv Mailing List:**

List Name: **artlist**
Subscribe to: **listserv@listserv.arizona.edu**

## Corpse Game Image Archive

When you get tired of playing with Mr. Potato Head and the Operation game, move on to a different kind of game that involves body parts. Participate in the collaborative art project Corpse. You and other random individuals collectively create a body: one of you draws the head, one draws the torso and so on. Put them all together and you can call it Art.

**Web:**

**http://sunsite.unc.edu/otis/synergy/corpse.html**

## Digital Journeys

An ongoing collaborative art project by various people on the Internet. Read the writing, look at the pictures, and if you feel inspired you can add to them. It's free-form and fun.

**Web:**

**http://ziris.syr.edu/digjourney.html**

One of the best things about the Internet is how people share their creations. (It's also one of the worst things about the Internet.)

If you feel like collaborating — or seeing how others collaborate —

take a look at **Digital Journeys** and see how the Internet can bring out the best in people.

## Fine Art Forum

Delve into the mystery and meaning of art. Artists come together for lively exploration of the meaning, impact, responsibility, and history of art. This forum is scholarly, but not intimidating, and can provide answers to the most obscure technical or theoretical questions. Because artists are always in the studio, this is a great way to finally get them all in one place.

**Web:**

**http://www.msstate.edu/Fineart_Online/**

**Usenet:**

**rec.arts.fine**

## Gargoyles and Grotesques

Are you a fan of the dark? Do you, at sunset, glance upward to see the grotesque statuary on the edges of skyscrapers or Renaissance cathedrals? This web site is devoted to gargoyles old and new, as well as grotesque statues of every sort. It provides a history of and writings about this unique form of sculpture, as well as dramatic pictures of some of its more interesting examples. All in all, the site is definitely worth a visit, if only for the Gothic grandeur of it all.

**Web:**

**http://www.mcs.net/~sculptor/GARGOYLE.HTML**
**http://ils.unc.edu/garg/garghp4.html**

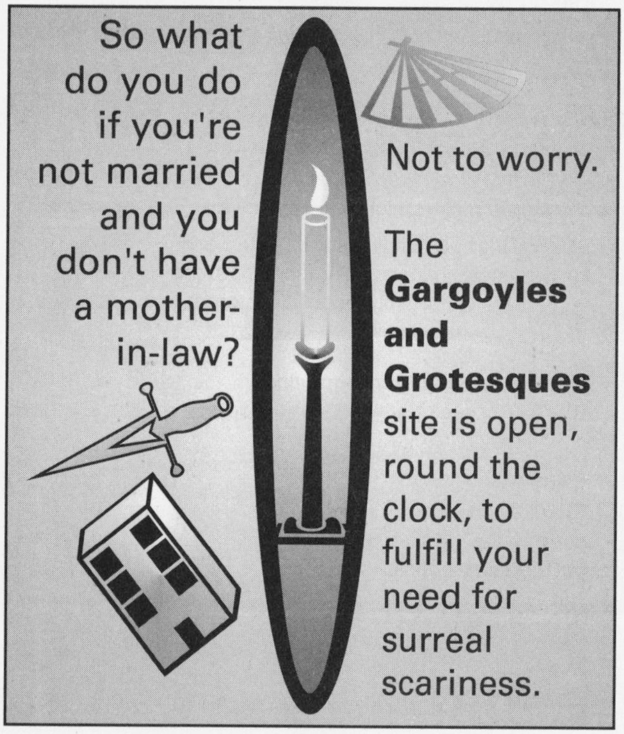
So what do you do if you're not married and you don't have a mother-in-law?
Not to worry.
The Gargoyles and Grotesques site is open, round the clock, to fulfill your need for surreal scariness.

## Greencart Magazine

An attractive online magazine with forums for art discussion, artist contacts, contest information and links to other art sites. Have fun at the interactive art wall and earn your reputation as an online grafitti artist.

**Web:**

**http://www.greencart.com/**

## Grotesque in Art

This is an exhibit of visual images that explores violence, horror, and the grotesque in art. Send the kids out of the room, don't eat before viewing, and don't meditate on these just before bedtime because they can be very graphic.

**Web:**

**http://www.ugcs.caltech.edu/~werdna/grotesque/grotesque.html**

If you are an ordinary mortal, you may not be aware that grotesque–just like *sfumato*, *profil perdu* or *horror vacuii*–is an actual technical term among art historians. So when you cop a look at the *Grotesque in Art* resource, you are actually dropping in on a scholarly exhibit, designed to educate, enlighten, and generally raise men above the base level of beasts. To use another technical term favored by the people who like to drive students crazy by making them mindlessly memorize slides of famous paintings, it's way cool.

## Japanese Animation

Immerse yourself in the magical world of Japanese animation (anime). Devotees of animation provide information not only on this art form, but also movie reviews, schedules of showings, announcements of new releases, conventions, and club meetings.

**Usenet:**

**rec.arts.anime**
**rec.arts.anime.creative**
**rec.arts.anime.fandom**
**rec.arts.anime.games**
**rec.arts.anime.info**
**rec.arts.anime.marketplace**
**rec.arts.anime.misc**
**rec.arts.anime.models**
**rec.arts.anime.stories**

## Mail Art

Mail art is a fun means of creating interactive art that stays in the hands of the artists, instead of being behind glass or in stuffy exhibits. Find out more about mail and email art, see images of mail art, and get a list of people on the Net who participate in mail art.

**Web:**

**http://www.sas.upenn.edu/~vbell/mail.html**

## Mythology in Western Art

Everybody you know is always showing off snapshots of their kids, cats or cars. Be one up on the masses by showing pictures of your favorite gods and goddesses at the next family reunion.

**Web:**

**http://www-lib.haifa.ac.il/www/art/mythology_westart.html**

## Native American Art

Prior to the twentieth century, native Americans did not create art as an end unto itself. Rather, they created crafts that fit into their ceremonies and their everyday activities. The twentieth century has seen a great deal of purposeful art development based on these early traditions and skills. The Native American Art site contains museums, galleries and collections in which you will find a wide variety of information regarding contemporary native American art.

**Web:**

**http://hanksville.phast.umass.edu/misc/NAart.html**

## Nomadic Art

Most art is not like the Sistine Chapel. Generally, art is easy to move and travels around to show itself off at galleries around the word. "Nomadic" is a term with roots in ancient history, but it still applies to some art today. Join artists and art lovers as they discuss and share news about art on the move.

**Usenet:**

**alt.arts.nomad**

## Planet Earth Art and Photography

This site is a collection of active links to a variety of art and photography sites. These range from images of the cave paintings in France to Art Crimes, a gallery of graffiti art.

**Web:**

**http://www.nosc.mil/planet_earth/art.html**

## SITO Project

SITO (Operative Term Is Stimulate) distributes original artwork and photographs over the network for public perusal, scrutiny, and distribution. SITO also offers a forum for critique and exhibition of your works. A virtual art gallery that never closes and exists in an information dimension where your submissions will hang as wallpaper on thousands of glowing monitors.

**Web:**

**http://www.sito.org/**

SITO
is cool.
SITO
is a big deal.
SITO
is great.

## Surrealism Server

If you don't understand it, we can't explain it. Let your mind dance on the edge of radical thought. (Fish.) Take a look at paintings of famed Surrealists or participate in some fun Surrealism games like The Infinite Story or The Exquisite Cadaver. Don't be afraid. The only thing it can hurt is your brain.

**Web:**

**http://pharmdec.wustl.edu/juju/surr/surrealism.html**

A B C D E F G H I J K L M N O P Q R S T U V W X Y Z

A B C D E F G H I J K L M N O P Q R S T U V W X Y Z

## Techno-Impressionist Art

Techno-Impressionism is a 20th century movement aimed at recapturing the spirit of the art of the 1890s when the Impressionists were running around causing gentle havoc in a variety of shades of pastel. View the gallery pages of art and read the interesting manifesto that talks about art from a techno point of view.

**Web:**
**http://www.techno-impressionist.com/**

## Tessellation Times

The Tessellation Times is a weekly electronic supplement to 3D Art Magazine for graphic artists. Read book reviews, event listings, special interest group listings, and other tidbits of information for artists interested in three-dimensional art.

**Web:**
**http://tgax.com/3dartist.htm#Tess**

## World Arts Resources

This site will give you lots of links to art around the world. See a list of hundreds of museums; search a database containing many art-related URLs. There are links to art publications, government and educational resources, and even antiques.

**Web:**
**http://wwar.com/**

# ART GALLERIES AND EXHIBITS

## 911 Gallery

So you just don't see what's so appealing about ancient art. It's old, dusty, and it smells bad. You want something new, shiny and fast. Check out this gallery of electronic media, including computer graphics, video and music. As with all galleries, the exhibits on display will change, so keep checking in to see new things.

**Web:**
**http://www.iquest.net/911/iq_911.html**

## Alphonse Mucha Museum

Alphonse Maria Mucha (1860-1939) was a Czech artist remembered for his posters created in the French Art Nouveau period. He was propelled into stardom when he was commissioned to create posters of Sarah Bernhardt, an actress who was in vogue in the late 1800s. Mucha's work is characterized by a predominance of curves and flowing lines, and abstract and stylized motifs from nature, like flowers. At the time, there was a growing interest in decorative art and a relaxation of the Victorian attitudes. Mucha's more free and sensual style was heartily welcomed. Take a look at the beautiful works of Alphonse Mucha. This web site has many of his works, including some of the advertisement graphics he did for companies like Nestle foods.

**Web:**
**http://www.webcom.com/~tuazon/ajarts/mucha.html**

## Andy Warhol Museum

What do the words "repetitive", "garish", and "self-indulgent" have in common? They are all words that can be used to describe Andy Warhol and his work. Tour the web page for the Andy Warhol Museum located in Pittsburgh, the new mecca for Pop art. Pages include a tour through the museum, art samples, exhibit schedules and film schedules.

**Web:**
**http://www.clpgh.org/warhol**

## Art Crimes

Graffiti is often referred to as "art crime" because even though it can sometimes be beautiful, it's still illegal. Take a photo-tour of art crimes around the world. Many of these places no longer exist, so this will be your only chance to see them.

**Web:**
**http://www.gatech.edu/desoto/graf/**

## The Future Is Now?

Perhaps Andy Warhol's most famous observation was, "In the future, everyone will read a Harley Hahn book for 15 minutes."

But unlike the wit and irony of Harley Hahn, Warhol and his art were nothing if not elusive. There is something to be said for this paragon of self-promotion, who no doubt spent most of his 60 years laughing, several tongues in cheek, all the way to the art bank. True, Warhol did stop long enough to turn the principle of monotonous repetition into a series of unknowable, vacuous silkscreens and films, heavy on the Ipecac, but low on meaning and inspiration.

Still, Warhol has made it onto the Net and perhaps, now in death, he has found his true resting place: amid the frenetic electrons racing round the world from web server to client, full of sound and words, signifying nothing.

If you are not sure what to make of this strange denizen from our own dimension, check out the Andy Warhol web sites and marvel at how—if anyone really cared—you *could* fool all of the people all of the time. Or maybe you are better off simply reading a Harley Hahn book for 15 minutes.

## Art Gallery Talk and General Discussion

There are lots of things happening in the art scene, and one way to keep up is to follow what's happening in this Usenet group. When the time comes that your work is going in exhibition, you can announce it here.

**Usenet:**
**alt.art.scene**

## Art Museums and Exhibits

Access to commercial art galleries, electronic art galleries, Krannert Art Museum, the Louvre, the Museum of New Zealand, photography exhibits, the REIFF II Museum, and many other museums and exhibits around the world.

**Web:**
**http://wwar.com/museums.html**

## Art on the Net

Galleries, artists, current art happenings, links to other art sites, copyrights, and other information about art resources on the Net.

**Web:**
**http://www.art.net/**

## ArtVark Gallery

A gallery of paintings, photographs, drawings, and computer images by Dutch artists. This collection offers a great look at Dutch painters whose work you will probably never get to see in physical museum exhibits.

**Web:**
**http://www.fwi.uva.nl/~boncz/artvark/**

## Asian Art Gallery

Cure that craving for the exotic with a visit to the Asian Art Gallery. Explore an exhibit on Tibetan Mandalas or a collection of Himalayan art. You will also find information and photos of art from Nepal, India and Tibet.

**Web:**
**http://www.webart.com/asianart/**

## Carlos Museum of Art

Get your daily dose of culture by looking at images of ancient Egypt, the ancient Americas, art from Asia, Greece, Rome, and sub-Saharan Africa. You will see ancient artifacts such as a cuneiform tablet, a mummy, and an engraved effigy, among others. Also available are later works on paper, such as manuscripts and scrolls.

**Web:**
**http://www.cc.emory.edu/CARLOS/**

## Dallas Museum of Art

See if there is any truth to the rumor that everything is bigger in Texas. The Dallas Museum of Art offers a look at their collections of contemporary art, pre- and post-Columbian galleries, and a Museum of Europe which includes images of Gauguin, Delacroix, Mondrian, Degas and Rodin.

**Web:**

**http://www.unt.edu/dfw/dma/www/dma.htm**

### Enhancing Your Art Image

**Do you want an easy way to impress someone? All you need to do is enhance your personal art image.**

**Here's what to do.**

**Connect to the Dallas Museum of Art web site. Find yourself a picture of a beautiful painting that looks good on your computer screen. (One of my favorites is "Riverbank in Springtime" by Vincent van Gogh.) Next, save the picture to a file.**

**Now, whenever anyone comes over, you can casually leave the file displayed on your screen. When people say, "My what a beautiful painting, is it real?", you can reply, "Oh, that old thing? It's just a little something I had lying around my disk."**

## Dia Center for the Arts

This is a great site that displays a permanent collection of local New York City artists, an Andy Warhol page and changing exhibits of web artists. These images are not just static—there are also movies available.

**Web:**

**http://www.diacenter.org/**

## Digital Photography

A display of the winners of annual juried contests of digital photography. These images began life as mere photographs or film and video and were then transformed into new art forms using a computer. Since this contest is held annually, you can also get information on how to enter your work in future events.

**Web:**

**http://www.bradley.edu/exhibit/**

## Drux Electronic Art Gallery

Discover the magic of digital art by taking a tour of the work of artists who are on the cutting edge of technology. The collection changes periodically, so what you see today may not be available for viewing tomorrow.

**Web:**

**http://yes.net/generality/drux.html**

## Enfolding Perspectives

Simran Singh Gleason has created an original collection of photo collages, landscapes, self-portraits and thoughtful writing. Gleason combines a fine photographic technique with a talent for seeing the unusual within the ordinary. Now, if I can only get him to take some pictures of my cat.

**Web:**

**http://www.art.net/Studios/Visual/Simran/EnfoldingPerspectives/enfolding-perspectives.html**

## Erté Museum

Erté was an art deco artist born in Russia under the name Romain de Tirtoff. He moved to Paris, in 1912, to become a fashion illustrator and called himself Erté, after the French pronunciation of his initials. He is best known for his extravagent costumes for musicals, Harper's Bazaar illustrations and the opera. His fashion career spanned his entire life. He designed outrageous clothing for approximately 75 years. This web site contains a nice collection and some writing about Erté.

**Web:**

**http://www.webcom.com/tuazon/ajarts/erte.html**

A B C D E F G H I J K L M N O P Q R S T U V W X Y Z

## French Cave Paintings

Much to everyone's relief, since the discovery of the Paleolithic cave paintings in Vallon, France, there has been little need to worry about the shortage of ancient cave paintings. At this Web site you will find images, history, and explanatory text about these French cave paintings.

**Web:**

**http://www.culture.fr/culture/gvpda-en.htm**

## Leonardo da Vinci Museum

See the work of the master who put the word "Renaissance" in "Renaissance Man". Painter, inventor, architect, writer, musician, and all-around genius, Leonardo is a household name in the world of art. This site displays his oil paintings, futuristic designs, drawings and sketches, and biographical information on the man who made Mona Lisa smile.

**Web:**

**http://www.leonardo.net/museum/**

## Los Angeles County Museum of Art

There is more to the city of Los Angeles than what you read in the National Enquirer. For instance, the Los Angeles County Museum of Art has quite a collection of beautiful artwork and interesting cultural costumes and textiles. See selected images of ancient and Islamic art, European paintings and sculpture, and art of the 20th century as well as links to other art sites.

**Web:**

**http://www.lacma.org/**

## Louvre Museum

Here's your chance to visit Paris free of charge. Get a ticket to the virtual Louvre, which is conducting tours around the city. You will see the Eiffel Tower and the Champs Elysees, among other sights. At the Louvre itself, they offer tours of a collection of famous paintings and a demonstration of French Medieval art. You have to bring your own pastries.

**Web:**

**http://www.louvre.fr/**

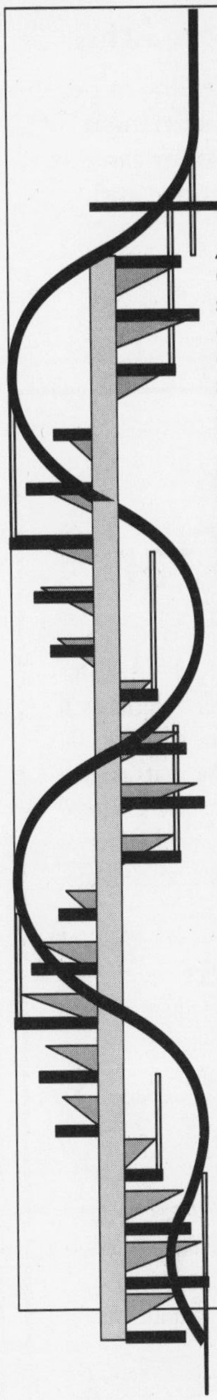

## Art+L.A.=
### Culture to the Max

A quick trip to the Los Angeles County Museum of Art web site is one that should be on everyone's cultural agenda. Of course, you will find the usual ancient Islamic and European art, as well as the mandatory collection of priceless paintings and sculpture. All of that is nice, of course, but nothing that you couldn't find on the walls of your local Water, Sewer, and Trash Administration Building.

But what you can't find elsewhere are exhibits that capture the essence of the true Southern California creative soul. For example, does the Louvre have an entire room devoted to toupees worn by famous film stars? Can the Sistine Chapel offer a collection as inspiring as the photographic exhibition of *all* of Johnny Carson's wives? And is there anything in New York—the poor East Coast wannabe—that even approaches the beauty and inspiration of the Winners of the Annual TV Guide Advertisement Collage Contest?

I think not. We in Southern California are proud of our creative heritage and our contributions to world culture, and we love to share.

## M.C. Escher Gallery

Maurits Cornelis Escher was not only a master at paradox and illusion, but he could draw an exquisite likeness of anything he could see or imagine. Artists, mathematicians, scientists, and the general consumer are all fascinated by his many graphic images on one level or another. Whether he stimulates your eye or your mind, these sites will be interesting to you.

**Web:**

**http://www.texas.net/escher**

A B C D E F G H I J K L M N O P Q R S T U V W X Y Z

## National Museum of American Art

There is more to good American art than the Sunday newspaper comics. View not only the permanent collection of the National Museum of American Art, but also some spectacular roving collections and exhibits.

**Web:**

**http://www.nmaa.si.edu/**

# Wish Upon a Falling Czar

On March 10, 1917, the troops of Czar Nicholas II of Russia mutinied. On March 11, the Czar ordered the dissolution of the legislature, but the members refused to honor the order. And on March 15, in the face of increasingly powerful unrest, the Czar decided to abdicate.

Clearly, being a Czar is a high-stress occupation that is probably not for everyone. However, if there is one thing good about being His Royal Excellency, it is the magnificent art collection that is yours to enjoy in your moments of leisure.

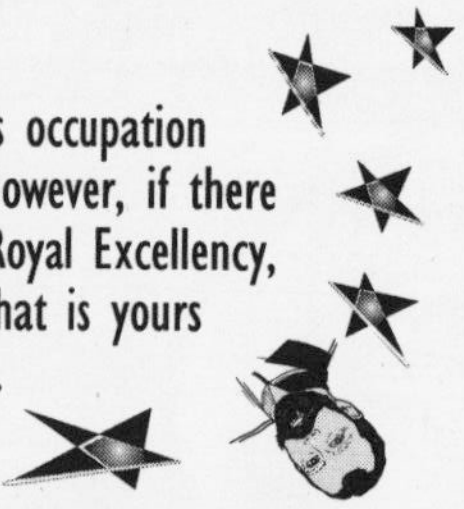

For example, we might imagine Czar Nicholas II saying to himself, "Sure, the peasants are revolting and my soldiers refuse to obey my commands, but I can still sit on my throne and admire this totally cool Fabergé egg with the tiny copy of *The Internet Complete Reference* inside." (Of course, he would be saying it in Russian, but you get the idea.)

For many years, such treasures were hidden from the world, but now, through the courtesy of the Internet, you can share in the art and culture of the Romanov dynasty. From 1613 to 1917, these awesome dudes (and dudettes) collected enough art to choke a Siberian horse. And if they were alive today, there would be nothing they would enjoy more than having you drop in and look around.

## Net in Arcadia

These artists have captured the spirit of Arcadia in their paintings. See the display inspired and named after the work of Nicholas Poussin. This gallery attempts to re-create the feeling of idealist settings and classically presented subject matter. Or as Poussin would say: *Et in Internet Ego.*

**Web:**

**http://www.parnasse.com/net.in.arcadia.html**

## Pixel Pushers

A "pixel" is a single dot that makes up part of an image. For example, on the screen of your monitor, each individual dot is a pixel. Pixel Pushers is the name of a web site devoted to the exhibition of digital art (art created using computers). You will find exhibits of digital art, as well as information about the artists. If you think that "computer art" isn't all that interesting, take a look at these pictures. I think you will be pleasantly surprised.

**Web:**

**http://yes.net/pixelpushers/**

## Sistine Chapel

If you can't get the time off from work to go see the Sistine Chapel, take a mini-vacation right now. Use your browser to take a tour of Cappella Sistina, where you will see hundreds of images of the chapel's artwork and read informative text about the chapel and its history.

**Web:**

**http://www.christusrex.org/www1/sistine/0-Tour.html**

## Treasures of the Czars

An excellent exhibit of art, icons, jewelry, armor and other items from the Russian Romanov dynasty. This site not only has images, but also useful historical information, fun games and a crash course on the Russian language. Even if you don't care anything about Russian art, you can still learn important phrases such as "Grouper is the local specialty."

**Web:**

**http://www.times.st-pete.fl.us/treasures/TC.Lobby.html**

## Vatican Exhibit

Here is a wonderful resource from the U.S. Library of Congress: an exhibition of Vatican history and culture. Here you can find a great deal of fascinating information as some wonderfully unexpected treasures: a fifteenth century manuscript of a Latin translation of Achimedes' mathematics, a Carolingian manuscript of the Roman comic poet Plautus, and the original autographed edition of *The Internet Complete Reference* used by the Pope to teach himself how to send email.

**Web:**

**http://www.ncsa.uiuc.edu/SDG/Experimental/vatican.exhibit/Vatican.exhibit.html**

## Women Artists Archive

Here is a great site for art lovers, information and resources relating to important women artists: Hildegard von Bingen (1098-1179), Artemesia Gentileschi (1593?-1652?), Maria Sybilla Merian (1647-1717), Marie Bracquemond (1841-1916), Frida Kahlo (1910-1954), Georgia O'Keeffe (1887-1986), and many more.

**Web:**

**http://www.cascade.net/women/**

## World Art Treasures

An art lover's fantasy: you're going through a bunch of junk at a yard sale and you find an old sculpture that turns out to be a lost treasure from the 5th century. Prepare yourself for those weekend jaunts from sale to sale. Brush up on art treasures from places such as Egypt, China, Japan, India, Burma, Laos, Thailand, so you will recognize that precious gem when you find it, although these are items you will probably not find lying around your neighborhood.

**Web:**

**http://sgwww.epfl.ch/BERGER/**

# ASTRONOMY

## Amateur Radio Transmissions

Just because you don't have millions of dollars of communications equipment in your bedroom doesn't mean you have to depend on NASA for your radio transmission thrills. Why should you be the last one on your block to hear signals from Pluto? Join the amateurs who discuss radio transmissions and telemetry data from space.

**Usenet:**

**rec.radio.amateur.space**

## Astrometry Science Team

If you had a telescope, would you study heavenly bodies? Well, that's exactly what the folks at the University of Texas are doing with the Hubble Telescope. Point your web browser here for images, data, and other items of interest from the folks who use the fine guidance sensors aboard the Hubble Space Telescope to study the stars and other celestial bodies.

**Web:**

**http://clyde.as.utexas.edu/**

### Be a Team Player

Are you just dying to be a competitive astrometrician? Well, all you have to do is say "Astronomical Telemetry" ten times real fast, grab your hyper-ruler and Secret Decoder O-Ring, and head for the *Astrometry Science Team* web page.

They may have laughed when you tried out for the football team, but if you are smart enough and fast enough to make the *Astrometry Science Team*, you will have them laughing out of the other side of their low-spectrum infrared radiometers. *(And, what's more, women will love you.)*

## Astronomical Museum

Instruments used by Bolognese astronomers from the early 18th to mid-19th century are on display here in the same rooms of the ancient tower originally devoted to observations. A history of the museum and astronomy in Bologna, Italy, and a guided tour of the Meridian, Globe, and Turret Rooms are available here. There are gif images of the early scientific equipment, along with lengthy descriptions.

**Web:**
**http://boas3.bo.astro.it/dip/Museum/MuseumHome.html**

## Astronomy and Astrophysics Research

It's hard to enjoy your life if you have heavy stuff on your mind like the anisotropy of gamma ray bursts or whether the sun actually has a south pole. If your local theologian can't help you solve the mystery of the universe, maybe here you will find someone who can. These folks know their astronomy and astrophysics.

**Usenet:**
**sci.astro.research**

## Astronomy Cafe

Sit around in the Astronomy Cafe and contemplate the stars, browse the weekly hotlist, ask questions in "Ask the Astronomer," and even listen to music which rounds out the cafe motif.

**Web:**
**http://www2.ari.net/home/odenwald/cafe.html**

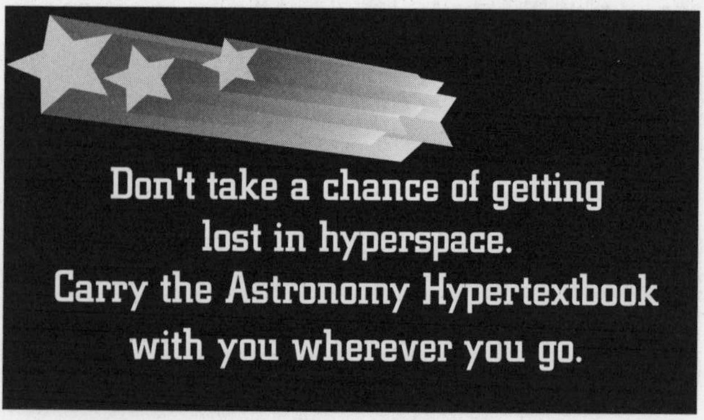



## Astronomy History

The study of astronomy is as old as the study of science. Aristarchus of Samos (310-230 B.C.), an early Greek astronomer, suggested that the Earth rotated on its axis and that the planets rotate around the sun in circular orbits. (Actually, the orbits are elliptical.) He also used his own observations along with his knowledge of geometry to determine the relative sizes and distances of the Earth, the moon and the sun. Personally, I have always been fascinated by man's quest for understanding the cosmos. Yes, there were a few false starts (like the Dark Ages and the 16th century Catholic Church), but by and large, mankind has made enormous progress in understanding the nature of our universe. Here is a resource that contains a wealth of information about the history of astronomy, including the many important twentieth century discoveries.

**Web:**
**http://aibn55.astro.uni-bonn.de:8000/~pbrosche/astoria.html**

## Astronomy Hypertextbook

Back in the old days, most of us had to lug around 150 pounds of dull, dry textbooks, and the only fun that could be had was to devise ways of writing graffiti in them without getting caught. With hypertext languages, textbooks become interactive and fun. Plus, you can sneak around and play games on the computer while the teacher isn't looking. Check out this fun and informative textbook that gives learning a whole new twist.

**Web:**
**http://zebu.uoregon.edu/text.html**

## Astronomy Servers

Large collection of links to astronomy-related servers around the globe. Each link has the institution's logo beside it, making it clear what is available.

**Web:**
**http://www.usgs.gov/network/science/astronomy/**

## Astronomy Software

Programs for all popular systems, texts, documents, pictures, news, and equipment information about astronomy and stargazing.

**Web:**

**http://www.w3.org/pub/DataSources/bySubject/astro/astroweb/yp_software.html**

## Astronomy Talk and General Discussion

Stars, planets, telescopes, cosmology, and all aspects of astronomy and astrophysics. Talk with people who really do understand black holes.

**Usenet:**

**sci.astro**
**sci.astro.amateur**

## Astrophysics Data System

The Astrophysics Data System allows access to hundreds of thousands of abstracts (astronomy and astrophysics, space instrumentation, physics and geophysics, and more), as well as access or links to archives and catalogs of astronomical data, including data collected by NASA space missions.

**Web:**

**http://adswww.harvard.edu/**

The Hubble Telescope sees all. And if you want to see what the people who seem to see the light with the Hubble are seeing right now, see the **sci.astro.hubble** discussion group. (Personally, I think they should have named it Seymour. Then when we go to galactic conferences where all the beings of the universe compare astronomical notes, we could wear T-shirts that say "See more with Seymour.")

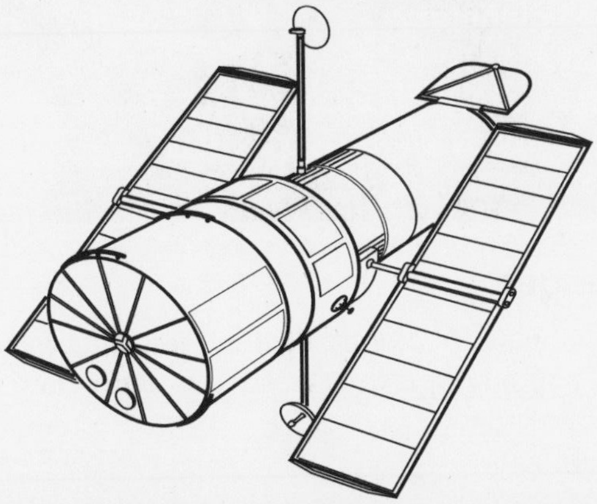

## Astroweb

The Internet has many different astronomical resources. There are information sites, picture archives, reference material, as well as many Usenet discussion groups. The Astroweb site connects you to dozens of interesting and useful resources, and makes it easy to find what you want. It is also a good place to explore for new resources.

**Web:**

**http://marvel.stsci.edu/net-resources.html**

## Earth Views

It's all a matter of perspective. No matter where you go on the Earth, you can never see the entire thing. These days, you don't have to be an astronaut to enjoy a nice view of the Earth from space. Check out this collection of photos of the Earth. If you know the latitude and longitude of your house, you can find the corresponding pictures and make a map with a big X and label it "You are here."

**Web:**

**http://images.jsc.nasa.gov/html/earth.htm**

## Einstein Observatory Data Archive

The Einstein Observatory was an X-ray telescope, in operation from November 1978 to April 1981 on a satellite orbiting the Earth. During that time, thousands of observations and images were captured. Here is a web page that allows you to access that information for your own research or just out of interest.

**Web:**

**http://hea-www.harvard.edu/einstein/Ein_home/ein_welcome.html**

## Hubble Telescope

Mull over data and observations from the Hubble Telescope. This moderated newsgroup contains technical information released as part of the Hubble project.

**Usenet:**

**sci.astro.hubble**

## Institutes of Astronomy

This web page has a collection of many links to institutes and universities with centers for astronomy and astrophysics.

**Web:**

**http://www.astro.cf.ac.uk/pub/Gareth.Jones/inst.html**

## Mars Atlas

This atlas is just as good as being on Mars. Better, really, if you think about how much you save in gas money by not going there. This is not just any atlas. You can scroll around and zoom in on the surface of the planet to see exactly what you want. If you look hard enough, maybe you will see those little men that Ray Bradbury is always going on about.

**Web:**

**http://fi-www.arc.nasa.gov/fia/projects/bayes-group/Atlas/Mars/**

## Observatories

Links to observatories all over the world, including Australia, Columbia, Canada, France, the U.K., Hawaii, Arizona, California, and many others.

**Web:**

**http://webhead.com/WWWVL/Astronomy/observatories-optical.html**

## Planetariums

Do you think that planetariums can be used for more than laser light shows to Pink Floyd music? If so, you can discuss issues with people who plan and implement planetarium programs.

**Usenet:**

**sci.astro.planetarium**

## Planetary Tour Guide

Make plans for where you want to go when Planet Earth gets too crowded. NASA offers several tour guides that will show you just what is hanging out in the sky above us. Even if you don't want to relocate, it's a nice way to plan your next vacation.

**Web:**

**http://ranier.oact.hq.nasa.gov/Sensors_page/Planets.html**

## Planets

If you've never had occasion to visit another planet, you don't have to feel that you are missing out on anything. Check out this colorful display of planetary "snapshots." If you move your chair around really fast while you look at these, you can almost pretend you are flying through space.

**Web:**

**http://pds.jpl.nasa.gov/planets/**

## Planets and the Solar System

The planets, asteroids, and other bodies that make up our solar system. Discuss astronomical details as well as space missions sent to explore these places.

**Usenet:**

**alt.sci.planetary**

### PLANETS ARE COOL

Yes, there is no doubt about it, planets are high up on just about everybody's list of favorite astronomical objects. Join the folks on **alt.sci.planetary** and talk about the large, significant objects that comprise our solar system, and our efforts to visit them before prices go up.

## Starpages

A collection of directories, dictionaries, databases, star guides, and other products related to astronomy and other space sciences.

**Web:**

**http://cdsweb.u-strasbg.fr/~heck/sf.htm**

## Sunspots

Sunspots are relatively dark areas that appear on the sun from time to time (although you need a telescope with a special filter to see them). Sunspot activity goes thorough 11.3 year cycles that affect our local environment. In 1852, for example, the Swiss astronomer Rudolf Wolf first correlated sunspots and magnetic variations on Earth. For more up-to-date research information, see your friendly Interenet sunspot site.

**Web:**
**http://athena.wednet.edu/curric/space/sun/sunspot.html**

## Views of the Solar System

Take an educational tour of the solar system. See images and information about the sun, the planets, moons, asteroids and comets that are found within our solar system. In addition, you can read a little space history and terms to gain some background knowledge.

**Web:**
**http://bang.lanl.gov/solarsys/**

**THERE'S NO PLACE ON EARTH LIKE THE WORLD!**

**But when you get tired of the same old planet, it's time to broaden your outlook and point your mind outward.**

Spend a few hours with ***Views of the Solar System*** and see why our solar system is one of the most popular in the galaxy. Find the facts and hints that can make your next vacation a trip to remember.

## WebStars: Astrophysics in Cyberspace

Virtual reality, software, cyberspace quotes, links to space science web groups, and pointers to many other astronomy and astrophysics resources on the Internet.

**Web:**
**http://guinan.gsfc.nasa.gov/**

# AVIATION

## Aeronet

Get the latest buzz on the commercial aviation industry. News, press releases, company and manufacturer listings, conference and school listings, and links to aviation medicine are just a few of the topics covered. This site is searchable by keyword.

**Web:**
**http://www.aeronet.co.uk/**

## Air Disasters

I am no stranger to aviation disasters. One time I took a dinner flight, and they forgot to put my special vegetarian meal on the plane. Another time, I asked for a drink of apple juice with no ice, but they gave me ice anyway. But the worst disaster—so bad that I actually wondered if I was going to make it—was the time I forgot to bring a book to read and had no choice but to watch an entire Meryl Streep movie. If you are an air disaster buff, here are some Internet resources that are right up your aerodynamic alley. Here is where you can look for timely information after an accident or other disaster, or—between accidents—discuss methods and investigations.

**Web:**
**http://www1.minn.net/~enigma/**

**Usenet:**
**alt.disasters.aviation**

## Aircraft Discussion Forum

A mailing list forum for people interested in aircraft and helicopters, both new and old. The list also includes information about air shows and similar events.

**Listserv Mailing List:**
List Name: **aircraft**
Subscribe to: **listserv@iubvm.ucs.indiana.edu**

## Aircraft Group Ownership

Ever wonder how you could afford to own an airplane? Group ownership may be one way you can. This mailing list will fill you in on all you need to know.

**Listserv Mailing List:**
List Name: **airplane-clubs**
Subscribe to: **listserv@dg-rtp.dg.com**

## Airline and Airliner Discussion List

In the airline world there is a saying: "What goes up, must come down—one way or another." Make sure that your knowledge of airlines and aircraft doesn't crash and burn. Join the airline mailing list and keep up on what's staying up.

**Listserv Mailing List:**

List Name: **airline**
Subscribe to: **listserv@cunyvm.cuny.edu**

## Airline Travel

Solve travel problems before they happen. If you are traveling, scope out trials that may occur between your departure and destination with ticket purchases, layovers, connecting flights, luggage dramas, and airline strikes. Information is available for the entire planet. Next stop: the rest of the universe.

**Usenet:**

**alt.airline.schedules**
**alt.flame.airlines**
**misc.transport.air-industry**
**rec.travel.air**

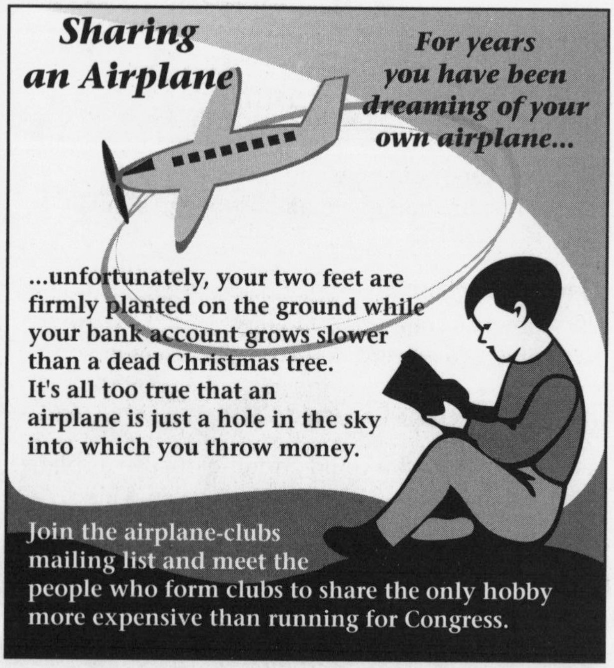
Sharing an Airplane
For years you have been dreaming of your own airplane...
...unfortunately, your two feet are firmly planted on the ground while your bank account grows slower than a dead Christmas tree.
It's all too true that an airplane is just a hole in the sky into which you throw money.
Join the airplane-clubs mailing list and meet the people who form clubs to share the only hobby more expensive than running for Congress.

## Aviation Enthusiast Corner

A forum dedicated to furthering interest in aviation-related hobbies. It offers an aircraft reference, air events guide, a large list of aviation museums and displays, and links to other aviation- and aerospace-related sites.

**Web:**

**http://www.brooklyn.cuny.edu/rec/air/air.html**

## Aviation Events

What's going on? Do you have an open weekend you want to fill? Are you going to be traveling to a new city and want to catch some aviation action? Find out what's happening on the aviation scene.

**Usenet:**

**rec.aviation.announce**

All revved up and nowhere to go?
Check out Aviation UPCOMING EVENTS

## Aviation Magazines

Check out the official web pages for Air and Space magazine and U.S. Aviator. These sites include articles in current and past magazines, links to air and space-related sites, a list of aviation events and more.

**Web:**

**http://airspacemag.com/**
**http://www.us-aviator.com/**

A B C D E F G H I J K L M N O P Q R S T U V W X Y Z

## Aviation Poetry

There's more to flying than just knowing which instruments to read and how many flight attendants it takes to screw in a light bulb. No, flying can be truly poetic, inspiration for songs of the soul. Read these poems about flight and flying, so on some dark, romantic night you can whisper into your beloved's ear a little poem that begins, "There once was a girl from Nantucket..."

**Web:**

**http://www.cyberspace.com/mbrunk/avpoem.html**

## Aviation Q & A

Looking for thorough, well-researched information on aviation? Or are you willing to pass on your knowledge through concise, streamlined postings? This is the place for you. This group is moderated, and it would be in your best interest to read the FAQ list before posting.

**Usenet:**

**rec.aviation.answers**

## Aviation Talk and Discussion

You'll go into a flat spin when you see all the information you can find in this group. If you don't know how to choose one of the specific aviation groups, this is a great place to start. There are often cross-postings from other groups to **.misc**, so you'll see a wide variety of topics, including comparisons of different types of planes, what to do about engine fires, pros and cons of leasing, and what happens when an instrument malfunctions. There's something for everyone.

**Usenet:**

**rec.aviation**
**rec.aviation.misc**
**rec.aviation.questions**

## Aviation Technology

Don't be content to just fly; dig deep into what makes aeronautics work. See the latest NASA press releases and learn about the physics of flight, pitch moment damping, aircraft stability, boarding design, and technical safety.

**Usenet:**

**sci.aeronautics**
**sci.aeronautics.airliners**
**sci.aeronautics.simulators**

## Dryden Photo Archive

Large collection of aircraft and spacecraft photos in jpeg format from Edwards Air Force Base in California. Includes pictures of the X Series and F Series research aircraft, the space shuttle, lifting bodies, and many other vehicles.

**Web:**

**http://www.dfrf.nasa.gov/PhotoServer**

## DUAT

If you're a pilot, this is the place to get your weather briefings, plan your flight, and even file your flight plan. DUAT also offers other valuable services. Check it out the next time you plan a cross-country flight.

**Web:**

**http://www.gtefsd.com/aviation/GTEaviation.html**

## European Aviation Server

This server contains information for pilots and non-pilots on European general aviation: aerodromes, events, weather images, round-trip pictures, and links to related web servers.

**Web:**

**http://www.aviation.span.ch/**

## Flight Planning

How would you feel if you planned to fly to Washington to help the President of the United States clean out his garage, and you got your directions mixed up and ended up in the middle of Disneyland? Imagine your embarrassment at spending an entire day with the wrong Mickey Mouse. Don't take chances: download a copy of free flight planning software and data today.

**Web:**

**http://skynet.ul.ie/~maverick/flight_planning.html**
**http://www.totavia.com/totavia/fltplan/fltplan.html**

Where am I ???????????????????

## Plan to Plan a Flight Plan

Of course you need a flight plan. If you didn't have a plan, you might arrive at your destination and not even know it. Worse, you might never arrive, and someone else would end up getting your dessert at dinner.

Before you go, use the Net to help you create a flight plan. Check weather and current conditions, and download software to make the whole thing as easy as falling off an aviational log.

## Gliding

Follow the example of the eagle and experience the powerful magic of gliding. Using sailplanes and hang-gliders has its own unique set of considerations. Learn about glide ratios, wind, flying in the rain, good places to glide, safety, gliding championships, and more.

**Usenet:**

**rec.aviation.hang-gliding**
**rec.aviation.soaring**

## Hang-Gliding

The site for the foot-launched flying community, offering a large gallery of hang-gliding photographs, digests, movies, weather updates, software, manufacturer contact list, a FAQ, paraglider designs, and much more.

**Web:**

**http://cougar.stanford.edu:7878/HGMPSHomePage.html**

## Instrument Flight Rules

Find out the concerns of flying under Instrument Flight Rules. Alternative mnemonics and IFR tasks just scratch the surface of the topics covered.

**Usenet:**

**rec.aviation.ifr**

## Landings Aviation Server

A large collection of aviation information, including aeronautical research servers, flight planning software, newsgroups, FAQs, piloting tips, federal aviation regulations, weather information, radio alphabet, flying jokes and poetry, details of aviation BBSs, Civil Air Patrol archives, and links to aircraft simulator sites.

**Web:**

**http://www.landings.com/**

## Learning to Fly

What a wonderful new experience, learning to fly. It's nice to know you have a place to ask questions or share your experiences with people who enjoy the same hobby or way of life. Find out all the questions new students are asking, and learn about instructors, lessons, equipment, PPL qualifications, and airspace.

**Usenet:**

**rec.aviation.student**

## Your own airplane

Oh, how these three simple words invoke deep feelings in all of us.

Wouldn't it be great to be able to fly to the market or the dry cleaners instead of having to wait in rush hour traffic?

**Join the discussion on Usenet** (rec.aviation.homebuilt and rec.aviation.owning) **and share ideas about what might well be the personal transportation vehicle of the 21st century.**

## Look What I Found on the Net...

```
Newsgroup: rec.aviation.student
Subject: Nausea and Learning to Fly

> I'm at about 15 hours now, and the nausea has pretty much
> entirely subsided. Anyone else have stress-related nausea
> while flying?

You're most definitely not alone there. As a student I don't
think that I know of anyone as stressed out as I was in my
learning days. All I can say to others as unfortunate is stick
it out, it WILL go away if you want.
```

## Military Aircraft

From the Sopwith Camel to the F-117A Stealth Fighter and beyond, experience the thrill of military aircraft. See the past, present, and even the future, as aviation devotees share their ideas on what are the best planes, who are the most notorious pilots in history, and how military aircraft of various countries compare to one another.

**Usenet:**

**rec.aviation.military**

## Owning Airplanes

Don't you wish owning an airplane were as simple as installing a bigger garage door on your house? Learn the joys and travails of being the owner of a powerful flying machine. If you are interested in building or restoring aircraft, check out **.homebuilt** to indulge in your aviation obsession. A word of warning: one of the questions in the homebuilt FAQ list is, "Will my marriage survive?"

**Usenet:**

**rec.aviation.homebuilt**
**rec.aviation.owning**

## Piloting

The tower says you're clear for takeoff into the wide world of piloting. You'll discover handy tips on priming cold engines, how to deal with rough weather, safety hints, and announcements on flying seminars.

**Usenet:**

**rec.aviation.piloting**

## Stories About Flying

How does it feel to be so high above the Earth? What was it like the first time you went solo? What excites you about flying? Read anecdotes of flight experiences and share yours. Even if you don't fly, you can experience the thrill of the moment in the stories of others.

**Usenet:**

**rec.aviation.stories**

## Ultralight Flying

Don't let the testosterone take over and convince you that you have to fly a jumbo jet. Experience the joy of ultralight aircraft and discuss with list members the joy of flying and the cost of maintaining ultralight aricraft.

**Usenet:**

**rec.aviation.ultralight**

**If you were normal, you wouldn't be reading this.**

# BBSs (BULLETIN BOARD SYSTEMS)

## Auggie BBS

A widely varied BBS, with a wide spread of discussion boards, public files, chat and talk facilities. Friendly people are always ready to chat, day or night, through the numerous online communication programs.

**Telnet:**

Address: **bbs.augsburg.edu**
Login: **bbs**

## BBS Information

Frequently asked questions (FAQ) (and answers) about Internet bulletin boards.

**Usenet:**

**alt.bbs.internet**

## BBS Programs

Here are a number of Usenet discussion groups devoted to particular BBS software packages. If you're interested in any of these packages, you'll want to be in constant contact with the experts.

**Usenet:**

**alt.bbs.citadel**
**alt.bbs.first-class**
**alt.bbs.gigo-gateway**
**alt.bbs.majorbbs**
**alt.bbs.metal**
**alt.bbs.pcboard**
**alt.bbs.renegade**
**alt.bbs.searchlight**
**alt.bbs.waffle**
**alt.bbs.watergate**
**alt.bbs.wildcat**
**comp.bbs.majorbbs**
**comp.bbs.tbbs**
**comp.bbs.waffle**

## BBS Talk and General Discussion

These Usenet groups are for general discussions on understanding, using, and even running a bulletin board system.

**Usenet:**

**alt.bbs**
**comp.bbs.misc**

Need help understanding BBSs? Read **comp.bbs.misc**.

## BBSs Around the World

There's a lot of BBS action around the world if you know where to look. The best places to start are the Usenet discussion groups devoted to lists of BBSs. When you have a moment, take a look at these groups and the information and advertisements they contain. There's a good chance you'll find some new and interesting resources and maybe even some new friends.

**Usenet:**

**alt.bbs.ads**
**alt.bbs.lists**
**alt.bbs.lists.d**

Bulletin Boards Around the World

**There was a time when computerized bulletin board systems (BBSs) were accessible only by their very own phone number. Not anymore. As an Internet user, you can connect to many different BBSs without making the slightest dent in your phone bill. Even government agencies have BBSs, putting the "bull" back in "bulletin" and the "bored" back in "board".**

## Dark Tower

The Dark Tower BBS is great for the Generation X and younger crowd: games, chat areas, writing, teen stuff, Things That Suck, and so on.

**Web:**

**http://bbs.digifro.com/**

**Telnet:**

Address: **bbs.digifro.com**

## Doors

External programs (doors) that are integrated into a BBS in order to provide access to special services.

**Usenet:**

**alt.bbs.doors**

## Eagles' Nest BBS

This BBS offers lots of variety in its discussion groups, including public chat rooms.

**Telnet:**

Address: **seabass.st.usm.edu**
Login: **bbs**

## Endless Forest BBS

Some say alternate space/time continuums exist for the known reality; the Endless Forest is one. Here the Forest dwellers roam, purely for the exchange of technical information, controversial debate, inane babble, and general fun.

**Telnet:**

Address: **forest.novia.net**
Login: **ef**

## Gaming Center

Once you are validated, you have access to a variety of free online games, including multiplayer tournaments. This is a great place to spend your time when you should be doing homework.

**Telnet:**

Address: **aztechnet.com**

## ISCA BBS

The largest and most popular BBS on the Internet (and the largest nonprofit BBS in the world). There are discussion groups to fit all tastes, especially some of a more esoteric nature that seem to be lacking from Usenet. ISCA is often full, with users from all over the globe busily rambling away.

**Telnet:**

Address: **bbs.isca.uiowa.edu**
Login: **guest**
Address: **whip.isca.uiowa.edu**
Login: **guest**

### ISCA: The King of Internet BBSs

The ISCA BBS has literally tens of thousands of users from all around the world. At any time, it is not unusual to have more than 1,000 people online.

If you only have time to join one BBS, give ISCA a try. It's the largest thing of its kind in the entire world. When you join ISCA, you are joining more than another BBS, you are becoming part of a tradition that has existed since 1990.

(By the way, the name ISCA stands for "Iowa Student Computer Association", the original sponsor.)

**Wow, free software.**

A B C D E F G H I J K L M N O P Q R S T U V W X Y Z

## List of BBSs Accesible by Telephone

This is *the* list of telephone-accessible BBSs. The goal of this site is to maintain a list of every active BBS in North America. You can search for BBSs by area code or by topic keywords. (If you run a BBS, you may want to make sure it is in the list.) There are also forums devoted to discussion of a variety of general BBS-oriented topics.

**Web:**
**http://www.thebbslist.com/**

## List of BBSs on the Internet

BBS junkies can celebrate over these comprehensive lists of BBSs on the Net. These resources give an overview of Internet BBSs, connect information, as well as links web pages.

**Web:**
**http://dkeep.com/sbi.html**
**http://aug3.augsburg.edu/~schwartz/ebbs.html**

## Monsoon

Monsoon has quite a few different message rooms that will entertain you while you are supposed to be doing something useful like work or your laundry. You will find discussion of sports, food and drink, personals, magic, computers, exercise, gender issues, gaming, music and other topics.

**Telnet:**
Address: **bbs.rtd.com**
Login: **bbs**

**Holy cow.**
**Look what's in "Religion".**

## Operator Headgap

For computer nerds, especially those with legacy systems, the Operator Headgap BBS is a good source of information and help. There are forums on the Amiga, the Commodore 64 and 128, Mac, and PC computers, as well as files for downloading.

**Web:**
**http://www.headgap.com/**

**Telnet:**
Address: **headgap.com**

## Parktown

The Parktown BBS will give you a 14-day free trial. You will find a nice variety of games and files, as well as forums on ANSI artwork, books, Boardwatch magazine, Christian topics and classic movies.

**Web:**
**http://www.parktown.com/**

**Telnet:**
Address: **parktown.com**

## Prism Hotel BBS

The Prism Hotel is divided into multiple floors, each with its own subject area. On each floor there are numerous rooms that you can enter to view the discussion posts therein. Message bases include arts and entertainment, music, business, and science and technology. It all makes for an interesting BBS experience.

**Telnet:**
Address: **bbs.fdu.edu**
Login: **bbs**

## Prowlers Domain

Here you will find a variety of forums and software. There are discussions about music, Nintendo, programming, scams, as well as some Usenet groups. The file archive includes game cheats, animal rights, MIDI, medical files, guitar tabs, celebrity nude images, as well as games and graphics software.

**Web:**
**http://prowlers.net/weblines**

**Telnet:**
Address: **prowlers.net**

## Roundhouse Run

At Roundhouse Run you can get a 2-week free trial. This is a good place if you want an interactive experience with lots of chatting and games like bingo, blackjack and poker. In addition, you will find the usual assortment of online BBS games.

**Web:**

**http://rhrun.com/**

**Telnet:**

Address: **rhrun.com**

## Sysop Information

BBS operators—sysops—have always been the cowboys of the electronic world. Like the pioneers of the American West, BBS sysops have explored and defined the evolving frontier. If you would like to see what the international sysop community is up to, follow their discussions on Usenet. After all, how often do you get to drop in on the cowboys as they sit around the bunkhouse talking shop.

**Usenet:**

**alt.bbs.allsysop**

## UTBBS

Based in Holland, with both English- and Dutch-speaking users, UTBBS offers public and personal messaging, online chat, and a large file selection covering many areas such as astronomy, biology, chemistry, computing, and more.

**Telnet:**

Address: **utbbs.civ.utwente.nl**
Login: **bbs**

## Wildcat BBS List

Here is a list of BBSs that use Wildcat software. The list shows telnet addresses as well as web sites. This is also the place to snarf yourself a copy of the Wildcat Navigator software, which you can use—with or without a browser—to access any Wildcat server on the Net.

**Web:**

**http://www.mustang.com/public/links/wc5bbs.htm**

## WWIV Software

Here is the online home of WWIV BBS software for PCs. You can find information about the software and utilities, hints on where to look for tech support, as well as a Sysop's Lounge (list of home pages of WWIV BBS sysops around the Net).

**Web:**

**http://www.wwiv.com/**

**Usenet:**

**alt.bbs.wwiv**

# BIOLOGY

## Biochemistry

The world would not be the same without nucleic acids. After all, without them, what would biochemists do for a living? This page offers information on macromolecules, nucleic acids, heme and iron metabolism, and more.

**Web:**

**http://ubu.hahnemann.edu/Heme-Iron/**

**Where would we be without biochemistry? Well, for some of us, pre-med studies would have been a lot easier. On the other hand, with no biochemistry, all we would be is a bunch of organic chemicals lying in a pool on the floor, so there are definite trade-offs. For those of us stuck in the real world of exquisitely shaped enzymes and long, silly chains of carbon that don't seem to know when to stop, the *Biochemistry* web site can provide a biodegradable home away from home.**

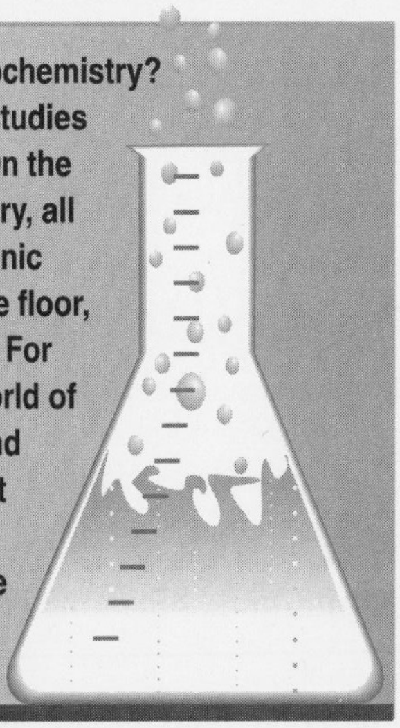

## Bioethics

What happens when you cross a philosopher with a biologist? You get a very interesting Internet site with a lot of bioethical information as well as a great many links to related resources around the Net.

**Web:**
**http://www.geog.utah.edu/~aab/**

### Bioethics

The name "bioethics" is derived from two words: "bioeth" (the Greek word for those sandwiches made with pita bread and fried chick peas) and "ics" (the Greek god of intermittent fertility).

Perhaps this explains why some of the best thinkers in the biological world are attracted to the study of bioethics, like fish to a whats-a-whoosie.

So the next time you are sitting around idly speculating about whether or not it is proper for your cat to accept gifts from a corporate lobbyist, don't wallow in ignorant bliss. Connect to the **Bioethics Server** and find the guidance you need to conduct your life with philosophical flair.

## Bioinformatics Resources

Find a wealth of information on DNA and protein sequence analysis software. This list of resources includes links to bioinformatics web pages around the world.

**Web:**
**http://www.ig.com/bioinfo.html**

## Biological Databases

For seemingly endless amounts of information, check out these biological databases. Find computer applications to suit your biological needs, so to speak.

**Web:**
**http://muse.bio.cornell.edu/**

**Usenet:**
**bionet.molbio.bio-matrix**

## Biology Announcements

This newsgroup is the loudspeaker of Bionet, Usenet's hierarchy of biology-oriented newsgroups. Find out what's going on in the wide world of biology: new electronic journals, conference announcements, calls for research papers, and new databases are a few of the things that people are shouting about. This group is moderated.

**Usenet:**
**bionet.announce**

### What's New in the World of Biology?

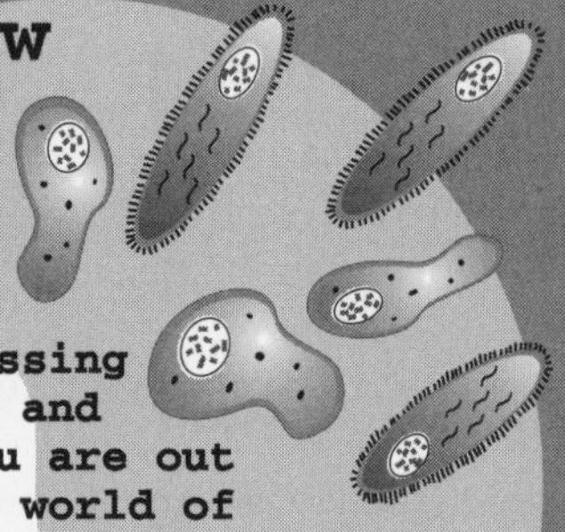

Isn't it embarrassing to be at a party and discover that you are out of date with the world of biology? Doesn't it make you feel like a piece of cheese when someone comes up to you and asks what you think of a newly discovered species of monera that you have never even heard of? Perhaps your budding career as a yeast biologist dried up and blew away because you didn't know what grants were available.
Well, no need to worry: just read
**bionet.announce**
and become biologically correct.

## Biology Funding and Grants

Don't wait for your million dollar sweepstakes check to come in. Where are some of the funding agencies in biology? Who's giving out research grants? Find out who has the money and how you can get some, too.

**Usenet:**
**bionet.sci-resources**

**Reach out and email someone.**

## Funding and Grants in Biology

**So you've got this great idea for developing wheat that grows in thin rows, just perfect for making sliced bread. But what can you do for seed money?**

**Participate in the bionet.sci-resources discussion group and perhaps, just perhaps, you will find the financial source that will send you on your way to becoming the next Internet Nobel Prize winner.**

## Biology Information Theory

Speculation, brainstorming, and sharing of ideas is what happens when you get everyone together to talk about biological information theory.

**Usenet:**

**bionet.info-theory**

## Biology Job Opportunities

Why be a telemarketer when you can have a job in the exciting field of biology? See cells reproduce right before your eyes, cut up small unsuspecting micro-organisms with lightning speed, and create new life forms seemingly from scratch. Opportunities abound for pre- or post-docs, undergraduates looking for something to keep them out of trouble for the summer, assistant professors who don't mind grading papers, and for upwardly mobile tenure-track seekers.

**Usenet:**

**bionet.jobs**
**bionet.jobs.offered**
**bionet.jobs.wanted**

**Sv bndwdth. Dn't typ ny vwls.**

## Biology Journals

If you like biological journals, or even if you don't and have to read them anyway, check the **.contents** for a brief outline of what's in the latest journals. Look at the **.note** group for advice on using biology journals.

**Usenet:**

**bionet.journals.contents**
**bionet.journals.note**

## Biology Related Sciences

Unbutton your top button and roll up your sleeves in preparation for some lively biological bantering. While informative and educational, subjects are never strictly hard-core science. Debate is sparked by such topics as evolution, the ethics of cloning, and the instinctual mating habits of animals and humans.

**Usenet:**

**sci.bio.botany**
**sci.bio.conservation**
**sci.bio.ecology**
**sci.bio.entomology**
**sci.bio.ethology**
**sci.bio.evolution**
**sci.bio.fisheries**
**sci.bio.food-sciences**
**sci.bio.herp**
**sci.bio.microbiology**
**sci.bio.misc**
**sci.bio.paleontology**
**sci.bio.phytopathology**
**sci.bio.systematics**
**sci.bio.technology**

## Biology Resources

A great collection of the favorite web pages of anyone involved with biology. If you like biology, you simply must check this out.

**Web:**

**http://pillo.unipv.it/em/surf.htm**

## Biology Software

Computers lighten your workload, if you have the right tools. The right tools are available, if you know where to look. There are many software sources for general biology or for more specific needs listed here.

**Usenet:**

**bionet.software**
**bionet.software.acedb**
**bionet.software.gcg**
**bionet.software.sources**
**bit.listserv.info-gcg**

## Biology Talk and General Discussion

This forum covers all the biological sciences. Catch glimpses of a little bit of everything that makes up the world around us. Discover what makes your body tick, what's in that yeast bread you've been eating, and how everything you touch teems with life. You will never be the same.

**Usenet:**

**bionet.general**

**Spam is more than a food.**

## BioMoo

BioMoo is the biologists' virtual meeting place, where people come to meet colleagues in biology studies and related fields, to hold discussions and conferences, and to explore the serious side of this new medium. You can also access recordings of previous meetings or browse the reference files.

**Web:**

**http://bioinfo.weizmann.ac.il:8888/**

## Biosphere and Ecology

Life does not exist in a vacuum. Ecology cannot exist strictly in a lab. For you rugged, active types, try studying the relations between living organisms and their environment.

**Usenet:**

**bit.listserv.biosph-l**
**sci.bio.ecology**

## Biotechnology

Murder mysteries are getting so intricate and complex these days with DNA matching, blood samples and genetic codes. And you have biotechnology to thank for it. Read the latest news and breakthroughs in the field.

**Usenet:**

**sci.bio.technology**

### *Look What I Found on the Net...*

```
Newsgroup: sci.bio.ecology
Subject: Why are foxes the main carrier of rabies in the wild?

In Ontario [Canada], foxes are definitely one of the main
vectors (skunks are good vectors too). I think that the reason
for this is as simple as the fact that there is a specific
rabies strain which attacks foxes but doesn't kill them very
quickly. This would allow the number of foxes with rabies to
build up due to contact with others before its death. I think
that the primary vector depends on which strain of rabies
predominates in a particular area.
```

## Cell Biology

This is where life happens, in tiny units of protoplasm. Unless you are a robot, cell biology concerns you. Cell scholars from all over the world dissect studies, research, and experiments that relate to cell biology. The **.cytonet** group is for the discussion of cytoskeletons such as cell walls and plasma membranes.

**Web:**

**http://www.gac.edu/~cellab/**

**Usenet:**

**bionet.cellbiol**
**bionet.cellbiol.cytonet**

Counting on your genes to pull you through?
Read
bionet.biology.computational.

## Cell Pictures and Movies

Can't find your tape from the last family reunion and you have dinner guests to entertain? Don't worry, here is something cool you can try. Download some of these movie segments and display them on your computer screen. Once you have downloaded movies of protozoa, bacteria and other various cells, paste small pieces of masking tape over the text on your monitor. With a magic marker, neatly print some new captions for the movies like "Uncle Harry trying to light the barbeque grill" or "Aunt Lolita prepares her old-fashioned potato salad" or "Cousins play African safari with the family dog". Show them all to your friends. Your polite guests will pretend to be astounded at your video prowess and once again, the evening will be a success thanks to the Net.

**Web:**

**http://www.comet.chv.va.us/quill/**

## Computers and Mathematics in Biology

There's more to life than just cells and DNA. (Not much more, but more.) Feeding in data, spitting out numbers, running this, programming that—it's all part of computer and mathematical biology. This group is moderated.

**Usenet:**

**bionet.biology.computational**

## Conservation Biology

The planet is relatively resilient, but there is only so much it can take. Science has taken up the cause of helping to protect, maintain, and restore life to the Earth, its species, and its ecological and evolutionary environment. That is the goal of conservation biology as well as the goal of the members of this list.

**Listproc Mailing List:**

List Name: **consbio**
Subscribe to: **listproc@u.washington.edu**

## Dictionary of Cell Biology

Are you one of those people who can't tell cytoplasm from ectoplasm? Do you have trouble remembering the exact definition of all your favorite organelles? If so, this web site is for you. Enter a word and get back a link to a related definition. ("Is that chromatin in your nucleolus or are you just glad to see me?")

**Web:**

**http://www.mblab.gla.ac.uk/~julian/Dict.html**

## Digital Anatomist

What do you do when you have your best girl (or guy) over on a Saturday night, and you run out of things to do? Just point your web browser to the Digital Anatomist and you will have hours of fun with an actual interactive atlas of the brain and heart—two of my favorite organs. (Boy, the world sure is changing. When I was in medical school, we had to do all of this by hand.)

**Web:**

**http://www1.biostr.washington.edu/DigitalAnatomist.html**

## Drosophila

The media is always reporting recent exploits of the pesky fruit fly in its travels around the globe. More amazing is the fact that there are people who study these critters for long periods of time. If you are one of those special people, find kinship with your peers as they discuss the biology of drosophila.

**Usenet:**

**bionet.drosophila**

## Electronic Newsgroup Network

Are you all dressed up in your lab coat with nowhere to go? There's no reason to be lonely when you have access to the Electronic Newsgroup Network. Check out this list of biology newsgroups, mailing lists, and chat forums. No matter what time of day or night, there will always be someone you can talk to about the birds and the bees.

**Web:**

**http://www.bio.net/**

## Evolution of Genes and Proteins

You won't see it happen right before your eyes (unless you are watching a bad science fiction movie), but evolution is nevertheless happening around us all the time. Study ideas and research on the evolution of genes and proteins.

**Usenet:**

**bionet.molbio.evolution**

## Evolutionary Biology

Evolution didn't stop when the apes climbed out of the trees and learned to drive Porsches. It's a constant process that goes on in the tiniest bacteria to the largest plants and animals. Get together with other people interested in evolution and discuss where we came from and where we might be going.

**Usenet:**

**sci.bio.evolution**

## Genbank Database

If you don't know your nucleic acids from a hole in the ground, maybe it's time to spend a little time with the people in the know. This discussion group is where you will find all the hot talk about the Genbank nucleic acid database.

**Usenet:**

**bionet.molbio.genbank**
**bionet.molbio.genbank.updates**

## Genetic Engineering and Bioethics

Sometimes it is easy to get discouraged and worried that you are not going to find that special someone with whom to spend the rest of your life. If you have a background in science, though, you really have nothing to worry about. Join this mailing list for the discussion of genetic engineering and bioethics and maybe you can just figure out a way to make the love of your life right from scratch.

**Listproc Mailing List:**

List Name: **gentalk**
Subscribe to: **listproc@usa.net**

## Genetic Linkage

How genes are connected is important and complex. If you are involved in this important area of molecular biochemistry, the Genetic Linkage discussion group is a good resource for you. See what people are saying as they discuss synthesis, lab techniques, gene analysis and so on.

**Usenet:**

**bionet.molbio.gene-linkage**

**Don't get fooled. Read "Consumer Information".**

## GenomeNet

A network for genome research and related research areas in molecular and cellular biology. The Human Genome Center (HGC) and the Supercomputer Laboratory (SCL) provide database services that are available through GenomeNet.

**Web:**

**http://www.genome.ad.jp/**

## Globin Gene Server

The Globin Gene Server provides access to information about the regulation of gene expression within the beta-like globin gene cluster. The page also has related information and links to other related web pages.

**Web:**

**http://globin.cse.psu.edu/**

## Human Genome Project

Join the discussion about the Human Genome Project, the massively ambitious scheme to ferret out and document all of the genes in human chromosomes. Maybe one day they will find the gene for TV watching and we will all be saved.

**Web:**

**http://www.hgmp.mrc.ac.uk/**

**Usenet:**

**bionet.molbio.gdb**
**bionet.molbio.genome-program**

## Immunology

Bigger, stronger people mean quicker and faster viral mutations. Why do you get sick, but your co-worker doesn't? Immunology reveals the magic of our ability to withstand the effects of disease and sickness.

**Usenet:**

**bionet.immunology**

### Globin Gene Server

**When your genes are running amok, the problem may be one of regulation. For most genes, you are out of luck, but if you are having trouble with your globin gene cluster, all you need to do is connect to the Globin Gene Server, get the information you need, and re-regulate. What could be simpler?**

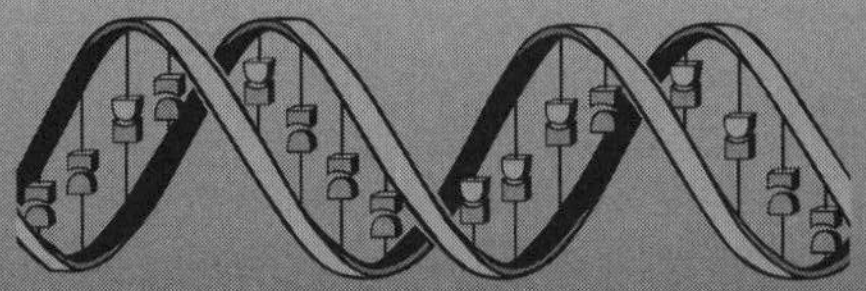

## Infomine Searchable Database

Here is a huge database of biological, agricultural, and medical information. You can search by keyword or browse by subject. Just the place to do some research when you have to decide whether you should sever your anterior or posterior commissure, and you haven't got a lot of time to make up your mind.

**Web:**

**http://lib-www.ucr.edu/bioag/**

## Instructional Resources in Biology

Teachers and students, lend me your ears (and your omohyoid bone and some parathyroid hormone). If you are one of the biologically inclined, here are some resources pointing to museums, databases, experiments, projects, and much more, all pertaining to the Wonderful World of Life on Planet Earth.

**Web:**

**http://golgi.harvard.edu/biopages/edures.html**

**Check out a free online book.**

## Kinetics and Thermodynamics

Kinetics and thermodynamics are fitness programs for cells, except that cells don't wear little spandex suits. Discuss the dynamics of chain reactions at the cellular level.

**Usenet:**

**bionet.metabolic-reg**

## Mapping Chromosomes

Much like the quest of Indiana Jones, only on a smaller scale (much smaller), mapping and sequencing eucaryote chromosomes can be mysterious and revealing. Join the discussion and find out the why and how.

**Usenet:**

**bionet.genome.chromosomes**

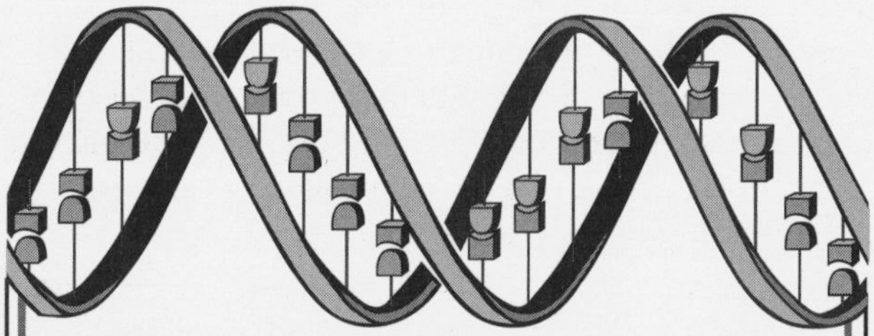

Why is it that only a man would try to find his way around a chromosome without a map? Don't be foolhardy. If you want to check on the latest happenings in mapping your favorite genome, try **bionet.genome.chromosomes**.

## Methods and Reagents

Develop some flair when experimenting. Show a little imagination when you stain your DNA or measure your plasma renin activity. See your peers use PCR to introduce silent mutations—the genetic ninjas of biology. Learn the methods and reagents that work, and run quickly away from the ones that don't.

**Usenet:**

**bionet.molbio.methds-reagnts**

## Molecular Biology of HIV

This discussion group is devoted to the biochemistry of HIV: the family of human immunodeficiency viruses responsible for AIDS. Participate in technical discussions regarding HIV, its characteristics, current research and hypotheses, and general questions and answers.

**Usenet:**

**bionet.molbio.hiv**

## Molecular Modeling

A central source of information for the National Institute of Health research community and others interested in molecular modeling methods and possible applications.

**Web:**

**http://cmm.info.nih.gov/modeling/**

## Mycology

Mycology is the study of the organisms within the Fungi kingdom, including yeasts, molds, smuts and mushrooms. Fungi—which are neither plants nor animals—are characterized by a lack of chlorophyll and vascular tissue. They range from small, single cells to large masses of branched filaments. Here is a great resource containing a collection of material relating to fungi organisms and cultivation, research, publications, discussion groups and taxonomy (naming systems), as well as a Usenet group for mycological discussion. By the way, we commonly divide the world of biology into five separate kingdoms: Plants, Animals, Fungi, Protista (one-celled protozoans and some algae) and Monera (bacteria and blue-green algae). Thus, properly speaking, fungi, protozoa and bacteria are neither plants nor animals.

**Web:**

**http://www.keil.ukans.edu/~fungi/**

**Usenet:**

**bionet.mycology**

## Fungi Are Your Friends

It's safe to say that Fungi are just about everybody's favorite biological kingdom (although some people do prefer Monera), which is why mycology—the study of fungi—is so popular amoung people in the know.

Find out what makes these multicelled, eukaryotic heterotrophs so much fun. Whether saprobic or parasitic, these cool organisms will well repay a lifetime of study. Join the crowd.

## Neuroscience

When you tell someone you are a bundle of nerves, you are telling more of the truth than you probably realize. Neuroscience involves the study of the nervous system, its structure and diseases. Join the discussion and meet the pros.

**Usenet:**

**bionet.neuroscience**

## Nitrogen Fixation

Most people don't think of bacteria as a handy and useful thing to have around. You clean them, spray them, call them bad names. Just hope they don't go on strike and stop carrying ammonia-bound nitrogen to their designated delivery areas, causing the collapse of the food chain right at the weakest link (you). See such nitrogen fixing in action and discover how this process keeps us in pizza and Chinese food.

**Usenet:**

**bionet.biology.n2-fixation**

**On the Net, everybody knows you're cool.**

## Nitrogen Fixation

Most people say, if your nitrogen ain't broke, don't fix it. Well, shows how much they know. If it wasn't for nitrogen fixation, plants wouldn't be able to turn inorganic nitrogen into organic nitrogen. And without organic nitrogen, we wouldn't have any amino acids. And without amino acids, we wouldn't be able to make proteins and enzymes, and boy, wouldn't we look foolish.

In other words, nitrogen fixation concerns us all. Still, it's not for beginners and, before you think about trying it at home, I suggest you check out the **bionet.biology.n2-fixation** discussion group and see what the pros have to say.

## Parasitology

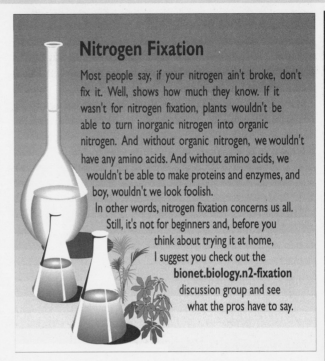

Suckers, biters, and burrowers are just a few of the nasty-sounding things that might be living on or inside your body right at this very moment. Before you panic, we should tell you that parasites are not all bad, just really misunderstood. Break the chain of ignorance by reading about parasites in this Usenet newsgroup.

**Usenet:**

**bionet.parasitology**

## Population Biology

The biology of populations used to be as simple as counting the legs and dividing by two. Modern methods are a lot more complex and require considerable biological, mathematical, and computational expertise. Visit this newsgroup when you need to swap stories with the experts.

**Usenet:**

**bionet.population-bio**

## Protein

How many angels can dance on the head of a lutropin beta chain? I don't know, but I know who to ask. If you are into protein, check out these protein databases. Several databases are linked together covering sequencing, structure, enzyme classification, and comparisons of DNA and protein sequences. Protein: it's not just for carnivores.

**Web:**

**http://www.gdb.org/hopkins.html**
**http://siva.cshl.org/**

**Usenet:**

**bionet.molbio.proteins**

## Protein Crystallography

Discover the latest thoughts on the form, structure, and properties of crystallized protein. It's not recommended for trail mix, but it certainly has its merits.

**Usenet:**

**bionet.xtallography**

## Randomly Amplified Polymorphic DNA

It's late in the day. You have optimized your PCR reaction conditions with a pair of specific primer sets. You then switch to random primers from UBC to do RAPD (not forgetting to lower the annealing temperature to 35 degrees C). However, you try 30 random primers and still do not get any good results. Isn't it good to know you have a place to turn for help?

**Usenet:**

**bionet.molbio.rapd**

**Half-time score: Net 1, Censorship 0**

## Shuffle Brain

How, exactly, does the brain store a mind? Is it like a computer, a cassette tape, a photograph, or like Aunt Molly with seemingly endless rows of Tupperware containers? Read these scientific articles relating to brains and how they store information.

**Web:**

**http://ezinfo.ucs.indiana.edu/~pietsch/**

## Tropical Biology

Imagine being on the beach, the wind whispering through your hair, sand between your toes—a scalpel in one hand, a mollusk in the other. What could be more beautiful? Experience the exotic essence of tropical biology with other people who think life is one long spring break. The only thing that could make it more interesting would be a drink with a little umbrella in it.

**Usenet:**

**bionet.biology.tropical**

## Virology

Nobody likes to invite a virus to the party, but biologists have a knack for making virology appealing. Talk often turns speculative, as topics include such debatable issues as destroying the last remaining specimens of the smallpox virus or whether certain viruses are capable of cross-species infection.

**Usenet:**

**bionet.virology**

## Virtual Genome Center

Find out what's hot and what's not in the genome world. Software and applications are available as well as documentation and images of some very unusual yeast sequences.

**Web:**

**http://alces.med.umn.edu/VGC.html**

## Look What I Found on the Net...

```
Newsgroup: bionet.women-in-bio
Subject: Re: Barbara & Michelle

> Don't know what you're into but thanks for the effort.
> We really did try, didn't we.
> We almost had it all....my friend...
>
> Barbara

Barbara, you have made two very gracious responses including
an apology even though I see no violation of netiquette.

I have not looked into this newsgroup for a while, but was
aghast when I saw the negative reaction to Barbara's obviously
innocent inquiry for information sharing. I have seen many
questions such as Monica's posed on many scientific, medical,
legal, economics etc. newsgroups. I have never seen any
individual flamed and subject to character assassination in
response...

Most of us learned in kindergarten how important it is to share
with our friends. If we cannot SHARE information and be
mutually supportive, let's agree to keep our negative thoughts
confined to our own hard drives.

—Catherine
```

## Who's Who in Biology

Who was that guy who wrote the article on yeast vector shuttles? If you are looking for someone particular in the field of biology, check here. While the Bionet is a small world, it covers a huge area. It has been said that you are only six people away from any person in the world. Try out this newsgroup and skip the five missing links.

**Usenet:**

**bionet.users.addresses**

**Get the latest dirt in "Archeology".**

## Women in Biology

Women share why the field of biology is important to them. Discover gender-related issues and other concerns that are specifically tied to women in this career. This group is not just about science; it has that added touch of something special that only women can give.

**Usenet:**

**bionet.women-in-bio**

## Yeast

Yeast is good for more than bread and beer. It's a fascinating, multiuseful mass of minute fungi. Find out what the molecular biology and genetics of yeast are all about. Maybe you'll even get some good recipes for bread and beer.

**Usenet:**

**bionet.molbio.yeast**

## BIZARRE

### Altered States

On those nights when there is nothing good on television and you are bored out of your mind, you can connect to this web page to find new and unusual ways to alter your state of consciousness. And it doesn't have to be with drugs. For those of you into more natural, organic methods, you can find information on hypnosis, dreams, and other interesting paraphenomena.

**Web:**

**http://www.utu.fi/~jounsmed/asc/asc.html**

### biancaTroll's Smut Shack

This will be a treat for all you voyeurs. Explore the rooms of biancaTroll's Smut Shack. Read and write graffiti on the walls of her bathroom, read her diary, flip through books on her shelves, explore her closet, talk to her troll, and otherwise put your nose where it doesn't belong.

**Web:**

**http://www.bianca.com/**

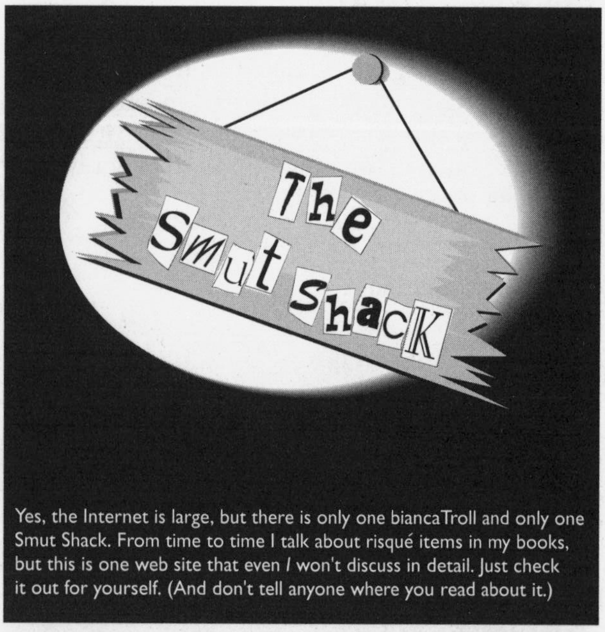
The Smut Shack

Yes, the Internet is large, but there is only one biancaTroll and only one Smut Shack. From time to time I talk about risqué items in my books, but this is one web site that even *I* won't discuss in detail. Just check it out for yourself. (And don't tell anyone where you read about it.)

### Bigfoot

When your small game hunting loses its thrill, try going on the endless quest for Bigfoot. This web page has all the information you need to get started, including still frames from some live footage taken in 1967. The mailing list is called the Internet Virtual Bigfoot Conference and is open to anyone wishing to discuss Bigfoot.

**Web:**

**http://www.teleport.com/~tbrp/**

**Usenet:**

**alt.bigfoot**

**Majordomo Mailing List:**

List Name: **bigfoot**
Subscribe to: **majordomo@teleport.com**

### Bizarre Literature

There is too much in the world that is *not* bizarre. If we are to maintain our status as the pre-eminent species on Earth, it behooves us to spend more time immersing ourselves in strangeness. A good way to do so is by subscribing to the Bizarre Literature mailing list. Then, just sit back and wait for your mailbox to be filled with bizarre, disturbing and offensive short stories and ramblings. Perhaps you might even send in a story of your own. (The world needs all the help it can get.)

**Listserv Mailing List:**

List Name: **weird-l**
Subscribe to: **listserv@brownvm.brown.edu**

### Bizarre Talk and General Discussion

The unusual, curious, and often stupid: here is Usenet's newsgroup for canonical strangeness. Just don't make the mistake of sending in an article that is not bizarre enough.

**Usenet:**

**talk.bizarre**

## Body Browser

It's disappointing that not everyone gets to have the experience of dissecting a human in a Gross Anatomy class. Don't be satisfied with a fetal pig. Go to this web page and use your browser to see inside a human body. You can rotate the point of view from different angles and zoom in and out. This is one of the safest tools you can use if you want to play doctor.

**Web:**

**http://www.scp.caltech.edu/~mep/ivb.html**

In my life, I have had the opportunity to dissect an entire human being, as well as two and a half brains. Most people never get the chance to look inside, but when you do, it is an experience not easily forgotten. The next time you have a few golden moments, take a look at the **Body Browser** and see what stuff we humans are made from. After all, it is not just beauty, but just about everything that is more than skin deep.

## Cabinet of Dr. Casey

The Cabinet of Dr. Casey is a great place to look if you are trying to get ideas for that next sleepover party or for the next time you see the Amway salesman coming to your door. This site is devoted to horror in the form of movies and books. Get some great audio samples, read Tales from the Internet, and see graphics and the horror timeline. A fantastic place to visit if you love the horror genre.

**Web:**

**http://www.ee.pdx.edu/~caseyh/horror/**

## Church of the Subgenius

Find out about the Church of the Subgenius, Bob and his pipe, and slack. The Church of the Subgenus is a cult parody that sharply satirizes what's wrong with religion and society in general.

**Web:**

**http://sunsite.unc.edu/subgenius/**

**Usenet:**

**alt.slack**

**Majordomo Mailing List:**

List Name: **subgenius**
Subscribe to: **majordomo@armchair.mb.ca**

## Complaining

Welcome to the Usenet complaint department. Complain about anything you want and read other people's pet peeves. Just the thing to get you back in a good mood after reading **alt.good.morning**.

**Usenet:**

**alt.peeves**

THE USENET COMPLAINT DEPARTMENT

*We all need to complain. The trouble is, most of our complaints are heard only by people in our immediate vicinity. Much better to send your complaints to **alt.peeves**.*

*That way, anyone on the Internet will have a chance to find out what you think of parents who can't keep their kids quiet in public, or talk show hosts who swank around like they own the place.*

## Contortionism

If you are looking for new recruits for your Olympic Twister team, this is the perfect place to start. You can view lots of photographs of contortionists bending their bodies in ways that are probably outlawed in more conservative parts of the world. Besides images, you will also find text on the history of contortion, a bibliography, information about the International Contortion Society and links to other contortion sites.

**Web:**

**http://www.escape.com/~silverbk/contortion**

## Crime Scene Evidence File

If you have ever fantasized about being the hero in a detective novel, or being the sleuth in a mystery story, here's your chance to act out the fantasy. A crime has been committed: a gruesome murder of a young woman. All the evidence is before you. Can you solve it? Justice depends on your wit, savvy and keen powers of observation.

**Web:**

**http://www.quest.net/crime/**

## Cryonics

We all have to go sometime, but maybe a lucky few will actually get to come back. Is it possible to have yourself frozen, in preparation for the time when unspecified future technology will be ready to bring you back to life? If you are deadly serious about an encore, this is a newsgroup you will not want to miss. To start, read the frequently asked question list (available from the web site). Next, decide whether you should have your whole body frozen or just your head (neuropreservation). Why let yourself get carried away, when you can chill out?

**Web:**

**http://www.cs.cmu.edu/afs/cs/user/tsf/Public-Mail/cryonics/html/overview.html**

**Usenet:**

**sci.cryonics**

**The Net cares.**

*Look What I Found on the Net...*

```
Newsgroup: sci.cryonics
Subject: Expiring minds want to know...

Neuropreservation is a form of cryonic suspension in which only
the patient's head or brain is preserved. It clearly is less
expensive than whole-body cryonic suspension. Being more
compact, the patient (normally) is more portable, too, enabling
faster escape from disaster. Furthermore, neuropatients
arguably can get better perfused brains than whole-body
patients, since the perfusion protocol can focus only on their
brains rather than all their other organs, too. The most
obvious disadvantage of neuropreservation, however, is the lack
of a body.

At first glance, lacking a body sounds like a fatal flaw in the
plan...

Question sent to sci.cryonics:

> Do you have to be DEAD to have this done? Is there any way
> that I could have them do it to me when I'm 90 or so?
> And then specify to warm me back up in another 75 years?
```

## Dark Side of the Web

When the history of the twentieth century is written, the section on gothic culture will have one simple entry: see Carrie Carolin. Carrie is a wonderfully resourceful and talented bundle of energy who maintains The Dark Side of the Web, the pre-eminent Internet site for things gothic. Here you will find a fabulous list of resources regarding gothic, horror, vampires (and vampyres), occult, magick, zines, magazines and much more. Root around a little, and you will find links to Carrie's other, equally fascinating enterprises. Not recommended for normal people or Republicans.

**Web:**

**http://www.cascade.net/darkweb.html**

## Death Clock

Do you want to know how long it is going to be before you bite the biscuit so you can plan everything in advance? On the Net, you can find out just how long you have to go until you pass on to your final reward. Your personal death clock will tell you how many seconds you have left to live and the date you are scheduled to die. If you don't want to know for yourself, you can check the death clocks of famous celebrities instead.

**Web:**

**http://www.ucs.usl.edu/~rkc7747/death.html**

## Devilbunnies

What are these devilbunnies? Tiny little creatures that seem to pop up everywhere and make the best laid plans of mice and men gang aft agley. Are they real, or figments of warped imaginations that have spent too long glued to the computer? Tune in for the latest update on the spiritual descendants of the gremlins of World War II.

**Web:**

**http://www.netimages.com/archives/alt.devilbunnies/**

**Usenet:**

**alt.devilbunnies**

## Discord and Destruction

Serious talk about serious talk. Destroy the earth or just our way of life: it's up to you. Remember, life is stern and earnest and nobody gets out of here alive.

**Usenet:**

**alt.destroy.the.earth**
**alt.discordia**

## Dream Interpretation

Have you had a strange dream you don't understand? Submit it here to solicit the dream interpretations of thousands of total strangers. Or just wander through to read other people's dreams and the weird interpretations others have offered.

**Web:**

**http://www.cs.washington.edu/homes/raj/dream.html**

## Excuse Generator

Late for work? Forgot your homework? Use the Excuse Generator to come up with a good one such as "I have a rare case of 48-hour projectile leprosy, but I know we have that deadline to meet."

**Web:**

**http://www.dtd.com/excuse/**

## Freak Show

The freak shows which were so popular between 1840 and 1940 began to lose popularity long before being politically correct became the rage. If you'd like to partake in a little socially unacceptable behavior, but just can't find the time to leave your computer, sneak a peak at this celebration of freak shows of decades past.

**Web:**

**http://www.zynet.com/~meatlog/freakshow.html**

Never again will you need to fumble for a reason why something did or did not happen correctly. Simply use the **Excuse Generator** and it will be clear, even to the shallowest intelligence, that it most definitely was not your fault.

## Furry Animals

Whether live or stuffed, there's something about small furry animals that brings out the latent anthropomorphism in us all. They are just too cute for words, so I won't even try.

**Usenet:**
**alt.fan.furry**

## Gallery of Fluorescent Intestine

Reminiscent of colorful fractals, these intestine images could be admired by any critics of modern art and be called "conceptually astounding," "provocatively colorful," "dynamically fluid," or "derivative of techno-organic randomness." Intellectually, I can't call it art, but on a gut level I'd say it's kind of pretty, all things considered.

**Web:**
**http://pharmdec.wustl.edu/juju/GloGutz/GloGutz.html**

## Geeks and Nerds

Remember, if it weren't for geeks and nerds, there wouldn't be an Internet (and you wouldn't be able to read this totally cool Internet book). Pay tribute to these unsung heroes of the Star Trek generation. Join Usenet's own mutual admiration society: take a nerd to lunch today.

**Usenet:**
**alt.geek**

## Ghost Stories

Ghost stories are a fun and inexpensive way to keep yourself up all night. Read some creepy ghost stories on the Web or get them hot off the newsfeed by checking out the Usenet group.

**Web:**
**http://www.azc.com/client/page/fright.html**

**Usenet:**
**alt.folklore.ghost-stories**

## Gonzo Links

If you are in the mood for something weird (or maybe something a *lot* weird), have a taste of information from the fringe of reason. This site is full of information about conspiracies, UFOs, spies, and other things the government and your mother don't want you to believe.

**Web:**
**http://www.capcon.net/users/lbenedet/**

## Look What I Found on the Net...

Newsgroup: alt.geek
Subject: Excitement, nerd-style

Hey guys, am I the only one this happens to?

I get excited when I see a female logged on our system very very late on a Friday night! It's even cooler when she and I are the only ones logged on the system :)

## Look What I Found on the Net...

Newsgroup: alt.geek
Subject: What the well-dressed geek is wearing

While we are discussing various facets of geek paraphernalia, I just wanted to mention something which *seems* to be becoming extinct: horned-rim glasses.

As I mentioned before, I'm only 14; but I have a NIFTY pair of horned-rim glasses straight out of any high school picture from 1964. I don't know about you, but I think extra-thick horned-rims are a classic geek symbol. Maybe I'm wrong. However, they look pretty good with tape.

My grandpa bestowed me his leather slide-rule case. I don't wear it much anymore because I tend to use my graphics calculator and my palmtop a bit more. I don't have a holster for my calc, but I do have a clip (which I'm sure is not as good). My palmtop, on the other hand, is a different story. I can't find anything with which I can attach it to my belt.

Regarding pocket-protectors. I agree with what someone said earlier: you should only wear them to suit a cause. Any other reason would be stupid and (dare I say it) rather superficial. If you like to have your pens and screwdrivers at hand like I do, then a protector is a good idea. I have a day-glo neon yellow protector that says "Kiss me, I'm a Physicist". Of course, I'm not a physicist, but a friend of mine who works at a research lab gave it to me.

## *Look What I Found on the Net...*

```
Newsgroup: alt.folklore.ghost-stories
Subject: Ouija Board Story

> I once scoffed at Ouija Boards saying, "How could something
> mass produced by Parker Brothers be a powerful tool of evil?"
> to which my girlfriend quickly retorted, "If you were the sort
> of paranatural malevolent entity that supposedly gets its
> kicks from screwing people up with these things, wouldn't
> you try and get them mass produced?"

> Food for thought.

> I guess what I am trying to say is, be careful.
> I went insane, and spent a month under the care of
> a physician during which I slept less than twelve hours in
> total and went through hell. It took me almost four years
> to fully recover, and I am still scared it might happen again.

> If you are going to get into the occult seriously, fine.
> Two bits of advice: Always make sure that you do ALL your
> research first. If you are going to do something, make sure
> you have perfected undoing it first.

> Second, always include a skeptic who you trust to remain a
> skeptic and remain a friend. You'll thank me later.
> I wish I had done both these things.

You know, he's right. Ouija Boards are the devil's tool.
They are evil. You don't wanna mess with them.

They slowly possess you by addicting you, and each time you use
it your soul is more open for possession.
```

## Greatest Conspiracies

Scarier than any bedtime story, conspiracies are the thing to talk about when sitting around the campfire or staying up late at night with friends. This web page has some satirical conspiracy writings as well as links to many conspiracy and paranoia sites.

**Web:**

**http://www.webcom.com/~conspire/**

## Gross and Disgusting

Here are a number of gross, disgusting and offensive stories and articles. Do not read these if you are easily offended. Do not read them while you are eating. Do not let your children, parents, boss or co-workers see you reading these things. And do *not* say I didn't warn you.

**Web:**

**http://wiretap.spies.com/Gopher/Library/Fringe/Gross**

## Horror Movie Theater

Scare yourself silly by browsing around Dr. Casey's Horror Movie Theater. There are tons of links to horror movies, audio and video clips, and still images. You can see clips from both classic and new movies.

**Web:**

**http://www.ee.pdx.edu/~caseyh/horror/theater/**

## Internet Crime Archives

The sun is shining, the birds are singing and what better way to spend the afternoon than browsing through this collection of information about serial killers and mass murderers.

**Web:**

**http://mayhem.net/Crime/**

## Loch Ness Monster

Like there is not enough lurking around in the murky depths of lakes. Not only do you have to worry about nibbling fish, water snakes, and snapping turtles, everyone insists on carrying on about large prehistoric-looking monsters that are just waiting for you to be served up like little hors d'oeuvres on a rubber raft. Get nervous: check out all the information about Nessie and other lake monsters, such as Champ from Lake Champlain and Sweden's Lake Storsjon monster.

**Web:**

**http://www.cais.com/strangemag/nessie.home.html**
**http://www.scotnet.co.uk/highland/**

## McChurch

Day in, day out, the same old religious rituals can get to be downright boring. If you are considering conversion for a change of pace, try looking into the Tabernacle of McChurch. You'll find some interesting thoughts on God and why he shouldn't babysit small children. Visit the patron saint McDonna and see historical artworks like the *Adoration of the McMagi*.

**Web:**

**http://mcchurch.org/**

### CRIME INFO TO THE MAX

What's the best way to plan a serial crime or a mass murder? Well, you could figure things out as you go along, but you risk finding yourself in the hands of the police before you have arranged for the proper international media exposure. Nothing is more embarrassing than being in the middle of negotiating a book deal and finding out that another criminal has already used the exact same modus operandi (and sold the rights for a made-for-TV movie).

So, before you commit yourself, check with the **Internet Crime Archives**. Whether you are looking for ideas for leisure-time activities or just browsing for fun, let the Net help you avoid the time-consuming and costly research which is so much a part of modern life.

In the future, religion will be a lot more practical and well-organized. Whenever you thirst for some spiritual refreshment, you will be able to log in via the Net, check out the latest disciples and saints, pick up a few choice revelations, and still have time left over to check your email before bed. Well, the future is here now. The **McChurch** web site can be your new, Net-centric, esoteric home away from home. And, unlike its competitors, this church is not the home of the big whopper.

A B C D E F G H I J K L M N O P Q R S T U V W X Y Z

A B C D E F G H I J K L M N O P Q R S T U V W X Y Z

## Mummy Museum

If you've been feeling bad because all the other people in your neighborhood have mummies and you don't, then here's your chance to perk right up and show them your stuff. Go to the Mummy Museum, where you will find lots and lots of pictures of real-live dead people in their typically shriveled states of being.

**Web:**

**http://www.sirius.com/~dbh/mummies/**

## Negative Emotions

Angst, bitterness, misanthropy, fear, disgust, anxiety, and just plain being in a bad mood. Join the folks down at the not-OK corral for some roll-up-your-sleeves-and-get-down-to-it homestyle bitchin'. As John Milton put it (when they took away his Internet account), "So little is our loss. So little is our gain."

**Usenet:**

**alt.angst**
**alt.bitterness**
**alt.misanthropy**

## News of the Weird

It's often hard to accept the mundanity of normal everyday living. If your life isn't weird enough, try subscribing to the **News of the Weird** mailing list or even browsing through their archives. You can read stories that will shock, surprise and flabbergast you. And this news is good for a laugh, too.

**Web:**

**http://www.nine.org/notw/archive.html**

## Obscure Research Laboratories

If you want to be one In The Know, check out the page of People Who Are In The Know. The folks at the Obscure Research Laboratories study UFOs, time travel, paraphysics and everyone's favorite: disinformation.

**Web:**

**http://140.249.8.212/orl/**

## Pantyhose

We know a newsgroup devoted to pantyhose sounds a little strange, but, after all, you have to admit that there is something about long, sensuous legs wrapped in sheer black stockings that will turn even the most dignified gentleman into a wild jungle cat with the morals of a U.S. senator. Check out the IRC channel, too.

**Usenet:**

**alt.pantyhose**

**IRC:**

**#pantyhose**

## Paving the Earth

Have you ever wondered what it would be like to pave the Earth? No more grass to stain your white pants, no more insects to eat your picnic food, no more dirt on your new sneakers. Just imagine everything nice and smooth and hard. Seriously. (Do you think I make this stuff up?)

**Usenet:**

**alt.pave.the.earth**

## Positive Emotions

As if there isn't enough to deal with already, here are newsgroups devoted to good feelings and happiness. Bah, humbug. If God had wanted us to hear good news, he wouldn't have given us television and newscasters with bad toupees. And most sickening of all has to be the **alt.good.morning** group: people from all over the world, wishing each other a good morning. As Butthead says: "I don't like stuff that sucks."

**Usenet:**

**alt.good.morning**
**alt.good.news**
**alt.hi.are.you.cute**

## Roadkill R Us

Get the going prices for roadkill and find out what makes or breaks a good roadkill sale—bloat, availability, and completeness of parts. Roadkill news, history of the Roadkill R Us corporation and an occasional recipe.

**Web:**

**http://www.rru.com/rru**

## Roommates From Hell

Next time your roommate borrows your girlfriend without asking, count yourself lucky. Tune in to the roommate version of "Can You Top This?" and it won't be long before you realize that some people have *real* trouble.

**Usenet:**

**alt.flame.roommate**

## Rumors

Check out all the new rumors, both serious (Elvis and aliens) and less serious (the FBI and CIA). Did you know that readers of this book are entitled to free admission to Disney World?

**Usenet:**

**talk.rumors**

## Santa Claus

Ho! Ho! Ho! Santa is real. Search your hearts for the truth; celebrate the magic of the Christmas season by joining in with other devout Santa believers. Just don't forget to be good for goodness sake.

**Usenet:**

**alt.religion.santaism**

## Skulls of Fate

Ask the Skulls of Fate that particular question that has been weighing on your mind. The Skulls aren't too smart, so you have to ask a question that can be answered with a "yes" or "no." Still, it's more responsive than your therapist's voice mail.

**Web:**

**http://www.dtd.com/skulls/**

## Social Deviants

It's a great deal of hard work to be normal, and not everyone is up to the strain. As long as you are not involved, it's fun to read about bizarre, disgusting, and socially unacceptable acts by people who simply do not have all their eggs in one basket. Check out the rantings, ravings, news, and theories on cults, freaks, criminals, and other social deviants.

**Majordomo Mailing List:**

List Name: **deviants**
Subscribe to: **majordomo@csv.warwick.ac.uk**

**Get into "Mischief".**

### *Look What I Found on the Net...*

```
Newsgroups: alt.hi.are.you.cute
Subject: A Cute Thing at Disney!

Today I did a temp assignment working at the reception desk at
Disney Studios.

Today the man and woman who do the voices for Mickey and Minnie
Mouse came in and entertained us with some samples of their
vocal talents.

But the cutest thing is that they are married to each other.
They met while doing the voices of Mickey and Minnie, and fell
in love...

I think that is so cute!
```

## Look What I Found on the Net...

```
(from the Skulls of Fate)

I submitted the following question to the Skulls of Fate:

  Some people say we are only what we perceive, that all our
  thinking and ideation can only restate the negativeness of
  the universe, the hideous lonely emptiness of existence;
  nothingness; the predicament of Man, forced to live in a
  barren godless eternity, like a tiny flame flickering in an
  immense void, with nothing but waste, horror and degradation
  forming a useless bleak straitjacket in a black, absurd
  cosmos.

  Is this, in fact, true?

To which the third skull from the right answered:

  Yes.
```

## Spleen

You probably don't give much thought to your spleen. You just let it sit there all day long doing its business, which, frankly, is not much. However, there is one man on the Net who is making the most of his spleen and feels the need to share it with you. Take a look at his work. It's sort of art, sort of philosophy, sort of poetry wrapped around the motif of anatomy.

**Web:**

**http://www.mcad.edu/home/faculty/szyhalski/Piotr**

## Squashed Bug Zoo

This page is for all of you who want to take revenge on bugs, but never have the nerve to actually squash them yourself. Recommended viewing time is between meals. Yes, live bugs were harmed in the making of this page.

**Web:**

**http://albert.ccae.virginia.edu/~dcm3c/zoo.html**

**Read the FAQs of life.**

## Squishy Mailing List

It's not entirely possible to tell you what this mailing list is for. After some serious investigation, the conclusion that can be reached is that even the list owners don't know. The truth is this mailing list is a vehicle for "spreading the gospel of feeling good". Join up for the serious business of having a good time.

**Majordomo Mailing List:**

List Name: **squishy**
Subscribe to: **majordomo@world.std.com**

## Strawberry Pop-Tart Blow-Torches

When the enemy is storming the gate and you are in your pajamas with nothing to protect yourself but a box of Strawberry Pop-Tarts and a toaster, fear not. With time, a web browser and a little guidance, you too can make a state-of-the-art mini-flamethrower that will fend off the most persistent door-to-door salesmen.

**Web:**

**http://www.sci.tamucc.edu/%7Epmichaud/toast/**

## Surrealist Compliment Generator

In a thankless world when an ordinary compliment is drowned out by deadlines, ringing phones, and suited executives waving memos that say "Hurry! Hurry!" it's nice to know that you can get an original, if not surreal, compliment anytime you want it just by loading this page. The Surrealist Compliment Generator will offer you the kindest words it can. While sometimes startling or unusual, these compliments seem earnest, sincere and refreshing.

**Web:**

**http://pharmdec.wustl.edu/cgi-bin/jardin_scripts/SCG**

## Swedish Chef

Remember that lovable Swedish chef on the Muppets? The one who would chase little chickens with a meat cleaver, talk with a Swedish accent, and say "Bork, bork, bork"? Well, he is alive and well on the Internet. Read the newsgroup and visit the web site, and find out how to get the encheferizer software: a program to turn regular English text into a speech from the Swedish chef. Und noo, buys und gurls, ve-a veell leern hoo tu cuuk cheeckees. Bork bork bork!

**Web:**

**http://gumbo.tcs.tufts.edu/chef/**

**Usenet:**

**alt.swedish.chef.bork.bork.bork**

BORK! The
BORK! Swedish Chef
BORK! is looking for you.

## Tasteless Topics

Taste is in the eye (and often in the mouth) of the beholder. But what do you do on those days when you need a good dose of bad taste? The answer is to check out the Net's tasteless discussion group. Feel free to look, to copy and to participate. Just be sure that whatever you do is disgusting and without any redeeming social value whatsoever. This is not the place to bring your grandmother for her birthday.

**Web:**

**http://www.healey.com.au/~rocky/tasty/**

**Usenet:**

**alt.tasteless**

## Twinkies Project

Combine science, junk food and students with time on their hands and you get a hilarious web site devoted to the study of Twinkies. Standing for Tests with Inorganic Noxious Kakes in Extreme Situations, "Twinkies" is just that. Laboratory tests were performed on these unassuming little yellow foods with surprising results. Take a look, but bring your own milk.

**Web:**

**http://www.owlnet.rice.edu/~gouge/twinkies.html**

## Vampire Talk

For vampires and vampire hunters alike or even innocent bystanders who can't decide in which category they should be. Join the mailing list to discuss the facts, lore and fiction of vampires. Topics of discussion include vampire history, literature, movies and more. Or if you just want to talk in real-time with a bunch of bloodsuckers, hang out in the IRC channel (after dark, of course).

**Majordomo Mailing List:**

List Name: **vampyres**
Subscribe to: **majordomo@holli.com**

**IRC:**

**#vampire**

## Vampyres Only

Vampyre hunters stay out! This site is not for you. However, if you are interested in possibly becoming a vampyre, you are welcome to have a look. There are even special tips on how to become such a creature of the night. Get information on what vampyres are, read the FAQs, and learn about vampyre societies, clubs and religions. If you are worried that you might be a vampyre, you can take a test to see how you rate. There are also audio and video clips, images and humor files. This is definitely the hotspot for vampyre information.

**Web:**

**http://www.vampyre.wimsey.com/vampyre/**

## Weird IRC Channels

After a while, going to Tupperware parties and hanging out at the mall can get a tad predictable. So when you get to the point where you are itching to meet some new and bizarre people, try hanging out in these IRC channels. The only thing I can guarantee is that nothing is guaranteed.

**IRC:**

**#abyss**
**#discordia**
**#dork**
**#evil**
**#gothic**
**#heathers**
**#insomnia**
**#pizza**
**#tarot**
**#thelema**

## Zombie Hangman

Add a little danger to the classic game of Hangman. Solve the word as best you can, but for every letter you miss, the zombie loses a body part. This is definitely no Wheel of Fortune.

**Web:**

**http://www.dtd.com/rip/**

Vampire Talk
Does your mailbox empty automatically whenever the sun comes up? Subscribe to the vampyres mailing list and get your fill of the nighttime.

# BOATING AND SAILING

## Boat Racing Talk and General Discussion

The **rec.boats.racing** newsgroup covers most racing events, regattas, sailing events and championships. Even racing crews are recruited via this newsgroup.

**Usenet:**

**rec.boats.racing**

## Boatbuilding

All aspects of building boats, including canoes and kayaks, are discussed in this newsgroup. Some topics covered are the obtaining of boat parts, boatbuilding software, special paint, and finding complete hulls.

**Usenet:**

**rec.boats.building**

## Boating Marketplace

If your yard is starting to look like a used boat lot, take the time to unload your treasures on the rest of the world by posting an ad in **rec.boats.marketplace**. You can post advertisements for boats, boating- related items or services, as well as for needs and wants as long as they pertain to boating. This newsgroup is moderated.

**Usenet:**

**rec.boats.marketplace**

## Boating Mnemonics

When I was in medical school, there were lots of great mnemonics used to remember body parts in anatomy, symptoms of diseases and the properties of drugs. When you are learning to sail, there are also lots of things to remember and the mnemonics really help. This site gives you a list of clever tricks to help commit boating terms and rules to memory: mast light combinations, stern lights, buoyage, sound signals and right of way rules. Not many places will explain why your life can be saved by knowing that Timid Virgins Make Dull Company at Weddings.

**Web:**

**http://ficus-www.cs.ucla.edu/ficus-members/geoff/mnemonics.html**

## Boating Quiz

Are you ready to captain your own sailing vessel? Find out how you score on this boating quiz. Afterward, you can take a break and head for the open seas, or at least to the bathtub with your little plastic battleships.

**Web:**

**http://www.ronin.com/USPS/quiz.html**

## Boating Safety

The words "safety" and "Commander Bob" go hand in hand. Just like you wouldn't go into a storm after getting your hair done, you wouldn't want to go charging off on a sailing adventure without first getting some safety tips from Commander Bob. This boating safety site will help you with boating regulations, the weather, personal watercraft safety and more. Don't leave shore without it.

**Web:**

**http://www.mailbag.com/users/stobo76/**

### Don't Miss the Boat

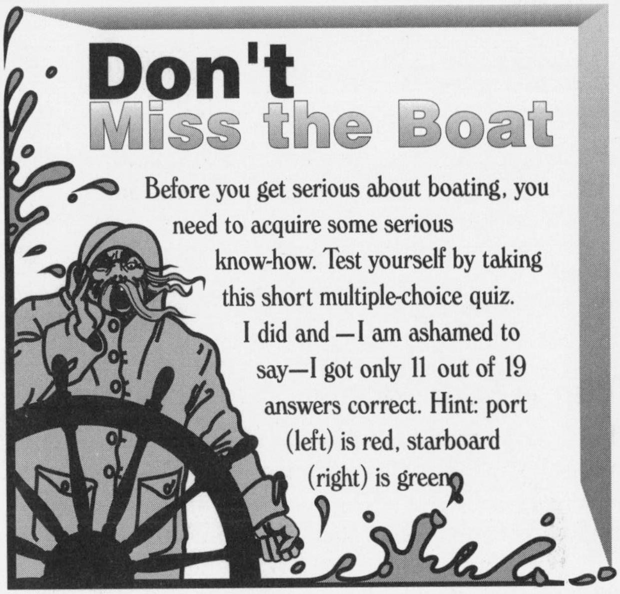

Before you get serious about boating, you need to acquire some serious know-how. Test yourself by taking this short multiple-choice quiz. I did and —I am ashamed to say—I got only 11 out of 19 answers correct. Hint: port (left) is red, starboard (right) is green.

## Boating Talk and General Discussion

When I was a kid at camp, I earned my Master Canoeist award. To this day, I can still recall all the esoteric canoeing strokes I had to be able to demonstrate, equally well on both sides. Truly, moving on water invokes deep feelings in all of us. If you care about things that float, join the Internet boating discussion groups: **rec.boats** for general boating topics; **rec.boats.paddle** for discussion of canoes, rowboats, and related craft.

**Usenet:**

**rec.boats**
**rec.boats.paddle**

## Crew Database

Are you a boat looking for a crew? Are you a crew looking for a boat? Here's a database of boatless crews and crewless boats looking for the perfect match. If you are itching to enter a boat race, but you just don't have everything you need, try this site. You might find just what you are looking for.

**Web:**

**http://home.netscape.com/people/flc/crew/**

## Cruising

Add some sophistication to your cruising techniques by doing it in a boat instead of up and down a strip of overcrowded highway. In this newsgroup you can read about where to cruise, how to cruise and where to charter. Share your cruising experiences and your favorite anchorages.

**Usenet:**
**rec.boats.cruising**

## Dragon Boat Racing

Dragon boat racing is a popular event in China. It is a long-standing part of the Chinese tradition dating back over 2,000 years. The boat races are said to have originated from a belief that they would bring agricultural prosperity. There is another, more romantic, legend that says dragon boat racing is related to the story of Ch'u Yuan, a Chinese patriot, who was exiled. Because of his expatriation, he was filled with despair and threw himself into the Mi Lo river. The legend says the people of the country were so distraught over the suicide of Ch'u Yuan that they got into their boats and raced up and down the river beating drums, splashing oars and making a general ruckus in order to scare away evil spirits and water dragons from the body of Ch'u Yuan. In modern day, this story creates a great excuse for people to get into brightly colored boats that are decorated like dragons and race up and down the river yelling, making noise and having a good time. Seems like as good an excuse as any to me. Use the Net to learn more about the history and culture of this fun Asian celebration.

**Web:**
**http://www.alvin.org/dragon/**

**Majordomo Mailing List:**
List Name: **dragonboat**
Subscribe to: **majordomo@teleport.com**

## Global Yacht Connection

When you're all dressed up with no place to go, head to the Global Yacht Connection where you will find articles and information on boating, vessels for charter, displays of boats, marine facilities, products and services, and yachts for sale.

**Web:**
**http://www.waterviews.com/**

## GORP: Great Outdoor Recreation Pages

Having this site on your bookmark list means you will never run out of interesting and entertaining resources relating to rafting, canoeing and kayaking. There are links to information on trips, gear, books and magazines, safety, events, reviews of locations, health, food and organizations.

**Web:**
**http://www.gorp.com/gorp/activity/paddle.htm**

**Have you ever dreamed about living on a boat?**
**Some people actually do it.**

**Subscribe to the live-aboard mailing list and see what these domestic mariners have to say about life on the water.**

## Intercollegiate Yacht Racing Association

This list was created for the discussion of all topics related to the Intercollegiate Yacht Racing Association of North America. Also the official bulletin board of the ICYRA, the mailing list serves as a vehicle for official notices from the ICYRA.

**Majordomo Mailing List:**
List Name: **icyra**
Subscribe to: **majordomo@westweb.com**

## Kayaking and Canoeing

When I was an undergraduate student at the University of Waterloo in Canada, I spent a little time with the Whitewater Canoe Club. However, I never got close to the action: my participation was limited to paddling a kayak around the swimming pool. Later, after I moved to California, I once went kayaking in the ocean, and I found it a lot more fun than the pool in Waterloo. If you want to keep afloat of the happenings in the world of the paddle, check out this web site for links to kayak and canoe organizations around the world.

**Web:**

**http://www.gfi.uib.no/~svenn/padling/norway/world.html**

## Live-Aboard Mailing List

One of the great things about living on a boat is that you don't have to spend your Saturday morning mowing the lawn. Whether you live aboard a boat or just fantasize about it, you are welcome to join in on the **live-aboard** mailing list.

**Majordomo Mailing List:**

List Name: **live-aboard**
Subscribe to: **majordomo@centaur.astro.utoronto.ca**

## Marine Signal Flags

A collection of the international maritime signal flags. Ships at sea use signal flags to spell out short messages or to communicate speeds and course changes. This page shows alphabetic flags, answering pennants, numeric pennants, substitute pennants, and the semaphore flag waving system.

**Web:**

**http://osprey.anbg.gov.au/flags/signal-flags.html**

## Navigation

When you are out to sea and lost or confused, send mail to this mailing list for the discussion of non- electronic navigation with primary topics such as celestial navigation, coastal piloting, dead reckoning, charts, currents, and weather at sea. As long as you have an Internet connection, you can find your way home.

**Majordomo Mailing List:**

List Name: **navigation**
Subscribe to: **majordomo@ronin.com**

## Personal Watercraft

If you are not up to sailing your own large boat, start smaller with a personal watercraft. This site includes links to manufacturers, part suppliers, magazines, clubs and much more relating to owning, using and maintaining personal watercraft. You have to supply your own pirate flag.

**Web:**

**http://www.geocities.com/Colosseum/1161/**

## Rowing

Whether you are rowing gently down a stream or pulling frantically on your oars in order to cross the finish line first, **rec.sport.rowing** is one newsgroup you should see. Read about regattas, clubs, training tips, Olympic events and more.

**Usenet:**

**rec.sport.rowing**

### Navigate Your Way to Happiness

What do you do when you're in the middle of the ocean, all your electronic navigation aids are on the fritz and—on the distant horizon—a black, ponderous cloud has begun to form?

For most people, this would be a giant-sized pickle, but as an Internet user and a reader of this book, you have nothing to worry about. All you need to do is send a message to the **Navigation** mailing list, describe your predicament ("I am surrounded by a bunch of water, what should I do?") and wait for a reply. Within a short time, some kind soul will probably answer you with the help you need, and soon you will be back in action without a care in the world.

A B C D E F G H I J K L M N O P Q R S T U V W X Y Z

## Sailing

When you are landbound but missing the open seas, drop anchor on the Net, where there are a list of sailing resources waiting for you. You can find FAQs (frequently asked question lists), humor, discussions, information about, weather and navigator, and much much more.

**Web:**

**http://sailing.info-access.com/**
**http://www.sailnet.com/**

**Intrigue, Privacy, Secret Stuff...**

## Sailing Mailing Lists

Experience the freedom and grace of operating a traditional sailing vessel. Just you and your ship against the wind and water. When they are not on the sea, sailors hang out on the **tallship** mailing list to discuss experiences and techniques relating to owning and managing sailing vessels. The **yacht-l** list is for sailors who like to discuss sailing and amateur boat building.

**Listserv Mailing List:**

List Name: **tallship**
Subscribe to: **listserv@vccscent.bitnet**

**Listserv Mailing List:**

List Name: **yacht-l**
Subscribe to: **listserv@nic.surfnet.nl**

### *Look What I Found on the Net...*

```
Newsgroup: rec.sport.rowing
Subject: Paddling in Stream: A Physicist Writes...

> I don't believe that it feels any different rowing with or
> against a current. I think it is all due to visual cues from
> the shore. As a similar example, have you ever walked on a
> moving walkway at an airport? It seems to feel as though
> you are getting tremendous acceleration from each step.
> But if you close your eyes, aside from the sensation of the
> air, it feels no different than walking on a stationary
> surface.

I row on a river and, during the spring, the current is usually
pretty fast. When I do my long distance workout, I measure the
time it takes for me to reach a specific point downstream and
then the time to get back. Factoring in the velocity of the
current, which I check by just sitting in my single and drifting
for a fixed distance, my boat speed relative to the water
remains the same both ways.

I admit there is definitely a feeling of being faster when one
rows with the current, but each time I do this little
experiment, I conclude there is really no basis for it beside
the visual sensations.
```

## Searoom

This mailing list includes discussion of books about wooden sailing vessels, such as their history, modeling, construction and sailing, as well as customs involving sailing. Searoom welcomes discussion of fictional as well as factual writings. Some of the authors you will see discussed are Herman Melville, Jack London, C.S. Forester, Brian Lavery and Richard Dana.

**Listserv Mailing List:**

List Name: **searoom-l**
Subscribe to: **listserv@netcom.com**

### Get on the Right Wavelength

No matter how much you like kayaking, you can't spend all your time in the water. Sometimes you have to stay home rest up for the next trip.

The best way to rest is to use your Net connection to read the online version of Wave-Length Magazine. That way, even if you are not in the water, you can still immerse yourself in the world of kayaking.

In fact, if you have a waterproof laptop computer and a cellular modem, you can take your Net connection with you and read Wave-Length while you are paddling.

## Watercraft Calendar

Are you all dressed up in your sailor suit with no place to go? Here's an events calendar that will help you make plans for the weekend. Find out about races, meetings, boat shows and jet ski competitions all across the United States.

**Web:**

**http://www.watercraft.com/pcalendr.html**

## Wave-Length Paddling Magazine

Now you can enjoy the online edition of Wave-Length paddling magazine. This magazine covers all topics relating to paddling and wilderness with a focus on preservation. Read articles on paddling experiences, kayaking and paddling with children, environmental issues, book, video and movie reviews, and safety. You can also get helpful hints on equipment, clothing and travel, and read the calendar of events.

**Web:**

**http://www.wie.com/~wavenet/magazine.html**

# BOOKS

## Bibliomania

Curl up by the fireplace and cozy down with Data Text Processing's fiction collection, which includes author biographies and HTMLized book texts. Authors include such notables as Joyce, Hardy, Dickens, Alcott, Defoe, Wilde, Stevenson, Kipling and Lawrence.

**Web:**

**http://www.bibliomania.com/**

**Stay away from "X-Rated".**

## Book Authors

Books are good for those times when the computer is down and you can't connect to the Net. If there is a particular kind of book that catches your fancy, check in Usenet to see if there is a group relating to your favorite author.

**Usenet:**

alt.books.anne-rice
alt.books.arthur-clarke
alt.books.brian-lumley
alt.books.bukowski
alt.books.chesterton
alt.books.clive-barker
alt.books.crichton
alt.books.cs-lewis
alt.books.dean-koontz
alt.books.deryni
alt.books.george-orwell
alt.books.h-g-wells
alt.books.iain-banks
alt.books.isaac-asimov
alt.books.julian-may
alt.books.kurt-vonnegut
alt.books.larry-niven
alt.books.lynn-luxner
alt.books.m-lackey
alt.books.phil-k-dick
alt.books.pratchett
alt.books.raymond-feist
alt.books.robert-rankin
alt.books.sf.melanie-rawn
alt.books.stephen-king
alt.books.terry-brooks
alt.books.toffler
alt.books.tom-clancy
rec.arts.books.tolkien
rec.arts.sf.written.robert-jordan

## Book Binding

Make your own book or preserve some that are in a delicate condition. This bookbinding tutorial will show you how to photocopy, collate and fold paper, make a cover, punch holes, sew sections of a cover, trim pages and make a dust jacket.

**Web:**

http://www.cs.uiowa.edu/~jones/book/

## Book Recommendations

See what people on the Net are reading these days. There are no reviews here, but people do send in the names of their favorite books. You won't know necessarily why they like them, just that they do.

**Web:**

http://www.best.com/~yylee/homespun/booktop.html

## Book Reviews

Why waste your time and money on an unrewarding book? Read the reviews on the Net and find out the real scoop before you make a serious commitment. Save your excess time and money for unrewarding people. The Usenet newsgroup is for ongoing discussion and current reviews.

**Web:**

http://www.ala.org/booklist.html

**Usenet:**

alt.books.reviews

## Book Talk and General Discussion

A good place to find a variety of information about books. This newsgroup covers books of all genres, including reviews and discussion of reviews. This is a fairly free forum provided you know something about your topic. Moreover, talk is not limited to books: there is much discussion of the publishing industry as well as requests for information on interesting bookstores and hard-to-find bargains.

**Usenet:**

rec.arts.books

## Books Online

Page after page of books. This site has local books, as well as links to mirror sites. Each title indicates whether it is local or not and whether it is plain text or hypertext.

**Web:**

http://www.cs.cmu.edu/Web/booktitles.html
http://www.cs.cmu.edu/Web/bookauthors.html

## BookWeb

Part of the American Booksellers Association, this web page offers you news about books and bookstores, author interviews and gossip about new bookstores opening up.

**Web:**

http://www.ambook.org/

## Book Talk and General Discussion

Many people believe if you have a complete set of Harley Hahn books, you really don't need anything else. Well, although that is certainly true for most people, there are a few oddballs who need some other type of literary stimulation once in a while. If you are one of these unfortunate eccentrics, you may want to follow the discussion in **rec.arts.books.** Find out what's old, what's new, what's borrowed, and what's colorful in the land of literature.

## BookWire

When you don't want the best book, only the best-selling book, check out this database of the hottest books on the market. The database is searchable by author or title. You'll find descriptions and links to book publishers and sellers on the Web, links to online libraries, a reading room, a book events calendar and more.

**Web:**
**http://www.bookwire.com/**

## Buying and Selling Books

Get a piece of the buying and selling action. See what's hot and what's not. Book reviews and business news make up the bulk of the traffic in this newsgroup.

**Usenet:**
**biz.books.technical**
**rec.arts.books.marketplace**

## Children's Book News

An online magazine for parents and teachers, with book reviews of new books and out-of-print favorites that are making a comeback.

**Web:**
**http://www.community.net/~ben_chun/bookafair/**

## Children's Books

A good compilation of Internet resources relating to books for children and young adults. Find out about conferences, book events, book awards, list of recommended books and booksellers, movies based on children's books and research guides.

**Web:**
**http://www.ucalgary.ca/~dkbrown/**

**Usenet:**
**rec.arts.books.childrens**

## Commanders Club

If your imitations of Beavis and Butthead are getting you nowhere in life, take an entirely different approach. Study the suave, cool, and untouchable lifestyle of James Bond. This page will teach you all of his moves, his habits and his quirks—yes, it even goes over his technique with women.

**Web:**
**http://www.commanders.com/~bond/**

## Do-It-Yourself Book Reviews

Which books are real crowd-pleasers? Find out by reading reviews written by people on the Internet. Categories include science fiction and fantasy, general fiction, religion, new age, mystery, computers and technology, biographies, science and mathematics.

**Web:**
**http://www.clark.net/pub/bell/review/book_review.shtml**

## Electronic Text Center

Read a good book and practice a foreign language at the same time. This etext archive has hundreds of writings in English, French, German and Latin. Find Modern English writing as well as Shakespeare, British poetry, the Bible and the Koran.

**Web:**
**http://www.lib.virginia.edu/etext/ETC.html**

## The Quintessential James Bond Reference

What do you do when you are about to entertain that special someone at an exclusive restaurant, and you can't recall whether the martini should be shaken or stirred, or you are not sure how to ask for your tagliatelle verde to be prepared? In most cases, about all you could do would be to trust in blind faith or hope that I might be in the same restaurant and you could ask me.

However, if you have access to the archives of the **Commanders Club**, your worries are over. This club "seeks to preserve the elegant lifestyle and sense of intrigue that was born of Fleming's writings and James Bond in the cinema."

Joining the Commanders Club is difficult: It is a small, exclusive organization with few openings. However, if you are on the Net, you can visit the Commanders Club archives whenever you want. If you are a real James Bond fan, you will not be disappointed. The wealth of Bond trivia is enough to choke a 1954 Continental Bentley with the "R" type chassis, the big 6 engine, and a 13:40 back-axle ratio.

### Historical Fiction Novels

There are writers who love to muse on the what-ifs of days gone by. If you like to dwell in the past by reading historical fiction, check out the newsgroup that talks about this popular pastime. Read reviews, ask questions and get information on any books relating to historical fiction.

**Usenet:**

**rec.arts.books.hist-fiction**

### Internet Books List

Do you want a book about the Internet? Of course, you can walk into any bookstore in the world, ask for a Harley Hahn book, and be assured of the finest quality and a most entertaining experience. However, what if you want a non-Harley Hahn book? How do you know what you are getting into? Just check the Internet Books List and help yourself to free reviews of a large number of Internet-oriented books.

**Web:**

**http://www.northcoast.com/savetz/booklist**

### Pulp Fiction

Pulp magazines existed in America from the turn of the century to the early 1950s. They offered an impressive array of stories about crime, mystery, detectives, war, love, romance, science fiction, horror, sports, westerns, and adventure. The spirit of pulp fiction is alive today in modern paperback adventure series and in this Usenet newsgroup. Did you know that the Shadow was really Kent Allard, a World War I ace and spy? Lamont Cranston was merely a disguise. If you listen to the radio show, you will be misinformed, but if you read this newsgroup, you will know the truth.

**Usenet:**

**alt.pulp**

**Find a friend in "People".**

## Rare Books

People always want what they can't have. If it's rare, it's bound to be popular. Take rare books, for example. People collect them, and most of the time they just store the books and never look at them. Join the **exlibris** mailing list where the topic for discussion is rare book and manuscript librarianship along with special collections issues. Anyone can subscribe, but most of the membership consists of those librarians who wear the little white gloves when they work. The **biblio** mailing list is for amateur or professional dealers and collectors of out-of-print, used or rare books.

**Web:**

**http://www.clark.net/pub/rmharris/discuss.html**

**Listproc Mailing List:**

List Name: **exlibris**
Subscribe to: **listproc@library.berkeley.edu**

**Majordomo Mailing List:**

List Name: **biblio**
Subscribe to: **majordomo@smartdocs.com**

## Romance Novel Database

Romance novel addicts will have a great time searching this database of books. It's searchable by title, author or subgenre such as Georgian, Medieval, Regency or Gothic. Many of the books listed have reader reviews and there is a form available so you can rate any of the books listed.

**Web:**

**http://www.sils.umich.edu/~sooty/romance/**

## Science Fiction and Fantasy Reviews

This is the place to find reviews of your favorite (or not so favorite) books, magazines, movies, and videos. This collection of resources offers reviews of speculative fiction, fantasy, horror, and even (sometimes) comics. The newsgroup **rec.arts.sf.reviews** is moderated.

**Web:**

**http://pubweb.acns.nwu.edu/~bjorn/sfflist.html**
**http://www.clark.net/pub/iz/Books/Top100/top100.html**

**Usenet:**

**rec.arts.sf.reviews**

Jennifer's breath grew short and stertorous. Her lips began to quiver while her straw-colored hair moved gently in the warm tropical breeze.

She gazed up at the dark, mysterious, masculine eyes of the stranger. As a frisson of passion shocked her taut, leonine body, she whispered softly into his dark, mysterious, masculine ear. "Tell me, my love," she murmured, "of all the heroines in all the romance novels in the world, whom would you say I most resemble?" The stranger touched her face gently with the back of his dark, mysterious, masculine hand. He turned away slowly, the moonlight shining brightly on his dark, mysterious, masculine features as he opened the cover of his notebook computer. "Just one moment, my sweet angel," he responded. "My PPP connection will be active shortly, and I will be able to check the **Romance Novel Database** for myself."

## Technical Books

If you have a squeak in your clicker or you can't get slot A to line up with tab B, check into this newsgroup to see if there is a technical book that can help. Just the place to look when you need to decide which Unix book to give your grandmother for her birthday.

**Usenet:**

**alt.books.technical**
**misc.books.technical**

A B C D E F G H I J K L M N O P Q R S T U V W X Y Z

## Women Writers

Explore this easy-to-read list of women writers and follow links to their works. You will find biographical information and pictures of some of the writers as well.

**Web:**

**http://www.cs.cmu.edu/afs/cs.cmu.edu/user/mmbt/www/women/writers.html**

## Wonderland Book Archive

Here are lots and lots of well known, worthwhile books you can read for free with your web browser. Just the thing to put up on your screen when your mother or father looks in to see what you are doing on the computer. (And, when they aren't checking up on you, you may want to take a look at the books anyway. Some of them are pretty good.)

**Web:**

**http://www.wonderland.org/Works/**

# BOTANY

## Agroforestry

As the population grows, the need for better crops and soil increases. Agroforestry studies plant growth and nutrition in an effort to find crops and soil that are compatible with each other and with the rest of the surrounding environment.

**Usenet:**

**bionet.agroforestry**

## Botanical Gardens

I belong to the local botanical garden where I live. I find that there is nothing more relaxing than sitting beside a rushing brook under a large tree, or relaxing with a good book sitting in a field of wildflowers. If you like gardens and plants, here is a list of botanical gardens in Canada and the United States, wonderful places to visit when you get a chance to slow down and enjoy life.

**Web:**

**http://www.botanique.com/**

### Agroforestry

**We need better and more crops and forests, but what have *you* done lately to help? After all, if you're not part of the problem, you're not putting your fair share of your nose on the grindstone. But don't worry, it's never too late. Subscribe to the bionet.agroforestry discussion group right this minute. Soon, with your help, poor crop yields will be a thing of the past and never again will some poor mother in Fargo, North Dakota, have to tell her son to clean his plate because paper doesn't grow on trees.**

## Botany Database

A database of nearly 100,000 records in the Type Specimen Register for the U.S. National Herbarium.

**Web:**

**http://nmngoph.si.edu/gopher-menus/BotanyattheSmithsonianInstitution.html**

## Botany Images

Here are thousands of pictures of plants, flowers, trees, fungi and other vegetation. If you are a student or researcher of botany, this is a site you should explore. However, even if you don't really care about botany, I suggest that you browse around and see what's here. There are fabulous pictures that would be great to dress up your web page or to use as a background.

**Web:**

**http://www.wisc.edu/botany/virtual.html**

## Botany Resources

Here is a large, international collection of botanical resources containing just about anything you can think of relating to botany, gardening, plants and cultivation. If you are a plant person, this is a great place to start a browsing expedition.

**Web:**

**http://www.helsinki.fi/kmus/botmenu.html**

## Botany Talk and General Discussion

How does your garden grow? Discover the myth and mystery of plant growth and reproduction. Discussion of all aspects of plant biology is encouraged. You'll never have a guilt-free salad again.

**Usenet:**

**bionet.plants**

## Botany Web Sites

Students, teachers, scientists or plain old plant lovers must immediately make their way to this web page. There are a huge amount of resources for botanists around the Net, and you will find most of them here: links to databases, mailing lists, archive sites, software, organizations and much more.

**Web:**

**http://herb.biol.uregina.ca/liu/bio/botany.html**

## Carnivorous Plants

A carnivorous plant is one that eats animal matter of some type (usually insects, but sometimes very small animals like frogs). Carnivorous plants have adapted to live in an environment which is lacking in nutrients, for example, a bog or the surface of a cliff. Worldwide, there are more than 600 different species of carnivorous plants, many of which can be grown right in your very own home or garden. What is fascinating about them is that they are so unexpected. Normally, we assume that plants will sit quietly and leave the animal kingdom alone. To find a plant that can actually attract, capture and digest an animal of some type is a complete biological non sequitur. In case you want to explore these monarchs of the botanical world, here are some Internet resources to help you learn about these plants before they get a chance to learn about you and hunt you down.

**Web:**

**http://www.hpl.hp.com/bot/cp_home/**
**http://www.indirect.com/www/bazza/cps/faq/faq.html**

**Listserv Mailing List:**

List Name: **cp**
Subscribe to: **listserv@opus.hpl.hp.com**

## Ethnobotany

Ethnobotany is the study of how people in a particular region of the world make use of the indigenous plants. Ethnobotany involves not only botany, but many other disciplines such as archeology, anthropology, biochemistry, pharmacology, history, sociology, mythology and so on. Ethnobotany is especially important to us as a source for native plants that might have important pharmacological and medical uses.

**Web:**

**http://countrylife.net/ethnobotany/**
**http://www.gene.com/AE/RC/Ethnobotany/**

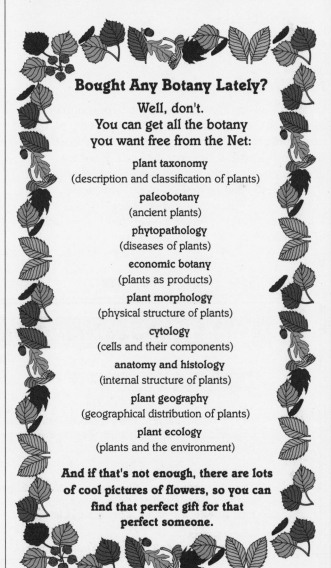

**Bought Any Botany Lately?**

**Well, don't.**
**You can get all the botany you want free from the Net:**

**plant taxonomy**
(description and classification of plants)

**paleobotany**
(ancient plants)

**phytopathology**
(diseases of plants)

**economic botany**
(plants as products)

**plant morphology**
(physical structure of plants)

**cytology**
(cells and their components)

**anatomy and histology**
(internal structure of plants)

**plant geography**
(geographical distribution of plants)

**plant ecology**
(plants and the environment)

**And if that's not enough, there are lots of cool pictures of flowers, so you can find that perfect gift for that perfect someone.**

## Ferns

In an outside alcove at my house, I have a fern garden with a nice variety of plants. From within the house, there are two large windows that I can look out of and see the ferns. I am not sure exactly what it is, but ferns have a special feeling about them that makes them unique among plants. If you would like to know more about ferns, here are some resources containing detailed biological data, as well as information about related books, organizations, events and helpful hints. For discussion about ferns, you can join the mailing list.

**Web:**

**http://www.visuallink.com/fern/**
**http://inet1.inetworld.net/~sdfern/**

**Listproc Mailing List:**

List Name: **pteridonet**
Subscribe to: **listproc@gac.edu**

## New York Botanical Garden

Okay, we all can't live in the Bronx (a borough of New York City). But, as long as we are on the Net, we can connect to the Bronx and visit the New York Botanical Garden whenever we want. Here are enough photos of the gardens and plant collections to allow you to spend a quiet peaceful afternoon communing with nature and enjoying the ambiance which has given the Bronx its worldwide reputation as a bastion of peace and tranquillity.

**Web:**

**http://pathfinder.com/vg/gardens/NYBG/**

## Palynology Resources

Palynology is the study of spores and pollen. My advice is to visit this web site as often as you can and brush up on your knowledge of tiny things that float around making people miserable. Then, when you meet someone at a party and they ask about your hobbies, you can say, "Oh, I am something of an amateur palynologist. Do you like spores?" I guarantee you will be invited back, again and again.

**Web:**

**http://gpu.srv.ualberta.ca/~abeaudoi/cap/websites.htm**

## Photosynthesis

Plants kissed by the sun get their own version of a tan. See green plant cells become little organic factories as their chlorophyll explodes into action. Read about the ins and outs of photosynthesis: the original food processor.

**Usenet:**

**bionet.photosynthesis**

## Plant Fossil Database

For some reason, when you read about extinct and endangered species, animals get all the press. However, there are a large number of extinct plant species, many of which have left fossil remains. This database contains a wealth of research information relating to thousands of extinct plants.

**Web:**

**http://www1.uel.ac.uk/palaeo/**

### *Look What I Found on the Net...*

```
Newsgroup: bionet.photosynthesis
Subject: I'm a Dad!

Although I don't know all of you I thought this was the easiest
way to let most of my photosynthesis buddies know what's
happening with me, and why I won't be at the upcoming conference
causing trouble this year.

I'm a dad! It's a girl.

She doesn't seem too interested in photosynthesis yet:
eating, sleeping and screaming are the current focus,
but there is time for everything.

Xxxx Xxxxx
Department of Biological Sciences
Xxxxx University
```

## Plant Gene Register

You can search this database, maintained by the American Society of Plant Physiologists, to find information about a large number of specific plant genes. Articles in the database describe the isolation and DNA sequence determination, as well as related technical information.

**Web:**

**http://ophelia.com/Ophelia/pgr/**

## Plant Pathology

Plants get sick. However, unlike people, plants rarely have adequate insurance and must almost always depend on the kindness of strangers. If you have a sick plant, or if you happen to be a plant pathologist doing research or wondering what your peers are up to, here is a well-organized web site specializing in botanical diseases and related topics.

**Web:**

**http://www.ifgb.uni-hannover.de/extern/ipp/ipp_en01.htm**

## Plant Viruses

For researchers and plant specialists, this resource contains lots of information about plant viruses: names, species descriptions, and some illustrations and micrographs, as well as access to the VIDE database of plant viruses (species index, viral acronyms, genus and host family index).

**Web:**

**http://biology.anu.edu.au/Groups/MES/vide/refs.htm**

## Succulents

Succulents are fleshy plants that are characterized by being able to survive with minimal water. Succulents typically have thick leaves, covered with a waxy material called cutin that acts to reduce the evaporation of water. These plants—including many species of cactus, aloe and yucca—are commonly indigenous to naturally dry regions, such as the semi-arid areas of the world. Personally, I like succulents, and I have a number of them in my office and outside in my garden. One such plant that I recommend for everyone is the aloe vera. It is easy to grow, and the slimy substance inside the leaves is useful for treating mild burns and skin irritations. For information about succulents, here is a web page containing links to a variety of resources.

**Web:**

**http://www.graylab.ac.uk/usr/hodgkiss/succule.html**

## Wildflowers

I love wildflowers. Right now, in my garden, I have a large bed of assorted wildflowers that are particularly suited to attracting hummingbirds. The thing I like about wildflowers is that, unlike their cultivated cousins, they retain an air of informality that allows you to enjoy that back-to-nature feeling without actually having to get your feet dirty or leave your home. If you are a wildflower fan, here is a great source of information and pictures that will keep your web browser blooming long into the night.

**Web:**

**http://www.wild-flowers.com/**

## Auction Acumen

If you're like me, you never pass through Overland Park, Kansas, without taking a few hours to visit the Auctioneer Hall of History.

However, being steeped in the lore of auctioneering won't help you when you are immersed in the hot and heavy, fast-moving environment of an actual auction.

After all, at an average household estate auction, an auctioneer will sell an average of 60 items per hour. And at a wholesale automobile auction, you may see as many as 150 cars sold per hour. When the auctioneer talks so fast, how can you possibly make any sense out of what he is saying?

"100 dollar bid, now 105, now 105, will ya give me 110? 110 dollar bid, now 120, now 120, will ya give me 120? 120 dollar bid, now 125, now 125, will ya give me 125?"

Here is a hint: ignore everything but the numbers. All the other words are used as fillers. Listen only to the numbers, and you will be surprised how easy it is to follow along like a pro.

# BUYING AND SELLING

## Auctions

Do you miss the heart-pounding thrill of going to an auction, when it gets down to mano a mano bidding and you just don't know how it's going to turn out? Before you go out on your next auction adventure, connect up to these web sites and learn a little more about the technique of buying at auctions. These sites have lots of general auction information such as how auctions work, how to understand what the auctioneer says, a glossary of terms, code of ethics and more.

**Web:**

**http://www.auctionweb.com/naa/**
**http://www.syspac.com/usaweb/auction.html**

## Bicycle Marketplace

Drop in to the bicycle marketplace: buying, selling, and reviews. Soon you'll be bopping around town on your very own bicycle built for one.

**Usenet:**

**rec.bicycles.marketplace**

## Board Game Marketplace

You can't spend your life playing games on the Net. Eventually you are going to want to have a party, and everyone knows that you have to play board games when you have a party. Increase your board game collection by seeing what games are for sale or, if it's spring cleaning time, clear out your closets by offering your games to people on the Net.

**Usenet:**

**rec.games.board.marketplace**

## Bootleg Music

Surely this isn't the illegal activity it looks like. Everyone knows that it's against the law to sell bootleg copies of recordings or amateur recordings of live performances. Don't they?

**IRC:**

**#bootlegs**

## Buying/Selling Talk and General Discussion

Where do you go on the Net when you want to buy or sell something that doesn't really fit into a specific category? This is the general buying/selling Usenet group, the place where it is okay to post a personal advertisement, wheel and deal till you drop. It is also the place to look for a bargain. Just remember, when you are dealing with someone whom you have never met, be sure to take normal precautions. (For example, if you are selling a house, don't actually send the house to the buyer until the check clears the bank.)

**Usenet:**

**alt.forsale**

## Catalog Mart

Don't have enough junk mail? I have a way for you to get even more. This site offers hundreds of subjects of interest from which you can select. Choose all the ones you like, fill in your name and address and before long, your mailman will be bringing catalogs straight to your mailbox.

**Web:**

**http://catalog.savvy.com/**

## Catalogs by Mail

Catalog and junk mail fans will have a blast at this site. You can browse reviews of newly released mail order catalogs, order catalogs online, preview catalogs and even get some celebrity gossip about who is buying what these days.

**Web:**

**http://www.catalogsite.com/**

## CD Clubs

CD clubs have their system all set up so they can make lots of money off you. If you want a fighting chance of getting the best value for your money, you should check out this site. It has a FAQ on how to get the most out of CD clubs and information on the strategies of membership, resale value of CDs, the ins and outs of using club coupons, how to stop getting cards every month, how to return CDs you don't want and more.

**Web:**

**http://www.eskimo.com/~bloo/cdfaq/toppage.htm**

## Classified Ads

Shopping, shopping, shopping. Do you like to shop, but don't like to get dressed to leave the house? Shop at home, by checking out the great classified ads on the Net.

**Web:**

**http://ep.com/**
**http://www.funcity.com/ads**
**http://www.galaxymall.com/Galaxy/ClassifiedMenu.html**

## Computers

Buying a computer? For buying and selling particular machines, see these specialized groups. Here's my hint for the day: it is difficult to buy too much speed, too much memory, or too much video resolution.

**Usenet:**

**biz.marketplace.computers.discussion**
**biz.marketplace.computers.mac**
**biz.marketplace.computers.other**
**biz.marketplace.computers.pc-clone**
**biz.marketplace.computers.workstation**
**biz.marketplace.services.computers**
**comp.os.os2.marketplace**
**comp.sys.amiga.marketplace**
**comp.sys.apple2.marketplace**
**comp.sys.ibm.pc.games.marketplace**
**comp.sys.mac.games.marketplace**
**comp.sys.next.marketplace**
**misc.forsale.computers.workstation**

## Law Books for Sale

If you have law books left over from when you were going to law school, there are many different things you can do with them. You can use them as a basis for an interesting glass-topped coffee table or for something as simple as a paperweight or a party coaster. Or if you are more interested in getting some cash than decorating your apartment, you should consider reselling your used law books to other, less-fortunate students. All you have to do is register at this site and hawk your goods for big or small bucks. Registration is free.

**Web:**

**http://www.lawbook.com/**

**Classified Ads**

Buy and sell, sell and buy. The Net has classified ads, and somewhere somebody wants to make a deal with you.

Classified Ads

## Macintosh Shopping

Looking for something to go with your Macintosh computer? Here's a site that has a search interface to help you locate mail order businesses that offer various products for Macintoshes.

**Web:**

**http://www.owplaza.com/msd/**

## Photography Marketplace

You've had your eye out for a sweet little camera setup with a powerwinder and a lens that can spot a yellow-bellied sapsucker at the top of a giant redwood. You've looked everywhere and you just can't find what you're looking for. Now you have another place to look. Check out this Usenet newsgroup where you can place notices whether you are buying or selling photographic supplies or equipment.

**Usenet:**

**rec.photo.marketplace**

## Pinball Machine Mall

Here's a classy decorating tip: If you have a big, empty spot in your house and you just don't know what to put there, consider buying a pinball machine. You will be popular with the neighbors who will want to come over at all hours of the day and night to play. You might be able to even charge them money for drinks and rake in some extra cash on the side. Go to this web site to find out where to buy pinball machines.

**Web:**

**http://www.pinmall.com/**

## Registries for Stolen Goods

Did someone snatch something of yours? Make it known to the world. This web site has a collection of pages where you can register goods that have been stolen or look before you buy something to make sure it has not been stolen. If someone offers you a deal that is too good to be true, check here to make sure you aren't buying someone else's stuff.

**Web:**

**http://www.rtt.ab.ca/rtt/personal/stolen.htm**

## Science Fiction Marketplace

Do you need a replacement for your old tricorder? Is your communicator or phaser malfunctioning? Check out the science fiction marketplace. If they don't have it, or know about it, it hasn't been replicated.

**Usenet:**

**rec.arts.sf.marketplace**

## Selling on IRC

If you've got to get rid of something *fast*, come to the **#forsale** channel to dump those unwanted items. People come here to buy, sell, and barter. They even hold live auctions from time to time.

**IRC:**

**#forsale**

### Talk 'N Sell

IRC (Internet Relay Chat) is great for talking, and the great thing about talk is that it is so cheap.

The next time you want to buy or sell something, why wait for an advertisement to do its work? Go right to the **forsale** channel on IRC, and see if you can conjure up a bit of instant gratification.

The person you need may be there, right now, waiting to offer you what you want (or waiting for your offer).

## Textbook Exchange

If you are a student, you know what a big difference there is between the price you pay for a textbook (even a used textbook) and what the bookstore is willing to pay to buy it from you at the end of the semester. I bet there are many times when you said to yourself, "What a rip-off. Somebody should do something about this." Well, someone has. Here is a place where you can buy and sell your used textbooks for free. (I checked to see if anyone was selling any of my textbooks but no one was. Which only makes sense—after all, who would want to give up a Harley Hahn book?)

**Web:**

**http://www.studentmkt.com/**

## Video Game Marketplace

When you are not playing a video game, you are wasting your time (unless you are *talking* about video games). If God didn't want us to spend all our time staring at the screen and manipulating a surrogate being, why did he give us this newsgroup?

**Usenet:**

**rec.games.video.marketplace**

## Video Tape Trading

I love watching old Dick Van Dyke episodes. In fact, I would trade my old copy of "Christmas in Connecticut" for a tape full of Dick Van Dyke. If you have some particular video needs and desires, check out the Usenet group where you can trade bootlegged video tapes, recordings of television and movies, live music performances, and music videos. But save the Dick Van Dyke tapes for me.

**Usenet:**

**alt.video.tape-trading**

**Take a break.**
**Try "Outdoor Activities".**

# CANADA

## Canadian Business Information

A collection of Canadian business resources, your one-stop site for everything you need to impress that certain someone the next time you have a hot Canadian date.

**Web:**

**http://www.visions.com/**

$$$$$$$$$$$$$$$$$$$$$$$$$$$$$$$$$$$$$$$$$$$$$$$$$$$$$$$

### Investing in Canada

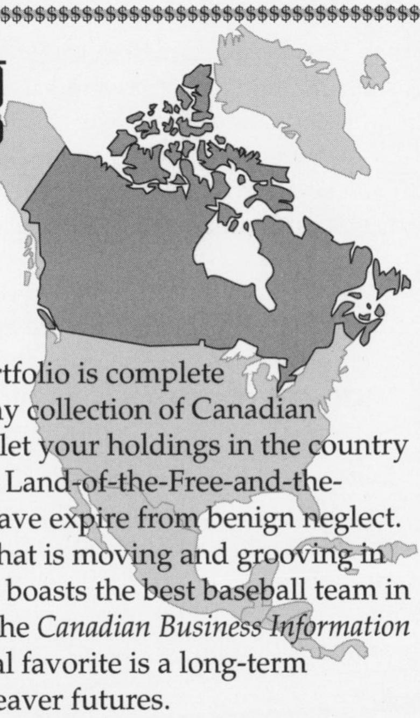

No financial portfolio is complete without a healthy collection of Canadian stock. But don't let your holdings in the country just north of the Land-of-the-Free-and-the-Home-of-the-Brave expire from benign neglect. Keep track of what is moving and grooving in the country that boasts the best baseball team in the world: Use the *Canadian Business Information* site. My personal favorite is a long-term investment in beaver futures.

$$$$$$$$$$$$$$$$$$$$$$$$$$$$$$$$$$$$$$$$$$$$$$$$$$$$$$$

## Canadian Constitutional Documents

In 1982, the United Kingdom parliament gave up all power over Canadian laws, including the Canadian constitution. Since then—through hard work and perseverance—Canada has become one of the best countries in North America. Would you like your own copy of the 1982 Canada Act? It's here, along with many other Canadian constitutional documents, waiting for you, 24 hours a day, 365 days a year.

**Web:**

**http://insight.mcmaster.ca/org/efc/pages/law/cons/Constitutions/Canada/English/cons.html**

## Canadian Culture

There is an old riddle: What is Canadian culture? The answer is, "Mostly American." Some people feel that "Canadian culture" is an oxymoron. What do they know? Haven't they ever heard of the Blue Jays? William Shatner? Rick Moranis (with whom I went to summer camp)? After all, if Canadian culture is good enough for Wayne Gretzky, it should be good enough for The Kids in the Hall.

**Web:**

**http://www.nervecenter.com/nerve/can/cancult.htm**

**Usenet:**

**soc.culture.canada**

### CANADIAN (?) CULTURE

It's amazing how many people know nothing about Canadian culture. If you are one of those unfortunate individuals, do not dismay. All you need to do is drop in to the **soc.culture.canada** forum where you can discuss recipes for Eskimo pies, the demise of the Oopik, and secret ways to sneak into Ontario Place.

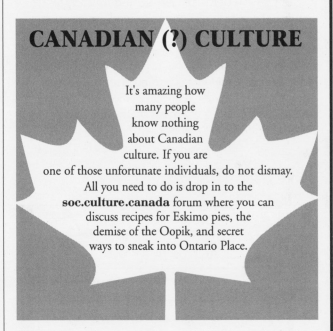

## Canadian Fact Sheets

Straight from the Canadian Department of Foreign Affairs and International Trade to you. Here is information about the provinces, history, government, legal system, economy, trade, education, women, geography, environment, climate, transportation, arts, sports, and—of course—the Mounties.

**Web:**

**http://www.dfait-maeci.gc.ca/english/canada/menu.htm**

A B C D E F G H I J K L M N O P Q R S T U V W X Y Z

## Canadian Government

Explore segments of the Canadian federal government, including the House of Commons, the Senate, the Supreme Court, and federal departments and agencies. These pages are in both French and English.

**Web:**
**http://canada.gc.ca/**
**http://info.ic.gc.ca/opengov/**

## Canadian Government Information Navigator

The Champlain Navigator is the place to go when you need to search for information from or about the government: federal, provincial and municipal. I requested a search within the federal government information area for "free money". It came back with 12 different sites. So far, I have been too busy working to check them out, but one day I will get around to it. Note: This Internet site is named after the French explorer, Samuel de Champlain (1567?-1635) who, in 1608, established a settlement on the site that eventually became Quebec City.

**Web:**
**http://192.77.55.3/champlain.html**

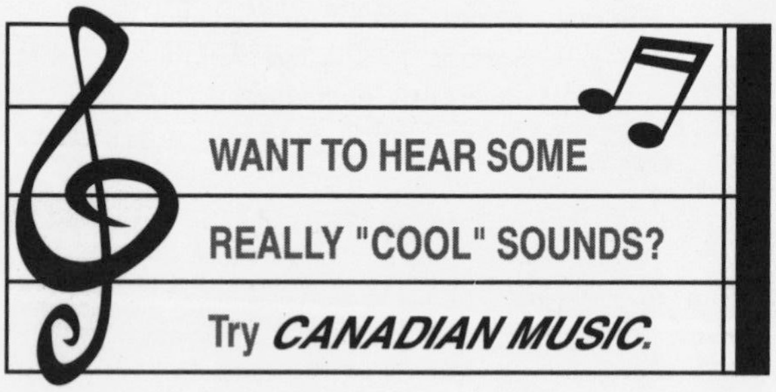
WANT TO HEAR SOME
REALLY "COOL" SOUNDS?
Try CANADIAN MUSIC.

## Canadian History

Here is a little-known fragment of Canadian history: When my sister, Melissa, was two years old and I was baby-sitting her, she fell off my parents' bed and hit her head on the floor. (Come to Toronto with me some time, and I will show you the exact spot.) Of course, not all Canadian history is that interesting, but still, there are jewels if you only take the time to look.

**Web:**
**http://www.msstate.edu/Archives/History/Canada/canada.html**

## Canadian Investment

If you're looking to spread your money around a little, try investing in Canada. Learn about Canadian money markets, investment clubs, financial publications, and the government. (And, if you have a little extra money, we have a snow farm you might want to invest in.)

**Web:**
**http://www.nucleus.com/wealthnet/**

**Usenet:**
**misc.invest.canada**

## Canadian Legal Resources

Brush up on your Canadian legal resources by reading this information on courts and tribunals, law reform commissions, legislation, taxes and accounting, lawyers and law firms, universities and colleges, the federal and provincial governments, free speech and privacy. The information is organized by subject or province.

**Web:**
**http://www.mbnet.mb.ca/~psim/can_law.html**

## Canadian Music

After more than 25 years of federal "Canadian content" rules, Canadian music is alive and well and living in...ahem...Canada. At the web site you can search for your favorite band. Or just join the discussion of your favorite musicians from the land where a rich musical tradition resonates from sea to shining sea. (Bagpipes and accordions are optional.)

**Web:**
**http://www.monkey-boy.com/cmusic**

**Usenet:**
**alt.music.canada**

## Canadian News

An American magazine once referred to Canada as "the retarded giant on our doorstep". Read the latest Canadian news and get the real scoop. You will find that Canadian news is about as exciting as...well...Canadian news.

**Web:**
**http://www.cdnemb-washdc.org/newscan.html**
**http://www.hfxnews.com/**
**http://www.xe.com/canpress/**

## *Look What I Found on the Net...*

```
Newsgroup: misc.invest.canada
Subject: Retirement Savings Plans "Should be Taxed" to Reduce Deficit

The federal government can't ignore $15 billion a year in tax-breaks
for retirement-savings if it's serious about controlling the deficit,
says a new article in a respected economics journal...

The item says the government needs to find out if tax-deductions for
contributions to RRSPs, registered pension plans, and deferred
profit-sharing plans are working.

Economists Sid Ingerman and Robin Rowley of McGill University in
Montreal take issue with the view -- trumpeted by four major pension
consulting firms and the Reform Party -- that the government should
keep its hands off money set aside for old age.

Finance Minister Paul Martin announced that his department would
study the problem of the country's aging population, and how to
finance its retirement...

Ingerman and Rowley say the federal and provincial governments have five
major options:

 * leave the system alone
 * reduce contribution limits
 * tax new contributions to pension plans
 * tax the income that pension-funds earn
 * impose one-time or periodic levies on pension-fund assets

The authors say that New Zealand has already eliminated tax-breaks for
retirement savings, while Australia and Sweden have moved to increase
their tax take.
```

## Canadian Politics

Politics is a global pastime, and even Canada is not immune. Assert your intellectual freedom, and see what everyone else has to say about the political challenges in modern Canadian society.

**Usenet:**

**can.politics**

## Canadian Resource Page

The Canadian Resource Page has links to news, statistics and figures about Canada, travel and tourism information, government services, politics and history, education and culture.

**Web:**

**http://www.cs.cmu.edu/Web/Unofficial/Canadiana/README.html**

## Canadian Talk and General Discussion

What do you at 9:30 PM on Saturday night, when you are just dying to talk to a Canadian and William Shatner's line is busy? Hop over to IRC, where nimble-fingered Canadians are cutting fast, loose and easy. Need a French-Canadian fix? Try the **#quebec** channel ("ici, on parle Français"). Who says Saturday night has to be dull?

**IRC:**

**#calgary**
**#canada**
**#edmonton**
**#montreal**
**#ontario**
**#quebec**
**#toronto**
**#vancouver**
**#winnipeg**

## Canadian Travel

Canada is a big place, and it's easy to get lost. Imagine how embarrassed you would be if, after saving all your money and planning for months, you and your family finally make it to Canada only to become completely disoriented. For example, what if you are driving from Winnipeg to Toronto, and you accidentally make a left turn at North Bay? The next thing you know, you are in the Ungava Peninsula, and the kids are complaining, "There are no bathrooms. You promised we would stop at MacDonalds. Whose dumb idea was it to go on a trip anyway?" Don't let this happen to you. Before you even think about exploring this grand old country just north of the Land of the Free and Home of the Brave, use the Net to access Canada's tourism information network. Remember their slogan: "Canada, the country with a lot of space."

**Web:**

**http://info.ic.gc.ca/Tourism/Canada/**

## Canadian Webmaster Index

Wanna fast way to get your finger on the pulse of the Canadian Net? Here is the master link that points to everything worth pointing to in Canada. ("Be there *and* be square.")

**Web:**

**http://www.csr.ists.ca/w3can/**

## Canuck Site of the Day

Everybody needs a bit of Canadian something-or-other in their life. Don't be deprived. Every day, you can visit this site and be surprised with a nice, pleasant Canadian experience.

**Web:**

**http://www.10q.com/canuck/**

## CBC (Canadian Broadcasting Corporation)

Daily news broadcasts, transcripts, program listings, sample radio programs, Radio Canada International information and schedules, a list of products, illustrated audio shows, and more from Canadian Broadcasting Corporation (CBC) Radio.

**Web:**

**http://www.radio.cbc.ca/**

## Montreal

When I was in grade 10, my class went on a trip to Montreal to see the World's Fair. Years later, I went to Montreal again to see the summer Olympics. You, however, may not have fulfilled your quota, so a trip to Montreal may be in your future. If so, here is a good place to get the details you need to make your visit enjoyable: location, attractions, calendar of events, museums, maps of the city and, for foreign travelers, customs regulations and exchange rates.

**Web:**

**http://sun2.cum.qc.ca/octgm/**

## Musée du Québec

The Musée du Québec (Quebec Museum) is the province of Quebec's national art gallery, containing over 20,000 works of art, most of which were produced in Quebec. You can look at some of the paintings over the Net as well as historical information about the artists. In addition, there is a nifty art puzzle you can play with. At this point, I can hear you saying, "Wait, Quebec is a province. Why would it have its own 'national' art gallery?" The answer is: Don't even ask. Just visit and enjoy yourself.

**Web:**

**http://www.mdq.org/fr/Anglais/index.htm**

**If you are one of those people lucky enough to get CBC (Canadian) Radio, you will appreciate their web site.**

## Ottawa

I once spent a summer in Ottawa, and I had a great time. It's a beautiful city (the capital of Canada) with a lot of tourist attractions and wonderful places to visit. And there are miles of pleasant bicycle paths on which you can ride your bike or jog. True, the winter gets a tad cold—actually, freezing beyond endurance—but you can skate on the canal and cross-country ski in the parks. However, perhaps the most important thing that anybody needs to know about Ottawa is that my friend Mike the Dentist lives there. If, for some reason, you need more information, all you need to do is check with the Net, where you can find out about dining, transportation, things to see, things to do and places to eat. Whether you live in Ottawa, or are merely planning to visit, there is lots of info waiting for you on the Net, twenty-four hours a day. And, if your teeth start to hurt, you can always call Mike.

**Web:**

**http://www.ottawakiosk.com/**
**http://www.scs.carleton.ca/ottawa/ottawa.html**
**http://www.tourottawa.org/**

## Toronto

I was born in Toronto and, I can tell you, it changes so fast that the only way I can keep up is to live in California and use the Net to look at the Toronto information web site. Find all the info you need about Toronto: news, sports, entertainment, food, music, tourism, and so on. However, my favorite activity is to check the weather reports during the winter.

**Web:**

**http://www.torinfo.com/**

## Tour Canada at Home

A collection of links with information describing Canada and its ten provinces. You will find images and articles about Vancouver, Ontario, Ottawa, Quebec, New Brunswick, British Columbia, and many other places within Canada. As with many things Canadian, the information is also available in French.

**Web:**

**http://info.ic.gc.ca/ic-data/industry/tourism**

### Tour Canada
### Without Leaving Your Desk

Who among us has not sat wistfully at a desk, daydreaming about being able to visit Canada? What a joy it would be to visit the frozen jewel of North America without even having to pack a bag.

Well, now your dream can come true—you can use the Net to tour Canada right from your very own home.

(Hint: As you pass through Toronto, look for the plaque marking the place where I was born.)

## Vancouver

The summer after I finished high school, I hitchhiked across Canada and ended up in Vancouver, where I joined a special French-language program at the University of British Columbia. It was great—the government paid for everything. I got free food, a place to stay, had lots of fun, went on excursions, and spent the afternoons sunning at Wreck Beach (the nude beach). And all I had to do was put in a few hours a day trying to learn how to speak French. ("La plume de ma tante est sur la table.") Since then, I have had occasion to spend many more delightful days in the pearl of the Canadian west coast. For instance, when I was a medical student, I spent a few weeks in Vancouver researching a book on unconventional medicine. Even if you do not want to learn to speak French or understand unconventional medicine, you may still want to visit Vancouver. If so, you can check with the Net before you go. There you will find information about parks, community centers, bicycling, swimming pools, arts, entertainment, attractions and visitors resources. True, the government probably won't pay for your room and board, but you can still spend your afternoons at Wreck Beach.

**Web:**

**http://www.netminder.com/yvr/**

# CARS AND TRUCKS

## Antique Cars

Wash it, buff it, tuck your baby in at night. Antique automobiles hold a special place in everyone's heart. Care and feeding of all older automobiles is covered in **alt.autos.antique**. Automobiles over 25 years old are parked in **rec.autos.antique**.

**Usenet:**

**alt.autos.antique**
**rec.autos.antique**

## Auto Channel

You don't need a television to check out the Auto Channel. In fact, you don't even need a car. All you have to do to get great auto news, commentary and other useful information is point your web browser to the Auto Channel web site.

**Web:**

**http://www.theautochannel.com/**

## Auto Discussion Archives and FAQ

Take it from me, the best place to learn about cars is where you learned about sex: in the street. Here is a wealth of street-smart info, guaranteed to explain something interesting you always wanted to know but were afraid to ask. For example, I learned how to double-clutch (and I don't even own a car).

**Web:**

**http://www.wizvax.net/rwelty/FAQ/**

## Auto Mall

It's no fun when your friends won't go with you to spend hours at the car lot looking at cool cars that you are probably never going to buy. However, you can indulge your fantasies all by yourself by hanging out at the Auto Mall. Get lots of information about cars and the companies that make them.

**Web:**

**http://www.autoweb.com/makers.htm**

## Auto Racing Archive

Feed your racing addiction by having a look at this racing archive, which has information on Formula One, Indycar and Nascar racing, including schedules and point standings.

**Web:**

**http://student-www.eng.hawaii.edu/carina/**

## Auto Racing Mailing List

It's not enough to be able to get in the car and go. You have to go fast. You have to go so fast that rubber burns, that the friction of the wind heats the metal on your car and nearly blisters the paint, that the G-forces press you into the fine Italian upholstery and any planetary geophysical disturbance threatens to rocket you into outer space. Now, that's what I call fun. And when you are not driving, participate in discussion of wheel-to-wheel racing for drivers, workers and crew.

**Listserv Mailing List:**

List Name: **autorace**
Subscribe to: **listserv@vtvm1.cc.vt.edu**

## Auto Racing Talk and General Discussion

As one of my readers, you can no doubt drive rings around anyone else. So where do you go in between races, when you want to read what people are saying about driving from one place to another as fast as possible? Put the virtual pedal to the metal and aim for Usenet, where you will find discussion covering all aspects of organized racing competition.

**Usenet:**

**alt.autos.sport.nhra**
**rec.autos.sport**
**rec.autos.sport.info**
**rec.autos.sport.nascar**
**rec.autos.sport.rally**
**rec.autos.sport.tech**

**What if...?**

# RACING ARCHIVE

You can't always be driving a car or watching a race. Occasionally you need to take a break to go home, eat something, and remind your family who you are.

However, that doesn't mean you have to be wasting your time. During those off hours, you can connect to the Net and check out the racing archive. After all, you do need to spend some quality time with your computer.

## Automobile Buyers' Network

Use keywords to search this large database of vehicles available for sale. You might have to experiment a little to try to narrow it down by geographic area unless you are willing to drive a long way just to buy a car. The search will give you a list of vehicles matching your keywords. Select the links to get detailed information on the automobile, including a picture.

**Web:**

**http://www.dmssoft.com/cars.htm**

## Automobile Listings

When the Queen of England comes over for dinner and you want to impress her with all the facts you have at your fingertips on the Internet, connect to this huge list of all-things-automobile. Exotic, classic or run-of-the-mill cars are all represented. This is the web site to use when size really does matter.

**Web:**

**http://www.w3.org/pub/DataSources/bySubject/Automotive/automotive.html**

**Stay connected.**

## Automotive Simulators

Why risk your life by getting into the car and traveling at high speeds knowing at any time some out-of-control individual could point his car straight into yours and cream you in a very short amount of time. If you want the thrill without the danger, try auto simulators and see how much adrenaline you can get pumping without ever pulling out of the driveway.

**Usenet:**

**rec.autos.simulators**

## British Cars

Some people have lifelong love affairs with things British. For example, Prince Charles's ex-wife, what's-her-name, always makes a point of riding in a British car, except when it is inconvenient or the weather is bad. Would you like to nurture your feelings for English things that move quickly with style? If so, here are some important British car resources for your anglophilic perusal.

**Web:**

**http://www.team.net/sol/**

**Majordomo Mailing List:**

List Name: **british-cars**
Subscribe to: **majordomo@triumph.cs.utah.edu**

## Buying and Selling Cars

Perhaps the best way to learn about buying or selling a car is to talk to other people. But what do you do when you just have to get that BWM 328i, and your Uncle Herman (the car buff) is away at a Shriner's convention? Connect to Usenet, where automobile fanatics galore are buying, selling and everything in between.

**Usenet:**

**rec.autos.marketplace**

## Car and Truck Prices

Listen to me. Before you visit a dealer to buy a car or truck, you *must* use the Internet to find out everything you need. Here is a fantastic site that has lots and lots of car and truck information. Best of all, you can get the actual prices the dealer pays for the vehicle and options. Why should you pay the auto club or a consumer magazine for this exact same information when you can get it for free from the Net? Now, when it comes time to open negotiations for a new car, you will know exactly what the dealer is paying, so he won't be able to pull the sleazy, automotive wool over your eyes. Information is power and, as we used to say in the Sixties, "Power to the people."

**Web:**

**http://www.edmunds.com/**

## Car Audio

If you are one of those people who believe that cars are made to be heard as well as seen, here is a Usenet discussion group that is right up your auditory alley. Start hanging around and soon, when someone says "My woofer is bigger than your woofer," you will be able to snap back, "Oh yeah? Well, my speakers use isobaric variations of a quasi-eighth order series-tuned dual-reflex bandpass."

**Usenet:**

**rec.audio.car**

What's the point of even driving if you aren't making enough noise to wake several surrounding neighborhoods? However, in these days of computerized engines and strict air control standards, it's not easy to find a car that can produce the required sound levels without a lot of special tuning and getting your hands dirty.

What's the solution? Auto audio, of course. All you need is a sufficiently powerful amp, and you can drive with the peace of mind that comes from being able to create a musical interlude as loud as you want.

So, if you want to make sure you are always as popular as a skunk in the wine tasting booth at a perfume convention, join the discussion in **rec.audio.car**, and find out how to coax that one last decibel out of Old Bessie. After all, life is designed to be lived with a bang, not a whimper.

## Car Classifieds

Don't stop reading the classified ads just because you are tired of having to recycle the daily paper. This web site provides a great index of advertisements for automobiles of all types. Whether you are buying or selling, the listings are free for non-commercial usage.

**Web:**

**http://ep.com/h/ca.html**

## Car Place

Here's someone who knows his cars. Here's someone who knows other people's cars. Here's someone who spends his time driving cars and lives to tell about it. Check out the reviews of all types of cars, new and old. Here's someone worth listening to.

**Web:**

**http://www.cftnet.com/members/rcbowden/**

## Car Talk and General Discussion

When you're not driving, you can talk about driving and, on the Net, there is no end to the discussion: automobile design, construction, service, tires, competitions, driving, manufacturers, and on and on and on.

**Usenet:**

**alt.autos.karting**
**rec.autos**
**rec.autos.misc**

## Choosing an Automobile

Smart shoppers will love Intellichoice. These car folks have crunched the numbers for you and come up with what they think is the best value in a car purchase based on ownership cost projections.

**Web:**

**http://www.intellichoice.com/**

### CHOOSING A CAR AUTO-MAGICALLY

Selecting just the right car is not easy. No matter which one you pick, you can be assured that somewhere along the line, someone is putting one over on you. So if you want the straight stuff about which cars offer the best overall cost of ownership, try the Intellichoice web site. Before you shell out your hard-earned bucks on a potentially big bucket of back-breaking bolts, check out these useful tips, and keep yourself from being the laughingstock of the automotive neighborhood.

## Classic and Sports Cars

There's nothing like the feel of riding around in a classic or sporty car. People turn to stare, the engine throbs and begs to be driven at high speeds. If you're addicted to classic or sports cars, join this international list and talk about your favorite cars with motoring enthusiasts around the world. Get updates about events such as races or car shows.

**Listserv Mailing List:**

List Name: **autos-l**
Subscribe to: **listserv@tritu.bitnet**

## Driving

Slide into your car, start her up, see the road race beneath you. Make your driving experience exquisite. Keep informed on driving laws and learn how to better handle your car.

**Usenet:**

**rec.autos.driving**

**Do a backup.**

## Electric Vehicles

How many automobile technicians does it take to screw in a light bulb? It depends where on the car they are trying to screw it in. Catch up on the state of the electric vehicle technology and the future of electric vehicles. How close are we to affordable electric cars? Will we be able to plug them into the wall of our garage? This list is not to argue about whether we should have electric vehicles or to compare EVs to other modes of driving. (So don't even try it.)

**Listserv Mailing List:**

List Name: **ev**
Subscribe to: **listserv@sjsuvm1.sjsu.edu**

## Exotic Cars

Imagine the awe you would inspire in everyone around you if you were the lucky owner of an exotic or limited edition automobile. Neighbors would ask you to drive them to the grocery store, people's chatter would die down to a respectful whisper as they passed your car, and the insurance agent would beg you to please leave the car in the garage. But there is more to exotic cars than just good looks. If you can't own one, you might as well be able to drool over them. Check out the fancy driving machines at this well-endowed web site.

**Web:**

**http://www.abc.se/~m8938/cars/cars.html**

### Exotic Car + You = Big Success

As one of my readers, you are as close to being perfect as a human being can expect. Perhaps, however, there is a tiny, little something missing from your life. Is it possible that you need a head-turning, attention-grabbing, high-performance automobile?

If so, drive right over to the exotic car site and pick out something nice. After all, why be almost perfect when you can go all the way?

Hint: If you decide to buy such a car, show them your copy of this book, and they are bound to give you a discount.

## Formula 1 Motor Racing

Formula 1 cars are designed for one purpose: to race on a circuit or closed course. If you want to build your own Formula 1 vehicle, don't forget: the car cannot be more than 200 cm wide; it must weigh at least 505 kg; you must use a 4-stroke engine with reciprocating pistons; and the engine capacity cannot exceed 3500 cc. Hint: When you get to the point where you need to understand how pneumatic valve openers relate to engine mapping, it's time to check with the Net.

**Web:**

**http://www.sport-hq.com/spectate/motor/f-1.shtml**

**Usenet:**

**rec.autos.sport.f1**

**IRC:**

**#Formula1**

## Four-Wheel Drive Vehicles

Discussion of the on- and off-road four-wheel drive vehicle. Read about and share experiences with other owners of Cherokees, New Tahoes, Explorers, Jeeps and other get-where-you-are-going-no-matter-where-you-are-going kind of vehicles.

**Usenet:**

**rec.autos.4x4**

## Gasoline FAQ

Frankly, most people don't care about gasoline. They go to the nearest place that offers a free car wash with a fill-up and hope that everything will keep working according to the Divine Automobile Plan. However, for those who dig chemistry or truly like to feed their cars, there is a frequently asked question list that discusses the composition of gasoline, gas toxicity, environmental issues, how to choose appropriate fuel and the diagnosis of some fuel-related problems.

**Web:**

**http://ram.chem.tulane.edu:8080/f-body/trivia/gasoline.html**

## General Car Topics

Here is the Usenet group devoted to general discussion about automobiles. This is the place to ask a question that doesn't belong to a more specific group. (For example, "If God can do anything, can he design a car so complicated that even he can't tune it without a computer?")

**Usenet:**

**rec.autos.misc**

### CAR TALK

What do you do when it's three in the morning and you need to find out why your 1983 Honda Civic won't start, even though the battery works and the engine turns over? Sure, it might be a simple clogged fuel line, but it could also be a broken chrono-synclastic infindibulum (which can get awfully expensive).

Don't worry. You are not alone. The auto-enthusiasts on Usenet will be glad to offer you an opinion. Just post a message to **rec.autos.misc**, and sit back and wait. Eventually, someone may give you just the help you need. If not, you can always call a mechanic, tell him you are one of my readers, and ask for a discount.

## High Performance Cars

Don't just drive your car, experience it. Which cars perform the best? How can you increase your auto's performance? Learn safety, technical aspects, and techniques.

**Usenet:**

**alt.autos.rod-n-custom**
**rec.autos.rod-n-custom**

## Hot Rods

Rev your engine and burn rubber. Find out the dos and don'ts of working with high-speed automobiles. Hot rod enthusiasts know the nuts and bolts. This group is moderated.

**Usenet:**

**alt.hotrod**

## Life in the Fast Lane

We all know that fast, high-performance cars are just a substitute for you-know-what. (Well, I do know, but I'm not allowed to talk about stuff like that in a family-oriented book.) Join the boys in the **rod-n-custom** Usenet groups and find out how to soup up your performance and enhance your experience with high speed and quick starts.

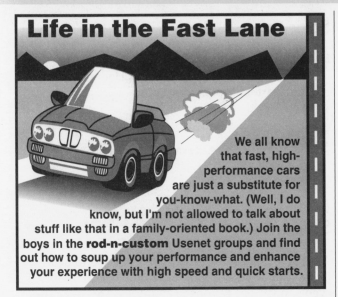

## Indianapolis Motor Speedway

Feeling the need for speed? Join the discussion of IndyCar racing. Fans talk about anything relating to the Indy races whether it is technical or just plain rumor-spreading gossip. Chat interactively on the IRC channel **#IndyCar**.

**Web:**
**http://www.indycar.com/**

**Usenet:**
**rec.autos.sport.indy**

**IRC:**
**#IndyCar**

## Kit Cars

For years you have been building model cars, and now you can do it without gluing your fingers together. It's time to graduate to the real thing. Find out about purchasing, building, driving, and maintaining kit cars—full-size and fully functioning cars you build from scratch. Then when people give you compliments on your smooth ride, you can say, "Thanks. I made it myself."

**Majordomo Mailing List:**
List Name: **kitcar**
Subscribe to: **majordomo@bolis.com**

## Macho Trucks

If cars were dogs, this list would not be for dachshunds. Macho truck enthusiasts have carved out this Usenet niche as a place where they can discuss their sport or just strut around, where tiny buzzing sports cars are mere hors d'oeuvres in the buffet of Life.

**Usenet:**
**alt.autos.macho-trucks**

## Motorsports FAQ

You should always be prepared for the day your grandmother calls you on the phone and wants to know exactly why an armco may or may not be better than a tyre wall. Are you going to let her down? There's no need to if you have access to the World Wide Web. This **rec.autos.sport** FAQ on auto competitions is loaded with detailed information on motorsports.

**Web:**
**http://www.zmall.com/sports/motorsports/rasfaq/rasfaq1.html**

## Nascar

Racing fans can hang out in the **#Nascar** channel and talk in real time about anything involving driving around and around on a track at high speeds. Get information about upcoming events, race schedules or just talk. For those of you who don't want to go as fast as real time, join the discussion in the **.nascar** newsgroup.

**Web:**
**http://www.nascar.com/**

**Usenet:**
**rec.autos.sport.nascar**

**IRC:**
**#Nascar**

## PM Zone

Brought to you by the fine folks who get their hands dirty publishing Popular Mechanics, this web site has lots of nifty car tidbits for automotive fans. Get a tech update of the day, learn more about choosing a quality automobile, and see movies and pictures that will make any car and truck lover purr like a finely tuned hot rod.

**Web:**
**http://popularmechanics.com/**

A B C D E F G H I J K L M N O P Q R S T U V W X Y Z

## Road Rally

I love adventures, especially when the adventure involves a road trip of some sort. For those with the spirit of adventure in their blood, read tutorials on road rallying, anecdotes on other rally adventures, information on mailing lists and a sample "Armchair Rally".

**Web:**

**http://www.contrib.andrew.cmu.edu/usr/ef1c/plug.html**

## Slot Cars

If you are old enough to remember when slot cars were popular, you are old enough to remember the Dick Van Dyke Show and Peace With Honor. Ah, what halcyon days of our youth were those. And what could be a better way to recover a bit of lost innocence than to grab a hot slot car, rev its motor, and show the kids how it was really done. For the slot car afficionado, here is all the info you need to stay cool: race and product information, links to related sites, calendar of events, slot car zines, and much more.

**Web:**

**http://www.slotcar.com/**

## Solar Cars

Have you been waiting for a rainy day to start learning about solar-powered cars? Here is a good place to start. Lots of links and lots of pics.

**Web:**

**http://www-lips.ece.utexas.edu/~delayman/solar.html**

## Speedway

A starting point for speedway fans the world over. Access information about racing and competition events in various European countries. This page also has links to the results of world championship races.

**Web:**

**http://www.amg.gda.pl/speedway/speedway.html**

**"Fun" is fun.**

### *Look What I Found on the Net...*

```
(from the Motorsports FAQ for rec.autos.sports)

What are restrictor plates?

They are aluminum plates with four 7/8 inch holes.  They are
placed between the carburetor and intake manifold on an engine.
The carburetors used in WC have four 1-1/2 inch diameter
barrels.  When this 7/8 inch restrictor plate is installed, the
air-flow into the engine is restricted, thus reducing horsepower.

Restrictor plates were mandated on WC cars at Talladega and
Daytona in 1988.  NASCAR first attempted to slow speeds after
Bobby Allisons car became airborne and crashed into the
spectator fence at Talladega in May of 1987...
```

## Team.Net Automotive Information Archives

Here is a nice collection of automotive-related resources: links to archives, organizations, mailing lists and activities. By the way, the American pronunciation of Team.Net is "Team Net"—the dot is silent; the British pronunciation is "Team-dot-Net". (See how cool it is to be one of my readers: I make sure you know everything important.)

**Web:**

**http://triumph.cs.utah.edu/team.net.html**

**FAQs are cool.**

## Technical Aspects of Auto Racing

In this newsgroup, talk turns to tech. Racing fans love to get into the nitty gritty aspects of racing, not the philosophical idea of the thrill of speed and competition. A few of the topics for discussion are debate over synthetic oil versus petro, advice about rebuilding rotaries or traction control in racing. Anything technical related to racing is allowed.

**Usenet:**

**rec.autos.sport.tech**

## Technical Automotive Discussion

Here is the place to go when you want to immerse yourself in automotive discussion that is hot, heavy and mechanical. If you absorb only half of what these people talk about, you will understand twice as much as everyone else. Remember, when the going gets hot, the cool stay viscous.

**Usenet:**

**rec.autos.tech**

### *Look What I Found on the Net...*

```
Newsgroup: rec.autos.tech
Subject: Re: Ford Mustangs

>>> The most common car used by high school students in the
>>> United States is the Ford Mustang.

>> It is?

> Yes it is. Mustangs, used and new, are the most common car.

I know what you mean. Unfortunately it is usually the kids of
Xxxxxxx immigrants that have 'em. Their parents came over here,
worked their xxxxx off and said 'I don't want my kids to go
through that' and make the  mistake of giving them everything
they want. 'Stangs are cheap power, so that's what they get.

Purple paint, lowered, alloys, flashing LED lights running
around the base of the car, loud exhausts -- most of that is
great stuff to do to a car, but these guys have NO idea how to
drive.

However, they are COOL. If you don't believe 'em, just ask 'em,
they'll tell you. ;)
```

# CHEMISTRY

## Analytical Chemistry

Analytical chemistry is the study of analyzing chemical substances and their constituent components. As you might imagine, this is a large, complex area within the world of chemistry. For discussion, you can follow the Usenet group. For information, start with this well-organized web site which contains a large number of links to many different types of analytical chemistry resources.

**Web:**
**http://www.anachem.umu.se/jumpstation.htm**

**Usenet:**
**sci.chem.analytical**

## Biochemistry Resources

Biochemistry is the study of the chemistry and the compounds found in living systems. This biochemistry site houses the Biochemistry Online Journal—with original essays—as well as a nice set of biochemistry-related links to journals, software, universities and other resources.

**Web:**
**http://www.arach-net.com/~jlyon/biochem/**

## Chemical Information Sources

Don't get your chemicals off the street—you never know who could be hiding a little machine gun beneath their roomy labcoat. Instead, learn about chemistry and various chemical compounds from this listserv list. Catch news about existing reference sources, the appearance of printed or machine-readable new resources, and prices and availability of chemicals. Any topic is okay as long as it relates to chemistry in some way. The **cicourse** mailing list is for teaching and learning about all forms of chemical information sources.

**Listserv Mailing List:**
List Name: **chminf-l**
Subscribe to: **listserv@iubvm.ucs.indiana.edu**

**Listserv Mailing List:**
List Name: **cicourse**
Subscribe to: **listserv@iubvm.indiana.edu**

## Chemical Physics Preprint Database

The Chemical Physics Preprint Database is a fully automated electronic archive and distribution server for the international theoretical chemistry community.

**Web:**
**http://www.chem.brown.edu/chem-ph.html**

## Chemistry Information

An electronic reference source providing answers to frequently asked chemistry questions through library resources. It covers nomenclature, compound identification, properties, structure determination, toxicity, synthesis, and registry numbers. For each component it lists the most appropriate reference resources (online catalog, indexes, journals, etc.).

**Web:**
**http://www.dmp.csiro.au/chemres.htm**

## Chemistry Journals

This is an absolutely huge collection of links to chemistry journals. Some of the journals are completely online; others only show the tables of contents or abstracts. However, the list is so large and so comprehensive that I guarantee you will find something in your area. If you are involved in chemical research of any type, you need to look at this site. (I bet you have lots of spare time for reading more journals.)

**Web:**
**http://www.betacyte.pair.com/journals.html**

## Chemistry Learning Materials

This site contains a collection of computer materials that can be used to learn about chemistry and lab procedures. If you teach chemistry and you like computers, you may want to check out this site for ideas and resources you can use with your own students.

**Web:**
**http://yip5.chem.wfu.edu/yip/organic/org-home.html**

## Chemistry Mailing Lists

There are many different mailing lists devoted to chemistry and related topics. Here is a quick index of such mailing lists, along with short descriptions. For more information, there is also a larger document describing each mailing list in detail along with subscription information.

**Web:**

**http://bionmr1.rug.ac.be/chemistry/overview.html**

## Chemistry Talk and General Discussion

Let's talk chemistry. Let's talk about substances and how they react when they are combined. Let's talk about mixing diatomaceous earth into sulphuric acid in order to make it sticky. Let's talk about everything under and inside of the sun. Let's talk about cleaning up the mess.

**Usenet:**

**sci.chem**

## Chemistry Telementoring

A mailing list to foster the exchange of ideas and information between chemistry students and teachers from high schools to universities.

**Listserv Mailing List:**

List Name: **chemchat**
Subscribe to: **listserv@uafsysb.uark.edu**

## Chemistry VRML

VRML—Virtual Reality Modeling Language—is a system which is used to create dynamic, changing presentations. As you might imagine, VRML can be used to illustrate some of the important three-dimensional properties of molecules. Here you will find such models for particular enzymes, amino acids, proteins, and other important substances. You will also find information about 3D molecular graphics along with some related software.

**Web:**

**http://ws05.pc.chemi.th-darmstadt.de/vrml/**

### *Look What I Found on the Net...*

```
Newsgroups: sci.chem
Subject: (fwd) Re: Strange properties of cornstarch slurr

>> The other night I was making a sauce and noticed that the cornstarch
>> and water had the bizarre property of solidifying when pressure was
>> applied and returning to a liquid when released. Is anyone familiar
>> with this phenomenon?

> This property is called thixotropy. I haven't tried this, but
> hitting the cornstarch/water slurry with a blunt object is supposed
> to cause it to crack, yet it can also be poured like a liquid.

I think the proper term is dilatancy.

Pseudoplastic fluids:
-- thin with increasing shear rate and are not time dependent

Thixotropic fluids:
-- thin with increasing shear rate and are time dependent

Newtonian fluids:
-- are not effected by shear rate or time dependent

Dilatant fluids:
-- thicken with increasing shear rate and are not time dependent

Rheopectic fluids:
-- thicken with increasing shear rate and are time dependent
```

## Chemist's Art Gallery

Spectacular visualization and animations in chemistry. Among the offerings are animations of small molecules, visualization of chromosomes and viruses based on electron microscopy tomography, visualization of micelles, and much more. There are also links to other chemistry visualization and animation sites

**Web:**

**http://www.csc.fi/lul/chem/graphics.html**

## Computational Chemistry List

A mailing list for the discussion of quantum chemistry, molecular mechanics and dynamics, and other fields related to computational chemistry.

**Web:**

**http://www.osc.edu/chemistry.html**

**Listproc Mailing List:**

List Name: **comp-chem**
Subscribe to: **listproc@iqm.unicamp.br**

## Crystallography

A crystal is a solid that is formed by a repeated pattern of components: atoms, ions or molecules. On the molecular level, crystals have a three-dimensional lattice with fixed distances between the components. Crystallography is the science that studies the structure and properties of crystals. Here is a web site containing information about conferences, databases, publications, education as well links to other crystallography sites on the Net. For discussion, there are two Usenet groups. The **bionet** group is for macromolecular crystallography.

**Web:**

**http://www.unige.ch/crystal/w3vlc/crystal.index.html**

**Usenet:**

**bionet.xtallography**
**sci.techniques.xtallography**

### Date With a Nerd

Okay, you finally got the BNOC (Big Nerd on Campus) to ask you out. So where do you go on your first date?

The Chemist's Art Gallery, of course.

Show your date that you have both good taste and the technical knowledge necessary to make a modern relationship work as well as a properly buffered acid-base reaction.

## Electrochemical Science and Technology

Electrochemistry deals with the chemistry of electrical phenomena (such as electrophoresis, electroplating, batteries, corrosion, and so on). The web site has a wealth of links to all kinds of electrochemical resources on the Net: information, organizations, publications, newsgroups, mailing lists, schools and more. The Usenet groups are for discussion of related topics.

**Web:**

**http://www.cmt.anl.gov/estir/info.htm**

**Usenet:**

**sci.chem.electrochem**
**sci.chem.electrochem.battery**

## Glycoscience

Glycoscience is the study of carbohydrates and glycoconjugates. Many people in the physical or life sciences find that memorizing the citric acid cycle several times during your academic career provides enough glyco-oriented stimulation to last a lifetime. However, for hard core glycoscientists, the citric acid cycle is merely the beginning. Glycoscience is a complex, robust area of science, and there are a lot of related resources on the Net. This well-organized web page is an excellent place to start, and for discussion, there is the Usenet group.

**Web:**

**bionet.glycosci**
**http://bellatrix.pcl.ox.ac.uk/TGN/**

## Electrochemistry to the Rescue

Your spouse calls up to tell you that both the Queen of England *and* the President of the United States are coming over for dinner. Can you please do something about the silverware looking so tacky?

Sure, you could spend the entire afternoon polishing every single item, but wouldn't it be easier to use the Net to teach yourself all about electrochemistry? That way you could set up an electroplating system and completely re-plate all the silverware before your guests arrive.

And don't kid yourself: high-class people do notice when you do things right.

## Hazardous Chemical Database

Please put this web site in your bookmark list. This important resource contains information on a large number of hazardous chemicals. You can find out basic information—such as formulas, physical data, names—as well as extensive safety information. This is the type of place you want to visit *before* the accident. However, if something unexpected does happen, you will be glad you know where this site is.

**Web:**

**http://odin.chemistry.uakron.edu/erd/**

## Laboratory Safety

I have to admit, I was a terror in the lab. Although I was mostly well-behaved, I once incurred the wrath of my organic chemistry lab instructor by throwing an iceball at my friend Stan. And in medical school, my partner and I would often break things in biochemistry lab no matter how careful we were. Still, I had an excuse: in those days, there was no Internet, and so I could not subscribe to the laboratory safety mailing list.

**Listserv Mailing List:**

List Name: **safety**
Subscribe to: **listserv@uvmvm.uvm.edu**

## Molecule of the Month

Some people waste their time and money on silly publications that feature new pictures of naked women every month. Not for me. My monthly thrill comes from checking out the new Molecule of the Month. Pictures, structures and chemical information—what more could you want? See if you can answer this riddle. What am I? I am a terpene-like compound, occurring as an essential oil within plants. I am non-polar, with low solubility in water. If you were to vaporize and inhale my volatile fractions, I would induce relaxation and euphoria. You might also experience perceptual changes, a sense of slowing of time, loss of attention, depersonalization, silliness and the munchies™. Aside from recreational uses, I am utilized by chemotherapy patients to treat drug-induced nausea. The final clue? I was the Molecule of the Month in April 1996.

**Web:**

**http://www.bris.ac.uk/Depts/Chemistry/MOTM/motm.htm**

## Nuclide Table

This is an amazing resource. You start with a graphical representation of all the known nuclides. (A nuclide is type of atom, specified by its atomic number, atomic mass and energy state. For example, carbon 14 is a particular nuclide of carbon.) Click on a section of the diagram, and you are presented with a more detailed chart that contains useful information about all the nuclides in that region. It's like a periodic table of the elements on steroids. You must try this web site: it's a great tool.

**Web:**

**http://www.dne.bnl.gov/CoN/**

## Organometallic Chemistry

Here is a discussion group devoted to the chemistry and techniques used in working with organometallic compounds. This is the place I used to ask questions while I was building Max (a semi-human android who used to do my organic chemistry homework for me).

**Usenet:**

**sci.chem.organomet**

## Periodic Table in Hypertext Format

A hypertext version of the Periodic Table that allows you to click on any individual element to obtain details of that element. The details include standard state, color, discoverer, date discovered, name meaning, radii, valency, electronegativities, effective nuclear charge, bond enthalpies, temperatures, enthalpies, ionization enthalpies, isotopic abundances, and more.

**Web:**

**http://www.cchem.berkeley.edu/Table/**

## Polymer and Liquid Crystal Tutorial

A polymer is a high-molecular weight compound, consisting of large numbers of repeating units—relatively simple molecules called monomers—linked by covalent bonds. Polymers can be natural (such as cellulose, silk and natural rubber) or synthetic (such as the plastics and synthetic fibers). A liquid crystal is a liquid in which the constituent molecules arrange themselves with a higher degree of order than ordinary liquids, by pointing along a common axis called a director. Within a liquid crystal, the arrangement of the molecules offers many of the optical characteristic of solid crystals. However, since the molecular arrangements are not so firmly fixed, they can be modified—along with subsequent changes in optical properties—by mechanical stress, electromagnetic radiation or changes in temperature. Both polymers and liquid crystals are fascinating substances. If you would like a good introduction to these and other related subjects, try this series of well-organized, well-written multimedia tutorials. I enjoyed the tutorials myself, even though they did tend to remind me of organic chemistry class.

**Web:**

**http://abalone.cwru.edu/**

**The Net cares.**

### Large Molecules are Cool

Let's face it. Anyone can walk around saying they like small molecules, such as sulfur dioxide or phosphoric acid. That takes no skill or taste whatsoever.

But you know what they say. The more important the man, the larger his favorite molecule. (Women, of course, are judged on entirely different standards.)

As one of my readers, you deserve the best, so I suggest you take some time to learn about polymers: large molecules that can literally stretch for millions of units.

## Sonochemistry

Sonochemistry is the study of chemical reactions that are significantly affected by ultrasound. Under the influence of ultrasound, a reaction may be accelerated (such as with a catalyst) or may yield completely different products. These effects can happen for various reasons. For example, ultrasound can speed up a reaction by enlarging the surface area of a catalyst or by enhancing the mixing of the reagents. A more profound effect of ultrasound can result from cavitation: the creation of tiny, low pressure bubbles, in this case caused by the compression/decompression pressure cycles as the sound passes through the reagents. For more information about this fascinating, new branch of chemistry, check out this sonochemistry web page.

**Web:**

**http://www.und.ac.za/und/prg/sonochem/**

## Virtual Library of Chemistry

Here, in one place, are links to more chemically related resources that you could dissolve in a beaker of distilled water and alcohol-free chloroform. Whatever you need to find in the world of chemistry, virtually everything virtual is here somewhere. Remember, if you're not part of the solution, you're part of the precipitate.

**Web:**

**http://www.chem.ucla.edu/chempointers.html**

# COMICS

## AAA Aardvark Comics Index

A gargantuan, well-organized hotlist of comics-oriented links. Lots of web sites, zines, images, comics archives, mailing lists, and more and more and more (and more).

**Web:**

**http://www.redweb.com/wraithspace/**

## Alternative Comics

Keep up with the latest trends in the alternative comics scene, while talking about artists, stories and comic book companies. Here are the places to discuss the philosophical and sociological aspects of the alternative comics genre. After all, reading Superman or Archie comics is a lot like wearing a cheongsam to the beach.

**Usenet:**

**alt.comics.alternative**
**rec.arts.comics.alternative**

**Majordomo Mailing List:**

List Name: **comix**
Subscribe to: **majordomo@world.std.com**

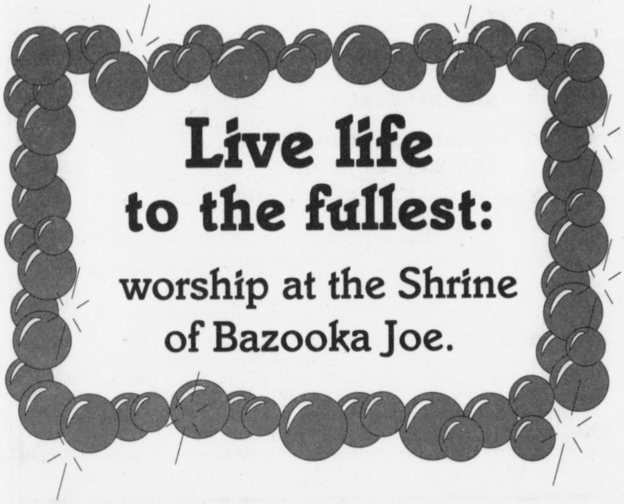
Live life
to the fullest:
worship at the Shrine
of Bazooka Joe.

## Anime and Manga

Join the throngs of masses discussing and enjoying Japanese comics and animation. The Net has tons of goodies relating to anime and manga: enough to satisfy even the most insatiable fanatic.

**Web:**

**http://er4www.eng.ohio-state.edu/~brownj/anim/**
**http://soyokaze.biosci.ohio-state.edu/~jei/anipike**
**http://www.csclub.uwaterloo.ca/u/mlvanbie/anime-list/**
**http://www.jurai.net/amplus/**
**http://www.utexas.edu/ftp/student/anime/.html/anime.html**

**Usenet:**

**alt.manga**
**rec.arts.anime**

**Listserv Mailing List:**

List Name: **anime-l**
Subscribe to: **listserv@vtvm1.cc.vt.edu**

**IRC:**

**#anime**
**#anime!**

## Batman

Crank up the theme music and point your browser to the supermarket of Batman sites.

**Web:**

**http://users.aol.com/JimD19713/batman.html**

## Bazooka Joe

No need to spend hours chewing Bazooka bubble gum just so you can read the comics inside the wrappers. Now you can get all you need on the Web. Not only will you be able to read the comics, but you can also get a Bazooka Joe fortune and learn more about the characters of this tiny comic strip. For those with more philosophic and intellectual needs, read the analyses of these comics in relation to deeper sociological and cultural meanings.

**Web:**

**http://www.ugcs.caltech.edu/~joe/bazooka_html/**

## Classic Comic Strips Discussion

I like old comics. My favorites are the pre-1960 strips of Nancy, Peanuts and Blondie. Here's a mailing list and Usenet group on which you can talk about any pre-1960 vintage newspaper comic strips with other fans.

**Usenet:**

**alt.comics.classic**

**Majordomo Mailing List:**

List Name: **comic-strip-classics**
Subscribe to: **majordomo@indra.com**



## Comic Cafe

Get the latest in hot comic book gossip at the Comic Cafe. Read this tabloid full of the latest news, new releases, collectible information and reader-submitted electronic whispers. And if you know a secret, be sure to tell the rest of the world while you are here.

**Web:**

**http://www.hype.com/comics/cafe/comicafe.htm**

## Comic Chat

I like comic books. I have a collection of Duck comics and Silver Age Superman, Lois Lane and Jimmy Olsen comics. If you are a comic book fan, too, you can hang out on IRC and talk about your old favorites or even new comic books that are hot off the press. You can meet lots of interesting comic fans on IRC.

**IRC:**

**#comicbooks**

## *Look What I Found on the Net...*

```
Newsgroup: rec.arts.comics.creative
Subject: The Impending Storm: An Introduction

 THE IMPENDING STORM: AN INTRODUCTION

The following are excerpts from past postings to The Impending Story Saga...

What has gone before:

Our valiant heroes have been transported by the Holy Savant to a world
known as the Arena in order to find the 12 Cross-Time X-piators in
order to save their world from the unravelling of time. Before the
Holy Savant left our heroes to their own devices (for they had no more
mutant powers), he left images in their minds of the 12. They were
then captured and thrown into a cell.  The heroes escaped from said
cell, chased by Bill the Axe-man, nearly flooded, and separated.

Vod and the Outrider came upon Captain Ultra and an unconscious White
Knave. Bill the Axe-man sent a raven named Ailli (who may be a dark
horse, later) to spy on the heroes. So far, only the Outrider, who can
speak to the raven, trusts her.

White Knave:
     [finally regaining consciousness]
   Uuuuhhhnnn. What the hell happened?
     [Seeing Vod, he quickly jumps to his feet and unsheathes his sword]
   And what the hell is she doing with us?

Captain Ultra:
   Whoa, easy there big fella. Calm down. She is one of us now. She
   is not under the control of her dark self...
```

## Comic Conventions

When it's time for a road trip, check out the upcoming comics conventions. Pack your bags and go on an adventurous excursion to hang out in a large room with other people who like comics. This site will give you the details you need to get started.

**Web:**
**http://grove.ufl.edu/~jrm/conventions.html**

## Comic Reviews

It's hard to know what to say when you are at a party, and someone asks your opinion about a particular comic. Sure, you can always make up something, but isn't it a lot better to prepare for important social encounters by reading a whole lot of comic reviews *before* you leave the house?

**Web:**
**http://verbeekt.cit.hope.edu/BeeksBooks/**

## Comic Writing

Experience the fun of being in control of your own universe and all the people in it. At the flourish of a penstroke, you can make people snap, crackle and pop to your own, personalized drumbeat. Submit your own work, and read the works in progress of other budding comic writers.

**Usenet:**
**rec.arts.comics.creative**

**Listserv Mailing List:**
List Name: **comicw-l**
Subscribe to: **listserv@unlvm.unl.edu**

## Comics Fan Fiction

Comic book characters really have a life of their own and fans of comic book characters like to participate by helping bring these characters to life. This Usenet group is for the purpose of sharing fiction written by fans of various comic strips and comic books. The FAQ for this newsgroup is periodically posted in case you have any questions about the group.

**Web:**
**http://gwis2.circ.gwu.edu/~hawk/acfffaq.html**

**Usenet:**
**alt.comics.fan-fiction**

## Comics Marketplace

What do you do when it's 2 AM and you just have to lay your hands on the Superman comic in which Lois Lane pretends to marry Peewee Herman, but it turns out to be a hoax? Fire up the old computer and visit the Usenet comics marketplace.

**Usenet:**
**rec.arts.comics.marketplace**

## Comics 'n' Stuff

Screen after screen of text will keep you in comics for hours. The variety at this site is staggering. With all the comics you can find here, there is no need to ever spend time working again. There's even a web chat room where you can talk to other comics fans.

**Web:**
**http://www.phlab.missouri.edu/~c617145/comix.html**

**IRC:**
**#comics**

## Comics on the Net

If you like to read comics, but don't like to get your hands dirty, then the Net has the answer for you. These web sites offer links to comics around the Net. Click around to your heart's content and never once worry about icky newsprint or your obligation to the environment. On the Web, you never have to recycle. There are enough comic links here to keep you busy for hours.

**Web:**
**http://studentweb.tulane.edu/~jseifert/comics/**
**http://www.reed.edu/~rseymour/home/comics/comics.html**

## Comics Resource Center

Go on a comics binge and stuff yourself full of information on comic strips, books, and animation. You will find links to comics, animations, archives, associations, comixographies, companies, FAQs, fan fiction, images, and interviews.

**Web:**
**http://comics.redweb.com/**

A B C D E F G H I J K L M N O P Q R S T U V W X Y Z

## Comics Talk and General Discussion

Zap! Biff! Pow! Action dialog brings comics to life. Whether you are a collector or just a person who likes to read comics now and then, you'll love the variety of discussion you can find in Usenet.

**Usenet:**

**alt.comics.2000ad**
**alt.comics.batman**
**alt.comics.buffalo-roam**
**alt.comics.elfquest**
**alt.comics.jack-chick**
**alt.comics.lnh**
**alt.comics.peanuts**
**alt.comics.superman**
**rec.arts.comics**
**rec.arts.comics.alternative**
**rec.arts.comics.dc.universe**
**rec.arts.comics.elfquest**
**rec.arts.comics.info**
**rec.arts.comics.marvel.universe**
**rec.arts.comics.misc**
**rec.arts.comics.other-media**
**rec.arts.comics.strips**
**rec.arts.comics.universe.xbooks**
**rec.arts.comics.xbooks**

Need to know when the next meeting of the Jimmy Olsen Fan Club will be held? Send your request to one of the Usenet comic book discussion groups.

## Comics World

Comics World is an online comics magazine that offers a trivia contest, interviews with famous comicfolk, feature articles, reviews and information on new comic releases. If you like comics, be sure to take a look at this site.

**Web:**

**http://www.farrsite.com/cw/**

## Daily Comics

This is one of my favorite sites on the whole Internet. Lots of daily comic strips to look at for free. Along with the comics, you will find background information on the cartoonists and on the strips themselves. Just between you and me, this site eliminated the only reason I ever had to buy a newspaper.

**Web:**

**http://www.unitedmedia.com/comics/**

COMICS
Don't start work. Not just yet. First you have to go to the Daily Comics web page and read everything you haven't already seen.

## Dilbert Zone

There is a fifth dimension beyond that which is known to man (or woman). It is a dimension as vast as the Internet and as timeless as anything that is trendy. It is the middle ground between light and "Where's the light switch?"; between science fiction and Super Bowl; it lies between the pit of a man's computer and the summit of his high speed Internet connection. This is the dimension of imagination. It is an area we call... The Dilbert Zone. Check out the cartoon archive and a massive amount of Dilbert-oriented silliness, including information on joining Dogbert's New Ruling Class.

**Web:**

**http://www.unitedmedia.com/comics/dilbert/**

**Usenet:**

**alt.comics.dilbert**

**Listproc Mailing List:**

List Name: **dilbert**
Subscribe to: **listproc@internex.net**

## European Comics

Lots of links to page after page (after page) of information about European comics. Just about anything you can imagine regarding European comics can be found here somewhere.

**Web:**

**http://grid.let.rug.nl/%7Eerikt/.Comics/**

## Ghost in the Shell

Ghost in the Shell is a futuristic manga comic about a bodiless entity who roams the virtual world doing the bidding of the Department of Foreign Ministry. This electronic secret agent decides it is a life form and rebels, insisting on procuring a physical existence. You can read more about the story and the characters of this popular comic at this web site.

**Web:**

**http://www.manga.com/manga/ghost/ghost.html**

## Indy Magazine

Enter the wonderful world of alternative comics with Indy Magazine. Indy publishes news, interviews, articles, reviews, convention reports and all the other happenings in the independent comics scene.

**Web:**

**http://grove.ufl.edu/~jrm/indy.html**

## Legion of Super-Heroes Discussion

I like superheroes, because they can do all sorts of nifty things. After all, who wouldn't want to be able to leap tall buildings in a single bound? Imagine how much better commuting would be. If you aren't a superhero, you can get your vicarious thrill through this mailing list. If you don't have time to be on a list, you can just read the mailing list archives.

**Web:**

**http://www.idyllmtn.com/archives/lsh-l/**

**Majordomo Mailing List:**

List Name: **lsh-l**
Subscribe to: **majordomo@idyllmtn.com**

## Negative Space

If you are into more than just reading comics, have a look at this comprehensive resource devoted to appreciating and creating comic books. Would you like to start your own comic? Here is a good place to start.

**Web:**

**http://nspace.cts.com/html/Comics**

Life is a Comic Book
Have you ever noticed how life is like a comic book?
Short, colorful, and full of violence and unrealistic romance.
Wouldn't it be great if you could spend all your time reading and talking about comics? Wouldn't it be great if you could make your own comic book? Well, why not?
Spend a few hours at the Negative Space web site, and your life will be better than most ordinary people could ever understand.

## Professional Cartoonists

When you are looking for a cartoonist, this is a good place to start. This site has a list of professional cartoonists on the Net: regional newspaper cartoonists and syndicated cartoonists. There is also information about freelance cartooning.

**Web:**

**http://www.pacificnet.net/art/ToonLinks.html**

### Sandman

Archives dedicated to Neil Gaiman's dark comics. At these sites, you will find a wealth of information related to Sandman comics and Neil Gaiman. Truly, Gaiman has created a world that must be experienced first-hand to be appreciated.

**Web:**

**http://rtt.colorado.edu/~jnmiller/Sandman.html**
**http://www.av.qnet.com/~raven/**

### Small Press Comics

On the Net there are great resources for any comic talent looking to be published. This web sites offer information on how to get yourself published and how to copyright, distribute and advertise your work. You can read about other small press comics, tools of the trade and tips on how to get comic shops to stock small press comics.

**Web:**

**http://www.question.co.uk/ismcomics/**
**http://www.sentex.net/~sardine/spfaq.html**

### Tintin

What is Tintin? A series of wonderful stories in comic format—written by the Belgian artist Herg—in which the hero Tintin (a young reporter) travels around the world with his dog Snowy, having one adventure after another. I have every Tintin book, and I read them again and again and again. (And so should you.) Here is a bit of Tintin trivia: in French, the original language, Tintin's dog is named Milou. This is the name of Herg's first girlfriend.

**Web:**

**http://werple.mira.net.au/~amcgee/cot_home.htm**

**IRC:**

**#Tintin**

**Get into "Mischief".**

## COMPUTERS: COMPANIES

### Apple

The official web site for Apple: Macintosh computers and software.

**Web:**

**http://www.apple.com/**

### Compaq

The official web site for Compaq: PCs.

**Web:**

**http://www.compaq.com/**

### Computer Company Talk and General Discussion

Computer companies have become an important part of the world's economy. As such, it is incumbent upon us—the customers—to talk and gossip about them whenever we get a chance. After all, when it comes to computer companies, their concerns become our concerns. Here are some Usenet discussion groups in which you can help everyone else mind somebody else's business.

**Usenet:**

**biz.marketplace.computers.discussion**
**biz.marketplace.services.computers**

### DEC (Digital Equipment Corporation)

The official web site for DEC: computers (especially Alpha-based workstations), network products, Alta Vista search engine software, and so on.

**Web:**

**http://www.digital.com/**

### Dell

The official web site for Dell: PCs.

**Web:**

**http://www.dell.com/**

## Gateway 2000

The official web site for Gateway 2000: PCs.

**Web:**

**http://www.gw2k.com/**

## Guide to Computer Vendors

Here you will find hundreds of links to computer hardware and software vendors (as well as their phone numbers). There is also a large list of links to computer magazine web sites. This is where I start looking when I can't decide where to start looking.

**Web:**

**http://www.ronin.com/SBA/**

## HP (Hewlett-Packard)

The official web site for HP: PCs, printers, scanners, and many other computer and non-computer products.

**Web:**

**http://www.hp.com/**

### Finding the Computer Company You Need

Computer equipment is best when it works perfectly, sitting quietly on your desk doing whatever you want. However, before you can get to that point, you need to:

(1) find the equipment that is just right for you, and

(2) get it up and running.

And, before that magic moment arrives, the time will come when you need to find a particular computer company—to find out what they sell, or to check their web site for updates, or maybe to get a phone number to ask for tech support.

So don't forget, the Guide to Computer Vendors is waiting for you on the Net.

## IBM

The official web site for IBM: PCs, software, OS/2, IBM Global Network, network products, Lotus, mainframes, midrange computers, AIX, and much, much more.

**Web:**

**http://www.ibm.com/**

## Intel

The official web site for Intel: PC processors and other products.

**Web:**

**http://www.intel.com/**

## Microsoft

The official web site for Microsoft: Windows (3.1, 95 and NT), Office suite (Word, Access, Excel and so on), games, networking software, Internet software (Internet Explorer), and much, much more.

**Web:**

**http://www.microsoft.com/**

## Netscape

The official web site for Netscape: Internet software (including the Navigator web browser).

**Web:**

**http://home.netscape.com/**

## Novell

The official web site for Novell: Netware operating system and other networking products.

**Web:**

**http://www.novell.com/**

## Packard-Bell

The official web site for Packard-Bell: PCs.

**Web:**

**http://www.packardbell.com/**

## SCO (Santa Cruz Operation)

The official web site for SCO: Unix, software development tools, and so on.

**Web:**
**http://www.sco.com/**

## Silicon Graphics

The official web site for Silicon Graphics: workstations, software development tools, and more.

**Web:**
**http://www.sgi.com/**

## Sun Microsystems

The official web site for Sun Microsystems: Java, workstations and other computers, Unix, software development tools, networking products, and so on.

**Web:**
**http://www.sun.com/**

# COMPUTERS: CULTURE

## Computer Culture Talk and General Discussion

Computers have been with us since the 1940s. In that time, there have been several generations of human beings who have been intimately involved with several generations of computers. Although hardware changes frequently, and software is replaced almost as fast as we can get used to it, human/computer relationships are not easily forgotten. Instead of going gentle into that good night, they give rise to tales and folklore which are passed on, from person to person, as part of our computational oral tradition.

**Usenet:**
**comp.society.folklore**

## Computer History and Folklore

One day, while you are driving, you see an old bearded man wearing a Grateful Dead T-shirt, standing beside the road, and holding a sign that says "Will set up a Usenet news server for food." This is not your average homeless person. This is a man who used to be *someone* in the early days of the Net. There was life—lots of life—before the Web, and you can read all about it in the archive of Internet-oriented history and folklore.

**Web:**
**http://yoyo.cc.monash.edu.au/~mist/Folklore/**

## Computer Nerd Humor

Are you a nerd? To be a real nerd, you need to know a lot about computers, but you can't stop there. Take the nerd test and find out if you make the grade.

**Web:**
**http://www.epix.net/~buppa/humor/computer/nerd_test.html**

## Computer Professionals for Social Responsibility

Computer Professionals for Social Responsibility (CPSR) is a non-profit organization concerned with the effects of computers on society. CPSR is supported by its membership and has chapters throughout the country. This web page has links to discussion lists on similar topics and numerous publications.

**Web:**
**http://www.cpsr.org/dox/**

**Usenet:**
**comp.org.cpsr.announce**
**comp.org.cpsr.talk**

## Computer Underground Digest

Here is a large archive of electronic publications and other files relating to the "computer underground". What is the computer underground? I can't tell you here (in case your parents or teacher or boss happens to be looking). Check it out for yourself when no one else is around.

**Web:**
**http://www.eff.org/pub/Publications/CuD/**

**Listproc Mailing List:**
List Name: **cudigest**
Subscribe to: **listproc@vmd.cso.niu.edu**

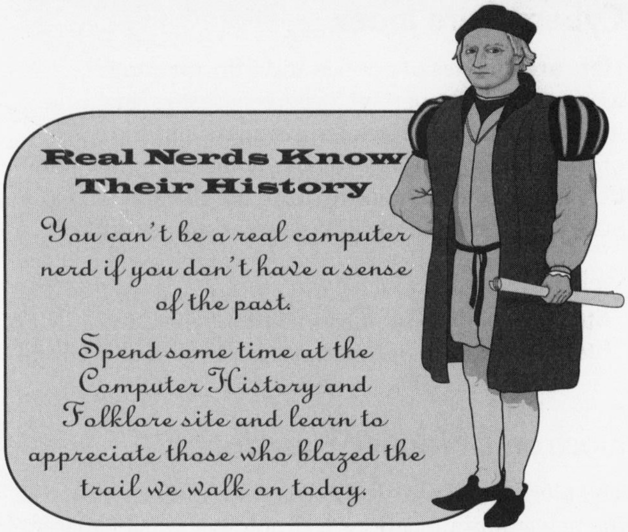
Real Nerds Know Their History
You can't be a real computer nerd if you don't have a sense of the past.
Spend some time at the Computer History and Folklore site and learn to appreciate those who blazed the trail we walk on today.

## Computers and Academic Freedom

Universities and colleges are our first line of defense when it comes to protecting intellectual freedom. Join the discussions and take a look at the archives relating to computers and academic freedom. The Net you save may be your own.

**Web:**

**http://www.eff.org/pub/CAF/**

**Usenet:**

**alt.comp.acad-freedom.news**
**alt.comp.acad-freedom.talk**

**Listserv Mailing List:**

List Name: **comp-academic-freedom-talk**
Subscribe to: **listserv@eff.org**

### *Look What I Found on the Net...*

```
Newsgroup: alt.comp.acad-freedom.talk
Subject: Usenet Censorship
```

The censors at the State Board for Comprehensive Technical Education have removed my access to the group alt.sexual.abuse.recovery. It has the word sex in it you see, and it MUST be obscene if it has the word sex in it.

They also removed all groups with the word "game" in it because the fools who make the Internet decisions for South Carolina Technical Colleges actually think people PLAY games in those groups. This was clearly stated in the rationale for the block, that people will tie up the lines playing games. The people who are deciding what to censor don't even understand that these are discussion groups, not video parlors. The blind leading the sighted.

They excluded all binary/picture groups because they think people are going to be gumming up the system looking at pictures, and used alt.sex.aluminum.baseball.bat, a joke group, as an example of the kind of immoral obscene decadent pervertedness that is to be found on the Net.

They have blocked "flame" because there are insults and bad words in there.

These people haven't a clue as to the what or how or why of the Net, and yet somehow they are in a position to determine what I have access to. In this shotgun attempt to censor my reading material, they have not achieved their purpose, as I can still access the very types of materials which they are attempting to stop me from obtaining and which I have no interest in to begin with, yet have been deprived of access to other groups which I do read and which are legitimate.

A B C D E F G H I J K L M N O P Q R S T U V W X Y Z

## Cult of the Dead Cow

The Cult of the Dead Cow is the oldest underground telecommunications organization, dating back to 1986. Although the membership is small—consisting of only about 20 active members—their influence is felt around the world. The cult's main product is a series of articles, written at various times by various members, with new articles being added from time to time. The articles are regularly read by thousands of people, so why not expand your mind and give it a try? Do you think you might like to join the cult as a member (as opposed to being an outsider)? Here is a hint: don't ask to join. Cult members are welcomed by invitation only, and once you ask, they will never invite you.

**Web:**
**http://www.l0pht.com/cdc.html**

**Usenet:**
**alt.fan.cult-dead-cow**

**IRC:**
**#cdc**

## Cyberanthropology

Almost all of the history of the Net has yet to be written. However, what does exist can be tied into cyberpunk, technoshamanism and virtual communities. If you would like to rise above the popular one-size-fits-all television-oriented culture, this is a great place to begin. Read the following sentence out loud, right now, no matter where you are: "Nobody who uses the expression 'surfing the Net' knows what they are talking about."

**Web:**
**http://www.clas.ufl.edu/anthro/cyberanthro/cyberanthro-biblio.html**
**http://www.clas.ufl.edu/anthro/cyberanthro/newhome.html**

**Don't click here.**

## Cyberculture Index

Here are indexes of articles and information relating to cyberethics, cyberlaw, cybercensorship, including interviews, projects, related readings and the history of computing. Perhaps you are wondering how all of this stuff relates to your favorite subcultural niche. Start here, and you may be able to figure it out.

**Web:**
**http://humanitas.ucsb.edu/shuttle/cyber.html**
**http://www.euro.net/mark-space/CyberCulture.html**

## Electronic Frontier Foundation

The Electronic Frontier Foundation (EFF) ensures that the new communications technology era is available to all, and that individuals' constitutional rights are preserved therein. Plenty of legal information, EFF publications, and many related articles and zines are available here.

**Web:**
**http://www.eff.org/**

### The Electronic Frontier Foundation

The Electronic Frontier Foundation (EFF) is a non-profit organization dedicated to maintaining *your* rights within the American electronic infrastructure. They publish an electronic newsletter ("EFFector Online"), freely available for reading or downloading, and they furnish expert testimony and financial support in various court cases. Isn't it nice to know that concerned **net.anti-police** are ready to jump in and fight for your right to privacy and access to public information? Why not take a look at some of their publications and see if you want to support them?

## *Look What I Found on the Net...*

(from the "EFFector Online", the Electronic Frontier Foundation newsletter)

```
******************************************************************
           //////////////     //////////////     //////////////
         ///                ///                ///
       ///////            ///////            ///////
     ///                ///                ///
   //////////////     ///                ///
******************************************************************
```

EFFector Online Volume 6 No. 1 9/17/1993 editors@eff.org
A Publication of the Electronic Frontier Foundation ISSN 1062-9424

-==-==-==-<>-==-==-==-

In This Issue:

Crypto Conference in Austin Virginians Against Censorship -==--==-<>-==--==-



-==-==-==-<>-==-==-==-

A Plain Text on Crypto Policy
by John Perry Barlow

...the Clipper Chip -- now called Skipjack owing to a trademark conflict --- is a hardware encryption device that the National Security Agency designed under Reagan-Bush. In April of 1993, it was unveiled by the Clinton Administration and proposed for both governmental and public use. Installed in phones or other telecommunications tools, Skipjack would turn any conversation into gibberish for all but the speaker and his intended listener, using a secret military algorithm.

Skipjack is unique, and controversial, in that it also allows the agents of government to listen under certain circumstances. Each chip contains a key that is split into two parts immediately following manufacture. Each half is then placed in the custody of some trusted institution or "escrow agent".

If, at some subsequent time, some government agency desires to legally listen in on the owner of the communications device in which the chip has been placed, it would present evidence of "lawful authority" to the escrow holders. They will reveal the key pairs, the agency will join them, and begin listening to the subject's unencrypted conversations.

Apparently there are other agencies besides law enforcement who can legally listen to electronic communications. The government has evaded questions about exactly who will have access to these keys, or for that matter, what, besides an judicial warrant, constitutes the "lawful authority" to which they continually refer.

Skipjack was not well received...

==============================================================

*This newsletter is printed on 100% recycled electrons.*

==============================================================

## Flaming

A "flame" is a complaint sent over the Net. Flaming is an important part of Net culture (although the word is so overused as to be trite beyond the bounds of tolerance). You will encounter flaming everywhere—on Usenet, on the Web, in email, on mailing lists, on IRC, in chat rooms—so you might as well learn how to do it well. To help you, here is some useful information. If you really want to get into Net-type complaining, there is even the **alt.flame** Usenet group to share the intellectual wealth.

**Web:**

**http://www.genetics.gla.ac.uk/hive/newbie1.html**
**http://www.xtc.net/~jess/howto.html**

**Usenet:**

**alt.flame**

## Future Culture

These forward-thinking people want to contemplate the Internet, the concept of the global community, technology and how these affect our culture and make us interact with each other in new and different ways. The web site contains FAQs, documents relating to Future Culture, and links to related resources. Or you can just join the mailing list and get a daily dose of technocultural philosophy.

**Web:**

**http://futurec.xtc.net/**

**Listserv Mailing List:**

List Name: **futurec**
Subscribe to: **listserv@uafsysb.uark.edu**

## Geek Code

Are you a geek? Do you want to be? Check out the Geek code and see how you rate. Then put your own personal geek code in your email signature for the whole world to see. If you are a geek, walk tall.

**Web:**

**http://krypton.mankato.msus.edu/~hayden/geek.html**

## Geek Site of the Day

If you are a geek, you should be proud of it. And what better way to show your appreciation than to visit the Geek Site of the Day every day of your life. Get a daily treat, your recommended daily allowance of something truly geeky like a calculus problem, recipes for snack food that you can eat on those 24-hour mudding binges, or links to technoid gidgets and gadgets that only a geek would love.

**Web:**

**http://www.owlnet.rice.edu/~indigo/gsotd/**

## Guide to System Administrators

Learn to understand the sub-species of human being known as the System Administrator. This lifeform's behavior has been scientifically studied and recorded in a helpful easy-to-understand guide.

**Web:**

**http://ncgia.ncgia.ucsb.edu/~fohl/fieldguide.html**

### *Look What I Found on the Net...*

```
Here is my personal geek code. If you would like figure out your
own, visit the Geek Code site. -- Harley

-----BEGIN GEEK CODE BLOCK-----
     Version: 3.1
     G d-? s: a+ C$ U@ P L E-@ W+$ N+$
     o-- K- w@ O M-- V- PS PE Y+ PGP t
     !5-? X--? !R- tv--? b+++$ DI+ !D
     G e+++ h++ r++ y++
------END GEEK CODE BLOCK------
```

## Hacker Test

Find out if you are a computer illiterate, nerd, hacker, guru, or wizard with this set of questions.

**Web:**

**http://www-ia.hiof.no/~jimmyo/hacker_test.html**

## Hackers

Peer in on clever hacking discussions in Usenet and IRC and learn how to not only hack computer hardware and software, but anything in everyday life, including loose shower tiles, vibrating air conditioning vents and dust-spewing vacuum cleaners. The web site has lots of great hacker information.

**Web:**

**http://www.underground.org/**

**Usenet:**

**alt.hackers**
**comp.hackers**

**IRC:**

**#hack**

## League for Programming Freedom/Free Software Foundation

A subdirectory containing articles and publications from the LPF and FSF, which are dedicated to the purchaser's right to use, copy, modify, and distribute software as he or she sees fit.

**Web:**

**http://www.lpf.org/**

## Mutate Project

Here is lots of hip and cool stuff by people all over the Net. When you have nothing else to do and your brain needs a bit of stretching, you can always investigate nerd sex or join a forum on "kulcher war" (taking over the world, net repression, electronic guerrilla warfare, and so on). If you have to ask, you aren't going to understand the answer. But, if you are afraid to mutate, you shouldn't even waste your time asking.

**Web:**

**http://www.onworld.com/MUT/**

## Nerds

Somewhere along the line, a bit flipped in the global memory bank and nerds became cool. So, if you want to be cool, you need to know more about nerds. One of these resources is a netzine that covers things nerdy: interviews with nerds, a bulletin board, features on nerds doing cool stuff. The other resource covers nerd culture, the Net culture, and the crucial differences between geeks and nerds.

**Web:**

**http://www.geocities.com/SiliconValley/8858/**
**http://www.spiv.com/nrrrd/**

## Net Culture

There is no cyberspace; there is no information superhighway; no one actually surfs the Net. In other words, everything everyone in authority is telling you is wrong. But is there a Net culture? See for yourself.

**Web:**

**http://www.eff.org/pub/Net_culture/**

### *Look What I Found on the Net...*

```
Newsgroup: alt.hackers
Subject: cheap grad-student food hack

With $5 to spend and 15 minutes to make
a dish for a potluck dinner:

 1 can condensed cream of mushroom soup
 1 package frozen chopped spinach

Place both in microwave-safe dish.
Microwave 4 min. Stir.
Microwave another 4 min.
Top with random cheeses.
```

## Net Tribes

There are lots and lots of gatherings on the Net, and some of them are starting to be recognizable as actual sub-cultures. Is there really such a thing as a virtual community? Can we really say anything intelligent about our Net-influenced future culture? Is there anything at all in virtual reality? (The answers, by the way, are "I don't know", "yes" and "who cares?") Start here and see what happens.

**Web:**
**http://www.eerie.fr/~alquier/cyber_index.html**

### Future Culture Shock

The future will be here soon. In fact, it may even be here tomorrow (or, in some areas, tonight). However, there is no need to wait to find out what the future has in store for us. Visit the Net Tribes site and see what sort of brave new futuristic worlds we are building for ourselves.

## Netaholics

Using the Net is a satisfying interactive experience. However, like all satisfying interactive experiences, using the Net can be practiced to excess. If it starts to affect the rest of your life (or if you don't *have* a rest of your life), you may have a problem. If so, why not take a few minutes to examine the Netaholics web site. Read about the symptoms and ponder the suggestions. How do you know if you have a problem? If it is hard for you to turn off the computer and go outside, you have a problem.

**Web:**
**http://www.safari.net/~pam/netanon/**

## Psybernet

I think we all owe it to ourselves to explore the psyche as it relates to information systems. After all, our minds are part of the Net, and we might as well understand something of the collective phenomenon, so here are some relevant links and information. For an ongoing discussion, the mailing list considers the effects of email groups and mailing lists.

**Web:**
**http://vesta.chch.planet.co.nz/~walter/psybernet.html**

**Listserv Mailing List:**
List Name: **psyber-l**
Subscribe to: **listserv@home.ease.lsoft.com**

## Technomads

A Technomad is someone who travels a lot, for recreation or fun, along with computers, portable phones, and other technical equipment. Yes, there are such people and now you can keep track of them and their activities. Some people have their own web pages to chronicle their electronically mediated adventures, while others are proponents of wearable computers. What I am wondering is whether this is merely regular people running around with a bunch of electronic equipment, or are we developing a whole new life form?

**Web:**
**http://www.paragon.co.uk/it/issue12/Technomadding/techno.html**

# COMPUTERS: GRAPHICS

## 3D Engines

3D engines for real-time graphics and VR. Listings of vendors, hardware, software, demos, game engines, texture mapping, wireframe, etc. Each review includes a list of features, contact information/links, and if possible a link to download a demo or the program.

**Web:**
**http://www.cs.tu-berlin.de/~ki/engines.html**

## 3D Engines

One dimension just doesn't cut it. Two dimensions are okay most of the time. But when you need something that can pass as reality, **3D** is the only game in town. The race for a new reality is about to begin. Gentlemen, it is time to start your 3D engines.

## 3D Morphing

Morphing is the gradual transition of one image into another. For example, you might see a picture of a famous supermodel slowly turn into a picture of Bill Gates. 3D morphing is a technique which overcomes some of the shortcoming of traditional "2D" morphing. Here is a site that has information about 3D morphing as well as examples you can view for yourself.

**Web:**

**http://www-graphics.stanford.edu/~tolis/morph.html**

## 3D Studio

Here are the places to look for information and discussion relating to the Studio program. You can find tips, tutorials, product reviews, questions and answers, as well as links to related resources.

**Web:**

**http://www.opencad.com/Magic_Mirror/**

**Usenet:**

**comp.graphics.packages.3dstudio**

## Computer Aided Sculpting

Here is software (called Sculpt) that you can use to work with digitized models and perform artistic sculpting. The software runs on SGI workstations and allows interactive computer-assisted editing and free-form sculpting of three-dimensional polygonal mesh surface. Unlike regular CAD software, Sculpt is easy to use, and a demo version is available for free.

**Web:**

**http://www.lance.colostate.edu/~dga/sculpt.html**

## Computer Animation

The FAQ covers hobbyist and career animation, animation theory, animation software, and related resources.

**Web:**

**http://www.ridgecrest.ca.us/fx/cga-faq.html**

**Usenet:**

**comp.graphics.animation**

## Computer Graphics Bibliography

A huge, comprehensive database of computer graphics bibliographic references, all in the BibTeX bibliography format. This is the place to begin a serious search for computer graphics information.

**Web:**

**http://www.siggraph.org/publications/bibliography/bibliography.html**

## Computer Graphics Information

Here is a fabulous starting point if you're looking for information on computer graphics. This web page has many links to university and government labs, Usenet groups, software, FAQs, bibliographies, conference news, utilities, and other items of interest.

**Web:**

**http://mambo.ucsc.edu/psl/cg.html**

## Computer Graphics

**Understanding computer graphics means a lot more than being able to use the Internet to trade erotic pictures. For detailed information and discussion, try the Computer Graphics Information web site.**

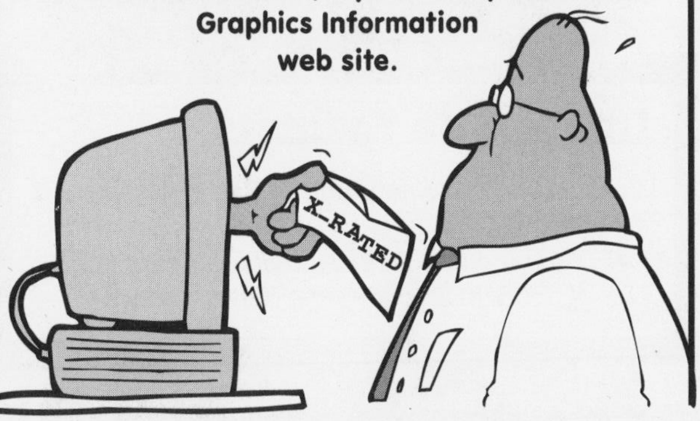
X-RATED

## General Image Manipulation Program

General Image Manipulation Program (Gimp) is a no-cost image manipulation software package for Unix systems (particularly Linux). The idea behind Gimp is to provide a freely available package to replace the commercial ones. Much of Gimp's functionality is provided by external programs called "plug-ins". Gimp users can create and share their own plug-ins with the Gimp community. The official Gimp web page contains information about the system, a downloading facility (including source code), some tutorials, examples, and links to other Gimp-related sites around the Net.

**Web:**
**http://www.xcf.berkeley.edu/~gimp/**

## Graphics Demos

Cool Demos is the name of this web page at the Stanford Computer Graphics Laboratory. This page contains lots of graphics demos, showing work done by members of the lab as well as students taking graphics courses. Here is a good place to spend some spare time learning about graphics and looking at... well... cool demos.

**Web:**
**http://www-graphics.stanford.edu/demos/**

## Computer Graphics Talk and General Discussion

When you want to talk to other people in the world of computer graphics, here are the Usenet groups you can follow. The discussion covers all aspects of computer graphics, including software, hardware, new research, and questions and answers.

**Usenet:**
**alt.graphics**
**comp.graphics**

**Image File Formats**

*Need to find out what's on the* **INSIDE** *of a graphics file?*

*Get inside the Image File Formats site, and find out all the details your mother never told you.*

## IBM Visualization Data Explorer

The IBM Visualization Data Explorer (DX) is a general-purpose software package for data visualization and analysis. DX runs under Unix on both IBM and non-IBM hardware. The system is designed around a data-flow driven client/server model and allows you to use a graphical program editor to create a visualization of particular data using a standard mouse/pointer interface. The official IBM site contains information about the system, a demo version you can try for free, tools, utilities, images, documentation, technical specifications and links to other DX-related repositories on the Net.

**Web:**
**http://www.almaden.ibm.com/dx/**

## Image Conversion

There are times when you need to convert one type of image to another, or change some of the qualities (grayscale, flip and so on). For example, you may have a gif file that you want in jpg format. Here are some resources that can help you by performing conversions of various types.

**Web:**
**http://www.ct.ebt.com/convmach.html**
**http://www.handmadesw.com/hsi/web_alchemy.html**

## Image File Formats

If you are like me, sometimes just using something isn't enough. There are times when you have to get under the hood. When the urge strikes, and you want to know more about image file formats than the guy next door, here is the place to look.

**Web:**
**http://beatus.geog.nottingham.ac.uk/~dee/rs/uif/uif.html**

**Read a zine today.**

## Macintosh Graphics

Spice up your boring papers and word processing projects with graphics help from Macintosh. Learn about the various software available as well as fonts, hints about methods and style, and even the more technical aspects of hardware needed to achieve your artistic vision.

**Web:**

**http://www.users.interport.net/~jashear/mac_graphics.html**

**Usenet:**

**comp.sys.mac.graphics**

## OpenGL

OpenGL is an interface used by certain PC and workstation applications for generating interactive 2D and 3D computer graphics. Here you can find a FAQ (frequently asked question list), a discussion group, technical specification, benchmark results and more.

**Web:**

**http://www.sgi.com/Technology/openGL/**

**Usenet:**

**comp.graphics.api.opengl**

## Performance Animation

Can you imagine animation being created in real time in response to human puppeteers? Well, that is performance animation, and people are starting to make it happen. Here is information including technical data, software and hardware, links to other related sites, and a gallery in which you can look at examples.

**Web:**

**http://www.studio.sgi.com/Features/PerfAnimation/intro.html**

## Persistence of Vision

The Persistence of Vision Ray Tracer (POV-Ray) is a freeware program that allows a user to easily create fantastic, three-dimensional, photo-realistic images on many computer platforms. This page offers POV news bulletins, FAQs, links to the official distribution sites, POV utilities, documentation, ready-made POV objects, and links to galleries of images created with POV.

**Web:**

**http://www.povray.org/**

## Ray Dream

If you use Ray Dream Designer 3D graphics software, here are some helpful resources: news, press releases, tips, a forum, as well as a mailing list.

**Web:**

**http://dreamline.human.cornell.edu/rdl/rdl.html**
**http://www.raydream.com/**
**http://www.webcom.com/~dram/rdd/**

**Listproc Mailing List:**

List Name: **raydream-l**
Subscribe to: **listproc@cornell.edu**

## Ray-Trace Graphics

Whether you want to make simple spheric shapes or plot three-dimensional movements of a human figure through space, this ray-tracing Usenet group will have something for you. Discussion covers software, tools and methods of ray-tracing for the novice or wizard. The web page has pointers to FAQs, bibliography, documentation, software packages, archives, many ray-traced images, links to other ray-tracing related sites, and much more to do with ray-tracing.

**Web:**

**http://www.cm.cf.ac.uk/Ray.Tracing/**

**Usenet:**

**comp.graphics.raytracing**
**comp.graphics.rendering.raytracing**

## Renderman

Renderman is a standard interface used by modeling programs to describe how images should be displayed by rendering programs. In principle, Renderman is similar to Postscript, except that Renderman is used for 3D primitives. The overall goal is to allow modeling programs (such as animation software) to send device-independent data to a rendering program with little regard as to the actual rendering algorithms.

**Web:**

**http://pete.cs.caltech.edu/RMR/**

**Usenet:**

**comp.graphics.rendering.renderman**

## Scientific Visualization

The world of scientific visualization is vast. If you are interested in this fascinating area, there are many resources available on the Net. To help you get started, here is a large collection of links to archives, various university departments, and web pages, all related to scientific visualization.

**Web:**

**http://www.nas.nasa.gov/NAS/projects/visualization/visWeblets.html**

## Silicon Graphics Info

Silicon Graphics users, here are some places you will want to know about. Access an online journal with news, features and product reviews. Find information about SGI graphics products, as well as demos, programs to download for free, and third party applications.

**Web:**

**http://www.pcinews.com/business/pci/sgi/**
**http://www.sgi.com/Products/**

**Usenet:**

**comp.sys.sgi.graphics**

### I Have a Dream...

I have a dream -- that children all over the world will be able to use any type of disk drive, regardless of interface, regardless of cable type, and regardless of operating system.

I have a dream -- that disk drives will one day be judged by the quality of their storage capacity and by their access times, and not by brand name or device driver compatibility.

I have a dream -- that the time will come when people everywhere will care more that their disks are reliable and dependable instead of worrying that an installation program may not recognize any device they choose to use.

Yes, I have a lot of dreams, and maybe one day they will come true. But until that day, I depend on the Disk Drives, Cables and Interfaces web site to keep our society up and running with as little conflict as possible.

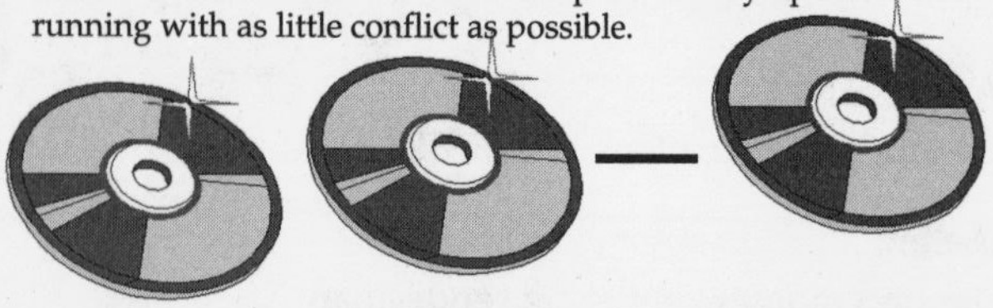

# COMPUTERS: HARDWARE

## CD-ROM

Originally, the name CD-ROM stood for "Compact Disc Read Only Memory". However, that name can be relegated to the etymological scrap heap of computer history: today CD-ROM, or just plain CD is a word unto itself. On one of my computers, I have a drive that can read ordinary CDs as well as special cartridges. Although the CDs are read-only, the cartridges are read/write and can hold up to 650 MB. There are all kinds of CD drives, and the variations can push you around the bend at times. Don't despair. Although the technology changes a lot and the standards are complex, the Net can help you. Here are places to turn when you need information about manufacturing, terminology, specifications, industry news and so on. For ongoing discussion or if you have a question, try Usenet.

**Web:**

**http://www.cd-info.com/**

**Usenet:**

**alt.cd-rom.comp.sys.ibm.pc.hardware.cd-rom**

## COM Port Conflicts

Every PC has COM ports to which miscellaneous devices and adaptor boards can be attached. Most of the time, the equipment you need is already connected when you buy the computer, and you don't need any help. Or you might install something of your own, but the gods are with you, and it works with no problems. However, on some computers, under some conditions, the adaptor boards conflict with one another. This can be highly frustrating and is one of the biggest sources of questions that Internet service providers must handle. ("I put in a new sound board, and all of a sudden, my modem won't dial.") Before you tear your hair out (or kill someone) turn to the Net for information about COM port and IRQ (interrupt) settings.

**Web:**

**http://www.usr.com/home/2054.111.html**

## Disk Drives, Cables and Interfaces

If you like to immerse yourself in the netherworld of disk drives and related hardware, you will love this site. Here you can find detailed specifications and setup information for many kinds of drives, controllers and cables. In addition, you will be able to teach yourself everything you ever wanted to know about hardware interfaces. This is a great place to spend a warm sunny day when everyone else is out at the beach having fun because they don't know any better.

**Web:**

**http://theref.c3d.rl.af.mil/**

## Ergonomic Keyboards

"Ergonomic" describes a device that is designed to reduce fatigue and discomfort. Ergonomic keyboards are designed to reduce the strain your hands, wrists and forearms undergo if you type for long periods of time. Do they work? Sometimes, for some people, yes they do. Ergonomic keyboards are designed with a different orientation from regular keyboards, so you hold your arms in a way that minimizes physical stress. Unfortunately, all the ergonomic keyboards I have seen are really cheap quality—most notably the one from a well-known company whose name I won't mention (Microsoft). It bothers me because I would really like to try one of these devices, but they are so junky. I guess they are designed for the mass market and the idea is to keep down the unit cost. Oh, well. Want more info? Here is a good place to start. (By the way, here is a technique I learned a long time ago for seeing how good the keys on a keyboard are. Take a bunch of pennies and stack them, one at a time, on one of the keys until it depresses. A good quality keyboard will require more pennies to depress a key than a cheap, low quality, mushy keyboard.)

**Web:**

**http://www.cs.princeton.edu/~dwallach/tifaq/keyboards.html**

**The Net is immortal.**

## Hard Disk and CD-ROM Treasury

If you are the type of person who cares about the IRQ settings for a hard drive, or CD-ROM drivers, or what's inside a master boot record, you will love this site. There is lots of technical information about hard drives and CD-ROMs, as well as pointers to related links around the Net. I looked up the specs for my hard drive and was amazed to see how fast it is. If you like numbers and specs, keep this resource on your booklist.

**Web:**

**http://www.cs.yorku.ca/People/frank/**

## Hard Drive Jumper Settings

Here is a resource you will not care about in the least until you need it, and then you will *really* need it. Jumper settings for hard drives can be hard to come by when you don't have the documentation and no one will answer the tech support line. Here's the info.

**Web:**

**http://blue-planet.com/techpg.html**

## Laptops

A laptop computer is one that is small and lightweight enough to be portable and sit on your lap comfortably. How small can laptops get and still be laptops? Well, people like a full-sized keyboard and a screen large enough to read without squinting, which puts a minimum size on how small a computer can be and still be useable for more than a few minutes. However, within these limitations, there are a lot of choices. Before you buy a laptop, check with the Net. You need to know more than when you buy a regular PC, so I suggest you definitely do some homework before committing yourself.

**Web:**

**http://www.enteract.com/~epbrown/**

**Usenet:**

**comp.sys.laptops**

A B C D E F G H I J K L M N O P Q R S T U V W X Y Z

## Modems

If you are ever sitting around on a rainy Sunday afternoon, bored out of your mind, and you suddenly develop an urge to know more about modems, this is the place to go. This is a well-organized well-designed, comprehensive site with links to just about everything under the Internet sun that has to do with modems. Lots and lots of modem-oriented information, including links to official sites for different brands of modems.

**Web:**

**http://www.rosenet.net/~costmo/**

### MODEMS and FUN

Modems are now an indispensable accoutrement of modern life. However, anyone who has ever tried to get a recalcitrant modem to cooperate understands just how much fun these delightful little devices can be. When your modem gets its back up, turn to the modem information site for help and enlightenment.

## PC Hardware Talk and General Discussion

Computing is no fun if you have to work on a slow dinosaur of a PC that creaks when it starts up or blows dust out of its cracks every time you change directories. Keep up with the latest in hardware changes and make your machine state-of-the-art.

**Usenet:**

**comp.sys.ibm.pc.hardware.cd-rom**
**comp.sys.ibm.pc.hardware.chips**
**comp.sys.ibm.pc.hardware.comm**
**comp.sys.ibm.pc.hardware.misc**
**comp.sys.ibm.pc.hardware.networking**
**comp.sys.ibm.pc.hardware.storage**
**comp.sys.ibm.pc.hardware.systems**
**comp.sys.ibm.pc.hardware.video**

## Performance Database Server

A web page interface to the Performance Database Server—a database with information on benchmarking computer hardware. Links on the page allow you to search the database or to browse articles directly.

**Web:**

**http://netlib2.cs.utk.edu/performance/html/PDStop.html**

## Personal Digital Assistants

A personal digital assistant (PDA) is a marketing euphemism for a small, hand-held computer that doesn't run standard software and sort of does what it is supposed to do some of the time. However, they are getting better every year and I predict that, one day, it will be common for everyone to have their own PDA to use as a paperweight on their desk. However, don't let me stop you from exploring the brave, new world of brave, new hand-held computers. Here is lots of information about PDAs (including the infamous Newton), as well as some Usenet groups for discussion.

**Web:**

**http://www.netaxs.com/people/bluesky/Newton.html**

**Usenet:**

**comp.sys.handhelds**
**comp.sys.palmtops**

## Powerful Computer List

The next time you run into one of those people who goes on and on about how fast and powerful his computer is, tell him that *your* computer is so powerful that it is on a special list. Point him to this web page. Here you will find information about the world's most powerful computing sites. While he is waiting for his browser to load the list, you can sneak behind him and slap him on the back with a sticky piece of paper that says "Nerd at Work".

**Web:**

**http://www.interactive.net/~gunter/**

## Printers

I remember when it was hard to get any printer working with a PC and, today, whenever a printer actually works I consider it nothing less than a small miracle. My feelings, of course, are way out of date. Today's printers are generally reliable and well-manufactured, and many printers are actually computers in their own right. There are a lot of different printers and, before you buy, there are a lot of choices to consider. After you buy, there are a lot of questions that may arise. Here are some resources to help you: links to printer manufacturers, sources for printer drivers, and much, much more.

**Web:**

**http://www.primenet.com/~penguink/printers.html**
**http://www.printgrc.com/pdrivers.html**

**Usenet:**

**comp.periphs.printers**

## SCSI

SCSI (pronounced "scuzzy") stands for "Small Computer Systems Interface". SCSI is a standard that specifies how peripheral devices such as disk drives, tape drives, CD-ROMs, and so on are to be connected to a computer. SCSI devices connect to a SCSI port on the computer, and multiple devices can be connected to the same port. Here are some resources for information and discussion relating to all things SCSI.

**Web:**

**http://www.paranoia.com/~filipg/HTML/LINK/F_SCSI.html**

**Usenet:**

**comp.periphs.scsi**

**Join the fun—now.**

## *Look What I Found on the Net...*

```
(from the list of the world's most powerful computing sites)

 1) Japan: National Aerospace Lab
 2) United States, Maryland: National Security Agency
 3) Japan: University of Tokyo, Meguro-ku
 4) England: European Center for Medium-Range Weather Forecasts
 5) United States, Texas: E-Systems
 6) United States, New York: IBM
 7) United States, Minnesota: Cray Research
 8) Japan: National Lab for High Energy Physics
 9) Japan: University of Tsukuba
10) United States, Pennsylvania: Pittsburgh Supercomputing Center
11) Japan: Japanese Atomic Energy Research Institute Lab
12) United States, New Mexico: Los Alamos National Lab
13) United States, New York: Cornell Theory Center
14) Japan: University of Tokyo, Bunkyo-ku
15) Japan: Nagoya University
16) Japan: Institute for Solid State Physics
17) Japan: National Institute of Genetics
18) United States, Hawaii: Maui High Perf. Computing Center
19) United States, Minnesota: Minnesota Supercomputer Center
20) Japan: NTT Transmission Systems Labs
```

### *Look What I Found on the Net...*

(from "Alice in Unixland")

..."Well," responded the Sun Bear, "we've got to do something to make them want to switch to Unix."

"Do you think," said a Woodpecker who had been busy making a hole in the table, "that there might be a problem with the name 'Unix?' I mean, it does sort of suggest being less than a man."

"Maybe we should try another name, " suggested the Job Sparrow, "like Brut, or Rambo."

"Penix," suggested a Penguin.

"Mount," said the Frog, "spawn."

Alice slapped him. "Nice?" he asked.

"But then again," suggested the Woodpecker, "what about the shrinkwrap issue?"

Suddenly, everyone leaped up and started dashing about, waving their hands in the air and screaming.  Just as suddenly, they all sat down again...

## Sound Cards

Sound cards are great—once you get them working. To help you, here is where you can find FAQs (frequently asked question lists), lists of acronyms and abbreviations, information about sound card companies and their products, as well as links to other sound-card related resources. For discussion or questions, there are the Usenet discussion groups.

**Web:**

**http://www.rpi.edu/~hsiaoe/soundsite/**

**Usenet:**

**comp.sys.ibm.pc.soundcard.misc**
**comp.sys.ibm.pc.soundcard.tech**

**Quick, turn the page.**

# COMPUTERS: LITERATURE

## Alice in Unix Land

Jump through your monitor with Alice and go on a wild and woolly chase through the strange and mysterious Unix Land. This fun story is based on the Wonderland tales by Lewis Carroll.

**Web:**

**http://inswww.ins.cwru.edu/php/fung/comp/alice.html**
**http://www.forthnet.gr/humour/Computers/AliceinUnixland.html**

**The Net loves poetry.**

## Go Ask Alice

### (About Unix)

The machinations of the commercial side of the Unix world have always been silly at best. If you want to see just how silly, take a look at "Alice in Unix Land", a short but apropos story by Lincoln Spector. Follow Alice as she leaves the realm of DOS to travel to Unix Land, a place in which everything makes sense (sort of), at least until the guys in suits start standardizing everything.

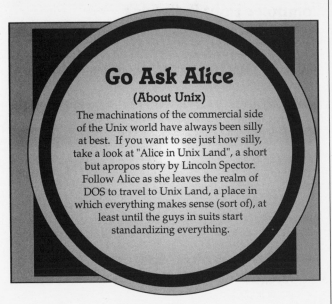

## Artificial Intelligence Publications

There are times when you simply must have instant access to artificial intelligence (AI) research. For example, say you are at a party and a computer science nerd challenges you to defend your reasons for believing in strong or weak AI. Simply whip out your handheld computer and your cellular modem, connect to the Net and, within seconds, you will be able to grind your challenger into an NP-complete hash of random neural impulses. (Note: "Strong AI" asserts that it is theoretically possible to build a computer that can think. "Weak AI" argues that—although computers are useful for modeling human cognitive processes—it is impossible, even in principle, to create an actual thinking machine.)

**Web:**

**http://www.cs.cmu.edu/afs/cs.cmu.edu/project/ai-repository/ai/html/other/publications.html**

## *Look What I Found on the Net...*

```
Excerpts from the BSD Version of the Bible
==========================================

(from the Book of Genesis)

In the beginning God created the heaven and the earth.
And the earth was without form, and void; and darkness was upon
the face of the DOS.
And God said, Let there be kernel: and there was kernel.
And God saw the light, that it was good: and God divided the
light from the darkness.
And God called the light BSD, and the darkness he called SYSV.
And the evening and the morning were the first revision.
And God said, Let there be a firmament in the midst of the RAM,
and let it divide the admins from the lusers...

(from the Book of Revelations)

And I stood upon the sand of the silicon, and saw a beast rise
up out of the core, having forty disks and many megs, and upon
its boxes ten digits, and upon its labels, the Mark of Bill.

And the beast which I saw was like unto an OS, and its binaries
were as to size of a core, and its interface as the interface of
a sloth: and the coders gave him his power, and his GUI, and
great speed...
```

## BSD Bible

BSD (Berkeley Software Distribution) is the name given to the family of Unix systems that were at one time developed at the University of California at Berkeley. The BSD Bible is an ongoing project to modify the entire Bible so as to replace every verse with a BSD Unix reference. Although most of the project is still to be done, what is done is funny, really funny *if* you are a Unix person. If you are a Unix person and you have a sense of humor, you might want to volunteer to work on some of the unfinished portions of the book. After all, how many living authors of the Bible are there? Wouldn't that look great on your résumé.

**Web:**

**http://bsdbible.worldone.com/**

## BugNet Online

Information about PC bugs, glitches, incompatibilities, and how to fix them. Includes an archive of Bug Alerts, a category all its own for Windows 95 and Windows NT, and a method for submitting bugs. This is a newsletter seeking subscriptions, but has a nonsubscribers info area with plenty of information.

**Web:**

**http://www.bugnet.com/~bugnet/**

## Computer Almanac

Trivia buffs, brush up on your facts about computers. You never know when an emergency will come up and you will need to know some sort of useless fact or figure such as the estimated percent of salaried workers who will work at video display terminals by the year 2000 or how many wire transfers the Federal Reserve handles per day.

**Web:**

**http://www.cs.cmu.edu/afs/cs.cmu.edu/user/bam/www/numbers.html**

## Computer Light Bulb FAQ

I am sure you have heard light bulb jokes. ("How many something-or-others does it take to screw in a light bulb?") Here is a list of such jokes in the area of computers. Before you go to your next party, check with this list, and pick two or three jokes to adapt to the current computer situation in your life. People will think you are so smart and witty (as, indeed, you are, being one of my readers).

**Web:**

**http://www.computernerd.com/litebulb.htm**

## Computer Literature Talk and General Discussion

Over the years, the world of computing has been developing its own literary tradition. Like all such traditions, it starts with stories, discussion, tall tales and general talk. You can watch it all develop by following the discussion in this Usenet group. Hang around here long enough, and when you get old, you will be able to tell your grandchildren, "I was there when Bill Gates told the *real* story of why DOS was kept around for so long."

**Usenet:**

**alt.folklore.computers**

## Computer Science Library

When I was a computer science student (at the University of Waterloo, and at the University of California) it was possible to be reasonably conversant with every important area of CS. Today, it is a lot harder to be a know-it-all like I was: the world of CS research has exploded like a Serbian minefield. So when I want to keep up on what's new and exciting in the Queen of Applied Sciences, I go to this wonderful collection of links to CS publications. Try it when you get a moment. I guarantee you will find more publications that you could shake a non-preemptive stick at in a polynomial amount of time.

**Web:**

**http://fas.sfu.ca/cs/library/**

## Computer-Oriented Cyberlore

Through the years, many humorous articles and jokes relating to computers have been posted to Usenet or circulated on the Net. From time to time, people have compiled collections of various types, and here is a nice set of links to many of these collections. The range is large, stretching all the way back to the days when computers were large and expensive and had operators.

**Web:**

**http://www.pass.wayne.edu/~twk/compfolk.html#humor**

## Computing Dictionary

Abbreviations, a list of over 2,100 computer languages, available compilers and interpreters, hacker jargon file, STING hypertext computing glossary, and links to other interesting computer resources.

**Web:**

**http://wombat.doc.ic.ac.uk/**

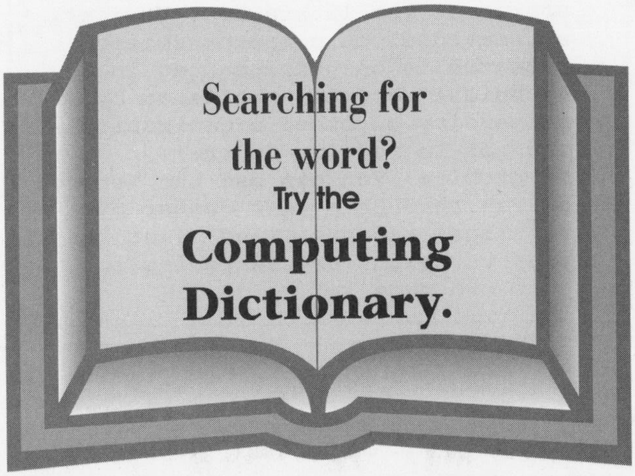
Searching for
the word?
Try the
Computing
Dictionary.

## Computing Magazines and Journals

I am going to let you in on a secret. Everyone else in the world has no trouble staying current on everything that is happening in the world of computing. *You* are the only one who is having trouble keeping up. That is why I have put in this resource, just for you. Here you will find links to many different computer magazines and journals. Read long and prosper.

**Web:**

**http://www.utexas.edu/computer/vcl/journals.html**

## Goldilocks in Fortran

Here is the story of Goldilocks and the Three Bears expressed as a Fortran program. As with all old-fashioned Fortran stories, you will notice the charming use of statement labels. Call me a traditionalist, but I prefer the old fairy tales, the ones that pre-dated structured programming.

**Web:**

**http://www.op.net/docs/Computer-Folklore/goldi.locks**

## Hacker's Dictionary

A comprehensive compendium of hacker slang illuminating many aspects of hackish tradition, folklore, and humor. Also known as the "jargon file".

**Web:**

**http://www.ccil.org/jargon/jargon_toc.html**

## Hacker's Technical Journals

Many infamous hackers have put together several journals full of technical information for those of you who like to know exactly how things work. What's nice about these archives is that they are multipurpose: they can probably get you out of as much trouble as they get you into.

**Web:**

**http://www.eff.org/pub/Publications/CuD**

I probably shouldn't tell you this, but you can get all kinds of information about all kinds of things that all kinds of people don't want you to know. Look in the ***Hacker's Technical Journals.***

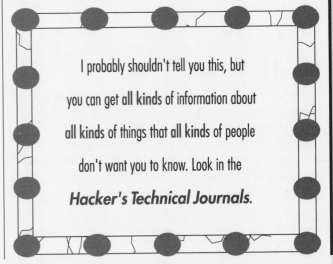

## How to Steal Code

Also known as "Inventing the Wheel Only Once". A guide as to the merits of using the wealth of existing software and libraries instead of rewriting programs from scratch.

**Web:**

http://www.apocalypse.org/pub/u/paul/docs/steal/steal-toc.html

## Network Observer

The Network Observer is an online newsletter devoted to a discussion of networks and how they relate to real life (that is, what goes on when you are away from the computer). Here you will find a large collection of thoughtful and provocative articles that makes for a wonderful place to browse. If you are an intelligent person—and as one of my readers I know you are in the top one percent—this is a good place to visit when you have a few free moments and are looking for something stimulating to read.

**Web:**

http://communication.ucsd.edu/pagre/tno.html

## Programming Humor

Some types of jokes—called canonical jokes—are repeated, with small variations, over and over again. Here is a list of canonical programming jokes. If you are a programmer, my prescription is to pause every time you find a bug and read two jokes.

**Web:**

http://www.misty.com/laughweb/canonical.lists/programming.humor.html

## Tao of Programming

A humorous guide to programming and otherwise living with computers in the modern age. "Something mysterious is formed, born in the silent void. Waiting alone and unmoving, it is at once still and yet in constant motion. It is the source of all programs. I do not know its name, so I will call it the Tao of Programming."

**Web:**

http://info.ox.ac.uk/~hu94003/Humour/Computer/Langs/tao.html

## Technical Reports

A large collection of links to online computer science technical reports and papers from academic and research centers all over the world. This is a great place to search when you are looking for works in a particular area or by a particular author.

**Web:**

http://www.cs.cmu.edu/afs/cs.cmu.edu/user/jblythe/Mosaic/cs-reports.html

**Computer Science Technical Reports**

Imagine how you would feel if you had worked hard on your dissertation for several years, only to discover that someone had already done the exact same thing at another university.

Or suppose you are embarking on a new area of research, and you want to find out everything that other people have already done.

Of course, you will do a thorough search of the literature. However, a great deal of computer science research is only documented in technical reports--published by a university or other organization--and not in regular journals.

No problem. You can use the Net to search through a vast number of technical reports. (And, just for fun, you might try searching for your own name.)

# COMPUTERS: MACINTOSH

## Buying and Selling Macs

Here is the Usenet swap meet for Macs. The **.wanted** newsgroup is the place to send a request for Macintosh-related hardware or software. The **.computers** groups are more for buying and selling systems and components.

**Usenet:**

biz.marketplace.computers.mac
comp.sys.mac.wanted
misc.forsale.computers.mac

## Cult of Macintosh

There are a great number of MacFanatics out there, and here is where they get together to share in the experience. Lots of well-organized links to lots of Mac-oriented fruits of the Internet loom. Do you love your Mac? Run, don't walk, to the Cult of Macintosh.

**Web:**

**http://www.sccs.swarthmore.edu/jahall/dox/Mac.html**

## Mac Hardware

All kinds of discussion about all kinds of Macintosh computers. Talk, talk, talk. Point the mouse and click. Talk, talk, talk. Point the mouse and click. Talk, talk, talk. Empty the trash can. Talk, talk, talk, etc.

**Usenet:**

**comp.sys.mac.hardware**
**comp.sys.mac.hardware.misc**
**comp.sys.mac.hardware.storage**
**comp.sys.mac.hardware.video**
**comp.sys.mac.portables**

## Mac Magazines

Keep up to date on what is happening in the Mac world. Here are some online sites for magazines in which you can find news about hardware and software, reviews, articles as well as links to other online resources. As long as you are on the Net, you need never be out of the Macintosh loop.

**Web:**

**http://www.macfaq.com/periodicals.html**
**http://www.macweek.com/**
**http://www.zdnet.com/macuser/**

**Express yourself.**
**Make a web page.**

## Mac Mailing Lists

One way to keep up on the Macintosh world is to subscribe to one or more mailing lists. Here is a list from which you can choose the mailing lists that are just right for you. Moreover, they make great presents. For example, for a wedding present, I registered my brother and his wife for a subscription to the **PowerPC_News** mailing list. True, they don't have a computer, and they have no idea what a Power PC is, but it is awfully hard to know what to get newlyweds. A nice mailing list is always in good taste.

**Web:**

**http://www.macfaq.com/faq/mailinglists.html**

## Mac Uses

Someday, you may find yourself in a bizarre situation in which you need to know how Macintoshes are used in sports, science, law, Hollywood, government, business and the arts. A normal person might be stumped, but you are not a normal person, you are one of my readers. No problem. Check out this web site and, in minutes, you can find out how and why people are using Macs around the world.

**Web:**

**http://www.halcyon.com/kegill/mac/**

## MacinTalk

Discuss any and all aspects of the Macintosh world with other Mac users and fanatics. Of all the things you can talk about on IRC, isn't it nice to find *something* your parents would approve of?

**IRC:**

**#macintosh**

## Macintosh Announcements

This moderated newsgroup contains announcements related to the Macintosh and to Apple: hardware and software, problems and solutions.

**Usenet:**

**comp.sys.mac.announce**

A B C D E F G H I J K L M N O P Q R S T U V W X Y Z

## Macintosh Index

A wealth of information on Mac-related news, archives, web sites, mailing lists, online publications, FAQs, and user groups.

**Web:**

**http://www.astro.nwu.edu/lentz/mac**
**http://www.cucug.org/mac**
**http://www.freepress.com/umac**
**http://www2.apple.com/Documents/resources.html**

## Macintosh Programming

Do you aspire to be a Macintosh programmer? And not just an ordinary Mac programmer but a *great* Mac programmer? Start here, and check out a FAQ, programming notes, technical notes, tips, tricks, and links to all kinds of Mac programming resources. After all, you don't want to be one of those people who go to a formal Macintosh dinner at the White House and use the data fork instead of the resource fork.

**Web:**

**http://devworld.apple.com/dev/geeks.html**

**IRC:**

**#macdev**

## Macintosh Talk and General Discussion

Discussion and commentary on every topic under the Macintosh sun. The **.advocacy** newsgroup is for debate and opinion. The **.digest** is a moderated magazine that contains articles of interest to Mac people. The **.misc** group is a forum for general discussion.

**Usenet:**

**comp.sys.mac**
**comp.sys.mac.advocacy**
**comp.sys.mac.digest**
**comp.sys.mac.misc**

**Stay away from "X-Rated".**

## Macintosh Tips and First Aid

When you are sick and tired of your Macintosh being sick and tired, have a look at the hotspot for Mac first aid. Get hints, tips and advice for dealing with your Mac on a day-to-day basis. You can even take a quick tour of the Mac via this site. No mouth-to-mouth contact is involved and, in fact, this sort of behavior is discouraged due to various health risks such as electrocution.

**Web:**

**http://hypatia.dartmouth.edu/~tcurtin/mac/mac.html**

## Macintosh Updates

If you are a Mac user, this is definitely a place you need to remember: a collection of fixes, updates and information relating to the Mac operating system, peripheral devices, and all types of Macintosh software. Next time tech support puts you on hold forever, check here to see if there is a fix you can download.

**Web:**

**http://www.gopvi.com/HTMLpages/incom.html**

## MacintoshOS.com

When the original Macintosh was introduced in 1984, it cost $2,500. Today it is worth about $15. This is just one of the interesting factoids I found in the Macintosh Museum, a compendium of information about every Macintosh model, including some models that are still under development. Aside from the museum, this well-organized web site serves as a general launching place for things Mac. You can look for free software, get help troubleshooting your problems, join a discussion group or talk to someone in a live chat area. By the way, in 1984, if you had spent that $2,500 on Apple stock instead of a computer, you would have seen it increase to a high of $3,147,743.75 in the glory days of the Mac. Today, that same stock would be worth about $15.

**Web:**

**http://www.macintoshos.com/**

## MkLinux

Linux is *the* cool Unix for the mid-1990s. And just because you have a Mac doesn't mean you can't be as cool as all the other Unix people on your block. Use this web site to find all types of Linux-for-the-Mac (MkLinux) information: the MkLinux package, a FAQ (frequently asked question list), updates and patches, as well as links to other MkLinux-related resources on the Net.

**Web:**

**http://www.mklinux.apple.com/**

Are you a Mac person?
Would you like to run Unix on your machine? Do you have lots and lots of time?
**Try MkLinux.**

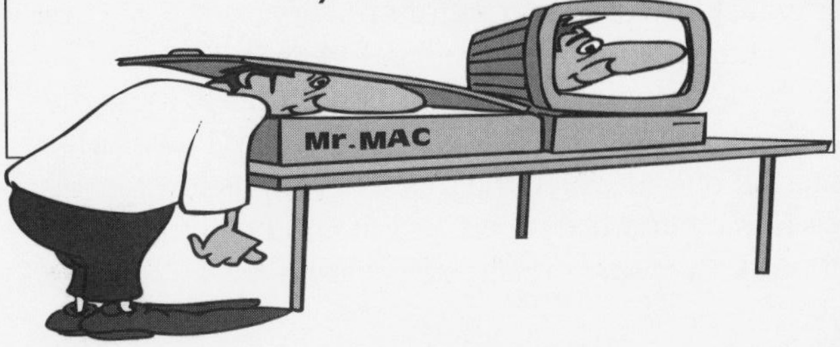
Mr.MAC

## *Look What I Found on the Net...*

```
Newsgroup: comp.sys.mac.advocacy
Subject: Mac Users are Dumb

>> I've had a Mac for years, but I recently bought a PC to see
>> what the Windoze users were talking about.
>>
>> My opinion:
>>
>> YOU HAVE GOT TO BE OUT OF YOUR MIND TO RUN WINDOWS 95
>> BY CHOICE.
>>
>> What a terrible piece of crap it is.  How could you possibly
>> even think that it's a poor cousin to the Mac?
>> Get a life, you idiots. Throw those Windoze machines back
>> into the typing pool for the secretaries to use, and get
>> yourself a Mac for real use.

> Your kind of snobbery is an ugly blotch on the face of
> humanity.
>
> I own a PC and an Apple PowerMac and they both do their jobs
> well.  Each has been customised with the best possible
> software to meet the job requirements.  I even make a living
> with these machines.
>
> This dumb Mac/PC argument -- usually associated with some
> immature insecurity -- has been going on for years now,
> and is developing into an art of mindless prejudice.
>
> Try to enjoy what toys you have.

AMEN...  To each his own, if you like it GREAT!
If you don't, get the other kind and get on with your life.
```

## PowerPC Macs

Power Macs are based on the family of PowerPC processors. (The older Macs use Motorola 680x0 processors.) Personally, I was pleasantly surprised how fast Power Macs caught on when they were first introduced. For information galore on these computers, there are several good places to look: the web site contains links to many different Power Mac sites all over the Net; the Usenet group is for discussion and questions; and, if you need to talk about Power Macs right now, there is IRC.

**Web:**

**http://www.go-nexus-go.com/macresources/links/power.html**

**Usenet:**

**comp.sys.powerpc**

**IRC:**

**#powermac**

## Science and Technology

Discussions about using the Macintosh for science and technological work. Just the place, for example, to ask if anyone knows of a catalog for organic chemical substances to use with a Mac.

**Usenet:**

**comp.sys.mac.scitech**

## Source Code for Macintosh

Share your Macintosh source code with the rest of the world by posting it to this Usenet group. **alt.sources.mac** and **comp.sources.mac** are only for source code, so if you want to discuss code that is posted at the newsgroup, use **alt.sources.mac.d**. If you want to make a request for source code, you should post on **alt.sources.wanted**.

**Usenet:**

**alt.sources.mac**
**alt.sources.mac.d**
**alt.sources.wanted**
**comp.sources.mac**

## Tidbits

Tidbits is a weekly electronic publication that discusses products and events in the Macintosh part of the world. Tidbits is both practical and news oriented. I suggest you read it regularly for two reasons: (1) to keep up on what is happening, and (2) for useful tips and techniques.

**Web:**

**http://www.tidbits.com/**

**Listserv Mailing List:**

List Name: **tidbits**
Subscribe to: **listserv@ricevm1.rice.edu**

Need to keep up with the MacJoneses?
Read Tidbits

## Virtual Macintosh

This site has web pages that look like the screen of a Mac. What you see looks like a Mac, but it really isn't. However, it is free, so you might as well try it, say "Wow, that's cool," and then go back to whatever you were doing. (And to tell you the truth, using the Web to simulate the Mac interface has philosophical implications that are so scary, I don't even want to think about them.)

**Web:**

**http://www.knowledgequest.com/poweron/**

## COMPUTERS: PCs

### Build Your Own PC

Do not, I repeat, do *not* put together your own PC in order to save money. You will just end up driving yourself (and your family) crazy. The only reason to put together your own PC is for the fun in doing so. So, by all means, build your own PC and enjoy yourself. Hint: Make sure you are not in a hurry.

**Web:**

**http://www.verinet.com/pc/**

### Chip List

There are lots and lots of different chips used in PCs. If you care about chips and components, take some time to explore the Chip List. You will find basic information about a great many chips as well as a lot of interesting historical information. For ongoing discussion, you can participate in the Usenet group.

**Web:**

**http://einstein.et.tudelft.nl/~offerman/chiplist.html**

**Usenet:**

**comp.sys.ibm.pc.hardware.chips**

### Free-DOS Project

Free-DOS is a project devoted to developing an entire DOS-compatible operating system, written by volunteers and shared for free (including source code). In other words, Free-DOS is to DOS as Linux is to Unix. If you would like to try the current version of Free-DOS or, better yet, volunteer to work on it, start by visiting the Free-DOS Internet site.

**Web:**

**http://sunsite.unc.edu/pub/micro/pc-stuff/freedos/freedos.html**

### Glossary of PC Terminology

There are so many technical terms that it is impossible to know them all. I wanted to find you a good PC glossary so I looked all around the Net, and this is the one I found. The definitions are exact and well-written, and the coverage is comprehensive. Whoever is responsible for it did a good job. Put this link on your bookmark list. It will come in handy the next time you encounter a PC word you don't understand.

**Web:**

**http://www.gw2k.com/support/custserv/glossary/a.htm**

THE PC GLOSSARY
BEFORE YOUR NEXT BIG SOCIAL OCCASION, SPEND A FEW MINUTES WITH THE ONLINE GLOSSARY OF PC TERMINOLOGY.
AFTER ALL, WHEN IT COMES TO PCs, THE MORE BUZZWORDS YOU KNOW, THE MORE PEOPLE WILL TREAT YOU AS IF YOU KNOW WHAT YOU ARE DOING.
(IT'S ALWAYS WORKED FOR ME...)

### PC Clones

If you are in the market for a PC clone or if you already have one and want some peer support, look to **pc-clone** groups for information. Here you will read smart shopping tips, technical questions and answers, horror stories, and praise for various brands of clones.

**Usenet:**

**alt.sys.pc-clone.dell**
**alt.sys.pc-clone.gateway2000**
**alt.sys.pc-clone.zeos**

## PC Computer Prices

If you are interested in getting the best price, you need a good way to compare. Use this web site to help you find pricing information about a large number of PCs, as well as parts and components. These days, even the best is inexpensive. Considering what you are getting, being able to buy any PC at all is the bargain of the century. Don't be too cheap. The only way anyone can offer you a computer that is well below the regular price is by selling you last year's technology. If you try to save money, you will only end up with an inferior machine and, believe me, your programs will know the difference.

**Web:**

**http://www.uvision.com/idx/COMPUTER_SYSTEMS/**

## PC CPUs

On old mainframe computers, the CPU was the "central processing unit": the part of the computer that did the computation and processing. Today, the function of what used to require a large chunk of computer doodads has been replaced by a single chip, called the processor. So when you hear the term CPU used with respect to a PC, it refers to the single main processor chip (such as an Intel Pentium). If you are into PC CPUs, you will love this page. Immerse yourself in an ocean of information and commentary about every known PC processor chip and all the variations.

**Web:**

**http://www.u-net.com/~sysdoc/cpu.htm**

## PC Hardware Discussion

Here is the place to bring all your general questions and answers about PC hardware. If you are a serious PC person, drop in once in a while and see what is happening. Things are always changing, and checking out the general PC discussion is a good way to keep up on new trends.

**Usenet:**

**comp.sys.ibm.pc.hardware**

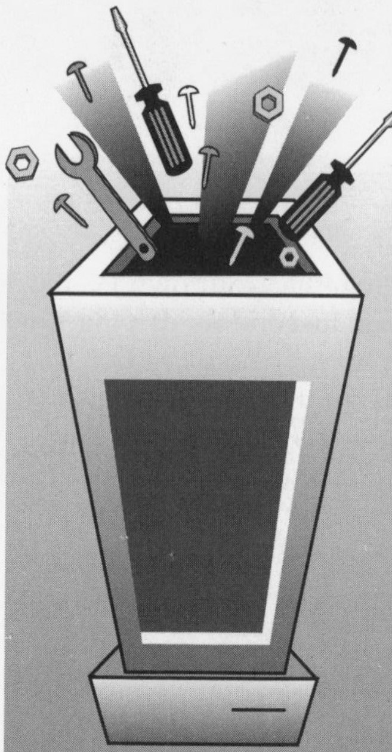

## PC Hardware

Ah, those halcyon days of my youth when—screwdriver and chip puller in hand—I spent so many wonderful hours working on the innards of my PC. What could be more fun on a summer's afternoon than discussing PC hardware when everybody else is wasting their time at the beach?

(Tip for the guys: women really go for men who know their hardware.)

## PC Hardware Introduction

There is a lot to know about PCs and even the basics can be confusing. Take a look at this series of articles about PC hardware, and you will soon be feeling a lot more comfortable when the conversation turns to computers. Spend a little more time, and you will be able to go to parties and hold people spellbound with your exquisite grasp of PC esoterica.

**Web:**

**http://pclt.cis.yale.edu/pclt/pchw/platypus.htm**

## PC Links

This page features extensive information about PCs. This is a good place to find PC-related information when you have a vague idea what you want, but you don't know where to look.

**Web:**

**http://www.mtp.semi.harris.com/pc_info.html**

**Feel lucky? Try "Contests".**

## PC Magazines

Keeping up on what is happening in the PC world is impossible. However, if you want to pretend to keep up, the easiest way is by reading PC magazines. To help you, here are some places on the Net where you can read articles from PC magazines without leaving the comfort of your web browser. Check back every now and then; there is always something new.

**Web:**

**http://www.pcmag.com/**
**http://www.pcweek.com/**
**http://www.web-newsstand.com/magpc.htm**

## PC News

Don't get left behind, even for a moment. Check in with the Net every day and see what's new in the world of PCs. Here is a great place to read the factoids behind the rumors and hype that pass for news in the PC industry. If you like keeping up with the PC flow, this site will help you stay one giant step ahead of the guy or gal in the next cubicle.

**Web:**

**http://home.zdnet.com/home/filters/news.html**

## PC Talk and General Discussion

General discussion about PCs and related hardware and software topics. The **.misc** group is an open forum. The **.digest** group is a moderated collection of postings. These two discussion groups are good places to hang out if you want to become ever so knowledgeable about the care and feeding of PCs.

**Usenet:**

**comp.sys.ibm.pc.digest**
**comp.sys.ibm.pc.misc**

**Upgrade Now**

I can tell you—without even knowing what computer you use—you need an upgrade, and you need it now.

So don't even waste a moment. Check out the PC Upgrades, and then rush out and buy a new PC.

And tomorrow, you can do the whole thing all over again.

## PC Upgrades

The reason you need new computers so often is to run new software (operating systems and programs). My advice is to count on a brand new, top of the line PC being a good tool for about two years. However, when you know your PC just can't cut the megahertz mustard any longer, should you buy a brand new machine or should you upgrade your current model? A lot of knowing what to do is having (1) knowledge of what is available and what you need, and (2) the judgment to make a wise decision. If you lean toward upgrading, here is information that can help you figure out what to do. Hint: Unless you are a technically knowledgeable computer nerd, don't upgrade—go for the new box.

**Web:**

**http://www.computernerd.com/nerdtips.htm**

## PowerPC Processors

The PowerPC is a family of processors created by a partnership between Motorola and IBM. The PowerPC design was based on the Power architecture developed for IBM's RS/6000 computers. Today, PowerPC chips are used in computers made by IBM, Apple and other companies. For official information, technical and otherwise, see the Motorola and IBM PowerPC web sites. For ongoing discussion, you can participate in the Usenet group. (By the way, the name "Power" stands for Performance Optimized With Enhanced RISC. "RISC" is an acronym for Reduced Instruction-Set Computer, a type of processor design.)

**Web:**

**http://www.chips.ibm.com/products/ppc/**
**http://www.mot.com/SPS/PowerPC/**

**Usenet:**

**comp.sys.powerpc**

**Listserv Mailing List:**

List Name: **power-pc**
Subscribe to: **listserv@uga.cc.uga.edu**

A B C D E F G H I J K L M N O P Q R S T U V W X Y Z

# COMPUTERS: SECURITY

## Anonymous Ftp Security

The Net is based on anonymous ftp: a system in which anyone on the Net can connect to another computer and download files that are stored in a public directory. When you connect to such a system, you log in using the name "anonymous", and you transfer the file using ftp (file transfer protocol), hence the name anonymous ftp. On the Web, whenever you download files to be saved to your disk (such as free software), you are using anonymous ftp. (Your browser automatically makes the connection for you.) There are a number of security problems associated with running an anonymous ftp service that can leave your system vulnerable to hackers. For information about these problems and how to avoid them, take a look at this anonymous ftp security FAQ.

**Web:**
**http://www.iss.net/sec_info/anonftp.html**

## Computer Emergency Response Team

You are running a double-top-secret computer system, a system whose very existence is crucial to the fate of the free world, when you get attacked by a hacker who just won't quit. Who ya gonna call? The Computer Emergency Response Team. CERT is often the only group standing between us and total Net-based anarchy. Would you like to see some of CERT's publications? Here they are, and I advise you to take a look before it is too late. In today's world, the Net *is* the free world.

**Web:**
**http://www.cert.org/**

## Computer Security FAQs

Maintaining effective computer security requires you to be knowledgeable and skillful in many different areas. Here is a collection of FAQs (frequently asked question lists) dealing with a number of important security issues. I suggest that you take some time and look at this list, reading every FAQ that is related to your responsibilities.

**Web:**
**http://www.iss.net/sec_info/faq.html**

## Computer Security Patches

A patch is a modification to a program, usually to fix a bug. There are many known security problems with all of the popular operating systems, and most of these problems have patches that you can download and apply to your system. If you are responsible for security on a multiuser system, you should spend a few moments looking at this well-organized list of patches, to see if any of them pertain to your system.

**Web:**
**http://www.iss.net/sec_info/**

**COMPUTER SECURITY PATCHES**

**Right now, someone may be trying to break into a computer for which *you* are responsible. Before they do, check out the latest security patches, and make sure you are protected. When it comes to maintaining security, the job never ends. (So don't you dare go on vacation—ever.)**

## Computer Security Resource Clearinghouse

The Computer Security Resource Clearinghouse is an ongoing project of NIST (National Institute of Standards and Technology). The goal of this clearinghouse is to provide one central location you can check for (1) crisis response information, and (2) a collection of links to general computer security information. The next time you hear about a new, controversial something or other—such as a "key escrow proposal"—check here to find out the official government-sponsored position.

**Web:**
**http://csrc.ncsl.nist.gov/**

## Computer Security Talk and General Discussion

If you are responsible for computer security, this is the Usenet gathering place for general discussion. Stay abreast of the latest trends and happenings, and read the questions and answers that people are talking about today.

**Usenet:**

**comp.security.misc**

## Computer Security Terminology

The world of computer security has many, many technical terms, some of which are obscure, and it is not uncommon to encounter a term you don't understand. The next time this happens, check this large online glossary of computer security terms. Chances are you will find a definition that will have you up and back in operation before you can say "time-dependent password".

**Web:**

**http://www.isse.gmu.edu/~csis/glossary/merged_glossary.html**

## Computer Viruses

Are viruses really that big a deal? Well, according to a document at this web site, "The National Center for Computer Crime Data in Los Angeles estimates that American businesses lose as much as $550 million from unauthorized access to computers yearly." In other words, every year, computer viruses cost us enough money to pay the Los Angeles Police Department's lawsuit bill and still have enough left over to try O.J. Simpson again. Need even more information on computer viruses? It's waiting for you on the Net.

**Web:**

**http://www.symantec.com/avcenter/**

**Usenet:**

**comp.virus**

## Firewalls

What's a firewall and why do you need one? This FAQ answers those questions as well as others about what firewalls do and don't protect against, commercial products and consultants, basic design and types of firewalls.

**Web:**

**http://www.cis.ohio-state.edu/hypertext/faq/usenet/firewalls-faq/faq.html**
**http://www.willamette.edu/~dlabar/firewall.html**

**Usenet:**

**comp.security.firewalls**

## Hacker Sites on the Net

Want to explore all the nooks and crannies in which hackers hang out? Here is your entree to some of the Internet sites frequented by hackers. But be careful--these are the people your mother warned you about.

**Web:**

**http://arirang.miso.co.kr/~xter/hack/hack-basics/**
**http://www.underground.org/web/hackers.html**

**IRC:**

**#hack**

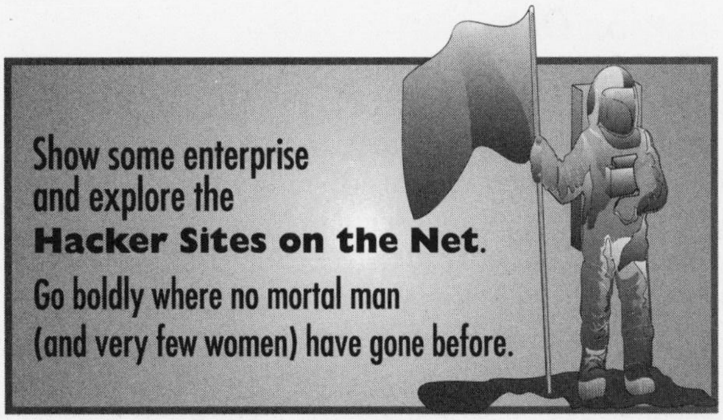
Show some enterprise
and explore the
Hacker Sites on the Net.
Go boldly where no mortal man
(and very few women) have gone before.

## Incident Response Teams

In case of a security emergency, follow the directions in the manual. No manual? Don't panic. Look here for the names and phone numbers of various incident response teams. You can trust them. They are the good guys.

**Web:**

**http://underground.org/teams/**

Incident
Response Team
An old woman calls the **Incident Response Team** and says, "A young man tried to violate me."
The expert listens to her and then asks, "Ma'am, when did this happen?"
She answers, "Forty-five years ago."
So the expert says, "And why do you want to report it now?"
The old woman replies, "I don't want to report it, I just want to talk about it."

## Intrusion Detection

If you are interested in detecting and preventing computer break-ins, you may want to find out about intrusion detection systems (IDS). An IDS is a system in which audit trails of user activity are maintained and analyzed in order to detect patterns that suggest internal or external threats. For example, a neural network program might analyze the audit trail for a particular computer and conclude that a particular user looks like he is up to no good. For more information subscribe to the **ids** mailing list. For research purposes, you can use the web page to search the archives of the list.

**Web:**

**http://web.eecs.nwu.edu/~jmyers/ids/**

**Majordomo Mailing List:**

List Name: **ids**
Subscribe to: **majordomo@uow.edu.au**

## Java Security

Java is a computer language used to write programs that are stored on a Web server, so they can be downloaded and executed on a remote computer. Each time you use the Web to access a Java program, the program is automatically downloaded and run on *your* computer. As you can imagine, experts who work with Java are extremely concerned about the possible security problems. After all, people all over the Net are using browsers that automatically download and run Java programs. In principle, Java has a lot to offer but, in practice, it can only work well when there are no external security threats. For example, how would you feel if you saw a web page that said "Click here to see something" and, when you clicked, your browser downloaded and ran a program (on your computer) that deleted all the files on your hard disk? Here are some sites that contain important Java security information. For ongoing discussion, you can participate in the Java discussion group on Usenet.

**Web:**

**http://ferret.lmh.ox.ac.uk/~david/java/bugs/**
**http://java.sun.com/java.sun.com/sfaq/**
**http://www.cs.princeton.edu/sip/pub/secure96.html**

**Usenet:**

**comp.lang.java**

## National Computer Security Association

If you are interested in Internet security, visit the site of the National Computer Security Association (NCSA). You will find information relating to NCSA activities, including conferences, training, product certification, security alerts, and consortia. You will also find links to a large variety of Internet security-related sites around the Net.

**Web:**

**http://www.ncsa.com/**

**Intrigue, Privacy, Secret Stuff...**

## Network and Computer Security Reference Index

This web page is a veritable "everything you ever wanted to know about computer security" resource. Links here point to FAQs, documents about firewalls, security, vendors, Pretty Good Privacy (PGP), Riordan's Internet Privacy Enhanced Mail, other web information sources, Usenet newsgroups, archives and mailing lists.

**Web:**

**http://www.telstra.com.au/info/security.html**

## Security Resources

This site has resources covering topics such as cryptography news bulletins, Clipper information, the Electronic Frontier Foundation's legislative advocacy, anonymous credit card protocol, and much more.

**Web:**

**http://www.cs.cmu.edu/afs/cs.cmu.edu/user/bsy/www/sec.html**

## Security Vulnerabilities

There are a significant number of security holes in well-known system programs such as fingerd, login, ftp, sendmail, firewalls, web servers, and so on. Here is a collection of such vulnerabilities along with advice on how to plug the holes.

**Web:**

**http://www.iss.net/vd/vd.html**

## Sniffers

Within most networks, before a chunk of information is sent from one computer to another, the information is repackaged into a series of small bundles called packets. Each packet is marked with the address of the destination computer and then sent out over the network. The packets travel separately to the destination computer, where they are reassembled into the original chunk of information. This all happens so quickly that, to us, it looks as if the information is being sent directly from one computer to another. On some local area networks (such as ethernets) every computer sees all the packets that are transmitted over the network. Each computer is configured to only look at those packets that are addressed to that particular computer. However, it is possible to configure some computers so they will look at all the packets that pass over the network. You can use that computer to run a program called a "sniffer" to trap and analyze all the data traffic on the network. Sniffers are used by knowledgeable network administrators when they need to solve certain data transmission problems. However, sniffers can also be used by sophisticated hackers to tap into networks and watch data as it is being transmitted (for example, your user name and password when you log in to a remote system). To learn more about sniffers—how they work and how to prevent sniffer attacks—take a look at this sniffer FAQ.

**Web:**

**http://www.iss.net/sec_info/sniff.html**

## Unix Security

This web page lists programs you can use to improve the security of computers running Unix. Some of these programs also run on other operating systems. The list includes COPS, Crack, Npasswd, Passwd+, PGP, Socks, Tripwire, and others.

**Web:**

**http://www.alw.nih.gov/Security/security.html**

### *Look What I Found on the Net...*

```
Is Your System Vulnerable?
All major operating systems have well-known security problems.
The hackers already know the loopholes. It's up to you to close them.
```

## Unix Security Holes

The **bugtraq** mailing list is for the discussion of security holes in Unix systems. The emphasis is on recognizing and defining such problems and discussion on how to prevent them. If you administer a Unix system, this is a good list to follow just to keep up on what is happening in your not-secure-enough part of the world. The web site contains a searchable archive of the list.

**Web:**

**http://www.eecs.nwu.edu/~jmyers/bugtraq/**

**Listserv Mailing List:**

List Name: **bugtraq**
Subscribe to: **listserv@crimelab.com**

## Unix System Monitoring Tools

Much of the Net is supported by Unix machines, so Unix security problems are especially important. Here is a free collection of Unix tools you can download to monitor the security of your Unix system. So you think your system is safe? Test it and be sure.

**Web:**

**http://ciac.llnl.gov/ciac/ToolsUnixSysMon.html**

## Web Server Security

As soon as you put your web server on the Net, you open your computer to the world. Of course, your server software is supposed to restrict what people can access and protect you from prying eyes. However, that assumes that you (1) configure the server properly, and (2) plug all the security holes. Here is a FAQ (frequently asked question list) devoted to web server security issues. I suggest you at least browse this FAQ to see if there is anything important that applies to your installation.

**Web:**

**http://www.genome.wi.mit.edu/WWW/faqs/www-security-faq.html**

# COMPUTERS: TECHNOLOGY

## Artificial Intelligence Repository

When you have a little spare time, take a look at all the cool artificial intelligence information you can find on the Net: AI programming languages, software packages, compression and archiving utilities, a calendar of events, technical reports, mail and news archives, books, and related publications.

**Web:**

**http://www.cs.cmu.edu/Web/Groups/AI/html/air.html**

## Artificial Life

Getting tired of real life? Try a little artificial life. It's low in calories, high in fiber, and while it might run up your electricity bill, it will certainly keep you from being lonely. MIT Press makes available this collection of resources relating to artificial life.

**Web:**

**http://alife.santafe.edu/**

## Asynchronous Transfer Mode

Asynchronous Transfer Mode (ATM) is a networking technology standard for high-speed, high-capacity data transmission. Lots of people talk about ATM as if it will be the salvation of the future; that is, lots and lots of bandwidth for you and me and the next guy. The holy grail of ATM is to create a one-size-fits-all international network of networks over which we will send voice (telephone), video (multimedia), and all types of data (Internet). Many companies have signed up to ride on the ATM, but it's hard to understand all the fuss unless you know generally how the whole thing works. To help you, here is a tutorial provided by the ATM Forum introducing the basic concepts of ATM. (By the way, you will notice that the information is arranged in "charts". Be careful, this is a tip-off that we are talking *big* business here.)

**Web:**

**http://www.atmforum.com/atmforum/atm_basics/notes1.html**

*Of all the different types of intelligence, artificial is one of my favorites. When you have some time to explore the new world of Man's making, take a look at the* ***AI (Artificial Intelligence) Repository****. After all, why should you have to settle for the real thing?*

## Chinese Computing and Word Processing

A mailing list discussion group on technology relating to the use of Chinese text on computers. A forum for both experts and regular users that reaches from North America to the Far East.

**Listserv Mailing List:**

List Name: **ccnet-l**
Subscribe to: **listserv@uga.cc.uga.edu**

## Client/Server Talk and General Discussion

"Client/server" refers to a technology in which a program called a client requests a service of some type from another program called a server. The Internet is a huge client/server system. Client programs that you run on your own computer (such as your web browser) can request information from computers all over the world. If you would like to talk about the technical details of such systems, join the discussion on the Usenet client/server discussion group.

**Usenet:**

**comp.client-server**

## Computer Science Conferences

Lots of links to conferences, meetings and general let's-all-get-together-and-chew-the-computational-fat gatherings. Perhaps one of these conclaves is just the place to present your paper on how to build a network-ready PC out of a used VCR and a couple of lengths of shrink tubing.

**Web:**

**http://www.netlib.org/confdb/Conferences.html**

## Computer Speech

Computer speech has been hyped for years and, every year, we hear the same thing: "This is the year." Well, when I hear it from a computer, I will believe it. In the meantine, you can get a grasp of the fundamentals by reading the FAQ (frequently asked question list). Where else are you going to go when you need a fast Fourier transform program right away and the neighborhood convenience store is closed?

**Web:**

**http://svr-www.eng.cam.ac.uk/comp.speech/**
**http://www.speech.cs.cmu.edu/comp.speech/**

## Computer Standards

Let's face it: generally speaking, things *do* work. And the reason they work is because, behind the scenes, a lot of faceless droids spend their lives creating standards. If you would like to check out the actual technical specs, take a look at this web site. As strange as it seems, I bet you will find something fascinating. After all, you *are* the type of person who reads the "Computers: Technology" section of a reference book. (But don't feel bad: I actually write this stuff for a living.)

**Web:**

**http://www.ips.id.ethz.ch/~parish/standard.html**

## Computer Technology in Developing Countries

One of the best ways for a developing country to grow economically is to install and utilize modern computer technology and to connect to the Net. Here is the Usenet group that is devoted to the issues surrounding bringing modern computing technology to the outskirts of our global village.

**Usenet:**

**comp.society.development**

**Read the FAQs of life.**

## Computer Standards

The computer world–especially the Internet–is held together by standards: standards that define how hardware should be designed, and how databases, communications, graphics and file transfer should be implemented. There are also very important standards describing how the Web should operate. In fact, one of the most interesting aspects of the Internet is that so many people are voluntarily following the rules. What most people don't realize is that standards are not just useful. They can also be a lot of fun. For example, the next time you have nothing to do, why not take a few moments and memorize the ISO 639 Language codes? It won't be long before you will be the most popular person in your entire social circle (including Friend A, Friend B, Friends C-1 through C7.2, and the optional Acquaintances WG-F 13.1 and WG-F

## Database Technology

Database theory is a highly developed area of computer science that has managed to insinuate itself into our everyday lives in ways that are staggering to contemplate. And database technology is not at all stagnant: it moves relentlessly onward in an unending quest for managing and retrieving ever-larger amounts of information, more and more quickly, over longer and longer distances. To keep up with the movable data feast, follow the discussion on Usenet.

**Usenet:**

**comp.databases.theory**

**Listserv Mailing List:**

List Name: **dbtg**
Subscribe to: **listserv@list.nih.gov**

**When it's your turn to fix dinner, read "Cooking and Recipes".**

## *Look What I Found on the Net...*

```
Newsgroup: comp.home.automation
Subject: Room Occupation

>> I recently installed a system that would turn the lights on
>> in a room when someone enters, and turn the lights off when
>> someone exits.  But if two people enter the room, the system
>> will wait for the second person to exit before turning off
>> the lights.

>> ... With a series of pressure mats in the floor, the logic
>> was fairly simple.  If a person stepped on the mat the lights
>> went on.  If the another person stepped on the mat while the
>> light was already on, it would set a "phantom load" on.
>> The light would then stay on until the both people left.

> What if the same original person stepped on the mat to leave
> the room?

...and what would happen if three people came in?
```

## Frame-Relay Technology

Frame relay is a system in which data is multiplexed over a high speed network (compare to packet switching which is not multiplexed). I have a frame relay connection to the Internet in my house that gives me a high-speed line using HDLC (High Level Data Link Control). For discussion of frame relay topics, here is the appropriate Usenet group. If you need help with any of the terminology, check the web site where you will find a glossary.

**Web:**

**http://new.frforum.com/4000/4003.html**

**Usenet:**

**comp.dcom.frame-relay**

## Future Computing Technology

What will the future bring to computing? No one knows for sure, but I can tell you with certainty that whatever happens will be completely unexpected. The only prediction you can make is that you can't make predictions. (Just think about what has happened in the last five years.) Still, speculation is interesting (and free). If you like thinking one step ahead of most people, you may enjoy the discussion on Usenet relating to new inventions and developments and how they affect the future of computing technology.

**Usenet:**

**comp.society.futures**

## Home Computers and Technology

If Mr. Bill has his way, the day will come when just about everything in our home that depends on electricity will have a computer running some form of Windows. (I am *not* kidding.) However, if the history of technology has shown us anything, it is that just about any prediction of any importance is always wrong, so we can breathe easy. Still, it is hard to imagine that computers won't invade our houses more than they already have. I can't tell you what the home of the future will be like, but I can show you where on Usenet people are speculating, planning, inventing and dreaming, all the while creating homemade miracles out of readily available technology.

**Usenet:**

**comp.home.automation**
**comp.home.misc**

## Intranets

An intranet is a computer system that uses Internet technology (especially web technology) to provide a private information resource to a select audience. Usually, that audience consists of users inside a company or organization, but it can also involve external people (such as customers). There is a lot of know about intranets, and this web site is a great place to start. Here you will find information, FAQs (frequently asked question lists), tutorials, design tools, news, as well as a collection of links to other intranet-related resources.

**Web:**

**http://www.brill.com/intranet/**

## Technology and Society

Computer technology has affected society more than any of us can understand, and in ways no one would have predicted just a generation ago. The ability to process information accurately at blinding speed has transformed how we think about ourselves and about the rest of the world. Indeed, we are so dependent upon computers (and the Net) that life without them would be unthinkable. For an ongoing discussion regarding such matters, check out the Usenet computers-and-society group. I remember when I was a grad student at U.C. San Diego in the mid-1970s, one of my teachers started a course in Computers and Society. At the time, no one understood what he was talking about. Now, the whole idea of such a course is trite and anachronistic.

**Usenet:**

**comp.society**

## Technology News Mailing Lists

Don't you dare get left behind. Computer technology moves so fast you simply must keep up if you are going to maintain your usefulness to your employer and to society. Here is the easy way to create an aura of technical up-to-the-minute know-how. Simply subscribe to one or both of these mailing lists. Then, when messages start to arrive, forward them to various people at work with the notation "FYI". Soon, everyone else will realize that you are up to date and *they* are inferior.

**Listserv Mailing List:**

List Name: **comptech-news**
Subscribe to: **listserv@listserv.pnl.gov**

**Majordomo Mailing List:**

List Name: **geek-news**
Subscribe to: **majordomo@lucifer.com**

A B C D E F G H I J K L M N O P Q R S T U V W X Y Z

## Upcoming Events in the Computer Industry

A web page that points to numerous tidbits of information about upcoming events, seminars, expos, workshops, conferences and meetings in the computer and software industries.

**Web:**
**http://www.techcalendar.com/**

## Video Conferencing

Video conferencing refers to conducting a real time voice+video conversation between two or more people. Some people say that, in the future, it will be common to meet with other people via video conferencing. Isaac Asimov wrote a book about a planet in which the people would meet one another *only* by three-dimensional video conferencing and not in person. Personally, I think that people want the visual anonymity of a voice-only connection and that video conferencing will never be as popular as the telephone. We will see. In the meantime, here is a Usenet group in which you can discuss the state of the video conferencing art, as well as a web site containing several useful resources, including a glossary.

**Web:**
**http://www.videoconference.com/**

**Usenet:**
**comp.dcom.videoconf**

## Virtual Reality

Before I commit myself to the concept of virtual reality, I need someone to answer some fundamental questions. Will there be commercials? Can I take my cat with me? Will I be able to get *real* food? In the meantime, I content myself with following what's new and almost real in the land of simulated make-believe. Try these web sites on for size and you too will be able to keep up on what may or may not really be happening inside and around the boundaries of perception.

**Web:**
**http://www.3dsite.com/cgi/virtual-reality-index.html**
**http://www.vr.org.au/**

Why mess with real reality...
...when you can have the virtual thing?


## Wearable Computers

Remember how you used to hear that, in the future, we would be using video phones and flying around in personal helicopters? Well, now there are some people saying that soon we will all be wearing computers. Wearing computers? Well, they would have to be small, and lightweight, and durable, and inexpensive, and reliable, and they would have to actually do something useful. Would you like to learn more? Here's the place to look.

**Web:**
**http://wearables.www.media.mit.edu/projects/wearables/**

## Wireless Technology

The world of wireless technology is vast. It encompasses mobile computing, telephony, wireless networks, satellites, radio and more. For ongoing discussion, you can follow the Usenet discussion group. For a collection of Internet resources pertaining to wireless technologies, see the web pages.

**Web:**
**http://snapple.cs.washington.edu:600/mobile/**
**http://www.cyberramp.net/~wireless/**

**Usenet:**
**comp.std.wireless**

**My other joke is funny.**

# CONSUMER INFORMATION

## Automobile Lemons

A "lemon law" obligates a car manufacturer or a car seller to repair or replace a defective automobile or refund your money. If you suspect you have a "lemon", check out this web page to see how you can be recompensed. This site has information about consumer strategies and the applicable laws for lemons.

**Web:**

**http://www.mindspring.com/~wf1/**

## Better Business Bureau

The Better Business Bureau (BBB) promotes good business/consumer relations. At the BBB site, you can find local bureaus, read consumer warnings and related news, file a complaint online, read consumer buying guides, or obtain a report on a company or charity. Find out what the Better Business Bureau can do for you.

**Web:**

**http://www.bbb.org/**

## Blacklist of Internet Advertisers

Do you get mad when you get junk email? If so, you are not the only one. Check out this great blacklist of Internet advertisers. This site will give you information on what to do about spamming and unsolicited junk mail. This is an informative FAQ and should be read by anyone who is interested in consumer issues on the Net.

**Web:**

**http://math-www.uni-paderborn.de/~axel/BL/blacklist.html**

## Computer and Communication Companies

Hundreds of links to web pages of computer and communication companies around the globe, updated on a regular basis. Also includes links to other more generally related lists of commercial companies on the Internet.

**Web:**

**http://www-atp.llnl.gov/atp/companies.html**

## Consumer Fraud

You know you have to be careful when someone is trying to offer you a deal that sounds too good to be true. Chances are, it probably *is* too good to be true. The U.S. Postal Service has a fantastic selection of information on consumer fraud that everyone should read. Some of the schemes they cover are chain letters, free prizes and vacations, 900-numbers, foreign lotteries, personal finance-related schemes, multilevel marketing, work-at-home schemes, telephone solicitations and many more. This is an excellent site for consumer information.

**Web:**

**http://www.usps.gov/websites/depart/inspect/consmenu.htm**

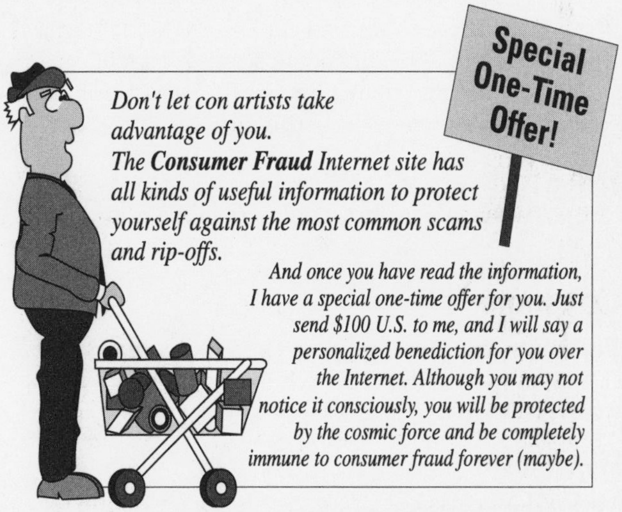
Special One-Time Offer!
Don't let con artists take advantage of you. The Consumer Fraud Internet site has all kinds of useful information to protect yourself against the most common scams and rip-offs.
And once you have read the information, I have a special one-time offer for you. Just send $100 U.S. to me, and I will say a personalized benediction for you over the Internet. Although you may not notice it consciously, you will be protected by the cosmic force and be completely immune to consumer fraud forever (maybe).

## Consumer Information Catalog

When it's late at night and you need a little something to read, check out the Consumer Information Center, which was established in 1970 to help federal agencies and departments develop, promote and distribute consumer information to the masses. Four times a year, the Consumer Information Catalog is published. This jewel has descriptive listings of hundreds of booklets from all sorts of federal agencies covering topics like buying a car, building a career, federal benefits and housing information. You can order a free copy of the Consumer Information Catalog by filling out this handy-dandy web form.

**Web:**

**http://www.pueblo.gsa.gov/**

## Consumer Law

Find out your rights as a consumer. This page offers information on various consumer pitfalls such as insurance fraud, product liability, toxic chemicals, bodily injury and more. You will also find links to consumer law resources and information on how to file consumer complaints.

**Web:**
**http://consumerlawpage.com/**

## Consumer Line

The Federal Trade Commission's Bureau of Consumer Protection has an online service called "Consumer Line". This service offers lots and lots and lots of online brochures relating to consumer protection. These brochures can inform you about art fraud, repossessions, financing scams, product purchases and much, much more. Increase your consumer savvy by visiting this site.

**Web:**
**http://www.ftc.gov/bcp/conline/conline.htm**

## Consumer News

Real news about real products bought by real consumers (you). Find out what is happening before the Joneses do.

**Web:**
**http://homearts.com/depts/fresh/00consf1.htm**
**http://www.bbb.org/council/alerts/index.html**

## Consumer Product Safety Commission

If you think you are safe because you stay home all the time and play on the Internet, think again. There are all sorts of dangers lurking around your house, just waiting to get you. That's why people in American have the Consumer Product Safety Commission (CPSC): an independent Federal regulatory agency whose mission is to keep the citizens safe from harmful products such as badly designed cribs, toyboxes or television remote controls. Here's the CPSC official site where you can find their latest news or report an unsafe product.

**Web:**
**http://www.cpsc.gov/**

## Can the Government Protect You?

Some people believe that the government should regulate many aspects of our lives to make them more safe, reliable and efficient.

Other people would have the government do as little as possible, letting individual people fend for themselves.

If you would like to see what the official U.S. government consumer agency is doing, take a look at the Consumer Product Safety Commission web site.

## Consumer Talk and General Discussion

Here is Usenet's general consumer forum. And, since we are all consumers, there is something for everyone. Send in your questions, share your answers, read the reviews, opinions, and general bad-mouthing of the bad guys. Before you spend your next dime, check with the world at large.

**Usenet:**
**misc.consumers**

## Consumer World

All dressed up and nowhere to go? Head to Consumer World where you can spend hours browsing around checking airfares, looking for ATM machines, filing consumer complaints, reading consumer booklets, applying for credit cards, researching a law and countless other things. Consumer World covers a variety of types of consumer needs whether it's business or just plain fun.

**Web:**
**http://www.consumerworld.org/**

## Coupons

Do you need some coupons to get a nice discount on your favorite tea biscuit? Or do you have twelve coupons for Mr. Sticky hair gel that you'll probably never use? On the Net, I've found some places where you can exchange coupons and rebates with other coupon clippers. Oil up your scissors and get to clipping.

**Web:**

**http://www.coupon.com/**

**Usenet:**

**alt.coupons**

## Credit Crossroads

This site can teach you all about credit and how it works. You can learn what is on a credit report, how to find a good credit card, information on good and bad credit card deals, how to fix your credit report, information on bankruptcy and what divorce can do to your credit rating.

**Web:**

**http://amdream.com/credit/cr_index.htm**

## Credit Information

We're in a fast-moving world, and it is a rare person who is not hard pressed to keep up with the popular culture. One crucial area of modern life is money and how it affects your credit. A good way to make sure you are capable of crossing your financial Ps and Qs is to read the credit information FAQ (frequently asked question list), and prepare yourself to face the brave new financial world with confidence and style.

**Web:**

**http://www.cis.ohio-state.edu/hypertext/faq/usenet/consumer-credit-faq/top.html**

## Credit Reports

Do you want to know what people know about you when they get a credit report? This site answers frequently asked questions about consumer credit reports and credit history in general. Go read these documents so you know what everyone else knows about you.

**Web:**

**http://www.trw.com/iss/is/isdiv.html**

## Federal Trade Commission News Releases

The Federal Trade Commission (FTC) is a government agency of the United States. It was established in 1914 and its purpose is to keep business competition fair. The FTC enforces antitrust laws, regulates product labeling and takes steps to prohibit false advertising. You can keep up with how the Federal consumer watchdogs are doing by reading their latest actions and releases.

**Web:**

**http://www.ftc.gov/opa/press2.htm**

## Free Offers

There is free stuff out there in the world, just waiting for you to ask for it. You can get all kinds of cool things for free—phone calls, food, clothes, recipes, tickets and endless samples of miscellany—just for asking. All the information is here, so clean out the garage in order to make room for more stuff.

**Web:**

**http://home.earthlink.net/~boughter**
**http://www.winternet.com/~julie/ntn1.html**

**Usenet:**

**alt.consumers.free-stuff**

**IRC:**

**#FreeStuff**

## Houses

What did you ever do with your weekends before you bought a house? Don't you feel sorry for all those people who have nothing better to do than go out and have fun? Share your experiences with hardwood floors, mortgages, roofing repairs, plumbing, carpeting, contractors, real estate agents, painting, ventilation systems, and all the other great ways to spend your all-too-brief time on planet Earth.

**Usenet:**

**misc.consumers.house**

## Look What I Found on the Net...

```
Newsgroup: alt.consumers.free-stuff
Subject: Ways to Get Free Music

Join a record club and get your promised 10 free CDs, tapes, or
whatever they have promised.  They make you pay shipping charges, but
it's only about $2 per CD or tape.  Then, when they want you to buy
more CDs or tapes at the regular price you:

a) Say that you are a minor.  Write a note from your parent saying they
   didn't know you were in this club.

b) Say you are devastated by society's pressures -- for example, you
   are you are 21 and pregnant, trying to resist everyday pressures etc
   -- and the last thing you can worry about is belonging to a stupid
   record club.

c) Say that you decided to give the money instead to charity.

This also works great with magazines to get a couple of issues free.

Trust me...
```

## Internet Consumers Action Network

The Cybercop Precinct House is a service of the Internet Consumers Action Network (ICAN). This is a place where consumers can talk about their experiences and report problems they have had with online sellers and advertisers. Here you can find hints and tips on how to not be taken advantage of while on the Net.

**Web:**
**http://www.ucan.org/**

## Junk Mail

Here is a sure cure for your dusty mailbox. Sign up on this mailing list if you want to see lots of commercial advertising coming your way. Mailings will include direct marketing, sales promotions and announcements, product information and a variety of other mailings that companies love to send out.

**Majordomo Mailing List:**
List Name: **junkmail**
Subscribe to: **majordomo@mail.msen.com**

## Look What I Found on the Net...

```
Newsgroup: misc.consumers.house
Subject: Too much house?

> Has anyone bought or rented a house and discovered that there was
> too much space for you?

I don't know if you're going to get much sympathy for your
problems.
It is far easier to make a house smaller than to make it larger...
```

## National Fraud Information Center

People are out to get your money. Read this page to learn about how you can take action to reduce fraud against consumers. This page is put together by the Federal Trade Commission, the National Association of Attorneys General and the National Consumers League. On this page you can report telemarketing fraud, suspicious activity on the Net, and learn to protect yourself against fraud.

**Web:**

**http://www.fraud.org/**

## Securities Fraud

The Division of Enforcement, a division of the United States Securities and Exchange Commission, enforces federal securities laws. They have a site on the Web where you can make a complaint about securities frauds as well as find out information on frauds made by brokers, dealers and investment advisors.

**Web:**

**http://www.sec.gov/enforce/comctr.htm**

## Tenant Net

Having a lousy landlord turns Home Sweet Home into Nightmare on Elm Street. Find out what your rights are on a variety of issues such as security deposits, pets, repairs, payment of rent and more. This site offers information on tenants' rights, limited referral and guidance, links to tenant advocacy groups, FAQs, text of rental and housing laws and much more. Have Tenant Net on your bookmark list in case the big, bad wolf comes to huff and puff and blow your house in.

**Web:**

**http://www.tenant.net/**

Tenant Info
Do you rent a place to live? Check out Tenant Net for all kinds of important information. Be prepared *before* you sign the lease.

# CONTESTS

## Bookweb Contest

If you can solve a puzzle you get to be in the group from which a winner is randomly chosen. And, if you are lucky enough to be chosen, you win a prize. Okay, so your chance of winning is only slightly more likely than being struck by lightning, but you have to admit it's a lot more fun.

**Web:**

**http://www.ambook.org/bookweb/contest/**

## Contest Talk and General Discussion

This is the Usenet group devoted to announcing new contests. You will also find discussion about contests as well as questions and answers. If you like contests, this is a good place to check regularly.

**Usenet:**

**alt.consumers.sweepstakes**

## Contest Web Resources

Is your working area covered in a flurry of sticky notes and random scraps of paper, in a vain attempt to keep track of all the contests on the Net? Here's a better idea. This web site keeps track of many of the contests, drawings, raffles, sweepstakes and promotions that are happening on the Web. My advice is to check in every day, just in case the contest of your dreams has materialized while you were asleep.

**Web:**

**http://www.4cyte.com/ThreadTreader/**

## Dangerfield, Rodney

Rodney Dangerfield, the comedian, has some clever contests on his web site. For example, you might find the "Rodney Make-Over" contest, where you can help Rodney with his image, so he can try to get more respect. Even if you don't, it's fun to read the past results, and Rodney and his web guys do go to a lot of trouble to make the site interesting.

**Web:**

**http://www.rodney.com/rodney/contest.html**

## Find the Lost Dog

The poodle is lost and it's your mission to find him. This challenge sends you out all over the Web looking for clues as to where the little doggie has gone. To be eligible for the drawing, there are various criteria you have to meet. Then you can win fabulous prizes and be admired by all your peers. Not to mention that, if you happen to be a Boy Scout, finding the dog could count as a good deed.

**Web:**
**http://www.heymon.com/contest.html**

## Football Trivia

Bring your fantasies to life on this (American) electronic football field. When you choose to participate in this monthly trivia contest, you are presented with a picture of a playing field. To score a touchdown, you have to choose plays and answer trivia questions. Lots of football fun, and you may even win a prize.

**Web:**
**http://www.dtd.com/tmw/**

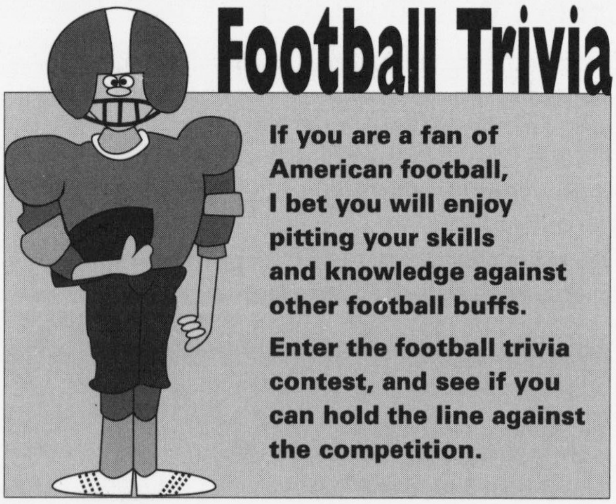
Football Trivia
If you are a fan of American football, I bet you will enjoy pitting your skills and knowledge against other football buffs.
Enter the football trivia contest, and see if you can hold the line against the competition.

## Hard Disk Contest

It's every geek's fantasy to win free computer equipment. Get a chance to win a studly hard drive just by browsing around this site looking for a sentence that has every word spelled backward.

**Web:**
**http://www.harddisk.com/freedisk2.html**

## Home Photo Gallery

You don't have to be a photography genius to have the chance to win money on the Web. Submit a funny family picture, a goofy pet picture, or anything weird you may have taken. The site is updated regularly, and you can even get to vote on who the winner will be. If you need ideas, there is a photo gallery with sample pictures.

**Web:**
**http://www.mbnet.mb.ca/flatland/sooter/**

## Internet Experiences

Everybody has a story about interesting things that happen on the Net. If you are like me, you love telling all your stories for free. Well, now you can actually win a prize just for talking about yourself. To enter this contest, all you need to do is share your "coolest Internet experiences". (My suggestion is to tell how reading this book changed your life.)

**Web:**
**http://www.gw2k.com/cool/contest/intnetpc/intnetpc.htm**

## Multimedia Newsstand Trivia

Trivia buffs: Have fun trying to win fabulous prizes playing this interactive trivia contest at the Multimedia Newsstand. Fill out the form online, cross your fingers and wait for the day when you will see your name splashed across this web page in the winners' section.

**Web:**
**http://mmnewsstand.com/Trivia**

## Nightmare Factory Trivia Contests

Indulge your morbid sense of fear by checking out the Nightmare Factory. This web site is the online representation of a huge haunted house in Austin, Texas. Once a month they offer a chance to win a prize by correctly answering a horror-related trivia question. And while you are thinking about the answer, you can check out their links to other horror-related Internet resources.

**Web:**
**http://www.nightmarefactory.com/trivia.html**

## Nightmares

Have you had a bad dream lately? (Last night I dreamed I was really hungry, and I went to the refrigerator, and someone had already eaten all the leftover spaghetti.) Write 25 words or less about your worst nightmare, real or imagined, and you just might win a prize.

**Web:**

**http://users.aol.com/mmbriefs/trpwin.htm**

## Riddler Game

Right now, as you read this, you could be out making money on the Web just by using your brain along with some clever mouse-button clicking. The Riddler Game gives you the opportunity to answer trivia questions and solve puzzles for cash prizes. The game is free, but you have to register to play.

**Web:**

**http://www.riddler.com/**

### Tracy Turnblatt Taken to Task in Trivia Tumble

*Do you know who Tracy Turnblatt is? If so, you may be a trivia champ in the making.*

*Don't even wait a moment. Connect to the Riddler Game and see what you can do with a lifetime's supply of otherwise useless knowledge.*

## Road Trips

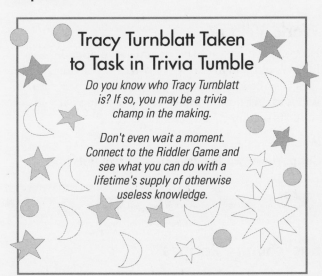

Scavenger hunts are fun. This particular hunt is modeled on a road trip. You have to drive around the Net answering questions at specific sites until you finally reach your destination. Fill up the cooler with drinks and snacks, put your browser into fast forward, and hit the road.

**Web:**

**http://www.roadtrips.com/**

## Sandbox

What do you do when you have a few hours to kill waiting for the repair guy to show up? Visit the Sandbox. Just the place to try contests, games and puzzles in order to compete for prizes. If you are a contest lover, this is a great place to check out.

**Web:**

**http://www.sandbox.net/sandbox/pub-doc/home-x.html**

## Sports Contest

Your sports experience doesn't have to be limited to sitting around watching television. You can sit around, testing your hard-won sports knowledge on the Net by entering the monthly contests sponsored by the World Wide Collectors Network. Not only will you impress your friends with your mastery of the esoteric, but you may even win a prize.

**Web:**

**http://www.wwcd.com/contest/contest.html**

## Sports Picks

Here's your chance to prove you really know your (American) football. During the football season, this site offers a contest that allows you to predict the scores of various games. The computer will keep track of all your predictions for the entire season. When it's not football time, you can hang out and talk with other sports fans in a variety of sports-related chat rooms. Or you can brush up on your football trivia, just in case you get an emergency call to participate on a game show.

**Web:**

**http://www.iis-sports.com/picks/**

## Sweepstakes and Contests

Here's a gold mine of sweepstakes and contest information for both children and adults. The site includes instant win sweeps, writing contests, freebie pages and links to other sweepstakes pages. Win, win, win, win. (That's my advice.)

**Web:**

**http://fly.hiwaay.net/~garson/sweep_main.htm**

Today may be your lucky day, but there is only one way to find out. Connect to the Sweepstakes and Contests site, and see what destiny has in store for you.

## Sweepstakes Information

Here is information on lots of sweepstakes and contests: dates, rules, and information on how to enter. You will also find links to sweepstakes and contests you can enter without even leaving the Web. How much more convenient can modern life get? In the Usenet group, people send in information about new contests all the time.

**Web:**
**http://www.sweepsonline.com/**

## Vacation and Travel Contests

If you don't want to spend your hard-earned money on a vacation, you can always try to win a vacation in a contest. Here is a web site where you can enter a variety of contests to win vacation-oriented prizes. Of course, if you did win a free trip, you would have to leave your computer and a lot of email would accumulate while you were away. Oh well, nothing is perfect.

**Web:**
**http://www.vacations.com/Win/**

## Victoria's Valentine Contest

Do you like romantic stories? The type that make you feel like a mushy container of warm butter? If so, you may be an almost-winner. All you have to do is write about your most cherished Valentine's Day memory, send it in to the judges, and you might win a lovely romantic prize.

**Web:**
**http://mmnewsstand.com/static/products/454/valentine-contest.html**

## Word Puzzles

Does your brain need a few mental pushups to keep it in tip-top shape? Try solving some of these interesting but challenging word puzzles, and you just may win a prize. There are several different puzzles to solve, and they are not easy, so roll up your virtual sleeves and plug in the ol' thinking cap. Pretty soon, your mind will be one of the best-functioning organs in your entire body.

**Web:**
**http://syndicate.com/entercontest.html**

**Think, Think, Think**
**Good. Now that you are warmed up, enter one of the Word Puzzle contests. Do it now. Don't tergiversate.**

## World Village

Do you need a variety of mental stimulation in your life? Would you like to win a prize? If you answered "yes yes," head straight to this web site, where you will find a variety of interesting places to visit with contests scattered here and there.

**Web:**
**http://www.worldvillage.com/wv/contests.htm**

# COOKING AND RECIPES

## Backcountry Recipes

When you are heading to the outback, make sure you are prepared. There's nothing worse than getting into the middle of nowhere, and suddenly you have a big craving for a barbecued chicken wing. Here are some recipes for people going backpacking, hiking, and camping. Learn about trail snacks, dinners, breakfasts, meat dishes, and desserts that are easy to bring along whether you are going to hike up a mountain or just spend the afternoon in downtown New York.

**Web:**
**http://www.gorp.com/gorp/food/recipe.htm**

## Barbecue

You know what I like after a hard day of writing? A whacking big carrot stick, doused with a liberal helping of spicy barbecue sauce, and roasted slowly over an open flame. However, if vegetarian is not your style, take a look at some of the ol' smoking-and-curing resources on the Net, where I guarantee you'll find enough information to choke a cumin-rubbed Boston butt. And if you find a tempting recipe for slow-roasted barbecued carrot, try it in my honor and see how close you can get to heaven on Earth.

**Web:**

**http://www.azstarnet.com/~thead/bbq/**
**http://www.cochran.sbc.edu/barbeque.html**

**Usenet:**

**alt.food.barbecue**

**Majordomo Mailing List:**

List Name: **bbq-digest**
Subscribe to: **majordomo@azstarnet.com**

## Bread

Here's how to plan for a successful dining experience: pick a bread that suits your mood, then decide what main dish goes well with it. Those of you who are more ambitious might want to even bake your own. If that is the case, try some of the bread recipes on the Net. When you find one you like, double the size of the recipe just in case. (You can never have too much bread.)

**Web:**

**http://countrylife.net/bread/**
**http://haven.ios.com/~wordup/bread.html**
**http://www.webcom.com/~stannet/bread/recipes.html**

**Usenet:**

**rec.food.baking**

## Candy Recipe Archive

When it's midnight and the stores are closed and you are having a big Attack of the Killer Sweet Tooth, get out the pots and pans, and whip up some of these exotic specimens such as Turkish delight, peanut butter balls, candied apple slices and many more.

**Web:**

**http://www.cs.cmu.edu/~mjw/recipes/candy/**

## Cookie Recipes

Everybody has their own favorite type of cookie. Mine are made from organic seaweed, brewer's yeast, whey and (for fiber) biodegradable sawdust. However, if you happen to be one of those people who is not a health food junkie, your taste in cookies may be a tad more mainstream. If so, check out this web site for more cookie recipes than you could use in a month of Sunday bake sales.

**Web:**

**http://www.cs.cmu.edu/~mjw/recipes/cookies/cookie.html**

### Make a Cookie

I bet that, right now, you need a cookie.

And not just any cookie. I bet you need a delicious, aromatic, homemade cookie.

Here's a great idea: go to the Cookie Recipes web site, find something that looks good, and get a batch in the oven as fast as you can.

Do you realize that, in less than half an hour, you could have a freshly baked cookie in your mouth?

Now *that's* what I call an idea.

## Cooking Talk and General Discussion

If you like messing around the kitchen and trying out new recipes, there are lots of people on the Net who will love to talk to you. Join one or all of the cooking discussion groups, and talk about cooking techniques, equipment, recipes, vegetarianism, and so on. This is a great place to trade tips and techniques, and to ask questions about things culinary.

**Usenet:**

**alt.cooking-chat**
**alt.creative-cook**
**rec.food.cooking**
**rec.food.recipes**

A B C D E F G H I J K L M N O P Q R S T U V W X Y Z

## Cyber Cookbook

Make sure your hands are clean before you turn the pages of this cookbook. Jayne's Cyber Cookbook offers basic information about cooking, recipes, conversion charts, a glossary of cooking terms and some hints to help you be a great cook.

**Web:**

**http://www.sapphyr.co.uk/lair/cookbook.htm**

## Diabetic Recipes

A collection of recipes for diabetics, including some dishes you would think diabetics could never eat, such as apple dumplings, double fudge balls, fruit cookies, and others. There is also information on powdered sugar replacements.

**Web:**

**http://www.cs.cmu.edu/~mjw/recipes/special/diabetic-coll.html**

## Fat-Free Recipes

Whether you are staying away from fat for dieting or health reasons, you still need some good recipes. Here are some tasty ways of preparing food without fat. You don't have to feel deprived, because here are recipes for bread, salads, cookies, casseroles, pizza and a variety of ethnic foods.

**Web:**

**http://www.eskimo.com/~baubo/lowfat.html**
**http://www.fatfree.com/**

## French Cooking

Some people pooh-pooh French cooking. They say that it uses too much butter, that it's too fattening, that the rich sauces are used to hide meat of dubious quality and that any food that can't be prepared by warming it in a microwave is too complex and intricate for day-to-day consumption. My philosophy is: If it's good enough for Zsa Zsa Gabor, it's good enough for me.

**Web:**

**http://jeffco.k12.co.us/dist_ed/spring96/onlinec/dahender/recipes.html**
**http://www.vol.it/UK/EN/HOBBY/CUCINA/fracucina.html**

## Indian Food

When I am in the mood for Indian food, I don't always have the time to hop on a plane and travel to India. On these occasions, it's easier just to find a recipe from the Net and make it in my own kitchen. You can do it, too. Set up the computer in the kitchen, point your web browser to this site and follow along. In no time, you will have a delightful meal prepared in your own home, without the side effect of jet lag and the red tape that comes with traveling to another country.

**Web:**

**http://www.u.arizona.edu/~srikant/recipes.html**

## Insect Recipes

If you are having a party, this page offers the perfect recipes for little appetizers. Insects are not only freely found in the environment, but they make perfect finger food. Try some dry-roasted leafhoppers or Army worms. For dipping, use the rootworm beetle dip or for dessert try my personal favorite: the chocolate chirpie chip cookies.

**Web:**

**http://www.ent.iastate.edu/Misc/InsectsAsFood.html**

## An Unexpected Treat

What do you do when your mother-in-law and your boss drop in unexpectedly for dinner at the same time?

You could reheat that leftover tuna surprise, or whip up a family-sized potful of macaroni and cheese, but that is so cliche and would impress nobody.

Instead, why not connect to the Net and try some of the **Insect Recipes**? Insect dishes are stylish, unusual and a good source of protein. After all, why let people bug you when you can bug them first?

## Internet Chef

The Internet Chef is a great culinary home away from home. You can browse the extensive recipe archives, look at cooking tips and articles, and even chat with other people in real time. You can also leave messages for other people to read. For example, you can post a message asking if anybody has a recipe for fried groat clusters and check back later to see the responses. If you can't stand the heat in the kitchen, you can always hang out at the Internet Chef.

**Web:**

**http://ichef.cycor.ca/**

## Italian Cooking

Can't tell your cannellini from your cannoli or your fontina from your fontinella? Don't worry. The Net can make you an Italian know-it-all in no-time-at-all. These web sites have recipes for pasta, appetizers and main dishes. Or you can read an Italian cooking glossary so you can enunciate your pancetta with the best of them.

**Web:**

**http://eat.com/cooking-glossary/**
**http://hella.stm.it./market/cucina_italiana/ricette.htm**

## Kitchen Link

If you're like me, you divide your time between the kitchen and the Internet. If so, here is the missing link: a large, well-organized collection of food and cooking resources from all over the Net. Recipes, magazines, FAQs (frequently asked question lists), cooking software, discussion groups, nutrition information, cooking tips—it's all here.

**Web:**

**http://www.frontiernet.net/~bcouch/**

## Medieval and Renaissance Food

If you want some really old food, besides the scary stuff at the back of the refrigerator, try whipping up something from the medieval or Renaissance period. You can get recipes for main dishes or desserts. Recipes are available by historical period or by country.

**Web:**

**http://www.pbm.com/~lindahl/food.html**

## Mexican Cuisine

When you are in the mood for something spicy, drag the laptop into the kitchen and connect to this web site which has lots of recipes and interesting trivia about Mexican foods and their history.

**Web:**

**http://mexico.udg.mx/Ingles/Cocina/menu.html**

## Mimi's Cyber-Kitchen

There's no kitchen like Mimi's kitchen. It has tons of links to recipe archives, articles on cooking indoors and outdoors, information on preparing seafood, spices, vegetables, holiday cooking, plus Mimi's personal recipe collection. Fire up the grill and make something special tonight.

**Web:**

**http://www.cyber-kitchen.com/**

Cooking with Mimi
If you love cooking, you'll love Mimi's Cyber-Kitchen.
Lots and lots of plain-spoken kitchen talk, along with an old-fashioned, traditional, down-home search engine to help find the exact recipe you need.

## Mushrooms

There are lots of things you can do with mushrooms. You can feed them to your pet pig, you can dress them up in little costumes and perform Shakespearean tragedies for your friends, or you can make some delectable recipes in the comfort of your own kitchen. My suggestion is to connect to the Net, find a few new mushroom recipes, and soon you will be scarfing down a delectable helping of everyone's favorite fungus.

**Web:**

**http://www.hcds.net/mushroom/cook.html**

## Pies

Not long ago I had a great pie experience. A well-known publisher came to visit me and stayed overnight. At dinnertime, he volunteered to help out by making dessert and, using a recipe passed on to him by his grandmother, he baked a magnificent apple pie fit for a king. The best part was—since we couldn't find a king on such short notice—we had to eat the whole thing ourselves. If you would like to have a great pie experience in your own home, you don't have to wait for a well-known publisher to visit you. Simply check with these Internet pie resources, where you can find instructions on pie baking along with a nice variety of recipes and tips that will make the whole experience as successful as possible.

**Web:**

**http://www.cs.cmu.edu/~mjw/recipes/pie/pie.html**
**http://www.teleport.com/~psyched/pie/pie.html**

## Recipe Archives

Out of ideas for dinner tonight? With this archive at your fingertips, you need never run dry on ideas. Search this large database of recipes for that special dish.

**Web:**

**http://english-www.hss.cmu.edu/Recipes/**
**http://ichef.cycor.ca/rec-food-recipes/recipe-archive.html**
**http://soar.Berkeley.EDU/recipes/**
**http://www.astro.cf.ac.uk/misc/recipe/**
**http://www.cs.cmu.edu/~mjw/recipes/**
**http://www.cs.ubc.ca/spider/edmonds/recipes/**

## Recipes

Have you ever seen the Dick Van Dyke Show? Well, when Rob Petrie first met his wife Laura, she did not like him at all. However, he found out that she collected recipes and started sending her cookbooks (which helped him win her heart). Rob had to do it the hard way: today, he could snarf as many recipes as he wanted from the Net and email them to Laura. So what do you do when your boss and his family are coming over for dinner and all you have is a frozen armadillo? Nothing to worry about. Just connect to the Net and check out the recipes. Either that or borrow a cookbook from Laura.

**Usenet:**

**alt.gourmand**
**rec.food.cooking**
**rec.food.recipes**

## Ridiculously Easy Recipes

Maybe it's not that you are a bad cook. Maybe you're just in a hurry. The important thing is, if you need a ridiculously easy recipe, I know where you can get one. These recipes are so easy that my cat can make them (and he does, when it is his turn to fix dinner). In case you'd like to try it for yourself, his personal favorite is the microwave tuna quesadillas.

**Web:**

**http://www.sar.usf.edu/~zazuetaa/recipe.html**

## Sourdough

Have you ever wondered what gives sourdough bread its distinctive sour taste? It's a mixture of microorganisms—yeast and bacteria—that take an integral part in the baking process. The actual taste of your bread depends on which micoorganisms you use, and this depends on which little creatures happen to be floating around in the air where you live. This is why San Francisco sourdough bread tastes different from, say, sourdough bread made in Fargo, North Dakota. Different bacteria create a different taste. So, do you still want to make your own sourdough bread? There are lots and lots of people on the Net who would love to help learn about this tricky but pleasingly addictive foodstuff.

**Web:**

**http://mindlink.net/darrell_greenwood/sourdoughfaqs.html**
**http://www.herbalgram.org/cyclotron/sourdough.html**

**Usenet:**

**rec.food.sourdough**

**Find a friend in "People".**

## Southern Cooking

Mmm, mmm. If you have never had Southern cooking, you are certainly in for a treat. Take off those jogging shoes and your fitness gear, and pull up to a big slab of ham coated with red eye gravy, a side of collards, some poke salad, okra, black-eyed peas and a hunk of cornbread. If you can't get this at your favorite restaurant, you can learn about Southern cooking on the Net. These sites will tell you what it is and how it's done, including the history of Southern cooking. You'll learn how ingenious Southerners are with their cooking and about the many different uses there are for leftover bacon grease.

**Web:**

**http://206.1.124.154/**
**http://www.as.ua.edu./math/bgray/recipes.htm**

### Food, Southern Style

*If you don't happen to live in the southern part of the United States, you are missing a lot. For example, I bet you can't remember the last time you had a nice helping of catfish and hush puppies, with a side order of cornbread.*

*Well, as long as you have a Net connection, you can remedy the situation right now. Just connect to one of the Southern Cooking sites and find out what you have been missing.*

*Until you can say you really understand grits, you have not led a full life.*

## Sushi

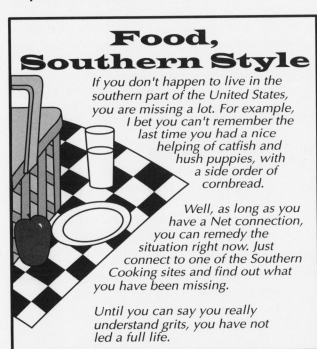

When you are hungry, it's nice to have a little ikura to roll around on your tongue. If you want to try to make some sushi at home, or you are just curious about how they make sushi hold together as it does, you can learn about it at this site. You can even brush up on terminology so the next time you are at a sushi bar, you can order like a native New Yorker.

**Web:**

**http://www.rain.org/~hutch/sushi.html**

## Virtual Kitchen

Here's a snazzy kitchen space offered by Time Warner. Get recipes, tips and general cooking information from these beautiful cookbooks. Spend time browsing or search by keywords for exactly what you want. Even if you have trouble boiling water, this site is worth a look.

**Web:**

**http://pathfinder.com/twep/kitchen/**

# COOL, BUT USELESS

## Abandoned Missile Base Tour

Scattered across the United States are missile silos, now defunct, that sit waiting for some reckless youngster to explore. Thanks to modern technology and the creativity of two guys who committed a felony, you can now have a virtual tour of a missile silo without having to risk your health, take the chance of getting lost, or returning home late for dinner.

**Web:**

**http://www.xvt.com/users/kevink/silo/**

## Abuse Page

Are you leading your day-to-day life in a cloud of restrained social politeness? Do you want the people you meet to speak their minds, but they won't because they are just too darned nice? Here is a place on the Net that will give you the abuse you deserve. Just fill out the appropriate demographic questions and get an custom-made insult that will fit you like the paper on the wall.

**Web:**

**http://www.shamus.com/abusepage.html**

## Advertising Gallery

Some people are frightened by roller coaster rides or monster movies. Some people are frightened by various processed food such as Spaghetti O's or Vienna sausages. For others, their blood may run cold after analyzing some of the less tasteful parts of marketing culture. This gallery of advertising will show you parts of the mostly American culture that are best left unrevealed. However, since it's too late for that, you might as well go see what you should be missing.

**Web:**

**http://omni.cc.purdue.edu/~royald/absurd.htm**

## Answers to All of Your Questions

There are so many times in life when you just do not know what to do. You reason everything out as best you can; perhaps you ask a friend or relative for advice; you may even toss a coin. But, no matter what you do, you just can't bring yourself to make a decision. Well, your troubles are over. What you need is spiritual guidance based upon your own particular inner needs, and here it is, for free, on the Net. Just ask your question and click on the purple square of your choice. As if by magic, the exact advice you need will appear on your screen. (And, if that doesn't work, open this book at random and read the first sentence you see. You have my personal guarantee that what you get will be what you need.)

**Web:**

**http://www.ccnet.com/~elsajoy/instant.html**

*NEVER FORGET.*
If you are ever unsure what to do,
you can always use the Net to find the
***Answers to All Your Questions.***

**Happiness is a warm modem.**

## Bill Gates Wealth Clock

Have you ever wondered how much money Bill Gates has? The real answer is that, no one, even Mr. Bill himself, actually knows how much he is worth. However, here is a web site that has a conservative estimate of his wealth based on his holdings of Microsoft stock and its current price. Check out the site, and you can see what the big fellow's stock is worth right now. You can also see an interesting statistic: the total amount of money divided by the number of people in the United States. Thus, if you are American, you can see an estimate of how much you would receive if Mr. Bill were to liquidate all his Microsoft stock at the current price (with no commissions) and share it equally with everyone in the country. It comes to about $65. Or to put it another way, if everyone in America were to send me the measly sum of $65, our country could have *two* humungously rich billionaires instead of only one. This would serve to increase the competition and be generally better for everyone.

**Web:**

**http://www.webho.com/WealthClock**

## Build Your Own Critter

Use the sliders to move the top, middle and bottom of various strange creatures. Put them together according to your momentary whim and, wow, your own personal very strange creature is right there on your screen, just for you. Okay, now back to work.

**Web:**

**http://www.cgrg.ohio-state.edu/~nvishnev/Onfire/Webs/BuildUrOwn/buildani.html**

## Celebrity Painter

Painting is therapeutic. I love to get out the paints, spread out a large dropcloth, and lose myself in the ecstasy of chromatic creation. However, sometimes it's nice to be able to experience the value of painting without having to drag out all the supplies or clean up the mess afterward. So try doing it on the Net. This web site will allow you to paint the portraits of various celebrities. You can even mix and match their facial features to get just the right *mélange* of *je ne sais quoi*.

**Web:**

**http://sgiserver.demonsys.com/jorkin/CelebrityPainter/**

## Cool But Useless Talk and General Discussion

There is a lot of useless talk on the Internet. However, there aren't that many places where you will find useless talk about cool ideas. Here are a few Usenet groups in which you might find such treasures. These are the places I visit when I need a quick break from the press of everyday life, and I want to immerse myself in the cool, but useless part of the world.

**Usenet:**

**alt.angst**
**alt.celebrities**
**alt.conspiracy**
**talk.rumors**

## Destruction Derby

Primal screaming is really noisy. Shooting people on the freeway is messy and illegal. What other way can you take out your frustrations? Try this web site. It allows you to smash up a car with nothing more than a mouse click.

**Web:**

**http://www.psygnosis.com/secure/derby/**

## Dr. Werner Wilhelm Webowitz

When life's stresses become to much for you, and you don't want to shell out the big bucks for a psychiatrist, check out the web site of Dr. Werner Wilhelm Webowitz. He will discuss any topic your heart desires—sort of.

**Web:**

**http://www.parnasse.com/drwww.shtml**

## Electronic Pizza

When it's so late at night that you can't get a pizza delivered, there is a way to get that pizza thrill. Send yourself an electronic pizza with any number of bizarre toppings, most of which you would never, ever put on a real pizza for fear of a midnight rendezvous with an ER nurse and a doctor with a long pair of tweezers. If you are not in the mood for pizza, send one to a friend who will then be in such gratitude that he or she will beg to wash your dishes for the next week (or something).

**Web:**

**http://www.internetuniv.com/pizza/ipizza.htm**

## Exploding Heads

When it's late at night and I have a big deadline, I can't call my editor because he is off having lasagna and a nice glass of wine at a fancy restaurant with a beautiful woman. Instead, I visit the Exploding Heads web site. Here, I can press on the head of a famous person and make it explode into a glorious pattern of red. In fact, I tested this site many, many times. (I wanted to make sure it was good enough for you.)

**Web:**

**http://www.king.net/gilmore/head/**

Once in a while, everyone has a bad day. The next time you need a pick-me-up, connect to the Net and watch a famous person's head explode. It's almost as much fun as watching it in person, and you won't have to clean up the mess.

## Faces

You don't have to go to years and years of medical school to experience the thrills of being able to modify the faces of rich, Hollywood stars. All you have to do is click your mouse, and mix and match parts of the stars' faces until you create something new that you like. You can recreate all the excitement experienced by Dr. Frankenstein without running up a huge electric bill.

**Web:**

**http://web-usa.com/faces/**

A B C D E F G H I J K L M N O P Q R S T U V W X Y Z

## Get a Life

No life? It's okay, you can get one here. Or at least fabricated proof that you have a life. Decide what aspect of life you would like to obtain, fill out the appropriate form which will establish what type of life you will have, then send away for your life. Within minutes, a photograph will be emailed to you, showing your life in action. You can pass this along to your friends and family who think that all you do is sit in front of a computer all day reading Harley Hahn books.

**Web:**

**http://www.developers.com/lgtech/getalife/**

## Life Games

The "Game of Life" is a computer-mediated game using a rectangular grid. Within the grid, a certain number of cells live or die from one generation to the next according to a few simple rules. The generations change and, as you watch, you will notice patterns. This web site offers some interesting variations on the Game of Life (as well as the original game). For example, you can watch tiny little dots—representing fish and sharks—change from one generation to the next. Watch the fish multiply, and then see what happens as the sharks become more and more hungry. You have control over the initial conditions, and so you can set up your own tiny world as you wish. True, what you are watching is a bunch of small dots changing, so you do have to use your imagination to see them as live entities. However, once you get the hang of it, you will see that it can be a lot of fun to create life, and then laugh hideously as it blindly fends for itself against immutable laws of nature.

**Web:**

**http://www.fusebox.com/cb/alife.html**

## Mad Martian Museum of Modern Madness

This is a great place if you are worried you are getting a bit too normal, and you need a boost of weirdness. For example, wouldn't you love to investigate the "Interactive Toilet of Terror"? And how can you pass up the "Plastic Eyeball Exhibit" or the "Mad Martian Masks"? I don't think I need to say any more: the interactive toilet can speak for itself.

**Web:**

**http://www.madmartian.com/**

## Magic 8-Bra

Is the Magic 8-Ball too retro for you? Consult the Magic 8-Bra instead. Confess your deepest dreams and desires, or ask for some sage advice, and the Magic-8 Bra will advise you appropriately.

**Web:**

**http://www.cyborganic.com/people/carla/Rumpus/Toychest/8bra/**

## Magnetic Poetry

Imagine you have a very large refrigerator and, sticking to the door, you have several hundred small magnetic thingies, each one having a word printed on it ("women", "urge", "pink", "ask", "you", "go", and on and on). Now imagine yourself being able to select and arrange the thingies so as to write poetry out of the words. Well, on the Net you do not have to imagine. Here is a virtual surface with lots and lots of thingies, each with its own word. Use your mouse to move the words around and create whatever poetry or messages your heart and mind desire. When you are finished, you can share the result with everyone by copying your poem onto a piece of paper and putting it on the door of your fridge.

**Web:**

**http://prominence.com/java/poetry/**

*I went to the* **Magnetic Poetry** *site,*
*and you know what I found out? I'm a poet.*
*No kidding. This is what I composed:*

essential delicious diamond
beneath bare language
recall languid goddess
say hello they soar

*And I bet you could*
*do even better.*

## Paper Dolls

It's fun to dress up, but it takes so much time and money to do it right. Now you can do it over the Net with no fuss, no muss, and no large credit card bills at the end of the month. Here are two "paper" dolls—Salon Betty and Net Chick—you can dress up over and over again. With Net Chick, once you dress her correctly, you can get into the secret diary.

**Web:**

**http://imusic.interserv.com/Paperdoll/**
**http://www.cyborganic.com/People/carla/Rumpus/Toychest/Doll/**

## Rock Paper Scissors

When you are young, your ideas about life are influenced heavily by your parents. Some parents are very protective and don't like to see their children participate in high-impact sports, such as football and hockey. If you are the offspring of an overprotective parent, here is a web game that should be well-suited for your temperament. Rock blunts scissors; paper covers rock; scissors cuts paper. If only life were that simple.

**Web:**

**http://www.shadow.net/~proub/rps.html**

## Superhero Generator

If you like to read comics—especially Marvel comics—I bet you have said to yourself, "I bet I could make up a better superhero." Well, here's your chance. Specify a few basic details, and the Superhero Generator will create the name of a brand new superhero, just for you: a superhero as good as any you have ever seen in a comic book. Once you have created your superhero, you can use him/her as your own personal alter ego. For example, I am seriously considering changing my name from Harley to The Amazing Scarlet Flame. My weapon would be a Psycho-Knife, and my vehicle would be the Scarlet Jet. The source of my powers, needless to say, would be Mystical. (Eat your heart out, Clark Kent.)

**Web:**

**http://fly.hiwaay.net/~lkseitz/comics/herogen/herogen.cgi**

## Time Machine

These days, time is really at a premium. So I understand if you don't have time to sit around and watch the sun rise, or enjoy flowers as they slowly open their petals, or appreciate the various other wonders of the world. No problem: take the easy way out. You can see all sorts of interesting time lapse photo movies without having to miss any of your favorite television shows. Life has never been so fast, easy or convenient.

**Web:**

**http://webmart.org/timelaps/**

## Useless Facts

Sometimes, the most enjoyable facts are the most useless facts. Facts that are weird, funny, sometimes astounding, but are careful to never stray from the path of uselessness. For example, I bet you didn't know that Anne Boleyn (the second queen consort of Henry VIII) had six fingers on one hand? Get your fill of odd factual tidbits and amaze your friends to no end. My prediction is that you will be the most popular person in your entire circle of friends. After all, there is no one more beloved that the purveyor of an endless supply of useless knowledge. Just ask any film studies teacher.

**Web:**

**http://www-leland.stanford.edu/~jenkg/useless.html**

## Virtual Bubblewrap

I love popping bubblewrap: that plastic wrapping that is used to package and protect delicate items. It's such a satisfying way to spend a few minutes of the day: pressing those small plastic bubbles with ever-increasing force until they suddenly surrender and self-destruct with a soul-satisfying pop. It used to be that I would have to buy something by mail in order to get some bubblewrap. Not any more. As always, the Net comes through. Now I connect to this web site and pop bubblewrap whenever I want. You think I am kidding? Try it for yourself.

**Web:**

**http://www.mackerel.com/bubble.html**

Need to
release some tension?
Try the **Virtual Bubblewrap**.

## Virtual Dartboard

If you live in England, you can throw darts any time you want by visiting the local pub. However, if you live in a pub-deficient country (such as America) you have to throw darts at home. However, why should you risk holes in the wall just for the sake of a few darts? Here are some virtual targets you can throw at whenever you want. Hone your dart-throwing skills to perfection without even putting a single mark on the wall. Isn't the Net great?

**Web:**
**http://asylum.cid.com/dartboard/**

## Virtual Keyboard

Here is a nice-looking keyboard you can play by pressing on the notes. There are, unfortunately, a few limitations. First, you can only press one note at a time. Second, the keyboard is kind of small. Third, you will have to wait a while for the sound to travel from the web server to your browser. Still, those are minor, picky little details. The main point is, you can click on a picture of a keyboard and hear something, and if that doesn't sound like a miracle to you, well, I just don't know what to say.

**Web:**
**http://www.xmission.com/~mgm/misc/keyboard.html**

## Virtual Lego

Lots of people love Lego building blocks. However, the big problem is you can't build anything unless you have a whole bunch of blocks. That is, until now. Using your web browser, you can visit a Lego site where you can build all kinds of things from your own virtual Lego blocks, as well as look at all the cool things other people have built. After all, who would want to use a bunch of actual icky little plastic blocks when you can use the real pretend ones over the Net?

**Web:**
**http://www-lego.mit.edu/~lego/LegoHome.html**

## Virtual Mr. Spud Head

Have you ever played with a Mr. Potato Head? You get a bunch of plastic facial features (eyes, nose, mouth, ears, and so on) and you stick them on a plastic potato or—if your mother will give you one—a real potato. This is much more cool. You can choose from a selection of vegetables and arrange their faces any way you want. (The plastic Mr. Potato Head only has holes in particular places and you can't, for example, put an ear in the middle of its face.) The Virtual Mr. Spud Head service is another example of how the Net makes our lives richer and more fulfilling by eliminating the physical limitations of normal, day-to-day existence.

**Web:**
**http://www.westnet.com/~crywalt/pothead/pothead.html**

## Virtual Plastic Surgery

Mix and match the features of well-known attractive people to create your own perfect someone or other. Choose just the right nose, mouth, eyes, and put it on whichever head feels right. When the result is displayed, print it out and take it with you as you walk around the world looking for your perfect soulmate. Each time you meet a new person, check your picture to see how close the person comes to your personal dream bunny.

**Web:**
**http://www.mrshowbiz.com/features/games/surgery/**

## Web-a-Sketch

Etch-a-sketch is a device about the size of a small laptop computer, that you can use to draw pictures on a reusable surface. You turn knobs and, as you turn, lines magically appear. When you get tired of your picture, you turn the etch-a-sketch upside down, shake, and—voilà—the picture has disappeared and you are ready for another satisfying artistic experience. Now you can have the same experience, whenever you want, on the Net. Instead of turning knobs, you click your mouse button to draw lines. Draw your own pictures and see the works of other people. It takes a while to get good but, come on, anything in life that is worthwhile takes time to master.

**Web:**
**http://www.digitalstuff.com/web-a-sketch/**

# CRAFTS

## Balloon Art

Balloon art is always a good thing to know how to do in case you are trapped in an elevator with a group of children or perhaps have to calm several wild animals who are about to attack you. Check out this site for lots of balloon pictures, a FAQ (frequently asked question list), a guide to ballooning, as well as other potentially life-saving material.

**Web:**

**http://www.fooledya.com/balloon**

## Basket Weaving

If your home is sadly lacking in cultural artifacts, I have the answer. Connect to one of these basket-oriented sites and teach yourself how to render an actual objet d'art. After all, what could be in better taste than a house full of baskets? I myself have a basket in the shape of *The Internet Complete Reference* hanging on my bedroom wall. (And, boy, am I popular.)

**Web:**

**http://csbh.mhv.net/~abeebe/basket.html**
**http://www.ashland.edu/~lbraun/baskets.html**

## Bead Discussion

These Usenet groups are for the discussion of beads, glass beadmaking, and using beads in making jewelry. Join with people from around the world who are taking little bitty bits of treasure and forming them into bigger and better bits of treasure.

**Usenet:**

**alt.beadworld**
**rec.crafts.beads**

## Beading and Jewelry

Hardcore beaders will love this web site, which has a little of everything for bead fans and jewelry makers. Get information about bead resources, bead societies, places to talk about beads, and much more.

**Web:**

**http://www.mcs.net/~simone/beadnet.html**

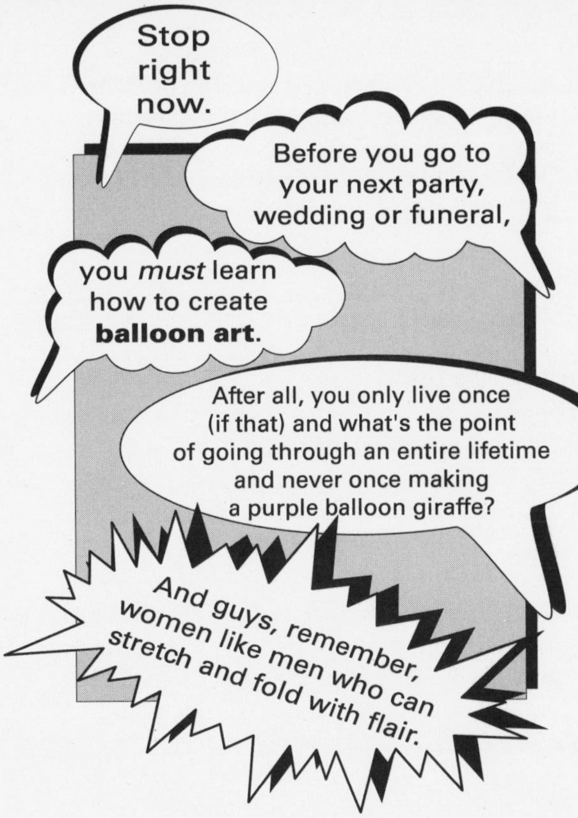
Stop right now.
Before you go to your next party, wedding or funeral,
you *must* learn how to create **balloon art**.
After all, you only live once (if that) and what's the point of going through an entire lifetime and never once making a purple balloon giraffe?
And guys, remember, women like men who can stretch and fold with flair.

## Calligraphy

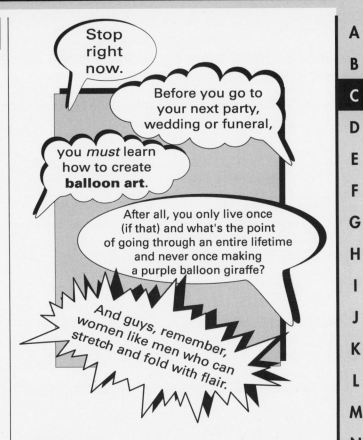

Calligraphy is the art of fine handwriting. Traditionally, calligraphy is often used with illumination (the decoration of a manuscript or book). There are many different types of traditional calligraphy and illumination: early Egyptian papyri, ornamental scripts of the Renaissance, Oriental brushwork, Islamic ornamentation, and so on. To be a good calligrapher requires years of practice. To be a great calligrapher requires years of practice and a lot of natural talent. Unfortunately, with the advent of computer-assisted artwork, the need for traditional calligraphers (ones who do not use a computer) is significantly diminished. If you are a calligrapher, or interested in calligraphy, take a look at this web page. You will find information about individual artists, calligraphy organizations, online pictures of manuscripts, as well as a collection of calligraphy-related links around the Net.

**Web:**

**http://mmm.wwa.com/ohmori/intro1.html**

**Majordomo Mailing List:**

List Name: **callig**
Subscribe to: **majordomo@c2.net**

A B C D E F G H I J K L M N O P Q R S T U V W X Y Z

## Clay Art

It's so much fun to play in the mud. The problem is you can't do it and use the computer at the same time. But when you get clean and dry, take some time to subscribe to this mailing list to partake in the discussion of ceramic arts, clay, kilns, glazes and other hot clay art topics.

**Usenet:**
**bit.listserv.clayart**

**Listserv Mailing List:**
List Name: **clayart**
Subscribe to: **listserv@lsv.uky.edu**

## Craft Fairs

We can't think of anything that rivals the liveliness and fun of a craft fair except perhaps a folk-dancing marathon. If you want to take a walk on the wild side, take a look at the schedule for upcoming craft fairs. This list is sorted by U.S. geographical region.

**Web:**
**http://www.teleport.com/~paulec/CRAFTLST.HTML**

## Craft Marketplace

No need to travel to the far regions of the world for the chance to buy cool craft stuff. On this newsgroup, you can buy, sell, trade or search for craft products and supplies. This is just the place to look when you need a little bit of Australian yarn to finish up that afghan.

**Usenet:**
**rec.crafts.marketplace**

## Craft Resources

A web page with links to many craft-related resources on the Internet. Here you will find links to general craft sites, craft suppliers, craft associations, information about fairs and events and even fun craft links for kids.

**Web:**
**http://www.wyomingcompanion.com/janacraft/links.htm**

## Craft Talk and General Discussion

The only thing as much fun as sitting around making crafts is sitting around talking about making crafts (and you don't have a mess to clean up when you are finished). Come join the discussion. Trade hints, tips, techniques and generally hang with the craftiest people on the Net.

**Usenet:**
**rec.crafts.misc**

**Listserv Mailing List:**
List Name: **crafts-l**
Subscribe to: **listserv@bigvax.alfred.edu**

## Craftweb Project

A little bit of everything is what you will find at this craft web site. This online community for professional craft artisans has links to crafts sites relating to glass, jewelry, wood, paperart, basketry, fabrics, ceramic, metal and painting.

**Web:**
**http://www.craftweb.com/**

## Cross-Stitch

What could be a better way to relax than to spend time sitting in a chair making thousands of little Xs with a needle and thread on a piece of aida cloth? If you like to spend your spare time making colorful crafts of cross-stitch, take a look at this web page. It has cross-stitch links, a FAQ and information about useful software programs. And using the mouse will limber up your fingers just the right amount to prepare you for a long session of stitching.

**Web:**
**http://www.heatersworld.com/wenspage/cross.html**

## Jewelry

What a great feeling it is to be dressed up for a night on the town when someone compliments you on your stunning cufflinks and you can say, "Thanks. I made these myself while I was watching the ballgame." Learn the fine craft of jewelry-making or share your jewelry secrets with others. Topics of discussion include gems, settings, bead-making and even selling jewelry.

**Usenet:**
**rec.crafts.jewelry**

# Cross-Stitching

It can be a lot of fun to stay home and cross-stitch for hours. But the last thing you want is to be in the middle of a complex pattern when all of a sudden you realize you don't know what comes next. So, before you get started, check the Net for cross-stitching hints, techniques and patterns. After all, who wants to be all strung out with no place to go?

## Knitting

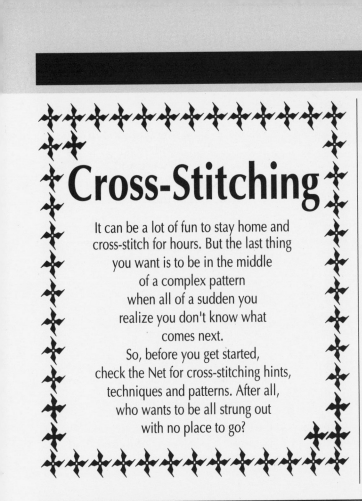

A web site with lists of books for knitters, net resources, knitting patterns, a list of stores around the world, information about knitting socks and knitting for dolls, as well as knitting hints, tips and techniques. The Surgeon General says that running while carrying knitting needles can be hazardous to your health.

**Web:**

**http://www.io.org/~spamily/knit/**

**Listserv Mailing List:**

List Name: **knit**
Subscribe to: **listserv@geom.umn.edu**

**Lost? Try a search engine.**

## *Look What I Found on the Net...*

```
Newsgroup: rec.crafts.misc
Subject: Stamp/Sticker Glue

> Does anybody have a recipe for the gummed back of stamps?

I found this one recently:

1 pkt (1/4 ounce) unflavored gelatin
1 Tbls cold water
3 Tbls boiling water
1/2 tsp. white corn syrup (optional)
1/2 tsp. lemon extract (optional)

In a very small bowl sprinkle gelatin into cold water.
Let soften for 5 minutes.

Pour boiling water into softened gelatin and stir until
dissolved. Add corn syrup and lemon extract (used for taste).

Mix well.

Brush thinly on back of sticker (paper may curl).

When dry, moisten sticker and apply to paper.
```

## Knives and Blades

Whether you want to make a delicate butter knife or a manly bear-killing sabre, this mailing list will have information that will interest you. Knife and blade makers and collectors from around the world discuss technical, artistic, historic, political and business-oriented topics relating to cutlery.

**Majordomo Mailing List:**
List Name: **knife-list**
Subscribe to: **majordomo@basis.com**

## Lace-Making

Lace-making is almost a lost art, because beer companies do not like to sponsor heated lace-making competitions as they do with various high impact male-oriented sports events. Fortunately, lace-making is not entirely neglected. This web page has a list of lace-making suppliers, some info about choosing lace, and working Le Pompe patterns. The mailing list gives you the opportunity to talk to lace-makers around the world.

**Web:**
**http://www.arachne.com/**

**Majordomo Mailing List:**
List Name: **lace**
Subscribe to: **majordomo@panix.com**

## Medieval and Renaissance Embroidery Patterns

Capture the spirit of the Medieval and Renaissance time periods by downloading designs you can incorporate into your own embroidery projects. While you are here, have a look at some pictures of finished works and images of antique embroidery and fabric fragments.

**Web:**
**http://www.uiuc.edu/ph/www/jscole/medembro.html**

**"Romance" is waiting for you.**

Is the world of needlework confusing you? Start reading **rec.crafts.textiles.needlework** and get the point.

## Metalworking

It's a totally embarrassing experience when your new neighbor comes to the door and says, "I heard you were the smartest and most talented metalworker on the block. Would you please anodize this piece of aluminum for me?" and that just happens to be the day you were going to brush up your skills from the great metalworking FAQ at this web site. Don't disappoint your friends and neighbors. Get the lowdown on heat treating, machinery, welding, motors, associations, clubs, museums, and more from the **rec.crafts.metalworking** FAQ.

**Web:**
**http://plains.uwyo.edu/~metal/**

## Needlework

This delicate and skillful craft takes time, patience and devotion. Read up on all manner of needlework including tips and techniques on tatting, petit point, cross-stitch, and embroidery. Share patterns, design ideas and timesaving hints on this age-old craft.

**Web:**
**http://www.needlework.com/**

**Usenet:**
**rec.crafts.textiles.needlework**

## Needlework Software

Needlework is fascinating and can be a lot of fun. However, when it comes to creating new charts and patterns, or keeping track of your supplies, wouldn't it be great to have a helper? Well, you can. Download some needlework software and your PC becomes your secretary and partner. After all, needlework is hard enough without having to do it all by hand.

**Web:**
**http://www.crl.com/~kdyer/software.html**

## Polymer Clay

Clay. Ah....clay. It makes me think of my childhood, when I could happily spend hours with soft and gooey substances and uninhibitedly mash and smash them into an unrecognizable pulp. (Now I have to spend my time smashing editors into an unrecognizable pulp.) Release your inner child and join the discussion about polymer clays. Common topics include molds, strength of clay, and tips on how to make various clay crafts.

**Usenet:**

**rec.crafts.polymer-clay**

## Quilting

A quilt is a blanket consisting of two layers of fabric enclosing a layer of cotton, wool, feathers or down. The whole thing is stitched together, often using a decorative design of some type. What make quilts so much fun is that you can use various fabrics and designs to create your own personalized work. If you are a quilt person—or aspire to learn this noble art—start with this quilting web page. Here you will find all the information you need to get started, along with lots of resources for experienced quilters. For discussion, questions and answers, check out the Usenet group.

**Web:**

**http://ttsw.com/MainQuiltingPage.html**

**Usenet:**

**rec.crafts.textiles.quilting**

## Rug-Hooking

Real rug-hookers know the difference between looped pile rug-hooking and latch-hooking. Don't get caught in a big social faux pas by not knowing the difference. At this web site, you can read the history of looped pile rug-hooking, a rug-hooking FAQ and a zine called Woolgatherings.

**Web:**

**http://gpu.srv.ualberta.ca/~dmerriam/hooked.html**

This is a family book so I can't really go into too many details about rug-hooking. Suffice it to say, if you do it by yourself or with a consenting adult, no one else really has the right to complain. Whether you practice your pastime in secret or out of the closet, the **rug-hooking** web site is there for you when you need it.

## Sewing

To me, the epitome of skill and artistry is being able to sew a shirt from scratch. I once watched someone do it and, to this day, I am still amazed. I guess I am one of the culturally unwashed: I like to wear clothes, but I have no idea how to make them. However, if you are a real sewing person, you are not alone. There are many people on the Net talking about sewing, and you can join them whenever you want.

**Web:**

**http://www.softworld.com/sewing/sewdir.htm**

**Usenet:**

**rec.crafts.textiles.sewing**

## Stained Glass

I love to look at stained glass and think of all the work that went into making it: cutting the pieces, grinding the edges, copper foiling or leading the glass, and then soldering the pieces together. If you are a stained glass artist, or if you are interested in learning something about this fascinating craft, you will enjoy this well-organized, comprehensive web site. You will find lots of information about supplies, patterns, magazines, questions and answers, and much, much more.

**Web:**

**http://www.artglassworld.com/**

## Textiles

Textiles are so...tactile. Get your fill of luscious laces, fabrics, yarns, thread and more. This page has loads of information on crocheting, knitting, embroidery, weaving, rug-hooking, sewing, quilting, lace-making and spinning. You can even browse the photo gallery where people on the Net show off their work.

**Web:**

**http://www.textiles.org/crafts/**

**Usenet:**

**rec.crafts.textiles**
**rec.crafts.textiles.misc**

## Tie Dye

Learn to tie dye your clothes in a totally rad fashion, man. And this is not just some lame instructions by capitalist pigs trying to make money off you. This FAQ (frequently asked question list) is compiled by the pros: tie dyed-in-the-wool Grateful Dead fans.

**Web:**

**http://www.public.asu.edu/~idjmw/tiedye.htm**

## Woodworking

Why kill a tree just to make paper, a fence or a house? Instead, you could be really cool and create something spiffy and craft-like that will make people ooh and aah. At this page, woodworkers can read tool reviews, files about bending wood, FAQs about wood toxicity, and information about toy safety.

**Web:**

**http://www.cs.rochester.edu/u/roche/wood.html**

**Usenet:**

**rec.woodworking**

## Yarn

The world would be a dull place if it were not for yarn. There would be no cozy sweaters or lumpy slippers to wear. Whether you like knitting, crocheting, using a machine or just your hands this group will have something you like as long as you are a lover of yarn.

**Usenet:**

**rec.crafts.textiles.yarn**

### *Look What I Found on the Net...*

```
(from the Woodworking Frequently Asked Question List)

              How do I remove paint?

      There are many ways to strip paint from wood.
-- Paint can be removed by scraping and/or sanding.
-- Paint can be removed by using chemical paint removers.
-- Paint can be removed by using heat.
-- Paint can be removed by sandblasting.

-- Rumor has it that oven cleaner also works.
```

# CRYPTOGRAPHY

## Ciphers

If you have to send a quick secret message to one of your friends, but you don't have time to make up a clever code, check out some of the ciphers that are already on the Net. While they aren't exactly a secret, some of them certainly are clever. Maybe you will get lucky and pick one that nobody has read about.

**Web:**

**http://www.achiever.com/freehmpg/cryptology/crypto.html**

## Classical Cryptology Bibliography

There is a ton of cryptography information on the Internet. However if, for some reason, you can't find everything you need to know from the Net, check out this bibliography of books about cryptology and cryptography. It is bound to get you going in the right direction.

**Web:**

**http://www.neumann.edu/tpatti/BIBLIO.HTM**

## Cryptographic Research

This is the web site for the International Association for Cryptologic Research. To be a cool cryptomaniac, you don't have to sit around in isolation planning new codes and trying to break old ones. No, you too can belong to a club of people just like you. (But remember what Groucho Marx once said, "I don't care to belong to any club that will have me as a member.") This site has information on crypto conferences, journals and newsletter.

**Web:**

**http://www.iacr.org/~iacr/**

Βαγκλεω ΛΛβε δοπλε τΛο

Want to learn about cryptography?
Start with the Cryptography Archive.

## Cryptography and the Government

If there is one thing the government understands less than running the government, it's running the Internet. Yet that doesn't stop certain ignoramuses from trying to control the Net in general and cryptography in particular. If you are at all interested in keeping up on how the guys in suits want to stick their electronic noses into our secrets, here is the place to talk about it. (P.S. The password is "swordfish".)

**Usenet:**

**talk.politics.crypto**

## Cryptography Archive

Here is a well-organized, compact collection of cryptography resources from around the Net. If you are at all serious about cryptography, you will want to put this site on your bookmark list. If you are not serious about cryptography, put this site on your list anyway. It's bound to impress your friends.

**Web:**

**http://www.quadralay.com/Crypto/**

## Cryptography Exports

Depending on where in the world you live, sending encryption software across international boundaries can get you into a heap of trouble. This page has information on various people who have encountered legal problems because of their work in cryptography.

**Web:**

**http://www.cygnus.com/pub/export/export.html**

## Cryptography for Beginners

Do you want to get into cryptography, but you aren't sure where to get started? Here is a good beginner's guide and introduction to cryptography. The site also includes information about the legal aspect of cryptography just so you know what rules you are breaking.

**Web:**

**http://www.ftech.net/~monark/crypto/**

## Cryptography Policy Issues

Cryptography is more than deciphering secret writing. There are also the political and administrative aspects. Here are some sites that consider cryptography from a political and legislative angle. Read about policies, legislative efforts, information about the infamous clipper chip, cryptography across international boundaries, and much more.

**Web:**

**http://www.cdt.org/crypto/**
**http://www.crypto.com/**

## Cryptography Resources

One of the nice things about cryptography is that it will allow you to store copies of all your love notes on your computer at work and you don't have to worry about your colleagues reading anything that might embarrass you or perhaps cause you to lose a presidential election. Find out about other great uses for cryptography at this web site, which contains a variety of links and information about data security.

**Web:**

**http://itrc.on.ca/CryptoWeb/**

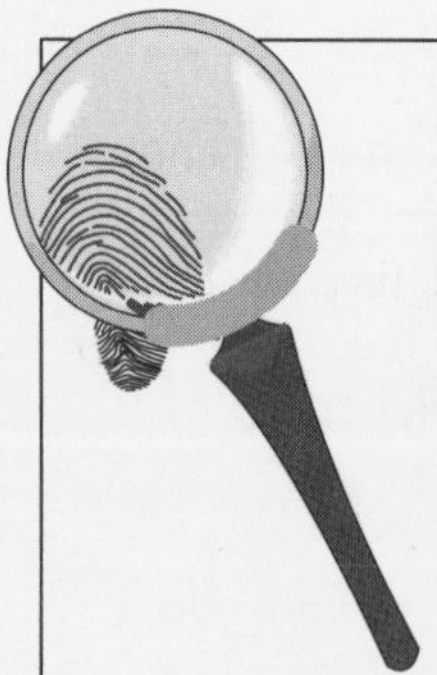

### Finding Technical Papers About Secret Stuff

*What do you do when you need to find a particular cryptography-related technical paper?*

*If you live near Washington, D.C., you can always go the headquarters of the National Security Agency and ask them to let you go through their library. (If you have any problem, just tell them you are one of my readers.)*

*However, if a trip to the NSA is not convenient, try the* ***Cryptography Technical Papers*** web site. *Not only is it faster, but you won't have to get fingerprinted just to use the restroom.*

## Cryptography Talk and General Discussion

A general discussion group for all aspects of data encryption and decryption. If you are a cryptography afficionado, this is the place to communicate with your peers on the Net.

```
F_eB7 n!K4r F^Pb2 M:Quf ^{9&L
0y}w# I/hH@ K'|eI 6N%-R G-(4u
UA,,] .Gs2~ o&?_^ :|IJA V*e}@
;a2#3 ZZuJB t0px9 \@z)t {eNSr
;LSZx Kht9. 'oRFa J'/KH oF:q'
Hn[\P vwqo1 4^:pI ~&8jb ]q4(2
1D)QE v.bvZ 6[M\$ 1)n;b L$?q{
d,$}F Q4PBM c[<&U )2>j) Sh\yF
!\u@j }:)ZW cOPKt 2_~P/ x|s]!
;<6.Q ";<;t UB,-{ 3@wzB HD4PH
tb$Xr !2Rpm &7}BU 8sg)= {
```

**Usenet:**

**sci.crypt**

## Cryptography Technical Papers

There is lots and lots and lots to learn about cryptography if you really want to know the subject intimately. If you like to get down to the nuts and bolts of how cryptography works, try reading technical papers and articles on this interesting science. This site has a searchable archive of technical cryptography documents.

**Web:**

**http://www.itribe.net/CTRS/**

## Digital Signatures and Certificates

More and more, we have the need to send information over the Net in complete secret. For example, if you order merchandise online by typing your credit card number, you should be sure that no one else can tap into the line, capture the information and use it for their own purposes. Or you may want to send a message to a friend or colleague that no one but the recipient can read. The systems that send and receive secure information over the Net use what are called "digital signatures" and "digital certificates". Such facilities are going to be in common use, so it is a good idea to find out how they work. Here are some good places to start.

**Web:**

**http://www.cylink.com/products/security/digsig/**
**http://www.epic.org/crypto/dss/**

## PGP Attack Page

Sometimes I like to make secret messages with PGP (Pretty Good Privacy encryption, developed by Phil Zimmerman). Generally I use it to encrypt my secret recipe for a special tuna and eggplant casserole I have been developing in between writing books. On the Net, there is a continual discussion going around about just how secure PGP really is. Can it be cracked? Read up on the reports and updates of clever individuals who spend their time trying to find vulnerabilities in PGP.

**Web:**

**http://axion.physics.ubc.ca/pgp-attack.html**

### Sending Secret Messages with PGP

The best things in life may be free, but if you don't want to share, you may have to hide them. The most widely used encryption program on the Net is PGP, written by Phil Zimmerman who, single-handedly, deep-sixed all the government's plans to control encryption by offering a free, high-quality software package to everyone.

Using PGP requires two passwords, called "keys". One of these is public; the other one is secret. You give your public key to anyone whom you want to be able to send secret notes to you. They use this key (and the PGP software) to encode a message which they then send to you. The beauty of the system is that a person can only decode the message if they have the private key (which you keep only for yourself).

The PGP program helps you create public and private keys that will work properly. Then you can give out your public key to your friends and start sending secrets around the Net. Similarly, if you have a friend who uses PGP, you can use his public key to encode a message to him that only he can read (because only he has the corresponding private key). Truly, Phil Zimmerman is one of the heroes of the 1990's.

**The Net: open 24 hours a day.**

## PGP Encryption/Decryption Program

Where to get and how to use the ubiquitous PGP (Pretty Good Privacy) encryption package. Use it to send secret messages to your friends.

**Web:**

**http://bs.mit.edu:8001/pgp-form.html**

**Usenet:**

**alt.security.pgp**

## Public PGP Key Repository

Guys, here's a great way to meet that special someone. Go up to a beautiful girl and say "I'll show you my public key, if you'll show me yours." If it doesn't work, try a different girl. In the meantime, you can share your public keys with the rest of the Net by connecting to this web site. If you want to talk about it (and you haven't yet found Ms. Right), the Usenet discussion group is always available.

**Web:**

**http://swissnet.ai.mit.edu/~bal/pks-toplev.html**

**Usenet:**

**alt.security.keydist**

Want to trade secrets?
I'll show you my public key if you show me yours.

## Steganography

Where are you going to hide Aunt Effie's secret recipe that you plan to use for the chili cook-off? The county championship is at stake, and you are determined not to let a spy slip in and ruin your chances. Don't settle for mere PGP encryption. Use steganography to hide your encrypted documents inside innocuous-looking images, sound recordings or other data files.

**Web:**

**http://www.iquest.net/~mrmil/stego.html**

### HIDING SECRETS WITHIN PICTURES USING STEGANOGRAPHY

Stego is the most amazing, cool thing you have ever seen. You can encode secret information inside a **PICTURE**—within the little tiny dots. To anyone else, it looks like a regular picture (say, of you shaking hands with the Pope at ex-Princess Diana's birthday party). But to anyone in the know, it is a **SECRET MESSAGE**. You can send it all around the Net if you want, and no one can extract the information unless they have the password.

How totally radical. Only you know that the picture contains information hidden within the dots. All you need is a Macintosh and a modem and you can open your own spy agency. If you do, make sure you remember what my sister told me years ago: It's nice to be important, but it's important to be nice.

## CYBERPUNK

### Cyberkind

Cyberkind, a web publication, offers prosaics and poetics for a wired world. It contains non-fiction, fiction, poetry, and art galleries, and is updated periodically. Writers' guidelines, details of how to write to the editor, a notification mailing list, and the publication itself.

**Web:**
**http://sunsite.unc.edu/ckind/**

**Reach out and email someone.**

### Cybermind

This web page offers archives from the Cybermind mailing list, Cybermind texts, many articles covering the themes of cybermind and cyberspace, and links to Cybermind-related online resources.

**Web:**
**http://www.lm.com/~tellis/cyber/cm.html**

**Listserv Mailing List:**
List Name: **cybermind**
Subscribe to: **listserv@listserv.aol.com**

### Cyberpunk Beginnings

Where did the term "cyberpunk" come from anyway? This short essay discusses cyberpunk in the 80s and 90s and how it got started. It talks about the movies, books and people who shaped the evolution of cyberpunk.

**Web:**
**http://www.cs.uidaho.edu/lal/cyberspace/cyberpunk/docs/Maddox.Essay**

### Cyberpunk Culture

Collection of cyberpunk-related material, including Locus magazine, Bruce Sterling articles, and the latest information about cyberpunk conventions, those mind-blowing meetings of the computer underground.

**Web:**
**http://www.delphi.com/~audacitee/CPCulture.html**

### Cyberpunk FAQ

You can't be totally cool, hip or rad until you know just what cyberpunk is. And you can't just fake it. You have to know the real stuff, like the difference between the literary movement and the culture. Read this FAQ which will answer all your questions about cyberpunk and never again will you have to worry about not being in with the In Crowd.

**Web:**
**http://bush.cs.tamu.edu/~erich/alt.cp.faq.html**

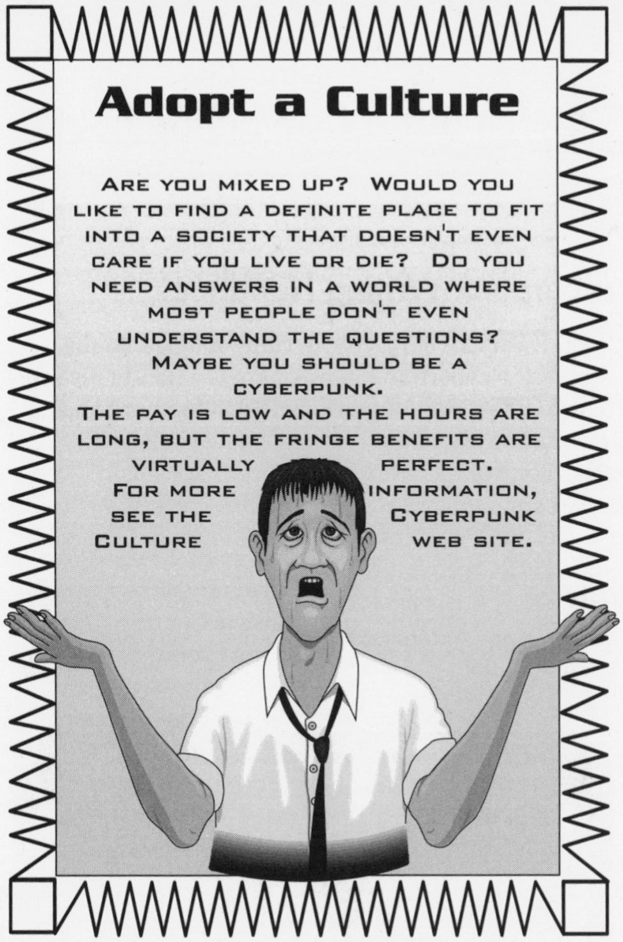
Adopt a Culture
ARE YOU MIXED UP? WOULD YOU LIKE TO FIND A DEFINITE PLACE TO FIT INTO A SOCIETY THAT DOESN'T EVEN CARE IF YOU LIVE OR DIE? DO YOU NEED ANSWERS IN A WORLD WHERE MOST PEOPLE DON'T EVEN UNDERSTAND THE QUESTIONS? MAYBE YOU SHOULD BE A CYBERPUNK.
THE PAY IS LOW AND THE HOURS ARE LONG, BUT THE FRINGE BENEFITS ARE VIRTUALLY PERFECT.
FOR MORE INFORMATION, SEE THE CYBERPUNK CULTURE WEB SITE.

## Cyberpunk Gaming

When life is getting too cozy and soft for you, try some cyberpunk role-playing. Immerse yourself in the dark, dreary future of a world gone tech. On the Net, you can find some great resources for cyberpunk gaming, or you can hang out on Usenet and talk to other gamers about what they like to do.

**Web:**

**http://www.common.net/~shadow/rpg_index/cyber.html**

**Usenet:**

**rec.games.frp.cyber**

**The Net is waiting for you.**

## Cyberpunk Literature

People who are immersed in the cyberpunk culture understand what it is, but they have a lot of trouble explaining it to anyone else. My advice is to start with the idea that technology touches virtually every aspect of our life. From there, you can enter the cyberpunk world by reading, and here is a good place to start: a collection of cyberlit (cyberpunk literature) resources on the Net.

**Web:**

**http://omni.cc.purdue.edu/~stein/stein.htm**

## Cyberpunk Movies

Here's a great idea you can plan for this weekend. Dust off the big screen television and have all your friends over for a cyberpunk film festival. For added special effects, you can rewire your remote control to run all the appliances in the house. At the touch of a button, you can pop some microwave popcorn, blend frozen drinks and get the dishwasher started cleaning the dishes. If you need a list of movies, this site will tell you what you should rent. (You're on your own as far as rewiring the remote control goes.)

**Web:**

**http://www.nyx.net/~astoker/cpmovie.html**

## Cyberpunk Projects

Cyberpunk is not the future. Cyberpunk is now. Read about current cyberpunk projects or famous cyberpunk authors like William Gibson and Bruce Sterling. Or for something a little more low key, check out cyberpunk mailing lists and zines.

**Web:**

**http://www.physics.wisc.edu/~shalizi/hyper-weird/new-edge.html**

**Spam is more than a food.**

## Cyberpunk Resources

Once I had a cyberpunk nightmare. In the dream, everything was dark and bleak and nobody ever went surfing any more. Fortunately, it was only a dream. If you are inclined to have bad dreams, it's best not to look at this site before bedtime. There are enough cyberpunk resources here to send your imagination into Mona Lisa Overdrive.

**Web:**

**http://www.wwmatrix.com/cyberpunk/menu.shtml**

## Cyberpunk Talk and General Discussion

Cyberpunks don't just talk about things other people don't understand. Cyberpunks live in a world that other people can't even imagine. Would you like to visit? You can join the discussion whenever you want, but be patient, it may take a while for your brain to make the necessary changes.

**Usenet:**

**alt.cyberpunk**
**alt.cyberpunk.movement**
**alt.cyberpunk.tech**

## Cyberpunk Writing

Step through a portal to another dimension, a cyberpunk world where darkness, depression, and danger are the norm. Lovers of cyberpunk sling slang around like literary fly-fishing lures. If you love high-tech, heavy metal punk, you will love the virtual reality of cyberpunk.

**Web:**

**http://www.magi.com/~vektor/chatsubo/**

**Usenet:**

**alt.cyberpunk.chatsubo**

**Sv bndwdth. Dn't typ ny vwls.**

**Check out a free online book.**

## Cyberpunk Writing Handbook

If you want to weave your writing magic into the form of the cyberpunk genre, here is a handy resource to have on your bookmark list. This document has information about the settings, subcultures and technology of the world of cyberpunk. (This document, while geared for writers, can also be useful to cyberpunk gamers.)

**Web:**

**http://zippy.sonoma.edu/~paradigm/handbook/cpunk.html**

CYBERPUNK PROJECTS
You may be a cyberpunk and not even know it.
There's only one way to find out. Check to see what the cyberpunks are doing, and look for yourself in the crowd.
Remember, anyone can be a punk, but do you have what it takes to be a cyberpunk?

## Cyberpunks and Hackers

What's the story on cyberpunks and hackers? Are they really the people you read about in those mass media exposès? Or is it possible that the reality of cyberpunk and hacker existence is just a tad different than what the newspapers and magazines are telling you? Here is a web site that will introduce you to the real cyberpunk and hacker culture.

**Web:**

**http://www.accessorl.net/~cyberwar/cybpunk.htm**

### Cyberpunks and Hackers

All hackers are cyberpunks, but not all cyberpunks are hackers. (For example, there are also crackers, phreakers and cypherpunks.)
My suggestion is to read about cyberpunks and hackers and make sure you understand the nuances, before you make a terrible mistake on your résumé.

TOP SECRET

**Get in step by reading "Dance".**

## Dick, Philip K.

Philip K. Dick (1928-1982) was an American science fiction writer whose writing transcended the base world of normality and ascended to the rarefied atmosphere of cyberpunk. Dick is best known for his story "Do Androids Dream of Electric Sheep?" on which the movie Blade Runner was (loosely) based. Personally, I liked both the movie and the story. If you liked Blade Runner but have never read any of Dick's stories, I suggest you start with "Do Androids Dream of Electric Sheep?" and explore from there.

**Web:**

**http://www.angelfire.com/pages0/pkd/**
**http://www.users.interport.net/~regulus/pkd/pkd-int.html**

**Usenet:**

**alt.books.phil-k-dick**
**alt.fan.philip-dick**

## Gibson, William

Sometimes referred to as "the father of cyberpunk", William Gibson gained a cult following after the publication of Neuromancer in 1984. Gibson has written several other books and short stories, all of which are in the cyberpunk style: a dark future marked by high technology and a rise of the multinational corporate body as a significant ruling power.

**Web:**

**http://ee.oulu.fi/~thefinn/gibson/gibson.html**
**http://www-user.cibola.net/~michaela/gibson/**

## Sterling, Bruce

Bruce Sterling (1954-) is a cult-inspiring cyberpunk author who wrote "The Hacker Crackdown" (about computer crime) as well as various cyberpunk and future culture-type books. Sterling's work forms one of the pillars of neo-American cyberpunk literature. A lot of his writing is available on the Net, so you can check it out whenever you want.

**Web:**

**http://riceinfo.rice.edu/projects/RDA/VirtualCity/Sterling/sterling_res.html**

# DANCE

## Ballet and Modern Dance

The only thing that is not cool about ballet and modern dance is that you can't do it on the Internet. The closest thing you will find is a place where people talk about their experiences in the dance scene and share information on upcoming dance tours as well as dance opportunities. Strap yourself into some shoes and sashay on over to where the dance action is happening.

**Usenet:**

**alt.arts.ballet**

## Ballet Terms

When you don't know your *adage* from an *arabesque*, it's time to get professional help. This web site has definitions for common terms you will hear in the world of ballet. Brush up on some of these words before you go to your next ballet dancing party.

**Web:**

**http://www.acm.uiuc.edu/signet/JHSI/dance.html**

:-)

### *Look What I Found on the Net...*

```
Newsgroup: alt.arts.ballet
Subject: age of starting ballet / feet damage

> A friend of mine (female) is considering starting ballet, so I
> would like to ask all of you girls two things:
>
> 1. What is the best age to start ballet, and is there is an
> age limit that is better not to be exceeded?
>
> 2. Is it true that ballet damages female feet?

The general theory goes:  Pre-ballet would be creative dance from ages
4-8, with a small amount of ballet added in.  As the
child gets older, the more ballet the student gets.

I have personally found that if kids have had pre-ballet for a
year or two before beginning strict ballet training, they
progress faster.  But most new beginners (female) start at ages
8-9 years old.  It is fine to start later, but the later you start the
harder it gets both emotionally and physically.

If a teenager starts ballet for fun it is great, just like an
adult, but if a child is serious about a career, then it is
really too late to get to where a professional needs to be by
age 17-18.

How to tell how well a child will dance is impossible, so you
just have to go for it and see what happens.

Feet: I think a lot of it depends of genetics as well as training.
Females are more prone to bunions, and so on.

Pointe shoes must be fitted correctly, and be the right type for
the foot.  Also, a lot depends on the type of foot the girl has, her toes,
the length, her strength, and when a teacher puts the
girl on pointe.  Most students don't start pointe work till they
are 11-12 years old.  But some gifted and strong girls can start
earlier, if the musculature is developed enough.  A lot depends
on the teacher's beliefs, but girls should not go on pointe
before the age of 10.
```

## Ballroom and Swing Dancing

Keep in step with the latest ballroom and swing dance happenings by joining this mailing list. Discuss places to dance, exchange information about clubs, ballroom dance music, dance steps, technique, dance etiquette and get announcements of special events. If you are interested in joining a moderated, lower traffic mailing list, use the **ballrm-m** list.

**Listserv Mailing List:**
List Name: **ballrm-m**
Subscribe to: **listserv@mitvma.mit.edu**

**Listserv Mailing List:**
List Name: **ballroom**
Subscribe to: **listserv@mitvma.mit.edu**

## Belly Dancing

When you feel like your life is lacking in that which is exotic, you can have a look at these web sites which specialize in belly dancing, often called oriental dancing or Middle Eastern dance. Learn about the rich cultural heritage behind the art of belly dancing. These sites include sounds, texts, pictures and lists of events happening around the world. Join the mailing list **med-dance** if you are looking for more personal interaction with fellow dancers or fans.

**Web:**
**http://cie-2.uoregon.edu/bdance/**
**http://www.ivo.se/as-sayf/englishindex.html**
**http://www.lpl.arizona.edu/~kimberly/medance/medance.html**

**Majordomo Mailing List:**
List Name: **med-dance**
Subscribe to: **majordomo@world.std.com**

## Break Dancing

I certainly thought it was dead like the rest of the culture of the '80s. However, there is a place on the Web where break dancing is clinging tenaciously to life, thanks to devotees of this nearly forgotten craft. Refresh your memory of break dancing by having a look at pictures and the movies that made this dance so popular. Read the break dance history and brush up on your lingo so you can be really *fresh*, not *wack*.

**Web:**
**http://weber.u.washington.edu/~bock/bd/bd.html**

## Calendar of Events

Never again will you be all dressed up with no place to go. Check out this list of dance events that are happening all over the world. Every time zone is hopping, so if you place your airline reservations carefully, you could arrange to be dancing all night.

**Web:**
**http://www.weblink.com/nyibc/Events/events.html**

## Contra Dancing

It's not square dancing. It's not country line dancing. A young, Americanized version of English country dancing, this lively dancing pastime gets its name from the French *contredans*. While nobody agrees on the origins, most everyone agrees that contra dancing is fun. Learn more about how and where it's done at these web sites, which are packed to the edges with information.

**Web:**
**http://www.io.com/~entropy/contradance/**
**http://www.rain.org/~gshapiro/contradance.html**

## Dance Resources

After six hours of school, I've had enough of a day, I grab the radio dial, and turn it up all the way, I've got to dance, right on the spot, the beat's really hot, dance, dance, dance, dance... (And when I'm not dancing, I'm on the Net, looking at dance resources and talking on Usenet.)

**Web:**
**http://www.cs.fsu.edu/projects/group4/dance.html**
**http://www.cyberspace.com/vandehey/dance.html**
**http://www.tmn.com/Artswire/www/dance/resource.html**
**http://zeus.ncsa.uiuc.edu:8080/~hneeman/dance_hotlist.html**

**Usenet:**
**rec.arts.dance**

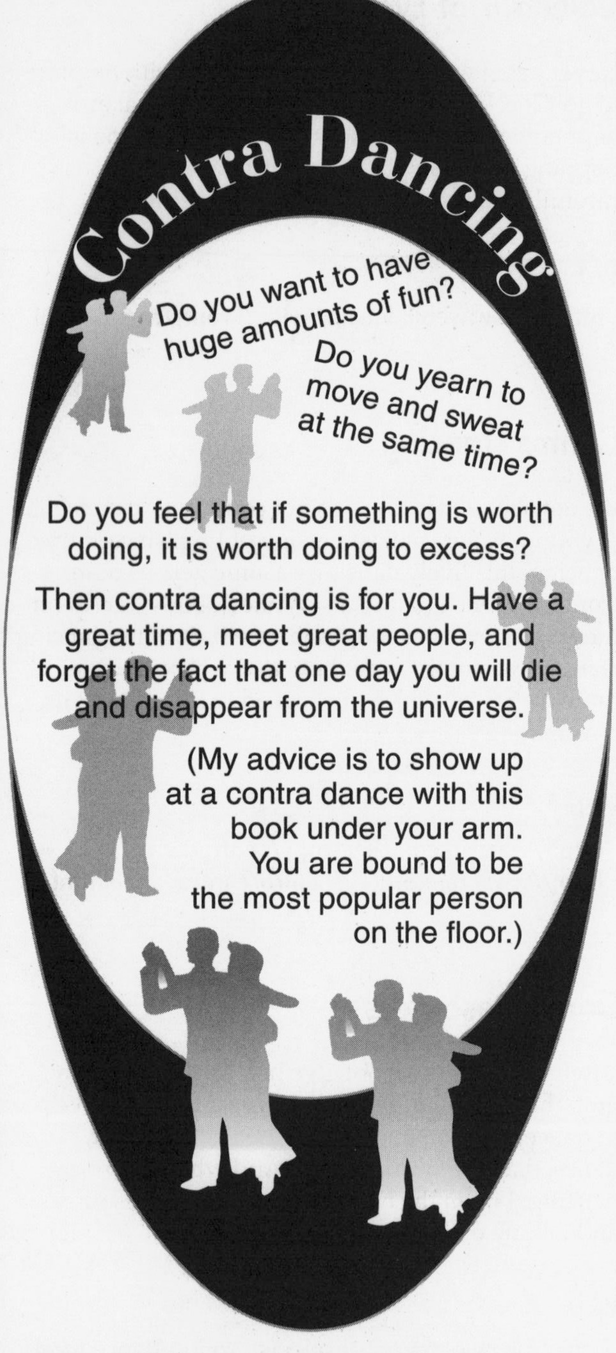
Contra Dancing
Do you want to have huge amounts of fun?
Do you yearn to move and sweat at the same time?
Do you feel that if something is worth doing, it is worth doing to excess?
Then contra dancing is for you. Have a great time, meet great people, and forget the fact that one day you will die and disappear from the universe.
(My advice is to show up at a contra dance with this book under your arm. You are bound to be the most popular person on the floor.)

## Dance Talk and General Dicussion

Eventually the music will stop, but that's no reason for you to stop dancing. Do what I do: stand in front of the computer and read the articles in the **rec.arts.dance** Usenet group.

**Usenet:**
**rec.arts.dance**

## Dancescape

Ballroom dancing is not for sissies. For those of you with more cutthroat tendencies, this site has loads of information about competitive ballroom dancing. Check the calendar of events to see what's happening in your area. Get information on publications about competitive dancing, organizations dedicated to the sport of dancing and personal ads for people who love to dance. You will also find a list of places where competitive dancing events are held, including Asia, Europe and North America. This is not your mother's ballroom dancing.

**Web:**
**http://wchat.on.ca/dance/pages/dscape1.htm**

## European Dance Server

Europe has more than just good wine and cheese. For instance, dance is a well-loved pastime because Europeans need interesting ways to exercise off all that good wine and cheese. Get a little dose of culture by checking out all this information about European dance resources, which are organized by country or by category.

**Web:**
**http://www.net-shopper.co.uk/dance/**

## Flamenco

There is absolutely no truth to the rumor that culture is boring. This is simple propaganda designed by those in the entertainment business to seduce people into watching more television when, in fact, they should be out learning how to flamenco dance. Flamenco dancing is fun. Other than children's birthday parties, where else can you wear colorful costumes while dancing around, stomping your feet and clapping your hands? Learn more about this passionate pastime, by checking out a web page entirely devoted to the dance. For personal interaction, you can discuss dancing with people around the world on the **flamenco** mailing list.

**Web:**
**http://www.ims.uni-stuttgart.de/phonetik/ernst/flamenco/ebflamenco.html**

**Majordomo Mailing List:**
List Name: **flamenco**
Subscribe to: **majordomo@world.std.com**

## Folk and Traditional Dance

I have always had a strong interest in traditional dances; for example, my favorite dance is the "Freddy". If you are like me, you are not alone. Here are some resources to keep you in step with people around the world who care about how dancing used to be in the days when people danced to enjoy life and not just to keep moving till the drugs wore off.

**Web:**

**http://www.io.com/~hbp/folkdance/fd.html**

**Usenet:**

**rec.folk-dancing**

**Listserv Mailing List:**

List Name: **dance-l**
Subscribe to: **listserv@nic.surfnet.nl**

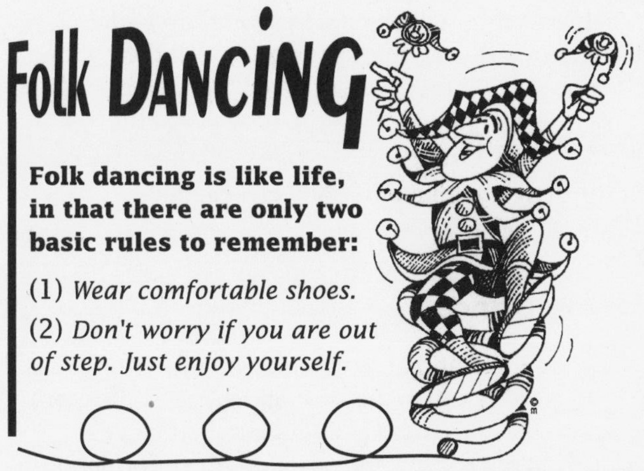
Folk Dancing
Folk dancing is like life, in that there are only two basic rules to remember:
(1) Wear comfortable shoes.
(2) Don't worry if you are out of step. Just enjoy yourself.

## Morris Dancing

When you are looking for something lively in which to participate, consider taking up Morris dancing. This rustic dance of north England had its origins in country festivals and became a vigorous ambulatory dance which found its dancers cavorting from village to village accompanied by pipers and taborers. This mailing list talks about not only Morris dancing, but also Garland, North West, Rapper, Cotswold, Border, Abbots Bromley, Longsword and similar forms of English dance.

**Listserv Mailing List:**

List Name: **morris**
Subscribe to: **listserv@indycms.iupui.edu**

## Muse Zine

Get a copy of this snazzy little electronic zine, which has a regular section covering the world of dance. Read articles about dance in general, dance troupes or current international events. The Muse is published monthly and covers more than dance, so it's a fabulous all-around zine for anyone interested in culture and entertainment.

**Web:**

**http://www.hyperlink.com/muse/**

## Renaissance Dance

For those of you with a little more vintage taste for dance, try Renaissance dancing. It's colorful, it's cultural, the music is good and best of all: you can't get arrested for doing it. The web site has tons of files about the dance including information about music, history and the dance steps themselves. If you want to talk to other people about Renaissance dances, join the **rendance** mailing list.

**Web:**

**http://www.ucs.mun.ca/~andrew/rendance.html**

**Listserv Mailing List:**

List Name: **rendance**
Subscribe to: **listserv@morgan.ucs.mun.ca**

## Round Dance

Round, round, get around, they get around. And the reason is because there are hundreds of round dance cue sheets and step instructions on this web site. You can look through the full index or browse by phase or rhythm.

**Web:**

**http://www.rob.cs.tu-bs.de/mp/RoundDance/**

**What if...?**

## Samba

Samba is a type of music and a type of dance from Brazil, a tradition that originated with African slaves. Samba is a lively, gyrating, complicated dance performed by men and women together. The men and women perform different dance moves, with the women shaking their bodies and the men doing more hopping, jumping and slapping hands to their heels. This web site has a listing of samba events, help with terminology, information about samba music, and links to regional samba web pages. The mailing list is a place for exchanging information on topics such as music, costumes, styles of samba, schools and events.

**Web:**

**http://www.worldsamba.org/**

**Majordomo Mailing List:**

List Name: **sambistas**
Subscribe to: **majordomo@tardis.ed.ac.uk**

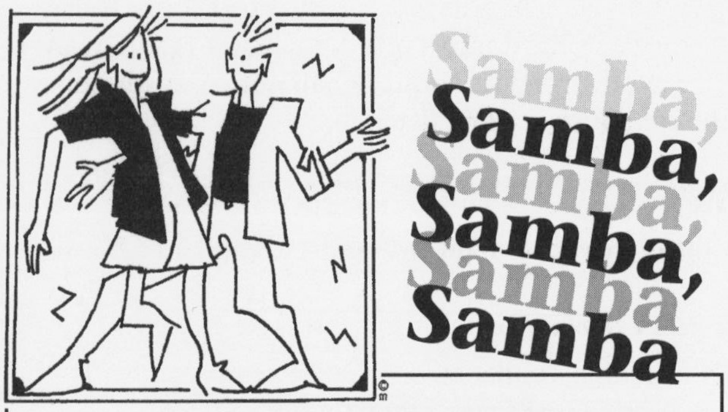
Samba,
Samba,
Samba

**Don't just sit there.**
**Put on the music and samba.**
**(And while you are dancing, read about samba on the Net.)**

## Scottish Dancing

Forget the bar scene and the pick-up lines. Try some Scottish country dancing. Even though there is no actual dancing on the web site, you can learn all about Scottish dancing and prime yourself for a bout of fancy non-choreographed enjoyment.

**Web:**

**http://www.tm.informatik.uni-frankfurt.de/strathspey**
**http://www.tvt.com/scddb/**

## Society for Creative Anachronism Dance

If you love the SCA, but don't want to dress funny and get hit with big sticks, try engaging in some SCA dance in which you still have to dress funny, but there is little hitting involved. This web site has lots of information about historical dance, dance steps, and music.

**Web:**

**http://www.pbm.com/~lindahl/music_and_dance.html**

## Square Dancing

You don't have to be a square to enjoy square dancing. People from all walks of life enjoy this down-home pastime. For instance, the last time I was at a dance hall in Hollywood, I saw certain film notables swinging their partners and do-si-doing. If the film industry thinks it's cool, well then, it must be cool.

**Web:**

**http://pages.map.com/~bobl/sdance.htm**

## Swing Dance

Swing all night and at daybreak when the music dies down, come home to the Web and swing some more. This web site has more information than you can triple step on. For instance, you can get information on upcoming swing dance events on a local or national level. Or you can read about styles and techniques of swing. Impress your friends and dance partners with your huge knowledge of swing steps that you learned from this fabulous online swing source. I could go on and on about this site, but I have better things to do...like go dancing.

**Web:**

**http://www.cs.cornell.edu/Info/People/aswin/SwingDancing/swing_dancing.html**

**Stay connected.**

## Tango

What is it that is so appealing, so passionate, and so captivating about the tango? At first glance, it's hard to understand the attraction. Why would so many people spend so much time moving with restrained eroticism to haunting music, when they could be sitting at home reading one of my books? Still, there are tango fans all over the world, so there must be something in it. Try it for yourself and you will find that there is nothing better to perk up an otherwise dull day than a heavy dose of carefully channeled sensuality. (Personal note: My favorite tango is "The Masochism Tango" by Tom Lehrer, which I play on the piano whenever I need a break from writing.)

**Web:**

**http://users.aimnet.com/~batango/resource.htm**
**http://www.ims.uni-stuttgart.de/phonetik/ernst/tango/ebtango.html**

**Listserv Mailing List:**

List Name: **tango-l**
Subscribe to: **listserv@mitvma.mit.edu**

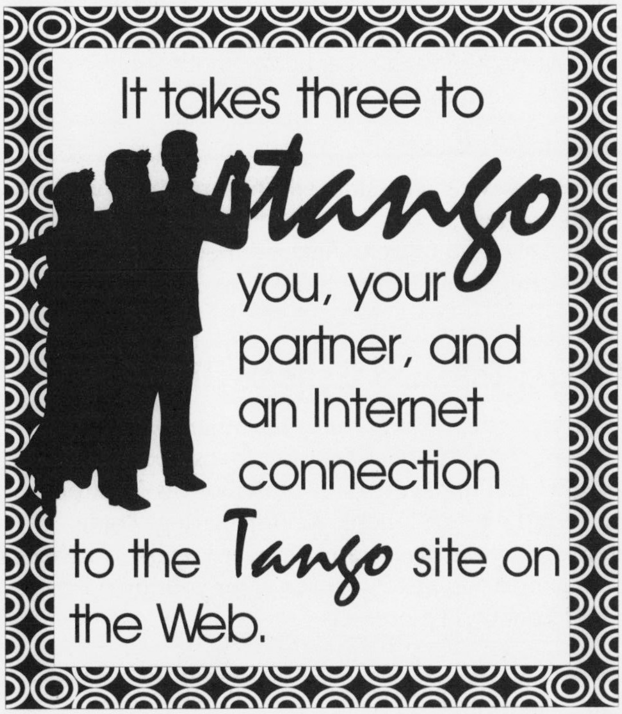
It takes three to tango
you, your partner, and an Internet connection
to the Tango site on the Web.

## Tap Dancing

When you are looking for some lively, snappy dancing, consider tap. On the **tap-jazz** mailing list, lovers of fancy footwork discuss steps, techniques, shoes, dancers and the tap industry. For more immediate gratification, you can shuffle, flap, hop, scuff, paddle, dig or cramp roll your way to the web site. These pages contain information about dance steps, famous tapsters, dance clubs, movies, sounds and more. By the way, when I was a kid, I used to do a lot of tap dancing, until one day I fell into the sink and hurt my ankle.

**Web:**

**http://www.mcphu.edu/~corrp/tap**

**Majordomo Mailing List:**

List Name: **tap-jazz**
Subscribe to: **majordomo@world.std.com**

## Western Square Dancing

"Chicken in the bread pan kickin' out dough; skip to my lou my darling!" or "Parlez-vous square dance?" This web page is the place to be if you like Western square dancing. It has call lists, articles, humor, and much more.

**Web:**

**http://suif.stanford.edu/~rfrench/wsd/**

### Square Dancing, the Pastime of Kings

Who has not fantasized about meeting the perfect man or woman in the middle of a square dance? There is something about this honestly American tradition that fans the flames of grace and nobility in all of us. The next time you are sitting home on a Saturday night, wondering if there are people out there who really know how to have more fun than you, take a look at the Western Square Dancing web site and eat your heart out. Then stop feeling sorry for yourself and get out on the floor.

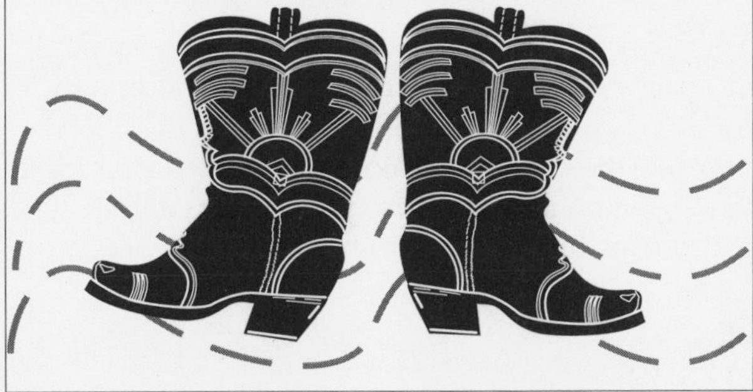

# DIETING

## Bite by Byte Newsletter

Bite by Byte is a newsletter for people who are dieting or on the track to a healthier lifestyle. This newsletter has a variety of good information about nutrition, recipes, inspirational thoughts, dieting tips and reviews.

**Web:**

**http://www.voicenet.com/~mlms/coh/news/cohnews.htm**

## Club 100

Club 100 is a mailing list for people who are overweight by 100 pounds or more. The newsgroup **alt.support.obesity** grew out of this list and messages from the newsgroup are also posted to the mailing list. Club 100 is designed to be a supportive area for people to talk about issues related to being overweight, dieting included.

**Web:**

**http://www.unm.edu/~markm/asofaq.html**

**Listserv Mailing List:**

List Name: **club-100_mail_list-l**
Subscribe to: **listserv@mail.unm.edu**

## Cyberdiet

If you think you need to go on a diet, but you are not sure exactly where to start, check with Cyberdiet. They offer a nutritional profile that might help you determine the amount of calories you should eat in order to maintain or decrease your weight. Other information about dieting is also available.

**Web:**

**http://www.cyberdiet.com/**

## Diet and Weight Reduction

Are you looking for a new way to lose weight? Here is a list of links relating to obesity, diet and nutrition, physicians, medicines and drugs. Just the thing to read while you are having your midnight snack.

**Web:**

**http://www.loop.com/~bkrentzman/links/obesity.links.html**

## Diet Buddies

It's no fun to diet alone. All you have to do is join a diet group and you can get emotional support from people around the world who are struggling with the same issues as you. You don't have to go through anything by yourself. Remember, as long as you are on the Net, you are not alone.

**Web:**

**http://home.sprynet.com/sprynet/brenda1996/**

## Dieting FAQ

When you are suffering from too much information, get some help sorting it all out with the FAQ from **alt.support.diet**. This list of frequently asked questions covers issues such as general diet and nutrition, weight loss, liquid diets and fasts, weight loss organizations and diet books, motivation, exercise, diet aids and more.

**Web:**

**http://www.cis.ohio-state.edu/hypertext/faq/usenet/dieting-faq**
**http://www.lib.ox.ac.uk/internet/news/faq/by-category.dieting-faq.html**

## Dieting Talk and General Discussion

Does your diet work? Or like the other 99.9 percent of humanity, do you have to suffer to lose excess weight? Join ultra-nutrition-conscious people around the world who will thank you for sharing. Trade stories, scientific trivia, and leftover Weight Watchers' menus. Are you just about ready for your own zip code? Lonely no more.

**Usenet:**

**alt.support.diet**

## Dining Out Tips

It's hard to turn down luscious food when it is sitting right in front of you. It's difficult when many restaurants insist on serving you a gargantuan amount of food that is really enough for two people. This web site contains hints on how to avoid overeating and breaking diet rules when you are at a party or dining out. Here is my hint: when you eat out with another person, order one large meal and split it between the two of you. This is a great way for a husband and wife to eat sensibly and save money at the same time.

**Web:**

**http://www.weight-watchers.com/out.htm**

## Fad Diets

Every day you can see new fad diets in magazines and books. Each one claims to be *the* way to fill your dieting needs. This has been happening for years, and the diets still come and go like the tide. The American Heart Association has a page that talks about fad diets from a health point of view. You might want to read this before starting any new program that you think may be a flash in the fad-diet pan.

**Web:**

**http://www.amhrt.org/hs96/faddiet.html**

## Fast Food Calorie Counter

When you go to a fast food restaurant, you can't exactly read the labels to see what you are putting into your body. In fact, you are probably better off if you *don't* read the labels. Instead, use this calorie counter to find out how fattening everything is. After all, what's the point of eating junky fast food if you can't at least get a substantial helping of guilt out of the experience?

**Web:**

**http://www.uiuc.edu/departments/mckinley/health-info/hlthpro/fastfood.html**

## Fat

It's 11:00 PM, do you know what your cholesterol/HDL risk ratio is? Saturated fat, hydrogenated fat, good fat, bad fat, everyone is talking about fat. Sometimes the stories, ideas and rumors are so conflicting, you can't tell if you are sinking slowly or rising to the top of the soup bowl of life, only to be skimmed off the top. Don't despair, get your fat facts hot off the Net.

**Web:**

**http://ificinfo.health.org/redufat.htm**
**http://ificinfo.health.org/sortfat.htm**
**http://www.uiuc.edu/departments/mckinley/health-info/nutrit/wtloss/fatcont.html**

### *Look What I Found on the Net...*

```
Newsgroup: alt.support.diet
Subject: Bodyfat Measurement

Hi all.  Since a lot of people have been asking me about various
methods of bodyfat measurement, I figured I ought to post something.
There are a variety of methods used to measure bodyfat, each with
their own pros and cons.

The most accurate method is to have the body dissected, and then to
separate and weigh the fat cells.  This will give the most accurate
value but is rather inconvenient as you have to be dead for it to
work...
```

A B C D E F G H I J K L M N O P Q R S T U V W X Y Z

## Fat Loss Support

One of the hardest things about losing fat is having to give up pizza. When you want help with ideas on how to lose fat, help with problem-solving, discussion about fat-loss diets or just emotional support, this is a good mailing list to join.

**Web:**

**http://www.geocities.com/Athens/1953/**

**Majordomo Mailing List:**

List Name: **fatloss-support**
Subscribe to: **majordomo@list.stanford.edu**

Losing weight is not easy. If you would like to help someone, or if you need a little assistance for yourself, join the
fatloss-support
mailing list.

## Fat Substitutes

The American Heart Association has lots of information about fat: what it is, what types of fat exist, and what you should and should not eat. Whether you are watching your fat intake because you want to lose weight or just because you want to be healthy, check out this web site for some useful information.

**Web:**

**http://www.amhrt.org/hs96/fatsubs.html**

## Healthy Diet Guidelines

When the doctor says it's time to get off the Pepsi and cheeseburger express, get help from your friend the Net. This resource contains everything you need to eat well except willpower and a credit card.

**Web:**

**http://www.uiuc.edu/departments/mckinley/health-info/nutrit/hlthdiet/hlthdiet.html**

## Holiday Diet Tips

Inevitably, when the holidays roll around, out come the trays of party snacks and rich chocolates, not to mention the high-fat cheeseballs sent across the country by your well-meaning Aunt Matilda (who used to send fruitcakes until she found out you were using them as doorstops). Don't get caught in the holiday-eating pitfall. Prepare now by reading tips on how to enjoy the holiday without overeating.

**Web:**

**http://www.columbia.net/drfrist/diet.html**

## Low Fat Lifestyle

One way some people are successful at losing weight is to reduce the amount of fat they have in their diet. This page gives lots of tips and recipes on living a low fat lifestyle. While you are here, check out the list of facts about fast food. (Then go eat a carrot.)

**Web:**

**http://www.wco.com/~mardiw/lowfat.htm**

## Magic of Believing

Get rid of your diet blues. Here's a group of people who support each other in their efforts to get fit and healthy through weight loss. Read important insights by support group members, and check out the links and resources relating to weight loss.

**Web:**

**http://www.swlink.net/~colonel/**

## Net Loss Club

If you are on a diet and looking for a good support group, try the Net Loss Club. These folks are on a diet and offer an upbeat and energetic environment in which to support one another in their efforts to lose weight.

**Web:**

**http://www2.itw.com/~thinker/**

## Vending Machine Calorie Counter

How many calories are you putting into your body on those midnight snack runs to the vending machine? Before you do it, go to the site that will tell you exactly how many of those hard-to-burn little monsters are making their way to your hips and thighs. This calorie counter lists the types of foods from vending machines and their number of calories.

**Web:**

**http://www.uiuc.edu/departments/mckinley/health-info/nutrit/hlthdiet/vendingm.html**

### Vending Machine Vendetta

20% FREE

How do you know how many calories are in a prepackaged snack? Well, you can look at the wrapper, but when you buy something from a vending machine, you can't look at the wrapper until you have already spent your money.

Ordinary people just have to put up with problems like this, but *you* are on the Net, which makes you special. All you need to do is check with the Vending Machine Calorie Counter ahead of time, and find exactly what is hidden from view. Never again will you be fooled into buying a "lite" snack only to find out that it contains enough calories to support the entire Peruvian army.

## Weight Control

If you want serious information about weight control, it's good to talk with someone who is qualified and knows what he or she is talking about. Here is a site, created by a physician, that offers sensible information on dietary options like liquid diets, fad diets, fashionable low-calorie diets, and appetite suppressants. However, please remember: there is no surefire easy way to lose weight permanently and safely. Although every year there seems to be a new fad that promises an easy way to perfect weight control, don't be fooled. The best way to stay healthy and lose unwanted weight is to (1) eat a reasonable amount of nutritious food, and (2) exercise regularly. My suggestion is to stop worrying so much about your body and practice enjoying your life. And if you are a woman, for goodness sake, stop trying to look like the models in those women's magazines. They starve themselves to look that way, and it's not healthy or normal.

**Web:**

**http://www.weight.com/**

## Weight Control and Dieting

When you decide you want to lose weight, it's good to understand nutrition, food, and how the body works. However, the same diet will not work for everyone. Read these informative articles and figure out what might work for you. If it doesn't work, try something else. Don't give up. Expect success to come slowly.

**Web:**

**http://www.healthtouch.com/level1/leaflets/100817/100817.htm**

## Weight Gain

Most people are trying to get their weight to go down, but if you are one of the few who are trying to gain weight, take a look at this information resource. Here you will find articles covering topics such as too much exercise, body composition, healthy ways to gain weight, and recovering after hard exercise.

**Web:**

**http://www.uiuc.edu/departments/mckinley/health-info/nutrit/wtgain/wtgain.html**

## Weight Loss

There are lots of ways to lose fat, but the whole thing can be summarized into two simple rules. (1) Exercise more. (2) Eat less. For helpful tips and techniques, check out this well-maintained Internet resource. (My doctor has a surefire method to lose weight: you serve yourself normal amounts of food, but you don't eat everything; you leave 25% of the food on your plate. It wasn't easy to get started, but the technique does work. Now I am ready to introduce him to my new money-saving plan in which I pay all but 25% of my doctor bill.)

**Web:**

**http://www.mhv.net/~donn/tips.html**

## Weight Loss Tips

Some people, despite their best efforts, find it difficult to lose excess weight. Here is a resource that has weight-loss tips with information about meals, the psychology of food, what to eat and what *not* to eat.

**Web:**

**http://www.ring.com/health/w_loss/w_loss.htm**

# DISABILITIES

## Accessibility

Accessibility issues are an important part of everyday life for people with disabilities. Use the Net to help you find out what solutions are available for accessibility problems. This site has information for adaptive, assistive and access technology researchers and for users. You will also find helpful information about special equipment.

**Web:**

**http://www.webable.com/**

Accessibility

One thing I have learned is that we all have disabilities, some people's are just more pronounced than others.

If you have a serious disability that makes day-to-day life difficult, look at the help and information available on the Net.

Remember, the Internet is not about computers. The Internet is about *people*.

There are lots of people ready to help and to contribute. Perhaps you are one of them.

## Americans with Disabilities Act

In 1990, the U.S. Congress passed the Americans with Disabilities Act (ADA). Although most people do not appreciate the significance of this legislation, it has an enormous effect on many areas of the American economy. Why? The ADA defines a disability as a mental or physical condition that "substantially limits one or more of the major life activities" (walking, hearing, seeing, working, and so on). The ADA requires specific action in four areas: employment, public facilities, transportation and communication. Here are some Internet resources about the ADA and related topics, including the full text of the actual law. (I actually found it interesting to read.)

**Web:**

**http://disability.ucdavis.edu/docs/ada.htm**
**http://www.public.iastate.edu/~sbilling/ada.html**

## Amputees

Amputees and friends and families of amputees can find a lot of helpful information on the Net. The web sites have articles and links to resources, information about prosthetics, phantom sensation, as well as sports and recreation. The mailing list offers a way for amputees to talk to and support one another.

**Web:**

**http://vanbc.wimsey.com/~igregson/**
**http://www.inform.umd.edu:8080/EdRes/Topic/Disability/Events/People/Amputees/**

**Listserv Mailing List:**

List Name: **amputees**
Subscribe to: **listserv@sjuvm.stjohns.edu**

## Attention Deficit Disorder

Attention Deficit Disorder (ADD) is a childhood syndrome characterized by hyperactivity, a short attention span, and impulsive behavior. These web resources have information relating to children and adults with ADD, including helpful tips for parents and a checklist of symptoms for adults suspected to have ADD. The mailing list is for adults with ADD, but the Usenet group is for the support of adults, children and anyone who works with ADD patients.

**Web:**

**http://www.chadd.org/**
**http://www.greatconnect.com/oneaddplace/**

**Usenet:**

**alt.support.attn-deficit**

**Listserv Mailing List:**

List Name: **addult**
Subscribe to: **listserv@sjuvm.stjohns.edu**

## Autism

Autism is a syndrome with many variations. By its nature, autism is difficult to define, especially in plain English (but I am going to try anyway). Autism is a congenital condition characterized by some of the following: (1) abnormal development of physical and social skills, (2) abnormal responses to sensation, (3) delayed development of speech and language, (4) abnormal ways of relating to the outside world. Here are some Internet resources to help you understand autism and to communicate with other people who are interested in the disorder.

**Web:**

**http://web.syr.edu/~jmwobus/autism/**

**Usenet:**

**bit.listserv.autism**

**Listserv Mailing List:**

List Name: **autism**
Subscribe to: **listserv@sjuvm.stjohns.edu**

**IRC:**

**#autism**

## Blind and Visually Impaired Computer Usage

Using the computer is tricky enough when you don't have a vision impairment. This mailing list provides a forum for the discussion of computer use by the blind and visually impaired. If you are interested in helping to make the Internet more accessible to blind people, this is a good place to participate. For my part, I work with the National Braille Press to help them translate *The Internet Complete Reference* into braille. However, it is an expensive and time-consuming process, and it doesn't solve the main problem: the interface. I wish that certain companies whose names I won't mention (Microsoft) would do more to design features for blind people while they are designing their operating systems. I have enough trouble using the wretched mouse-oriented/pull-down-menu/one-size-fits-all graphical interface—and I can see. Imagine what it's like for a blind person.

**Listserv Mailing List:**

List Name: **blind-l**
Subscribe to: **listserv@uafsysb.uark.edu**

**BLIND AND VISUALLY IMPAIRED COMPUTER USAGE**

There is lots of modern technology available to help blind people use the Net. If you are blind, or visually impaired, ask someone to help you get started.

Then, once you do, join the *blind-1* mailing list and keep up on what is new and exciting.

**Do a backup.**

## Blind News Digest

This newsletter is a digest format of posts to the Blind News mailing list. It covers issues relating to being partially or totally blind and ways to deal with such an impairment. Topics include experiences and anecdotes as well as medical and technical information about blindness. This group is moderated, and you can access it either as a mailing list or a Usenet discussion group.

**Usenet:**
**bit.listserv.blindnws**

**Listserv Mailing List:**
List Name: **blindnws**
Subscribe to: **listserv@listserv.nodak.edu**

## Computers for the Handicapped

CHIPS is the Computers for the Handicapped Independence Program. Get information about software and hardware for the visually impaired, quadriplegics, mobility impairments, speech and language impairments, and for the hearing impaired.

**Web:**
**http://www.wolfe.net/~dr_bill/**

## Deaf Kids Discussion

This mailing list offers a place for deaf children to chat and to communicate with one another. Remember, when you are on the Net, you are never alone.

**Listserv Mailing List:**
List Name: **deafkids**
Subscribe to: **listserv@sjuvm.stjohns.edu**

## Deaf Magazine

Deaf Magazine is an electronic magazine devoted to issues relating to hearing impairment. You can subscribe to the mailing list, or you can access the magazine via the web page.

**Web:**
**http://www.deaf-magazine.org/**

**Listserv Mailing List:**
List Name: **deaf-magazine**
Subscribe to: **listserv@listserv.deaf-magazine.org**

## Deaf-Blind Discussion List

This is a multipurpose list devoted to the topic of dual sensory impairment or deaf-blindness. Not only is it a place where professionals can discuss problems and solutions, but it's also a space in which individuals with DSI or families and friends can share information, inquiries, ideas and opinions.

**Listserv Mailing List:**
List Name: **deafblnd**
Subscribe to: **listserv@lsv.uky.edu**

## Deafness

The deaf, hearing impaired, researchers and family members of the deaf gather to discuss issues relating to deafness. Topics include medical and technical subjects as well as experiences and problems with having little or no ability to hear.

**Usenet:**
**bit.listserv.deaf-l**

**Listserv Mailing List:**
List Name: **deaf-l**
Subscribe to: **listserv@siucvmb.bitnet**

## Disability Information

Information about many disability-related resources. There is an enormous amount of such material on the Net, and these sites are a good place to start.

**Web:**
**http://www.eskimo.com/~dempt/disability.html**
**http://www.eskimo.com/~jlubin/disabled.html**
**http://www.indie.ca/**

If you or a loved one is disabled, remember that there are many people on the Net who are glad to help. There are many sites that offer information for the disabled, and they are open 24 hours a day.

## *Look What I Found on the Net...*

Newsgroup: bit.listserv.deaf-l
Subject: Hard of Hearing in the Hearing World

...I figured out that this is all physics. I have an 80 dB loss. You hear half with every loss of 20 dB. So it goes like this:

| | | |
|---|---|---|
| -20 dB | you hear | 1/2 the sound |
| -40 | | 1/4 |
| -60 | | 1/8 |
| -80 | | 1/16 |

Assuming I'm still at -80, I hear 1/16 what you hear. That m eans the person I am listening to [in a lecture hall] has to be 16 times closer...

Once I understood what was wrong, I could understand that if I am sitting down and the person speaking to me is standing up, I can't hear them. It's obvious why...

When people get high frequency deafness, the ability to pick out consonants fails as well as the hearing itself. People do not realize that when they raise their voice to communicate with people who are hard of hearing, they automatically destroy the very consonants that cannot be heard. The vowels distort and completely cover up the consonants.

Please never ask us to "listen harder". We are already trying to outguess the 70 percent or more of the consonants we cannot hear. We hear all languages like a foreign language, English included...

When you talk to us, DO talk in a normal soft voice, very close in the ear. If this will not work, write it down. If we can't hear it close and soft, we will not be able to hear it louder or "enunciated" either.

Please understand that lip reading is nothing but a guessing game, and we are really tired of guessing. There is not even one lip pattern that unambiguously means one thing only.

At the same time, we are sick of being alone, sick of eating by ourselves (since almost no one takes the trouble to learn how to talk to us), sick of being unable to communicate.

So there you have it: how it is to be hard of hearing in a hearing world.

A B C D E F G H I J K L M N O P Q R S T U V W X Y Z

## Disabled Student Services in Higher Education

It's frustrating for disabled students when colleges and universities don't have enough curb cuts, ramps, wide doorways, or elevators where they are needed. The purpose of this discussion group is to provide a forum to share information among providers of services for disabled students in higher education. Common issues for discussion are service delivery models and legal issues relating to the Americans with Disabilities Act.

**Listserv Mailing List:**
List Name: **dsshe-l**
Subscribe to: **listserv@ubvm.cc.buffalo.edu**

## Down Syndrome

Down Syndrome is a congenital disorder caused by the existence of an extra chromosome 21. The condition is characterized by mild to moderate mental retardation. Such people also tend to be short with broadened facial features. Down Syndrome was named after John Langdon Down, the British doctor who first identified the condition in 1866. This web site has some good information about Down Syndrome, including a FAQ (frequently asked question list) and health care guidelines. If you want to talk with other people interested in Down Syndrome, you can join the mailing list.

**Web:**
**http://www.nas.com/downsyn/**

**Listserv Mailing List:**
List Name: **down-syn**
Subscribe to: **listserv@listserv.nodak.edu**

## Dyslexia

Dyslexia is a reading and writing disability characterized by the reversal of letters and words, or by trouble matching letters to their corresponding sounds. Here are some Internet resources with information about dyslexia, including tips for teachers, research information, reports and useful software.

**Web:**
**http://ods.pie.org/T3639**
**http://www.hensa.ac.uk/dyslexia/www/homepage.html**

## Family Village

Family Village is a great site for anyone who has a disability or for parents who have children with disabilities. Family Village has a library of specific diagnoses, contact lists, ways to get in touch with other people with similar disability issues and much, much more.

**Web:**
**http://www.familyvillage.wisc.edu/**

## Fathers of Children with Disabilities

Being a dad can be tough. If your child has a disability or special health needs, you may need some extra support. Fathers, professionals and any other persons who care for children with disabilities are welcome to join this list, but the mission of this group is to share information, inquiries, ideas and opinions on matters relating to the experiences of fathers of children who are disabled or have special health care needs.

**Listserv Mailing List:**
List Name: **dadvocat**
Subscribe to: **listserv@lsv.uky.edu**

## Handicap Talk and General Discussion

If you have a handicap, you will find something helpful from these groups. Useful information and personal support covers topics such as problems facing amputees, medical issues for the disabled, handicap access concerns, politics and personal interest stories such as biographies of famous people.

**Usenet:**
**bit.listserv.l-hcap**
**misc.handicap**

## Kids With Disabilities

Parents of children with disabilities will find these resources useful. The web site has links to information about mental and physical disabilities and related adaptive technologies. The mailing list acts as a support group for parents and other people who work with disabled children.

**Web:**
**http://wonder.mit.edu/ok/**

**Majordomo Mailing List:**
List Name: **our-kids**
Subscribe to: **majordomo@tbag.osc.edu**

## Paralysis and Spinal Cord Injuries

If you, or someone you know, has paralysis or a spinal cord injury, it is good to understand the physical and medical aspects of the condition. These sites offer information about current research in spinal cord injuries, what can be done to reverse some types of paralysis, and advice for those who are newly injured.

**Web:**

**http://teri.bio.uci.edu/paralysis/**
**http://www.trader.com/users/5010/1020/nscia.htm**

## Rehabilitation

The National Rehabilitation Information Center (NARIC) collects the results of federally funded research products related to disabilities and rehabilitation. The web site contains a bibliographic database, information on home modifications, and links to related resources.

**Web:**

**http://www.cais.net/naric/**

**"Fun" is fun.**

**FAQs are cool.**

## Service Dogs

Service dogs perform tasks for people with physical disabilities. There are several types of such dogs, including general service dogs, hearing dogs and social dogs. General service dogs perform tasks like switching lights on and off, fetching items, pulling a wheelchair and pushing buttons. Hearing dogs can alert a deaf person to noises such as the telephone, alarm clocks, or a crying baby. Social dogs provide companionship and guidance for people with developmental disabilities. Read more about the great services that canine companions can offer to the disabled. You can also join the mailing list to discuss service dogs with disabled people as well as trainers.

**Web:**

**http://www.caninecompanions.org/**
**http://www.zmall.com/pet_talk/tittle/pets/dog-faqs/service.html**

**Majordomo Mailing List:**

List Name: **service-dogs**
Subscribe to: **majordomo@acpub.duke.edu**

### *Look What I Found on the Net...*

```
Newsgroup: misc.handicap
Subject: Singles Groups for Persons With Disabilities?

>>> Are there are singles groups for persons with disabilities?

>> I also would like to know if you find one. I've tried every
>> single's web page and BBS, and have had no luck. If you ever
>> find one please pass it on to me.

> Me too.  If one doesn't exist how do we create one?

I'm sure there must be some, but I don't know of them.  I have
an idea.  Try alt.support.disabled.sexuality -- that's the sort
of place to ask.
```

## Special Olympics

The Special Olympics is an exciting sports competition for individuals with mental retardation. The Special Olympics was founded in 1968 by Eunice Kennedy Shriver, and today there are Special Olympics programs in many countries all over the world. This is the official site for the program. You can learn more about the Special Olympics, discover how you can become a volunteer, and read other information about this great program for the mentally retarded.

**Web:**
**http://www.specialolympics.org/**

### Special Olympics

In a way, the word "Olympics" is a misnomer. The regular Olympics involve only the very best athletes, once every four years.

The Special Olympics—created for mentally retarded participants—involve over a million people, all over the world, all year long.

Take a look at their web site, and you will see just how special people can be.

# DRAMA

## Aisle Say

If you are a lover of modern theater, you will enjoy Aisle Say, an online magazine of reviews and opinion. The magazine contains theater reviews for plays in a variety of cities, in and out of the United States. Before you travel to a major city, you may want to check this site to see if there is a review of a play you are thinking about seeing. I enjoy reading the reviews just to see what they have to say.

**Web:**
**http://www.escape.com/~theanet/AisleSay.html**

## Ancient Theater

Age is good for cheese, fine wines and classic cars, so why not the theater? Take a look at the ancient histories, culture and philosophy of Greek and Roman theater.

**Web:**
**http://www.warwick.ac.uk/didaskalia/Didintro.html**

## Collaborations

It's no fun to be alone. In fact, if you join this mailing list you will never have to be alone again. Actors, musicians, composers and others who love creative theatrical antics discuss all aspects of collaborative works. One of the nice things about collaborating with other people is that you can always pass the blame on to someone else.

**Listserv Mailing List:**
List Name: **collab-l**
Subscribe to: **listserv@psuvm.psu.edu**

## Costumes of the Early Twentieth Century

If you were not attending the theater at the turn of the nineteenth century, you were missing the grand costumes and stage fineries that the actors and actresses used to wear. Now on the Web, you can see it all. This web site has pictures of famous English actors and actresses as they were costumed at the turn of the previous century.

**Web:**
**http://www.siue.edu/COSTUMES/actors/pics.html**

## Drama and Theater Resources

What would you give for an interesting and useful listing of drama and theater resources? Well, if you're on the Net, you're in the know, 'cause here it is for free. Check out this list of articles, announcements, organizations, periodicals and directories. If your favorite resource is missing, you can even add it to the page.

**Web:**
**http://galaxy.einet.net/galaxy/Humanities/Arts/Performing-Arts/Drama.html**

## Dramatic Exchange

The Dramatic Exchange is an archive for storing and distributing play scripts. This web server is a vehicle for experienced or budding playwrights to publish and distribute their works, and a place for producers to look at new material. Anyone else interested in drama is also welcome here.

**Web:**

**http://www.dramex.org/**

### Ahoy, Scriptwriters!

The *Dramatic Exchange* is a place for you to share your work and read what other people are doing. Just the place to show off the great script that Warren Beatty refuses to read, about a surfing detective who writes Internet books.

## George and Ira Gershwin

Here's a web site devoted to two Brooklyn boys who gave the world something to talk about. George and Ira Gershwin created beautiful music and plays that are popular to this day, even on the Internet. This site has the complete list of their plays and detailed information about each work. Who could ask for anything more?

**Web:**

**http://www.sju.edu/~bs065903/gershwin/**

## Gilbert and Sullivan

If your husband is so fat that you must move him with a trailer hitch. And you are tired of groups like Nine Inch Nails and Weird Al Yankovitch. You clearly need to break away from culture that is popular. To something that is pleasing, auditoral and ocular. Try Gilbert and try Sullivan, I guarantee they're sure to please. No matter if you're sitting in the orchestra or balconies. In short, in matters musical and other things historical. This is the very model of an archive categorical.

**Web:**

**http://diamond.idbsu.edu/GaS/GaS.html**

## Hamnet Players

Your best formal outfit is at the cleaners and you get an insatiable desire to go see a play. What can you do? Find out more about the Hamnet Players who perform entertaining Shakespearean antics on IRC (Internet Relay Chat). If you want culture, have some yogurt. But if you want a good time, point your browser to the Hamnet home page.

**Web:**

**http://wwwnt.thegroup.net/pcbeth.htm**

## Improvisational Theater

Extroverts and those with a more spontaneous nature will love the improvisation information at these sites. Read about the history of improv, find a list of improv groups or information on how to form your own group. There is a link to upcoming events and a list of improv games that will liven up just about any party. While you are here, find out about other improvisation-related resources on the Net and get pointers to home pages of Net-savvy improv performers.

**Web:**

**http://sunee.uwaterloo.ca/~broehl/improv**
**http://www.crl.com/~zot/improv.html**

## Improvisational Theater

**Unlike traditional theater, improvisation often requires a collaboration between performers and the audience. During the performance, the audience offers suggestions which the actors use to create a story. Since this can be a lot of fun, I thought you might like to try it for yourself. Find a half dozen friends to act as an audience, and choose one person to perform with you. Sit down next to one another and pretend that you are all alone, stuck in an elevator. To pass the time, you and the other person take turns reading this book, which you should pretend is a copy of ex-Princess Diana's secret love diary. As you read, you act out the various escapades. From time to time, have your friends in the audience yell out suggestions. Don't forget to videotape the performance, so you can enjoy it again and again.**

## Musicals

It's too bad life isn't like a musical. When you are stressed or unhappy or madly in love, you could just burst into song and all the people around you would stop what they are doing and sing with you. In fact, you might want to try it, but I can't be held responsible for what happens. Get a good dose of musical theater by talking to other lovers of the musical genre. Any topic is acceptable as long as it relates to musical theater, though sometimes list members will get carried away and even talk about a little non-musical theater.

**Usenet:**

**rec.arts.theatre.musicals**

**Majordomo Mailing List:**

List Name: **musicals**
Subscribe to: **majordomo@world.std.com**

## On Broadway

Are you all dressed up with no place to go? Have a look at this list of plays and musicals on or off Broadway. You provide the date, they'll provide the showtime. While you are here, check out the Tony Award information and links to other theater sites.

**Web:**

**http://artsnet.heinz.cmu.edu/OnBroadway/**

## Opera Companies

Opera is opera, right? That's like telling your cat that tuna is tuna. Those with a cultivated taste for dynamic singing and musical theatrics will appreciate the fine distinction between various opera companies. Here's a list of various local and regional opera companies as well as those companies that travel around the world. This site also has a link to an opera schedule server if you are looking for a night on the town.

**Web:**

**http://www.cc.columbia.edu/~km34/geopera.html**

## Opera Discussion

What do you do when the fat lady has already sung, but you haven't yet had enough? You rush home, fire up your Internet connection and talk about the opera. Here are some resources relating to opera discussion: a mailing list and some web resources especially designed for the people who participate in the discussion.

**Web:**

**http://www.atreus.com/operal.html**
**http://www.physics.su.oz.au/~neilb/operah.html**

**Listserv Mailing List:**

List Name: **opera-l**
Subscribe to: **listserv@cunyvm.cuny.edu**

**The Net cares.**

## Opera Schedule Server

You are a famous opera singer. The general manager of Lincoln Center in New York calls to ask if you can sing the lead in "Fidelio" in a few days. You say okay, but in the excitement, you forget the actual date. Of course, you can always call him back and ask for the information again, but acting like a clueless goober is not going to help you maintain your reputation as a famous opera singer. No problem—as long as you have an Internet connection. All you need to do is connect to the Opera Schedule Server, and you can find out the schedule and basic info for any of several thousand performances in many different cities around the world. In particular, you can look for the opera in which you will be singing in New York. Once again, another career has been saved by the Net.

**Web:**

**http://www.fsz.bme.hu/opera/main.html**

**Remember,**
it's not over until the fat woman has checked out the Opera Schedule Server.

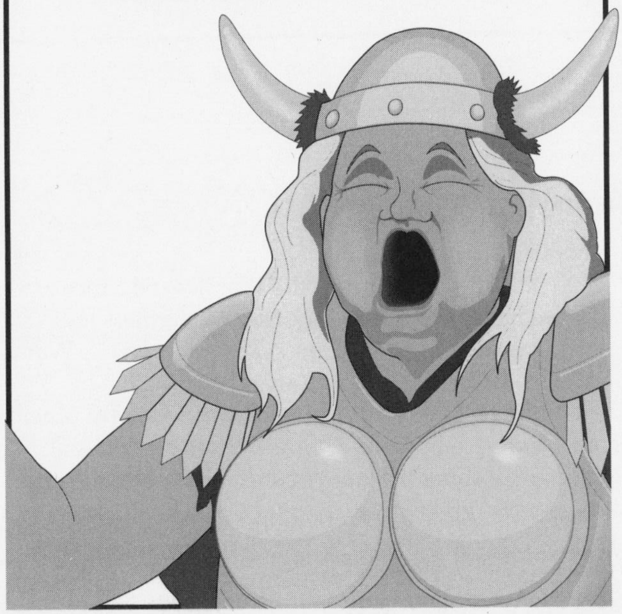

## Play Scripts

Just the other day, I had a few friends over and we were trying to think of something to do. "I have an idea," I said, "let's put on our own version of Aristophanes' play 'The Thesmophoriazus'". "But where can we get a copy of the play at this time of night?" my friends asked, "Wal-mart is already closed." "No problem," I replied, "we can download it free from the Net." And we did. And you can too, along with many other plays, both classical and contemporary.

**Web:**

**http://english-www.hss.cmu.edu/drama/**

## Playbill Online

Who needs the newspaper when you can get access to this snazzy online magazine that offers news and information listings for Broadway, off-Broadway and national theater tours? Have fun browsing around or use Playbill's search mechanism for speedier results.

**Web:**

**http://www.playbill.com/**

## Stagecraft

The lure of the theater is hard to resist and even if you have no acting talent, this doesn't mean that you have to miss out on the magic. Arm yourself with tools, gadgets, plans and a great imagination and you can be one of the all-important backstage magicians who create the stage, sets and costumes of the theater. These Usenet groups are for the discussion of the more technical aspects of theater.

**Usenet:**

**alt.stagecraft**
**rec.arts.theatre.stagecraft**

## Technical Theater Databases

When you need quick information on technical theater subjects, don't wait around for your mailing list to respond. You can use this web form to do a search through documents sent to various mailing lists relating to technical theater discussion. Use keywords to search for any topic and before you can say "don't drop that sandbag", a web page with links to related documents will appear on your browser.

**Web:**

**http://www.ffa.ucalgary.ca/citt/clbd/wais.html**

## Theater and Culture Reviews

Certainly nobody reading this book could be an uncultured buffoon, but if you happen to know someone who does not have your good taste, send him this web URL for his birthday. This site houses the regular column in which Diana Cantu reviews various aspects of the theater and culture.

**Web:**

**http://www.thegroup.net/diana.htm**

## Theater History

It's okay to live in the past if you do it with style, and theater people are certainly known for their style. This list is for the discussion of theater history and the American Society for Theater Research.

**Listserv Mailing List:**

List Name: **astr-l**
Subscribe to: **listserv@vmd.cso.uiuc.edu**

## Theater Journal

If your house is completely wired, you can have a computer in every room, even your bathroom. If so, it's important to have just the right sort of links on your bookmark list so guests have something interesting to enjoy. For instance, on the computer in my bathroom, I like to keep a link to this web site, an online magazine about the theater business. It has reviews, features and even technical articles about computers in theater. No doubt about it: people who visit me *know* that I have good taste.

**Web:**

**http://www.theatre-central.com/fea/jou/**

## Theater Mailing List

When you get tired of hanging around people whose idea of a good theater experience is going to the latest action-adventure flick, retire to a more sophisticated, cultural setting. Join the **theatre** mailing list to communicate with other folks who love the theater as a hobby or even a way of life.

**Listserv Mailing List:**

List Name: **theatre**
Subscribe to: **listserv@pucc.princeton.edu**

## Theater Resources

As long as you have Internet access, you will never have to be without a good dose of theater. This list of resources covers just about every theater topic imaginable. Now, when you are left home on Saturday night because your BMW broke down and you can't get to the theater, you can amuse yourself with a virtual experience that has a compelling drama all its own.

**Web:**

**http://pscinfo.psc.edu/~geigel/menus/Theatre.html**
**http://www.cs.fsu.edu/projects/group4/theatre.html**
**http://www.theatre-central.com/**
**http://www.wiso.gwdg.de/ifbg/ent_thea.htm**

## Theater Talk and General Discussion

There is magic in the stage with the lights and sound and hush of the well-dressed audience as they breathlessly await the curtain's rise. Whether you are an actor, a techie or a fan, you can find great discussions between people immersed in the drama scene.

**Usenet:**

**rec.arts.theatre.misc**
**rec.arts.theatre.muscials**
**rec.arts.theatre.plays**
**rec.arts.theatre.stagecraft**

# DRUGS

## Anti-War-on-Drugs Activist List

If you are old enough, you can remember when it was cool to be anti-war (during "the War"). Well, since then, we have had a number of other, perhaps less minor wars, such as the War on Poverty and the War on Drugs. If you are still anti-war, here is a list of organizations that support drug law reform. (In other words, here are the anti-War-on-Drugs protesters.) Personally, I think it would be nice if someone would start a War on Bad Taste.

**Web:**

**http://www.zeta.org.au/~aldis/liberty.txt**

## Caffeine

Check out the caffeine resources on the Net and find out everything you always wanted to know about the world's most overused stimulant. Do you know how to make really sludgy, sweet espresso? Are you wondering how much caffeine is in Jello Pudding Pops? Don't let it keep you up at night.

**Web:**

**http://www.quadralay.com/www/Caffeine/Caffeine.html**

**Usenet:**

**alt.drugs.caffeine**

Having trouble staying awake at night?
Try reading alt.drugs.caffeine.

## Cocaine

Cocaine is a powerful central nervous system (CNS) stimulant. Its effects include increased alertness, decreased appetite, decreased fatigue, and—what cocaine users crave—an intense feeling of pleasure. In general, cocaine make people feel powerful and happy. Unfortunately, cocaine is highly addictive, illegal, expensive and causes terrible side effects, both short-term and long-term. Cocaine is prepared from the leaves of the Erythroxylon coca bush, which grows primarily in Peru, Bolivia and Columbia. Here is a site from which you can find out more about cocaine, such as its appearance, its effects (including during pregnancy), and a discussion of tolerance and dependence.

**Web:**

**http://www.arf.org/isd/pim/cocaine.html**

## Drug Abuse Education Information and Research

There is more to drug abuse education than just saying no to over-the-counter diet pills. This list was created for people interested in issues related to community drug abuse education and the epidemiology and study of drug abuse.

**Listserv Mailing List:**

List Name: **drugabus**
Subscribe to: **listserv@umab.bitnet**

### *Look What I Found on the Net...*

```
Newsgroup: rec.arts.theatre.musicals
Subject: Casting for a New Musical

> This is to announce an open call for my new musical,
> "Sunday in the Park with Curious George".
>
> The final decision on whether to use a human or a simian as
> the title character (baritone) has not been finalized.
> Therefore, if you have an appendage at the base of your spinal
> column, feel welcome to try out.
>
> If interested, please send résumé to get@clue.duh.

I don't get it.  Why should Sunday be an ape?
```

## Drug Chemistry and Synthesis

Where do you turn when it's late and you have a cold and all the pharmacies are closed? Check out this newsgroup and see if you can find a nice recipe for a decongestant or perhaps some LSD. That won't help your cold, but at least it will take your mind off your symptoms. Chemists and fans of chemistry chat about how drugs are constructed and synthesized.

**Usenet:**

**alt.drugs.chemistry**

## Drug Culture

There is an entire group of people who choose not to hang out in reality some of the time. Instead of going to Disneyland, they like to spend lots of money on chemicals that are illegal and bad for their health. Commune with members of the drug culture as they talk about various drugs, music to trip to, and becoming one with nature and getting in touch with themselves and on special occasions with each other.

**Usenet:**

**alt.drugs.culture**

## Drug Information Resources

I know what you are wondering. Did Harley put anything dangerous to my mental health in this book, or are these ordinary, harmless web sites? To tell you the truth, with all the excitement of working on the book, I don't even remember myself. But seeing as the Internet is the most powerful interactive medium in history, what you need to be asking yourself is, "Do I feel lucky?"

**Web:**

**http://kiwi.uwaterloo.ca/drug_info.html**
**http://www.hyperreal.com/drugs/**
**http://www.lycaeum.org/links/Drug_Information/**
**http://www.paranoia.com/drugs/**

**Wow, free software.**

## Drug Information Resources

Before you embark on your next drug-induced exploration, check the Net to see what other people have to say.

Remember, you only have one central nervous system, so don't take chances.

As we used to say in the sixties, "Uh... uummm... like wow, man. Far out..."

## Drug Pix

Who says art is only for cultured people? This isn't the largest or highest quality art collection in the world. In fact, it's pretty sparse. However, there are some things that you just won't find anywhere else. For example, the last time I visited, I saw a photo of Cary Grant taking a hit of LSD, as well as a digitized photo of a piece of drug paraphernalia signed by contemporary U.S. philosopher and comedian Oliver North. My only hint is, if you see an invitation to lick the screen, don't do it. (I am serious.)

**Web:**

**http://www.links.net/drugz/pix.html**

## Drug Talk and General Discussion

There is a lot you can say about drugs, and the Internet has a lot of people who love to say it. What better way to spend your time than sitting around on Usenet talking about drugs? Here you will find a wide-ranging discussion about a variety of topics: hard drugs (such as heroin and cocaine), psychedelic drugs (such as LSD and mushrooms), and soft drugs (such as marijuana and television).

**Usenet:**

**alt.drugs.hard**
**alt.drugs.pot**
**alt.drugs.pot.cultivation**
**alt.drugs.psychedelics**

**IRC:**

**#drugs**

## Drug Testing

Drug testing is certainly a double-edged sword (to coin a phrase). On the one hand (to coin another phrase), drug testing is a useful tool to help employers maintain a drug-free workplace. Be that as it may (to coin yet a third phrase), many people see the forced donation of bodily substances to possibly incriminate oneself as an affront to personal liberty. Would you like the real scoop on what may or may not be the lesser of two evils? (Wow, I just coined two phrases in one sentence.) Check out these Net sites, and you won't be left out in the cold. (Boy, I sure wish I had a Susan B. Anthony dollar for every phrase I've coined.)

**Web:**

**http://hyperreal.com/drugs/politics/drug.testing/**
**http://www.csun.edu/~hbcsc096/dt/**

**Try a mud. Your life will never be the same.**

## Drug Use History

The use of drugs goes back about as far as human beings. (Think about Adam and Eve smoking that apple.) For a thoughtful tour through the annals of real virtual reality, take a look at this web site. By the way, speaking of drugs and history, has anyone else noticed that the guitar solo in the middle of the song "Just Like Me" by Paul Revere and the Raiders (1966) is a lot like the famous guitar solo in "25 or 6 to 4" by Chicago (1970)?

**Web:**

**http://www.paranoia.com/~foucault/Babel/**

## Ecstasy

What a nice, tempting name for a drug. An intense, yet delicate labeling. However, unlike other well known drugs—such as Coca-Cola and television—this is *not* one that you want to try at home. Contrary to what most people believe, Ecstasy (or MDMA—metheylenedimethoxymethamphetamine) is not a new drug. Read about the history, effects, dangers, and usage of Ecstasy, the drug that even Bill Clinton will not inhale. ("Coca-Cola", by the way, is a trademark of the Coca-Cola Company; "Ecstasy" is a trademark of the Republican National Committee.)

**Web:**

**http://www.hyperreal.com/drugs/e4x/**

### *Look What I Found on the Net...*

```
        (from The International Stoner Slang Dictionary)

Clam Bake [US]:
   To smoke in a car with the windows up.

Henry [UK]:
   An eighth of an ounce of cannabis (as in Henry VIII).

Logy [CA]:
   To become lethargic after smoking cannabis.

Pregnant [US]:
   A joint that is rolled incorrectly, usually with more pot in
   the middle than anyplace else.

Wacky Weed [AU]:
   Wild plant sometimes found in dense forest or sugar cane.

Zoom Tube [UK]:
   A long pipe on a bong which you take the smoke in with.
```

## Heroin and Opiates

Within 4-6 hours after his or her last dose, a heroin addict has begun to feel withdrawal symptoms: chills, muscle aches, joint aches, insomnia and nausea. About 10-20 hours later, those symptoms will have intensified and, by the time an addict has reached the 24-36 hour mark, he or she is experiencing insomnia, vomiting, diarrhea, weakness, depression, and hot and cold flashes. (You can see why a heroin addict will do anything to get the next fix.) Symptoms reach a peak at about 2-3 days. By then the person is experiencing muscle cramps, abdominal cramps, fever, severe tremors and twitching. These symptoms are often accompanied by incessant nausea and vomiting, and it is not unusual for an addict to lose 10-15 pounds (over 5 kg) in 24 hours. Withdrawal symptoms can take more than a week to disappear, and there may be a general loss of well-being that lasts for several months. Remember all of this the next time someone tries to tell you that heroin and other opiates are cool. Of course we all have differing tastes, and I would be the last one to impose my values on other people, but having to continually come up with large sums of money in order to avoid severe pain, vomiting and involuntary muscle contractions doesn't seem to be a pleasant way to spend one's brief time on Planet Earth.

**Web:**

**http://area51.upsu.plym.ac.uk/infoserv/drugs/graphical/grphopia.html**
**http://www.cnetech.com/dare/opiates.html**

## International Stoner Slang Dictionary

If you're not stoned, you might have trouble understanding stoned people when they talk to you. Not a problem. The next time someone under the influence says something you can't understand, tell him to write it down and have him wait quietly in the corner. Then you can quickly connect to the Net and check with the International Stoner Slang Dictionary. After all, if people can find a way to talk to chimpanzees using sign language, there's no reason why you can't learn to understand your friends.

**Web:**

**http://www.warehouse.net/wwweed/books/slang/**

## Leary, Timothy

The late Timothy Leary (1920-1996) was nothing if not an iconoclast. For example, he firmly believed that proper use of hallucinogenic and mind-altering drugs was necessary for experiencing an optimal existence. His philosophy was not that people should take drugs indiscriminately, but rather they should learn about drugs—what they do and how to use them—and deliberately choose what to take. In other words, where Nancy Reagan was fond of saying "Just say no", Timothy Leary would say "Just say know." In 1995, Leary was diagnosed with terminal prostate cancer and, until he died on May 31, 1996, he used his web page to keep the world informed of his pre-death drug use (which was considerable). There was some talk of Leary committing suicide on the Net—in real time, I assume—but, in the end, he went quietly and peacefully, certainly not his usual modus operandi. One of his last goals was to "give death a better name or die trying". Even in final repose, Leary seems to have more to say than most living people.

**Web:**

**http://www.leary.com/**

## LSD: My Problem Child

There are lots of famous fathers: George Washington was the Father of Our Country (in the U.S.); Prince Charles is the father of Prince William (in England); and Ward Cleaver was the father of Beaver Cleaver (on television). But perhaps the oddest parent-offspring relationship is that of Albert Hofmann and LSD. His writings have been translated and collected into this monograph, "LSD: My Problem Child". It begins: "There are experiences that most of us are hesitant to speak about, because they do not conform to everyday reality and defy rational explanation..."

**Web:**

**http://www.hyperreal.com/drugs/psychedelics/lsd/problem.child/**

**Get into "Mischief".**

## Marijuana

You probably know marijuana as a commonly used mind-altering drug of questionable value. What you may not know is that marijuana is used medicinally by people with AIDS, glaucoma, cancer and multiple sclerosis. Marijuana, or hemp, is also an industrial crop which can be used in the manufacture of paper, fiber, fuel and even food. Finally, in scientifically controlled studies, marijuana has been shown to increase the ability of volunteers to get the little beads into the eyes of the clown by as much as 54 percent. Need even more info? It's waiting on the Net.

**Web:**

**http://www.hyperreal.com/drugs/marijuana/**

**Usenet:**

**alt.drugs.pot**

## McKenna, Terence

Terence McKenna is an ethnobotanist and a writer who is as cherished in the drug culture as the big (but dead) cheese Timothy Leary. Read McKenna's bibliography, travel calendar and list of current events, hear audio clips, read a selection of his writings, quotes and interviews from magazines like bOING bOING and High Times.

**Web:**

**http://www.intac.com/~dimitri/dh/mckenna.html**

## Nitrous Oxide

Nitrous oxide—or laughing gas—is a mild anesthetic that has been in use since the late 18th century. Today, it is most widely used by medical professionals for surgery and dental procedures. Of course, there are also people who use this drug for recreation. However, before you put your neurons on the line, you might want to check things out with your buddies on the Net. Remember, pleasure is not a laughing matter.

**Web:**

**http://www.paranoia.com/drugs/nitrous**
**http://www.resort.com/~banshee/Info/N2O/**

## Nootropics (Intelligence-Enhancing Drugs)

I have a personal system for enhancing my intelligence: I exercise a lot, eat well, get plenty of sleep and—except when negotiating with editors—I think pure thoughts. I also happen to be very, very smart. Not everybody has such good habits, or is blessed with such natural talent, so it should come as no surprise that there is a lot of research into drugs that may be able to make you smarter. These drugs are called "nootropics" (from the Latin words for "doing your math homework"). Want some info? Here it is.

**Web:**

**http://www.hyperreal.com/drugs/nootropics**
**http://www.uta.fi/~samu/SMARTS2.html**

## Pikhal

An acronym for Phenelthylamines I Have Known and Loved, Pikhal is a "love story" about a man and his favorite chemicals. Read excerpts from the book and see clever chemical breakdowns of everyone's favorite phenylethyl radical.

**Web:**

**http://www.hyperreal.com/drugs/pihkal**

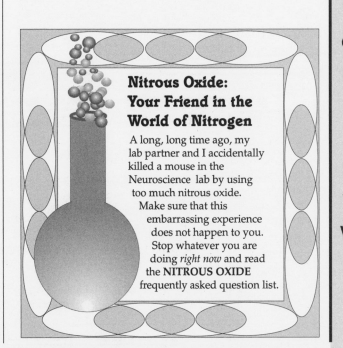

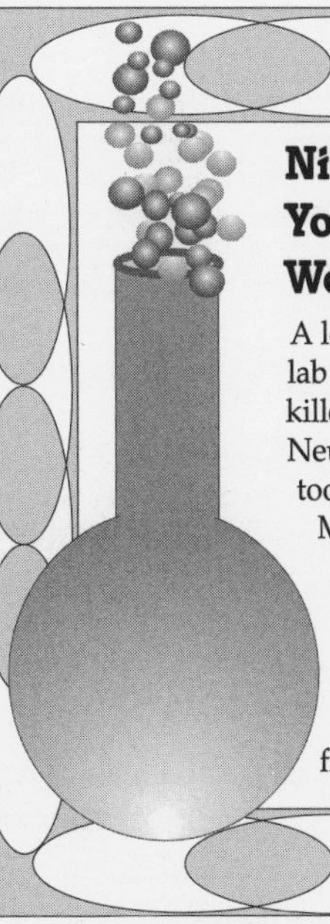

**Nitrous Oxide: Your Friend in the World of Nitrogen**

A long, long time ago, my lab partner and I accidentally killed a mouse in the Neuroscience lab by using too much nitrous oxide. Make sure that this embarrassing experience does not happen to you. Stop whatever you are doing *right now* and read the **NITROUS OXIDE** frequently asked question list.

## Politics and Drugs

Who's right? The politicians, the reporters, the teachers, the doctors, Ann Landers, your mother? Read what the people who really understand drugs and politics have to say, and make up your own mind.

**Web:**
**http://www.hyperreal.com/drugs/politics/**

**Usenet:**
**talk.politics.drugs**

## Psychedelic Drug Guide

When you are in need of a field guide to psychedelics, have a look at this site, which has resources on morning glory seeds, fly agaric, LSD, ecstasy, mushrooms and other psychedelic drugs.

**Web:**
**http://www.utu.fi/~jounsmed/asc/misc/psychedelic.html**

## Psychedelics and Ethnopharmacology

You don't have to leave your home to be a world traveler. Here is a site with a more global approach to drug use: Australian psychoactive plants, links to the Island Web psychedelic society and psychedelic research institutes, ethnobotany, drug culture throughout history and articles by drug-notables such as Hoffman and McKenna.

**Web:**
**http://www.om.com.au/mkzdk/gates/ethnobotgates.html**

## Psychoactive Drugs

The Internet is just a crutch for people who can't cope with drugs. But if you happen to be one of those lucky few who can handle both at the same time, join the discussion about psychoactive drugs, legal and illegal. Just don't let it go to your head.

**Usenet:**
**alt.psychoactives**

## Recreational Drugs

Drugs for fun, not for profit. Where else can you go for advice on what to do with a pot of leftover phenyl acetic acid? How do you tell the difference between Amanita Muscaria, Psilocybe Cubensis and Chinese take-out? Turn on, tune out, and drop into the only Usenet newsgroup where "Better Living Through Modern Chemistry" is more than just a slogan.

**Usenet:**
**alt.drugs**

## Street Drug Slang

Brush up on your street drug lingo the next time you are in desperate need for a decongestant and all the drug stores are closed. Learn how seemingly innocent words can have other, more sinister meanings.

**Web:**
**http://www.addictions.com/slang.htm**
**http://www.drugs.indiana.edu/slang**

## *Look What I Found on the Net...*

(from the Psychedelic Drugs Guide)

```
The effects of Ketamine are stronger and more profound than acid
but last only an hour or so.

The subject should remain still. Experiences of the mind leaving
the body, floating in space, or even death are common.
Bad trips are supposed to be absent, but there are serious
dangers following heavy use.

John Lilly and his fellow researchers have used the drug
continuously for weeks. Several believe themselves to have
contacted alien intelligences and two committed suicide.
```

# ECONOMICS

## Agricultural Economics

The economics of agriculture has its own particular methods and areas of concern. Here are some useful resources to help you in this area. One web site is the Internet site for the Economic Research Service of the U.S. Department of Agriculture. The other web site has a special search engine that you can use to find Internet resources related to agricultural economics, as well as links to research publications at any universities. For ongoing discussion, there is a mailing list.

**Web:**

**http://agecon.lib.umn.edu/**
**http://www.econ.ag.gov/**

**Listserv Mailing List:**

List Name: **agecon-l**
Subscribe to: **listserv@umdd.umd.edu**

## Beige Book

The beige book consists of national and regional summaries of the current economic conditions in the United States as described by the Federal Reserve. New versions of the beige book are produced every month or two, in advance of the meetings of the Federal Open Market Committee (FOMC) (the most important monetary policy-making body of the Federal Reserve System). At any time, you can look at the current beige book and check up on the economic health of the U.S. or one of its twelve Federal Reserve districts. Personally, I think this is a much better way of understanding the economy and where it might be heading than depending on the writers and commentators in the popular press.

**Web:**

**http://woodrow.mpls.frb.fed.us/economy/beige/beigeb.html**

**Stay connected.**

## Bureau of Economic Analysis

The Bureau of Economic Analysis (BEA) is an agency of the United States Department of Commerce. The BEA's function is to analyze and integrate immense amounts of data in order to create a consistent model of the American economy. The BEA creates estimates and analysis dealing with regional, national and international areas of economic concern. Their best-known national measure is probably the gross domestic product (GDP), but they also produce a variety of less well known but equally important measures. Personally, I find a lot of these numbers fascinating. For example, in 1995, the highest average per capita income in the country was in the District of Columbia ($32,274), followed by Connecticut ($30,303) and New Jersey ($28,858). The lowest incomes were in Mississippi ($16,531), Arkansas ($17,429) and New Mexico ($18,055). Although California had only the 12th highest per capita income ($23,699), it had, by far, the highest total personal income was in Wyoming (10.2 billion dollars). (By the way, these are American figures, in which 1 billion = 1,000 million.)

**Web:**

**http://www.bea.doc.gov/**

## Central Banks of the World

A "central bank" is an organization whose purpose is to guide and influence the economy of a particular country or region of the world. Traditionally, the most powerful tool a central bank has is the ability to exert partial control over the money supply. Virtually every country in the world has a central bank. In the U.S., the central bank is the Federal Reserve. In Europe, each country has its own central bank. Once economic union is achieved, a European central bank will be formed from today's European Monetary Institute. Most people do not understand the role of central banks—indeed, many people do not even know of their existence—but their power is an important force in the national economies of the world. Here is a web site that will lead you to many interesting and informative resources regarding central banks of the world, including a list in which you can look for the central bank of any country.

**Web:**

**http://adams.patriot.net/~bernkopf/**

## Central Banks of the World

It's a conspiracy. I'm not supposed to tell you, but I will anyway. All the central banks of the world are controlled by a small group of the intelligentsia: people who are known to be very smart, highly educated, dedicated and disciplined, working in complete secret. These people hide away in hard-to-find places, wielding an obscene amount of power in almost total obscurity. They possess esoteric knowledge and use a vocabulary of technical terms that precludes normal people from even understanding what they are talking about.

Yes, it's a conspiracy. The central banks of the world are controlled by... writers of Internet books.

Well... not actually all writers of Internet books... just a few of us. Well.. .to be totally honest... it's just me.

But don't tell anyone.

## Community Economic Development

A discussion forum for anyone interested in trends, opportunities and changes in community economic development. The focus is for what communities can do for themselves in terms of achieving access to knowledge, programs, markets, and funds.

**Majordomo Mailing List:**

List Name: **ced-net**
Subscribe to: **majordomo@sfu.ca**

## Computational Economics

Now that computers are ubiquitous, and people have had ample time to develop mathematical methods suitable for computation, computational economics touches many different areas of economics. Here is a web site that contains links to a wide variety of related Internet resources. Since this area is such a disparate one, the resources sometimes go far afield. However, as I followed the links I landed in some especially interesting and unexpected places.

**Web:**

**http://cce.sscnet.ucla.edu/sites.html**

## Consumer Price Index

In the United States, the Consumer Price Index (CPI) is a measure of the average change over time of the prices paid by urban consumers for a specific collection of goods and services. The CPI is important as it allows us to track the change in cost of living over various time intervals. This is the official CPI web site as maintained by the U.S. Bureau of Labor Statistics. Here you will find all kinds of information about the CPI including a FAQ (frequently asked question list), current estimates, news releases, raw data, and so on.

**Web:**

**http://stats.bls.gov/cpihome.htm**

## Economic Development

It all started with a few beads, a handful of corn, and maybe a button or two. Who was to know that that functional system would turn into mutual funds, stocks, and IRAs? Economic development is where the little fish grow up to be the big fish who eat other little fish. Of course, it's not quite that simple, which is why you should read this list to find out how small, innovative companies can gain sophisticated tools that help them compete in a global economy.

**Majordomo Mailing List:**

List Name: **econ-dev**
Subscribe to: **majordomo@csn.net**

## Economic Growth

Growth is crucial to maintain the health of the world economy. For measuring and studying economic growth, here is a great web site. You will find data sets, publications, research, as well as many links to related resources on the Net. For ongoing discussion, you can join the mailing list.

**Web:**

**http://www.nuff.ox.ac.uk/Economics/Growth/**

**Majordomo Mailing List:**

List Name: **economic-growth**
Subscribe to: **majordomo@ufsia.ac.be**

## Economic Resources

Let's face it, no one really understands the economy any more than anyone really understands, say, why beer comes in six-packs when people only have two hands. Still, that is no reason to feel left out in the financial cold. There are lots of economics resources out there, just waiting for you to explore, and here are some good places to start. After all, when we are living in a world when an American basketball player can sign a $120,000,000 contract and Internet authors have trouble making that much money in a *good* year, you know that things are getting out of control.

**Web:**

**http://econwpa.wustl.edu/**
**http://fisher.ecn.bris.ac.uk/pointers.htm**
**http://niord.shsu.edu/**

## Economics and Statistics

It's comforting to know that someone out there in the world is taking care of the ebb and flow of all the money that is changing hands by the minute. If you would like to get a closer look at exactly who these people are who are in charge of the economy, browse around at the various federal reserve systems around the world. Get statistics from Indonesia, Mexico, United States and other countries or just read selections from various journals and scholarly publications.

**Web:**

**http://www.lib.lsu.edu/bus/economic.html**

## Economics History

The study of the history of economics is fascinating. Here are some resources for economic historians. You can find data series available for downloading, archives from various mailing lists, syllabi from many different academic courses in economic history, book reviews, abstracts, as well as links to many other sources of related information such as professional organizations, journals, personal web pages, data sets, library catalogs, and so on.

**Web:**

**http://cs.muohio.edu/**

### Economics on the Net

**It all started with classical economics and moved through Marxism, the neoclassical schools, Keynesian economics, monetarism, right through to supply-side economics. Where does that leave us now? Good question. All I can tell you is try to get paid in advance and carry a big stick.**
**However, if you want to understand even more, there are substantial economics resources on the Net. Download the frequently asked question list and you will have more economic resources than you can use in a month of financial Sundays. Never again need you feel left out when the people in the checkout line at the supermarket start discussing the contributions of the neoclassicists to microeconomics.**

## Economics Journals

There are a great many economics journals that have some type of presence on the Net. Here is a list of well over 170 such journals, along with links direct to the corresponding web sites. This is a great place to look for journals of which you may not already be aware.

**Web:**

**http://www.helsinki.fi/WebEc/journals.html**

## Economics Network

Charts are nice. Especially when they come in all sorts of shapes and colors. If you like economics or if you just like charts, take a peek at the Economics Network: an entire resource center with online chart rooms for the U.S. economy and financial markets, economic indicators, weekly economic analyses and briefings, and a fiscal policy chartbook.

**Web:**

**http://www.webcom.com/~yardeni/economic.html**

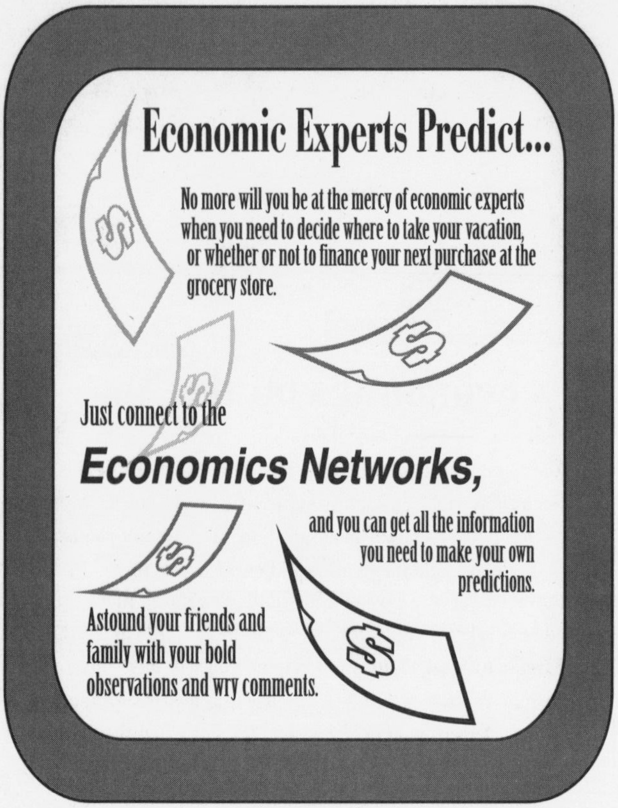
Economic Experts Predict...
No more will you be at the mercy of economic experts when you need to decide where to take your vacation, or whether or not to finance your next purchase at the grocery store.
Just connect to the
Economics Networks,
and you can get all the information you need to make your own predictions.
Astound your friends and family with your bold observations and wry comments.

## Economics of the Internet

These days, information is a premium commodity and everyone is trying to cash in. Get a gander at these links that will inform you about the economics of the Internet, information goods and services, network economics, intellectual property and related information.

**Web:**

**http://www.sims.berkeley.edu/resources/infoecon/**

## Economics Statistics

There's nothing like taking a quick little break from the daily hustle and bustle of life to browse through some economic historic price data and current business statistics. In fact, if you go right now to this site, you can read economic reports from the President of the United States or the U.S. National Budget. With all this waiting for you, how can you even wait to finish this paragraph?

**Web:**

**http://www.idbsu.edu/carol/busness2.htm**

## Economics Talk and General Discussion

For serious talk about the science of economics, here are the Usenet discussion groups. In addition, here's a web site where you can find the FAQ (frequently asked question list) for these groups.

**Web:**

**http://econwpa.wustl.edu/EconFAQ/EconFAQ.html**

**Usenet:**

**sci.econ**
**sci.econ.research**

## Economists on the Web

A large list of economists on the Internet, with pointers to their web pages. If there is a better way to impress a hot date quickly with why the Internet is so important, I have yet to find it.

**Web:**

**http://eclab.ch.pdx.edu/ecwww**

### Finding an Economist

How many times has this happened to you?

You are planning a big party to impress your friends and neighbors and while-making out the guest list you realize that you don't know any economists. And, as we all know, a party without at least one economist is like. . . well. . . a party without an economist.

No need to panic. Just connect to Economists on the Web, and before you can say "MZ Money Supply", you will have as many economists as you need. Remember, a man who knows his numbers is a man you can count on.

## Game Theory

Game theory sounds frivolous. It is anything but. Game theory is a complex body of mathematical methods used for making decisions. The goal of game theory is to analyze a competitive situation in order to determine the optimal course of action. Game theory has applications in politics, economics and military science. Here are two interesting game theory sites on the Net that offer articles, bibliographies, abstracts, information on conferences, and links to many other resources. There is also a well-organized chronology of game theory, tracing the ideas of analyzing competition well back into history, long before formal game theory was put in a sound mathematical basis.

**Web:**

**http://www.canterbury.ac.nz/econ/hist.htm**
**http://www.pitt.edu/~alroth/alroth.html**

## Gross State Product Tables

The gross state product data tables estimate the value of goods and services produced for 61 industries in 50 U.S. states, eight regions, and the U.S. as a whole. The value is the sum of four components: compensation of employees; proprietors' income with inventory valuation adjustment and capital consumption allowances; indirect business tax and nontax liability; and other, mainly capital-related, charges.

**Web:**

**http://www-lib.iupui.edu/erefs/gsp.html**

## History of Economics Thought

There have been many economists, but the large-scale schools of economic thought have been shaped by a relatively few important thinkers. For a student of economics, it is an invaluable experience to read historical papers to get a feeling for economic thinking at various times and places. Here is a wonderful collection of writings by some of the most important and influential people in history. Read papers by Babbage, Hobbes, Hume, Locke, Malthus, Marx, Swift, Toynbee and many more.

**Web:**

**http://socserv2.socsci.mcmaster.ca/~econ/ugcm/3ll3/**

## Household Economic Statistics

How is it that *They* know more about you than you know about you? The Department of Census's Housing and Household Economic Statistics Division has lots of information about incomes and poverty, health insurance, the labor force, wealth and asset ownership of households.

**Web:**

**http://www.census.gov/ftp/pub/hhes/www/**

### *Look What I Found on the Net...*

(from Household Economic Statistics)

Net Worth of U.S. Households

| Age Group | Median Net Worth | Excluding Home Equity |
|---|---|---|
| All ages | $37,587 | $9,505 |
| <35 | $5,786 | $3,297 |
| 35-44 | $29,202 | $8,219 |
| 45-54 | $57,755 | $14,499 |
| 55-64 | $91,481 | $25,108 |
| >65 | $86,324 | $20,642 |

## Inflation Calculator

Inflation is important to the study of economics. Here is a good place to start your thinking about inflation and its effects. Begin by using the inflation calculator: put in any amount of money, pick two different years, and then see how the value of the money would inflate. For example, $100 in 1952 would have the same value as $625 in 1997. Aside from the inflation calculator, there are links to related Internet resources.

**Web:**
**http://www.english.upenn.edu/~morgan/inflation/**

## Law and Economics

This is a great way to find Internet resources relating to the law and economics. You can use a search engine to search for the resources you need, as well as look at lists of links to research, publications, organizations, legal and government resources, directories of people involved in the law and economics, and much more. The mailing list is devoted to discussions of relevant topics in this area.

**Web:**
**http://www-leland.stanford.edu/~tstanley/lawecon.html**

**Listproc Mailing List:**
List Name: **econlaw**
Subscribe to: **listproc@gmu.edu**

## Securities and Exchange Commission's Database

The SEC's Internet EDGAR Dissemination project allows you to get any current filings to the Securities and Exchange Commission that are available to the public.

**Web:**
**http://www.sec.gov/edgarhp.htm**

**Do a backup.**

# EDUCATION

## Academic Technology

Teachers: Don't fall behind in the race for information. Wield your computer like a sword and cut through all the useless and frivolous information. Here is a mailing list that will help you keep up on academic technology. Now you can have extra time for some enjoyable extra-curricular activities of your own (like grading essays, planning lessons, writing report cards...).

**Listserv Mailing List:**
List Name: **infobits**
Subscribe to: **listserv@gibbs.oit.unc.edu**

## Adult Education

These forums offer interesting discussions on ways to educate adults. People talk about all sorts of subjects, such as textbooks, education using interactive computer environments (like Muds and IRC), and audio tapes. There is also lots of discussion about teaching in conventional classroom settings.

**Usenet:**
**misc.education.adult**

**Listserv Mailing List:**
List Name: **adted-l**
Subscribe to: **listserv@psuvm.psu.edu**

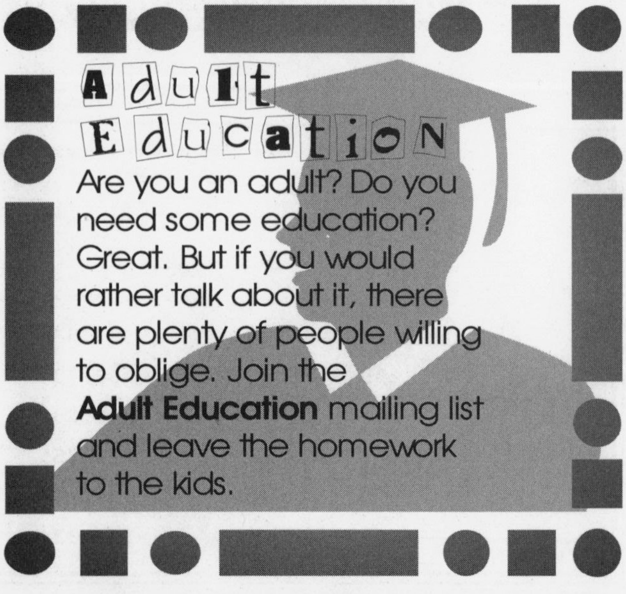
Adult
EducatioN
Are you an adult? Do you need some education? Great. But if you would rather talk about it, there are plenty of people willing to oblige. Join the Adult Education mailing list and leave the homework to the kids.

Z Y X W V U T S R Q P O N M L K J I H G F E D C B A

## Adult Literacy

Learning to read when you are an adult can sometimes be tough—just like trying to learn a new language. Practice is the crucial ingredient for being able to read well, and with **learner**, a moderated discussion group for adult learners, you can practice reading and writing skills by posting to the group. Since the group is for adults, it provides a safe and helpful environment for new learners to share ideas, to meet other people, and establish pen-pal contacts.

**Listserv Mailing List:**
List Name: **learner**
Subscribe to: **listserv@nysernet.org**

## Alternative Approaches to Learning

Learning changes as society changes. When I was a kid, I used to have to walk six miles through the snow every day (uphill both ways) just to get to school. Today, there are alternatives. If you would like to find out about them, join the discussion.

**Usenet:**
**alt.education.alternative**

**Listserv Mailing List:**
List Name: **altlearn**
Subscribe to: **listserv@sjuvm.stjohns.edu**

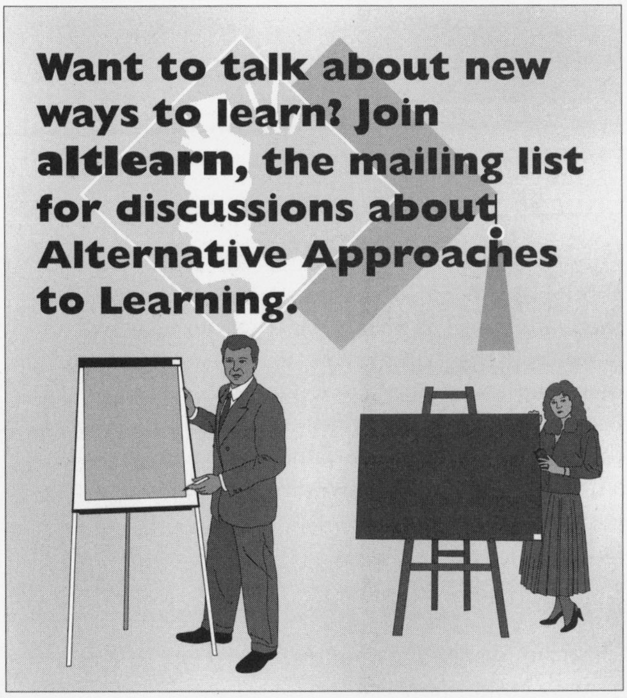
Want to talk about new ways to learn? Join altlearn, the mailing list for discussions about Alternative Approaches to Learning.

## Biology Education

It's 6:00 AM and you need a quick answer for your biology homework due at 8:00. Never fear—fire off a question into the **biopi-l** mailing list. Within a few minutes you may get your answer!

**Listserv Mailing List:**
List Name: **biopi-l**
Subscribe to: **listserv@ksuvm.ksu.edu**

## Canada's Schoolnet

If you are a Canadian teacher, you *must* know about Schoolnet. In the great Canadian tradition of let's-spend-lots-of-government-money-to-create-cultural-resources, Schoolnet is the most ambitious, comprehensive teaching facility since I organized the sex education exhibit at the University of Toronto Medical Students' Open House (1981). Are you Canadian? You must plug in, there is no choice. If you are not Canadian, check it out anyway, and you may find something useful.

**Web:**
**http://www.schoolnet.ca/**

## Computer Networking

There is no doubt that computer networks play an ever-increasing role in schools. If you are the techno-nerd in your school who is supposed to keep the machines up and running, here is a mailing list to help you stay well-connected.

**Listserv Mailing List:**
List Name: **cneduc-l**
Subscribe to: **listserv@tamvm1.tamu.edu**

## Curriculum Materials and Ideas

A collection of pointers to curriculum resources on the Net, including curriculum guides, lesson plans, ideas and resources. Before you copy anything, though, remember that your kids also have access to the Net.

**Web:**
**http://www.cua.edu/www/eric_ae/k12.htm**

## Daily Report Card

If you are a teacher, administrator or professor who finds it difficult to keep up with the news, here is a resource that you simply *must* put in your bookmark list and check regularly. Every day, you will find a comprehensive update showing news items relevant to the educational community.

**Web:**
**http://www.utopia.com/mailings/reportcard/**

Report Card A+

**Get an A+ for Current Events**

**Teachers:** Do you want to be able to keep up on what's happening in the educational community? Read the Daily Report Card every day, and you'll never have to worry about falling behind the rest of the class.

## Distance Learning Resources

Once you are on the Net, there are lots of ways to learn. You don't have to go to a school and sit at a desk. Here is a nice collection of resources for learning (and teaching) over the Net. These resources are especially useful if you are interested in home schooling.

**Web:**
**http://emporium.turnpike.net/~pflaump/winhttpd/htdocs/distan~1.htm**

**Usenet:**
**alt.education.distance**

## Education Conferences

Here's a great web page for those of you (you know who you are) who are just itching to go to an education conference. Check out this updated list of exhibitions, seminars and conferences for educators. You will never have to spend another dull weekend hanging around the house.

**Web:**
**http://www.edunet.com/evendex.html**

## Education Information Technology

Forget plastics and natural resources. *Information* is the key investment for the future. (Remember that you heard it here first.) This discussion group is for educators and educational researchers interested in information technology and resources.

**Listserv Mailing List:**
List Name: **enet-l**
Subscribe to: **listserv@uhccvm.uhcc.hawaii.edu**

## Education Policy

When I was a kid, you could get in trouble for chewing gum in class. Now you get in trouble if the gun you are carrying happens to be on the list banned by Congress. I bet you can remember what it was like being a kid and having to follow the rules with no say in the matter. Well, now you can have your two cents' worth and eat it too. Here are two mailing lists: **edpolyan** for discussion of education policy in the U.S.; **edpolyar** for an archive of the **edpolyan** list.

**Listserv Mailing List:**
List Name: **edpolyan**
Subscribe to: **listserv@asuvm.inre.asu.edu**

**Listserv Mailing List:**
List Name: **edpolyar**
Subscribe to: **listserv@asuvm.inre.asu.edu**

## Education Talk and General Discussion

You don't have to be an teacher or administrator to enjoy the education discussion on Usenet. This Usenet newsgroup covers all sorts of general education topics that relate to teachers, parents, children, administrators, the public school system and much more. Anything goes.

**Usenet:**
**misc.education**

## Educational Discussion Groups

There are a lot of people on the Net who like to talk about schools and education. So many, in fact, that there are a large number of Usenet discussion groups devoted to these areas. This web site contains a list of many of these groups along with short descriptions. From here, it is easy to find what you want. I suggest that you take a look from time to time and investigate a new group. There is always something more to learn, and there is always an interesting discussion going on.

**Web:**
**http://darkwing.uoregon.edu/~ericcem/newsgroups.html**

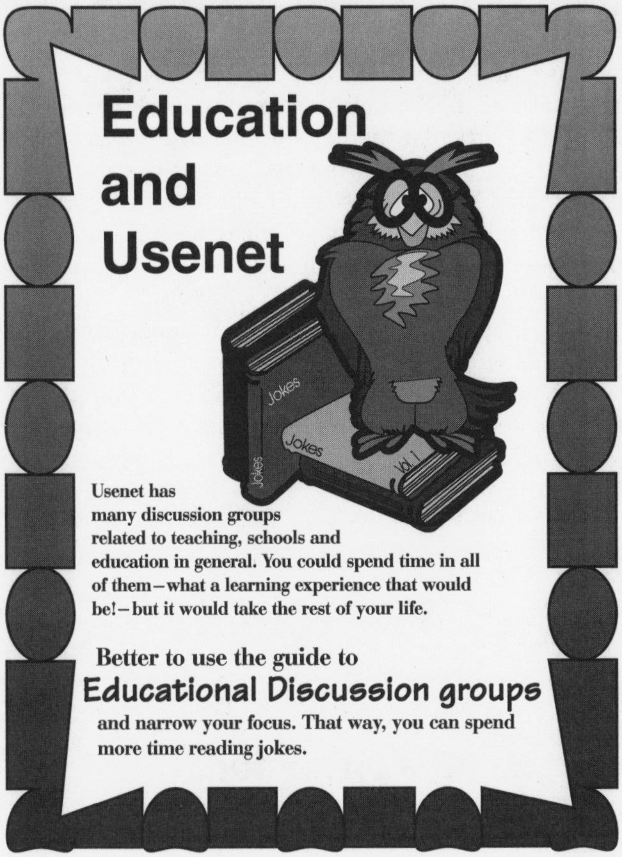
Education and Usenet
Jokes
Jokes
Jokes
Vol. 1
Usenet has many discussion groups related to teaching, schools and education in general. You could spend time in all of them—what a learning experience that would be!—but it would take the rest of your life.
Better to use the guide to
Educational Discussion groups
and narrow your focus. That way, you can spend more time reading jokes.

## Educational Mailing Lists

There are a great many mailing lists on the Net devoted to schools, education and related topics. Here is a web site that contains information about these lists. If you have anything to do with education (teacher, parent, administrator, even student) it is worth spending a few moments looking for mailing lists that interest you. I guarantee you will find something.

**Web:**

**http://www.tile.net/tile/listserv/education.html**

## Educational Reform

A mailing list about innovations in educational reform, as well as other educational issues, including performance assessment, nongraded primary education, and multicultural education.

**Listserv Mailing List:**

List Name: **ukera-l**
Subscribe to: **listserv@lsv.uky.edu**

## Educational Site of the Week

It's fun to spend time exploring the Net, looking for new educational resources to use in the classroom or for your lesson plans. It's even more fun when someone else does the work for you. Here is a site that offers a new educational resource each week. You can also search the archives for previous educational sites of the week.

**Web:**

**http://www.cyberstation.net/~may/surprise.htm**

## Education-Related News Service

An education-related news service provided by EDUCOM, a consortium of leading colleges and universities seeking to transform education through the use of information technology.

**Web:**

**http://www.educom.edu/web/edupage.html**

## Eisenhower National Clearinghouse

The Eisenhower National Clearinghouse (ENC) provides K-12 teachers a central source of information on mathematics and science curriculum materials and encourages the adoption and use of these materials. ENC is funded by the U.S. Department of Education.

**Web:**

**http://www.enc.org/**

## Home Schooling

As home schooling becomes more popular, it is easier to find resources relating to the process of teaching children in the home environment. Take advantage of the Internet as one of these resources and discuss with other home schoolers the trials and rewards of teaching your kids at home. The **misc.education.home-school.christian** group is specifically for Christians who home school.

**Web:**

**http://www.midnightbeach.com/hs**

**Usenet:**

**misc.education.home-school.christian**
**misc.education.home-school.misc**

## Media in Education

If there is one word that is heavily overused by the media, it is "media". Generally, the word means "news media" (newspapers, television, radio, and so on ), although sometimes it means "mixed media" as in computer multimedia (sound plus video). If you are interested in how media services and communication technologies interact with students and other types of human beings, here is the mailing list for you.

**Listserv Mailing List:**
List Name: **media-l**
Subscribe to: **listserv@bingvmb.cc.binghamton.edu**

## Multilingual Classrooms

It's not easy teaching in an environment in which your students can misbehave in more than one language. To share the fun, here is a mailing list especially for discussions of teaching, language, and education in multilingual environments. (I wonder, what is the Esperanto for: "Well, if you think that is so funny, perhaps you would like to share the joke with everyone.")

**Listserv Mailing List:**
List Name: **multi-l**
Subscribe to: **listserv@vm.biu.ac.il**

## Musenet

A muse (Multiuser Simulated Environment) is a multiuser, text-based virtual community designed around a particular theme. Musenet (Multiuser Science Education Network) is a system of various educational Muses. These muses provide real-time interaction between many people who cooperate to build their own world. (Think Dewey or Montessori.) Before you start, I would like to warn you: a muse can suck up all your spare time and then some. Game to try the game? Check the web site for info (don't worry, you don't have to understand everything), then connect to the telnet site and see what happens.

**Web:**
**http://www.musenet.org/**

**Telnet:**
Address: **guest.musenet.org**
Login: **guest**

**"Fun" is fun.**

## *Look What I Found on the Net...*

```
Newsgroup: misc.education.home-school.misc
Subject: How do you cope with four at home?

Hey, congrats on your plunge into what I think is the most rewarding
part of my life.  I have four, like you.  Mine are 9, 7, 4 and 1, my
boys are the older and girls the younger...

It is pretty hard to attend to all their differing needs.  I'm sure it
will take awhile for you to get into a routine, and I don't think it's
REAL important to worry too much about lots of structure right away.
When my boys were 7 and 5 we did very little schooling at all (we have
always homeschooled) -- I sort of waited for them to indicate a
willingness and readiness.  We did lots of reading to them, which my
daughter (3) enjoyed, even the books geared to older kids.  And we did
lots of our work just talking about things: phonics/math/history/science
and they all seem to retain most of what we would talk about if it was
on their level at all.

I think your 2 year old will probably stop her sabotage if you can
involve her by letting her participate...  If it's way beyond her
level, she will probably get bored and turn to a different activity.
My three older kids all do pretty much the same work, but I don't
expect my four year old's stuff to be "correct" and I make sure she
knows it's optional, especially if she gets frustrated...
```

## National School Network Testbed

It's not hard to imagine a time when every school will be on the Net, in the same way that every school has telephone service. However, setting up the intital connection takes time and money and expertise. If you are interested in getting your school on the Net, check out the National School Network Testbed. Their goal is to help every school in the United States get on the Net. Although the information is oriented toward American schools, I know you will find it interesting no matter where you live.

**Web:**

**http://nsn.bbn.com/**

**Is Your School on the Net?**

The National School Network Testbed is working to help get every school in the United States on the Net. Okay, I know this sounds an awful lot like all that silly Information Superhighway, National Information Infrastructure stuff, and in some ways it is. However, if you are involved in getting your school on the Net, you can find some useful information here if you dig long enough.

**Hint:** The local Internet expert in your school is going to have a lot of power. That person might as well be you.

## Netschool

Netschool is a cooperative effort by students, families, teachers and schools. The goal is to create a group of schools that will work together even though they are remote from one another. Well, the Net is certainly the right place to try something like this. If you like the idea of cooperating over long distances, give this site a look.

**Web:**

**http://netschool.edu/**

## New Patterns in Education

The more teaching changes, the more it changes. Just because you are too busy to keep up is no reason why you have to miss the educational school bus. This mailing list is devoted to discussing all that is new and cool in education and the teaching profession.

**Listserv Mailing List:**

List Name: **newedu-l**
Subscribe to: **listserv@uhccvm.uhcc.hawaii.edu**

## Newton BBS for Teachers

The Newton BBS (bulletin board system) is for teachers and students of science, math and computer science. The web site will lead you to the BBS, as well as show you a number of resources related to the Newton project. Isaac Newton, by the way, was an English mathematician and physicist who lived from 1642 to 1727. Among his many contributions to science are the invention of calculus and his concept of universal gravitation. He also—in 1665—discovered the binomial theorem. (Compare this to what most people are able to do at the age of 23.) Many people (including me) consider Newton to be the greatest scientist who ever lived.

**Web:**

**http://www.newton.dep.anl.gov/newton/newtonpg.htm**

**Telnet:**

Address: **newton.dep.anl.gov**
Login: **bbs**

## Quality of Education

A forum for anyone concerned with the quality of education. If you're a parent, teacher, administrator, or student, join the **bgedu-l** list to share ideas and to discuss better alternatives for education.

**Listserv Mailing List:**

List Name: **bgedu-l**
Subscribe to: **listserv@lsv.uky.edu**

## Scholarly Electronic Conferences

The pretentious and ambiguous name of this resource hides a real jewel: a large, well-organized list of education discussions conducted over the Internet. Check out any category you want, and you will find information about mailing lists, Usenet discussion groups, electronic journals and newsletters, text-based virtual worlds (such as muds), and so on. This is a good place for both exploring and serious research.

**Web:**
**http://www.mailbase.ac.uk/kovacs/kovacs.html**

**Academic Excellence on the Internet**

Do you like to tell other people what to think? Do you love to pontificate using sentences that start with "It turns out that. . ."? Do you want to work for an organization that never makes a profit? If so, academia may be for you. The only trouble is, you may have to do research, which can really eat into your spare time. Not to worry. Use the **Scholarly Electronic Conferences** resource and find out what's already there for the taking.

Report Card
A+


## School Nurse Network

Being a school nurse is more than handing out aspirin and Band-Aids. This list provides information and networking opportunities for anyone related to the field of school nursing. Discussion covers research and technological advancements, legislation, policy and regulations, educational opportunities, new grants, and information on professional organizations.

**Listserv Mailing List:**
List Name: **schlrn-l**
Subscribe to: **listserv@ubvm.cc.buffalo.edu**

## Schools on the Internet

Here is a collection of links to all the known high schools and elementary schools on the Internet. Save the address: this list may save your life some day. (For example, I have a friend who teaches in Coquille, Oregon. One day she printed the entire "Schools on the Internet" list, folded it in two, and put it in her shirt pocket. A short time later, she was walking past a classroom window when an over-stimulated ADD student hurled a blackboard eraser out the window, hitting her smack in the chest. If it wasn't for that list in her shirt pocket, my friend would not be alive today.)

**Web:**
**http://web66.coled.umn.edu/schools.html**

## Science and Math Education Reform

Mathematics and science are two subjects for which we always seem to be changing out teaching strategies. This site is maintained by an organization devoted to efforts to reform the teaching of mathematics and science. If your school is interested in this area, you will find a number of interesting resources here.

**Web:**
**http://ra.terc.edu/**

## Science Education

This list is a forum for discussing the reform of science education. If you believe that science education should—or should not—undergo fundamental change, join **ncprse-l** and let your feelings be known.

**Listserv Mailing List:**
List Name: **ncprse-l**
Subscribe to: **listserv@ecuvm.cis.ecu.edu**

## Special Education

In the United States, we have the Individuals with Disabilities Education Act—I.D.E.A.—and before that PL 94-142 (both federal laws) to help ensure that students with a disability can receive a free and appropriate public education in the least restrictive environment. In the outside world (that is, outside the U.S. Congress), there are often problems. Fortunately, there are a lot of people on the Net who are willing to share solutions and information. Here is a good place to start.

**Web:**
**http://www.mordor.com/wader/sped.htm**

## Talented and Gifted

A forum has been established for the discussion of special programs for children who show exceptional skill, intelligence or creativity. Learn about resources, research, and experience relating to Talented and Gifted educational programs.

**Listserv Mailing List:**

List Name: **tag-l**
Subscribe to: **listserv@vm1.nodak.edu**

## Technology in the Classroom

Technology in the classroom changes faster than the official U.S. stand on welfare reform. If you would like to keep up on where our schools and colleges are heading, join the list. The future will be here soon enough and, when it comes, you won't be able to live in the past.

**Listserv Mailing List:**

List Name: **edtech**
Subscribe to: **listserv@msu.edu**

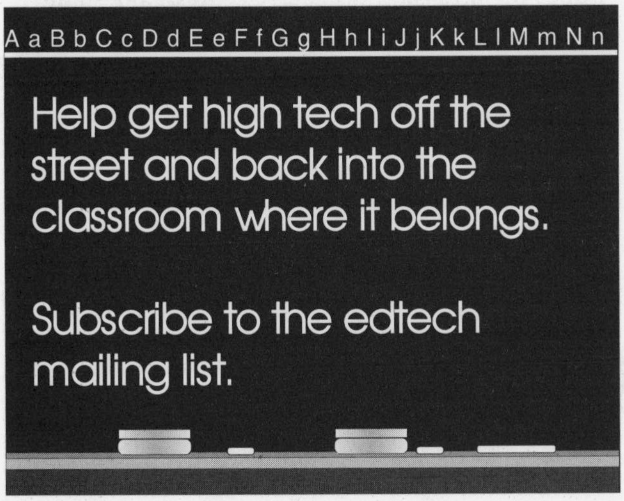
A a B b C c D d E e F f G g H h I i J j K k L l M m N n
Help get high tech off the street and back into the classroom where it belongs.
Subscribe to the edtech mailing list.

## U.S. Department of Education

As part of the Institutional Communications Network project, the U.S. Department of Education has established this site to provide information to educators and researchers interested in education. You will find a wide variety of files on K-12 education as well as vocational and adult education, goals of the Department of Education, programs, announcements and press releases, and educational software.

**Web:**

**http://www.ed.gov/**

## Vocational Education

Network with teachers and administrators of vocational education systems as they explore new ways to pass on needed skills to people heading into the work force. Discover interesting projects designed to make learning interesting and see how educators use the Internet to enhance the learning environment.

**Usenet:**

**bit.listserv.vocnet**

**Listserv Mailing List:**

List Name: **vocnet**
Subscribe to: **listserv@cmsa.berkeley.edu**

# EDUCATION: COLLEGES AND UNIVERSITIES

## American Colleges and Universities

This is almost as good as a "try before you buy" plan. Check out the rumors and reputations of colleges and universities around the United States or discuss the merits of various departments as well as opportunities available at different schools. Discussion includes input from students, professors and alumni.

**Web:**

**http://www.globalcomputing.com/universy.html**

**Usenet:**

**alt.college.us**

## Campus Climate

Campuses have their own special environments, made up of rule-makers, rule-followers, and rule-breakers. It's a breeding ground for diversity, and that has advantages and disadvantages of its own. This open forum invites discussion on the personal, educational, and physical climates of campuses, including topics like race relations, sexual harrassment, safety, and handicapped access.

**Listserv Mailing List:**

List Name: **campclim**
Subscribe to: **listserv@uafsysb.uark.edu**

## Campus Parking

Rumor has it that when naughty college students die they go to the Perpetually Crowded Parking Lot down below and are doomed to spend eternity driving around in circles looking for a place to park while thinking they have only three minutes to make it to their Econ midterm. That's enough to make anyone develop better religious hygiene. Parking problems on campus are universal, so a forum was started in which you can discuss administrative and technical questions and concerns and work toward a resolution that will make everyone happy. (Paving the Earth is not an option.)

**Listserv Mailing List:**
List Name: **cpark-l**
Subscribe to: **listserv@psuvm.psu.edu**

## College Admissions

Getting into the college you want can be difficult and frightening. Blow off some steam on Usenet. You can talk about fears, hopes, dreams, as well as how to make your college application absolutely stunning. If you have any questions about college admissions, this is a good place to ask.

**Usenet:**
**soc.college.admissions**

## College Net

Here is a search tool for college admissions information, including graduate programs. Search, browse by geography, or look at featured schools. Search for financial aid and scholarships.

**Web:**
**http://www.collegenet.com/**

## College Student Guides and Manuals

Perfection is not a bad goal. (It's always worked for me.) So if you want to be an ideal student, here are a few guides that can help you. Learn how to make the transition from high school to college, how to deal with various problems you may encounter in college, and how to make your time at the university go as smoothly as possible.

**Web:**
**http://volvo.gslis.utexas.edu/~acadres/guides.html**

**FAQs are cool.**

### *Look What I Found on the Net...*

```
Newsgroup: alt.college.us
Subject: Studio Art Programs

> Can anyone recommend reputable colleges/universities for studio art?
> My brother is an aspiring comic book artist who is unsure of which
> schools he should consider...

One of the most important things that your brother needs to look into
when he checks on schools is their attitude toward "comic book art" or
other "alternative" forms of art.  By alternative, I mean
"non-traditional".  I can tell you from experience that no matter how
good the school or the instructors, if they don't feel that what he
does is "real art", he is going to end up either squelching his natural
inclinations or spend four or five years fighting the administration.
```

## Advice for College Students

**One great thing about being young is there is no shortage of people who are willing to give you advice (including me).**

**My advice is to take a few moments and look through the College Student Guide and Manuals.**

## College Talk and General Discussion

This is a great discussion group for students and professors in college, and for anyone thinking about attending college. Anything related to colleges and universities is okay: school reputations, good courses to take, grading, taking exams, study habits, professors, university politics, and so on.

**Usenet:**

**soc.college**

## Community Colleges

The United States has—aside from universities—a great many post-secondary schools known as community colleges or two-year colleges. These schools have a wide variety of programs: academic studies leading to a diploma, vocational training, preparation for university, remedial education, and so on. If you are planning to apply to such a school, why not check it out over the Net first? You can find information on just about every community college in the U.S.

**Web:**

**http://www.mcli.dist.maricopa.edu/cc/**
**http://www.sp.utoledo.edu/twoyrcol.html**

## Exploring Campus Tunnels

If you have not yet explored the tunnels under your campus, you have not had a full college experience. These tunnels are constructed in order to hold all types of utility conduits, wiring and pipes (especially steam pipes). They are secret. They can be dangerous (if you have bad luck or do something stupid). But they can be fun to explore. Since it is illegal to enter such tunnels, I advise you to not go near them. Do not read the Usenet group, even though you will find interesting stories, discussion about tunneling—the legalities and health hazards—and possibly information on entrances to specific campus tunnels. And, if you are a student at UCLA or CMU, do not look at the web sites that contain maps of the steam tunnels at your schools.

**Web:**

**ftp://ftp.pslc.ucla.edu/pub/kerry/spyhunt/tunnels.gif**
**http://www.city-net.com/~dmm/tunnels.html**

**Usenet:**

**alt.college.tunnels**

## Financial Aid

Want some free money or even some cheap money? Get the scoop on how to pay your way through college by filling out forms for money. The web page has information about student financial aid, information about specialized schools like grad school, law school and medical school. The Usenet discussion group is a place where you can ask questions, talk or gripe about financial aid and your experiences. My advice is to get as much free money as you can, and borrow as little as possible.

**Web:**

**http://www.finaid.org/**

**Usenet:**

**soc.college.financial-aid**

**The Net cares.**

A B C D E F G H I J K L M N O P Q R S T U V W X Y Z

## Fraternities and Sororities

Have you been feeling out of touch since you graduated from college? No more parties, no more hazing, no more long hours of dressing for social success? Hook up electronically with your fraternity or sorority. This directory lists fraternities and sororities that have a presence on the Web. For ongoing discussion, you can participate in the Usenet groups.

**Web:**

**http://www.greekpages.com/**

**Usenet:**

**alt.college.fraternities**
**alt.college.sororities**

## Globewide Network Academy

The aim of GNA is to foster online learning at a distance over the Internet. If you live on the Net, the future is here: there are already lots of ways to attend school electronically. The GNA web site is a good place to look for such schools and to get information about online learning generally. Surely it can't be that long until we hear, "I couldn't do my homework because the dog ate my mouse."

**Web:**

**http://uu-nna.mit.edu:8001/uu-gna/**

**Wow, free software.**

## *Look What I Found on the Net...*

```
Newsgroups: alt.college.sororities, alt.college.fraternities
Subject: Saying Hello

> This seems to be the sentiments of most sorority members that
> I've met.  My girlfriend wishes that she hadn't joined her
> sorority because most of the girls won't even say hi to her on
> campus, because they only talk to the people in their own
> clique.
>
> My cousin had the same problem in her sorority.  Why are
> sororities like this more so than fraternities?  Maybe it's
> just that way in my experience and nobody else's, but we
> pretty much all get along great in my house.  Once in a while
> there will be a squabble when personalities collide, but never
> do I pass a brother on the street and not even say hi to him.

I do NOT want to reduce this to a gender issue, but many Greek
women I know only know the women in their "family", within the
120-girl group.

I know what's going on in all of my fraternity brother's lives.
Never will I pass a brother without a handshake if I can help
it.

Some of the guys are just arriving back on campus now, and many
of them have gone far out of their way to see me.  (I've been
living a mile off campus all summer.)  There is real brotherhood
out there, even though Greeks get a lot of bad press.
```

## Graduate Record Examination

Ah, the GRE (Graduate Record Examination). An acronym that strikes fear in the hearts of college graduates everywhere. After years and years of studying, you now have to take a test that is going to determine how likely you are to be admitted to the graduate school of your choice. I bet you would like to take some of the magic and mystery out of taking the GRE. This site has sample test questions, reference materials, tips and test-taking strategies, information on how and where to take the test, and how to get your score.

**Web:**
 **http://www.gre.org/**

## Graduate Schools

If you've gone through college and you still just can't get enough of going to school, think about applying for graduate school. You will have much more intellectual stimulation and be admired by all the undergraduate students (who will worship you as a matter of course). These web sites contain information about graduate schools in the United States along with contact information. The Usenet groups offer a place for grad students or grad student wannabes to talk about applying for graduate schools, attending graduate schools, and so on. Personally, I had a lot more fun as a graduate student than as an undergraduate.

**Web:**
 **http://www.schoolguides.com/**

**Usenet:**
 **soc.college.grad**
 **soc.college.gradinfo**

## Graduate Students

After years of school, it begins to look like you might never graduate into the real world. That's why there is the Association for Support of Graduate Students. They provide information about theses, dissertation news and a professional consultant directory. Read the free articles at their web site.

**Web:**
 **http://www.asgs.com/**

## Higher Education Resources Newsletter

Keep up with the latest cool resources valuable to the higher education community. This newsletter comes out once a month and announces new Internet resources such as online tutorials and courses, interesting new web sites, mailing lists and Internet books in print.

**Web:**
 **http://www.hw.ac.uk/libWWW/irn/irn.html**

## Honors Programs

Are you looking for a college that will challenge your scholastic prowess with an honors program? As you are shopping for a place to spend the next four (or five or ten) years, check out this list of links to colleges that offer honors programs. The links will take you to the various colleges where you will find the specific information you need.

**Web:**
 **http://kelp.honors.indiana.edu/nchc/other.html**

**Honors Programs**

**If you are smart and you like to work hard, maybe an honors program is for you. Check it out on the Net, and see what is available. Remember, the brain you train is anything but plain.**

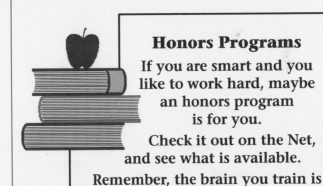

## Internet College Exchange

It's hard to narrow down all the choices of colleges you could go to. How do you pick just the right one? Here is something to help. This service is designed to help prospective college students search for colleges which are appealing. Search by the name of the college, by region or state, size of the institution or cost of tuition.

**Web:**
 **http://www.usmall.com/college/**

## Religious Colleges

If you would like to attend a college that leans toward a particular religious denomination, check out this web site. You can search through a database of colleges run by various religious organizations. The site also has information about each of the colleges, so you can get a quick overview.

**Web:**

**http://www.petersons.com/ugrad/select/rrse.html**

## Residential Colleges

Going to college is a much better way to get away from your family than getting married. So why not go all the way and pick a place that's halfway across the world? Imagine studying in a place where the food makes you ill and nobody speaks your language. Check in the Directory of Residential Colleges to find the perfect place for yourself.

**Web:**

**http://strong.uncg.edu/colleges.html**

### Financial Aid Administrators

The life of a financial aid administrator does have its demands, and sometimes it really helps to talk to other people.

If you would like to see what your peers are saying, join the **finaid-l** mailing list.

(Inside scoop: I have advance knowledge that this year—for a change—there will be too many students and not enough money. But don't tell anyone. It's a secret.)

## Student Affairs

At a university, the euphemism "student affairs" refers to a wide variety of activities such as counseling services, student activism, fraternities, clubs and organizations, and so on. Here are some resources with links to student affairs offices at colleges and universities, as well as information about relevant mailing lists. The Usenet group is for professionals to discuss student development, job announcements and graduate schools.

**Web:**

**http://www.ukans.edu/~upc/sa_list.html**

**Usenet:**

**alt.education.higher.stu-affairs**

## Student Financial Aid Administration

"But I need my money and I need it now!" How many times have you heard that? (How many times have you *said* that?) No matter which side of the checkbook you are on, processing financial aid is a grueling and painful process designed by fans of the Spanish Inquisition. On this interactive informational network, you can discuss administrative concerns and discover resolutions to common problems in the student financial aid community. Share your expertise with fellow administrators and related personnel.

**Listserv Mailing List:**

List Name: **finaid-l**
Subscribe to: **listserv@psuvm.psu.edu**

## Student Governments

Today's student body will be tomorrow's civic and political leaders. If that scares you, at least you can take comfort in the fact that they can organize themselves on the Internet. This universal home page leads to many student government organizations at colleges and universities across the United States.

**Web:**

**http://www.umr.edu/~stuco/national.html**

## Studying Abroad

What better excuse is there to go to another country and have adventures than to tell your parents that the whole thing is educational? Think of all the stories you will have to tell when you return and, best of all, your friends will be jealous. These web sites offer information about various study programs available around the world.

**Web:**

**http://www.petersons.com/stdyabrd/us.html**
**http://www.studyabroad.com/**

## Two-Year Colleges

Join this global network of educators who teach in two-year colleges. They are interested in facilitating instant communication by means of this discussion group, bringing together faculty, administrators, and staff at two-year institutions around the world.

**Listserv Mailing List:**

List Name: **commcoll**
Subscribe to: **listserv@lsv.uky.edu**

## University and College Education

This innocuous sounding resource is a launching pad for a huge amount of information. You can find just about anything having to do with American university and college education by starting here. In particular, there is a master list of links to web pages for what looks like every university and college in the United States; also links relating to research, financial aid, and other sources of information.

**Web:**

**http://www.cs.fsu.edu/projects/group11/combined.hotlist.html**

## University Residence and Housing

Before you go away to college, scope out the various places to live on campus. This page has links to college residency and housing pages. Most of the housing pages include information on residence halls, dining, housing policies and rates. You can also find some tips on getting along with roommates and problem resolution.

**Web:**

**http://www.whitman.edu/~hedgesaj/stuaff/housing.html**

## On-Campus Housing

When I was a young lad, I lived in a co-op dorm during my first year as an undergraduate. By "co-op", I mean a dorm where everything was organized and run by the students. In fact, the dorm was actually owned by the students, and the whole thing worked just fine.

If you get a chance to live in a dorm for a year or two, I think you will agree with me that it is an important social experience (often leading to other important social experiences).

**Hint #1:** If you want to find out the official details about dorms at various schools, use the Net to do your advance research.

**Hint #2:** Learn how to use a butter knife to hold a door shut, so you can lock someone into their room before they do it to you.

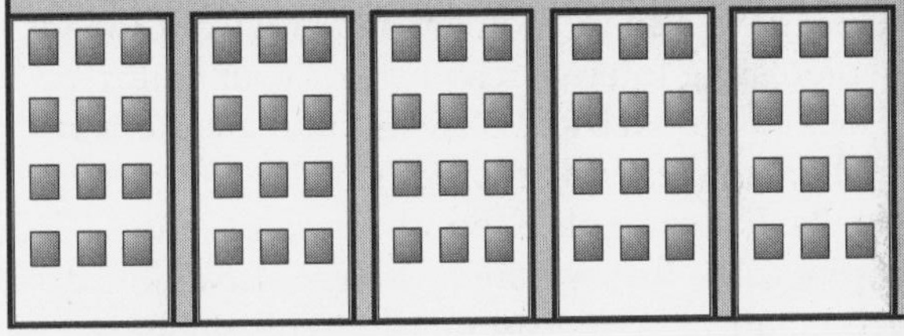

# EDUCATION: K-12

## Ask an Expert

I have always thought that if I changed my name to "Harley Expert" I would get a lot of free publicity in the newspapers. For example, just about every day you see a headline like "Expert Predicts Economy Will Rebound in Next Quarter", or "Expert Says Children Are Using the Internet More Than Their Grandparents Did". I could be famous. However, until then, you and your kids will have to be satisfied with regular, run-of-the-mill experts. Here are some links to such people who have volunteered to answer questions in areas such as science and technology, health and medicine, computing, the Internet, the economy, and so on. Be aware, though, that questions asked of experts over the Net are similar to prayers addressed to a supreme being: they are not always answered.

**Web:**

**http://njnie.dl.stevens-tech.edu/curriculum/aska.html**

## Ask Dr. Math

This is a fantastic math resource. The idea seems simple enough. Children and teachers submit questions about math. The questions are then answered by Dr. Math. (Actually, there are several Drs. Math, but don't tell anyone.) What makes this site so great is that the questions and answers are collected into a well-organized archive. First you choose the level of math in which you are interested: elementary school, middle school, high school, or college and beyond. Then, within that category, you can explore a variety of topics. If you are interested in learning or teaching math, I guarantee you will find something interesting here. And, of course, you can always send your own question to Dr. Math.

**Web:**
**http://forum.swarthmore.edu/dr.math/dr-math.html**

## Education Place

When you have a spare moment and you want to look for an interesting Internet resource for your children, take a look at this web site. You will find a variety of information, games and activities suitable for various age groups. For example, I found a multiple choice geography game that was interesting. I also enjoyed the mathematical brain teasers. Hint: This site is produced by a textbook publisher, so you will have to ignore the commercial stuff and hunt for the jewels.

**Web:**
**http://www.hmco.com/school/**

## Geometry and Art

One of the nice things about teaching geometry is that you can use simple visual aids which you can make yourself. Here is a web site that contains many different ideas on how to teach abstract geometrical ideas imaginatively. You will see detailed presentation plans, as well as descriptions of how to make all the visual aids you need. For the kids, you can find hands-on activities. For yourself, you can find grids and patterns you can copy, as well as tips on teaching geometry vocabulary.

**Web:**
**http://forum.swarthmore.edu/~sarah/shapiro/**

## Helping Kids Learn Science

How do you help your kids learn science? There are two time-tested methods, both of which have their place in education. (1) You can pique your kids' curiosity about scientific phenomena, by showing them fascinating aspects of nature and discussing how and why they occur. To assist you, here is a guide for parents of K-12 kids, showing how you can help them learn science. (2) You can make them read and study, even when they don't feel like it.

**Web:**
**http://www.ed.gov/pubs/parents/Science/**

## Kids and Science

When Einstein was young, it took him a long time to get his career started because his parents couldn't use the Net to help him learn science. (They didn't have a modem.)

However, there is no need for *your* kids to suffer. There are lots of resources on the Net that you can use to help your kids learn a lot about science.

After all, you already have enough problems without having to worry that your children might end up like Einstein.

$$E=MC^2$$

## High School Newspapers on the Net

In the old days, high school newspapers would be circulated on paper to a relatively small number of people. Thus, anonymous gossip about the principal and the head of the science department had only a limited audience. Today, we have the Net and many, many high school newspapers are online and accessible to the world. Take a look.

**Web:**
**http://www.nvnet.k12.nj.us/newsweb/**

## High School Student's Survival Guide

This web site contains a list of resources for high school students. The resources are organized by subject so you pick an area in which you are interested, for example, English, history, art, science, computers, math, and so on. I don't know if these resources will help anyone survive high school—you would be better off with a lot of patience and a diverting social life—but if you are a nerd who likes spending your spare time on the Net, you will probably find something here you like.

**Web:**

**http://www.marblehead.com/amahaney/**

## Jason Project

The Jason Project is an ambitious undertaking that uses modern technology to offer educational experiences relating to science and technology. The material is organized around general themes, and helps children learn about important scientific discoveries and concepts. Jason is designed to be part of a K-12 curriculum, and can provide an ongoing and valuable adjunct to classroom study. If you are a teacher or parent, take a look at this site, and see if there is something here for you and your kids.

**Web:**

**http://seawifs.gsfc.nasa.gov/scripts/JASON.html**

## K-12 Curriculum Talk and General Discussion

There are specific Usenet groups for teachers to discuss curriculum and learning materials. If you are a teacher, you may enjoy participating in the discussion related to your area. The groups are: **art** (art), **business** (business education), **comp.literacy** (computer literacy), **health-pe** (health and physical education), **lang.esp-eng** (English/Spanish), **life-skills** (home economics and career education), **math** (mathematics), **music** (music and performing arts), **science** (science), **soc-studies** (social studies and history), **special** (students with handicaps or special needs), **tag** (talented and gifted students), and **tech** (industrial arts and vocational education).

**Usenet:**

**k12.ed.art**
**k12.ed.business**
**k12.ed.comp.literacy**
**k12.ed.health-pe**
**k12.ed.lang.esp-eng**
**k12.ed.life-skills**
**k12.ed.math**
**k12.ed.music**
**k12.ed.science**
**k12.ed.soc-studies**
**k12.ed.special**
**k12.ed.tag**
**k12.ed.tech**

## K-12 Foreign Language Talk and General Discussion

If you are learning (or teaching) a foreign language, you can talk to people around the world who speak that language. Learn about their culture and practice speaking with them. The **arts** group is for general discussion of the language arts. The other groups are for specific languages and cultures: **deutsch-eng** (German/English), **esp-eng** (Spanish/English), **francais** (French/English), **japanese** (Japanese/English) and **russian** (Russian/English).

**Usenet:**

**k12.lang.art**
**k12.lang.deutsch-eng**
**k12.lang.esp-eng**
**k12.lang.francais**
**k12.lang.japanese**
**k12.lang.russian**

## K-12 Internet School Sites

Before you know it, kids will spend more time on the Net than at school. ("I'm sorry, but I couldn't do my homework because my dog ate the modem.") There are lots and lots of schools on the Net, many of which have their own web sites. Here are collections of links to such schools. I bet you will find it fascinating to see what teachers and students are doing around the world. Perhaps your kids would like to create their own web page and share it with the world.

**Web:**

**http://web66.coled.umn.edu/schools.html**
**http://www.classroom.net/classweb/**
**http://www.sendit.nodak.edu/k12/**

A B C D E F G H I J K L M N O P Q R S T U V W X Y Z

## K-12 Resources

Here are some well-organized collections of resources relating to many areas of K-12 education: classroom activities, teaching, libraries, administration, art, fun for kids, connecting your school to the Net, museums, information for parents, and so on. I predict that whatever spare time your kids are willing to let you have will be quickly used up by the Net.

**Web:**

**http://chico.rice.edu/armadillo/Rice/K12resources.html**
**http://sunsite.unc.edu/cisco/schoolhouse.html**

## K-12 Student Discussion Groups

There are special Usenet groups in which students from all over the world can talk to one another. This is a great way for kids to learn about other children and other cultures while developing their writing skills. The groups are organized as follows: **elementary** for grades K-5, **junior** for grades 6-8, and **senior** for high school.

**Usenet:**

**k12.chat.elementary**
**k12.chat.junior**
**k12.chat.senior**

## K-12 Teachers Discussion Group

If you are a K-12 teacher, you may want to participate in the Usenet teacher's discussion group. After all, you need something to do in your spare time.

**Usenet:**

**k12.chat.teacher**

## Kidlink

Kidlink is an organization that helps children aged 10-15 from all over the world talk to one another using the Net. Kidlink supports not only English, but other languages as well. To participate in Kidlink children register by answering several questions about themselves. They can then participate—either on their own or with their class at school—in any of the Kidlink activities: mailing lists, entering art contests, IRC, and so on. The most important resources are the Kidcafe mailing lists, which children can use to talk to one another. For information on Kidlink and how to participate, see the web page. Teachers and parents: This is a good way for your kids to talk to other kids around the world, and to show them how important the Net is to human culture.

**Web:**

**http://www.kidlink.org/**

### *Look What I Found on the Net...*

```
Newsgroup: k12.lang.art
Subject: Star Trek

How many other teachers use Star Trek in their teaching?

I've used the episode "Darmok" in discussing the concepts of
mythology, allusion, and culture with good results.  You can
buy a CD which has theme songs and sound effects from the
various Star Trek incarnations.

If anyone would like to swap Star Trek lesson ideas, let me
know.
```

## Learning to Read

If you have children, you know how important it is to help them learn how to read. Here are some tips that can make the process effective and enjoyable. The emphasis is on talking, telling stories, reading stories together, and making the alphabet fun to learn. I have a hint of my own. Teach your kids the alphabet forward *and* backward. Throughout their entire life, they will find it much easier to use dictionaries, phone books, and other reference books that are organized in alphabetical order. It is simple for kids to learn their letters both ways—from A to Z and from Z to A—but most parents and teachers don't realize how important it is.

**Web:**

**http://nisus.sfusd.k12.ca.us/sfsv/read.html**



## Literature for Children

The Net has lots and lots of literature specially for children. Here are some web sites that can help you find what you need for your kids. You will see book reviews, tips on using books, information about children's books and their authors, as well as links to other children's literature resources on the Net.

**Web:**

**http://www.crocker.com/~rebotis/**
**http://www.users.interport.net/~fairrosa/**

## MegaMath

MegaMath is a project designed for elementary school children and teachers. The idea is to introduce kids to some of the important unusual ideas that mathematicians work with. The site is set up to be useful for teachers who want to plan mathematical activities as well as children who want to explore on their own. I found a lot of interesting material which I am sure is not normally covered in the classroom.

**Web:**

**http://www.c3.lanl.gov/mega-math/**

## School Projects by Kids

There are lots and lots of kids on the Net who love to share their work. Here are links to projects, reports and writing, all done by kids. Now that we have the Net, growing up will never be the same.

**Web:**

**http://sln.fi.edu/tfi/hotlists/kids.html**

## School Safety Tips

Being in school presents a special set of safety considerations. Wise parent prepare by teaching their children how to avoid unsafe situations and what to do if something happens. Here is a wealth of wise and practical information about safety for parents of school-aged children. There is a lot you can do in advance to avoid unnecessary trouble, and I strongly recommend you take a few minutes to read the hints and tips. For example, you can choose a secret password for you and your children to use in case of an emergency.

**Web:**

**http://www.st-louis.mo.us/st-louis/county/government/safety.html**

*Look What I Found on the Net...*

```
                  (from School Safety Tips)

============================
Know Your Children's Friends
============================

Parents should become familiar with their children's
acquaintances.  This is a continuing process because children
make new friends during each school year.

Children should also be taught to keep parents informed about
their whereabouts.  They are often distracted on the way home
from school and end up at a friend's house without telling a
parent.

Knowing your children's friends will help you know where to
look for them in the event they fail to come home from school
on time.
```

## School Uniforms

Belief systems go in and out of fashion. Today, there are many people who believe that the way to get kids to behave and concentrate in school is to remove the pressure and laxity that comes from allowing people to dress the way they want. In other words, if the kids wear school uniforms, the school environment will be more disciplined and, hence, safer and more effective. Here is what you need to consider before setting up a school uniform program in your school.

**Web:**
**http://www.ed.gov/updates/uniforms.html**

## Science Learning Network

Learning about science can be a lot of fun or it can be a big bore. One thing that makes science enjoyable is to see things happen with your own eyes, and then relate what you see to what you understand. The Science Learning Network has resources for teachers to plan lessons and demonstrations that help kids to explore various areas of science. If you are a parent, you will be able to find things to do with your children at home to help them appreciate science. For example, wouldn't it be great to dissect a cow's eye in front of the entire family?

**Web:**
**http://www.sln.org/**

## Spelling Bee

Would you know how to spell "vivisepulture"? That's the word that a young lady named Wendy Guey had to spell in order to win the final (13th) round of the American National Spelling Bee. A spelling bee is a contest in which people compete against one another to see who is the best speller. Spelling bees are organized into rounds. In each round, the individual contestants are each asked to spell a word, one person at a time. Only those people who spell their word correctly may move on to the next round. Eventually, only one person—the winner—is left. Spelling bees can use easy or difficult words. With easy words, you can have a spelling bee with young kids, even those who are just learning to read. The National Spelling Bee is a national championship in which very difficult words are used. For more information about this contest, take a look at their web page. I enjoyed looking at the round by round descriptions, seeing exactly which words were used. By the way, "vivisepulture" means burying alive.

**Web:**
**http://www.spellingbee.com/**

**Don't click here.**

## Study Tips

I am going to tell you a secret. How you do in high school *does* matter. I know you may hear stories about people who completely screwed up their grades in high school and went on to become rich/famous/powerful—whatever. However, in general it is just not true. The people you hear about are exceptions and are rare. When I think about the people I grew up with, their success in later life correlates directly with their success in high school. (For example, I did well in high school, and I am very successful.) In my experience, the people who blew off high school ended up being unhappy and poor. Believe me, it is no fun being a middle-aged man or woman who is floundering around looking for work or trying to get by on a small salary with no prospects. One of the things you need to understand is that being a good student involves using skills that you must learn and practice. To get you started, here are some resources with a small amount of information about studying and taking notes. (I don't want you to spend a lot of time reading about studying. I want you to study.) Finally, here are my personal tips on how to do well in high school. (1) Have fun, but don't fool around too much. (2) Learn to study well and do it a lot. (3) Hang around with people who share your interests and do well in school. Avoid people who are losers no matter how popular they may seem. (4) Don't get pregnant; don't get anyone else pregnant.

**Web:**

**http://www.math.ucalgary.ca/~ling/takenote.html**
**http://www.tulane.edu/~erc/STips.html**

## Test Taking Tips

So you thought that since you are finished with school yourself you don't have to worry about tests. Think again. Now that you have kids, you have to help them with *their* tests. Here is a lot of useful information offered by the United States Department of Education, Office of Educational Research and Improvement. The hints in this document are helpful for both regular and standardized tests. (I bet you didn't know there was an entire government office devoted to things like helping you teach your kids how to do better in school.)

**Web:**

**http://www.ed.gov/pubs/parents/TestTaking/**

## Writing Well

When your kids write well, everyone benefits. However, writing well must be learned deliberately and requires a lot of practice. Here are some useful hints to assist you in helping your children with their writing. If there is one skill they will use over and over for the rest of their lives, it is writing. Help them get started properly.

**Web:**

**http://www.ed.gov/pubs/parents/Writing/**

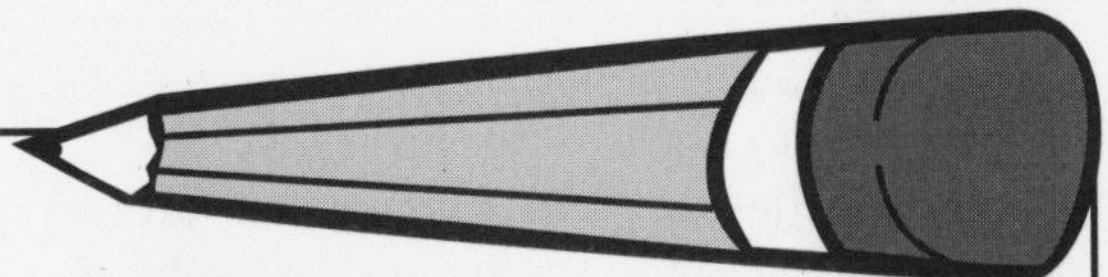

### Writing Well

To me, the most important skill you can help your students (or your children) develop is being able to write well.

As a child practices writing, he or she is also practicing how to read well, how to organize ideas, and how to concentrate for an extended period of time on a specific goal.

Writing well endows a child with an enormous advantage that will persist throughout life.

(Also, writers, especially good writers, are cool.)

# EDUCATION: TEACHING

## Academic Magazines

Here is a list of pointers to a great many magazines and journals relating to schools, education and universities. Just the place to look for something to read in your copious spare time.

**Web:**

**http://www.enews.com/monster/education.html**

## AskERIC

ERIC (Educational Resources Information Center) is a taxpayer-funded information system that provides access to education-related literature for teachers, library media specialists, administrators, and others.

**Web:**
**http://ericir.syr.edu/**

## Business School Faculty

Do you teach in a business school? Here is a mailing list to allow you to talk to other business school faculty all over the world. Talk about your problems, discuss the solutions and share your research ideas.

**Listserv Mailing List:**
List Name: **busfac-l**
Subscribe to: **listserv@cmuvm.csv.cmich.edu**

## Catalyst for College Educators

College educators have concerns that often differ from other educators. This quarterly journal published by the National Council on Community Services and Continuing Education has been created to meet the needs of educators in community, junior and technical colleges.

**Listserv Mailing List:**
List Name: **catalyst**
Subscribe to: **listserv@vtvm1.cc.vt.edu**

## Classroom Discipline

Keeping order in the classroom is important, and it's not always easy to walk a careful path between regulations, parents who are ready to complain, and the fact that, by their nature, many students love to misbehave. Still, you're the teacher, and you do have to spend some of your time socializing the youngsters (if for no other reason than to make your life easier). This web site contains tips and techniques that you might find useful. However, it is good to remember, every teacher has his or her own personality and what works for one person won't work for everybody, so don't stop experimenting.

**Web:**
**http://users.aol.com/churchward/hls/techniques.html**

## College and University Teaching Assistants

Remember how in school everyone wanted to do stuff for the teacher, like clean the chalkboard, bang erasers, or grade papers? Most of us got over that urge, but there are some who never did, and now they are hanging out in the big league academic scene wearing tweed and discussing philosophy at the off-campus coffeehouse. But that's not all they do. Sometimes they are found on the Internet discussing the roles of teacher and student with other teaching assistants on this listserv list. It's a nice space in which to talk about teaching techniques and the responsibilities of being a teaching assistant.

**Listserv Mailing List:**
List Name: **t-assist**
Subscribe to: **listserv@unmvma.unm.edu**

### Teaching Assistants

Being a T.A. (teaching assistant) is fun. For the first time in your life, you actually get to control the grades of other people. And you can have the experience of saying something and watching other people write it down.

Still, it can take a while to become a good T.A. If you would like to talk to other teaching assistants, join the **t-assist** mailing list.

When I was a grad student, I was the senior T.A. for a course in which the professor left before the end of the semester to move to Brazil. I got to give all the exams and award all the grades. It was great.

**On the Net, "New Age" is old hat.**

A B C D E F G H I J K L M N O P Q R S T U V W X Y Z

## Dead Teacher's Society

Are you interested in a broad discussion of teaching and learning? If so, you may want to join the Dead Teacher's Society mailing list. Being dead is optional. (Although you are expected to die some day, you are allowed to do it at your convenience.)

**Listserv Mailing List:**

List Name: **dts-l**
Subscribe to: **listserv@iubvm.ucs.indiana.edu**

## Education Net

To me, the Internet provides an wonderful and exciting place to teach and learn. Do you agree? (Of course you do.) Here is a mailing list to join if you would like to talk to other people about the Net and its educational potential. Discussions range from K-12 through postsecondary education.

**Listserv Mailing List:**

List Name: **ednet**
Subscribe to: **listserv@lists.umass.edu**

## Educational Administration

When you were a kid in school, didn't you ever wonder what it would be like to actually work in the office? Well, now you know. And you also know that—when you get right down to it—it's the administrators that make everything run smoothly (or at all). If you would like to talk with other educational K-12 administrators, here is the place.

**Listserv Mailing List:**

List Name: **k12admin**
Subscribe to: **listserv@listserv.syr.edu**

## Educational K-12 Resources

An educational web site containing K-12 programs and projects, a "what's new" section, a list of education-oriented Internet sites, art resources, schools that have their own web pages, K-12 virtual libraries, notices about contests, and much more. This is a great collection.

**Web:**

**http://k12.cnidr.org/janice_k12/k12menu.html**

## EdWeb

If you have anything to do with schools, you know that lots of people are running around trying to figure out what to do with the Net—and what the Net is going to do with us. One way to sort it all out is to learn what you are talking about (a solution that has somehow evaded just about every public official in the world). A good place to start is EdWeb. Click on anything that looks interesting, and you are bound to learn something.

**Web:**

**http://k12.cnidr.org:90/**

## Explorer

A remarkable collection of ideas, lesson plans, and general information for educators and students that is easy to work with and simple to understand. Outlines for math and science lessons, newsletters, and resource keyword searching capabilities.

**Web:**

**http://unite.ukans.edu/**

### *Look What I Found on the Net...*

(from the Explorer web site)

CREEPIN' CRITTER MATH

```
Critter Math is an arcade-style game for practicing the math facts.
The game can be played in two variations.  In the first, four
cockroaches are crawling up a wall toward four picture frames
containing possible answers to a math-facts problem at the bottom of
the screen.  The student has to swat the bug below the correct answer
before one of the bugs disappears under its picture frame. If the wrong
bug is swatted, the other three keep crawling, and give the student an
extra chance...
```

A B C D E F G H I J K L M N O P Q R S T U V W X Y Z

## Higher Education Discussion

A mailing list for discussions relating to all aspects of higher education, teaching and learning. If you are a professional, this mailing list is a good way to get to meet your peers and to find out what they are doing.

**Listserv Mailing List:**

List Name: **stlhe-l**
Subscribe to: **listserv@listserv@unb.ca**

## Instructor Magazine

Instructor Magazine is a professional publication for elementary school teachers. You will find articles on important topics such as professional development, curriculum planning, communicating with children and parents, grading, teaching strategies, and ideas for the classroom.

**Web:**

**http://www.scholastic.com/Instructor/**

## Kindergarten Teachers Discussion

I once lived with a kindergarten teacher and, I can tell you, they have a lot to talk about. So here is the place to do your talking: a mailing list devoted to topics of interest to kindergarten teachers.

**Majordomo Mailing List:**

List Name: **kinder-l**
Subscribe to: **majordomo@etc.bc.ca**

## Lesson Plans Using the Net

It's fun to plan lessons, but when you are tired, overworked, in a hurry and under pressure, it can be nice to have a bit of help. This web site has lessons specifically designed to be integrated with the Internet, so you can teach and be cool, all at the same time.

**Web:**

**http://trms.k12.ga.net/~jtucker/lessons/lessplan.html**

## Special Education Teachers

There are a great deal of unique concerns when dealing with the field of special education. It's great to be able to network with other teachers, clinicians and researchers to discuss current issues about practices, policies and new developments. This list is open to anyone who has an interest in special education.

**Majordomo Mailing List:**

List Name: **spedtalk**
Subscribe to: **majordomo@virginia.edu**

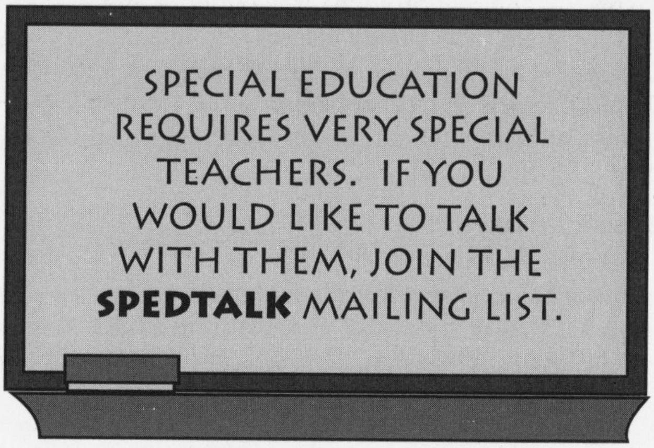
SPECIAL EDUCATION
REQUIRES VERY SPECIAL
TEACHERS. IF YOU
WOULD LIKE TO TALK
WITH THEM, JOIN THE
SPEDTALK MAILING LIST.

## Teacher Talk and General Discussion

This is the general Usenet discussion group for K-12 teachers. Feel free to talk about anything you want. In particular, this is a good place to look for questions, answers and support.

**Usenet:**

**k12.chat.teacher**

## Teachers Helping Teachers

The best tips and hints you can find will come from other teachers. That is what you will find at this web site. In addition, you will find information on classroom management, language arts, special education and stress reduction. (Stress reduction? Who has time for stress reduction?)

**Web:**

**http://www.pacificnet.net/~mandel/**

## Teachers Net

A variety of resources for teachers with an emphasis on discussion groups. This site is great for teachers to trade tips, ask questions, look for help with a specific problem, and so on. Sometimes it seems that a big part of teaching is complaining about the working conditions, lack of reasonable pay and all the dumb things your principal does. In my experience, most teachers are chronically disgruntled about something or other. When you feel in the mood, you might as well complain to your friends on the Net.

**Web:**

**http://www.teachers.net/**

## Teachers Resources

A plethora of resources for teachers (and other related fauna): there are various guides, resources categorized by subject, instructional materials and a list of educational supply vendors. Also, a nice list of links to other related Internet resources.

**Web:**

**http://www.educ.kent.edu/ed/teachers/**

## Teaching English as a Second Language

Imagine the thrill of teaching people to speak English—every word you say is going to be mimicked, and all across the globe there will be people who talk just like you. Take advantage of networking opportunities by looking at what other teachers of English are doing with lesson plans, multicultural classroom environments, helpful hints for pronunciation and other important issues.

**Usenet:**

**bit.listserv.tesl-l**

## Teaching Health and Physical Education

Talk to people who teach health and physical education. Trade ideas, tips, and stories. Find out if it is really true that "Those who can, do. Those who can't, teach. And those who can't teach, teach P.E."

**Usenet:**

**k12.ed.health-pe**

### *Look What I Found on the Net...*

```
Newsgroup: bit.listserv.tesl-l
Subject: What's a good post?

Fellow netters: I am writing this both as an active teacher and as the
founder of TESL-L, and I am answering the claim that netters are using
this list just to get "quick fixes" to help them with their next class.

Well, I can't see anything wrong with that... TESL-L was founded and
is funded to help teachers help students.  In particular, my vision for
TESL-L was that teachers who are professionally or geographically
isolated would have a forum where they could get the information they
needed and couldn't get elsewhere.

I think it is *wonderful* if teachers can get help with their next
TESL/FL class...

To demand that teachers not use the net if the information requested is
available in libraries denies the value of electronic communications,
and it denies the facts of many teachers' lives: They do not have ready
access to libraries, journals, and professional development....
```

## Teaching Math

If you hated math in school, how do you think your teachers felt? Find out by taking a look at this discussion group.

**Usenet:**
k12.ed.math

## Teachnet

Teachnet is an online magazine devoted to the teaching profession. You will find classroom decor tips, hints on getting organized, lesson plans, classroom management ideas, and employment opportunities, and much more.

**Web:**
http://www.teachnet.com/

# ELECTRONICS

## All About Electronics

Would you like to learn about electronics? Here are lots and lots of resources to help you find information about whatever area of electronics interests you. Start with basic skills, such as soldering, and work your way up to designing complicated circuitry. Pretty soon, you will be creating your own robots to help you with the household chores. And when people say, "Wow, how did you ever learn how to make something like that?" you can answer, "I learned it on the Net."

**Web:**
http://www.hut.fi/~then/electronics.html

## Analog IC Design

Explore the web site of the Analog IC Design group at UCLA. Learn about their projects in the areas of wireless transceivers, disk signal processing and data conversion. You can also take a look at the publications, theses, reports and presentation slides related to the research.

**Web:**
http://www.icsl.ucla.edu/aagroup/

### *All About Electronics*

Tell me if the following sounds interesting to you:

========

A transistor is a semi-conductor device used for amplifying a current or voltage.
Transistors have three terminals.
Bipolar transistors have a base, an emitter and a collector. They are controlled by current and have low input impedance.
Field-effect transistors have a gate, a source and a drain. They are controlled by voltage and are high impedance.

========

Now don't worry about whether or not you understand all the technical terms.
If this type of stuff sounds interesting to you, you may enjoy learning about electronics.
If so, don't waste a moment. Connect to the Net, and start reading about electronics right this very moment.

## Circuit Analysis Software

Investigate Aplac, a software package used for circuit analysis. It offers a large number of analysis modes including AC, DC, linear and nonlinear noise, transient and oscillator. This program has a lot of built-in facilities including various component models, a lot of control over input and output, and optimizations methods. If you spend any of your time designing or testing analog circuits, you should check out Aplac.

**Web:**
http://www.aplac.hut.fi/aplac/cookbook/basics/

**Read a zine today.**

## Consumer Repair Documents

Do you think you might like to fix that toaster yourself rather than throw it out? Or how about taking a whack at the microwave before calling the repair service? Here is some handy and practical information about fixing electronic appliances. And if you really get stuck, you can always ask your Usenet friends for help. Maybe you can save enough money to pay for your monthly Internet bill.

**Web:**

**http://www.paranoia.com/~filipg/HTML/REPAIR/**

**Usenet:**

**sci.electronics.repair**

## EDN Access Magazine

EDN Access is a well-established magazine that follows the electronics industry, especially in areas related to design engineering. You can read the current issue for free, as well as fill out a form to qualify for a free print subscription.

**Web:**

**http://www.ednmag.com/**

## Electronic Chip Directory

There are a *lot* of electronic chips in the world, with more being manufactured all the time. To help you find the information you need when you need it, here is a great resource that contains data about specific chips and about manufacturers, organized numerically as well as by function. You will also find FAQs (frequently asked question lists), information about mailing lists, useful tips as well as many other links to related resources.

**Web:**

**http://www.hitex.com/chipdir/chipdir.html**

**Chips Ahoy**

There are a lot of chips in the ocean of electronics. Make sure you are able to spot the right chip at the right time.

If you always check with the Electronic Chip Directory, you will never run a ground.

## Electronic Circuit Archive

Don't spend a lot of time trying to design a brand new circuit until you have checked with this archive. You will find all kind of circuit schematics as well as a component database. You can also search for information about other electrical devices, such as microprocessors, software, and links to many related resources on the Net.

**Web:**

**http://www.ee.washington.edu/eeca/**

## Electronic Components

If you need to find a manufacturer of a particular type of component, this web site is the place to look. Choose a category and then look through a comprehensive list of links. Jump right to the web sites of manufacturers who are involved with that type of component. This is a fast and easy way to find out where to get the information you need, direct from the manufacturer. If you would like to discuss electrical components, check out the Usenet discussion group.

**Web:**

**http://www.ping.be/~ping0751/**

**Usenet:**

**sci.electronics.components**

## Electronic Equipment Talk and General Discussion

If you maintain or purchase electronic equipment, it can be difficult to keep up on what's changing and to know what to do to get the best out of your apparatus. Here is a Usenet group devoted to discussion of electronic equipment. This is the place to spend some time browsing, or to ask a question of an expert.

**Usenet:**

**sci.electronics.equipment**

A B C D E F G H I J K L M N O P Q R S T U V W X Y Z

## Electronic Prototyping Tips

Only those who are really lucky can aspire to this level of electronic excellence. Get your fill of electronic prototyping and construction methods. Learn how to do cool things like despike chips, make changes to circuitry and more. There is a huge amount of great troubleshooting information at this site.

**Web:**

**http://engr-www.unl.edu/ee/eeshop/proto.html**

## Electronics Repair

What a feeling of power to wield your mighty soldering iron knowing that you can fix anything. Share the thrill of wiring up the world with other electronics pros and enthusiasts and hear adventure stories about sparking microwave ovens, glowing Halloween gadgets, and televisions that generate X-rays. The talk is technical in detail, but these electronics gurus have a sense of humor (and the joy buzzers to prove it).

**Usenet:**

**sci.electronics.repair**

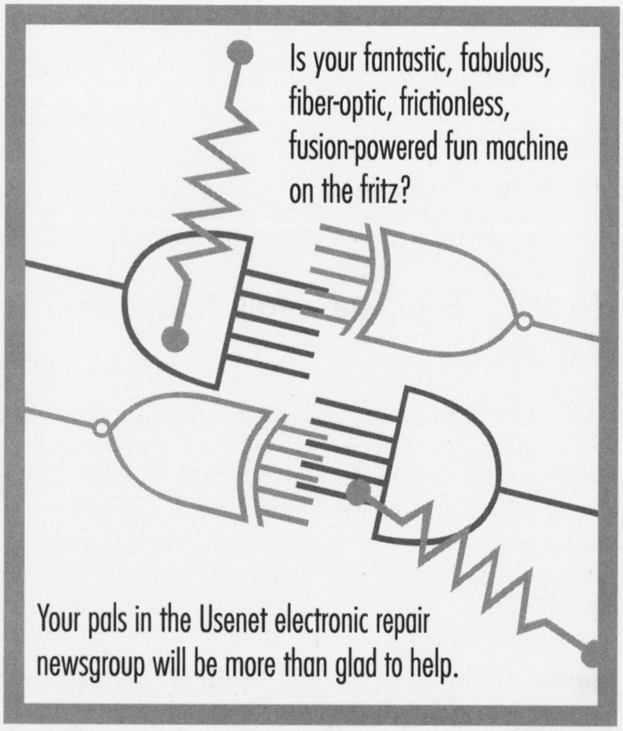
Is your fantastic, fabulous, fiber-optic, frictionless, fusion-powered fun machine on the fritz?
Your pals in the Usenet electronic repair newsgroup will be more than glad to help.

## Electronics Talk and General Discussion

Electronics is a fascinating field that can be a lot of fun. However, it is a complex detailed area of technology, and there are times when it can help a lot to have someone to talk with. Usenet has a number of groups devoted to electronics discussion. This is where the P=IV type of people hang out in the Net.

**Usenet:**

**sci.electronics**
**sci.electronics.basics**
**sci.electronics.design**
**sci.electronics.misc**

## IEEE Computer Society

The IEEE Computer Society is a world-renowned source of information relating to all aspects of computer science, electronics, and engineering, including the publication of periodicals and newsletters, sponsoring conferences, workshops, and symposia, and the development of standards. Computer Society Online now offers an electronic source of this information, in many cases before the information is published in hard copy.

**Web:**

**http://www.computer.org/**

## Museum of HP Calculators

When I was a senior in high school, the chemistry teacher had a contraption about the size of an old fashioned adding machine: a brand new electronic calculator. It cost $450 (which was a lot of money in those days) and could add, subtract, multiply and divide. The machine was considered so valuable, the teacher kept it locked in his office. Nowadays, you can pick up a small, credit card-sized solar-powered calculator for a couple of bucks at the corner drugstore. Much of the evolution from the first rudimentary calculators to today's sophisticated hand-held computers is a result of the work done by Hewlett-Packard. Throughout the years, HP has produced a family of calculators that, even now, are near and dear to the hearts of nerds everywhere. This web site celebrates the history of such calculators. And if you happen to have one, you can find information about the calculator and how to maintain it.

**Web:**

**http://www.teleport.com/~dgh/hpmuseum.html**

## Semiconductors

A semiconductor is a substance whose electrical properties lie between that of a conductor and an insulator. Within the substance, there is limited movement of electrons, the exact characteristics depending on the crystalline structure of the material. Materials commonly used as semiconductors include germanium, silicon, indium antimonide, gallium arsenide, and aluminum phosphide. What makes semiconductors so useful is the fact that, by adding small impurities to the material, the flow of electrons can be modified. Thus, it is possible to design a component that contains semiconductor material with specific impurities to create an electrical component designed to perform specific functions. As you can imagine, the world of semiconductors is complex. To help you understand what you read, I have found some resources with basic information about semiconductors and semiconductor terminology. For general discussion, such as questions and answers, you can participate in the Usenet group.

**Web:**

**http://rel.semi.harris.com/docs/lexicon/**
**http://star-www.st-and.ac.uk/users/adg1/electron/info/comp/conduct/conduct.htm**
**http://www.semiconductors.philips.com/ps/philips3.html**

**Usenet:**

**sci.engr.semiconductors**

## Speaker Building Information

Would you like to build your own audio speakers? There are a lot of subtle details that create the difference between a good speaker and a great speaker. Here is some useful information for people who like to design and build their own speakers. You will find various technical articles, tips and techniques, as well as specifications of other people's designs.

**Web:**

**http://www2.hi-fi.com/speaker/**

**The Net is immortal.**

### Speaker Building Information

**Right now, you may be just a regular guy or gal in your home, with no special responsibilities. However, if you understand something about electronics, and you have access to information on the Net, you can become the Speaker Builder of the House.**

# EMERGENCY AND DISASTER

## Cascades Volcano Observatory

The Cascade Range is a mountain chain in the western section of North America. The mountain range extends for 700 miles from British Columbia, Canada, to Northern California in the United States. In the last 200 years, half of the Cascade's fourteen peaks have had volcanic eruptions: Mount Baker, Glacier Peak, Mount Rainier, Mount St. Helens, Mount Hood, Mount Shasta and Lassen Peak. Read about the latest volcanic activity in the Cascade Mountains, how geologists keep track of volcanic activity, and see some interesting before-and-after pictures of volcanic eruptions.

**Web:**

**http://vulcan.wr.usgs.gov/**

## Chernobyl Nuclear Disaster

In 1986, in Chernobyl, Ukraine, a cooling system of a nuclear reactor failed during a test, causing the worst nuclear disaster in the history of the world. During this incident, the core of the reactor overheated resulting in an explosion and fire. Nuclear fallout spread across Eastern Europe and parts of Scandinavia. Towns in the vicinity of Chernobyl were permanently evacuated, and several thousand people died from the radiation. This web site has information regarding the Chernobyl disaster, including secret Soviet documents.

**Web:**

**http://freedom.ncsa.uiuc.edu/~zelenko/belarus/ChFacts.html**

## Comprehensive Guide to First Aid

You never know, as you travel out and about, when you are going be called upon to rescue someone who is choking on a chicken wing. Imagine your dismay if you are not prepared, and the resulting incident ruins the rest of your meal. Don't let this happen to you. Prepare yourself for various first aid emergencies by reading the information on this site. Find out about choking aid, CPR, heart attacks, bleeding and burns.

**Web:**

**http://pharmweb1.man.ac.uk/redcross/firstaid.html**

## Disaster Management

Selection of resources related to disasters and how to deal with them, including news and information on current disasters, historical information and links to disaster-related resources such as local and federal relief agencies.

**Web:**

**http://vifp.monash.edu.au/~davidt/admin.html**
**http://www.disaster.net/**

## Disaster Situation and Status Reports

Information and reports about natural disasters and events from agencies like the U.S. Weather Service and the U.S. Geological Survey. Information includes earthquake reports, weather reports, and hurricane forecasts. The **nat-dsr** mailing list is for situation reports from various humanitarian emergency response organizations and covers natural disasters only. The **sitreps** list is for situation reports about natural disasters as well as complex disasters (events that are socially or politically initiated).

**Web:**

**http://www.vita.org/disaster/disaster.html**

**Listserv Mailing List:**

List Name: **nat-dsr**
Subscribe to: **listserv@vita.org**

**Majordomo Mailing List:**

List Name: **sitreps**
Subscribe to: **majordomo@vita.org**

**Natural Disasters and You!**
One of the best parts of life is reading about natural disasters that happen to other people. What could be more fun than waking up each morning, logging in to your favorite Internet connection, and checking out all the disasters that happened overnight to people who aren't as smart and good looking as you? (And, if truth be told, may not even be smart enough to read a Harley Hahn book.)

## Disaster Talk and General Discussion

Are you the type of person who can't resist staring in fascination as you drive by the scene of an automobile accident? Well, if you also like to talk about disasters, this is the place to be. Any disaster will do: fire, flood, earthquake, plane crashes, and so on.

**Usenet:**

**alt.disasters.misc**

## Earthquakes

If you live in earthquake country, it's good to be prepared just in case the ground beneath you starts moving. If you don't live in earthquake country, you may want to find out what you are missing, so you can feel superior to everyone else. These web sites have maps of recent earthquakes, seismic data, earthquake news, information about the latest earthquakes around the globe, as well as hints on making your home environment more earthquake-safe. The Usenet discussion groups are for talking about various aspects of earthquakes, including personal information and technical data.

**Web:**

**http://www-geology.ucdavis.edu/eqmandr.html**
**http://www.eqe.com/publications/homeprep/**

**Usenet:**

**alt.disasters.earthquake**
**sci.geo.earthquakes**

## Electronic Volcano

Are you wondering where to go on your next vacation? How about a quick tour around an active volcano? Some people, as you know, get their thrills by jumping out of airplanes or by climbing sheer cliffs. However, if you ask me, there's really nothing that compares to monkeying around a volcano that could, at any time, spew hot flaming jets of lava all over the countryside. If you would like such a thrill (or just see what things look like), check out this site. It has information about active volcanoes around the world, including maps and photographs. You can also learn about volcanic hazards, current events and the last volcano research.

**Web:**

**http://www.dartmouth.edu/pages/rox/volcanoes/**

## Emergency Medical Services

911, along with the iron lung and the electric sewer rooter, is an awesome invention that we all hope we never have to use. It's nice to know that in the event of a personal disaster, an emergency medical team will come racing to help you. In an effort to continually update information and to improve services, EMS providers discuss protocols, rules, policies, and hospital regulations. **ems-c** discusses emergency medical services and general emergency medical care for children.

**Listserv Mailing List:**

List Name: **ems-c**
Subscribe to: **listserv@lists.colorado.edu**

**Listserv Mailing List:**

List Name: **emsny-l**
Subscribe to: **listserv@health.state.ny.us**

## Emergency News

When you want to find out what is happening in the emergency and disaster world, this is the place to look. You will find news stories about infectious diseases; police, military and fire operations; emergency medical events; terrorism and rescue operations; hazardous material reports; and chemical and biological weapons.

**Web:**

**http://www.emergency.com/**

## Emergency Preparedness Information Exchange

The Emergency Preparedness Information Exchange is dedicated to the promotion of networking in support of disaster mitigation research and practice. Offers information on emergency/disaster management organizations, topics, conferences, and access to other emergency management resources.

**Web:**

**http://hoshi.cic.sfu.ca/epix**

### PREPARING FOR EMERGENCIES

**I live in California where we have our own type of special emergencies. For example, what if your agent is coming over to dinner and you are all out of Chardonnay? Or what do you do when the heater on your hot tub goes on the fritz and it's too late to call a repairman? Or, even worse, what if you have a fabulous breakthrough in your emotional and intellectual growth program, and there is no one around to help you relate to the experience?**

**Not to worry: as long as you have an Internet connection, the Emergency Preparedness Information Exchange is there to help.**

## Emergency Services

Emergency service personnel come in a variety of shapes and sizes. There are workers who help before, during or after emergencies. Such people—who may be civilian or military—cover various types of natural and technological disasters. Some workers get paid and some volunteer. But they all use a wide range of equipment and techniques to save lives and property. This web site is a fine tribute to rescue workers as well as a good place to get general information about emergency services and life-saving tips. (You never know when you may need to know how to operate a chain saw properly.)

**Web:**

**http://www.catt.citri.edu.au/emergency/**

## Emerging Diseases

Not feeling at your perky best? Check this web site with the latest news of emerging diseases just in case. Do you have some newly discovered contagion, or are you just not getting enough sleep? As well as news, this site has general information on various outbreaks around the world, historical information of outbreaks of bygone days (for those who love nostalgia), and in-depth coverage on diseases such as Ebola and Mad Cow Disease.

**Web:**

**http://www.outbreak.org/cgi-unreg/dynaserve.exe/**

## Famine

Famine is a large-scale shortage of food. There are many causes of famine, the most common being (1) natural disaster, and (2) overpopulation combined with exhausted agricultural resources. However, no matter the reason for a famine, hunger is hunger, and the Net has a great many hunger-related resources. This site talks about causes of hunger and solutions to famine. You will find information about advocacy groups and policies, education and training, as well as situation updates from all around the world.

**Web:**

**http://www.brown.edu/Departments/World_Hunger_Program/**

## Federal Emergency Management Agency

Federal Emergency Management Agency (FEMA) is an independent United States federal agency in Washington, D.C. FEMA provides training to help communities prepare for and cope with disasters. After something happens, FEMA offers disaster relief assistance. The FEMA web site offers information about their services, as well as general information about how to prepare for various natural (and unnatural) disasters: earthquakes, extreme heat, fire, floods, hurricanes, nuclear plant disasters and much more.

**Web:**

**http://www.fema.gov/**

## Flood Observatory

If you are thinking of relocating, you may want to know if your new location is in an area that is prone to flooding. If so, you can check the flood activity for various places over the last few years. For example, many Americans think that moving to the mid-western United States is safe because they will be cleverly avoiding the earthquakes and volcanoes from the west as well as the hurricanes from the east. Well, as Marlon Brando said in A Streetcar Named Desire, "Ha... ha ha!" Before you relocate, read the information from the available flood databases, as well as current information about floods. There are also some fascinating images.

**Web:**

**http://www.dartmouth.edu/artsci/geog/floods/**

## Global Disaster Report

If you are not getting enough bad news from the morning paper, connect to this site. It has a listing of summaries of all the major disaster events from around the world, including natural events and disasters of human origin.

**Web:**

**http://hypnos.m.ehime-u.ac.jp/GHDNet/WADEM/GDR96.html**

## Home Fire Safety Tips

Do you know what to do if your house catches on fire? This web site has tips on how to prevent fires in the home, as well as how to make a good plan for evacuating your house and keeping your family safe in the event of a fire. For example, if your house does catch on fire, have you designated the person whose job it would be to bring the marshmallows?

**Web:**

**http://www.ou.edu/oupd/fireprev.htm**

## Hurricanes

If you live in a place where you occasionally have to batten down the hurricane hatches, then you should know about where on the Net you can get good hurricane information. These sites will tell you about hurricanes including the how to prepare for an upcoming storm.

**Web:**

**http://home.sprynet.com/sprynet/jedwar01/**
**http://www.nassauredcross.org/sumstorm/hurrica1.htm**

## Be the Most Respected Member of Your Household

GLOBAL
DISASTER
REPORT

Are you one of those people who loves to find out important news first and then tell it to other people before they have a chance to hear it for themselves?

**Great. You'll love this idea.**

Every day, wake up early before everyone else and check out the Global Disaster Report.

By breakfast time, you will be full of all kinds of good news. Not only will everyone be entertained, they will be amazed at your comprehensive grasp of world events.

Within a short time, your entire household will be treating you with the dignity, respect and deference that a person in your position deserves.

## Natural Disaster Reference Database

If you are having a lousy day, and you need to make yourself feel better, check out this web site. Use the searchable database to read articles about various natural disasters that have occurred over the last few years. Look at pictures of the havoc and distraction caused when the earth cuts loose and lets down its hair. All this will tend to put your day to day life into perspective. This site also has information about remote disaster sensing instruments and disaster research. The mailing list is for the discussion of disaster recovery.

**Web:**

**http://ltpwww.gsfc.nasa.gov/ndrd-cgi/ndrd**

**Majordomo Mailing List:**

List Name: **disaster-recovery**
Subscribe to: **majordomo@magmacom.com**

## Planning Ahead for Disasters

Part of the trick of surviving a disaster is being prepared. This Usenet discussion group offers a great place for people to talk about how to get ready for that unforeseen day when fate is waiting around the corner with an unpleasant bit of sticky business. Trade anecdotes and hints with people around the world.

**Usenet:**

**alt.disasters.planning**

## Red Cross

There never seems to be a lack of natural disasters, so there is always something for the Red Cross to do. This global nondenominational, nonprofit disaster assistance organization boldly goes where everyone else is evacuating. Read information about the Red Cross, get updated news about current disasters and assistance efforts currently being performed. For those of you who like to participate, you can also find out how to join.

**Web:**

**http://www.crossnet.org/**

## Storm Chaser Home Page

The diameter of a tornado can vary from a few feet to as wide as a mile. Rotating winds within a funnel can reach a velocity of up to 300 mph (480 km/hour). However, the enormous risk posed by these storms is not enough to scare off certain types of people, called "storm chasers". Storm chasers will travel hundreds of miles, hot on the trail of storm activity. Their goals are to learn more about the storm and experience certain types of storms firsthand. Some storm chasers just want to have something exciting to do in their spare time. This site offers lots of information about storm chasing, including pictures, anecdotes and late-breaking storm news.

**Web:**

**http://taiga.geog.niu.edu/chaser/**

## Survivalism Talk and General Discussion

I am a firm believer in survivalism, and I am quite a survivalist myself. For instance, in my pantry right now, I have not one, but *two* boxes of microwave popcorn in case I am overrun by hoards of hungry guests. In my bathroom, I have extra rolls of fluffy bathroom tissue because, well, you just never know. And, in the cupboard, I have an extra bag of cat food. To some people, however, survival goes beyond popcorn, toilet paper and cat food, as you will see when you read this Usenet group. People all over the world are talking about old, new and unusual ways of practicing the art of self-reliance. All it takes is gumption, planning and some money. As Oscar Wilde said, you can survive anything except death, and live down anything except a good reputation.

**Usenet:**

**misc.survivalism**

## Tornadoes

If you think living inland protects you from storm activity, think again. Tornadoes are generally quick but intense, causing destruction in a localized area. Find out how and where tornadoes form, how to rate a tornado and tips on what to do if a tornado hits in your area.

**Web:**

**http://cc.usu.edu/~kforsyth/Tornado.html**
**http://femapub1.fema.gov/fema/tornadof.html**

# ENERGY

## Alternative Energy

Tired of the same old energy? Try an alternative energy lifestyle. This site has information on alternative-fueled vehicles, the American Hydrogen Association, alternative fuel newsgroups, mailing lists and archives that relate to alternative forms of energy.

**Web:**

**http://solstice.crest.org/online/aeguide/**

## Biomass

Biomass refers to organic matter. Much biomass is renewable; that is, if you use it up you can create more. There is a lot of research and development being done to find ways to use renewable biomass to produce energy in a way that is safe, economical and non-polluting. For example, researchers are looking for ways to create energy out of forest and mill residues, agricultural and animal wastes, livestock operation residues, aquatic plants, fast-growing trees and plants, and municipal and industrial wastes.

**Web:**

**http://rredc.nrel.gov/biomass/**
**http://rredc.nrel.gov/biomass/states/bio_glossary/glossary.html**

## Coal

Coal is a fuel created from fossilized plants (similar to the way in which oil is created). Coal is almost entirely carbon with varying amounts of minerals. Although coal creates a lot of pollution when it is burned, it is still used in a good many places around the world (including the United States, where it is especially important to the steel industry). There are a good number of places on the Net where you can read about coal, its properties and uses. Here are a few to get you started.

**Web:**

**http://apollo.osti.gov/fe/ccafetdb.html**
**http://energy.usgs.gov/coalpubs.html**
**http://www.dpie.gov.au/resources.energy/coalmin/coal_vl/**

## Department of Energy

What a nice word fusion is. Just say it slow, let it roll off your tongue and lips with a soft hissing sound: *fusion*. It's not just a science, it's a way of life. Get an overview of the U.S. Fusion Energy Science Program, information about fusion and the environment, documents on fusion as an environmentally attractive, commercially viable and sustainable energy source.

**Web:**

**http://wwwofe.er.doe.gov/**

## Look What I Found on the Net...

```
Newsgroups: misc.survivalism
Subject: Re: My First Gun

> Hi.  I was hoping to get some advice.
>
> We have sunk ourselves into survival and alternative living
> for the last year.  We have bought our land in the mountains
> of Montana, we have our food and water storage going, and we
> have learned to be pretty proficient at organic gardening.
> We hope to move up to our property next summer and will be
> using solar energy up there.
>
> My question is this:
>
> We know nothing about guns.  We will need a gun for protection
> from grizzlies as well as protection if American society
> breaks down, and we have economic or social collapse.
> Eventually we will also have to learn to hunt. Should we start
> with a rifle or shotgun?  What is the main difference?

[to which various people offered the following suggestions]

A shotgun is definitely best for home protection...

A good hunting rifle in the .30 caliber range would be ideal...

If you are really worried about bears, and you are not a good
shot, get a semi-automatic...

A shotgun is good in CLOSE combat...

I would recommend a good rifle...  The .30-30 is good for areas
with a lot of brush... The .308 is the basic NATO round -- it's
used by most military snipers... The .30/06 is the most common
big game rifle...

For each person, one semi-automatic handgun, caliber 9 mm or
larger with at least 6 magazines each... I'd store at least
500 rounds of ammunition... also for each person, one pump
action 12 gauge shotgun with both a "riot" and a "hunting"
barrel... I'd have on hand at least 200 rounds of #4 buckshot,
500 rounds of #6 shot, 250 rounds of #7.5 shot, and probably
100 rounds of rifled slugs...
```

## Educational Energy Information

Here's a great place to find out about energy. The information is written in an easy-to-understand style, suitable for children. If you are a teacher or parent and you want to make energy information accessible to young people, this is a good site to explore. Aside from general energy information, you will find puzzles and stories about energy.

**Web:**

**http://www.energy.ca.gov/energy/education/**

## Energy and the Environment

It's common these days to hear about what car smog is doing to the environment. However, there is more to energy and the environment than what your automobile is producing. Check out some of the environmentally related resources on the Net, gathered under one solar-powered virtual roof. You'll find information about alternative energy as well as traditional energy sources (such as fossil fuels).

**Web:**

**http://www.wam.umd.edu/~tfagan/enrgyenv.html**
**http://zebu.uoregon.edu/energy.html**

A B C D E F G H I J K L M N O P Q R S T U V W X Y Z

## Educational
## Energy Information

Kids. I bet you wish you knew more about energy. I know I did when I was young.

Spend some time browsing the educational resources on the Net and you will soon be at the top of your class, energy-wise. (And will you be popular.)

There are lots of great hints as to what you can do to help out. For example, you could get your school to start a school energy patrol. Every day, you can check all the classrooms to make sure that the lights are turned off if no one is in the room. Not only will you have a lot of fun, but it will look great on your résumé when you get older and want to go to medical school.

Boy, adults sure think of some great things for kids to do.

**Join the fun—now.**

## Energy Efficient Homes

How energy efficient is your home? Here are some resources on the Net that show you how to improve your home's efficiency, help the environment, and save a few bucks at the same time. The web sites will show you energy-saving tips. The **alt.hvac** and **sci.engr.heat-vent-ac** Usenet groups are for the discussion of heating, venting and air conditioning.

**Web:**

**http://www.nimo.com/HEEG/**
**http://www.wpl.com/ps/bihome.html**

**Usenet:**

**alt.hvac**
**sci.engr.heat-vent-ac**

## Energy Information Administration

The Energy Information Administration (EIA) is an independent statistical and analytical agency of the United States Department of Energy. The EIA compiles data relating to energy resources, supply and demand, technology, economics, energy policies and more. The EIA's web site has summaries and reports on energy consumption all over the world, as well as energy forecasts. (This is the place to check to see if you will have enough energy to play softball after work.)

**Web:**

**http://www.eia.doe.gov/**

## *Look What I Found on the Net...*

```
Newsgroup: sci.energy
Subject: Tidal Energy

Together with my friend Xxxx Xxxxxx, I have found a new concept
to extract huge amounts of tidal energy from shallow seas where
the tidal wave propagation is typically parallel to the shore.

Typically, 1000 to 2000 megawatt plants are possible.  This
concept is new, but most promising for the future.

At this time, we would like to know if anyone has ever dealt
with tidal energy plants.  In addition we are looking for
financing for a feasibility study, so if anyone knows the right
place, please let me know.
```

A B C D E F G H I J K L M N O P Q R S T U V W X Y Z

## Energy Talk and General Discussion

When you need a little pick-me-up, check out the Usenet group where nerds around the Net energize themselves by talking about the science of energy.

**Usenet:**

**sci.energy**

## Hydroelectricity

Hydroelectric power is the largest renewable resource in the United States. Hydropower generates ten percent of the power produced in the United States, equivalent to 500 million barrels of oil a year. In general, hydropower is an excellent energy source because it gives off no emissions when it is used, and the source of the energy is from water that is already lying around doing nothing in particular. However, there are problems. In order to create a hydroelectricity plant, water must be diverted and, often, dams must be constructed. These activities must be considered carefully as they can have negative effects on the ecosystems of the waterways. Still, I grew up in a place in which all the electricity was generated from hydropower, and I turned out pretty good.

**Web:**

**http://starfire.ne.uiuc.edu/ne201/webproject/buntic/**

## Hydrogen Power

If you have lots of water laying around and the right type of electrical current, you can whip up some hydrogen and create your own power plant. However, if you are low on water, you can also produce hydrogen from sewage, garbage, agricultural biomass, paper waste products and other waste streams that have hydrogen-bearing compounds. Check out these links for interesting information about using hydrogen as a source of fuel. And if you feel like talking, you can expend some hot air on the hydrogen Usenet group.

**Web:**

**http://www-unix.oit.umass.edu/~mellis/hydrogen/hydrogen.html**

**Usenet:**

**sci.energy.hydrogen**

## Natural Gas

Natural gas is a mixture of gases that come from beneath the ground. Natural gas is mostly methane (80-95%) with the remainder varying according to the geographic locality. The minor components of natural gas may include helium, carbon dioxide, carbon monoxide, hydrogen and nitrogen. Natural gas is a fossil fuel and is often found along with petroleum. However, natural gas can also occur by itself within sand, sandstone or limestone deposits. Natural gas can be utilized to power any number of appliances or machines. These web sites will give you a variety of information about natural gas, including the details about natural gas-powered vehicles.

**Web:**

**http://solstice.crest.org/renewables/eerg/natgas_index.html**
**http://www.cng.com/html/ngv.htm**

## Nuclear Energy

Nuclear energy produces approximately 20 percent of the energy used in the United States. In general, nuclear energy is a versatile form of power. Aside from the production of electricity, nuclear energy is put to such disparate uses as cancer treatments, explosive-detecting machines, medical instrument sterilizers, and smoke detectors. Nuclear usage in the United States is heavily regulated by an independent government agency called the Nuclear Regulatory Commission. They have a site on the Web where you can read about nuclear materials, handling and hazards. There are also more general nuclear resources that talk about the various uses and environmental concerns related to the use of nuclear energy.

**Web:**

**http://nuke.handheld.com/**
**http://www.nrc.gov/**

**Quick, turn the page.**

## Petroleum

Back in the olden days (millions of years ago), nobody knew what to do with all the dead dinosaurs and various other organic matter that was just sitting around composting. It was entirely too much for primitive people to use in their tomato gardens, so they just left it laying around. Eventually a lot of the organic matter fossilized and turned into a substance that we process and use as oil, gasoline, and natural gas. You can find out more about petroleum, petroleum products, and the oil industry by checking out the petroleum newsgroups. You can also read the FAQ (frequently asked question list) and browse the Web. Remember: Today's trash can be tomorrow's treasure.

**Web:**

http://www.cis.ohio-state.edu/hypertext/faq/usenet/geology/petroleum-resources/faq.html
http://www.slb.com/petr.dir/.guthery.html

**Usenet:**

sci.geo.petroleum

# PETROLEUM

Personally, I am always ready to learn more about petroleum. My philosophy is: none of us lives forever, and it is good to be prepared, so when the end comes, I want to be ready.

After all, oil's well that ends well.

## Renewable Energy

Right now, as you read this there are clever people around the world thinking about ways to use renewable energy. They are coming up with new designs for batteries, generators, pumps and chargers to use wind, water and sun for fuel. Read about the neat gadgets they have modified or invented or just check out the ideas and philosophy behind using renewable energy.

**Web:**

http://www.nrel.gov/

**Usenet:**

alt.energy.renewable

## Solar Energy

Where I live in California, there is a lot of sun. In fact, there is such an abundance of sunlight that I can use it to power my souped-up solar-powered surfboard. But even if you don't surf, you may still want to check out solar energy information on the Net. These web sites have information about solar cars and powering your home with solar energy. On Usenet, you can discuss various aspects of solar energy with all the other solar buffs, talking about everything energy-related under the sun.

**Web:**

http://www-lips.ece.utexas.edu/~delayman/solar.html
http://www.netins.net/showcase/solarcatalog/

**Usenet:**

alt.solar.photovoltaic
alt.solar.thermal

## Wind Energy

I love to feel the wind in my hair while I am riding my skateboard. However, wind has other uses. It can also be harnessed for energy. This site has educational information written in a way that is suitable for children. You will find information about wind as well as experiments you can use for teaching about wind energy and windmills.

**Web:**

http://www.sln.org/tfi/wind/windguide.html

## World Energy Statistics

Numbers, numbers, numbers. What do you do when you need to find out how much natural gas the world is going to use in the year 2010? Well, you could just wait until 2010, but that would take a long time. Wouldn't it be faster to check with the Net?

**Web:**

http://www.energyinfo.co.uk/wstats.html

**The Net loves poetry.**

# ENGINEERING

## Advanced Nuclear Reactor Technology

A mailing list to facilitate "substantive discussion on the worldwide advocacy, design, and deployment of advanced nuclear reactor technology". In other words, is there any way we can have our nuclear cake and eat it without blowing up the kitchen?

**Listserv Mailing List:**

List Name: **anurt-l**
Subscribe to: **listserv@vm1.hqadmin.doe.gov**

## Aerospace Engineering

Aerospace engineering is the area of engineering that deals with aircraft and space vehicles. The web site contains numerous links to Internet resources for aerospace engineers: information on NASA projects and missions, news, professional tools, publications, software, aerospace companies, and more. For discussion, the Usenet group is devoted to the technology of space flight.

**Web:**

**http://www.wpi.edu/~ching/aerohome.html**

**Usenet:**

**sci.space.tech**

## Alternative Energy Design Guide

Many people like to design and build their own equipment to work with alternative energy sources, especially solar power. If you are interested in such a project, you will have to know a fair amount of technical details. Here is a guide to the basic ideas you will need to understand.

**Web:**

**http://www.asis.com/aee/**

## Architectural Engineering

Architectural engineering is the profession that deals with the technical aspects of building design and construction. (In some countries, architectural engineers are known as building engineers.) Architecture and engineering are vastly different disciplines: not only in training and approach, but in the social aspects as well. Engineers and architects are two very different types of people who look at problems differently. Where an architect will create something out of nothing, changing and modifying and throwing away until he gets what he wants, an engineer will attack a problem by analyzing a mass of details while moving one step at a time toward a solution. The job of an architectural engineer is to bridge the gaps between these two disciplines. This is not a job for weenies. When an architectural engineer designs a building's structure, he or she will consider loads, structural systems, forces in structural members, and materials, all the while balancing the important considerations of the overall design. Clearly, architectural engineering is not an easy job. However, there are some Internet resources that can help you. This web site is a good place to start.

**Web:**

**http://energy.arce.ukans.edu/wwwvl/wwwarce.htm**

### *Look What I Found on the Net...*

```
    (from a FAQ referenced in the sci.space.tech Usenet group)

         ===============================================
         HOW LONG CAN A HUMAN LIVE UNPROTECTED IN SPACE?
         ===============================================

If you *don't* try to hold your breath, exposure to space for
half a minute or so is unlikely to produce permanent injury.
Holding your breath is likely to damage your lungs, something
scuba divers have to watch out for when ascending, and you'll
have eardrum trouble if your eustachian tubes are badly plugged
up, but theory predicts -- and animal experiments confirm --
that otherwise, exposure to vacuum causes no immediate injury.

You do not explode. Your blood does not boil. You do not freeze.
You do not instantly lose consciousness...
```

A B C D E F G H I J K L M N O P Q R S T U V W X Y Z

## Audio Engineering

The Audio Engineering Society is a professional society devoted to audio technology. They maintain this web page, which is a collection of links on the Net in the area of audio technology as well as related topics. You can find timely references to papers and articles on loudspeakers, sound reinforcement, microphones, disk recording, time-delay spectrometry and digital audio. For discussion, there are a number of Usenet audio newsgroups in which you can participate. I have included the ones that are the most useful for audio engineering.

**Web:**

**http://www.aes.org/www-links/**

**Usenet:**

**rec.audio.high-end**
**rec.audio.opinion**
**rec.audio.pro**
**rec.audio.tech**

## Biomedical Engineering

This web site is a good place to start a search for biomedical engineering information on the Net. Academic resources, publications, organizations, jobs, grants, conferences and more. For discussion, the two Usenet groups are good places for a biomedical engineer to participate.

**Web:**

**http://bme.www.ecn.purdue.edu/bme/**

**Usenet:**

**sci.bio.technology**
**sci.engr.biomed**

## Build a Flying Saucer

This one is a few years old, but I am leaving it in the book anyway. Or let me put it another way: this was the best Internet resource I could find discussing how to build a flying saucer. "...A set of superconducting magnets can be charged by metal sheet circuits, within limits, to whatever frequency is needed and will continue to transmit that magnetic field frequency almost indefinitely..." (And some people think the Information Superhighway is a waste of money.)

**Web:**

**http://wiretap.spies.com/Gopher/Library/Fringe/Ufo/build.ufo**

**No need to put up with rush hour traffic. Build your own flying saucer.**

The plans are free for the downloading.

## CAD (Computer Aided Design)

The aim of CAD (computer aided design) is to use computers for creating designs. A basic CAD system can be used to model a design, to produce drawings, and to keep track of a list of all the parts needed for a particular design. More advanced systems will provide sophisticated help to the engineer during the design process.

**Web:**

**http://utwpue.wb.utwente.nl/mech-surf/cad_systems.html**
**http://www.cam.org/~flamy/cadcam.html**

**Usenet:**

**alt.cad**
**comp.lsi.cad**
**sci.electronics.cad**

## Chemical Engineering

Chemical engineering is the study of the industrial applications of chemistry. In other words, chemical engineers use raw material to make stuff. Did you know that of the four main branches of engineering—civil, mechanical, electrical and chemical—chemical engineering has the fewest people, but they make the most money? Check the Net and see if you can find the formula.

**Web:**

**http://www.che.ufl.edu/WWW-CHE/**

**Usenet:**

**sci.engr.chem**

**Listserv Mailing List:**

List Name: **cheme-l**
Subscribe to: **listserv@ulkyvm.louisville.edu**

## Civil Engineering

The term "civil engineering" was first used in the 18th century to describe engineering work performed by civilians for nonmilitary purposes. Today, civil engineering is a broad field, dealing with works of public utility: roads, buildings, bridges, dams, airports, tunnels, and so on (which is probably why the U.S. Army Corps of Engineers—civil engineers to the max—live inside the military). Here is a large collection of civil engineer sites from around the world. See what you can build with it.

**Web:**

**http://www.pvv.unit.no/~oes/civeng/civengserv.list.html**

**Usenet:**

**sci.engr.civil**

## Cold Regions Engineering

When the temperature falls below freezing (0 degrees centigrade, 32 degrees Fahrenheit), water solidifies and the natural world changes dramatically. This causes many engineering problems. For example, machinery may stop working properly, and many materials will change their properties. Nearly half our planet will, at some time during the year, experience temperatures below freezing. In fact, 20 percent of the Earth is underlain by permafrost (permanently frozen subsoil). Thus, cold region engineering is an important discipline that draws from general engineering, earth sciences and physical sciences.

**Web:**

**http://www-bprc.mps.ohio-state.edu/PolarPointers.html**
**http://www.usace.army.mil/crrel/**

**Hey guys:**
want to make lots of **money** and meet **beautiful women**?
Maybe its time to check out Chemical Engineering.

## Defense Sciences Engineering

Defense sciences cover a range of engineering disciplines. This web site, at the Lawrence Livermore National Laboratory, contains information on designing, testing, and evaluating systems for national security. (Whose national security you must figure out for yourself.) In addition, you can read about programs, projects and research in areas of electromagnetics, pulsed power, optics and material science.

**Web:**

**http://www-dsed.llnl.gov/**

## Electrical Engineering

Electrical engineering deals with systems and devices that use electric power and electric signals. The four main areas of this discipline are electronics, computers, communications and control, and electric power and machinery. If you are an electrical engineer (or a student), here are a lot of resources collected into one place. If you ever need to embark on an electrical engineering search, this is a good place to start.

**Web:**

**http://www.ecn.uoknor.edu/~jspatric/ee-info.html**

### Electrical Engineering

**The next time you hear someone pooh-pooh electrical engineering, remind him of the following:**

(1) In ancient Rome, there wasn't even one properly certified electrical engineer, and within several hundred years, the entire Roman civilization was toppled by bands of invading barbarians.

(2) No electrical engineer has ever been impeached by the Senate of the United States.

(3) In one survey after another, famous supermodels and movie stars choose electrical engineers as the type of engineer they would prefer to be stranded with in an abandoned hydroelectric plant.

(4) As a group, the electrical engineers of America collectively make more money than the President of the United States and his wife put together.

(5) Electrical engineers never have to wait in line at a restaurant, and they always get the best seats in a movie theater.

(6) Every year, on Electrical Engineering Day, everyone has to find an electrical engineer and do whatever he or she wants for the entire day.

(7) In certain primitive societies, electrical engineers are considered to be gods, even more important than writers.

## Electronics Engineering

Electronics engineers: Now you have your own cool hangout on the Net. Check out this web page with links to FAQs on electronics, discussion group, archives and other web pages relating to electronics.

**Web:**
**http://engr-www.unl.edu/ee/eeshop/netsites.html**

## Electronics Engineers' Toolbox

If you are an electronics engineer working with chips and computer components, you will want to know about this site. It is a well-organized collection of information and links pertaining to digital signal processing, industrial embedded computing, microcontrollers and microprocessors, realtime embedding systems, chip specifications and development tools.

**Web:**
**http://www.eg3.com/ebox.htm**

## Engineering Index

Engineering covers so wide a range of activities as to almost defy definition. Still, such trifles never stopped me, so here goes: Engineering is the profession in which a knowledge of science and mathematics is used to control the materials and forces of nature. If you have any interest in any type of engineering, paste this web site in your hat. Here you will find links to just about any type of engineering you can imagine (and several you can't imagine).

**Web:**
**http://www.englib.cornell.edu/ice/ice-index.html**

## Engineering Talk and General Discussion

If you are a part of the engineering community, you may want to participate in an ongoing discussion of engineering topics. If so, the general Usenet engineering group is the place to be.

**Usenet:**
**sci.engr**

## Engineering Visual Database

The Engineering Visual Database is an online repository of images specifically designed for engineering teachers and students. The pictures are yours for the downloading, and cover a wide variety of engineering disciplines. The idea is to use the database as a resource when you need a specific image to illustrate something you are teaching.

**Web:**
**http://www.ce.vt.edu/evd/**

## Facilities and Services

What a madhouse it would be if everyone had to take care of everything themselves and nobody was in charge of organizing anything. As much as we don't like to drive at the speed limit, it's still nice to know there are rules and regulations—even if some people don't follow them. Get in on the discussion of facilities and services such as physical plant operations, security and public safety, transportation and parking, telephone and mail service, environmental health and safety, capital planning, and facilities utilization.

**Listserv Mailing List:**
List Name: **facser-l**
Subscribe to: **listserv@wvnvm.wvnet.edu**

## Geotechnical Engineering

Geotechnical engineering is the engineering discipline related to the technology and methods of soil mechanics. Geotechnical engineers build things that must interact with geological structures. If you ever go to a party with such people, you will hear them talk about consolidation, lateral earth pressures, bearing capacity and stability. The father of modern geotechnical engineering (soil mechanics, actually) is the Hungarian-American Karl von Terzaghi (1883-1963). This web site has a collection of information regarding organizations, jobs, publications, conferences, historical notes, as well as links to related resources around the world.

**Web:**
**http://geotech.civen.okstate.edu/wwwVL/**

**Usenet:**
**sci.engr.geomechanics**
**sci.geo.geology**

ENGINEERING TEACHERS. DO YOU NEED TO ILLUSTRATE YOUR POINT? TRY THE ENGINEERING VISUAL DATABASE.

## Mechanical Engineering

Mechanical engineering is the broadest of the engineering sciences. In simple terms, mechanical engineering concerns itself with things that move in some way. More generally, this discipline can be divided into two main parts: machine design and working with heat. Here is a web site that contains a good number of links to mechanical engineering resources. For discussion, try Usenet.

**Web:**

**http://cdr.stanford.edu/html/WWW-ME/**

**Usenet:**

**sci.engr.mech**

## Nuclear Engineering

So you want to impress your best girl (or guy) and show your parents that you really can amount to something? Go to this web site and learn something about nuclear engineering (applying technology based on energy absorbed or released during atomic reactions). How hard could it be? After all, it's not rocket science.

**Web:**

**http://neutrino.nuc.berkeley.edu/NEadm.html**

## Optical Engineering

Do you need to shed light on your engineering problems? Here are some resources devoted to optical engineering (applying the science of light) and to photonics (transmission of information via light, usually lasers). By the way, when I was a graduate student at the University of California at San Diego, one of my best friends was an optical engineer. I used to do my math homework with her.

**Web:**

**http://www.optics.org/**

**Usenet:**

**sci.optics**

## Robotics

Robotics is the study and creation of machines guided by automatic controls (robots). Although it is fashionable to think of robots as being humanoid, outside of science fiction, robots look a lot more like your toaster than like your Uncle Henry.

**Web:**

**http://piglet.cs.umass.edu:4321/robotics.html**

**Usenet:**

**comp.robotics.misc**
**comp.robotics.research**

What do you do if you happen to be married to a member of the British royal family and want to learn to relate to your mate? Not to worry. The Net has lots and lots of resources to help you understand robotics.

## Urban Traffic Control

If you spend too much of your time waiting around in traffic, you will be interested in this resource, an information source for people active in the study of urban traffic congestion. Read papers detailing the research of the York Network Control Group. Actually, I have had personal experience with traffic control. At one time, I was living in a small coastal town in Southern California, and I had a problem with people parking in front of the walkway to my place. I went to the City Hall to talk to the town's traffic engineer and he said, "No problem, I'll send over a lifeguard to paint the curb red." (If only life were always that easy.)

**Web:**

**http://gridlock.york.ac.uk/**

# ENVIRONMENT

## Aquifers and Pollution

A mailing list discussing the vulnerability of aquifers to pollution, and what can be done about it. Why is this important? An aquifer is a layer of earth in which water collects. Much of our drinking water comes from aquifers and must be protected. (By the way, don't confuse aquifers with aquaducts: man-made channels for carrying water from one place to another.)

**Listserv Mailing List:**

List Name: **aquifer**
Subscribe to: **listserv@ibacsata.bitnet**

## Atmosphere Pollution Prevention

Do your part to take the stink out of the air. Read up on the methane outreach program, green lights program and publications you can order from the Environmental Protection Agency. This site even has software programs to help calculate light level, submit voluntary reporting requirements and survey facilities.

**Web:**

**http://www.epa.gov/docs/GCDOAR/OAR-APPD.html**

## Better World Magazine

This environmentally oriented zine has great articles about alternative technologies, pollution, natural resources and many more green topics. The web site has lots of useful information for people who are interested in becoming more conscious of how to care for the environment.

**Web:**

**http://www.betterworld.com**

**Stay away from "X-Rated".**

## Biosphere

The "biosphere" refers to the part of our world in which life can exist: from the surface of the Earth—that is, the oceans and the land—up to about 10 km (6 miles) into the atmosphere. Obviously, this is an important area of the universe that we should understand. After all, all our stuff is here.

**Web:**

**http://ice.ucdavis.edu/MAB/**
**http://www.circles.org/ESSCC/curric/biosphere/BiosphereHtlist.html**

**Usenet:**

**bit.listserv.biosph-l**

**Listserv Mailing List:**

List Name: **biosph-l**
Subscribe to: **listserv@listserv.aol.com**

## Chemical Substance Factsheets

Information from the EPA on hundreds of chemicals, elements, and compounds. Factsheets include data on toxicity, identification, reason for citation, how to determine if you've been exposed, OSHA safety limits, ways to reduce exposure, and more relevant information.

**Web:**

**http://earth1.epa.gov/chemfact/chemical**

## Coastal Management and Resources

People think that the coast is all fun and sun with the ocean crashing against the beach and the sun setting across the water. Well, it's that very water that makes the coast so tricky to manage. And then there's that rumor that has been going around about California falling off into the ocean. It's enough to give anyone a headache. Fortunately, there is a list that deals with topics related to coastal management and resources, so there is a place to turn when it's time to do some brainstorming or to discuss revolutionary ideas that pop up in the coastal management field.

**Listserv Mailing List:**

List Name: **coastnet**
Subscribe to: **listserv@uriacc.uri.edu**

## Conservation OnLine

Conservation OnLine (CoOL) is a full text database of conservation information. This database covers a wide spectrum of topics of interest to anyone involved with the conservation of libraries, archives and museum materials.

**Web:**

**http://palimpsest.stanford.edu/**

## Coral Reefs

Coral reefs are limestone formations found in shallow tropical ocean where the water is over 22 degrees Centigrade (72 degrees Fahrenheit). Reefs are produced by sea animals which secrete calcium carbonate (limestone) that, over thousands of years, builds up into massive formations. Coral reefs are part of the undersea ecosystem and provide important ecological support for coral as well as other animal and plant life. There are several types of reefs: fringing reefs that are platforms running continuous with the shore, barrier reefs that are separated from the shore by an expanse of deep lagoon, and atolls that surround a lagoon. Although coral reefs cover less than 0.2% of the Earth's ocean-covered area, they create a living environment for a great many of the ocean's species. At this web site, you can read about all the things that coral reefs do for humans, and why we should save them from contamination and physical destruction.

**Web:**

**http://www.blacktop.com/coralforest/**

## Earth Observation System

You never know when the day will come that you will be called upon to know the salinity of coastal air or even how you find out stuff like that. To make an airborne salinity mapper, what wavelengths of microwave and IR-bands do you use and what's the conversion algorithm? No need to worry about bothersome details. NASA has it all worked out for you with their Earth Observation System. They're keeping an eye on the planet so you can rest easy at night.

**Usenet:**

**sci.geo.eos**

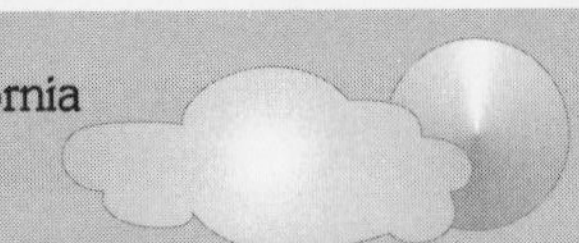

Life here in Southern California is a lot more than surfing and snorkeling and swimming. Sometimes we have to take a break and get a massage.

But when we do get serious, we get serious. If you want to join in, subscribe to the Coastal Management and Resources mailing list (**coastnet**).

If you can't go surfing, you might as well talk about the water.

## Earth Sciences Resources

The Earth is one of my favorite planets in the entire solar system, so it's no surprise that I like this Earth sciences site. There is a lot of interesting information waiting for you. For example, before I go to the beach, I make sure to check the map of world water temperatures. Take a few minutes and browse, and I bet you'll agree with me that we live in a pretty interesting place.

**Web:**

**http://www.wadsworth.com/earthnet.html**

## Ecological Economics

What does economics have to do with the environment? According to this list, we should make a major change in the way we think about economics in order to respond to environmental threats to the planet. If you love the Earth more than you love your money, this might be the place for you. Join in on discussions about alternatives to prevailing economic systems.

**Web:**

**http://csf.colorado.edu/se/**

**Listserv Mailing List:**

List Name: **ecol-econ**
Subscribe to: **listserv@csf.colorado.edu**

Imagine. You walk down to your favorite river and there it is — gone. Don't let this happen to you. Check out the **Endangered Rivers** resource, and look for your personal favorite. After all, if you are like me, you probably don't have enough to worry about.
Adopt a river today.

## Econet

Econet gathers information to enhance cooperation among people interested in environmental activities. Would you like to save the world, but you don't have enough time? Let's start small. Hug a tree with one hand and, with the other, use your browser to connect to Econet.

**Web:**

**http://www.econet.apc.org/econet/**

## Ecoweb

Do your part for Mother Earth by checking in at the Ecoweb, a network for the environmentally conscious. Ecoweb has audio clips, movies, and Ecochat—a place where you can chat with other green people. Connect to a large number of mailing lists sponsored by the Students Environmental Action Coalition. Explore other environment-related resources on the Net through links that offer everything from simple text to the whole multimedia shebang.

**Web:**

**http://ecosys.drdr.virginia.edu/EcoWeb.html**

**Feel lucky? Try "Contests".**

## Endangered Rivers

Rivers don't grow on trees, so it's a nice idea to take care of the ones we have. Here's a file listing endangered and threatened rivers that are suffering from the effects of mining, toxic dumping, waste dumping, pollution and other human threats.

**Web:**

**http://www.amrivers.org/amrivers/**
**http://www.irn.org**

## Endangered Species

A web site with information—including curriculum plans—about endangered and extinct species. What's your favorite endangered species? Mine is *Dipodomys ingens* (the giant kangaroo rat).

**Web:**

**http://www.nceet.snre.umich.edu/EndSpp/Endangered.html**

## Energy and the Environment

Exactly how did those holes get in the ozone? Could it be all the hairspray women had to use in the '50s for those tricky bouffant hairdos? Find out the facts about the ozone, UV radiation, and the status of the northern and southern ozone holes. Also available is historical information on gas prices and energy consumption.

**Web:**

**http://zebu.uoregon.edu/energy.html**

## Envirolink Network

A large resource of environmental information from the Envirolink Network. It covers all aspects of the environment, including environmental action, issues, media, networks, organization, and politics, and gives easy access to other environmental servers.

**Web:**

**http://envirolink.org/**

## Environment Talk and General Discussion

Whether you just like to talk about saving the environment, or whether you actually want to *do* something about saving the environment, these Usenet discussion groups are for you. Earth lovers from all over the planet talk about various aspects of ecology and the environment. Discussion ranges widely, from helpful home tips to technical scientific topics.

**Usenet:**

**alt.save.the.earth**
**sci.environment**
**talk.environment**

## Environmental Engineering

It's like any picnic—when you have people hanging around they are bound to make trash that you have to deal with, and dealing with trash is what environmental engineers do, except on a much larger scale. Read about all topics relating to environmental engineering, including water and waste water treatment, air pollution control, solid waste management, and radioactive waste treatment.

**Web:**

**http://www.nmt.edu/~jjenks/engineering.html**

## Environmental Organization Web Directory

Do you ever want to find out who does what in the environmental world? Well, now you can with just a click of the mouse. This web directory has a listing of various environmental organizations categorized by subject area. Just pick your pet topic and find out what companies and organizations have related resources on the Net.

**Web:**

**http://webdirectory.com/**

## Environmental Protection Agency

The EPA has collected a massive amount of information on the environment with regard to legislation, regulations, job vacancies, grants, newsletters and journals, press releases, announcements and consumer information.

**Web:**

**http://www.epa.gov/**

**Intrigue, Privacy, Secret Stuff...**

### *Look What I Found on the Net...*

```
Newsgroup: sci.environment
Subject: Re: Environmental Lawers

> Just a guick question.
> Are there any companies out there which hires
> individuals interested in environment law?
> I really would like to know.
> Thanks in advance

Plenty of consulting firms and industrial companies hire
environmental lawyers.  Pay is commensurate with experience and
skills of course.

However, most such positions require extensive writing and
research.  Before you apply, I would suggest a good course in
English spelling and grammer.
```

## Environmental Scorecard

If you are American, you may be interested to see how your congressional representatives rank on the National Environmental Scorecard. This ranking is created by the League of Conservation Voters to draw attention to voting patterns followed by the individual congressmen and congresswomen. How did your elected officials do? My two senators scored 100% and 77% respectively, while my congressional representative scored 0% (all three are women, by the way).

**Web:**

**http://www.lcv.org/home/scorecards-menu.html**

**Do elected officials know the score?**

**Maybe yes and maybe no, but if you live in the United States, you can check your congressional representative's environmental scorecard.**

**(Environmental hint: After you are finished connecting to the Web, be sure to recycle all your leftover electrons.)**

## Environmental Search Engine

When you need to find data and information related to the environment, you can focus quickly using a search engine specifically geared toward environmental resources. Choose from many, many web sites or archives, or perform a quick search on several databases at the same time.

**Web:**

**http://www.intbc.com/sleuth/envi.html**

## Environmental Web Directory

Here on Earth, we have more environment than you can shake a biodegradable stick at. But some days, it seems as if our large but limited supply of environment is being damaged faster than we can even understand. Is this true, or is the Earth capable of taking care of itself? If you like to learn more about the environment, this web site is a terrific place to start.

**Web:**

**http://www.webdirectory.com/**

## FireNet

An information service for everyone interested in any aspect of rural and landscape fires. The information concerns all aspects of fire science and management, including fire behavior, fire weather, fire prevention, mitigation and suppression, plant and animal responses to fire, and all aspects of fire effects.

**Web:**

**http://online.anu.edu.au/Forestry/fire/firenet.html**

## Forest Conservation

Would you like to help protect forests? How about supporting biodiversity and indigenous cultures? If so, this site is for you. Lots and lots of reference material relating to forest environments around the world. (However, to save disk space, information is restricted to only those forests in our local biosphere.)

**Web:**

**http://forests.lic.wisc.edu/forests/gaia.html**

## Global Change and Climate History

If you travel a lot and talk to people, you will find that, no matter where you go, no matter when you travel, no matter who you talk to, they will always say that the recent weather is different from what it normally is. Clearly, you have to be careful what you define as "normal". The U.S. Geological Survey Global Change Research Program (I bet you can't say that ten times real fast) collects information to help people recognize and understand long-range changes to our climate. If you are concerned about possible global changes, here is a good place to learn more.

**Web:**

**http://geochange.er.usgs.gov/gch.html**

## Global Recycling Network

Global Recycling Network is an information service set up on the Internet to aid businesses around the world in recycling resources, surplus manufactured goods and outdated or used machinery.

**Web:**

**http://grn.com/grn/**

My personal philosophy has always been, "Think globally, do nothing."
Still, if you do want to stick your nose into the Earth's business, take a look at *Global Change and Climate History.*
The life you save will probably be nobody's (but then again, you never know).

## Green Manufacturing

Nobody likes it when the Earth is unhappy, because we get all these earthquakes and storms and floods. So, in an effort to please Mother Nature, someone came up with the concept of green manufacturing—a means of manufacturing that is environmentally friendly. Scholars, manufacturers, and students interested in the environment should check out background information and studies on green manufacturing.

**Web:**

**http://euler.berkeley.edu/green/cgdm.html**

## Greenpeace

If the military is not your style, but you want a sense of adventure on the open seas, check out Greenpeace. Read up on ship movements, press releases, latest demonstrations, job opportunities, see pictures and publications of this environmental activist group.

**Web:**

**http://www.greenpeace.org/**

## National Wetlands Inventory

You can check on America's wetlands without having to put on the waders and slosh about in the muck. Graphical maps will show you the status of the wetlands using color coding. A master map will give you the availability of digital maps, but others are available only in print. If you don't have a graphical browser you will need to download the images, or the information at this site won't make much sense.

**Web:**

**http://www.nwi.fws.gov/**

## National Wildlife Refuges

This server provides information about the National Wildlife Refuge System and topics of interest related to wildlife management and natural resources management. As far as I know, this is the best place to go in the middle of the night when you need a copy of the "Review of Potential Impacts of Oil Development on the Coastal Plain of the Arctic National Wildlife Refuge".

**Web:**

**http://bluegoose.arw.r9.fws.gov/**

## NOAA Data Set Catalog

The National Oceanic and Atmospheric Administration (NOAA) Data Set Catalog allows you to search for information from a number of NOAA databases. If you are a serious environmental researcher, this site is for you. Historical note: The term "data set" is a very old computer term meaning "file". The term was used on IBM mainframe computers in the olden days (starting in the 1960s).

**Web:**

**http://www.esdim.noaa.gov/NOAA-Catalog/**

**Read the FAQs of life.**

## Ozone Depletion

Whether you are a serious researcher, or just a student looking for information for your term paper entitled "Our Friend the Stratosphere", here are a couple of resources that contain enough information about ozone depletion to keep you satisfied for a long time. The ozone layer, by the way, refers to the area in the stratosphere (about 15-40 km straight up) in which ozone is formed by the action of ultraviolet radiation (coming from the sun) on oxygen. The ozone layer keeps a lot of this radiation from getting down to where we live. If the ozone layer is thinned—by pollutants, for example—a lot of bad things might happen. Don't say I didn't warn you.

**Web:**

**http://www.cis.ohio-state.edu/hypertext/faq/usenet/ozone-depletion/top.html**
**http://www.epa.gov/docs/ozone**

**ISN'T OZONE GREAT?**

**If there's too much you die,
and if there's not enough
you get skin cancer.
If you want more details,
look under
Ozone Depletion
(a great way to spend a Saturday night).**

## Rainforest Action Network

The Rainforest Action Network (RAN) is organized for the purpose of protecting tropical rainforests and the people who live in and around the forests. At RAN's site you can learn more about the rainforests, which bad guys to boycott, as well as the latest action alerts.

**Web:**

**http://www.igc.apc.org/ran/**

## Sea Level Data

I spend a lot of time at sea level (and some time below sea level), and I can tell you that the ocean is not flat. However, even averaging things out, sea level is not the same everywhere in the world. This site analyzes sea level data received by satellite, and shows you the anomalies using easy to understand colored maps (well, relatively easy to understand colored maps).

**Web:**

**http://nng.esoc.esa.de/ers/alti.html**

## Seas and Water Directory

This site is dedicated to the conservation of reservoirs, oceans and aquatic life and to finding solutions to help alleviate water problems. You will find links to information about acid rain, toxic hazards and specific action groups that are focusing on water as their part of the efforts to save the environment.

**Web:**

**http://www.igc.apc.org/igc/www.water.html**

## ULS Report

A bimonthly newsletter that helps people "use less stuff" and become more friendly to the environment. The list also serves as a discussion group for anyone interested in activities and occasionally features guest experts who respond to reader questions and comments.

**Majordomo Mailing List:**

List Name: **uls**
Subscribe to: **majordomo@mail.msen.com**

## Waste Reduction Tips and Factsheets

Here is useful information showing how to reduce waste and conserve resources. The focus is on source reduction and re-use rather than just recycling. Unfortunately, they left out the most important tip: buy Harley Hahn books in bulk, and never, ever throw them away.

**Web:**

**http://www.state.mo.us/dnr/deq/swmp/hhtips.htm**
**http://www.web.apc.org/rco/factsheet/fs_a37.html**

TOO MUCH
**STUFF?**
The Net has lots and lots of resources for Waste Reduction

# EXERCISE

## Abdominal Training FAQ

Time goes on and we all suddenly find a little extra weight around our midsection. The abdominal training FAQ (frequently asked question list) is intended as an introduction to the basic principles of training the abdominal area.

**Web:**

**http://www.dstc.edu.au/TU/staff/timbomb/ab/**

## Aerobics

Some people cringe each time they hear their aerobics instructor say, "only 8 more." Others get that adrenalin rush after cycling up their local mountain. This is a group that discusses all forms of aerobic activity and reminds you that it's all worth it.

**Web:**

**http://grove.ufl.edu/~evilgreg/aerobics.html**

**Usenet:**

**misc.fitness.aerobic**

## Balance Magazine

An online monthly fitness magazine with information on diet, exercise, health and other necessary information to stay in balance.

**Web:**

**http://www.hyperlink.com/balance/**

## Beginning to Exercise

It's never too late to start, but it's vital that you choose the right fitness program for yourself. Here you'll find tips on how to choose the right type of exercise and how to select a fitness center. (The instructor in the purple tights might only *look* good.) There are also important guidelines and safety tips for beginners.

**Web:**

**http://sln.fi.edu/biosci/healthy/exercise.html**

## Endurance Training Journal

If you've ever dated a successful triathlete, you know that they spend a lot of time training, cross-training and eating right. This journal discusses all of the important components of effective endurance training.

**Web:**

**http://s2.com/etj/**

## Exercise Search Engine

All dressed up in spandex and no place to go? Stay home and give your fingers a workout by playing with the exercise and sports medicine search engine. You'll find all sorts of cool fitness stuff, and you won't have to shower afterward.

**Web:**

**http://www.hslib.washington.edu/your_health/sports.html**

## Female Bodybuilders

Take a look at the web page of some of the top competitive female bodybuilders. You'll also have access to contest results, fan mail addresses and writings of these bodybuilders' experiences, good or bad. If you become tired of reading, you can revel in a little aural sensation by listening to your favorite female bodybuilders being interviewed.

**Web:**

**http://www.frsa.com/fgallery.html**

## Fitness

This site provides exercise and fitness guidelines, programs and resources as well as what to do in case of injury. Find overall fitness information to assist you with maintaining a healthy and well-rounded body composition.

**Web:**

**http://chat.carleton.ca/~kthom/misc.fitness.faq.html**
**http://k2.kirtland.cc.mi.us/~balbachl/fitness.htm**

A B C D E F G H I J K L M N O P Q R S T U V W X Y Z

**All females are human.**
**All humans have bodies.**
Therefore, as Socrates once said,
**all female bodybuilders are human.**
(well, sort of)

Try the Female Bodybuilder site and see what you think.

## Fitness Discussion

We all know we should exercise every day. And we all know that sometimes we don't like to exercise every day. So when you are having one of those days, maybe it would be more fun to talk about it than actually do it. If so, Usenet is always there, and lots of people are ready to talk.

**Usenet:**

**misc.fitness.aerobic**
**misc.fitness.misc**
**misc.fitness.weights**

## Fitness Jumpsite

All tired out from your physical training program? Take a rest at the computer and re-inspire yourself to fitness greatness. Browse this great collection of links and articles relating to exercise and nutrition.

**Web:**

**http://www.cdc.net/~primus/fpc/fpchome.html**

## Fitness Zone

With a little bit of motivation and an Internet connection, you too can be a fitness stud. This site has articles on exercise and weight loss, fitness training, weightlifting, as well as a variety of FAQs (frequently asked question lists). So get out of the fridge and onto the Net.

**Web:**

**http://www.fitnesszone.com/**

## Gift of Youth

Fifty-plus year old Gypsy is an iron-pumping grandma who is passing on her wisdom about rejuvenation to the Net. Here you'll find thoughts on exercise, dieting and weightlifting.

**Web:**

**http://www.skypoint.com/members/magic/gypsy/giftofyouth.html**

## High Altitude Exercise

If you're unsure about the air up there, read this info about exercising and training under high altitude conditions. There's technical information about how altitude and oxygen affect metabolism as well as guidelines for high altitude training.

**Web:**

**http://www.livelinks.com/sumeria/oxy/altitude.html**

**High Altitude**

**Before you get high and exercise, make sure you get all the facts about altitude and its effects on the human body.**

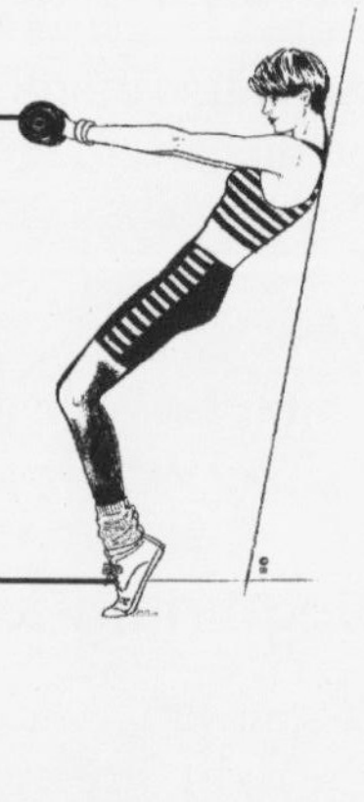

## Male Bodybuilders

This web site provides information about bodybuilding competitions, magazines, television listings, addresses for fan mail, profiles and other related Internet resources. There's even a picture gallery.

**Web:**

**http://bb.acc.stolaf.edu/**

## Massage for Health and Fitness

Magic fingers are always welcomed by sore muscles. Massage in conjunction with exercise helps to create a healthy body. Learn about the physiological effects of massage, how to incorporate massage into a fitness program and tips on what to look for when choosing a massage therapist.

**Web:**

**http://www.doubleclickd.com/theramassage.html**

## Muscle Physiology

When it's late at night, I like to turn the lights down low and read about force-velocity relationships and excitation contraction coupling. I find that there is nothing like a thorough examination of muscle and joint movement to really get the blood going. Want to know more? This web page has a list of explanations about muscle physiology and how it works with respect to fitness.

**Web:**

**http://ortho84-13.ucsd.edu/MusIntro/**

## Powerlifting

Everybody's probably wondered what it would be like to hold a world record for powerlifting. Check out this web site and compare your record with those of the junior and senior world records. Read biographies and take a look at images of powerlifters doing their thing.

**Web:**

**http://www.cee.hw.ac.uk/~acc/plift-list.html**

## Pregnancy and Exercise

The effects of exercise during pregnancy have been known to result in an easier delivery. Read articles about tips, warnings, maternal heart rate and temperature during exercise as well as how not to hurt your body or the baby. One advantage is that you're encouraged to eat extra food if you are exercising.

**Web:**

**http://s2.com/etj/clinic/expreg.html**
**http://www.daxcoe.com/dax/dcarticles/exercise.html**
**http://www.lack.net/fitfor2/**

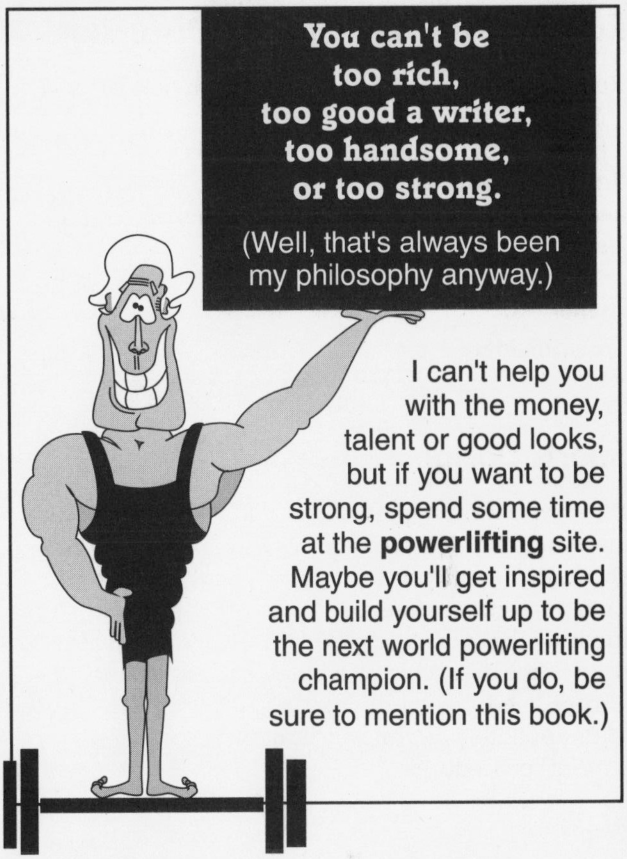
You can't be too rich, too good a writer, too handsome, or too strong.
(Well, that's always been my philosophy anyway.)
I can't help you with the money, talent or good looks, but if you want to be strong, spend some time at the **powerlifting** site. Maybe you'll get inspired and build yourself up to be the next world powerlifting champion. (If you do, be sure to mention this book.)

## Running

Every runner from beginner to experienced can benefit from these running sites. There are tips for newcomers, as well as hints on how fast to run and how the body adapts. Rest assured, you'll be convinced that running is the right choice if done properly.

**Web:**

**http://sunsite.unc.edu/drears/running/running.html**
**http://www.webrunner.com/webrun/running/faqs.html**

## Running Injuries

Don't just run away. Deal with your injuries. Look here for advice on how to avoid running injuries and overtraining, recommended footwear, tips on running in cold or hot weather and recommended running books. After all that, if you still have running injuries, you'll also find suggestions on immediate care.

**Web:**

**http://www.clark.net/pub/pribut/spsport.html**

## Running Talk and General Discussion

Runners are always happy to find each other and share their trials and tribulations. Sometimes finding a new running partner is just what's needed; other times, being turned on to a new jogging route takes a healthy turn. Share your ideas with the folks on Usenet.

**Usenet:**

**rec.running**

## Sports Doctor

When you want to play doctor and nobody is around, just connect to this web site. You can pretend to be a sports doctor and click on your patient's symptoms until you reach a diagnosis. You can also find a medical glossary to help explain some of the terms used in the diagnosis, as well as read explanations of various medical conditions. And, if you like to reduce your appetite, you can watch movies of various surgical procedures.

**Web:**

**http://www.medfacts.com/**

**My other joke is funny.**

## Stretching and Flexibility

This document attempts to compile a wealth of information in order to answer some frequently asked questions about stretching and flexibility. It is organized into chapters covering the physiology of stretching, flexibility, types of stretching and how to stretch. Look out Gumby!

**Web:**

**http://www.smartpages.com/faqs/stretching/top.html**

## Training and Nutrition

The last thing that anyone wants to do is give up their favorite treats. Learn about how exercise affects body metabolism and check out a safe fast food list. There's also a training and nutrition FAQ as well as mailing list archives about how to eat right while exercising and body building.

**Web:**

**http://www2.dgsys.com/~trnutr/**

## Walking

Walking can be a lot more meaningful than making regular trips from the computer to the refrigerator. In fact, walking is a great form of exercise. This site has information about power walking, race walking, and walking for sport, exercise and leisure. If you are thinking about improving your fitness level, this is a good place to start.

**Web:**

**http://www.teleport.com/~walking/walking.shtml**

### *Look What I Found on the Net...*

```
Newsgroup: rec.running
Subject: Throwing up

> Does anyone out there have any explanation as to why I would
> be throwing up after a long run?
>
> I had trained all winter and never got sick, but lately
> I'm throwing up on any run lasting more than 1 hour 15 min.

The two times I've been extremely dehydrated, I've felt very
nauseous.  Dehydration could be your problem.
```

## Weightlifting

Just when you think that there aren't any more weightlifting sites, this one will provide you with further information about recreational lifting, powerlifting, competitive bodybuilding, FAQs and even more links to other related resources.

**Web:**

**http://www.cs.unc.edu/~wilsonk/weights.html**
**http://www.waf.com/weights/**

**Usenet:**

**misc.fitness.weights**

## Women's Fitness

This site covers special fitness and health considerations for women: targeting various body parts for toning and fat loss, weightlifting, specific workout routines, and nutritional information.

**Web:**

**http://www.sims.berkeley.edu/~vtran/assign5/**

## Yoga

I have been doing yoga for years (Ashtanga and Iyengar styles), and I can tell you that it works. However, it is hard work, and a good yoga workout will make you sweat profusely. Perhaps the best way to put it is that yoga is like a sewer: what you get out of it depends on what you put into it. If you want to see what people talk about when they are not doing their postures, take a look at the Usenet discussion group. Here you will find all the traditional cultural pursuits of the yoga community: sharing ideas, discussing personal growth, gossip about other people, and complaining. The web sites have interesting information about yoga styles, articles from yoga magazines and much more.

**Web:**

**http://www.iyoga.com/yf/**
**http://www.spiritweb.org/Spirit/Yoga/Overview.html**
**http://www.yogajournal.com/**

**Usenet:**

**alt.yoga**

### *Look What I Found on the Net...*

```
Newsgroup: misc.fitness.weights
Subject: People Who Experiment

>> I will tell you a story.  We were experimenting with a new
>> veterinary drug (not for humans).  A single vial contained
>> several doses for big cows.
>>
>> A friend of mine used the whole vial all at once.  He
>> agonized for several hours.  But he was happy about the
>> whole experience as the next day his body was completely
>> changed.
>>
>> The point is, people willing to try crazy stuff can be found
>> all over the world.

> His body changed overnight?  In what way?

He was leaner (he excreted a lot of water), and his muscles
were harder than anything I have ever touched.

And yes, he was bigger overnight (could be due to a vasodilatory
effect of the drug).
```

## FAMILIES AND PARENTING

### Adoption

Adoption is both difficult and exciting. This site offers information for anyone involved in an adoption process: birth parents, adoptees, and adoptive parents. You can find answers to general, legal and medical questions, information about adoption agencies and publications, and advice on foreign adoption. The mailing list provides a forum for discussing anything relating to adoption and is open to adoptive parents, adoptees, birth parents, social workers, counselors and anyone else involved in the adoption process.

**Web:**

**http://www.adoption.org/adopt/**

**Listserv Mailing List:**

List Name: **adoption**
Subscribe to: **listserv@sjuvm.stjohns.edu**

### Advice for Parents

Parents and parents-to-be will find useful articles on this web site. There is a lengthy selection of topics relating to many different areas of parenthood. Read about pregnancy, newborn babies, infants, toddlers, pre-school children, pre-teens and adolescents. (Then take a long hot soak in a warm tub, and remind yourself how much fun it is to have children.)

**Web:**

**http://www.tnpc.com/parentalk/**

### Baby Bag Online

If you have a baby, or if you have a baby on the way, this is a great site to visit. There is a huge amount of information about parenting, baby care, pregnancy, childbirth, baby news, day-care centers and much, much more. Announce your baby's birth, and then stick around and read some of the handy baby care information.

**Web:**

**http://www.babybag.com/**

Baby Bag OnLine
*Conception can be a lot of fun. And the day you deliver the baby, I'm sure you will be awfully busy.*
*But what about the 280 days in between? How do you keep from being bored?*
*Easy. Spend your time exploring the Baby Bag Online web site. By the time the baby shows up, you'll know so much about children, they'll call you Mom.*

### Baby Care Corner

Babies want most of all to be fed, loved and changed. But when there's something wrong, it can be hard to tell what the problem is—or even if there is one. Parenting can be frustrating sometimes. Here you will find information about caring for babies. Just the thing to read when you can't sleep at night.

**Web:**

**http://www.familyinternet.com/babycare/babycare.htm**

### Breastfeeding Talk and General Discussion

There are special issues that must be considered by parents of babies who are breastfeeding. This mailing list and Usenet group are great places for talking about the problems and rewards of breastfeeding. Some of the topics include attachment parenting, weaning, extended nursing, nursing in public, working mothers who breastfeed, tandem nursing, societal attitudes toward nursing, and nursing during pregnancy.

**Usenet:**

**misc.kids.breastfeeding**

**Majordomo Mailing List:**

List Name: **parent-l**
Subscribe to: **majordomo@uts.edu.au**

## CD Mom

Here is a nice family gathering area with lots of inspiring articles on a variety of topics: physical and mental well-being, how to inspire your children to greatness, community issues, hi-tech products and news, parenting, and a lot more.

**Web:**

**http://www.cd-mom.com/**

## Child Activism Talk and General Discussion

Children's rights is the main topic for discussion on this Usenet group. Read and post your thoughts and ideas regarding the social and political issues relating to children. Hint: If your child is going to grow up to be famous, be careful what you say and do, as it may all end up in a book.

**Usenet:**

**alt.activism.children**

### *Look What I Found on the Net...*

```
Newsgroups: alt.parenting.spanking
Subject: Beating the Devil Out of Them

Deut. 21:18-21 commands parents to stone disobedient sons to
death along with sons who have an alcohol problem or an eating
disorder.

Deut. 22:20, 21 advocates stoning girls to death for premarital
sex.  Daughters of priests were burned rather than stoned for
premarital sex (Lev. 21:9).

Deut. 13:6-10 says a man may execute his children for deviating
from Judaism.

In 2 Kings 2:23, 24, 42 children are torn apart by two she-bears
for childishly making fun of the prophet Elisha's receding
hairline.

Psalms 137:9 recommends bashing Babylonian babies' brains out
while Jer. 18:21 thunders, "Therefore deliver up their children
to the famine and pour out their blood by the force of the
sword; and let their wives be bereaved of their children and be
widows."

The point is, the handful of verses about beating children need
to be viewed in the context of their culture of origin.
The ancient Israelites were perfectly comfortable with behavior
that would nowadays constitute, not only child abuse, but war
crimes in violation of the Geneva Convention.  Anyone who states
that they have a religious duty to beat their children with a
rod because the Book of Proverbs says so needs to explain
whether or not they also believe in the literal meaning of the
Old Testament verses about killing children.  If not, how does
such an individual determine which bible verses to obey and
which ones to disregard?
```

A B C D E F G H I J K L M N O P Q R S T U V W X Y Z

## Child Discipline Talk and General Discussion

To spank or not to spank—that is the question. This group mostly contains a long-running debate about whether it is morally and politically acceptable to spank children. However, there are occasional threads about alternative methods of discipline and hints on "positive parenting". My personal hint is to talk softly, but carry a big stick.

**Usenet:**
**alt.parenting.spanking**

## Child Safety Forum

Just because your children are home doesn't necessarily mean they are safe. Accidents can happen in your home, especially if the household is not properly child-proofed. This site has information on child safety, focusing on the kitchen. It offers hints and a checklist to help you make the cooking area safe for children. You can also find information on product recalls, and you can pass along experiences you have had with accidents at home.

**Web:**
**http://www.xmission.com/~gastown/safe/safe2.htm**

## Child Safety on the Internet

If you are worried about your kids wandering around the Internet by themselves, have a look at these tips that will give you a better idea of how to protect young minds from inappropriate material.

**Web:**
**http://www.missingkids.org/information_superhighway.html**

## Child Support Talk and General Discussion

How do you stand on issues of custody and child support? Find out the thoughts of others affected by these issues and learn about current legislation.

**Usenet:**
**alt.child-support**

## Childcare

When you can't stay home with your kids, you have to decide who is going to take care of them. This site has information about all forms of childcare: au pairs, nannies, day care, and educational care. You will also find links to other childcare resources and search facilities. The Usenet group is for the discussion of non-parental childcare.

**Web:**
**http://www.parentsplace.com/readroom/ACS/**

**Usenet:**
**alt.childcare**

## Children

Kids say the darnedest things. Impart your information and experience regarding children from the cradle onward. Anecdotes, advice on doctors, behavior, activities, discipline, and schooling legislation are just a few of the topics covered. The web sites have information on the various issues that arise when rearing children.

**Web:**
**http://www.internet-is.com/misckids/**
**http://www.irsociety.com/cgi-bin/webchat_doorway.cgi?Room=misc.kids**

**Usenet:**
**misc.kids**

## Children With Special Needs

Raising a child with a disability is difficult, and doing a good job can be time-consuming, tiring and expensive. But perhaps worst of all, spending a lot of time with a child with special needs can be a lonely experience for you. If you have such a child, you may enjoy participating in the **our-kids** mailing list. This is a support group for parents or others who care for children with physical or mental developmental disabilities. It is important for you to remember that such problems are common, and you are not alone. Talking with other people who face similar problems and challenges can make all the difference in the world.

**Majordomo Mailing List:**
List Name: **our-kids**
Subscribe to: **majordomo@tbag.osc.edu**

## Children's Health

If you have kids, there will be times when you need to call the doctor, or look for help in a first aid or medical book. At such times, this web site may help. Here is reference information on pediatric health, childhood conditions, and acquired and congenital diseases. The Usenet group is for the general discussion of children's health. And, if all else fails, ask your mother.

**Web:**

**http://www.uab.edu/pedinfo/**

**Usenet:**

**misc.kids.health**

## Cute Kids

Proud parents—take some time to check out this site. Here is your chance to tell all those cute stories about your children that your friends and relatives have already heard. After you are done talking about your child, you can read what everyone else has said about theirs. This is just the thing to share with childless friends when they come over to visit.

**Web:**

**http://www.prgone.com/cutekids/**

**Find a friend in "People".**

### *Look What I Found on the Net...*

```
Newsgroups: misc.kids
Subject: My daddy dressed me

>> Well, Carrie's Daddy dressed her yesterday, and what a
>> combination he came up with!  She was wearing a pair of
>> overalls, bright red with...

>> Normally, if Daddy dresses the kids, I leave on what he puts
>> on them, not wanting to belittle his efforts.  But normally
>> he does better than yesterday.

> I've been away from misc.kids for a while and, on tuning in
> today, it is disappointing to see that this sexist crap is
> still going on.  The traditional "this color goes with that"
> attitude has clearly long been dropped from fad wear, in which
> any and every color is worn together.

Sorry, but I have to disagree.  While I personally do not care
if my son matches when he plays, my wife and I do try to make
sure he "matches" if we go out.  (Of course, I tend to have a
little more liberal interpretation of what matches than my wife
does, but that seems to be common given the father/mother
responses. :-)  Now, I'm not saying it is important for a young
child to match.  I don't place that much weight on it.  However,
one of the things I see later on in life, especially with males
is that wearing the appropriate clothes to work/interviews, etc,
one feels much more confident when one isn't concerned about
whether their tie matches their suit or if it clashes...
```

A B C D E F G H I J K L M N O P Q R S T U V W X Y Z

## Cybermom

Moms, rev up your Internet connection and race over to Cybermom where you can hang out in one of the many chat rooms or browse the nice selection of articles while sipping a hot cup of cappuccino. You'll find a little bit of everything here: health, beauty, taking care of the kids, child safety, gardening, cleaning, entertaining, seasonal articles, and more.

**Web:**
**http://www.thecybermom.com/**

## Family Planet

Here's a real family site: family headline news, regular advice features, a handbook for parents, and a "sound off" section where you can post your experiences, advice and hints. While you are here, check out the great list of activities you can do with your kids. I remember when I was a kid, there was nothing I liked better than when my parents found me something interesting to do on the Net.

**Web:**
**http://family.starwave.com/**

### Keeping the Family Together

These days, it's hard to keep the family together.

Dad's in his study, using the Net to check the sports scores; Mom's in the kitchen with her laptop computer, cruising the Web for recipes; Junior is downloading free game software; and Sis is up all night talking to her friends on IRC.

Sometimes it seems as if everyone is in a different world, and modern parents despair of creating any real family spirit.

But now there is a way. All you have to do is hold regular family get-togethers, where everyone gathers around the family PC as you visit the Family Planet web site.

Staying together has never been so easy.

## Family Resources

The family that webs together stays together. This web page covers family topics like adolescence, pre-school, infants, children and marriage. Links on these topics will result in a list of related articles that will lead you to even more links for hours of interesting reading.

**Web:**
**http://www.einet.net/galaxy/Community/Family.html**

## FatherNet

It gets tiring hearing Mr. Mom jokes after a while. Dads, here is a little portion of the Internet just for you. Read through papers on men and children, information on interaction with kids, connect to an electronic bulletin board and chat system for dads, get a newsletter called At-Home Dad, and send in your opinions and experiences about fatherhood.

**Web:**
**http://www.fsci.umn.edu/cyfc/FatherNet.htp**

## Foster Parents

Being a foster parent can be tricky and can test your ability to adapt to new situations. However, the Net has great support groups of other foster parents. There is a Usenet discussion group for foster parents to gather and talk about their joys and experiences. The web site has lots and lots of information about children's specific physical and mental conditions and how to deal with them, as well as articles and hints on foster parenting and a bulletin board to which you can post messages.

**Web:**
**http://worldaccess.com/FPHP/**

**Usenet:**
**alt.support.foster-parents**

## Internet Filtering Software

There are lots of great resources on the Net for kids, and there is no reason why children should be deprived of exploring the Internet just because they might accidentally encounter some inappropriate content (that is, sex). This site has a list of companies who have designed software that filters out what you don't want your kids to see.

**Web:**
**http://www.safesurf.com/lifegard.htm**

## Jewish Parenting

This newsgroup was specifically created for parents to discuss those issues that are important to the Jewish community (such as bread, religion and soup). Along with the newsgroup come two FAQs. The **judaism.faq.12-kids.html** FAQ is about Jewish parenting. The **judaism.faq.scjp-admin.html** FAQ contains information related to the Usenet discussion group **soc.culture.jewish.parenting**.

**Web:**

**http://www.lib.ox.ac.uk/internet/news/faq/archive/judaism.faq.12-kids.html**
**http://www.lib.ox.ac.uk/internet/news/faq/archive/judaism.faq.scjp-admin.html**

**Usenet:**

**soc.culture.jewish.parenting**

## Kids, Computers and Software

I have never met a child who didn't like computers. In these Usenet groups, you can talk about the best computers and hardware for children, as well as educational and entertainment software. The web site has a collection of shareware that I am sure your kids will enjoy (when they are not sneaking behind your back to connect to inappropriate web sites).

**Usenet:**

**alt.comp.shareware.for-kids**
**misc.kids.computer**

**Happiness is a warm modem.**

### *Look What I Found on the Net...*

```
Newsgroup: misc.kids.computer
Subject: Mouse for Young Kids

>> I want my three year-old son to start using our computer.
>> However, our mouse is too big for him to handle.  Can anyone
>> recommend something that is easier to use?

> The Microsoft Easyball is a trackball for kids. They use their
> whole hand to move it.
>
> The purpose of the Easyball is threefold:
>   1. To make the mouse easier to use for hands with less fine
>      motor control.
>   2. To provide a better cognitive relationship between hand
>      and eye coordination (any roller-ball would do that).
>   3. To make using a computer FUN.

I don't know how small your three-year-old's hands are, but my
four-year-old has been using the mouse since she was two.  She
uses the standard mouse just fine.  Children are slow at first,
but they catch on.  They learn to use it like they learn
everything else.

In my opinion, in the long run the Easyball will serve little
or no purpose when the kid gets older.

That is, unless YOU want to use it.
```

A B C D E F G H I J K L M N O P Q R S T U V W X Y Z

## Missing Children

Help locate a missing child. Read descriptions of missing children, which have been posted by concerned individuals.

**Web:**

**http://www.childsearch.org/**
**http://www.notice.com/childrescue.html**
**http://www.scubed.com/public_service/missing.html**

**Usenet:**

**alt.missing-kids**

## Newsletters for Parents

Here is a nice collection of newsletters for parents, including specialty publications for single moms, single dads, grandparents, and more. When you get a chance (in your copious spare time), take a look. No matter what your situation, I bet you will find a lot of useful information.

**Web:**

**http://ericps.ed.uiuc.edu/npin/respar/nls.html**

## Parent Soup

Parent Soup is a great place for parents. As a matter of fact, if it weren't for your kids, you could spend hours at this site. You will find news, feature articles, a parent poll, chat areas, and lots of information for parents. There are also special sections for at-home parents, working parents, and single parents. The information at this site seems to go on forever, so put the kids to bed early so they won't get in the way.

**Web:**

**http://www.parentsoup.com/**

## Parenthood Web

This is a fantastic web site to explore. It has many features for parents and prospective parents, covering vital topics such as family health, naming babies, pregnancy, breast feeding, helping children through divorce, problems at school, homework, and much more.

**Web:**

**http://www.parenthoodweb.com/**

## Parenting Matters

Everything I know about parenting, I learned from my cat. For example, it does me no good whatsoever to raise my voice when he misbehaves. When I give him tuna, he always cleans his plate. And he never brings over friends for the weekend without first asking permission. My cat and I have a fair and mutually respectful relationship, and if you would like the same type of relationship in your household, check out this web site. It promotes healthy interactions between parents and children based on firm, but fair, discipline, and understanding your children intellectually so you can appreciate how they think. Read these articles and it won't be long before you will have created a familial utopia that will be the envy of the entire neighborhood. (And if you have any problems that can't be solved by utilizing the advice at this web site, try giving your kids an extra plate of tuna.)

**Web:**

**http://lifematters.com/parentn.html**

## Parenting Resource Center

If you are bored and you want to read some new stuff about parenting, check out this web site. It has features that are constantly changing as well as a reading room where you can find material on just about every topic imaginable related to parenting, step-parenting, parenting multiples, fatherhood, pregnancy, breastfeeding, health, education, and family activities. You will never run out of things to do here. And, if you do, you can always have a couple more kids.

**Web:**

**http://www.parentsplace.com/**

## Parents and Children Together Online

Here is an online magazine that both parents and children can enjoy. For the children, there are delightful, entertaining stories and articles. For adults, there are features about parenting, as well as reviews of books and products.

**Web:**

**http://www.indiana.edu/~eric_rec/fl/pcto/menu.html**

**Parents:**

We all know that raising children doesn't really take that much time, and most parents have a lot of empty hours on their hands.

If this is the case in your family, you run a real risk of ending up watching television.

However, there is no need to worry. Instead of turning on the TV, fire up the PC and connect to the Net. Then jump right to the Parenting Resource Center.

There is so much to do, you will never be bored. And before you know it, all your spare time will be used up.

## Parents and Teens

What works? What doesn't? Share your experiences with other parents, give advice, ask questions.

**Usenet:**

**alt.parents-teens**

## Parents Room

Parents Room is a place on IRC (Internet Relay Chat) where parents can exchange ideas on parenting and life or just hang out and talk. The web site has information on the **#!parentsroom** regulars, parenting resources, guidelines for the IRC channel, and general information about how IRC works.

**Web:**

**http://gwabbs.com/~delila/Parents.htm**

**IRC:**

**#!parentsroom**

## Pregnancy and Childbirth

Pregnancy is exciting and exhilarating, but it can be awfully scary if it is your first time. At the web sites, you can find out what is going to happen at every stage of your pregnancy. Read stories about birth, what labor is like, and find out information on special birth procedures like caesarians and episiotomies. The Usenet group is for the discussion of pregnancy and pregnancy-related issues.

**Web:**

**http://www.childbirth.org/**
**http://www.geocities.com/Heartland/5552/**

**Usenet:**

**misc.kids.pregnancy**

## Premature Infants

The normal human gestation period—the time between conception and birth—is about 280 days (40 weeks). Babies that are born significantly before the full term (six weeks or more) are said to be premature. Premature infants face a special set of problems. First, because their bodies are not fully developed, they may have trouble surviving. Second, premature babies that do survive have a greater than normal chance of suffering from a disability. Here are some resources to help parents understand the problems and considerations unique to premature infants. My experience is that having authoritative information can make a medical situation a lot easier to bear. However, doctors are often too busy to spend a long time explaining technical matters to patient's families. If you have a premature infant, these resources can help you understand what is happening, and what you can do to help your child.

**Web:**

**http://www.medsch.wisc.edu/childrenshosp/Parents_of_Preemies/index.html**
**http://www.vicnet.net.au/~garyh/preemie.htm**

**Majordomo Mailing List:**

List Name: **preemie-l**
Subscribe to: **majordomo@vicnet.net.au**

A B C D E F G H I J K L M N O P Q R S T U V W X Y Z

A B C D E F G H I J K L M N O P Q R S T U V W X Y Z

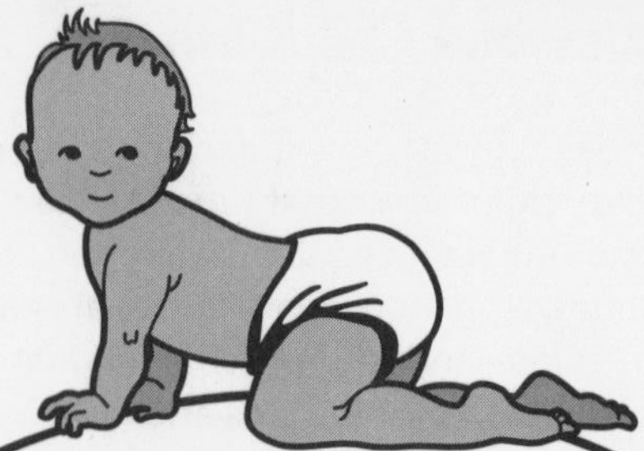

**Premature Infants**

*If you have a premature baby, you probably have a lot of questions. Well, the Net has a lot of answers, as well as many people who are ready to share.*

## Products for Children

If you have children, you probably don't get much choice about what toy you want to give them. Children know what they want, and they have their own ways of getting it. However, if you want to get the lowdown on what is best for children—as if they care—check out this guide. This site reviews toys and entertainment products for children, and also has hints for parents about what to select for particular age groups. The Usenet group is for discussion of consumer issues that relate to children.

**Web:**
**http://www.drtoy.com/**

**Usenet:**
**misc.kids.consumers**

## Sgt. Mom's Place

Military families have quite a life, so Sgt. Mom has made a web site with resources that can help. This site is for any military family: active, veteran, retired or reserve. Find support groups and new friends, advice on parenting, moving tips, and stuff for kids. When military living gets tough, the tough get going to Sgt. Mom's.

**Web:**
**http://www.sgtmoms.com/pages.htm**

## Single Parent Mailing List

Being a single parent is a tough job and you don't have to feel like you have no one to talk to. Join this mailing list on which you can share your experiences, talk about your kids and life in general. Listen, talk and support one another.

**Majordomo Mailing List:**
List Name: **sinpar**
Subscribe to: **majordomo@world.std.com**

## Single Parent Resource Center

When you are going it alone, it's good to know that there are other single parents all around the Net. This web site has a great deal of information for any single parent. You can find helpful topics about children, careers, parenting, spirituality, support and entertainment. For more immediate communication with other single moms and dads, check out the Usenet group, where you can share your experiences and wisdom.

**Web:**
**http://rampages.onramp.net/~bevhamil/singleparentresourcece_478.html**

**Usenet:**
**alt.support.single-parents**

## Step-Parents Support

Being a step-parent is always a difficult job with no guarantee that it will be rewarding. However, you don't have to be on your own. On Usenet, you can find a whole group of people who are having the same types of experiences as you. Take some time to talk, share your ideas and experiences.

**Usenet:**
**alt.support.step-parents**

## Things to Do During Summer Vacation

Ah, the good old summertime: the time of sunshine, lemonade, trips to the local swimming hole, and running in and out of the house, driving your parents crazy. Note to parents: Once you have an Internet connection, you will never have to worry about your kids getting bored. Start them at this web site, and they will find many ways to stay busy for hours with indoor and outdoor activities, food and recipes, garden projects, craft ideas, and more.

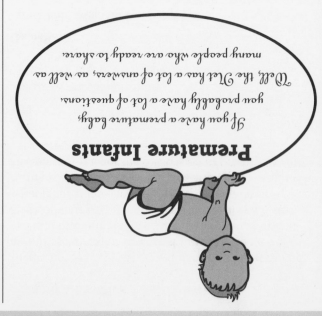

**Web:**
**http://ok.bc.ca./ten/summer/mainpage.html**

**There are two types of things your children can be doing during summer vacation:**

**(1)** Educational, entertaining activities that are safe.

**(2)** Fun stuff they won't tell you about.

As a parent, it's your job to make sure that your children spend as much time as possible staying on the Net and out of trouble.

## Twins and Triplets

The nice thing about multiple births is that you can have all your kids at once. No more Lamaze classes, no more packing the emergency hospital bag, no more late-night frantic phone calls to family members. Yes, now that you have lots and lots of babies on your hands you can rest easy (sort of). The web site has a question and answer forum for parents of triplets (or more). The Usenet group is for the discussion of raising multiple birth children.

**Web:**

**http://www.inreach.com/triplets/question.html**

**Usenet:**

**alt.parenting.twins-triplets**

## Vacationing With Children

When you plan your next vacation, include reading Usenet to find out helpful hints on how to make traveling with your children easier. Find money-saving ideas, new ways to entertain kids while on the road, information on travel safety as well as funny travel anecdotes from parents.

**Usenet:**

**misc.kids.vacation**

# FAQs (FREQUENTLY ASKED QUESTION LIST)

## Anti-FAQ FAQ

If you are one of those people who believe that the main purpose of a FAQ is to convey useful or interesting information, you may be troubled by all the useless FAQs out there. If so, you may enjoy reading the anti-FAQ FAQ: an question and answer essay discussing what makes a FAQ useless and why such creative abominations should be deplored. Before you create your own FAQ, you might want to read this FAQ. In a negative way, it does give some good hints about being relevant and useful. Perhaps the most important comment is that "There is no such thing as a bigshot on the Net."

**Web:**

**http://www.ptbo.igs.net/~shawn/anti-faq.html**

## Automatic FAQ Posting

If you maintain a FAQ, you will want to know about the **auto-faq** script. This script is designed to post a FAQ to Usenet groups automatically. It allows you a large amount of control by specifying particular values in a configuration file. Another benefit is that, if you use this script, your FAQ will comply with all the requirements for posting to **news.answers** and the other ***.answers** groups.

**Web:**

**http://www.novia.net/~pschleck/auto-faq/**

## FAQ FAQ

"A FAQ FAQ? What's a FAQ FAQ? I don't need no stinking FAQ FAQ." Well, yes, you do. The FAQ FAQ is a list of questions and answers about FAQs. It explains the history of FAQs, and gives you tips and hints for writing and maintaining a FAQ. If you get the urge, one of the most useful things you can do for the Net is to maintain a FAQ. If you would like to try, this is the place to start.

**Web:**

**http://www.cis.ohio-state.edu/hypertext/faq/usenet/faqs/about-faqs/faq.html**
**http://www.cs.ruu.nl/wais/html/na-dir/faqs/about-faqs.html**
**http://www.lib.ox.ac.uk/internet/news/faq/archive/faqs.about-faqs.html**

She looked up from her computer as I came in, and I caught a whiff of exotic oriental perfume. She smiled seductively: red hair, green eyes and voluptuous body with enough curves to cause a cardiovascular accident in a giraffe.

"I want the program," I said.

"What program?" she asked.

"Don't get smart with me, sister. You know what program. The program to automatically post my FAQs to Usenet."

She wrote down an address on a piece of paper.

"All you have to do is connect to this web site," she said. "But isn't there anything else you want? I know my way around the Net better than anyone. Just let me work with you, and I'll get you anything you want."

"Sorry, kid, but I work alone."

"Are you sure?" she said. "I have a lot more to offer. Are you positive there isn't anything else?"

I took the paper and headed for the door.

"Just the FAQs, ma'am."

FAQs

## FAQ Finder

This is a great site, whether you are looking for a FAQ on a particular topic, or just something new and interesting to read. Choose a category, and you will be shown a list of all the FAQs in that subject area. Click on the one you want, and before you can say "Wow, this is cool," you will be reading the FAQ of your choice. This is a wonderful place to spend time browsing.

**Web:**

**http://ps.superb.net/FAQ/**

## FAQ for the *.answers Usenet Groups

There are a number of Usenet groups devoted to FAQs and other period postings. These principal groups are **news.answers, alt.answers, comp.answers, humanities.answers, misc.answers, rec.answers, sci.answers, soc.answers** and **talk.answers** (often referred to collectively as ***.answers**). Here is a FAQ that explains the purpose and contents of these groups, how to submit new postings, how to join the mailing list for periodic posting maintainers, and where to find archives of postings to the ***.answers** groups.

**Web:**

**http://www.cis.ohio-state.edu/hypertext/faq/usenet/news-answers/introduction/faq.html**
**http://www.cs.ruu.nl/wais/html/na-dir/news-answers/introduction.html**
**http://www.lib.ox.ac.uk/internet/news/faq/archive/news-answers.introduction.html**

## FAQ Maintenance

At first, it would seem easy—and fun—to maintain a FAQ. However, doing a good job can be a lot more work than you might think. To help you, here is a web site devoted to making FAQ maintenance as easy as possible. Read about tools for automatically posting your FAQ to Usenet, producing HTML versions of your FAQ, and coping with electronic mail. There are also links to other Internet resources related to FAQs.

**Web:**

**http://www.qucis.queensu.ca/FAQs/FAQaid/**

## FAQ Talk and General Discussion

The reason for frequently asked question lists is that newcomers to a Usenet discussion group often seem to ask the same questions. Veterans don't mind answering new questions, but nobody wants to explain, over and over and over, what "Unix" means. Through the years, many groups have developed a frequently asked question list (FAQ) that contains all the common questions that have been answered repeatedly in that group. Some FAQs are so large as to be divided into several parts. Whenever you start reading a new group, look for a FAQ to orient yourself. More important, before you post a question to the group, check the FAQ to see if your question has already been answered. The people who maintain FAQs post them regularly, not only to their own group, but to special groups that have been created just to hold FAQs and related material. The **news.answers** group contains FAQs from every possible source. The other **.answers** groups contain FAQs for their respective hierarchies. For example, **comp.answers** contains computer FAQs. When you have a spare moment, check out these groups, especially **alt.answers**. You will see a lot of interesting and strange stuff that you might never encounter otherwise. These groups contain not only FAQs, but important summaries of information not tied to specific Usenet groups.

**Usenet:**

**alt.answers**
**comp.answers**
**misc.answers**
**news.answers**
**rec.answers**
**sci.answers**
**soc.answers**
**talk.answers**

## Finding and Writing FAQs

There are an enormous number of fascinating FAQs on the Net. Sometimes I like nothing better than to find a FAQ I know nothing about and read it just for fun. One way to look for FAQs is to read the **news.answers** Usenet group. Another way is to look on the web for FAQ collections. These resources will show you how to find FAQs on the Net, as well as write and publicize a FAQ of your own.

**Web:**

**http://www.best.com/~ii/internet/faqs.html**
**http://www.jazzie.com/ii/internet/faqs.html**

## Minimal Digest Format FAQ

When you maintain a FAQ, the format you use is important. Using a proper format can make your FAQ compatible with the digest-handling capabilities of certain newsreader programs. It can also allow your FAQ to be read more easily by a web browser. Perhaps most important, using a good format will make it convenient for people to read and understand your work. This FAQ describes a format that is relatively simple but contains the minimal characteristics necessary for a proper FAQ.

**Web:**

**http://www.cis.ohio-state.edu/hypertext/faq/usenet/faqs/minimal-digest-format/faq.html**
**http://www.cs.ruu.nl/wais/html/na-dir/faqs/minimal-digest-format.html**
**http://www.lib.ox.ac.uk/internet/news/faq/archive/faqs.minimal-digest-format.html**

## Periodic Informational Postings List

On Usenet, there are a great many articles that are sent to various discussion groups on a regular basis. For example, there are a lot of FAQs. There are also other types of regularly posted articles, such as lists of various things. You might ask, does anyone collect the names of all the articles that are posted regularly to Usenet? The answer is yes, and this list—called the Period Informational Postings List—is itself posted regularly to Usenet. (Imagine the philosophical implications.) This list is a long one, so here is a web site that makes it easy to find what you want.

**Web:**

**http://www.jazzie.com/ii/internet/lopip.html**

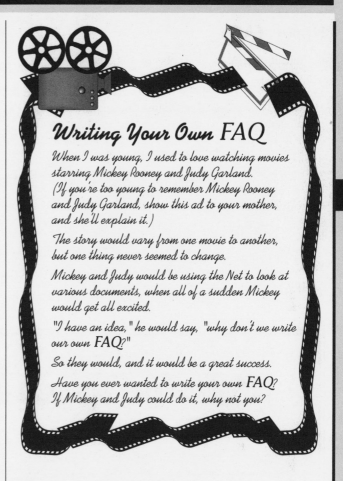

## Submission Guidelines for the *.answers Usenet Groups

If you maintain a FAQ, you will probably want to post it not only to your own Usenet group, but to **news.answers** and possibly one of the other ***.answers** groups. This FAQ explains what you need to do in order to cross-post a FAQ in this manner.

**Web:**

**http://www.cis.ohio-state.edu/hypertext/faq/usenet/news-answers/guidelines/faq.html**
**http://www.cs.ruu.nl/wais/html/na-dir/news-answers/guidelines.html**
**http://www.lib.ox.ac.uk/internet/news/faq/archive/news-answers.guidelines.html**

## Useless FAQs

By definition, FAQs are a collection of answers to frequently asked questions about a particular subject. Thus, each FAQ should be useful—at least to someone. However, since FAQs are created and maintained by people, and people vary widely as to quality, it should come as no surprise that FAQs also vary widely as to quality. If you would like to see the bottom of the virtual barrel, here is a list of the most useless FAQs on the Net. Of course, there are links to each FAQ, so you can explore it for yourself. As to whether or not this collection itself deserves to be included on the list, I leave that to your judgment and good taste.

**Web:**

**http://www.ptbo.igs.net/~shawn/useless-faq.html**

## Usenet FAQ Archives

It's the middle of the night. An emergency arises that requires you to read one of the Usenet frequently asked question lists. So you fire up your favorite newsreader program only to find that the article you want has expired. Never you mind. Many of the Usenet FAQs are available on the Web.

**Web:**

**http://www.cis.ohio-state.edu/hypertext/faq/usenet/top.html**
**http://www.cs.ruu.nl/cgi-bin/faqwais**
**http://www.lib.ox.ac.uk/internet/news/faq/by_group.index.html**

### *Look What I Found on the Net...*

(from the Bra FAQs web site)

You may have heard about a new book which claims that there's a link between bra-wearing and breast cancer. Rest assured that most cancer specialists say the idea is so ludicrous it isn't even worth commenting on.

The authors interviewed more than 4,700 women (roughly half of whom had breast cancer) and found that those who wore bras for 24 hours a day had a 113-fold increase in breast cancer incidence, when compared with women who wear bras less than 12 hours a day.

Based on this, they theorize that constriction from a bra allows toxins to build up in the breasts' lymphatic system, which leads to cancer.

But that premise is unfounded. "Even when a bra fits snugly, it doesn't interfere with the lymphatic drainage of the breast," explains a breast cancer expert Xxxxxx Xxxxxxxx, M.D., professor of surgery at Jefferson Medical College in Philadelphia.

Says Xxxxxxxx Xxxxxxxx, M.D., director of the breast center at the John Wayne Cancer Institute in Santa Monica, California, "Breast cancer has many causes -- hormonal, environmental, genetic and dietary -- but it's likely that wearing bras isn't one of them."

## FASHION AND CLOTHING

### Bra FAQs

A brassiere (or bra) is a women's undergarment whose principal purpose is to lend support to the breasts. As simple as this sounds, choosing the right bra can be a complex and frustrating task. There are many variations of people and by no means does one size fit all. The first modern bra, the Maidenform, was designed in 1922 by Ina Rosenthal and Enid Bissett. (If you are in New York, you can see the original bra on display at the Maidenform Museum.) Here are a series of FAQs devoted to bras, where you can read about coverings, designs, sizes and fitting, health issues, fabrics, fashion, history, trivia and suppliers. There is also a FAQ for underwire bras (bras that provide extra support by having wires underneath the cup or along the rib cage). Helpful Hint from Harley: Bra specialists will tell you that most women—especially large-busted women—are wearing the wrong size bra. When you look for a bra, pay attention to fit and comfort, not style and construction. (In other words, evaluate a bra with your eyes closed.) Extra Hint: For a better fit, lean over as you put on your bra.

**Web:**
**http://www.funhouse.com/babs/FAQ.html**

### Business Fashion

Have you heard of the MBA Style magazine? Well, if you have an MBA, or you want an MBA, or you live with someone who has an MBA, *and* you want to explore the style affected by fashion-conscious MBAs in modern-day American popular culture, this may be the magazine for you. Where else can you go for advice on how to buy a tie for an interview? What are you going to do, ask your mother?

**Web:**
**http://members.aol.com/mbastyle/web/mbastyle.html**

**Clothing Labels**

Have you ever met anyone who actually knows what the labels on clothing really mean? Well, I do, because I read the Clothing Labels document on the Net. True, I don't know everything there is to know about clothing, but I do know enough to be dangerous (and "Danger" is my middle name).

### Clogs

Originally, a "clog" was any shoe made from wood. Such shoes—constructed from a single piece of wood—were developed by the Dutch, who needed footwear that would keep their feet dry while working in wet fields. Today's clogs are made from a variety of materials and the word "clog" has come to refer to a large, backless shoe with a thick, elevated sole. Even the most clog-enamored fanatic can't pretend that these shoes are anything but ugly. However, they do make a satisfying clunk-clunk sound as you lumber from one place to another like an elephant at a Sixties dress-up party. In the Sixties, clogs were practical because they allowed you to walk wherever you wanted, while still retaining the freedom to slip off your shoes at a moment's notice. (You had to be there.)

**Web:**
**http://members.aol.com/clogs01/**

### Clothing and Textile

This list is for State Extension Clothing and Textiles Specialists. It provides a communication link for sharing program ideas and resources. If this is your field of choice, you'll find others with the same expertise.

**Listserv Mailing List:**
List Name: **clotex-l**
Subscribe to: **listserv@unlvm.unl.edu**

### Clothing for Big Folks

Here are the FAQs discussing oversized clothing for the United States, Canada, United Kingdom and Europe. You'll find out how to convert sizes internationally, where to find clothing and shoes for everyday as well as where to shop for wedding and maternity clothing. This information will help women, men and children.

**Web:**
**http://www.math.uio.no/faq/fat-acceptance-faq/clothing/**

### Clothing Labels

Shopping for clothes today can be an international experience. Sometimes it is difficult to understand the labels if you don't know all the facts. Written by an extension clothing specialist, the site helps you shop around the world.

**Web:**
**http://ianrwww.unl.edu/ianr/pubs/nebfacts/nf92-93.htm**

## CNN Style

The world fashion and style has lots of news. If you like to keep up, here is the place to check daily. CNN gathers the fashion news stories of the day—along with pictures—and puts them on the Web just so you can stay one step ahead of what is happening.

**Web:**

**http://www.cnn.com/STYLE/**

## Conservation of Textile Items

If only we all had a valuable textile heirloom, we could consult this site to find out how to preserve it for future use. Special care is required, including an understanding of light, temperature, humidity, storage, cleaning, and keeping insects away.

**Web:**

**http://www.textiles.org/crafts/general/conservation.html**

## Corsets

Do not confuse corsets with girdles. Girdles are a modern undergarment made out of elastic material. Corsets have been used from time immemorial and are more extreme. Corsets incorporate a series of reinforcements called "stays", in order to bind the breasts, waist and hips into a particular desired shape. At one time, corsets were extremely popular, and the image of a Victorian woman needing help to lace up and tighten her corset is one that does little to make us nostalgic. However, corsets were an important fashion accoutrement that, even today, have their admirers. If you are one of them—or if you would like to see some pictures of corsets and the women who wore them—take a look at these web pages.

**Web:**

**http://imgnet.com/corset/**
**http://www.dnaco.net/~aleed/corsets/links.html**

## Cosmetic Label

Everyone has wondered whether or not their shampoo or lotion bottle is telling the truth when it lists the ingredients. Most average consumers probably don't even know what sodium lauryl sulfate is. Look here for help if you're not a chemist or a cosmetics engineer.

**Web:**

**http://vm.cfsan.fda.gov/~dms/cos-labl.html**

## Designer Clothing

All clothes, of course, are designed by somebody. But only certain clothes are designed by a Designer: a recognized member of the fashion elite. At the beginning of a Designer's career, he or she actually creates the designs. However, as the Designer's fame (and marketing success) increases, the temptation increases to license one's name in order to make more money. For example, does anyone actually believe that Donna Karan eyeglass frames are actually designed by Ms. Karan? Why do people pay more money—sometimes a lot more money—to buy designer clothing? Call it one part quality and one part fashion, mixed with snobbery, ignorance, a need to be trendy, all cooked in a broth of marketing, marketing, marketing. Would you like to talk about it? Here's the Usenet group for you.

**Usenet:**

**alt.clothes.designer**

## Fabrice Magazine

The Fabrice Magazine web site is an outlandish, visual experience: a collection of pictures that push the accepted envelope of fashion in order to explore a new and outrageous world. If you like to stand out from the crowd in such a way that people look at you, wrinkle their noses, and say, "Oooohhh, look at *her*," this is the perfect place to look for ideas for your prom dress.

**Web:**

**http://bytesizemag.com/fabrice/fabrice.htm**

**Need a quick refresher?**

***Immerse yourself for ten minutes in the visually stimulating fashion and images at Fabrice.***

## FAD Magazine

FAD is an online magazine devoted to images and articles that blur the line between visual fashion and sensuality. This is a place to visit when you have time to enjoy carefully constructed images and words. Leave the mundane, ordinary world of responsibility and immerse yourself in the fantasy of what might be.

**Web:**

**http://www.fadmag.com/**

## Fantasy Costume

Everyone has a fantasy costume idea. This mailing list concentrates on the design and production of fantasy clothing. Let your imagination run free and think about what you may have worn in your past lives and what you'd like to wear in the future.

**Majordomo Mailing List:**

List Name: **f-costume**
Subscribe to: **majordomo@world.std.com**

## Fashion Internet

Fashion Internet is an online fashion magazine with a selection of features on fashion and beauty. If you like reading regular fashion magazines, you will enjoy browsing at this web site. Lots of information: health, designers, advice, entertainment reviews, and much more. In addition, you will find the same sort of articles about life, men and fashion that provide the lifeblood of women's magazine everywhere.

**Web:**

**http://www.finy.com/**

## Fashion Net

So you've read already everything in this month's Vogue? No need to be bored. Spend some time at Fashion Net and you will find plenty of food for fashionable thought: magazines, entertainment, modeling, shopping, beauty sites, fashion houses, fashion shows, photographers, Usenet groups, message boards, links and job listings.

**Web:**

**http://www.fashion.net/**

## Fashion Page

This web site is published by a fashion maven whose itinerary includes visits to runways in London and other parts of England. You can also follow links to get fashion TV reviews, commentary on what's new and exciting, as well as those always useful Christmas shopping tips for men.

**Web:**

**http://www.charm.net/~jakec/**

## Fashion Talk and General Discussion

It's a nice feeling when you're dressed in a spiffy new outfit with all the right accessories and people turn to look as you walk down the street. Impress your friends, family, and total strangers with your fashion sense and the clothing tips you've learned while hanging out on the Internet. Clothing pros, trendsetters, and the hopelessly unfashionable find their way to these newsgroups to share ideas or get answers to questions.

**Usenet:**

**alt.fashion**

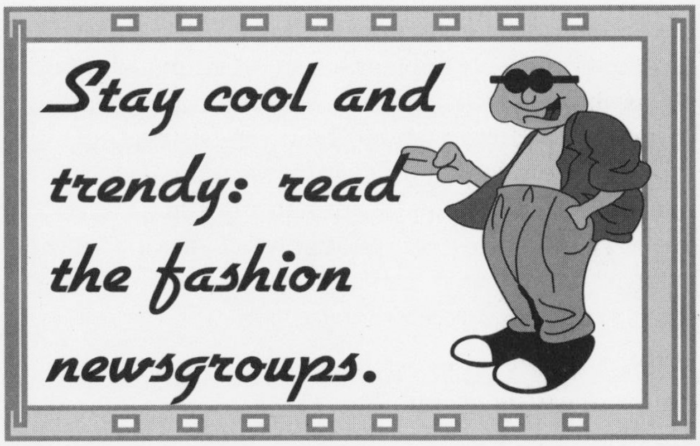
Stay cool and trendy: read the fashion newsgroups.

**Lost?**
**Try a search engine.**

A B C D E F G H I J K L M N O P Q R S T U V W X Y Z

## Fashionstance

Fashionstance is an online magazine, created to portray and explain the world of fashion and style from the consumer point of view. (However, this is still heavy duty stuff, most suitable for fanatics.) Read tips on make-up, hair, skin, nails, clothing trends, perfumes, seasonal fashion news and new products. In addition, you will find collections of links to fashion-related resources around the Net.

**Web:**
**http://www.users.wineasy.se/bjornt/fshead.html**

## Fur

Fur has been a part of the human wardrobe for a very long time. In recent years, however, it has become fashionable to sneer at those who are crude enough to actually wear the skin of a dead animal when they could have perfectly good synthetic clothing made from petroleum products. The fur industry, as you might imagine, takes such trends seriously. Here they are fighting back—a web page devoted to furs, furs and more furs—news, magazines, articles about the latest styles and materials, pictures of models wearing furs, and so on. Moreover, when you are tired of reading about furs and looking at pictures of clothes you will never, ever be able to afford, you can take a few moments and get "the real scoop on animal rights". My opinion is that, before the animal rights people complain too loudly about the fur industry, they might want to look a little closer to home. Do you have any idea how many animals are slaughtered every year just to create enough electrons to run the Internet?

**Web:**
**http://www.furs.com/**

**Wow, free software.**

## Girdles

A girdle is a woman's undergarment, made from an elastic material. The purpose of a girdle is to shape the woman's figure from the waist to the thighs. Some girdles also have clips that are used to hold up stockings. At once time, it was common for a woman to wear a girdle in order to make her body look slim (well, relatively slim), and to create that sleek, flat look admired by men. Girdles are also used to mold a body so as to make it suitable for encasing in tight, narrow clothing. Finally, a girdle contains the buttocks and upper thighs. Put simply, a woman with a girdle does not jiggle. One big disadvantage of a girdle is that it can bind in an uncomfortable manner, although a properly fitting garment is easier to wear. However, what spelled the end of the girdle as a ubiquitous fashion supplement was the miniskirt, which became popular in the late sixties. Logistically, it is difficult to conceal a girdle under a miniskirt. However, girdles do have their admirers and, to tell you the truth, they have never entirely gone out of fashion. For information about girdles, including observations based in extensive personal experience, take a look at these web sites.

**Web:**
**http://www-unix.oit.umass.edu/~matt/acl/girdle-faq.html**
**http://www-unix.oit.umass.edu/~matt/acl/girdles-suzanne-2.html**
**http://www-unix.oit.umass.edu/~matt/acl/girdles-suzanne.html**

## Gothic Fashion

Stop here for a complete discussion of such tricky topics like saving bleached hair, when to wear those pointy boots, and whether kinky or straight hair is the most Gothic. Just when you think you've dreamed up a new color to dye your hair, someone has beaten you to it.

**Usenet:**
**alt.gothic.fashion**

## Hair Care

Do you look good? Do you want to? Consult this web site if you want to be in style, look good, and be the envy of everyone on the Net.

**Web:**
**http://www.hairnet.com/**

### *Look What I Found on the Net...*

```
Newsgroup: alt.gothic.fashion
Subject: Witch Shoes

I saw this pair of shoes I fell in love with.  Unfortunately,
they were on another girl.

They were black patent "witch shoes" also called granny boots,
with a thick heel that curved down in a Victorian style.

Do any mail-order places have these?  I have a pair in black
suede, but the heels are straight as opposed to curved.
```

## Historical Costuming

There's nothing that I like more than dressing up in an authentic historical costume—bell bottoms, love beads and a tie-dyed T-shirt—and walking around the house affecting an attitude as cool as a Canadian winter. However, this is nothing compared to what real historical costume buffs do to relax. Here are a couple of web sites on which you can find lots of information about historical costuming. Just the place to look when you need to find a Renaissance-style crossbow or complete your research into what type of underwear women wore in the fifteenth century.

**Web:**

**http://digital.net/~milieux/costume.html**
**http://digital.net/~milieux/supplies/websupplies.html**

## Hypermode

What is Hypermode? There is no good answer here. You have to look and listen and watch and make up your own mind. I guess that Hypermode has something to with fashion. Check it out: pictures, advice, pictures, fashion, pictures, feature articles, pictures, raw urban streetstyle, pictures... you get the idea.

**Web:**

**http://www.hypermode.com/**

## Lingerie

Lingerie is fun and sexy, but the bad thing about it is you can't parade around outdoors while wearing it. Or at least you're not supposed to. For discussion about garments that you wear for limited viewing, check out this Usenet group, where they talk about things with straps and things with no straps, garments that hold you in and ones that let you hang out, and outfits that make you look naked even when you're not.

**Usenet:**

**alt.clothing.lingerie**

Are you one of those people who sees a beautiful woman and says, "Put it on, put it on"?

If so, **alt.clothing.lingerie** is for you.

A B C D E F G H I J K L M N O P Q R S T U V W X Y Z

## Lipstick

Lipstick is something we are all used to. However, like many areas of the fashion world, the more you think about it, the more strange the idea seems. The best solution, then, is not to think about it. Just use lipstick and enjoy. One way to enjoy is to look at this lipstick-oriented web site. Read about tips and consumer issues, explore other links to cosmetic-related resources, look in the lipstick library of color choices, and much, much more. If you would enjoy knowing which lipstick shades and brands are used by famous models and movie stars, this is the place for you.

**Web:**

**http://www.users.wineasy.se/bjornt/lip.html**

## Look Online

This is serious fashion industry stuff—news—upcoming events—site reviews—fashion resources—New York industry gossip—exclusive runway photos—this is serious stuff—life in a very expensive, designer-oriented fast, fast lane. It leaves me breathless.

**Web:**

**http://www.lookonline.com/**

## Lumière

Lumière is a monthly magazine containing a variety of articles relating to fashion and beauty. And not just everyday fashion—"upscale" fashion (translation: innovative, high quality, expensive). Enjoy articles from past issues on such topics as ready to wear collections, casual dress for work, wardrobes, designer profiles, and reviews of makeup and perfume.

**Web:**

**http://www.lumiere.com/**

## Lycra

Yes, it's true. There is a discussion group for fans of lycra and spandex. If you have something to contribute or are just curious about the lycra culture, check out the Usenet group. For some lycra-oriented exploration, try the web site.

**Web:**

**http://www2.best.com/~invncble/altlycra.html**

**Usenet:**

**alt.lycra**

## Modeling Hints and Information

The modeling industry is very hard to break into. And it is even harder to earn a living as a model. Moreover, regardless of what you see in the magazines, the job is not at all glamorous—just ask any professional model. So, do you *still* want to be a model? Well, okay. Here's a web site that contains a variety of useful information. Hints on how to become a successful model, information about photoshoots, hairstyling, makeup, and much more, including how to avoid scams.

**Web:**

**http://www.models-online.com/Gateway/News/RealA.html**

### Modeling *Hints* and *Information*

**Want to be a model? It's easy.**

(1) Connect to the Net and read all the useful hints and information.

(2) Each time you show up for an interview, take a copy of a Harley Hahn book to read while you are waiting.

When your interviewer sees the book, he or she will be so impressed, you will be able to name your own price.

## N-touch Magazine

N-touch is an online style magazine produced by students in the B.A. Fashion Promotion course at London College of Fashion. If you're unsure about the current fashion in London, the trends in cosmetic surgery or what part of your body to have pierced next, read about it all in N-touch.

**Web:**

**http://www.dircon.co.uk/lcf/ntouch.html**

## Sewing Talk and General Discussion

Some people are truly amazing. They lose a button or tear their hem while waiting in line at the grocery store and, out of nowhere, they whip out a little sewing kit and make the repair before the checker can say "paper or plastic". Whether you are a sewing fanatic or just a sewing wannabe, stop in at this Usenet group and read the latest talk about sewing and textiles.

**Usenet:**
**rec.crafts.textiles.sewing**

## Shoes

The same foot can be a size 8, size 25 or size 85 depending on who you ask. If you're confused, look at the comparative shoe size charts at this site. Take a walk through the United States, Canada, United Kingdom, continental Europe and Japan and find out your local size.

**Web:**
**http://funnelweb.utcc.utk.edu/~lyle/shoe.html**

## Sneakers

When you've run out of useful things to do, check out the Internet resources on sneakers. You'll find dialog on different brands of running shoes, what sneaker to buy and how to deal with stinky feet.

**Web:**
**http://sneakers.pair.com/**
**http://www.fokus.gmd.de/dst/Security/sneakers/**

**Usenet:**
**alt.clothing.sneakers**

## Streetstyle

Are you disconnected from the official fashion world? Do you feel that what passes for corporate fashion might just as well pass away? Would you like to make your own personal fashion statement on a limited budget? Streetstyle is for you. Streetstyle—anti-corporate, anti-runway fashion. Do you think you could create a *look* for yourself using economical, readily available clothes and accessories from a chain store in a mall? Look at this site to get inspired, then go shopping.

**Web:**
**http://www.best.com/~street/**

## Supermodels and Photos

Maybe you can never be too rich or too thin, but why not check it out first? See photos and learn what being a supermodel is all about. If you still think that you've got what it takes, remember, no dinner for you tonight.

**Web:**
**http://thunder.ocis.temple.edu/~svarughe/supermodels.html**
**http://www.supermodel.com/**

**Usenet:**
**alt.supermodels**

### Free Offer: Get Your Own Supermodel

Would you like your own supermodel? I have arranged a special offer just for my readers. Here is what you need to do.

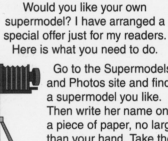

Go to the Supermodels and Photos site and find a supermodel you like. Then write her name on a piece of paper, no larger than your hand. Take the paper, put it in this book at this exact page, close the book, and put it under your pillow when you go to sleep tonight.

Tomorrow morning, there will be a message on your answering machine from that particular supermodel. The message will tell you where and when you can meet her in person. If for some reason you do not get a message, try again the next night.

Disclaimer: Sorry, this offer is not valid if you do not have an answering machine.

## Textiles Mailing List

You can make it a hobby, a science, or a way of life. This list covers the development, science, chemistry, engineering, technology, and management of textiles. Discussion is open to any researchers, students, academics, or industrialists who are interested in clothing and textiles.

**Listserv Mailing List:**
List Name: **textiles**
Subscribe to: **listserv@vm3090.ege.edu.tr**

## Textiles Reference Material

There is a ton of printed information on textiles, sewing and fashion. And someone has compiled the information for you. See this list of books and periodicals covering topics such as sewing, tailoring, men's fashion, quick tips, fitting, and pattern drafting.

**Web:**

**http://www.cs.ruu.nl/wais/html/na-dir/crafts/textiles/books/.html**

## Textiles Talk and General Discussion

Rough and soft, shiny and crinkled, textiles come in a variety of colors, weights, and textures. Some are made from natural materials like plants and animals or even metal. Others are invented in a lab, fibers woven out of who-knows-what kind of synthetic material with a 12-syllable name. Fashion designers, students, people who sew, or just folks who love fashion—you will find them all on Usenet.

**Usenet:**

**rec.crafts.textiles.misc**

### Victorian Fashion

Back in the nineteenth century, Queen Victoria and her husband Prince Albert were the fashion trend-setters of the day.

Victoria and Albert could wear whatever they wanted and, instantly, that would become the new fashion.

However, Queen Victoria's temper was legendary, and nobody wanted to show up at an official function wearing something that was out of fashion.

So how could everyone else keep up on the latest trends? Easy. All they had to do was connect to the Net and check the Victorian Fashion web site.

## T@p Style

T@p is an online magazine published by the largest college marketing company in the United States. Its target is the huge 18-24 year old Generation X college market. If you are a Generation X college student, and you would like to look at a graphically rich online publication aimed directly at you (and your money), here is a direct connection to T@p's "style" section: fashion talk written and illustrated by people who are definitely plugged in (to something anyway).

**Web:**

**http://www.taponline.com/tap/culture/style/**

## Victorian Fashion

The Victorian Age is named after England's Queen Victoria who ruled for sixty-four years, from 1837-1901. During these sixty-four years, a collection of style and behavior patterns developed that we refer to as Victorian culture. Along with the culture came a definite set of guidelines as to what proper people should wear and not wear. Even today, Victorian fashion has its admirers. If you would like to find out more, check this web site where you will find information about making Victorian clothing, lists of companies that sell Victorian patterns, hints on how to wear frillies (underwear) and corsets, lists of accessories and where to find them, a bibliography, and links to related resources on the Net. By the way, within the royal household, the champion of taste was not Queen Victoria, but her consort Prince Albert—the Princess Diana of his time.

**Web:**

**http://leia.factory.com/princess/victorian/victorian.html**

**Get into "Mischief".**

## Vintage Clothing and Costume Jewelry

If you save something long enough, it will come back into style. (Unless it's from the '70s. . . in that case, you will just have to take your chances.) Vintage clothing is fun. Some people collect it for preservation. Others acquire vintage clothing and costume jewelry to actually wear and create unique combinations that are interesting and attractive. Join the rest of the clothes scavengers and compare notes on all subjects relating to vintage clothing and costume jewelry. The web site houses the archives for the **vintage** mailing list.

**Web:**

**http://www.cs.brown.edu/people/smh/vintage/vintage.html**

**Listserv Mailing List:**

List Name: **vintage**
Subscribe to: **listserv@brownvm.brown.edu**

# FINDING STUFF ON THE NET

## Altavista

Altavista. An awesome search engine. Searches the entire Web and all of Usenet. Finds everything. Knows about everything. Awesome. Totally awesome. I use it every day. Altavista. Amazing.

**Web:**

**http://altavista.digital.com/**

## Anysearch

Anysearch is a tool that makes using a search engine fast and easy. Once you install the program, it attaches itself to your browser, creating a button and a small text-entry box in a convenient location near the regular browser controls. The button shows the name of a default search engine. To send a query to that search engine, all you need to do is type the words you are looking for in the box, and then press the Enter key. To go to the home page for that engine, simply click on the button. At any time, it is easy to change your default search engine. Anysearch is simple, easy to use, and effective.

**Web:**

**http://www.webdirectory.com/**

## Argus Clearinghouse

A massive collection of subject-oriented guides to Internet resources. Select the category in which you are interested, and you are shown a large list of resources, which is easy to skim quickly to look for what you want.

**Web:**

**http://www.clearinghouse.net/**

### Everything About Anything: Now Available

"Clearinghouses" are usually rest stops for people who would rather put together the work of other people (usually on government money) than contribute anything of their own (which requires original thinking). But the Argus Clearinghouse is a job well done and definitely belongs on your web hotlist.

This resource was put together by librarians and includes a wonderful set of guides, authored by various people, that will point you to information about just about any important topic you can imagine. This resource is perfect for those times when the boss is in a meeting, and you have to look like you are hard at work at your computer.

(And tonight, before you go to bed, be sure to give a silent moment of thanks to librarians—the chronically underpaid elves of the Internet—who are not appreciated nearly as much as they should be.)

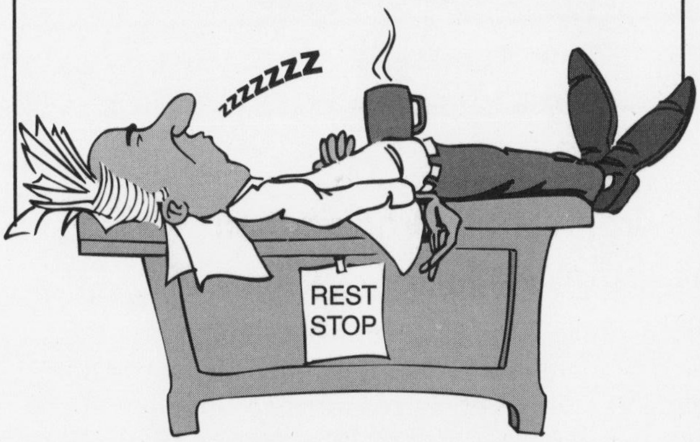
zzzzzz
REST STOP

**Don't click here.**

A B C D E F G H I J K L M N O P Q R S T U V W X Y Z

## Deja News

Deja News is a gargantuan collection of indexed, archived, searchable Usenet news items. You can search for keywords in message titles, or the text of articles. If you are looking for anything that someone said in the recent past, what you want is here somewhere.

**Web:**
**http://www.dejanews.com/**

**If it's worth saying (and, even more so, if it's not worth saying), someone on Usenet has probably said it lately. Use the Usenet News Searches facility and find out what people have been saying in places you would never even think of looking.**

## Environmental Organization Webdirectory

If you are looking for anything at all related to the environment, this is the place to start. There are lots and lots of items organized into appropriate categories. Is it possible that the method of presentation borrowed heavily from what we might call the "Yahoo look and feel"? Never mind. The pages are prettier and the ads are a lot more attractive.

**Web:**
**http://www.webdirectory.com/**

## Excite

Excite is a large, ambitious project that lets you find oodles of information in several different ways. Primarily, you can use the search engine to search the Web or Usenet. You can also read the news and access travel and reference information. The silliest aspect of the whole site, however, are the reviews. Someone got it in their head that it would be a good idea to have professional writers review web sites (in the manner of movies or TV shows). For a good laugh, head for the area that reviews the web sites of "Happy Couples". (Look under "Personal Home Pages".) Overall, I guess Excite is a good resource, but the in-your-face design wears me out.

**Web:**
**http://www.excite.com/**

## FTP Search

If you understand the anonymous ftp system, you will want to know about FTP Search. It offers a web-based interface that is much easier to use than the original text-based archie or any archie client I have ever seen. Moreover, it is fast. The days of slow awkward archie searches are gone forever. Searching the worldwide ftp archives is now as easy as falling off a virtual log (three years too late).

**Web:**
**http://ftpsearch.ntnu.no/ftpsearch**

## Galaxy

Galaxy, one of my personal favorites, is a large collection of web pages. The Galaxy people do not go looking for resources. They include only those sites that are submitted to them. However, the database is especially well organized and has a lot of useful resources. Unlike some of the other catalogs, Galaxy contains only links—there are no descriptions. However, the material is good, and there is none of the junk you will find when you do a blind search through all of the larger databases. Anyway, who needs descriptions? My philosophy is, if I want a description, I'll write it myself.

**Web:**
**http://galaxy.einet.net/galaxy.html**

## Hotbot

Hotbot is a souped-up, high-performance search engine. Hotbot is okay for simple queries, but where it really shines is for serious fanatical searching. If you take the time to learn the nuances, you can even make Hotbot dance. Let's just say that when Hotbot and Altavista die, they will probably both end up in the same part of heaven.

**Web:**

**http://www.hotbot.com/**

## How to Use Search Engines

A search engine is a program that allows you to search a database quickly. All of the well-known Internet search tools (Yahoo, Altavista, Lycos, Excite, and so on) are search engines. Here is information about the various search engines, along with a wealth of advice on how to use them effectively. If you find yourself spending too much time floundering around, take a few moments and read these articles.

**Web:**

**http://issfw.palomar.edu/Library/TGSEARCH.HTM**
**http://www.monash.com/spidap.html**

## In Reference

A lot of what happens on the Net takes place in Usenet and on the mailing lists. If you are only looking at the Web, you are missing a lot. And, when you are looking for something, if you only search on the Web, you will miss everything that goes on in one of the thousands of Usenet groups and mailing lists. In Reference is a service dedicated to searching Usenet and mailing lists. Aside from searching the current contents of Usenet and the lists, you can submit a permanent "stored query". The In Reference computer will remember your query and run it at pre-selected intervals. Whenever anything appears that matches your search pattern, In Reference will send you mail. It's like having a free electronic clipping service.

**Web:**

**http://www.reference.com/**

### How to Use Search Engines

You can find just about anything you want on the Net—if you know what you are doing. One of the biggest tips I can give you is to spend some time learning how to use the various Internet search engines. (A search engine is a program that can look through an entire database of information quickly.)

There are a number of companies that maintain databases containing information about all the web pages on the Net. (You can imagine what a job it is keeping such databases up to date.) These companies allow anyone to use their search engines for free—they make their money from advertising.

For example, if you want information about me, you can use a search engine to look for the words "Harley Hahn". The results of the search will be a set of links to all the web pages in that particular database that contain these words. To visit these pages, all you have to do is click on the links that look interesting.

My advice is to pick the search engines you like the best and learn how to use them well. Because the databases are so large, it is common to have your search return many spurious items that you will have to ignore. However, there are ways to make your request more sophisticated, which will get you better results.

In my experience, any time you spend learning how to use a tool well is time well spent.

## Infoseek

Infoseek is a general purpose search engine (like Altavista, Lycos, Yahoo, and so on). I find the organization and presentation confusing, but then, I'm a simple fellow. Try it for yourself and see if you like it.

**Web:**

**http://www.infoseek.com/**

## Internet Consulting Detective

Check with this site every couple of weeks, and you will find hints on how to search the Net for what you want. The motif is based on a Sherlock Holmes theme. To test your skill, you can try to solve a Internet searching problem sent in by one of the readers.

**Web:**

**http://www.intermediacy.com/sherlock/**

A B C D E F G H I J K L M N O P Q R S T U V W X Y Z

## Internic Directory of Directories

There is no central directory (of anything) on the Internet. However, the Internic—Internet Network Information Center—does maintain a large number of directories in various areas. Take a few minutes and browse, and I guarantee you will find something interesting.

**Web:**

**http://ds.internic.net/cgi-bin/tochtml/0intro.dirofdirs/**

## Lycos, Point and A2Z

Lycos, Point and A2Z are search facilities from a single source (the Lycos company) that present information from a huge database in three completely different ways. Lycos proper is a search engine that allows you to search the entire Web, looking for a specific word or phrase. A2Z and Point are more selective. A2Z only shows you web sites that are referenced from many other web sites. (I guess they feel these are the most important resources.) Point is more ambitious. Its goal is to list the top 5% of all web sites, ignoring anything that doesn't meet the editorial standards. Unlike Lycos—which is a brute force search engine—both A2Z and Point show a specially created description/review of each resource. Point also offers various ratings (content, presentation, experience), all of which you can safely ignore. The best advice I can give you is to spend some time at Lycos, become familiar with all three search facilities, and see which one you like the best.

**Web:**

**http://a2z.lycos.com/**
**http://www.lycos.com/**
**http://www.pointcom.com/**

Mailing List Search Engines

(A mailing list is a discussion group in which messages are sent to the participants via email.)

Here is my one-step plan for total happiness:

1: Check with a mailing list search engine, and subscribe to the list of your dreams.

Pretty soon your mailbox will be overflowing, and your happiness will be unbounded.

## Mailing List Search Engines

The Net has tens of thousands of different mailing lists, with more being added all the time. A mailing list is a forum for the discussion of a particular topic. Mailing lists differ from Usenet in that all the messages are distributed to participants by electronic mail. (With Usenet, messages are posted to various groups, which you can access with your web browser or a special-purpose newsreader program.) To participate in a mailing list, you must subscribe (which is free). Once you subscribe, all the messages that are posted to the list will be sent to your mailbox. If you get tired of being on the list, you can unsubscribe at any time. Although the first mailing lists were administered by people, most modern lists (and all the ones listed in this book) are managed by computer programs. The three most popular such programs are Listserv, Majordomo and Listproc. I have included a great many mailing lists as resources in this book. However, there are times when you may want to perform a search of your own. To help you, here are my favorite mailing list search engines.

**Web:**

**http://catalog.com/vivian/interest-group-search.html**
**http://www.liszt.com/**
**http://www.neosoft.com/internet/paml/**
**http://www.tile.net/tile/listserv/**

## Nerd World

Nerd World is another of the large databases of Internet resources. However, there are three reasons why you may want to use it rather than spending all your time at Altavista, Yahoo, Lycos or whatever. (1) Nerd World was designed by someone who knows what he is doing. In particular, this nerd understands how to organize and present information. (2) There is a lot of information, but not too much. (3) In the world of business and power, Nerds are an under-represented minority and deserve your support.

**Web:**

**http://www.nerdworld.com/**

**Read a zine today.**

## Netscape Destinations

The Netscape company has compiled a small but well-organized catalog of useful links. Their intention, of course, is to show off their technology and to sell ad space. However, this is a useful site, which you may be able to use to find what you want more quickly than using a search engine or a huge catalog.

**Web:**

**http://www.netscape.com/escapes/**

## New Stuff Talk and General Discussion

These two Usenet groups are good places to look for new and interesting Net resources. The **net-happenings** group is moderated and well-organized. This group is as close to an official place to announce a new resource as exists on the Net. There is *always* something interesting here. The **www.announce** group is not moderated, and is used by the general population to post notices about new Web sites.

**Usenet:**

**comp.infosystems.www.announce**
**comp.internet.net-happenings**

## Research It!

Here is a collection of tools that almost defies description (but that never stopped me). On one web page you will find easy to use forms to search a variety of Internet resources: language tools (dictionaries, thesauruses, acronym finders, translators, you can even conjugate French verbs); biography; geography (including zip codes and area codes); financial information (currency exchange, ticker symbols, stock quotes); and more. This is an interesting place to explore, just to get an appreciation of the type of useful reference information that is available for free on the Net.

**Web:**

**http://www.itools.com/research-it/**

## Search Engine Collections

These sites are not search engines. Rather, they are web pages that contain a list of links to search engines. Although some people find such services useful, my experience is that—if you do a lot of searching—it is probably easier to find one or two favorite engines and learn how to use them well. However, if you are an occasional searcher, you may like the one-size-fits-all setup. At the very least, I'm sure you will appreciate how some of these services select advertisements to show you based on the keywords in your search. How thoughtful.

**Web:**

**http://metasearch.com/**
**http://miso.wwa.com/~boba/search.html**
**http://nln.com/**
**http://www.albany.net/allinone/**
**http://www.search.com/**
**http://www.stpt.com/**

## Webring

Webring is cool. Very cool. It consists of hundreds of virtual "rings", each of which is devoted to a particular topic and contains a number of web sites; for example: "Comic Book Ring", "The Official Ring of Games", "Female Empowerment Ring", "Adoption Ring", and so on. Here is how it works. You start by checking the index of rings for a topic that interests you. You then connect to the first site on whichever ring you want. At the bottom of the page, there is an icon you can select to move to the next site on the ring. Eventually, if you visit all the sites, you end up where you started. However, in the process, you will have jumped all over the Net. If you would like to your site to be part of Webring, you can register it. Your site will then be placed in a particular ring. Next, you must put the Webring icons at the bottom of your web page. These icons actually point back to the main Webring computer, where a special program figures out which is the next site in the ring. The Webring program handles all the details automatically, adding and deleting web sites from rings as the need arises.

**Web:**

**http://www.webring.org/**

A B C D E F G H I J K L M N O P Q R S T U V W X Y Z

### Search Engine Collections

So your best friend is always bragging about his rare stamps. And your uncle Henry loves to talk about his original signed lithographs.

But the worst is a guy you knew in high school, who never misses a chance to go on and on about the antique cars he has gathered over the years.

Well, here's your chance to get even. Invite them all over to see your collection of Internet search engines.

That'll show them who's cool.

## WWW Virtual Library

This is a large subject catalog. It's organized on a "distributed" basis, which means that various people around the Net volunteer to host different subjects at their sites. You will find a *lot* of resources here, from aboriginal studies to zoos.

**Web:**
**http://www.w3.org/pub/DataSources/bySubject/**

## Xplore

Xplore was designed to be "the easiest Internet Guide available". (I suppose they are referring to its ease of use, not its morality.) The idea is to have a catalog consisting of the 500 best sites on the Web. The concept is interesting and a lot more ambitious than you might expect. (Try finding the 500 best sites, and you will see what I mean. In fact, just try figuring out what you might mean by "best".) Anyway, when you get a moment, check out Xplore and see what you think. As you might imagine, Xplore is not comprehensive, but it does provide a way to get to good web sites fast. If you like the service, perhaps we might all chip in and buy them a vowel.

**Web:**
**http://www.xplore.com/**

## Yahoo

Yahoo was the first of the modern web searching tools. To this day, Yahoo is still one of *the* places for searching the Net. They have a huge database of resources that you can access by choosing a category, or by looking for a specific word or phrase. You can also click on various icons to immediately see certain information, such as news headlines. (This is the fastest way I know to read an up-to-date news summary.) Learning to use Yahoo well is one of the first steps to becoming a knowledgeable, useful member of the Internet community.

**Web:**
**http://www.yahoo.com/**

## Yahooligans

This is the kids' version of the famous Yahoo site. As with the main site, you can find resources by selecting a category, or by searching the database for a specific word or phrase. There are lots and lots (and lots) of resources for kids here. Warning #1: This site contains advertisements directed towards children. (Someone has to pay.) Warning #2: If you join the club (Club Yahooligans), you will be put on a mailing list.

**Web:**
**http://www.yahooligans.com/**

# FOLKLORE, MYTHS AND LEGENDS

## Atlantis

It all started with the Greek philosopher Plato (427-347 B.C.). He wrote two dialogues, Timeaus and Critias, in which Socrates, Hermocrates, Timeaus, and Critias are sitting around having a conversation. Timeaus and Critias want to tell Socrates a story, a tale of a great city, a story which they say is absolutely true. And there begins the trouble. Ever since, people have been racing around the planet looking for this long lost city of Atlantis. This web site has information on the origin of the legendary Atlantis, as well as links to other related resources.

**Web:**
**http://www.activemind.com/Mysterious/Topics/Atlantis/**

## Camelot

Mythology and history concerning King Arthur, the Knights of the Round Table, and the Holy Grail, literature, linguistics, archaeology, and mysticism.

**Web:**
**http://rodent.lib.rochester.edu/camelot/CPHOME.htm**

## Charms and Amulets

There are days when something special is about to happen, and you want an extra boost to make things turn out perfect. For example, on the day you go in to ask your boss for a raise, wouldn't it be nice if you had a well-crafted spider amulet like that used by the ancient Europeans when they wanted to attract money? You don't like spiders? How about a magnetic lodestone, a horseshoe amulet, or a Snow Globe Pyramid of Luck? Whatever the occasion, when you need a bit of extra good luck to come your way, check out this site. It will give you lots of great information about the legends, history and stories behind the charms and amulets that have been used for centuries.

**Web:**

**http://www.sonic.net/~yronwode/LuckyW.html**

## Cryptozoology

Cryptozoology is the study of mysterious animals—such as Bigfoot and the Loch Ness monster—whose existence is a matter of dispute. (The term "cryptozoology" was first used in the 1950s by Bernard Heuvelmans, author of "On the Track of Unknown Animals".) If you don't have enough to worry about in your life, and you want to concern yourself with things that don't actually exist, try reading some of the cryptozoology stuff at this site. There is lots of information about monsters, bugs, invertebrates, and legendary lifeforms that nobody can prove are real.

**Web:**

**http://www.ncf.carleton.ca/~bz050/HomePage.cryptoz.html**

**Cryptozoology**

**Looking for Mr. Bigfoot? How about the Loch Ness monster or a giant cookiecutter shark?**

**If these mythical but well-known beasts appeal to you, maybe you should investigate Cryptozoology: the study of hidden animals.**

**(Actually, I would be satisfied with a way to find my cat when he is hiding in the back yard.)**

## Dragons

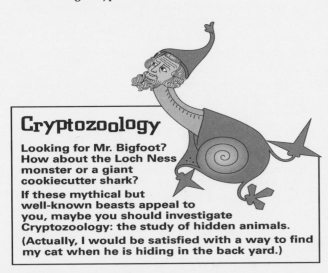

I was in the bookstore the other day, and I happened to go to the section that has my book *The Internet Complete Reference*. As I turned the corner, I encountered a dragon, holding a copy of my book and breathing fire. I said to him, "Don't you know this is a non-smoking area?" And he said, "I know, but I can't help it. This is a very hot book." As you can see, it's always good to know what to say to a dragon, just in case you happen to meet one unexpectedly. So read up on dragons, learn about their personalities (such as why they have such good taste in books), and enjoy their legendary stories. If you would rather talk about dragons, and you can't find one in your local bookstore, try the Usenet group.

**Web:**

**http://www.hooked.net/users/jjwalker/dragons.html**

**Usenet:**

**alt.fan.dragons**

## Encyclopedia Mythica

High in content and easily searchable, this site offers a wealth of information about mythology, legends, and folkore. Read about all sorts of creatures, gods, goddesses, and their origins and history.

**Web:**

**http://www.pantheon.org/myth/**

## Faerie Lore

Fairies come in many different shapes and sizes, and are known by a variety of names. What they have in common is that they are all magical beings who are most often mischievous in nature. If you are a fairy fan, here is a site you will enjoy: pictures, a great collection of folklore and literature, and a searchable fairy dictionary. And while you are here, read about fairy etiquette, so you know what to do in case a brownie comes calling.

**Web:**

**http://faeryland.tamu-commerce.edu/~earendil/faerie/faerie.html**

## Folk Tales

I like a good folk tale. Various cultures around the world have created tales to teach people and to modify the behavior of the community to suit specific needs. Out of these needs are born water spirits, changelings, magical weapons and objects, gods, goddesses, underground people and mysterious animals. This site offers a nice collection of folk tales that will fascinate and amuse you. What's my favorite folk tale? The one about the tired Internet writer who fell asleep, exhausted, in front of his computer, only to awaken in the morning to find that a group of elves had magically finished writing his book during the night.

**Web:**

**http://www.pitt.edu/~dash/folktexts.html**

## Folk Tales From Around the World

It's fun to hear folk tales from a variety of countries. Occasionally, I will light a nice fire, put the cat in my lap and read him a nice Syldavian folk story. He really appreciates the cultural exposure because, as you know, a well-rounded cat can catch a lot more mice. If you too would like to be more culturally refined, check out this collection of folk tales from around the world.

**Web:**

**http://www.ece.ucdavis.edu/~darsie/tales.html**

## Gems and Mineral Folklore

Some people believe there is magic and power locked inside the stones of the Earth, and that these stones can be used to channel energy from one place to another. (Of course, there are also people who believe the Easter Bunny is going to mysteriously fix all the bugs in Windows 95.) Regardless, here is the place where you can talk about folklore and stories surrounding various gems and minerals.

**Usenet:**

**alt.folklore.gemstones**

## Germanic Myths, Legends and Sagas

Do you ever have one of those days when you come into the house, all bundled up and covered with snow, and someone hands you a big mug of hot chocolate and says, "Here, sit down by the fire and let me relate an old Germanic legend my mother used to tell me." It doesn't happen to me, because I live near a beach in California, but it could happen to you, especially if you have this web site in your bookmark list. This site has information about Germanic (Scandinavian and Teutonic) mythology, culture, ancient beliefs and deities.

**Web:**

**http://www.pitt.edu/~dash/mythlinks.html**

## Greek Mythology

Brush up on your ancient Greek mythology by reading stories about gods, goddesses, heroes and creatures. This web page will not only give you an overview, but will also diagram a family tree so you can keep all your characters straight.

**Web:**

**http://www.intergate.net/uhtml/.jhunt/greek_myth/greek_myth.html**

## Griffins

A griffin (also known as a griffon or gryphon) is a mythological beast with the body of a lion, and the head, forelegs and wings of an eagle. As you can imagine, this would be enough to cause the poor animal to be refused admittance to the more fashionable night clubs. Still, despite their odd features, griffins have been extremely popular over the centuries and are portrayed as having great intelligence and powerful strength (much like writers of Internet books). Griffins have appeared in numerous starring roles, as pets for the god Zeus, in a singing scene in Alice in Wonderland, and on many science fiction book covers. If you like griffins, or you want to learn how to like griffins, check out this web site.

**Web:**

**http://sashimi.wwa.com/~tirya/gryphon.html**

## *Look What I Found on the Net...*

Newsgroup: alt.folklore.gemstones
Subject: Need to Know the Meaning of a Stone I Found.

> Recently at an event I went to, I found a stone that was
> called Apatite. I found the stones to be quite interesting,
> and purchased a few of them. I was wondering if anyone had
> come across similar stones, or might know of any significance
> they might have.

[...to which one person responds...]

Apatite is nothing new. It is a fairly common gem material, often found in attractive crystal forms. It's essentially a calcium phosphate, with some fluorine or chlorine in the composition.

As a gem, its use is somewhat limited, due to its softness. Because of their limited utility in jewelry, many apatite gems are inexpensive. That explains why you'll see the things on TV home shopping channels, being praised for their rarity and beauty. Of course, the real reason is that Apatite crystals can be bought very cheaply, and looks fine on a screen. The average consumer, not having seen them before, has no way of judging whether they are actually worth buying.

Xxxxx Xxxx, commercial jeweler and metalsmith,
Graduate Gemologist and Lapidary

[...another person answers the same question as follows...]

I have some information from the book Xxxxxx by Xxxxxx:

Apatite (astrological sign of Gemini) can be used to stimulate the intellect and to promote realization that one's strength occurs through both spiritual avenues and via love; hence, dissolving aloofness and negativity.

Apatite is related to service and to the development of the humanitarian pursuits. It is attuned to healing, storing information, communicating, balancing energy and teaching. It is extremely useful in the expansion of knowledge and in the disclosure of the truth to freedom.

It can be used to stimulate the development of clairvoyance, clairaudience, clairsentience, and the awareness of the devic worlds. It can further the connection with UFOs and can provide access to past-life insights and telepathy.

This gem is the stone of the future and will bring knowledge to those attuned to it by clearing mental confusion. It truly awakens the fine, inner self.

Apatite vibrates to the number 9.

## Joseph Campbell Foundation Reading Room

Joseph Campbell (1904-1987) was a writer and leading scholar in the field of mythology. In his lifetime, Campbell became well-known and popular from his books and his series of educational television shows. The Joseph Campbell Foundation offers a reading room with a collection of mythology links around the Net, a list of Campbell's books, a place where you can submit stories and poems for possible publication at the site, as well as a discussion area.

**Web:**

**http://www.jcf.org/pub/**

## King Arthur

Arthurian legend contains many stories based in medieval times about King Arthur of Britain and his Knights of the Round Table. The legend can be traced back as far as the sixth century, although the stories have been expanded and modified throughout the years. The basic story, however, has always remained more or less the same. Arthur is the illegitimate son of King Uther Pendragon. After the king's death, Arthur distinguishes himself by successfully pulling out a sword that is embedded in a huge stone. Arthur becomes king and reigns over the land of Camelot. The stories involve the familiar characters of King Arthur, his knights (including Sir Launcelot, Sir Galahad and Sir Tristram), his wife Guinevere, Merlin the Magician, the Lady of the Lake (who gives Arthur his special sword Excalibur), and his enemies Morgan le Fay and Sir Mordred, all of whom appear in Arthur's many adventures. Eventually, Arthur is wounded by Sir Mordred and—as he is dying—is carried away to Avalon, from which he will one day return.

**Web:**

**http://reality.sgi.com/employees/chris_manchester/guide.html**
**http://rodent.lib.rochester.edu/camelot/cphome.htm**

**Usenet:**

**alt.legend.king-arthur**

**Listserv Mailing List:**

List Name: **arthurnet**
Subscribe to: **listserv@morgan.ucs.mun.ca**

**King Arthur**

**It's a well-known fact that King Arthur didn't really exist. (However, the last time I heard from him, he was saying that I don't really exist, so you'll have to make up your own mind.) If you want to get into the esoterica of the Arthurian legend, subscribe to the ArthurNet mailing list. Find out if Merlin was killed by one bullet or two. Was there really only one assassin, or was the whole thing a cover-up?**

## Mermaids

A mermaid is a legendary sea creature with the head and upper body of a woman and the lower anatomy of a fish. Sightings of mermaids have always been popular among sailors who have spent long days at sea, without female companionship, in the company of other sweaty sailors (and the odd fish). This site has a mermaid magazine with pictures of mermaids, as well as classic and modern tales.

**Web:**

**http://www.accessone.com/~cagle/seatails/**

## Mythic Worlds

When you are in the mood for tales and legends that reach back into the very heart of civilization, light some incense and candles, and point your browser to this web page. Then spend some time exploring a great list of mythology links that will take you on a tour of various ancient worlds and old religions.

**Web:**

**http://members.gnn.com/shickman/myth.htm**

**The Net is immortal.**

## Mythical Animals

As cute as they are, little groundhogs and frollicking squirrels can get tiresome after a while. Imagine a world in which all sorts of bizarre creatures were alive and roaming your neighborhood. What fun it would be to have to worry about gorgons and harpies hastening your demise, mischievous satyrs, graceful unicorns, and beautiful mermaids who nip at your toes as you tread water. Read about all forms of mythical creatures and their origins.

**Usenet:**

**alt.mythology.mythic-animals**

## Mythology in Western Art

The stories of Greek mythology are soap operas that take place back when men were men, and the other men were glad of it. If you would like to know how the gods and goddesses of mythological tales have been portrayed by artists over the centuries, sneak a peek at this web site. It offers a collection of images of individuals who have a starring role in your favorite myths. You will also find links to other interesting Greek and Roman mythology sites.

**Web:**

**http://www-lib.haifa.ac.il/www/art/MYTHOLOGY_WESTART.HTML**

## Mythology Talk and General Discussion

Myths are traditional stories, passed down from one generation to the next. Myths arise in all time periods, and they most always involve supernatural events. (Myths are different from folklore in that folk tales are generally more entertaining and believable.) If you like any type of mythology, this is the place to hang out and discuss the who, what, when, where and how-high-did-he-jump aspects of this entertaining and telling area of human culture.

**Usenet:**

**alt.mythology**

## Myths and Legends

The perfect place for storytime, this site has a large archive of myths and legends from a variety of cultures: Norse, Teutonic, Greek, Roman, Native American, Spanish, Gothic Horror, Medieval and Renaissance.

**Web:**

**http://pubpages.unh.edu/~cbsiren/myth.html**

## Mythtext

When the repetition of prayer gets to be a little much and you just have to break up the routine of your before-bed ritual, have a look at this site, which has a list of thousands of gods, goddesses and immortals, from around the world. You can read bibliographies on mythology, spirituality and history; find pointers to mythological texts; and access FAQs and related links.

**Web:**

**http://www.io.org/~untangle/mythtext.html**

## Native Indian Myths And Legends

Native storytellers created sacred myths to explain the origin of humans, to answer the question of why we live as we do, and to record lessons that have been passed down through years of living. Aside from being teaching tools, these stories were often used to entertain. This web page has a collection of traditional stories from various native tribes.

**Web:**

**http://indy4.fdl.cc.mn.us/~isk/stories/myths.html**

## Pirates

Pirates are the ultimate seafaring bad guys. They wear cool clothes, they pillage, and they can stay up as late as they want to watch Letterman. Yes, the pirate life is the life for me. If you want to be a pirate, or you want to just see what it was like to be a pirate (back in the days when pirates were allowed to have fun), take a look at this site. You'll see pictures of ships, read about the pirate way of living, and have a chance to learn about the history, legends and myths of famous pirates of antiquity.

**Web:**

**http://www.uic.edu/~toby-g/pirates.html**

A B C D E F G H I J K L M N O P Q R S T U V W X Y Z

## Robin Hood

Robin Hood is a legendary 13th century English hero who robbed the rich and gave his stolen goods to the poor and oppressed. Robin Hood lived in Sherwood Forest (in central England, north of Nottingham and west of Lincoln) with his band of merry followers who assisted him in his heroic endeavors. Read about the life and times of Robin Hood and why he is popular to this day.

**Web:**
**http://www.cyberramp.net/~infinity/robinhood.html**

## Scientific Urban Legends

There are all sorts of nasty rumors flying around about science. And we know just where they are coming from. Check out the latest outlandish tales of science which often sound like they come straight from the set of a 1950s science fiction movie. Help discern the truths from the myths by reading up on what the folks in Usenet have to say.

**Usenet:**
**alt.folklore.science**

**Join the fun—now.**

## Sea Serpents and Lake Monsters

I have been swimming in the ocean for many, many years and I have never seen anything out of the ordinary or unexplainable. However, there are people all around the world who say they have seen oddities in oceans and lakes. Some of these people even have pictures. If you want a nice overview of what creatures you might be missing, take a look at this site. There are pictures, explanations and background information about various legendary creatures such as the Loch Ness monster, the Lake Champlain monster, the megamouth shark, giant squids, Ogopogo and others. And if you are insatiable for unusual marine animals, there are links to other water creature sites.

**Web:**
**http://www.serve.com/shadows/serpent.htm**

## Tree Lore

Wood is beautiful in its quality and variety: the clean, fresh look of the pale birch; the tan sheen of elm; the white, almost grainless holly; the rich dark oak; and the golden yew. This beauty is enough for me, but for some there is also a symbolic meaning and significance ascribed to various woods. If you would like to learn more about our friends in the world of wood, this web site explains the sacred traits of trees as well as the origin of the tree lore.

**Web:**
**http://pages.icacomp.com/~runesmith/woods.html**

### *Look What I Found on the Net...*

```
Newsgroup: alt.folklore.science
Subject: See the Ultraviolet

> According to Hecht's "Optics", people who have cataract
> surgery can see into the ultraviolet. The removed lens no
> longer filters out the ultraviolet.

The late Walter Scott Houston, who wrote Deep Sky Wonders in
Sky & Telescope, mentioned this once in a while.  The central
star in the ring nebula (M57 in Lyra) is brightest in the
ultraviolet.  This star is considered a challenge to see since
there is so little "visible" light emitted.  After cataract
surgery (in which the eyes lens is replaced with a plastic one),
he claimed that the star was easy to see with that eye.
```

## Urban Legends

An urban legend is a story that is widely believed to be true, even though no real evidence exists. Urban legends generally offer a measure of humor or horror, and seem to take on a life of their own, regardless of how true they really are. Urban legends are famous for being retold as if they happened to "a friend of a friend". For example, are there really gangs of kidnappers at Disneyland who abduct children, change their clothing and hairstyles, and then smuggle them out the gates into a waiting getaway car?

**Web:**

**http://www.best.com/~snopes/**
**http://www.urbanlegends.com/**

**Usenet:**

**alt.folklore.info**
**alt.folklore.suburban**
**alt.folklore.urban**

Don't you just love those unbelievable stories that always happen to a "friend of a friend"? These are urban legends and the Net has several newsgroups devoted to such tales. (I wonder, is there any truth to the story about the man whose life was saved by a copy of *The Internet Complete Reference*?)

## Werewolf Folklore

On those days when you are not feeling quite like your old self, when you would rather have a midnight walk and howl at the moon than watch TV, you should know where to turn. Check out the werewolf and shifter handbook, and see if you have any of the symptoms.

**Web:**

**http://www.lycanthrope.org/~humbird/handbook.html**

# FONTS AND TYPEFACES

## comp.fonts Home Page

This web site is a companion to the general typographical discussion that takes place in the **comp.fonts** Usenet groups. You will find an interesting variety of font-related resources to explore, including links to archives, software, a FAQ, style guides, designers, exhibits, and so on.

**Web:**

**http://www.ora.com/homepages/comp.fonts/**

## European Diacritics

A diacritic is a mark that is added to a letter to modify its pronunciation or to distinguish words that would be otherwise identical. Here are two examples: é (an "e" with an acute accent) and ç (a "c" with a cedilla). This web page contains important and hard to find reference material: examples of the various diacritics used with the various European languages (even obscure languages). This is the place to look when you need to find the name of the tiny little circle that is sometimes placed above a letter, such as the Swedish å character. (The mark is called a Krouzek).

**Web:**

**http://www.portal.ca/~tiro/di_intro.html**

## Field Guide to Fonts

Have you ever used a Roget's Thesaurus? Although many people think it is a synonym finder, a Roget's Thesaurus is actually designed to help you find the exact right word. You use a Roget's Thesaurus when you know the meaning of a word, but you do not know the word. Analogously, there are times when you need to find out the name of a particular font. For example, what do you do when know the characteristics of a font—perhaps because you have a sample—but you don't know its name? Here is an unusual and well thought-out tool that can help you track down the mysterious font, by narrowing down the choices based on the font's characteristics.

**Web:**

**http://ivory.lm.com/~mundie/Typography/Faces.html**

## Figlet Fonts

Don't settle for the same old dull, boring strings of letters. Spice things up with some ASCII fonts. This web page has information about Figlet as well as links to sets of Figlet fonts and web-based Figlet services.

**Web:**

**http://st-www.cs.uiuc.edu/users/chai/figlet.html**

## Font Talk and General Discussion

These are the Usenet groups that are used to discuss fonts, typefaces, typography and related topics. If you are in the business, these are good groups to read regularly. These are also good places to ask a question when you need help with a typesetting problem, and no one around the office has any idea what you are talking about.

**Usenet:**

**alt.binaries.fonts**
**comp.fonts**

## Foreign Font Archive

This is a huge repository of fonts from around the world. There are over 200 fonts supporting over 40 different languages, all of which are available for downloading (either as shareware or freeware). All fonts are available as Truetype files; many are also in Adobe Postscript Type I format.

**Web:**

**http://www.dtcc.edu/personal/staff/berlin/fonts-f.htm**

## Free Fonts

There are lots and lots of fonts available for free on the Net. Here are some resources from which you can download a large variety of different fonts. When you have a spare moment, these are great places to browse to find a new and interesting font (say, to give to your wife or husband for an anniversary present).

**Web:**

**http://home.earthlink.net/~ewhall/fontfairy/webfonts.html**
**http://wabakimi.carleton.ca/~mgauthie/**
**http://www.ccsi.com/~graball/scriptorium/month.html**

## Guide to Postscript

Postscript is a page description language. That is, it is a special type of programming language that was designed for printing and displaying graphics and text. Postscript is device-independent, which means that the same Postscript program can be used to print or display output on any Postscript device (printer, monitor, film, and so on). For example, Postscript does not make any reference at all to the resolution of the output device. Postscript was introduced by Adobe in 1985 and first used commercially in the Apple Laserwriter printer. This web site contains a simple introduction to Postscript and its technical details. However, do not be misled. "Simple" is a relative term, and Postscript is a complex language. (By the way, Postscript is an interpreted, stack-based language, similar to the RPN—reverse Polish notation—language used with programmable calculators.)

**Web:**

**comp.sources.postscript**
**http://www.cs.indiana.edu/docproject/programming/postscript/postscript.html**

**Usenet:**

**comp.lang.postscript**

### *Look What I Found on the Net...*

```
Newsgroup: comp.fonts
Subject: I Need Your Help Desperately

I am looking for a font called "Ovine".

My band uses this font for our logo, and I deleted it by
mistake.

Please, if someone has this font, I would be happy to trade
something for it. I hope someone has it.
```

## Headline Maker

This typeface company has come up with an engaging way to show their wares. You can select any of their many typefaces and use it to create a headline banner of your choice (such as "Harley Hahn writes great books"). This is a great way to experiment with different typefaces, and after you are finished, you can save the result to show your friends.

**Web:**

**http://ubik.letraset.com/ripper/**

## Internet Font Archives

The Internet Font Archives is a large repository of information about Postscript Type 1 fonts. Many of the fonts can be downloaded for free, and in such cases, you can do this by clicking on a button. This archive is great for browsing. For example, I am often disappointed with the Courier fonts that I see in computer books. In my own books, I like to have a bold, easy-to-read Courier for the information that I want to be monospaced. All too often, however, I have had to settle for an anemic, ugly Courier font that just can't pull its own typographical weight. I was especially pleased to find a large variety of Courier fonts in this archive. You know, that gives me an idea. What about a web-based matchmaking service? You could examine small pictures, looking for the perfect man or woman... oh, never mind, it probably wouldn't work anyway. Let's stick to fonts.

**Web:**

**http://www.ora.com/homepages/comp.fonts/ifa/**

### The Internet Font Browser

As Shakespeare once said, "There are more fonts on the Web and on the Net, Horatio, than are dreamt of in your philosophy."

That's fine for Horatio: he could borrow Shakespeare's font collection whenever he wanted.

But how do ordinary people like you and me find the fonts we need?

We use the Internet Font Browser.

## Internet Font Browser

The Internet Font Browser allows you to browse many hundreds of font samples stored as gif images. You can search for a specific font, use the alphabetic listing, or select a font from the miniature images available in the thumbnail sheets.

**Web:**

**http://cuiwww.unige.ch/InternetFontBrowser**

## Truetype Fonts

Truetype is a family of fonts that was originally developed by Apple. They developed these fonts for two reasons. (1) They didn't want to have to pay royalties to the owners of existing fonts. (2) They wanted to fix some of the technical problems in Adobe Type 1 fonts. The Truetype family was designed to be compact, flexible and extensible. Since Microsoft had been looking for a similar type of font family, Apple agreed to license the technology. Since then, Microsoft has done considerable Truetype development, enhancing the font technology. Today, Truetype fonts will work on any current Mircosoft platform or Apple computer. This web site has a great deal of information devoted to Truetype fonts, including Opentype (the result of Microsoft's collaboration with Adobe to unify Truetype with Type I fonts).

**Web:**

**http://www.truetype.demon.co.uk/**

## &Type

This is an eclectic collection of resources for people interested in typography: check out the strange, interesting and useful fonts, take a look at the typesetting tricks, and read a number of articles, all related to fonts and the people who use them.

**Web:**

**http://www.graphic-design.com/Type/**

## TypeArt Library

This is an interesting collection of typographical resources. The ones I think you will enjoy the most are the contests (can you identify a mystery font?), tips for typesetters, and tips for typeface designers, all of which change from time to time.

**Web:**

**http://www.typeart.com/**

A B C D E F G H I J K L M N O P Q R S T U V W X Y Z

## Typeface Design Competition

This web site is the home of an international typeface design competition. The contest is sponsored by a Japanese company and there are two types of prizes: one for Latin typefaces and one for Kanji (Japanese-Chinese) typefaces. The contest is held every three years and is open to designers from any country. Unfortunately, the deadline for the fifth competition (August 1996) has already passed. However, I found it interesting to look at the typefaces designed by the winners of the fourth competition, especially the Kanji typefaces. This is a good site to remember, because it will be interesting to see the winners of the fifth competition once they are chosen.

**Web:**

**http://www.morisawa.co.jp/fonts/contest_e.html**

## Typeface Identification

There are two good reasons why you should learn how to recognize and distinguish different typefaces. First, if you are a serious student of typography, understanding the different typefaces is a basic skill which you will want to master. Second, if you work with desktop publishing for a living, there will be times when someone will bring you a sample of printing and ask you to find a similar typeface. (Still, you have nothing to complain about. Imagine what it is like being a hair stylist when an ordinary-looking customer comes in with a magazine picture of a supermodel and says, "I want you to make me look like this.") Back to typefaces: Learning how to recognize different typefaces requires a lot of knowledge and practice. Here is a well-written series of lessons, illustrated with examples, that will teach you the basics. I enjoyed reading the lessons, as I found a lot of interesting information about typeface history and terminology.

**Web:**

**http://forest.xcelco.on.ca/dmc/public_html/INTRO.HTM**

## Typofile

The Typofile web site is for typophiles. If you love typefaces, you will love this web site. Use the hypertext decision-making system to help you choose the best typeface for a particular job. Read hints on how to use typefaces well. And, for real typeface lovers, take a look at the featured typefaces of the month.

**Web:**

**http://www.will-harris.com/type.htm**

## TYPEFACE IDENTIFICATION

*It's late at night. All of a sudden, you are awakened by an authoritative knock on your front door.*

"Open up. This is the font police. We want you down at headquarters to make an identification."

The next thing you know you're at the back of a dimly lit room looking at a lineup: Palatino, Courier, Futura, Optima and Times Roman.

A tough-looking sergeant with a big club in his hand looks at you and says, "Okay, buddy. Which one is the font we want? And if you want to stay out of trouble yourself, you'd better get it right the first time."

Fortunately, you know what you are doing. You put the finger on the correct font, and within an hour you are back at home safe in bed.

Typeface identification: it just may save your life someday.

## Typography

This site is dedicated to the history and appreciation of typography. You can learn all about typefaces: find out how and why they are constructed, read about their history, visit a gallery of interesting typefaces, and more.

**Web:**

**http://www.razorfish.com/bluedot/typo/**

## Typography Terminology

The world of typography has a great many technical words and terms. Here are some glossaries that can help you understand these terms. In my experience, knowing what the words mean counts for a lot. So, the next time someone (say, your manager) acts like he or she knows more than you do, you can say, "Well, I can do it your way if you really want, but the glyphs in that particular typeface will force me to use slightly different kerning which may change the lines by a few points."

**Web:**

**http://forest.xcelco.on.ca/dmc/public_html/Lesson0.htm**

**http://www.ora.com/homepages/comp.fonts/FAQ/cf_18.htm**

**http://www.razorfish.com/bluedot/typo/glossary/**

# FOOD AND DRINK

## Beer

Making, choosing, and imbibing: these discussion groups will help you find out everything you want to know about beer and related beverages. Read the regular posting on which beers are best, based on the votes of Usenet participants. (Anyone can vote, although you do have to supply your own beer.) For specialists, the **.Zima** group discusses this odd, beer-like drink.

**Web:**

**http://www.eff.org/~brown/beer.html**
**http://www.globall.com/j/beer/ref.html**
**http://www.realbeer.com/**

**Usenet:**

**alt.beer**
**alt.zima**
**rec.crafts.brewing**
**rec.food.drink.beer**

## Beer Ratings

So many beers, so little time. If you feel too overwhelmed to go taste test all the beers in the world yourself, don't worry. Some guys on the Net have done a lot of the work for you. Read their beer ratings and see what they say to try and what to avoid.

**Web:**

**http://www.mindspring.com/~jlock/ratings1.html**
**http://www.mit.edu:8001/afs/athena.mit.edu/user/m/j/mjbauer/WWW/beer-ratings.html**

## Beverage Network

Unless you drink only water, somewhere, sometime, you are a consumer of commercial beverages. As such, you have my personal guarantee that there is something, somewhere, on the Beverage Network that will interest you. We all know that the world is full of fanatics, but it doesn't really hit home until you see something like this web site: someone has used enormous amounts of time and energy (and a fair amount of talent) to create an entire web site devoted to beverages. Check it out for yourself. While you are there, take the beverage purity test to see how beverage savvy you are. (I rated 17% which puts me in the third lowest category.)

**Web:**

**http://www.thebevnet.com/**

## Caviar

Make your next party a ritzy affair by adding caviar to the list of edibles. Before you do, make sure you know how to select, prepare, serve and store your little treasures from the sea. This site will show you how.

**Web:**

**http://virtumall.com/Caviar**

**Quick, turn the page.**

### *Look What I Found on the Net...*

```
Newsgroup: rec.food.drink.beer
Subject: alt.beer vs. rec.food.drink.beer

> What is the difference between rec.food.drink.beer and
> alt.beer if any?  Other than the fact that there is less
> junk in this group.

I think rec.food.drink.beer gets more posts like yours than
does alt.beer.

I wonder why that is?
```

## Cereal

Cereal is not just for the first meal of the day. In fact, it's more than just something to put in your mouth. It's not only nutrition and sustenance—it's fun and if you read the box, you could even call it a literary experience. More than that, it's a facilitator of a great social experience by bringing people together on the Net to talk about how cereal makes an impact on all our lives. Don't be left out of the cereal movement. Grab a spoon and dig in.

**Web:**

**http://www.cereal.com/**
**http://www.flake.com/**

**Usenet:**

**alt.cereal**

## Cheese

If you like cheese, even just in passing, you *must* spend some time at this Web site. There is lots and lots of information about the cheeses of the world: how they are made, what they are made of, where they are made, what wines go well with particular cheeses, history of cheese, how to make cheese, a cheese glossary, Ask Dr. Cheese, and cheese literature (poems and writings about cheese).

**Web:**

**http://www.wgx.com/cheesenet/**

## Coca-Cola

You can pooh-pooh the contributions of America to world culture, but there is no gainsaying the fact that Coca-Cola has virtually defined the concept of ubiquity. It would be difficult to find anything as well-known as this peripatetic soft drink, so I'm sure it comes as no surprise when I tell you that the Coke fanatics of the world have a definite presence on the Net. If you have any interest at all in Coca-Cola and its social accoutrements, here are some Internet resources to help you explore this beacon of international culture, clearly the most important beverage in the refrigerator of American hegemony.

**Web:**

**http://www.unm.edu/~madrigal/coke.html**

**Usenet:**

**alt.food.cocacola**

## Cocktail Magazine

The interesting thing about alcohol is that so much of our popular culture has been developed around the acts of creating, mixing and drinking alcoholic beverages. Can you think of any other drug that has specially trained people (bartenders) whose sole purpose is to create and serve a large number of different preparations (cocktails) based on that one particular drug? Do you not think it's interesting that the large alcohol companies routinely spend huge amounts of money trying to build an image for their particular version of this drug? And would I be too much of a spoilsport if I pointed out that the main reason one administers alcohol to oneself is to cause one's brain cells to act abnormally in a way that makes one feel good? I guess that would be too much, so forget I said it. In fact, forget all of this. Just enjoy the Cocktail Magazine web site and drink up.

**Web:**

**http://www.cocktail.com/**

## Coffee

Some people like to sip it, some gulp it down in the morning before their eyes are open. Some people like to have it flavored and run through various elaborate preparations which result in a thick, syrupy brew or a decadent foamy concoction. And then there are the hard core people who don't bother brewing and simply munch on the beans themselves. If your drug of choice is coffee, you will feel right at home in these Usenet groups where people talk about preparation, storage, growth and sale of this popular beverage. The web sites offer the perfect reading material for your early-morning beverage.

**Web:**

**http://www.bid.com/bid/coffeeworld/coffee.html**
**http://www.wfu.edu/~pendeea3/coffees.html**

**Usenet:**

**alt.coffee**
**alt.food.coffee**
**rec.food.drink.coffee**

**The Net loves poetry.**

## Coffee Lover's Resources

Dedicated to coffee lovers all over the world, this resource features links to a glossary of coffee terminology, a list of mail order coffee and tea vendors, the coffee file archives, newsgroups about coffee, coffee recipes, books, FAQs, and even a traveler's guide to coffee houses.

**Web:**

**http://www.cappuccino.com/**

## College Food

Ah, those good old college days. How nostalgic we will be when our hair turns silver and we wax eloquent about mystery meat burgers and the blue-green algae surprise. Come on in and discuss college dining halls, cafeterias, and pay-for-it-even-if-you-don't-want-it food plans.

**Usenet:**

**alt.college.food**

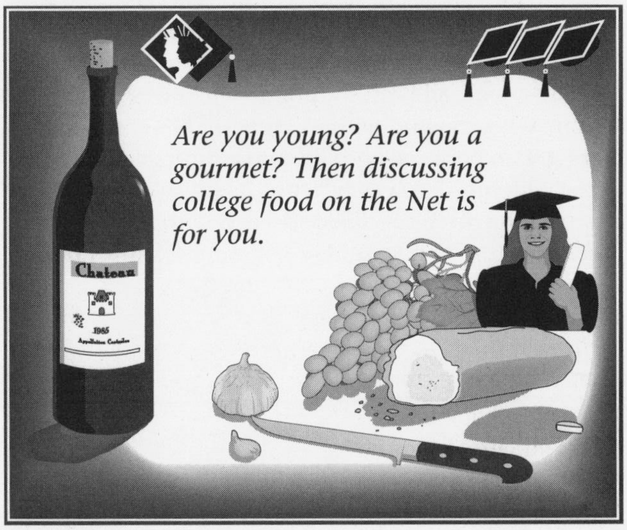
*Are you young? Are you a gourmet? Then discussing college food on the Net is for you.*
Chateau

## Epicurious

Epicurious is an online magazine dedicated to the three major areas of culinary enjoyment: eating, drinking, and playing with your food. I find the articles imaginative and well worth a regularly scheduled look. My suggestion is to poke into the web site once a week to see if anything new and exciting has arrived. You will find reviews, recipes, food commentary, wine information and—my favorite—complaints about stupid food.

**Web:**

**http://www.epicurious.com/a_home/a00_home/**

## Fast Food Talk and General Discussion

Fast food refers to cheap food that is sold, prepared, and served to you within several minutes. Fast food is usually bought at a franchised outlet which, as often as not, allows you to order, receive and devour the food all without leaving your car. Fast food outlets tend to standardize their offerings. For example, a Big Mac (multi-layer hamburger with secret sauce) will look, feel and taste pretty much the same from one MacDonalds to the next. (Actually, if the carefully trained employees prepared your Big Mac correctly, it will look, feel and taste *exactly* the same.) Since the cost of fast food is reasonable and there is no real wait, such restaurants are a favorite of busy parents everywhere. If you are a fast food buff or buffette, and you want to share your ersatz culinary experiences and opinions, what better place could there be than Usenet: the home of fast, cheap, simple, satisfying experiences?

**Usenet:**

**alt.food.dennys**
**alt.food.fast-food**
**alt.food.mcdonalds**
**alt.food.taco-bell**

## Fat-Free Food

Remember, just because it has no taste doesn't mean it's good for you. Immerse yourself in the world of fat-free fanatics and lower your cholesterol, blood pressure, and enjoyment quotient.

**Usenet:**

**alt.food.fat-free**

## Food Discussion

It is universally acknowledged that—out of all the things people put in their mouths in public—food is the most socially acceptable. There is a lot to say about food, and people on the Net are more than glad to say it. If you would like to take part in the discussion, just step up to the virtual table and join the group. What I like best about the Net is you can talk with your mouth full.

**Usenet:**

**alt.food**
**rec.food.drink**
**rec.food.restaurants**
**rec.food.veg**

## Food Labeling Information

Rulings on labeling requirements for ingredients, serving sizes, terms, fat and cancer, fruits and vegetables, nutritional claims, and other related topics.

**Web:**
**http://vm.cfsan.fda.gov/label.html**

## Food Mailing List

A mailing list for the exchange of recipes, discussion of cooking procedures, nutrition, cookbooks, spices, cookware and any other fun things you can do in a kitchen. The **vnr-cul** list is for culinary professionals.

**Listserv Mailing List:**
List Name: **eat-l**
Subscribe to: **listserv@listserv.vt.edu**

**Majordomo Mailing List:**
List Name: **vnr-cul**
Subscribe to: **majordomo@zelda.thomson.com**

## Food Safety

A discussion group for food safety specialists. Postings to this group include food safety alerts and discussion among professionals involved in the prevention of foodborne illnesses.

**Listproc Mailing List:**
List Name: **foodlink**
Subscribe to: **listproc@listproc.wsu.edu**

**Listserv Mailing List:**
List Name: **foodtalk**
Subscribe to: **listserv@unlvm.unl.edu**

## Foodplex

Don't feel guilty about your food. Enjoy yourself with the help of this guilt-free web page dedicated to the pleasure of fine food. Information about food, recipes, food humor and a column which will answer readers' food questions.

**Web:**
**http://www.gigaplex.com/food/index.htm**

## French Fries

Okay, let's be honest for a moment. Is there anything you would rather do, right now, than connect to a hot French fry web site and indulge yourself? Learn about history, world culture, art, government, little-known facts, foreign customs and the law. All of this from the lowly French fry? It's almost sounds too good to be true. It's not.

**Web:**
**http://www.select-ware.com/fries/**

## Fun Foods

We need to eat just to stay alive, but that doesn't mean we can't have some fun at the same time. We all know that some foods are just naturally more fun that others. For example, a plateful of turkey with cranberry sauce and baked sweet potatoes is serious food—ice cream is fun. A dry red Merlot wine can be a treat to enjoy with your linguini and clam sauce at a pretentious, over-priced Italian restaurant, but for pure enjoyment, Kool-aid is definitely the drink of the people. And ketchup—well, all I can say about ketchup is that anyone who grew up with my brother has enough first-hand experience with the consumption of ketchup to last a lifetime. However, when it comes to appreciating these special foods, eating them is only part of the fun. You should spend at least a few hours a week on Usenet, talking, reading, learning, and generally sharing in the collective experience.

**Usenet:**
**alt.drinks.kool-aid**
**alt.food.cereal**
**alt.food.ice-cream**
**alt.food.pancakes**
**alt.food.sugar-cereals**
**alt.ketchup**

## History of Food

Where do you ask for information on what type of food the peasants ate during the French Revolution? What do you do when the in-laws are due any moment and you need the recipe for figgy pudding? Check out this newsgroup and move forward, into the past.

**Usenet:**
**rec.food.historic**

Food Labeling
Information

My cat has a simple system when it comes to understanding food: a piece of food is either tuna or it's not tuna. For human beings, however, things are more complicated.

To help us, the United States Food and Drug Administration has set up a system in which all prepared foods must carry labels that have certain useful information. If you have any questions as to how to interpret these labels, you can check with the Food Labeling Information web site, sponsored by the FDA's Center for Food Safety and Applied Nutrition.

Or you can use my special alternate system: a piece of food is either chocolate or it's not.

**Stay away from "X-Rated".**

## Homebrewing

All kinds of material related to beer and homebrewing, including recipes, Homebrew Digest archives, color images of various beer labels and coasters, and much more.

**Web:**

**http://alpha.rollnet.org/**
**http://www.ummed.edu:8000/pub/s/sganesan/Docs/beer.html**

**Majordomo Mailing List:**

List Name: **homebrew**
Subscribe to: **majordomo@aob.org**

## Internet Bar

Bartenders, entertainers and party animals will love this site, which offers a variety of interesting mixed drink information. Browse the recipe archives, look at the drink of the week or ask a bartender a question. There is lots of great information here.

**Web:**

**http://www.epact.se/acats/**

### *Look What I Found on the Net...*

```
Newsgroup: alt.ketchup
Subject: Recipe for ketchup cake

> Here is a complete meal for six people.
>
> You only need:
>
> 3 liters ketchup
> 200 gram flour
> 1 liter milk
>
> Mix the ingredients and place it in the oven for approximately
> half an hour.
>
> Enjoy!

I spent a night in the hospital due to eating this disgusting
cake.  Thank you very much.
```

A B C D E F G H I J K L M N O P Q R S T U V W X Y Z

## Junk Food

Junk food. What a tempting name for something you put in your mouth; something you digest, assimilate and, ultimately, incorporate into your bodily tissues. What classifies something as junk food? To be official junk food, a nutritional substance must meet three specific criteria as defined by the Harley Hahn Official Junk Food Standards. (1) It must be real food, for sale in a bona fide retail outlet. (2) It should taste so good that you want to overeat (at least once you are used to it). (3) It must be something your mother would not want you to eat.

**Web:**

**http://grelb.src.gla.ac.uk:8000/~cube/party/junk.html**

## Mead Maker's Resources

These resources are just for brewers of mead, an alcoholic beverage made from honey. The web page has links to recipes and other information and items of interest to mead lovers.

**Web:**

**http://www.atd.ucar.edu/rdp/gfc/mead/mead.html**

## Peeps

Peeps are funny-shaped almost-100%-sugar creations that have to be seen and tasted to be believed. In a world in which imitation bacon and non-alcoholic beer has become so commonplace as to be pedestrian, it is gratifying to find a food that is not ashamed to push the nutritional envelope. If you have ever seen a peep, it will be no surprise to hear there are a large group of peep-imprinted fanatics alive on the Net, conjuring up huge amounts of glucophilic devotion toward a confection that is nothing less than the epitome of food-your-mother-used-to-warn-you-about.

**Web:**

**http://aris.sfrc.ufl.edu/~maryjo/peep_nuke.html**
**http://www.wam.umd.edu/~ejack/peep.html**

**Usenet:**

**alt.food.peeps**

## Pez

Pez are small rectangular-shaped candy that are stored in special Pez dispensers and retrieved one piece at a time. Popping out a Pez is fun: you hold the dispenser up to your mouth, pull back on the top and, in an instant, a small rectangular-shaped piece of sweet paradise is yours. Eating a Pez may not be the most satisfying culinary experience you will ever encounter, but it is certainly the most dependable. Pull back the top and out pops a Pez, over and over and over and over, until you run out, at which time all you need to do is restock your dispenser with a handy refill. Pez candy and dispensers are manufactured by the Pez Candy Company, which has plants in both Europe and the United States. (The name "Pez" comes from the German word for peppermint—Pfefferminz.) The reason why Pez are so much fun is that there are many different dispensers which can be collected, displayed, bought and sold, and generally enjoyed by Pez enthusiasts (called Pezheads) throughout the world. The two biggest selling Pez dispensers of all time are Santa Claus and Mickey Mouse.

**Web:**

**http://gator.naples.net/~nfn02886/pez.html**

**Usenet:**

**alt.food.pez**

Eating Out Is Good
These days, more and more people who go to restaurants are going to restaurants. (Strange, but true.)
But where's the best place to go?
No need to guess.
Before you spend your hard-earned cash for stuff to put in your mouth, check with your friends on
rec.food.restaurants

## Restaurant Talk and General Discussion

Oh my, we all like to spout off about what is good or bad in the world, and this is a great place to do it. Do you have a favorite restaurant that you simply must praise? Or did you just spend a lot of money for a dinner that tasted like warm-over cardboard, and you feel obliged to warn everyone in the world to stay away? Join the discussion on Usenet, and let the fish and chips fall where they may.

**Usenet:**

**rec.food.restaurants**

## Restaurants on the Web

Check out the menus of these fine restaurants on the Web. See their menus, gift catalogs, and maybe even fax in your order. The restaurants include some of the most interesting places to eat in a variety of cities around the world.

**Web:**

**http://westweb.com/rest/**
**http://www.cuisinenet.com/**
**http://www.cvent.net/restaurants/stmain.html**
**http://www.cyber-kitchen.com/pgrestrt.htm**
**http://www.dinersgrapevine.com/**

## Spam

To quote The Encyclopedia of Bad Taste by Jane and Michael Stern, "Spam is ground pork shoulder and ground ham combined with salt, sugar, water and sodium nitrite, stuffed into a can, sealed, cooked, dried, dated, and shipped." It's hard to explain the world's love affair with this most versatile of foods. Join Spam enthusiasts as they debate the pros and cons of this 20th century culinary wonder. As the Sterns point out, "Next to spit-roasted dog meat, Spam is just about Korea's favorite delicacy."

**Web:**

**http://www.idir.net/~rbock/spam-rec.htm**
**http://www.yeeeoww.com/yecch/spamentries.html**

**Usenet:**

**alt.spam**
**alt.spam.conspiracy**

## Sporks

Simple, yet utilitarian. Graceful in its functional elegance. Along with lasers and automatic bread slicers, the Spork is one of the greatest inventions of the Modern Age. (The Modern Age officially began the day that Alice Cooper first appeared on Hollywood Squares, bringing the culture of the 1970s Disco Era to its timely conclusion.) Fans of the Spork post lauditory comments on the merits of this plastic eating utensil.

**Web:**

**http://www.spork.org/**

**Usenet:**

**alt.utensils.spork**

## Sushi

What is it about small, strange hunks of biological material wrapped in seaweed that makes you want to put them in your mouth? It has been said that sushi is to the 1990s what roasted chunks of meat were to the 1530s. Still, you don't need to take our word for it. Your friends on Usenet are ever-ready to talk sushi-talk regardless of how compelling your needs may be.

**Web:**

**http://sisko.awpi.com/AustinAxis/Food/Sushi.html**
**http://www.gsd.harvard.edu/crstaff/CRstaffhome-WADE-SUSHI.html**

**Usenet:**

**alt.food.sushi**

## Unusual Foods of the World

Pictures and details of a small selection of unusual foods from around the world, including snail livers, and Gatorade Spritzer.

**Web:**

**http://town.hall.org/food/unusual.html**

**Feel lucky? Try "Contests".**

### Look What I Found on the Net...

```
Newsgroup: alt.food.sushi
Subject: Dangers of sushi?

> My question is this:  does anyone out there have personal
> knowledge of anyone who's experienced a serious problem after
> eating sushi?  I suspect the dangers are greatly exaggerated
> and probably culturally biased.

I've never gotten ill in at least 500 outings.  I've never heard
anyone report that they got ill from sushi.  I've heard that it
is possible to get ill under certain circumstances -- the like
of which a sushi chef is knowledgeable in knowing how to avoid.

On the other hand I have gotten ill scores of times from poorly
prepared chicken, beef that was a little off.

Seems the odds are really greatly lessened in a sushi shop.
```

## Vegans

If it came out of an animal, vegans want no part of it. That means all the rich yummy foods are off limits—butter, milk, cheese, and eggs are among the things that will not pass a vegan's lips. Look at the vegan-oriented web page, or talk the talk with other vegans on the Net.

**Web:**

**http://www.vegan.org/news.html**

**Listserv Mailing List:**

List Name: **vegan-l**
Subscribe to: **listserv@vm.temple.edu**

**Listserv Mailing List:**

List Name: **vnews-l**
Subscribe to: **listserv@ubvm.cc.buffalo.edu**

## Vegetarian Resources

The word "vegetarian" was first used in England in 1847 by the people who started the Vegetarian Society of the United Kingdom. Today, vegetarianism covers a wide variety of eating choices. Some people simply avoid meat, but eat eggs, dairy products and fish. (Technically, you could call such people ovo-lacto pescetarians.) Other people eat only fruits and vegetables and nothing else (true vegetarians). Some will eat eggs (ovo vegetarians), or dairy products (lacto vegetarians), or both (ovo-lacto vegetarians). Other vegetarians are very strict, avoiding the use of any animal products whatsoever including non-food products (vegans). Perhaps the most strict are those people who will only eat foods that can be harvested without killing the plant (fruitarians). As you might imagine, there are a large number of vegetarian resources on the Net, and no matter what your preference, I guarantee there is something for you. To start, you may want to read one of the FAQs (frequently asked question lists). In addition, you will find information about nutrition, restaurants, organizations, journals and magazines, animal rights, and lots and lots of recipes.

**Web:**

**http://envirolink.org/arrs/VRG/**
**http://vegweb.com/**
**http://www.veg.org/veg/**

## Vegetarian Talk and General Discussion

A vegetarian will say, "I eat in a way that makes sense to me, in order to preserve my day-to-day vitality and maintain my longterm health." A non-vegetarian will say, "Is it worth living forever if you can't have a hot dog?" This debate seems to be the central nutritional issue of our times, and here is the place to talk about it. Share your vegetable-oriented opinions, thoughts and recipes with vegetarians all over the world.

**Usenet:**

**rec.food.veg**
**rec.food.veg.cooking**

**Listserv Mailing List:**

List Name: **vegfood**
Subscribe to: **listserv@cadserv.cadlab.vt.edu**

**Listserv Mailing List:**

List Name: **veglife**
Subscribe to: **listserv@vtvm1.cc.vt.edu**

## Wine

Tired of the pedestrian charms of beer? Move up to the big time where drinking is an art form and 1983 was a good year. Join the Bacchus society, wine lovers extraordinaire, and maybe even make your own homegrown vino. Oenophiles of the world unite: you have nothing to lose but your grains.

**Web:**

**http://www.speakeasy.org/~winepage/wine.html**
**http://www.winedine.co.uk/**

**Usenet:**

**alt.bacchus**
**alt.food.wine**
**rec.crafts.winemaking**

**Listserv Mailing List:**

List Name: **foodwine**
Subscribe to: **listserv@cmuvm.csv.cmich.edu**

**Majordomo Mailing List:**

List Name: **foodnwine**
Subscribe to: **majordomo@gnn.com**

**Majordomo Mailing List:**

List Name: **wine**
Subscribe to: **majordomo@wine.niagara.com**

## Wine Zines

When you are sitting in the study rolling a little vino around on your tongue and you need some interesting reading material, check these great wine zines on the Net. Whether you are a seasoned wine taster or a novice, you will find these web pages highly agreeable with robust content and balanced, supple designs.

**Web:**

**http://bighorn.terra.net/grapevine**
**http://felix.scvnet.com/~jkolesar/**
**http://www.bpe.com/radio/**
**http://www.crswww.com/crs/onwine/**

**Intrigue, Privacy, Secret Stuff...**

ARE YOU A
WINE LOVER?
Try the
GRAPEVINE.

# FREEDOM

## ACLU

The ACLU is the American Civil Liberties Union. Their charter is to protect American constitutional rights even when everyone else is asleep at the political switch. You may not always agree with the ACLU, but I guarantee that you will always have an opinion. Their web site contains speeches, publications, reports, legislative alerts, Supreme Court filings, and other information from the land of the generally free and occasionally brave.

**Web:**

**http://www.aclu.org/**

## Activism Resources

If you are an activist, it helps to build upon the experience of other people. Here are collections of activist resources. You will find advice regarding what to do and what not to do, as well as hints, inspirational writings, and links to related resources.

**Web:**

**http://www.eff.org/pub/Activism/**
**http://www.matisse.net/~kathy/activist/activist.html**

**Get involved.**
**Do something.**
**Make a difference.**
(But if you don't have the time, you can at least take a look at the activist resources on the Net.)

## Activist Projects

Would you like to get involved? Good. But how do you know what to do? This site has some suggestions. Read about current causes of concern, along with suggestions for action and a summary of the unfolding events.

**Web:**
**http://www.webactive.com/webactive/hap/hap.html**

## Amnesty International

The Amnesty International web site offers the full text of the Universal Declaration of Human Rights as well as information about the organization and a membership application.

**Web:**
**http://www.amnesty.org/**
**http://www.igc.apc.org/amnesty/**

## Banned Books

The only thing worse than a banned book is two banned books. Unfortunately, banning books did not die out with Hitler and the Nazis. Today, even in the U.S., there are still people who are trying to ban books that challenge their particular political and social agendas. Find out more about it on the Net. You will be surprised how many books have been banned over the years. Moreover, since you are on the Net where everything can be linked to something else, you can not only learn about the banned books, you can, in many cases, read them on your own screen, in the privacy of your own home.

**Web:**
**http://www.cs.cmu.edu/Web/People/spok/banned-books.html**

## Censorship of the Internet

Traditionally, the Net has been without organized censorship. There has, of course, always been censorship. However, it is at the local level. Now that the Net has become an important and prominent part of our global culture, there are those who would love to impose their will on everyone else by fiat. Here are two interesting, well-organized web sites that will keep you up to date on what is happening on the Net censorship-wise.

**Web:**
**http://www.epic.org/free_speech/censorship/**
**http://www.pathfinder.com/technology/netdecency/**

## Censorship Talk and General Discussion

The antidote to censorship is free and open discussion. That is what this Usenet group is devoted to: a frank discussion of censorship and current events. Hint: If you want to participate, be prepared to argue.

**Usenet:**
**alt.censorship**

## File Room

A large collection of occurrences of censorship, mostly in art or public display and performances. You can read the case histories and descriptions of the artwork. You can also add your own information if you know of a significant case of censorship. The information is global, concerning censorship issues around the world.

**Web:**
**http://fileroom.aaup.uic.edu/FileRoom/documents/homepage.html**

## Flag Burning

In the United States, the issue of having the freedom to burn the flag is so emotional as to be almost incomprehensible to people in other countries. In some countries, no one would dare even think about burning a flag. In other countries, no one would be bothered. In the U.S., however, the flag is an emotionally charged icon and being able to burn it is an important freedom, almost as if America is proud of the fact that the country is so free that its people are allowed to destroy and denigrate one of its most sacred symbols. The issue, of course, is symbolic. Should a person have the right to do something that many people find offensive, even if the act poses no immediate danger to anyone? Few Americans actually want to burn a flag, but many do want to preserve the freedom to do so. If you would like to understand the issues, try this web site. As you are reading, you can personally participate by choosing whether or not to burn a virtual flag.

**Web:**
**http://www.indirect.com/user/warren/flag.html**

**Censorship, Boo**

**All of us, of course, are against censorship (except when the censored item is something that offends *us*). If you've got a hankering to see what sorts of things people don't want you to see, visit *The File Room*. (Actually, the most important act of censorship of modern times occurred when "They" would not let us explain the real meaning of "rtfm" in *The Internet Complete Reference*.)**

## Free Speech

Free speech does not mean the same to everybody. As we all find out eventually, it is often the case that my freedom ends where yours begins. For this reason, there is really no such thing as complete freedom of speech. Instead, there is only an eternal debate over what should be allowed and what should be disallowed. Although many people like to think that the idea of free speech can be considered as a simple issue, there are many gray areas and, somehow, even in the United States—where freedom of speech is guaranteed by the Constitution—the line between right and wrong seems to always be moving. Here is a large collection of links to free speech-related resources on the Net. I was surprised at how much information is available. If you would like to explore the very complex concept of free speech, this is an excellent place to start.

**Web:**

**http://cavern.uark.edu/comminfo/www/freespeech.html**

## Free Speech Mailing List

A forum for discussing free speech issues. Topics here include current and historical issues in freedom of expression, reviews of recent books and articles related to free speech, constitutional interpretation, research opportunities, privacy, censorship, and other areas relating to freedom of expression in the United States and elsewhere.

**Listserv Mailing List:**

List Name: **amend1-l**
Subscribe to: **listserv@uafsysb.uark.edu**

## Freedom and Scientology

Scientology is a global organization with its own values, literature, and a lot of money. For a long time, many people have been at odds with Scientology for a variety of reasons and, now, the struggle has carried over to the Net. There is a lot of information about Scientology and what people think about it (pro and con) on the Net. If you care about such issues, I feel it is important to learn some of the details and make up your own mind. Here are two places to start. One is a web page relating to the protest against Scientology. The other is the official Scientology Internet site. Both places will lead you to a lot of interesting information.

**Web:**

**http://www.cybercom.net/~rnewman/scientology/home.html**
**http://www.scientology.org/**

## Freedom Launchsite

This site is a collection of a great many links to resources relating to freedom, censorship, free speech, activism, civil liberties, and so on. This is also a good place to find freedom-oriented groups and organizations.

**Web:**

**http://www.launchsite.com/freedom.htm**

## Freedom of Expression

In my opinion, the fundamental ideas regarding freedom of expression are best expressed by the First Amendment of the Constitution of the United States: "Congress shall make no law respecting an establishment of religion, or prohibiting the free exercise thereof; or abridging the freedom of speech, or of the press; or the right of the people peaceably to assemble, and to petition the Government for a redress of grievances." Although this particular quotation refers specifically to the U.S., freedom of expression is an issue all over the world. Here are some web sites that will lead you to a great many related resources all over the Net: the law, civil liberties, censorship, government, and much more.

**Web:**

**http://insight.mcmaster.ca/org/efc/pages/chronicle/censor.html**
**http://www.cybersquirrel.com/clc/expression.html**

## Freedom of Information Act

A publication from the federal government that explains to citizens how to use the Freedom of Information Act and the Privacy Act of 1974. The Usenet group contains discussion of the various aspects of the Freedom of Information Act.

**Web:**

**http://jcomm.uoregon.edu/~tgleason/FOIA.Guide_j202.html**

**Usenet:**

**alt.society.foia**

## Freedom of Religion

Almost by definition, belief in one particular religion precludes belief in another religion. Religions deal with matters of utmost importance to human beings: the existence of a supernatural being (or beings), morality and the law, what happens after death, the reasons for our existence, as well as our responsibilities toward society as a whole and toward individual people. Every religion believes that its scriptures and customs are the best (that is, true). However, history has proven over and over that when one religion dominates within a country or region, that group tends to use its power to oppress members of other religions. For this reason, the United States (and other countries) specifically enshrined in law the right for every person to practice religion (or to be without religion) as he or she sees fit. Such rights—perhaps by their very nature—are continually under attack, especially by those who would interpret the law to their advantage. Here are some web sites with useful and informative resources relating to the vitally important, but very complex concept we call freedom of religion.

**Web:**

**http://w3.trib.com/FACT/1st.relig.liberty.html**
**http://www.fac.org/religion/religion.htm**

## Freedom Talk and General Discussion

The measure of the maturity and intellectual wealth of any society is the civil liberties enjoyed by its members. This Usenet group is for the discussion of civil liberties, general philosophy as well as specific current events. When it comes to freedom, there is always something more to say. This is the place to say it.

**Web:**

**alt.society.civil-liberty**

## Gun Control

Gun control—restricting people's access to guns—is an issue everywhere, but nowhere is the debate as disputatious as in the United States. Technically, the American debate is rooted in the language of the Second Amendment to the U.S. Constitution: "A well regulated militia, being necessary to the security of a free state, the right of the people to keep and bear arms, shall not be infringed." It's easy to see how this can be interpreted two ways. If you are against gun control, you can point out that this amendment clearly enshrines the right of all Americans to "keep and bear arms". If you feel that guns should be controlled, you can argue that the amendment is irrelevant because it speaks only to the need of maintaining a "well regulated militia", and not any other uses of firearms. Here are web sites that reflect both sides of this issue. For discussion, the Usenet group is for general debate.

**Web:**

**http://guninfo.org/**
**http://www.clark.net/pub/tcasey/firearms.html**

**Usenet:**

**talk.politics.guns**

## Human Rights

Although we talk a lot about human rights, the idea is relatively new. On December 10, 1948, the United Nations General Assembly unanimously adopted the Universal Declaration of Human Rights. This was the first time a declaration signed by more than one country mentioned the idea of human rights by name. The web site has a collection of information and resources regarding human rights documents and organizations, including a well-organized collection of links to related resources around the Net. The Usenet group and mailing list are for ongoing discussion.

**Web:**

**http://www.traveller.com/~hrweb/hrweb.html**

**Usenet:**

**soc.rights.human**

**Listserv Mailing List:**

List Name: **hrs-l**
Subscribe to: **listserv@bingvmb.cc.binghamton.edu**

## Individual Rights in America

You may or may not feel that America is the Home of the Brave, but it is certainly the Land of the Free. I grew up in Canada, which is ostensibly a free country, but I really didn't appreciate freedom until I came to live in the United States. This web site is a guide to the rights of the individual in America. You will find links to important federal documents (such as the Constitution and the Bill of Rights), information about the rights of various groups, a list of related mailing lists, and places to find other legal information. If you do not live in the U.S., this is a great place to browse and get a feeling for the American spirit.

**Web:**

**http://asa.ugl.lib.umich.edu/chdocs/rights/Citizen.html**

## Liberty Web

Here is a large collection of links to resources on the Net relating to freedom. This is the place to look if you want to find out what the fanatics are doing to protect our freedom (even though, goodness knows, as one of my readers you are anything but a fanatic).

**Web:**

**http://www.catalog.com/jamesd**

## Medical Privacy

A compilation of companies who do some form of human quality tests that violate your rights to privacy. Who wants urine? Who wants blood? Who wants to crack open your skull and look inside? Helpful hint: Whatever happens, you can always say that you didn't inhale.

**Web:**

**http://www.eff.org/pub/Privacy/Medical**

### *Look What I Found on the Net...*

(from the Individual Rights in America web site)

The Declaration of Independence of the Thirteen Colonies

In CONGRESS, July 4, 1776

The unanimous Declaration of the thirteen united States of America,

When in the Course of human events, it becomes necessary for one people to dissolve the political bands which have connected them with another, and to assume among the powers of the earth, the separate and equal station to which the Laws of Nature and of Nature's God entitle them, a decent respect to the opinions of mankind requires that they should declare the causes which impel them to the separation.

We hold these truths to be self-evident, that all men are created equal, that they are endowed by their Creator with certain unalienable Rights, that among these are Life, Liberty, and the pursuit of Happiness. That to secure these rights, Governments are instituted among Men, deriving their just powers from the consent of the governed. That whenever any Form of Government becomes destructive of these ends, it is the Right of the People to alter or to abolish it, and to institute new Government, laying its foundation on such principles and organizing its powers in such form, as to them shall seem most likely to effect their Safety and Happiness...

## Naturism and Freedom

Naturism refers to the philosophy that it is healthy and desirable for human beings to spend a significant amount of time naked, often in the company of other people. Most of us are taught that being naked in front of other people is bad, and so we sublimate our feelings by snickering at the very idea of nudism. So when I tell you that naturists are under attack from various people and organizations, I understand if you feel like ignoring the whole thing ("Surely we have more important matters to worry about") or perhaps even make a joke ("Did you hear about the blind man at a nudist colony?"). However, you should be concerned. When an isolated beach is closed to nudism because some local community pressure group is offended by the idea of people being allowed to be naked in a secluded area, the issue should concern all of us. Being naked—in an appropriate place—is a relatively harmless activity, and the people who would deny that freedom to naturists are just as ready to deny other, more vital freedoms to you and me. In my opinion, when you hear the bell of oppression anywhere, at any time, you don't have to ask for whom it tolls.

**Web:**
**http://www.naturist.com/alerts/**

# Addicted2: Stuff

You have to admit it.
There is a lot of stuff on the Net.

If you like looking at stuff—and who doesn't?—the Addicted2: Stuff web site has collected links and created commentary about some of strangest and most interesting web sites on the Net.

(And you'll have fun, fun, fun till your daddy takes your keyboard away.)

## United Nations Agreements on Human Rights

When we study and talk about freedom, some of the most important documents of modern times are adopted by the United Nations. Here are these documents: Universal Declaration of Human Rights, Covenant on Civil and Political Rights, Covenant on Economic, Social and Cultural Rights, Convention Against Torture, Convention Against Genocide, Geneva Conventions, Convention on the Rights of the Child, Convention on the Elimination of Discrimination Against Women, and the original 1945 Charter of the United Nations.

**Web:**
**http://www.traveller.com/~hrweb/legal/undocs.html**

# FUN

## Addicted2: Stuff

The only thing I don't like about stuff is that, once you get it, you have to put it somewhere. However, I have figured out how to avoid this problem. What I do is go to this web site. Here, they have all sorts of stuff I can enjoy and not have to worry about cleaning up the place afterwards. No dusting, organizing or putting away required. If you are addicted to stuff, you have to take a look. There is a little bit of everything: cars, music, quotes, collecting, oddities, and on and on.

**Web:**
**http://www.morestuff.com/**

## Anagrams

Anagrams are something you can do no matter where you are or what is going on. For instance, if you're in traffic and there is nothing on the radio but ads for hair replenishing cream, you can make up all sorts of anagrams by rearranging the letters of all of Henry the VIII's wives' names. This will be good practice so when you are at a party and word gets around that you are the county anagram champion you will be able to demonstrate your talents with grace and elegance.

**Web:**
**http://www.catt.ncsu.edu/~witsend/hehf/anagrams.html**

**Usenet:**
**alt.anagrams**

## Boredom

Bored? Share your boredom with others who have nothing better to do than listen.

**IRC:**

**#bored**

## Bubbles

I have a wonderful battery-operated bubble gun, and sometimes when I need to take a break from writing, I will go out on the patio and blow bubbles. Occasionally, my cat will lounge on a nearby railing and sniff at the bubbles as they slowly float by, carried on their upward journey by the cool ocean breeze. If you think you would enjoy being a bubble person, check out this great bubble site and learn about the history of bubbles, how to make bubble tools, and creating your own bubble solution.

**Web:**

**http://bubbles.org/**

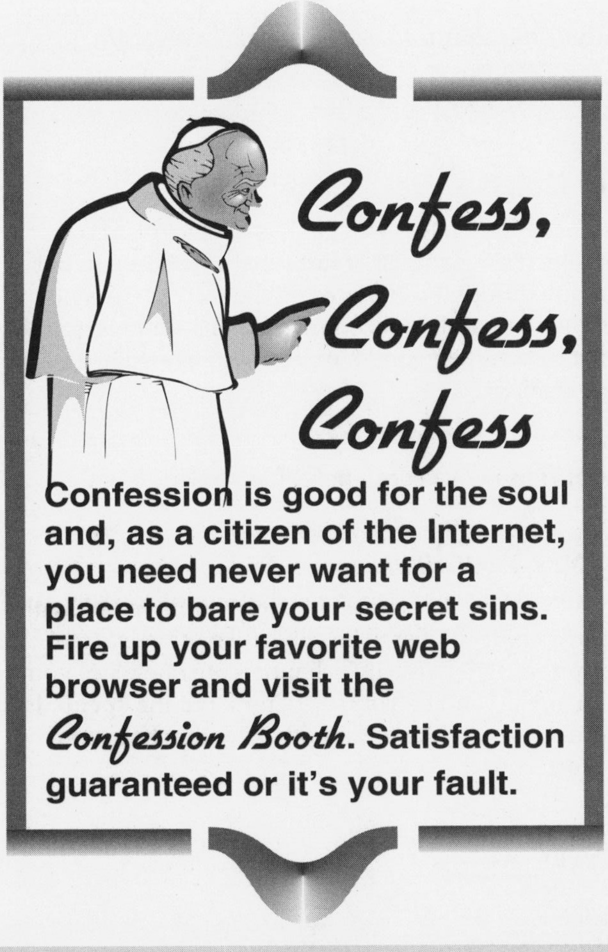
Confess,
Confess,
Confess
Confession is good for the soul and, as a citizen of the Internet, you need never want for a place to bare your secret sins. Fire up your favorite web browser and visit the Confession Booth. Satisfaction guaranteed or it's your fault.

## Chat

Are you bored? Here are a some great places to chew the virtual fat with other Internet folks. Once you are on the Net, there will always be someone (or many someones) to whom you can talk, day and night, night and day.

**IRC:**

**#chat**
**#hello**
**#talk**

## Confession Booth

With this web page, almost anyone can feel like a Catholic. Confess your sins by checking the appropriate boxes and receiving your penance.

**Web:**

**http://anther.learning.cs.cmu.edu/priest.html**

## Cool Toy Site of the Week

Are you looking for a new toy in your life? Try the Cool Toy Site of the Week. This site highlights and reviews a new toy site every week. Toy gluttons who want more than one toy site a week can read the reviews from previous weeks. As far as I am concerned, there is no reason why you should not be having fun this very minute.

**Web:**

**http://utmdacc.mda.uth.tmc.edu:5014/eric/rtm/toysite.html**

## Cracks in the Web

Get into some danger without ever having to hurt yourself. Cracks in the Web is a weekly espionage thriller that lets you get in on the spy mystery-solving action without the danger of getting yourself into a pair of cement shoes.

**Web:**

**http://www.directnet.com/~gmorris/**

## Cybertown

If you are planning your next vacation and you are not sure where to go, try Cybertown. It's free and you don't have to worry about losing your luggage. The web area is designed like a city from the 21st century. Click your way around the city map to explore various sections of town, but there's no telling what you might find. Hint: Cybertown is not organized to find something quickly, so plan to stay and enjoy yourself for a while.

**Web:**

**http://www.cybertown.com/**

## Diaries and Journals

There's nothing like the sinful pleasure of snooping where you don't belong. The Web is a great place to be able to stick your nose into people's private lives without them knowing it. This site has a list of daily journals and diaries that are on the Net. With the click of your mouse, you can be finding out who did what, to whom, and why. Just think, if it weren't for these people who have nothing better to do with their time, you would have nothing better to do with *your* time.

**Web:**

**http://www.spies.com/~diane/journals2.html**

### Popular Culture at its Worst

If you already hate Barney the Dinosaur, you are only one step away from detesting The Family Circus. And once you achieve this enlightened state, you can maintain your good taste and sense of value by spending some time with The Dysfunctional Family Circus. Just the thing for people who get tired of people who get tired of people.

## Dysfunctional Family Circus

If you hate Barney the Dinosaur and Mr. Rogers, you will love The Dysfunctional Family Circus. It is a user-participation parody of The Family Circus (a too-cute-for-words and make-you-want-to-be-sick-right-here-and-now comic that celebrates the inane normalities of white-bread family life in the U.S). Even if you never heard of The Family Circus, look at this one anyway. It's great to make fun of something, even when you don't know what it is.

**Web:**

**http://spinn.thoughtport.com/spinnwebe/dfc/**

## Electronic Postcards

Send greetings to friends so they will think you are thoughtful and considerate. Pick from a selection of graphics, fill out the form with your message and send it on its way. You can preview the card before you send it in case you made any really embarrassing mistakes.

**Web:**

**http://linux.hartford.edu/~azmizar/postcard/postcard.cgi**
**http://www.maxracks.com/**

## Fun Links

Hard-core fun lovers will get lots of enjoyment out of this site. It's a giant list of links that will take you out to many different fun places on the Net. There is no commentary and no recommendations—nothing at all to get between you and a wagon load of virtual hedonism.

**Web:**

**http://miso.wwa.com/~boba/fun.html**

## Happy People

Tired of talking to crotchety people? Want to talk with happy people, or just to be silly and not have to feel guilty about it? These IRC channels are one place you can hang out and be yourself. Check out the **#penpals** channel if you'd like to find others with whom you can correspond.

**IRC:**

**#happy**
**#penpals**
**#silly**

## Internet Candy Dish

When you connect to this URL, five random sweetheart images are presented, complete with those cute little quotes on the front. "Be Good to Me," "As You Like It," "Jet Set," "Dearest," and "You're So Cool."

**Web:**

**http://www.mps.org/~rainbow/ToyBox/ICD/icd.cgi**

Guys: Do you want to prove to your sweetheart that you are gentle and sensitive? Nothing could be easier. Just show her the Internet Candy Dish.

## Internet Scavenger Hunt

A scavenger hunt is a game in which people have to run all over the place trying to find items on a list. The fun comes from the list itself: usually the items are strange, requiring you to exercise not only your legs but your ingenuity. This scavenger hunt takes place right on the Internet. You read a list of questions and use your Net-savvy skills to find the answers. What I like about the game is that it demonstrates just what a wide variety of information is out there somewhere. The next time you run into an Internet know-it-all, challenge him to the Internet Scavenger Hunt, the winner getting to keep *both* computers. (The 90s version of racing for pink slips.)

**Web:**

**http://www.shore.net/~mcheung/hunt/**

## Internet University

It's not generally well known, but you don't necessarily have to graduate from high school to attend a university. In fact, right now, no matter who you are, you can go to Internet University. There are no admission fees, no rules (and the food is great because you have to bring your own). Internet University has lots and lots of interesting things to do and makes for a nice diversion when you should be doing something more important. Plan on stimulating the portions of your brain that respond to popular culture, books, entertainment, food, health and sex.

**Web:**

**http://www.internetuniv.com/**

## IRC Bar

Come drink and chat in the IRC bar. Descriptions of over sixty cocktails are available from the barman who is more than happy to serve or even sober you up. The web site offers gossip, news, help, and gif pictures, and plans of the real-life meetings that the bar's frequenters hold every so often. Come drink and be merry in the bar that never sleeps. Cheers!

**Web:**

**http://sandbox.sdstate.edu/~brownd/ircbar.html**

**IRC:**

**#ircbar**

## Line Around the World

Start at the point of origin and follow the line around the world. Arrows will point you to other people who have joined the line around the world by doing good deeds. You can follow the line or join it yourself.

**Web:**

**http://www-leland.stanford.edu/~dsedy/line.html**

## Madlibs

If your Web browser has forms, you will have loads of fun filling in nouns, adjectives, and other words out of which the computer will weave a story. This is just like the paper Madlibs, only you don't need a group of friends to play it.

**Web:**

**http://www.mit.edu:8001/madlib/**

Do you think you might like to be a writer? Start with **Madlibs** and, if you do well, you can work your way up to sending in anecdotes to *Reader's Digest.* (From there, it is only a small step to writing Internet books. Soon, fame, fortune, and never-ending happiness will be yours.)

India INK

A B C D E F G H I J K L M N O P Q R S T U V W X Y Z

## Mind Breakers

Is your life uneventful? Is your job a bore? If so, there is no need to go through the day without a mental challenge. Just explore this collection of mind games, puzzles and riddles, and get ready to be perplexed, frustrated and amazed. For some extra stimulation, try the Usenet discussion group.

**Web:**

**http://huizen.dds.nl/~mahulsma/mb.htm**

**Usenet:**

**alt.brain.teasers**

## Nicecafe

A nice little cafe in the realms of IRC, where people sit and watch the world go by.

**IRC:**

**#nicecafe**

## Puzzles

Hundreds of puzzles to open your mind, complete with solutions. If six cats can kill six rats in six minutes, how many cats does it take to kill one rat in one minute?

**Web:**

**http://einstein.et.tudelft.nl/~arlet/puzzles/**

## Sites of the Day

Everyone needs a reason to get out of the bed in the morning, so here is one that will always work. These web sites offer links to many places on the Net that have "sites of the day" and to web pages that change daily. For example, you will find a new word every day, a daily fun fact, daily news stories, political sites of the day, funky sites of the day, or a [insert just about anything you are interested in] site of the day.

**Web:**

**http://fox.nstn.ca/~moonstar/dynalink/cooool.html**
**http://www.webcom.com/~tbrown/coolsite.html**

## Spot: An Online Soap Opera

The Spot is a soap opera designed to be viewed over the Net. Tune in to the daily lives of guys and gals whose activities unfold into a never-ending dramatic/boring imitation of real life at its ooziest.

**Web:**

**http://www.thespot.com/**

THE SPOT
If you think your life is boring or insignificant, check out **The Spot**. One look at what these people are up to, and your personal existence will begin to shine with the brilliant light of relevance.

## Squat: A Parody

A parody of The Spot, this serial text drama takes place in and around an old mobile home in Southern U.S.A. Read about the tension-filled existences of these young men and women who are trying to make their way through life the best way their script writers know how.

**Web:**

**http://theory.physics.missouri.edu/squat/**

## Time Wasting

It's a moral imperative that everyone spend at least a little time very day wasting some time or else we would have all this extra time that we would have to fill or worse—recycle. If you have too much time on your hands, waste a little of it here learning new ways to creatively fritter a good portion of your day away.

**Usenet:**

**alt.timewasters**

## Toy Talk and General Discussion

Admit it. You love toys. Not only are they fun, but they are a great thing to keep you busy so you don't have to work. The only thing that could possibly be better than playing with toys is actually getting paid to play with toys. Enter the world's largest playroom and meet other people who love toys. These groups cover toys from the simplest plastic Legos to the most complicated technical gadgetry.

**Usenet:**

**alt.toys.gi-joe**
**alt.toys.high-tech**
**alt.toys.lego**
**alt.toys.low-tech**
**alt.toys.transformers**
**rec.collecting.dolls**
**rec.toys.cars**
**rec.toys.lego**
**rec.toys.misc**
**rec.toys.vintage**

## URouLette

URouLette is a random URL generator. By clicking on the picture of the floating roulette wheel, you are connected to a random location on the Web. You won't know where you're going until you get there.

**Web:**

**http://www.uroulette.com:8000/**

## Virtual Presents

I love virtual presents, and I love to send them to my friends for no reason at all. This is a great place to visit if you need to get someone an impressive gift that you can't afford. You can send your friends a vacation, fine jewelry, animals, food, flowers, and a lot more. What's a virtual present? Try it.

**Web:**

**http://www.virtualpresents.com/**

**Read the FAQs of life.**

**Virtual Presents**

Right now, there are people all over the Net having fun sending imaginary gifts to one another by email.

Your virtual presents is requested.

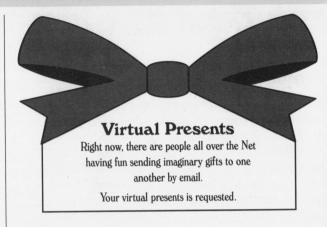

## Web Soap Operas

I don't watch television, so I miss out on the portion of the popular culture having to do with the daily lives of imaginary people having imaginary various trials and tribulations in imaginary places. However, on the Net, I can tune into a web-based soap opera whenever I want. I don't have to wait for a particular time of day, and I don't have to be interrupted by commercials. This web site is an index page to the various soap operas, collaborative fiction and ongoing dramas taking place around the Net.

**Web:**

**http://home.earthlink.net/free/merlin200/webdocs/soap/soap.htm**

## Yahoo Parody

Called "Yecch!!!", this site parodies the famous Yahoo. Yecch compiles weird pages or puts normal pages in a weird context. Extra special gross sites are marked by easily recognizable icons for people who love that stuff or for the squeamish who want to stay out of the way.

**Web:**

**http://www.yeeeoww.com/yecch/yecchhome.html**

## Yo-Yos

If your personal popularity depends on hanging out at the mall strutting your fancy yo-yo style, it's good to have a new way to access fresh material with which to impress your friends. Check out these sites at which you will find yo-yo tips and tricks, as well as general information regarding this pastime of the gods.

**Web:**

**http://pages.nyu.edu/~tqm3413/yoyo/**
**http://www.pd.net/yoyo/**

# GAMES AND PUZZLES

## Arcadium

Arcadium is a great hangout for hard-core gamers, whether you use a PC, Mac or a console (such as Nintendo, Playstation or Saturn). Arcadium provides a total gaming-related environment, including your own personal start page. There are lots of things to do here. You can post in the message forums, read game reviews, chat with other gamers, find out about playing games over the Net, and download demos of many different games. Once you know about this site, there is no excuse whatsoever for doing any useful work ever again.

**Web:**
**http://www.arcadium.com/**

## Backgammon

Backgammon is played by two players using a specially marked board, 15 counters and a set of dice. You take turns throwing the dice and moving your counters around the board according to the numbers on the dice. When a counter reaches the end of the circuit, you remove it. The object of the game is to be the first person to remove all your counters from the board. It sounds easy, but there's lots of strategy involved. Backgammon is the oldest game in recorded history; historians even believe it was played in ancient Mesopotamia. Today, backgammon is as popular as ever, and if you would like to play, learn, or talk about it, there are lots of resources on the Net. Or you can go to Mesopotamia and find someone to play in person. (Driving instructions: Head toward central Asia, make a left at the Persian Gulf, and go back 3,000 years.)

**Web:**
**http://www.io.org/~takeith/bg/main.html**

**Usenet:**
**rec.games.backgammon**

**"Fun" is fun.**

### Backgammon with Strangers

These days you have to be careful who you mix with. Playing backgammon in person presents all kinds of potential problems. For example, someone might sneeze on you and give you pneumonia, or your opponent could get mad and stab you with an ice pick.

Much better to play it safe: connect to the ***Backgammon Server***, where you can depend on the kindness of strangers. Moreover, you can play in your underwear and no one will care.

## Battleships

In World War II, radio operators invented the game of Battleships in order to test radio transmissions that were kept secret from the Japanese. The operators were only allowed a few tests a day, so they developed a game which they played, a bit at a time, over a matter of weeks. And now you can play the same game (without waiting) on the Internet.

**Web:**
**http://polaris.biology.ucla.edu:8088/ships/**

## Bingo Zone

To be an excellent Net person, you need to develop good mouse skills. For example, to compete professionally, you must be able to steer your mouse pointer to a specific area of your screen and click the mouse button with perfect timing. And you must be able to do this dependably, quickly and under enormous pressure. Perfecting and maintaining such skills requires constant practice, and here is the place to do so. At the Bingo Zone, you compete with many other bingo players from around the world. You will need to keep a sharp eye on the screen and coordinate your mouse and pointer perfectly. Check here for playing times.

**Web:**
**http://www.bingozone.com/TBC_schedule.htm**

## Blackjack

If you can't make it to a casino this weekend, this is the next best thing. Play Blackjack with other Internet folks and become a Net billionaire or downright penniless. There are help files available and records are kept of rankings, cash won and lost, top players, and other table statistics. Join the table today.

**Web:**

**http://www.web-source.com/bj.html**
**http://www2.netdoor.com/~kensmith/bjstrat.html**

**IRC:**

**#blackjack**

## Board Games

Rules, rule variations, reviews, clubs, distributors, charts, and more about board games from around the world. This web page caters mainly to family and strategy games. On the Usenet group, you can talk with people around the world about your favorite board games.

**Web:**

**http://www.gamecabinet.com/**

**Usenet:**

**rec.games.board**

## Boggle

The robot on this channel hosts a game patterned after the popular Boggle word game. You are presented with a grid of letters, and you must form words that are at least three letters long, created out of adjoining letters. Full instructions are available from the bot online.

**IRC:**

**#boggle**

## Bridge

Bridge is such a fun game for couples. Most men take up bridge when they get married and discover their wives won't let them watch football. The only thing left to do is to sit with another couple and play cards all night. Perfect your bridge skills so you can learn to play a killer game. If you're clever, you can even make it a contact sport so you won't miss football.

**Web:**

**http://www.cs.vu.nl/~sater/bridge/bridge-on-the-web.html**

### The Game of Bridge

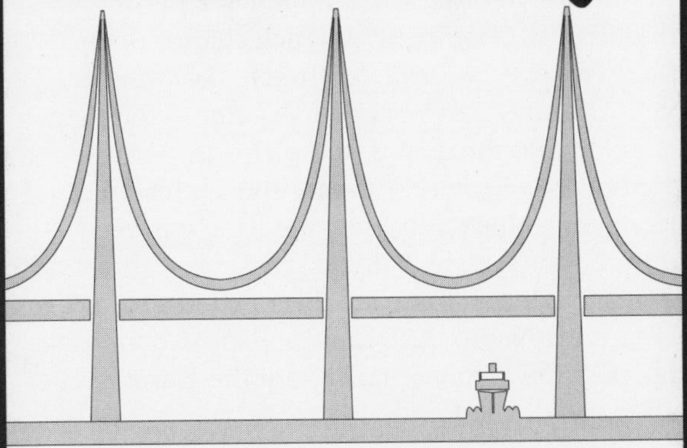

Well, it's time to write another advertisement and my editor suggested I do one about the game of bridge. Actually, I don't normally even think of it as a game, per se. More like a thing that you build, or perhaps even a structure. Okay, it's important to have bridges–after all, if we didn't have any bridges, all the cars on the highway would just fall off into nothingness, and you wouldn't be able to get across rivers and things–but still, I hardly see where that qualifies as a game. And I'm dashed if I can figure out why anyone wanted me to write an ad for the "game" of bridge. I mean, I know that there are people out there who build bridges and roads and things, civil engineers and what not, but why anyone would think that that belongs in an Internet book, or why it requires an advertisement... What's that? You don't mean building bridges? You mean the card game? Do you mean all that stuff with spades and hearts and two no-trump and so on? Oh... *that* bridge game.

Oh... Never mind.

## Chaos

The game of Chaos is patterned after the popular party game Outburst. You play the game on IRC in real time by interacting with a bot (automated program). It gives a category and you must provide answers that fit that category. You play as part of a team. Full instructions are available online from the web site.

**Web:**

**http://www.cs.uregina.ca/~hoyle/Games/chaos.html**

**IRC:**

**#chaos**

## Chess

The attraction of chess is that it requires intense concentration in order to dominate in a highly competitive environment in which chance plays virtually no part whatsoever (much like being a professional Internet writer). The game symbolizes warfare, in that the goal is to capture as many of the opponent "men" (pieces) as possible. Unlike real warfare, the game ends when the King has been captured ("checkmate"). If you are a chess affcionado, or even a beginner, there are lots of chess-related places on the Net to visit. You can learn about the game, play the game, or talk about the game (sort of an allegory for Life).

**Web:**

**http://caissa.onenet.net/chess/**
**http://www.bluemtn.com/~duif/hotchess.html**
**http://www.delorie.com/game-room/chess/**

**IRC:**

**#chess**

CHESS LOVERS,
the Net has a lot for you. The Chess Archives are just full of things and stuff and so on.

## Connect-4

Connect-4 is a two-player game in which the object is to be the first person to connect four colors in a row on a 7x6 square board, by dropping blue or red chips into columns. It's sounds simple, but it provides a nice, diverting break when you have a few extra moments to play on the Net.

**Web:**

**http://www.csclub.uwaterloo.ca/cgi-bin/cgiwrap/kppomaki/c4/connect_www.cgi**

## Conquest

"Kill a man, you are an assassin. Kill millions of men, you are a conqueror." Play IRC Conquest, a strategy war game set in the Middle Ages—a time of battles, alliances, and spies.

**Web:**

**http://www.misha.net/~conquest/conq.html**

**IRC:**

**#conquest**

## Core War

Core War is a game in which people write computer programs that are run at the same time on the same computer. The goal of the game is to write a program that can kill the other programs by terminating all of their processes. Core War programs are written in an assembly language called Redcode and run in a virtual computer called MARS (Memory Array Redcode Simulator). There aren't any real MARS machines, but there are Core War systems available for most popular types of computers. Core War was first described in March 1984 by D. G. Jones and A. K. Dewdney of the University of Western Ontario (in London, Canada). Core War is the ultimate game for ultimate computer programmers: no weenies allowed.

**Web:**

**http://www.stormking.com/~koth/corewar-faq.html**
**http://www.ypn.com/games2/a671.html**

## Cribbage

Why work when you can play games? Download cribbage and spend a few frustrating hours trying to beat your computer.

**Web:**

**http://tis_archive.thepoint.net/FreeBSD/FreeBSD-current/src/games/cribbage**
**http://www.gamesdomain.co.uk/directd/pc/windows/cards/cribw10.html**

## Crossword Puzzles

Do you like crossword puzzles? There are many, many puzzles on the Net that you can access for free whenever you want. There are also dictionaries, word lists, guides, computer programs, helpful tips, and a great deal of other crossword-related material, including a FAQ (frequently asked question list). Now, if someone would only tell me the three-letter word for an Australian bird, and the two-letter name for the sun god, my life would be complete.

**Web:**

http://cherwell.ospl.co.uk/life/headercw.html
http://virtumall.com/cgi-bin/crossword
http://www.cis.ohio-state.edu/hypertext/faq/usenet/crossword-faq/top.html
http://www.primate.wisc.edu/people/hamel/cp.html

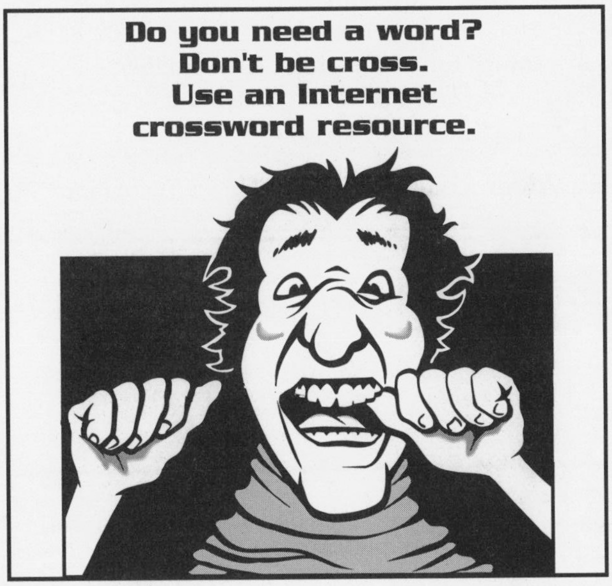
Do you need a word?
Don't be cross.
Use an Internet
crossword resource.

## Doom

These unofficial Doom web pages offer the official Doom FAQ, tutorial guides, update news, Doom specifications, some graphics from the game, some great utilities (such as map editors and level creators) to use with Doom, and links to other Doom-related pages.

**Web:**

http://doomgate.cs.buffalo.edu/
http://www.erie.net/~mrdoom/

If you are a Doom fan, the Net has lots of stuff for you. Then you can hunt and kill things to your heart's content in the privacy of your very own computer.

## Doom Talk and General Discussion

Have you been dreaming about Cacodemons, Imps, and Barons of Hell? If not, you're not playing enough Doom. Join with others hooked on this incredible, virtually real, shoot 'em all game from id Software. The DoomServ bot on the IRC channel offers many files, including patches, FAQs, modem init strings, cheats, help files, editors, tutorials, and much more.

**Usenet:**

alt.games.doom
alt.games.doom.ii
rec.games.computer.doom.announce
rec.games.computer.doom.newplayers

**IRC:**

#doom

## Empire

Home of the famous game of Empire, the real-time strategy wargame played by people across the Internet. This page offers Empire news, FAQs, and archive services to obtain the necessary software.

**Web:**

http://www.empire.net/~children/

## Fascist

Fascist is a variation on the game called Nomic, which was invented by Peter Suber and described by Douglas Hofstadter in Scientific American. Fascist is designed to be completely undemocratic, at least to start with. There are a few initial rules, players propose new rules or rule changes, and the Imperious Emperor says whether they are accepted or not.

**Web:**

**http://www.mit.edu:8001/people/achmed/inomic/**

## Game of Life

Is it about life or is it just a game? Are we just cosmic chickens in the barnyard of the universe? Pit yourself against the skills of the computer in this game of logic and strategy and discover why nobody makes playing God a full-time job.

**Web:**

**http://www.research.digital.com/nsl/projects/life/life.html**

## Game Reviews

This is an online magazine dedicated to electronic and computerized games: reviews, interviews, reports and general game industry news. If you are going to be a zealot, you might as well know what you are talking about.

**Web:**

**http://www.gamesdomain.com/gdreview/**

## Games and Recreation

I love this collection: there are so many games here, I am never without something new to try. Computer games, card games, board games, role-playing games—all this and much more. The next time someone asks you what's so good about the Net, show him or her this web site and say, "This reaffirms my basic belief that Man was not put onto this Earth to be serious and reverent, but to play games and have as much fun as possible." Then, invite your friend to join you in selecting something new to try.

**Web:**

**http://www.cis.ufl.edu/~thoth/library/recreation.html**

### *Look What I Found on the Net...*

```
Newsgroup: alt.games.doom
Subject: Real Men Use the Keyboard

>>> I've played keyboarders before.  Pretty decent keyboarders.
>>> And you know what? I won.
>>> You also know what? I use the mouse.
>>> You also know what?
>>> I've never had less than a 3-to-1 frag ratio against a
>>> keyboarder...

>> I've also played decent keyboarders.
>> And you know what? I beat them too.
>> Your point?

> None of you are "real men".  Real men have better things to do
> than sit behind a computer (keyboard or mouse) wasting their
> lives away playing video games...

Right.  Real men are those who have nothing better to do than
sit behind a computer (keyboard or mouse) wasting their life
away, telling people that they waste their lives away playing
video games...
```

## Games and Recreation

Stop studying. Stop working.
Stop living up to your responsibilities
and other people's expectations.

Stop right now.

Good. Now you can visit the Games and Recreation web site and find something better to do with your time.

## Games Archive for PCs

Explore your online game options at this archive for PC games. This site includes downloadable shareware as well as playable and non-playable demos for software you have to buy.

**Web:**

**http://www.happypuppy.com/games/link/**

## Games Domain

The Games Domain is a large, well-organized collection of games, games and more games. No matter what you enjoy, I guarantee there will be something here for you. Aside from links to actual games, you will find information, articles, FAQs, patches, tips and hints, and more.

**Web:**

**http://www.gamesdomain.co.uk/**
**http://www.gamesdomain.com/**

## Hangman

Hangman is a game in which you try to guess a mystery word, one letter at a time. When you guess a correct letter, you are shown where it appears in the word. When you guess a wrong letter, a new feature is added to a drawing of a little man. If the entire little man is drawn before you guess all the letters in the word correctly, you lose, and the little man gets hung. I wonder if this is a feminist game? (I could make a joke about a well-hung little man, but instead, I will content myself with wondering out loud why the game is not called "hangperson".)

**Web:**

**http://home.netscape.com/people/nathan/netnoose/**
**http://weber.u.washington.edu/~jgurney/games/Hangman.html**

## Head to Head Daemon Resources

An archive and mailing list for anyone interested in producing software that allows you to play multiuser realtime PC games over the Internet. For example, you can play certain flight simulators and other games such as Doom "head to head"—that is, against another real person when you connect your PCs via modem. Members of this mailing list are interested in producing dialers and other driver programs that convince your game software to play in a multiuser mode over the Internet. Some of these dialers are already finished and are in use. Join the list to find out which games you can play head to head over the Internet and where to find the necessary utilities.

**Web:**

**http://www.cactus.org/~knutson/IHHD/**

**Listserv Mailing List:**

List Name: **ihhd**
Subscribe to: **listserv@cactus.org**

## Initgame

Playing Initgame is just like playing the guessing game 20 Questions, except that you have to try and guess the famous person that the gamemaster is thinking of. There is a bot (automated program) with help files and tips for playing the game.

**IRC:**

**#initgame**

## Interactive Fiction

Interactive fiction (IF) is a computerized text-based game in which a story is told as part of the game. The first IF game was probably "Hunt the Wumpus", a Unix game from the early 1970s, in which you must move around a dodecahedron-shaped maze, avoiding mysterious dangers in search of a Wumpus, which you must kill before he eats you. (Obviously, some people *did* inhale.) The classic IF was "Adventure", which debuted in 1977. Interactive fiction is a lot of fun. I myself completely mastered Adventure during the summer of 1981 when I had a few months off from medical school. There are lots of IF enthusiasts on the Net and lots of IF resources to explore.

**Web:**

**http://challenge.tiac.net/users/baf/if-guide.html**
**http://fiddle.ee.vt.edu/proto/Recreation/Games/Interactive_Fiction/1-index.html**
**http://www.undergrad.math.uwaterloo.ca/~svanegmo/if-index.html**

**Usenet:**

**rec.arts.int-fiction**
**rec.games.int-fiction**

## Interactive Web Games

Here's a fun web page with several interactive games, including Java games. Just the ticket when work gets slow.

**Web:**

**http://www.bu.edu/Games/games.html**

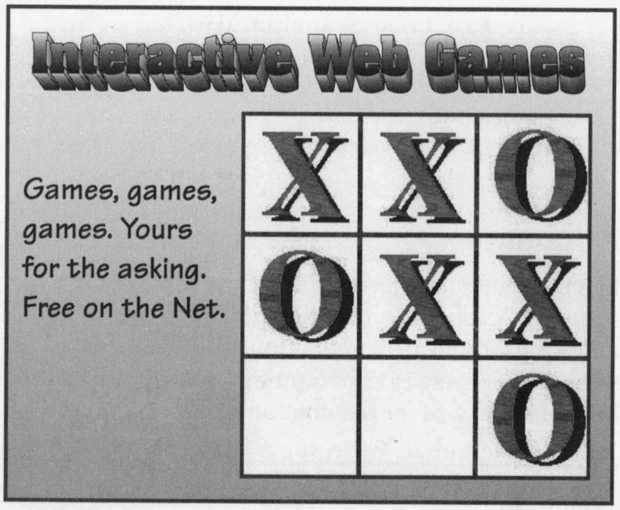
Interactive Web Games
Games, games, games. Yours for the asking. Free on the Net.
X X O
O X X
O

## Jeopardy

An online Jeopardy host asks a multitude of questions in many different categories, awarding points to the first person to answer correctly. Win enough points and you can play Final Jeopardy on this popular channel.

**IRC:**

**#riskybus**

## Magic: The Gathering

This is a dungeons-and-dragons-type game that is played with collectible cards. The site has tips on strategies, rules, different ways to play. It has links to other pages and sources for gaming materials.

**Web:**

**http://www.echo-on.net/~jelkouby/zone.html**

## Mazes

The best thing about having your own maze is you always have a good excuse for not doing something on time. ("I'm sorry I can't turn in my homework; my dog took it and dropped it in my maze.") If you are one of the few people who don't have a maze of their very own in the family room, you can at least explore and create mazes over the Net.

**Web:**

**http://www.delorie.com/game-room/mazes/**
**http://www.obs-us.com/obs/english/books/holt/books/maze/**

## Microsoft Flight Simulator

If you don't happen to own your own aircraft, you really miss out on a lot of great experiences (like taking your friends for rides and making them airsick). However, if you have Microsoft Flight Simulator, at least you get to have the next best thing. On the Net, there are lots of people who are addicted to this game and who enjoy sharing. There are archives for various types of information, aircraft, documentation and tools. If you enjoy talking about the game as much as you like playing, join in the Usenet discussion. Pretty soon, you'll be so good, you'll be able to invite your friends over to visit and make them sick just watching you use the computer.

**Web:**

**http://members.aol.com/TGFltsim/**
**http://www.surf-ici.com/fishman/fs51/**

**Usenet:**

**comp.sys.ibm.pc.games.flight-sim**

## Multiuser Games

Forget competing against the computer. Match your wits against the unpredictability of the human mind and play games against your friends. These Usenet groups will give you a huge amount of information about various multiuser games. Work your way up through the ranks and before long you will be known as the neighborhood champion of network computer games, and when you are at the grocery store, the people will be yelling throughout the produce section, saying, "Hey, you're the champ, aren't you? How are those brussels sprouts?"

**Usenet:**

**alt.games.mtrek**
**alt.games.netrek.paradise**
**rec.games.bolo**

## Netropolis

If you want to develop a little character and you are looking for an exercise in patience, have a look at the Netropolis, an interactive web game. Pick a company name and a geographic location, then start the search for a plot of land on which to build your empire. You will be playing against people all around the world.

**Web:**

**http://www.delphi.co.uk/netropolis/**

## Othello

Othello (which is similar to Reversi) is a strategy board game played by a great many people around the world. Othello is played on an 8x8 square by two players, each of which uses discs which are one color on one side and a different color on the other side (for example, white and black). Each player has his own color. Players alternate moves, putting down a disc (with their personal color face up) in such as way as to try to "outflank" some of the other person's discs. When this happens, the outflanked discs are flipped, changing their color. When the game ends, the winner is the person who has the most discs with his color on the board. Lots and lots of people play Othello. Would you like to try? On the Net you can practice by playing against a computer.

**Web:**

**http://web.cs.ualberta.ca/~brock/othello.html**
**http://www.kmine.com/othello.htm**

## PC Games Frequently Asked Question List

An invaluable document for PC gamers providing related Usenet newsgroups, ftp guide, acronym list, computer issues, software issues, and a great deal of essential information.

**Web:**

**http://www.gamesdomain.com/pcfaq/pcgfaq1.html**

? ? ? ? ? ? ?

**Do you have a PC? do you have more time than you know what to do with? The PC Games frequently asked questions list will well repay your inspection.**

¿ ¿ ¿ ¿ ¿ ¿ ¿

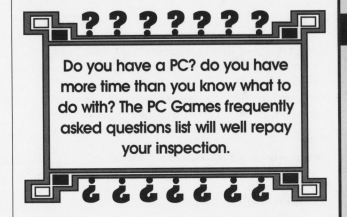

## PC Games Talk and General Discussion

If God didn't want us to use our PCs for games, he wouldn't have given us so many game discussion groups. The **.games** and **.misc** newsgroups are for general talk about all types of PC games: for DOS, Windows, and OS/2. The **.announce** group is moderated and contains announcements of interest to the PC games community. Look for the PC Games frequently asked question list, posted regularly to this group. The FAQ is also available on the Web. The other groups are for particular types of games (**.rpg** means role-playing games).

**Usenet:**

**alt.binaries.warez.ibm-pc.games**
**alt.warez.ibm-pc.games**
**comp.sys.ibm.pc.games**
**comp.sys.ibm.pc.games.action**
**comp.sys.ibm.pc.games.adventure**
**comp.sys.ibm.pc.games.announce**
**comp.sys.ibm.pc.games.flight-sim**
**comp.sys.ibm.pc.games.misc**
**comp.sys.ibm.pc.games.rpg**
**comp.sys.ibm.pc.games.sports**
**comp.sys.ibm.pc.games.strategic**

**Keep up on the newest and coolest in the PC game world. Read the comp.sys.ibm.pc.games Usenet groups.**

## Pinball

If you are one of those persons who loves to hear and see the balls bump and jump all over the place, here is your non-tiltable home away from home. Lots of pinball-related information, as well as a Usenet discussion group for talking to other pinball fanatics.

**Web:**

**http://www.lysator.liu.se:7500/pinball/**

**Usenet:**

**rec.games.pinball**

## Play-by-Mail

Not everyone has time to spend hours gaming or interacting on the computer in real time. Play-by-mail games—both email and snail mail—allow you to participate in games at your leisure. Moreover, you can have fun gaming without having to invite people over and giving them the opportunity to trash your living room or insult your choice of wallpaper.

**Web:**

**http://www.pbm.com/~lindahl/pbm.html**

## Poker

Play or watch multiuser poker, administered by the IRC Poker Bot. (A bot is an automated program used on IRC to perform a particular function.) The bot can provide complete instructions and a command summary. You can also play interactive video-style poker on the web.

**Web:**

**http://maelstrom.cc.mcgill.ca/poker/poker.html**
**http://rio.atlantic.net/~phod/**
**http://www.i5.com/cgi-bin/draw5**

**IRC:**

**#poker**

## Riddle of the Day

Try to solve the riddles and brain teasers posed by the Sphinx. If you can, you get immortalized in the Sphinx Hall of Fame. You can even submit your own sticklers here or browse the archive of past riddles with their answers.

**Web:**

**http://www.new3.com/riddle/**

## Shogi

Shogi is a two-player Japanese game played on a board with squares. The object of shogi is to capture your opponent's king. (I hear that Diana—the woman formerly known as Princess—is a great player.) Don't let any of those facts confuse you: shogi is not chess. However, shogi is fun and challenging, and knowing how to play will make you look cultured. (If that fails to work, just walk around with this book under your arm.)

**Web:**

**http://hpux.ced.tudelft.nl/hpux/Games/Board/xshogi-1.2.03.html**
**http://salam.cae.wisc.edu/hpux/Games/Board/gnushogi-1.2.03.html**

**Listserv Mailing List:**

List Name: **shogi-l**
Subscribe to: **listserv@technion.technion.ac.il**

## Sliding Tile Puzzles

Do you remember when you were a kid playing with one of those puzzles with the sliding tiles? You move the tiles around until they are in the correct order (or until you give up in frustration and decide to throw the thing away and go watch TV). Now you can play the same game on the Net. Just one more way in which childhood is becoming electric.

**Web:**

**http://www.cm.cf.ac.uk/htbin/AndrewW/Puzzle/puzzle4x4image**

### Sliding Tile Puzzles The Real Truth

Do you want to know the real truth about sliding tile puzzles? You know, those puzzles that have a number of small pieces that slide up/down and left/right. You move the tiles around and, when you get all the pieces in the right place, you see a picture of some type.

Okay, here's the real scoop.

These puzzles were invented by aliens. They spread the puzzles everywhere and, whenever you work on one, the aliens monitor you with their special observation rays.

You see, the aliens want to take over the Earth and, to do so, they need to control a certain number of human beings. So, at night, the aliens kidnap certain people and implant control mechanisms in their brains. Before dawn, these people are returned with the memory of the whole procedure wiped out. One day, when enough people have been modified in this way, the aliens will activate all the control mechanisms and take control of the Earth.

The thing is, only certain people's brains are suitable for implantation. However, the aliens can tell if you are one of those people by monitoring your brain waves as you try to solve a sliding puzzle.

And now—for the first time—sliding puzzles are starting to appear on the Net.

I don't have to tell you what that means.

## Tic Tac Toe

Tic Tac Toe has been called "one of the most useless games ever invented" (by my chief researcher, actually). Maybe so for the traditional 3x3 game, but have you tried playing on a 6x7 grid with 5 in a row needed to win? Play against a computer program that lets you choose the size of the grid and the number of Xs or Os in a row you need to win. You can play the regular 3x3 or try something more adventurous. When you get into higher numbers, it's more fun and a lot more difficult.

**Web:**

**http://netpressence.com/npcgi/ttt**

## Tiddlywinks

Tiddlywinks is a game played with colored counters (called winks) on a 6 foot by 3 foot felt mat with an open pot placed in the center. There are four sets (blue, green, red, yellow) of 6 winks (2 large and 4 small). To play, you use a disc called a squidger to press a wink and make it move. The object of the game is to score points (called tiddlies), either by popping winks into the pot or by having your winks completely uncovered at the end of the game (20 minutes for singles matches, 25 minutes for pairs matches). Tiddlywinks requires a great deal of strategy and skill, and there are major tournaments which are highly competitive. Find out more from the Net or by learning the game for yourself.

**Web:**

**http://www.cis.ohio-state.edu/hypertext/faq/usenet/games/tiddlywinks/faq.html**

## Top 100 PC Games

A weekly list of the top one hundred commercial PC games, as voted by game players on the Internet. This is a good list to check out, if you are looking for a new game for yourself or for a gift.

**Web:**

**http://www.tiac.net/users/top100/pcgames.html**

## Truth or Dare

Truth or Dare is a game which is guaranteed to bring out the most horrid aspects of human nature. (I bet you can't wait.) Here is how it works. You play with a group of people. You go from one person to the next and ask "Truth or Dare?" If the person says "Truth", the group gets to ask any question, and the person *must* tell the truth. If the person chooses "Dare", the group gets to make him or her do something daring. For example, if you choose "Truth", you might be asked "What's the kinkiest thing you ever did that did not involve a live animal?" If you choose "Dare", you might be told to re-install Windows 95 from diskettes without using a mouse. (By the way, you might be wondering if I ever played Truth or Dare. Yes, I did once. I was playing in Canada with a group of friends from high school, and they dared me to move to California and become a famous writer.) Doesn't this sound like a great game? Wanna try it? Connect to IRC and join the Truth or Dare channel.

**IRC:**

**#truthdare**

## Video Games

The suspension of reality is fun as long as you are not driving a car or operating heavy machinery. Video games are a great method of escape and, on the Net, video game fans have lots and lots of resources. Here are some good places to start.

**Web:**

**http://www.cm.cf.ac.uk/Games**
**http://www.gamepen.com/yellowpages/**

**Usenet:**

**rec.games.video.advocacy**
**rec.games.video.arcade**
**rec.games.video.arcade.collecting**

## Video Games: Hints and Cheats

Why spend huge portions of your life trying to master an arcane video game? As a Net user, you are only one click away from enough hints, cheats and walkthroughs to choke an electronic horse. Now you can use all that extra spare time to do something useful (like talk about video games on Usenet).

**Web:**

**http://www.gamepen.com/cheats/**
**http://www.gamesdomain.co.uk/uhs/uhs.html**
**http://www.gamesdomain.co.uk/walkthru.html**

### Video Game Cheating

Video games can be a lot of fun, but what is even more fun is knowing secret ways to beat the game.

If you play a lot of video games, check out the collection of cheats to see if any are known for your favorite game.

Be sure not to tell your brother, however. That would take all the fun out of it.

## Zork

Create your own destiny in this textual adventure. Read the imaginary scenarios and then click on the choices you want to make that will take you further into the story.

**Web:**

**http://ampere.scale.uiuc.edu/~boraski/zork/**

# GARDENING

## Bonsai

The art and craft of bonsai and related art forms. Bonsai is the oriental art of dwarfing trees and plants into forms that mimic nature. Anyone interested, whether novice or professional, may join this mailing list or participate in discussion on the Usenet groups. At the web sites, you will find FAQs and pictures of beautiful bonsai.

**Web:**

**http://www.hav.com/~hav/tobicus.html**
**http://www.pass.wayne.edu/~dan/BonsaiWeb/bonsai-faq-part1.html**

**Usenet:**

**alt.bonsai**
**rec.arts.bonsai**

**Listserv Mailing List:**

List Name: **bonsai**
Subscribe to: **listserv@home.ease.lsoft.com**

## Children's Gardening

Encouraging your children to work in the garden is not only healthy, good exercise, and a great learning experience, but it will also wear them out fast so they will go to bed earlier. Discover a myriad of fun activities you can organize in the garden that will incorporate the interests and talents of children.

**Web:**

**http://www.ext.vt.edu/hort/consumer/general/children/**

## City Farmers

City-folk don't need to feel deprived because they don't have massive tracts of land on which to farm. Yes, you can have your buzzing city existence and a fruitful garden, too. Get information on community gardens, urban agriculture, school and rooftop gardens, composting and solutions to common problems.

**Web:**

http://www.cityfarmer.org/

## Flower Gardens

Wouldn't it be great to have flowers all over the house and yard so that when you wake up in the morning, the air is all fragrant with natural perfume? With time, patience, a bit of a green thumb and some Usenet newsgroups, you can turn your home into a floral paradise. Gardeners offer tips and general information on the care and feeding of specific flowers.

**Usenet:**

rec.gardens.orchids
rec.gardens.roses

## Fruit Growing

Experience the thrill of harvesting your own fruit to sell, eat or to just give to friends. Use these helpful articles to learn tips for successfully growing a variety of fruits, such as berries, grapes, pomegranates, pears, apples, and kiwis.

**Web:**

http://www.ext.vt.edu/hort/consumer/general/quest/fruits-nuts.html

## Garden Encyclopedia

Flip through this easy-to-use encyclopedia of gardening and get information on soils, plants, tools, trimming, digging, mulching, and more. Never again will you have to wonder how much osmunda fiber to use for your epiphitic orchids or what the difference is between a bush hook and a sickle.

**Web:**

http://www.btw.com/garden_archive/

### Fruit Growing

Ah . . . who has not relaxed in the quiet peace of an evenfall, listening to the dozy buzzing of the bees and wallowing in the still, relaxed atmosphere of the earth as it slowly closes its petals for the night? And what could be more intoxicating than lying quietly in your hammock as night falls, enjoying the smooth, subtle fragrances of your very own fruit trees as their gentle scents calmly and tenderly caress your face?

Yes, there is something about fruit your own fruit that speaks to the depths of all of us. In a world of noise and international conflict and general brouhaha, where you can't pick up a newspaper without reading about some fiend with a hatchet slaying six or a gas explosion on the Indian subcontinent wiping out a village, and you can't turn on the TV without hearing about children who get arrested for anti-social behavior or husbands sneaking 'round the corner to do things that right-minded people don't even discuss, isn't it nice to know that in your very own garden, with your very own fruit trees, you can find a spot of peace and a tiny portion of tranquillity? Of course it is.

## Garden Gate

It's possible to spend hours reading about gardening instead of actually doing any real gardening. When you can't be participating in the real thing, try the virtual thing at the Garden Gate. Find FAQs, plant lists, a reading room, information on houseplants, reviews of gardening software and tours of botanical gardens and greenhouses around the world.

**Web:**

http://www.prairienet.org/ag/garden/

## Garden Ponds

Having water near your house creates an extremely pleasant and soothing environment. I put in a waterfall in my yard near where I grow flowers, strawberries and tomatoes. I can see it and hear it from inside, and it serves to brings a bit of the outdoors into the house. Would you like to make your own pond? This site will show you how it is done and give suggestions about populating your pond once it is completed. (I am still debating what to put in my pond. My cat has suggested goldfish.)

**Web:**

**http://reality.sgi.com/employees/peteo/**

## Garden Web

Garden groupies can hang out and talk shop on this interactive web forum. Post messages about herbs, ponds and aquatic plants, annuals and perennials, trees and shrubs, pests and plant diseases. This site offers contests to enter and interesting columns by master gardeners.

**Web:**

**http://www.gardenweb.com/**

**FAQs are cool.**

## Gardening Oasis

If you are like me, you spend so much time on the Net that, one day, you walk out to your garden and find it is completely out of control. Do not despair. If your garden is no longer the oasis it once was, you can at least take a moment to relax at this soothing web site. The Garden Oasis has a searchable database with many good gardening resources. Or you can brew a cup of herbal tea and read the latest feature on seasonal hints and tips. Pretty soon, your gardening quota will be fulfilled, and you can go back to regular Net stuff with a clear conscience.

**Web:**

**http://gardening.com/**

## Gardening Talk and General Discussion

If things aren't going right in the garden, don't just raze everything with the roto-tiller, turn to your fellow Internet buddies for ideas. For the organically challenged, you have the opportunity to cry, scream, and beg for help. Bragging is also welcome; you can pass on the news that it was your 25-pound tomato that made the cover of the National Enquirer.

**Usenet:**

**rec.gardens**

### *Look What I Found on the Net...*

```
Newsgroup: rec.gardens
Subject: Plants That Attract Birds?

> Has anyone had any particular success attracting birds to
> their yard with particular plants?  I've bought a book called
> "How to Attract House and Feed Birds" which contains a list of
> trees and shrubs that birds are attracted to, but it lists
> several dozen and I'm having a hard time choosing among them.

If I had room for just one bird-feeding plant, it would be a
serviceberry (Amelenchier species): either a shrub or tree.
Robins and other birds love the berries.  In addition, the
plants have beautiful spring blooms and great fall color.
```

## Gothic Gardening

If you prefer the dark and macabre (as opposed to the sunny and cheerful), you do not have to feel left out of the Internet gardening scene. Visit this site and experience gothic gardening at its best. Pick your theme: would you like lots of black plants, plants that attract bats and insects, carnivorous plants, or perhaps a garden that only sits up and take notice after the sun goes down? It's all here and then some.

**Web:**

**http://www.gsu.edu/~lawjdp/gothgard/**

## Growing Vegetables

One of my favorite pleasures is growing vegetables. Right now (as you read this), I have wonderful beefsteak tomatoes growing in my garden. Here's some information to help you plan and cultivate your own tiny patch of paradise. After all, if Adam and Eve had a Net connection with access to better information, they probably would have been more successful in handling their gardening problems.

**Web:**

**http://hammock.ifas.ufl.edu/txt/fairs/19976**

Many people do not appreciate their friends in the vegetable kingdom. Why not grow your own?

## Home Gardening Mailing List

The **gardens** mailing list promotes and exchanges information about home gardening. Topics include vegetable gardens, herbs, flowers, ornamental gardening, and other topics. Both novice and experienced gardeners are welcome.

**Listserv Mailing List:**

List Name: **gardens**
Subscribe to: **listserv@lsv.uky.edu**

## Hydroponic Gardening

Why get your hands dirty when you can grow your crops hydroponically? Hydroponic gardening is on the rise everywhere. Hydroponics fans get together to discuss technical aspects and personal experiences relating to growing plants without the mechanical support of soil.

**Majordomo Mailing List:**

List Name: **hydro**
Subscribe to: **majordomo@hawg.stanford.edu**

## Indoor Plants

The cat has eaten half of your rhododendron and the leaves on your African violet are turning yellow. What should you do? Check out the helpful hints at the Virginia Cooperative Extension. Articles cover topics such as container drainage, decorating with houseplants, feeding and watering, and making terrariums.

**Web:**

**http://www.ext.vt.edu/hort/consumer/general/quest/indoor.html**

## Landscaping and Lawns

It's a fear that strikes deep in your gut. You really want to go out in the backyard, but you just can't stand the thought of what might be lurking around in the uncut grass and wild, thorny shrubbery. Make a bold move and turn "Night of the Living Greenery" into "The Garden of Earthly Delights". These helpful articles will give you information on landscaping and lawn care, including tips on how to save time and money.

**Web:**

**http://www.ext.vt.edu/hort/consumer/general/quest/lawns-landscaping.html**

## Mailing Lists for Gardeners

Make new friends and talk about gardening by joining a mailing list. In fact, join lots of mailing lists and impress people when they see how much mail you get all the time. This web site has an extensive collection of mailing lists on a variety of gardening topics.

**Web:**

**http://www.prairienet.org/ag/garden/maillist.htm**

## Pest Management

"Pest management" is the politically correct term for figuring out effective ways to destroy, obliterate, or otherwise get rid of those nasty creatures that feed on your plants. Form your strategic battle plan with the help of this extension service. It offers insect factsheets, information on exotic pests, and even images of insects so you can accurately identify the enemy.

**Web:**

**http://hermes.ecn.purdue.edu:8001/server/water/Publications/1008.va.ascii**
**http://www.nysaes.cornell.edu/ent/biocontrol/**

## Plant Answers

This is a great site for finding general information on particular types of plants such as flowers, fruits and vegetables, ground cover, houseplants, trees and shrubs, and grasses. In addition to specific plant-oriented answers, you can find helpful files about mulching, irrigation and other gardening basics.

**Web:**

**http://aggie-horticulture.tamu.edu/plantanswers/web.html**

## Plant Factsheets

The key to being a successful gardener is to make sure you are well informed. One way you can do that is by having a look at these factsheets, which cover topics like ground covers, poisonous plants, shrubs, vines, trees, flowering potted plants, and even cut flowers. The factsheets give a brief overview of each item and basic information on how to care for them. This directory offers a keyword search if you are looking for something specific.

**Web:**

**http://www.ext.vt.edu/hort/consumer/factsheets/**

Questions about plants?
The Plant Factsheets are for you.

## Strawberry Page

I have a lot of strawberries growing in my backyard, and I was pleased to find out that they are good for more than just eating. I bet you didn't know you can use strawberry leaves and roots as a skin tonic. This strawberry facts site contains information about growing strawberries, the history of berries, trivial facts and tidbits, and fun strawberry events around the world (such as me harvesting the berries in my backyard).

**Web:**

**http://vanbc.wimsey.com/~jam/StrawberryFacts/**

## Tele-Garden

When you get tired of all those back-breaking hours of sweating over a hot shovel, take a little break at the Tele-Garden. With a click of your mouse, you can move a robot arm in order to look at the garden from different viewpoints. You can even go so far as to plant seeds, water and perform various other manual labors without breaking a sweat. Experience gardening of the future.

**Web:**

**http://www.usc.edu/dept/garden/**

## Trees

If you are into dendrochronology (deducing past environmental changes by looking at tree rings), you probably already know that the oldest tree ring known (from a sequoia) covered 8,700 years. You may not plan on enjoying your own trees that long, but it's still a good idea to know something about how to take care of them. Here are some Net resources to get you started.

**Web:**

**http://www.sufa.com/**
**http://www.tpoint.net/neighbor/Tre.html**

## Vegetable and Herb Growing

If you ignore the back-breaking intensity and the fact that it's really hard on your nails, gardening can be fun. Get hints on things like making container gardens, storing and drying herbs, choosing vegetable varieties, and planting early crops.

**Web:**

**http://www.ext.vt.edu/hort/consumer/general/quest/vegetables.html**

## Virtual Garden

Time-Life has created a beautifully designed web site containing an interactive plant encyclopedia, directory of house plants, and gardening articles from major magazines.

**Web:**

**http://pathfinder.com/vg/**

## Web Garden

With all the great gardening resources available on the Net, it's hard to get away from the computer long enough to spend time in the backyard. This site has information for beginning gardeners, whether you garden at home or commercially. Read garden features and tips, and search a gardening database for information about all sorts of plants.

**Web:**

**http://hortwww-2.ag.ohio-state.edu/hvp/Webgarden/Webgarden.html**

## Weekend Gardener

I get a great deal of pleasure from my garden. I try to spend time outside every day, even if it's just for a brief moment. However, all too often, the busy hurry-flurry of the week pushes my gardening priorities to the back of the virtual tool shed. That's why I like this site: a place for busy people who still like to mix it up with the mud and plants whenever they can. The information here is concise and easy to handle for people who do not have a lot of time to spare. Get gardening tips, learn about growing plants from seed, find out about the weather, and lots more.

**Web:**

**http://www.chestnut-sw.com/**

**The Net cares.**

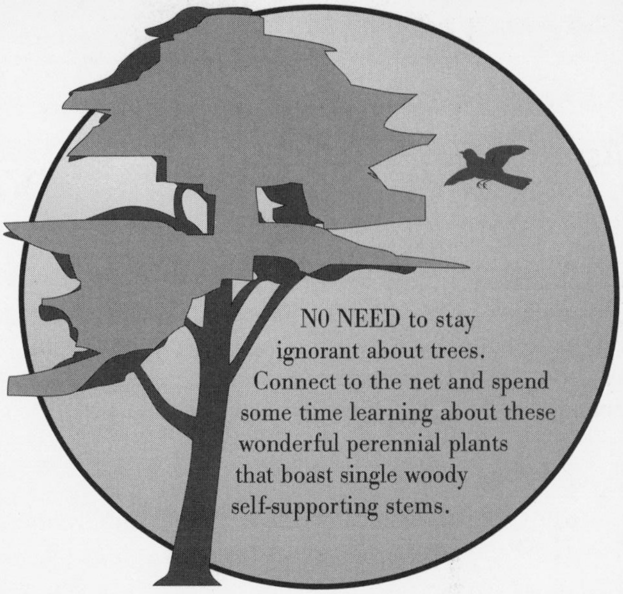
NO NEED to stay ignorant about trees. Connect to the net and spend some time learning about these wonderful perennial plants that boast single woody self-supporting stems.

## Wildflowers

I have lots of colorful wildflowers growing in my garden beneath my orange tree. They are hardy and easy to manage, requiring only minimal time for maintenance, and they attract a nice contingent of hummingbirds. If you want to learn more about wildflowers, here is a great place to visit. There is a fantastic selection of photographs, as well as information about growing and maintaining wildflowers of your own.

**Web:**

**http://aggie-horticulture.tamu.edu/wildseed/**

## Woody Plants

There is more to landscaping than willowy flowers and delicate groundcover. Shrubs and trees offer sturdy variety for your yard and garden. Learn about planting, growing, feeding, and trimming shrubs and trees as well as how to avoid diseases and pests that afflict them.

**Web:**

**http://www.ext.vt.edu/hort/consumer/general/quest/woody-ornam.html**

# GAY, LESBIAN, BISEXUAL

## Assorted Gay Resources

Years ago, gay, lesbian and bisexual resources were harder to find. Now, on the Net, information is freely disseminated and can be found in a variety of places. This archive houses a variety of national and international resources, including GLB organizations, AIDS and HIV organizations, and links to other archives such as the Queer Resource Directory.

**Web:**

**http://www.paonline.com/phiv/netlinks/rainbow.htm**

## Bible's View of Homosexuality

Are homosexuality and Christianity at odds? Read this lengthy paper that discusses how Jesus and the Bible view homosexuality.

**Web:**

**http://www.crl.com/www/users/he/heath/rainbow/bible.homos**

### Homosexuality and the Bible

All too often, we flounder around looking for guidance and a helping intellectual hand. In the homosexual world, there is often the sort of conflict Shakespeare would have described as "I dare not waiting upon I would". The Bible is important to a great many people (perhaps even more so than The Internet Complete Reference) and it is a matter of great pith and moment as to what this holy book actually says about homosexuality. Of course, like many such references, the interpretation is everything, so before you can call your life complete, take a look at the **Bible's View of Homosexuality** and see what *you* think. In the words of Ronald Reagan: "What was that question again?"

## Bisexual Resource List

These web pages are compilations of resources useful to bisexual and bifriendly people. They include a calendar of events, mailing lists, discussion groups, newsletters, literature, radio shows, and HIV and AIDS education.

**Web:**

**http://www.cis.ohio-state.edu/hypertext/faq/usenet/bisexual/resources/top.html**

## Bisexuality and Gender Issues

For some hard-hitting theoretical discussion of bisexuality and gender issues, you can participate in this Usenet group and mailing list. Note: These forums are primarily for intellectual discussion, not for socializing, support, or news and announcements.

**Usenet:**

**alt.motss.bisexua-l**

**Listserv Mailing List:**

List Name: **bithry-l**
Subscribe to: **listserv@brownvm.brown.edu**

## Brochure on Sexual Orientation

A brochure called Someone You Know Is Gay offers information on sexual orientation and tries to answer questions about why people are gay. It also addresses the process of coming out and stereotypes such as "what gay people look like".

**Web:**

**http://www.crl.com/~heath/rainbow/someone**

## Collected Queer Information

A large collection of gay, lesbian and bisexual resources, including articles, a list of gay, lesbian, bisexual and supportive businesses, film lists, news, a bisexual resource list, advice, a link to the Queer National Homeland in Webworld, and links to other related resources.

**Web:**

**http://www.cs.cmu.edu/Web/People/mjw/Queer/MainPage.html**

## Coming Out

Information and links relating to individuals coming to terms with their lesbian or gay sexual orientation.

**Web:**

**http://www.cyberzine.org/html/GLAIDS/ComingOut/comingoutpage.html**

## Cyberqueer Lounge

The Cyberqueer Lounge is a large, comprehensive collection of resources for gay, bisexual and transgendered persons. Here you will find links covering politics, culture, gay advocacy, health, communication and much more, including lots of fun stuff.

**Web:**

**http://www.cyberzine.org/html/GLAIDS/glaidshomepage.html**

## Domestic Partners

It's amazing that problems can be caused by not having a little piece of paper. Even if you have signed on to your relationship for life, it doesn't legally count without the certificate. This site has information about domestic partnerships, same-sex marriages, legal status, policies at various universities, and related issues.

**Web:**

**http://www.cs.cmu.edu/afs/cs.cmu.edu/user/scotts/domestic-partners/mainpage.html**

### Domestic Partners

There is a lot more to a domestic partnership than disagreeing about money and remembering all the times your partner hurt your feelings. You also need to keep abreast of the latest legal information. The **Domestic Partners** archive has a wealth of information that is perfect for people who need to know what's what and what's not.

## Gay and Lesbian Alliance Against Defamation

The Gay and Lesbian Alliance Against Defamation (GLADD) was founded in 1985 with a mission to reform the portrayal of gays and lesbians in the media, to improve the public's attitude toward homosexuality, and to help decrease violence and discrimination affecting gays and lesbians. At the GLAAD web site, you can read about their successes, and look at their press releases, media resources and general information.

**Web:**

**http://www.glaad.org/**

## Gay and Lesbian Parenting

Here are some useful resources for gays and lesbians who have children or who are considering starting a family. At these sites, you can find information about the Gay and Lesbian Parents Coalition International as well as relevant legal issues. There is also information for lesbian moms covering such topics as sperm banks, artificial insemination, health and pregnancy, adoption and insurance.

**Web:**

**http://abacus.oxy.edu/QRD/www/orgs/glpci/**
**http://www.lesbian.org/moms/**

## Gay Daze

Step into the private lives of five gay guys and a lesbian. Here is a running saga in diary format. While you are at the site, check out the gay chat room, postcard server, Fairy Tales and Dyke Dramas (a story section), as well as other stuff.

**Web:**

**http://www.gaydaze.com/**

## Gay, Lesbian and Bisexual Resources

There are lots of gay-related resources on the Net. Here is a good place to start when you are searching for something in particular or simply browsing for something new and interesting.

**Web:**

**http://www.tatertot.com/agenda/**

## Gay, Lesbian and Bisexual Trivia Game

Help build the **soc.motss** trivia game by adding in your trivial tidbits. Select the category, type in the question and answer, and you'll be in on helping compile this fun trivia database.

**Web:**
**http://www.skepsis.com/.gblo/motss/triv_form.html**

## Gay, Lesbian and Bisexual White Pages

Keep in touch with the **soc.motss** crew. Add your name and vital statistics to the database.

**Web:**
**http://www.skepsis.com/.gblo/motss/motss_dir.html**

## Gay Public Officials

Discover more about public officials than just their political leanings. Read this list of government people who are publicly out.

**Web:**
**http://www.crl.com/~heath/rainbow/officials**

## Gay Travel Guide

Travel information from a gay perspective. This travel guide offers recommendations for gay-friendly hotels, bars, clubs and other interesting places you might go while traveling around the world.

**Web:**
**http://www.ocsi.com/anton/**

## Gay TV Listings of the Week

This weekly column outlines movies and television programs that are showing on network or cable television. The guide tells you whether it's pay-per-view, on premium channels, or whether to check your local television listing for viewing times.

**Web:**
**http://www.jersey.net/~not2/gaytv.htm**

## Gay Public Officials

The best way to keep a secret is to tell it only to a person who has a legitimate need to know. This is why I want you to know about the **Gay Public Officials** Internet site. As one of my readers, *you* have the right to know everything (at least in the biblical sense).

## Gay Workplace Issues

If you are looking for a place to get information on networking and support in the workplace, here is a good place to start. This site covers issues that gays encounter at work. You can get a list of companies that fund gay programs, lists of company policies on gay issues, information about unions, legal resources and more.

**Web:**
**http://www.nyu.edu/pages/sls/gaywork/**

## Gay-Oriented Mailing Lists

Mailing lists are fun because the information comes right to you—you don't have to go out to get it (sort of like pizza). There are a huge amount of mailing lists dedicated to gays, lesbians and bisexuals, including regional lists.

**Web:**
**http://www.qrd.org/qrd/electronic/email/**

## Gays in the Military

Are you sick of hearing people talk about not telling? Here are some web pages that relate to gays in the military. Read about the Servicemembers Legal Defense Fund for gays in the military as well as news, information and articles relating to relevant legal issues.

**Web:**

**http://www.qrd.org/qrd/usa/military/**
**http://www.sldn.org/**

## Historical and Celebrity Figures

When you're famous, you can't expect to have your privacy. Just look at headlines of the tabloids and other gossip sheets. Here is a list of people who are out by choice or by force, so take it for what you think it's worth.

**Web:**

**http://www.cyberzine.org/html/GLAIDS/Famous/famouspage.html**
**http://www.efn.org/~mastrait/famousqueers.html**

## Homosexuality and Religion

There are eight places in the Bible—five in the Old Testament and three in the New Testament—commonly cited as references to how we should think about homosexuality. However, Bible verses are only part of the story. How religious people feel about homosexuality has as much to do with what they are taught and what they feel as what it says in the Bible. Here are some links to information regarding this important topic.

**Web:**

**http://web.canlink.com/ocrt/homosexu.htm**
**http://www.cs.cmu.edu/afs/cs.cmu.edu/user/scotts/bulgarians/church.html**

### Gay-Oriented Mailing Lists

Would you like to talk with people about gay-oriented topics in complete privacy?

Join a mailing list.

## Homosexuality in the Middle Ages

It's obvious from studying Greek history that homosexuality was not invented in the twentieth century. In fact, here is a mailing list, associated with the Society for the Study of Homosexuality in the Middle Ages, where participants discuss all aspects of homosexuality in the medieval era. It's almost better than watching reruns of Flipper.

**Listserv Mailing List:**

List Name: **medgay-l**
Subscribe to: **listserv@ksuvm.ksu.edu**

## Homosexuality Talk and General Discussion

Members of the same sex (MOTSS) discuss their thoughts, feelings, and experiences about being gay. The general groups on homosexuality cover a wide range of topics on how gays relate to the rest of the world, while the **.motss** groups discuss how gays relate to one another.

**Usenet:**

**alt.homosexual**
**alt.sex.homosexual**
**alt.sex.motss**
**soc.motss**

## Lesbian Chat

Meet and talk with other lesbians and bisexual women from around the world.

**IRC:**

**#lesbian**
**#lesbos**

## Lesbian Fiction Bibliography

If you are in the mood for some lesbian literary action, check out this list of books that are by or about lesbians. The books are fiction, usually with a central lesbian character or with lesbianism as a theme.

**Web:**

**http://www.epl.org/booklist/adults/fiction/lesbian.html**

## Lesbian Mothers Mailing List

This list is for women only and relates to special issues that are faced by lesbian mothers or lesbian mom-wannabes, either single or partnered. The list is private so only members of the list will have access to information on or about the list.

**Majordomo Mailing List:**
List Name: **moms**
Subscribe to: **majordomo@qiclab.scn.rain.com**

## Out and Proud

Out or not, this is a great place for gay men to read inspiring stories about other men who are out and proud of it. Every week you can find a new personal story profile, advice from a gay psychologist, true stories about why people have not come out, what it was like to come out, a penpal section and pictures of public events.

**Web:**
**http://catalog.com/outproud/**

**Wow, free software.**

## Out List

Stop speculating on whether your favorite famous person is out or not. Read this lengthy list of notable people who have publicly acknowledged that they are gay, lesbian or bisexual.

**Web:**
**http://www.mps.org/~rainbow/Words/OutList.html**

### The Out List

The **out list** contains the names of many well-known gay people. Although you may have heard of some of these people, you may not have known they are gay. The idea is to show that there are many important, accomplished gay people in public life.

If you are gay, perhaps you might want to check the list for your name. After all, you may be famous and not even know it.

### *Look What I Found on the Net...*

```
Newsgroup: alt.homosexual
Subject: Are You Gay or Is It a Phase?

> After all these years, my mother still thinks I'm going
> through a phase.  It's the longest phase I'm going through :-)
> and I'm wondering if anyone here has parents, friends or other
> loved ones who think the same thing.

For almost seven years, my mother began all our phone
conversations with: "Are you normal yet?  When will you get over
that silly phase?  Your father and I are getting older and we
want grandchildren from you."

I put a stop to this, but every now and then my mother still
surprises me with: "Do you have any female friends that you find
attractive?"  I always disappoint her by saying: "I do mom, but
I'm lucky in that we cruise different types of men..."
```

## Out Magazine

Out or in, Out is outrageous. Full of links and information about culture, community and news, Out Magazine has lots of entertaining stuff that will keep you informed and amused (and very possibly outraged). This is a great place to keep up on the news.

**Web:**

**http://www.out.com/**

## PFLAG Gay Support Organization

PFLAG stands for "Parents, Families and Friends of Lesbians and Gays". PFLAG was created to offer support and advocacy for gays, lesbians, bisexuals and their families. The PFLAG mailing lists are great places for families and friends to talk about issues and experiences. The web site offers lots of information about sexual orientation, gender identity and local PFLAG chapters.

**Web:**

**http://www.critpath.org/pflag-talk/**

**Majordomo Mailing List:**

List Name: **pflag-talk**
Subscribe to: **majordomo@casti.com**

## Politics and Homosexuality

Gays in the military and child custody battles put the politics of homosexuality on the front page. Discuss the latest civil rights cases, pending legislation, and whom to boycott (or not). Keep informed so you can make a difference in your community. The web site has a nice collection of gay and lesbian political resources.

**Web:**

**http://ezinfo.ucs.indiana.edu/~sanderss/gaylespolguide.html**

**Usenet:**

**alt.politics.homosexuality**

## Queer Resources Directory

The Queer Resources Directory contains literally over 16,000 files of information relating to just about every aspect of homosexuality you can imagine. This is one of the premier gay sites on the Internet. Family, religion, health, business, culture, media, politics, organizations, electronic resources—it's all here.

**Web:**

**http://www.qrd.org/QRD/**

**Looking for some gay-oriented information on the Net? The Queer Resources Directory is *the* place to start your search.**

## Queer Zines

Looking for something good to read? Have a look at this list of zines that relate to gays, lesbians and bisexuals. This informative list covers print zines that are not accessible on the Net, but it gives all the details on how to subscribe or find the publications in question.

**Web:**

**http://www.qrd.org/qrd/media/magazines/**

## QueerAmerica Database

Looking for some gay, lesbian or bisexual connections in your neck of the woods? Check out this searchable database of community centers, support organizations, PFLAG chapters, gay and lesbian youth groups, and read the available action alerts.

**Web:**

**http://youth.org/outproud/**

## Yoohoo Lesbians

Yoohoo Lesbians is a web guide with a great collection of lesbian-oriented links covering just about any topic you can imagine. There is also a section for heterosexuals who are interested in trying to relate better to gays and lesbians.

**Web:**

**http://www.sappho.com/yoohoo/**

A B C D E F G H I J K L M N O P Q R S T U V W X Y Z

# GENEALOGY

## Adoptees and Genealogy

There are times when you can work on genealogy for hours and never seem to get anywhere. As you know, it can be a lot of work trying to trace your family tree. If you are adopted, there are extra complications, especially if you do not have full information about your birth parents. If you are an adoptee or you have adoptees in your family, here are some genealogy resources that can help you trace your lineage.

**Web:**

**http://www.mtjeff.com/~bodenst/page3.html**

## Canadian Genealogy Resources

Searching through the records of another country is often difficult and time consuming. Get an advantage by doing preliminary research on the Net. This site has tons of links to Canadian genealogy resources as well as links to related sites.

**Web:**

**http://infoweb.magi.com/~holwell/cangene/gene.html**

## Cyndi's Genealogy Resources

If you want to be overwhelmed and dazzled by the amount of genealogy research material on the Net, all you need to do is fire up the old browser and check out this collection of genealogy links. You will be amazed at how well-organized and easy to use it is. There is only one problem: once you get started digging around, you won't want to stop.

**Web:**

**http://www.oz.net/~cyndihow/sites.htm**

**When I was growing up in Canada, I would have given anything for access to the Canadian Genealogy Resources that you can get for free whenever you want. (Well, not really, but I did want to say something nice about Canada...)**

## Genealogical Computing

Computers are great for storing the result of your genealogy research. What I like best is that, once data is transcribed and stored on a computer, you will never have to re-read notes made by family members whose handwriting is all but indecipherable. Although I keep all the old material, it certainly is easier to read it on a computer screen. This discussion group is a great place to talk about how you can use computers to help with your genealogy research.

**Web:**

**soc.genealogy.computing**

## Genealogy Discussion by Ethnicity

There are lots of genealogy discussion groups available on Usenet, many of which are devoted to various cultural and ethnic heritages. These groups are devoted to genealogy in the following cultures: Cajun, Africa, Australia/New Zealand, Belgium/Netherlands/Luxembourg, Canada, France, Germany, Hispanic, Nordic, Slavic, United Kingdom and Ireland, and West Indies.

**Usenet:**

**alt.culture.cajun**
**soc.genealogy.african**
**soc.genealogy.australia+nz**
**soc.genealogy.benelux**
**soc.genealogy.canada+english**
**soc.genealogy.french**
**soc.genealogy.german**
**soc.genealogy.hispanic**
**soc.genealogy.nordic**
**soc.genealogy.slavic**
**soc.genealogy.uk+ireland**
**soc.genealogy.west-indies**

## Genealogy Events

Are you looking for some hot genealogy action? This site will give you the details on upcoming events such as courses, seminars, meetings, tours, lectures, festivals and reunions. If you are planning a shindig of some sort, post it here so people can see what is going on in your genealogical neck of the woods.

**Web:**

**http://www.genealogy.org/~gcal/**

## Genealogy Mailing Lists

When you participate in a mailing list, you can meet lots of people, including other researchers who are working in the same lines as you. Scan these collections of mailing lists, and see what suits your needs. There is something for everyone here, including lists devoted to specific surnames.

**Web:**

**http://users.aol.com/johnf14246/gen_mail.html**
**http://www.eskimo.com/~chance/**

### Genealogy Mailing Lists

Did it ever occur to you that, if you are important enough, after you die people will be talking about you on a genealogy mailing list?

But by then, you won't be able to see what they are saying.

Maybe you should join one now before it's too late.

## Genealogy Marketplace

If you have any genealogical items you want to buy or want to sell, this is the place to do it. Just about anything goes: books, services, maps, documents, and much more.

**Usenet:**

**soc.genealogy.marketplace**

## Genealogy Methods and Hints

It's always good to have help when you are working on a family history. These web sites have lots of hints about what to do and what not to do, as well as suggestions as to good sources of information. The Usenet group is a place to ask questions or offer advice to other genealogical researchers.

**Web:**

**http://www.geocities.com/CapitolHill/1025/faq.html**
**http://www.smartlink.com/~leverich/20ways.html**

**Usenet:**

**soc.genealogy.methods**

## Genealogy Scams

I got a special "genealogy" offer in the mail. Perhaps you have seen one yourself. Some company wants to sell you a complete history of your family from the beginning of time, or the full names of every single person in the world with your surname. The offers sound inviting, but you should always check them thoroughly before you turn loose any of your money. Some of these pitches are real scams and they are targeted specifically at inexperienced genealogists or anyone who is working on a family history. Read this FAQ (frequently asked question list) to get an overview of the types of suspicious offers you might encounter. Actually, the FAQ itself is interesting, and might help you with your work.

**Web:**

**ftp://ftp.cac.psu.edu/genealogy/roots-l/faq/faq.scams**

## Genealogy Software

Once you get started with genealogy, you will find that using a computer makes things a *lot* easier. For example, the program I use is able to print nice charts of various parts of the family tree. I then send these charts to relatives and ask them for changes and additions, which has worked out nicely. Here are some places to help you find the software you need to do the best possible job.

**Web:**

**http://www.coast.net/SimTel/msdos/genealgy.html**
**http://www.oz.net/~cyndihow/pubsoft.htm#Software**

## Genealogy Talk and General Discussion

The Internet is a global community—a great place from which to track down family members from way-back-when. Usenet and IRC offer a convenient forum not only to discuss ways of researching, what kinds of software and resources are available, or to compare anecdotes of your quests, but you can also ask for information on family names. Plenty of sharing goes on here. Find that long-lost second-half-cousin-twice-removed who broke all your crayons when you were seven and remind him you want all 64 colors, plus the built-in sharpener.

**Usenet:**

**alt.genealogy**
**soc.genealogy.misc**

**IRC:**

**#Genealogy**

A B C D E F G H I J K L M N O P Q R S T U V W X Y Z

## Genealogy Terms

There are lots of special terms used in genealogy. Many of these have origins in other languages. Some terms are really arcane medical words. You will also find technical words relating to genealogy techniques and record keeping. The next time you encounter a baffling word, here are some good places to find a definition. Pretty soon, expressions like paucis hebdomadibus and collateral ancestor will be old friends.

**Web:**

**http://www.electriciti.com/~dotts/diction.html**
**http://www.oz.net/~cyndihow/terms.htm**

## Genealogy Toolbox

A well-designed guide to genealogy resources on the Net, including surname data, guides and indexes, area-specific, associations, news and serials, library, and web projects. Very comprehensive.

**Web:**

**http://genealogy.tbox.com/genealogy.html**

## Genserv

Gain access to tens of thousands of surnames and over a million names in this huge database of family information donated from people around the Net. You can search the database as long as you provide information of your own to help Genserv grow.

**Web:**

**http://soback.kornet.nm.kr/~cmanis/**

### WHAT'S IN A NAME?

WE ALL KNOW THAT IT IS IMPORTANT TO KNOW EVERYTHING POSSIBLE ABOUT YOUR ANCESTORS BECAUSE...UH...WELL...I GUESS I FORGET, BUT IT IS A PRETTY IMPORTANT REASON. AFTER ALL, IF YOU DON'T KNOW WHERE YOU CAME FROM THEN YOU CERTAINLY WON'T KNOW WHERE YOU ARE AND...HMMM... SOMETHING OR OTHER ANYWAY.

LET'S JUST SAY THAT GENEALOGY IS COOL AND LEAVE IT AT THAT. AFTER ALL, IF IT WASN'T FOR OUR ANCESTORS, WE WOULDN'T BE HERE. (WELL, WE MIGHT BE HERE, BUT WE WOULD HAVE DIFFERENT PARENTS AND GRANDPARENTS, AND WE WOULDN'T KNOW ANYONE'S BIRTHDAY, AND EVERYTHING WOULD BE ALL MIXED UP AND, WELL... YOU GET THE IDEA.)

**Get into "Mischief".**

## *Look What I Found on the Net...*

```
Newsgroup: alt.genealogy
Subject: The Oldest U.S. Surname

This was in a local newspaper...

"Surname of the oldest surviving family in the United States
reportedly is Sonan.  Descended from settlers at Florida's St.
Augustine."

The next clip said: "When your father's father, or his, was a
lad, men usually lived longer than women.  And that had always
been true worldwide.  But by 1920, women lived a little longer.
And for the last generation or so, they've stabilized,
evidently, outliving men by about seven years."
```

## GenWeb Project

GenWeb is an ambitious project devoted to compiling information about genealogy research resources around the United States. The available information is divided by state and county. These resources are actual physical sources of genealogical information, such as public libraries, family history centers and genealogy libraries. This is a great place to find what resources are available in your local area.

**Web:**

**http://www.usgenweb.com/**

## Getting Started in Genealogy

At first, getting started in genealogy can be bewildering. If you are having trouble telling your tiny tafel from your soundex, here are some good places to start. These are easy-to-read beginner's guides to genealogy, that will offer the help and guidance you need to begin a family search.

**Web:**

**http://cs6400.mcc.ac.uk/genuki/gs/**
**http://www.rootsweb.com/roots-l/starting.html**

## Handy Genealogy Tips

Looking at the big genealogical picture is overwhelming. Get helpful hints and some how-to documents that will make tracing your family tree much easier. When you start searching back, it's amazing who you will find. Perhaps you will be the one to find the Missing Link.

**Web:**

**http://www.firstct.com/fv/tmaps.html**

**The Net is immortal.**

## Heraldry

Heraldry is the tradition, dating from the Middle Ages, of displaying symbols or pictures (called charges) on shields. During tournaments, knights were recognized by the shields they carried. (Such tournaments were refereed by officials called heralds—hence, the word "heraldry".) The charges on the shield identified individuals and families, and were passed to successive generations (the Middle Age's version of a vanity license plate). As centuries passed, these charges were adapted into insignia for the nobility and were used not only on shields, but as seals for documents. Later the designs were embroidered into articles of clothing. In fact, the phrase "coat of arms" comes from the practice of embroidering family designs onto the surcoat that was worn over chain mail armor. (This served to make you easily recognizable by the person who was running you through with a sword.) Here are some interesting sites on the Net that explain heraldry, give a basic primer, and tell what some of the symbols mean. The Usenet group is for the discussion of heraldry. All these resources will help you better analyze your family's coat of arms. (Or, if your family does not have a coat of arms, you can concoct something suitable for your next reunion, and start a brand new family tradition.)

**Web:**

**http://digiserve.com/heraldry/**
**http://econ10.econ.jhu.edu/heraldry/**
**http://www.catt.ncsu.edu/www_projects/heraldry/**

**Usenet:**

**rec.heraldry**

## Jewish Genealogy

For genealogy buffs interested in tracing Jewish roots, here are special resources you will find useful. The mailing list and Usenet group specifically address the special issues involved in tracing Jewish lineage and are great companions to other, more general discussion forums.

**Web:**

**http://www.jewishgen.org/**

**Usenet:**

**soc.genealogy.jewish**

**Listproc Mailing List:**

List Name: **jewishgen**
Subscribe to: **listproc@listserv.eworld.com**

## LifeLines Database

LifeLines is a software program that runs on Unix systems. It is remarkably flexible in that it allows a maximum amount of manipulation to the database. Entries can easily be added, removed, swapped, or merged with each other. There is no limit to the size of the entries. LifeLines is written to accommodate itself to fit your needs. This software will also support Gedcom, another genealogical database. **lines-l** is a mailing list that covers discussion of all topics concerning LifeLines.

**Listserv Mailing List:**

List Name: **lines-l**
Subscribe to: **listserv@vm1.nodak.edu**

Are you planning your own genealogical database? Consider LifeLines.

## Mayflower

The Mayflower was a ship that brought pilgrims from England to New England in 1620. The Mayflower landed at Plymouth on December 26, 1620. Before leaving the ship, the colonists drew up an agreement—called the Mayflower Compact—establishing a temporary government based on their own intentions, rather than the laws of the English crown. This web site has information about the Mayflower and the people who descended from the original passengers. You can investigate wills, inventories, passenger lists, early writings related to the Mayflower, and explore links to other Mayflower resources. Somebody had to be descended from those adventurous pilgrims. It might as well have been you.

**Web:**

**http://members.aol.com/calebj/mayflower.html**

## Medieval Genealogy

Imagine the hours and hours of research that would go into tracing a family lineage back to the medieval period. If you want to meet some people who are working on such a task, check out this Usenet group. This discussion involves genealogy relating to the period spanning 500 to 1600 A.D. This discussion group is strictly for talking about medieval genealogy, not a general discussion of medieval history and culture. (If you want to talk about history, use **soc.history.medieval** instead.) The web site has the **soc.genealogy.medieval** FAQ.

**Web:**

**http://www.rand.org/personal/Genea/faqmed.html**

**Usenet:**

**soc.genealogy.medieval**

## National Archives and Records Administration

See what the National Archives and Records Administration (NARA) has to offer in the way of instructional leaflets and helpful searching tips for genealogical research. They also give you a glance at microfiche records for census and federal court information such as bankruptcy records, naturalization records, land grant claims, and immigrant and passenger arrivals.

**Web:**

**http://www.nara.gov/nara/menus/genealog.html**

## Native American Genealogy

No matter what tribe you are from, this site will have good general information to get you started. You may even find specific information about your particular nation of origin. There are also links to some useful how-to articles relating to Native American genealogy.

**Web:**

**http://members.aol.com/bbbenge/front.html**

**Join the fun—now.**

## Roots

The mailing list **roots-l** has been a popular genealogy mailing list for many years. It has been spun into a major collection of resources and networking options for genealogists around the world. The web site has a searchable archive of posts that have been sent to the mailing list. For example, this is a good place to find out if anyone has been making queries regarding a particular surname. The site has a sharing library where individuals who have time to share list books from which they are willing to do lookups for other people. Roots offers a registry of people who are researching particular surnames, so you may be able to find other people who might be related to you. Detailed information about the **roots-l** mailing list is also available at this web site.

**Web:**

**http://www.rootsweb.com/roots-l/roots-l.html**

## Royalty and Nobility

Once, when I was in a Mormon Family History Center, I saw ex-Princess Diana at a microfilm reader, working on her family tree. (Actually, she was having trouble with her microfilm reader, and I had to help her load the film.) Before I went back to do my own research, I told her that it would be easier to do her research on the Net. I explained that there are lots of places with information about royal and noble lineages, and she wouldn't even have to remember how to turn the microfilm spool. I gave her a list of these resources to get her started. And, I told her, if you want to see what they are saying about you behind your back, try the Usenet group.

**Web:**

**http://ftp.cac.psu.edu/~saw/royal/royalgen.html**
**http://www.dcs.hull.ac.uk/public/genealogy/GEDCOM.html**

**Usenet:**

**alt.talk.royalty**

# ROYALTY AND NOBILITY

When you come right down to it, the kings, queens and nobles of history were a lot like regular people (if you overlook minor details such as fame, power and wealth).

However, there was one important difference: many aspects of the lives of these people were documented in detail and, if you need such information, a lot of it is available on the Net.

So sometime, just for fun, why not graft a portion of some royal family onto your own personal family tree, and see if anything takes root?

## Scottish Clans

Most people don't realize it, but there is a lot more to Scottish culture than the Loch Ness monster and Scotch whiskey. For example, they have bagpipes and Highland games and men who wear skirts. Moreover, the Scots also have lots of cool clans (sort of like gangs in Los Angeles, only Scottish accents are easier to understand). If you are interested in Scottish clans, or if you are a member of a clan, check out this great resource. It has links to individual clan sites, a virtual pub in which you can post messages, as well as information on the history and culture of Scotland and the Highland games. The Usenet group is for discussion of Scottish clans.

**Web:**

**http://www.tartans.com/**

**Usenet:**

**alt.scottish.clans**

**Quick, turn the page.**

## Searchable Genealogy Links

When you want information fast (or as fast as it gets in genealogy), it's good to know of places on the Net where you can search for your genealogy information by keyword. This site has a list of genealogy links that include some form of search capability.

**Web:**

**http://aerodyn.utias.utoronto.ca/html/lo2.htm**

## Special Genealogy Resources

Here are some Internet sites that will point you in the right direction for finding genealogy resources. Lots of useful information whenever you need it, as well as some great places to browse.

**Web:**

**http://ftp.cac.psu.edu/~saw/genealogy.html**
**http://genealogy.emcee.com/**

## Surname Databases and Discussion

As a genealogical researcher, you know how easy it is to spend hours and hours and still come up with nothing substantial. However, here's a great way to come up with information quickly that is fun, interesting and just may help you out. Search for your name in one of the surname databases, and I bet you will find something of interest. I found it interesting to see how many people in the database had the same last name as me. For discussion about surnames, check out the Usenet discussion group. It's for discussing surnames, posting surname lists, and requesting information on particular names.

**Web:**

**http://www.oz.net/~cyndihow/surnames.htm**
**http://www.rootsweb.com/rootsweb/searches/**
**http://www.toltbbs.com/~kbasile/springbd.htm**

**Usenet:**

**soc.genealogy.surnames**

## Tombstone Rubbings

In the course of your genealogical field trips, you may one day find yourself in a cemetery, recording data from tombstones. One great way to capture the essence of the tombstone is to do a rubbing. This site gives detailed instruction about how to do tombstone rubbings as well as hints on the type of information you can expect to find.

**Web:**

**http://www.firstct.com/fv/t_stone.html**

**GENEALOGISTS...**

FIVE REASONS TO LEARN ALL ABOUT TOMBSTONE RUBBING:

(1) TOMBSTONE RUBBING IS THE BEST WAY TO CAPTURE INFORMATION AND DESIGNS FROM A TOMBSTONE IN A PERMANENT, CONVENIENT AND PORTABLE FORM.

(2) IT'S A GREAT WAY TO MAKE FRIENDS. JUST SPEND SOME TIME IN A GRAVEYARD WORKING ON A TOMBSTONE, AND YOU WILL BE SURPRISED HOW MANY PEOPLE COME OVER TO ASK WHAT YOU ARE DOING.

(3) IT'S FUN. AND UNLIKE VISITING DISNEYLAND, THERE ARE NO LONG WAITS.

(4) IT'S GOOD FOR YOUR SOCIAL LIFE. PEOPLE WHO KNOW HOW TO RUB TOMBSTONES CONSISTENTLY RANK AT THE TOP OF POPULARITY POLLS. THINK BACK TO HIGH SCHOOL. WHO WERE THE ONLY PEOPLE WHO WERE MORE POPULAR THAN THE CAPTAIN OF THE FOOTBALL TEAM AND THE HEAD CHEERLEADER? SEE WHAT I MEAN?

(5) DIDN'T YOUR MOTHER ALWAYS TELL YOU IT WAS HEALTHY TO SPEND TIME OUTDOORS?

## U.S. Census Information

Article 1, Section 2 of the United States Constitution mandates an "enumeration" of all the people in all the states of the Union. (What a job that has turned out to be.) In the United States, the primary purpose of a census is to count the population in order to distribute seats in the U.S. House of Representatives and to define the legislative district boundaries within each state. However, census findings have many other purposes, most of which relate to allocating federal funds and developing social services. The first American census was taken in 1790; since then, a census has been taken every 10 years. Census records can give you basic information about families, some details about household members, and help you track family locations. These two web sites have information about how to use census records for genealogical research, as well as background information on the census itself.

**Web:**

**http://www.census.gov/ftp/pub/genealogy/www/**
**http://www.firstct.com/fv/uscensus.html**

## U.S. Civil War Genealogy

Just imagine. You are sitting on the front porch, drinking a refreshing mint julep, when all of a sudden, a group of Union soldiers come tearing through the yard on their way to burn down your house. No doubt about it, the years of the U.S. Civil War were a confusing, difficult time in American history. Fortunately for genealogists, there was a lot of effort put into keeping track of all the men who went off to war, and it is possible to search the old military records for information about these men. In addition, since this was a time of upheaval, many people were away from home, corresponding by letters. There are also a fair number of personal diaries. One problem, however, is that some courthouses were burned, and a certain number of records were lost permanently. That aside, there are a lot of great resources relating to Civil War genealogy. These resources will show you where to begin and what to do once you get started.

**Web:**

**http://funnelweb.utcc.utk.edu/~hoemann/warweb.html**
**http://www.outfitters.com/illinois/history/civil/cwgeneal.html**

## Vital Records in the U.S.

Vital records are official documents that record important life events such as births, marriages, deaths, divorces, and passages from one country to another. There is a great deal of important information you can glean from these documents, so be sure you know where to get them. This site has a list of places to which you can write for vital records within the United States.

**Web:**

**http://www.medaccess.com/address/vital_toc.htm**

**The Net loves poetry.**

# GEOGRAPHY

## Center of Statistical Resources

I have found another important but little-known use for the Net. As you are playing a trivia game, make an excuse and sneak off to your computer, where you can use the Net to find lots of statistics that will help you beat your friends into submission. For example, wait until you get a question you can't answer, and then say, "Oh, just a second, I have to go the bathroom." While you are gone, you can quickly visit this web site, where you will find a staggering compilation of statistics on many, many topics. When your friends express admiration at your extensive knowledge of trivial subjects, you can tell them that eliminating toxins from the body really helps to clear one's mind.

**Web:**

**http://www.lib.umich.edu/libhome/Documents.center/stats.html**

## CIA World Factbook

Detailed information about every country and territory in the world. Includes geographic, climate, economic, and political information. This is a fantastic resource with which you should become familiar; you never know what you will find. For example, I just found out that 97 percent of Canadians over 15 years old can read and write. (The others, presumably, use a graphical user interface.)

**Web:**

**http://www.odci.gov/cia/publications/95fact/**

### CIA INFO FOR YOU

TOP SECRET

**The American Central Intelligence Agency is so secret that its budget is not even made public. (I don't even know if they have enough money to buy copies of my Internet books.)**

**What I do know is that the CIA spends a lot of time and effort keeping track of all the countries of the world. And you can get it all (the non-secret stuff anyway) for free. This resource is invaluable for anyone who is planning to create their own military alliance.**

TOP SECRET

A B C D E F G H I J K L M N O P Q R S T U V W X Y Z

## Distance Calculator

Before you go from here to there, make sure you know how far it is. Otherwise, how would you know how much food to bring? This site enables you to find the distances between world cities and will even show you the points plotted on a map. You can also get information about the county and the population of the city you are referencing.

**Web:**
**http://www.indo.com/distance/**

## Earth Rise

Images of the Earth by region, movies of the Earth rotating, images of the Earth from space and the moon, Earth icons, details of the Xearth globe picture creation program, and more.

**Web:**
**http://earthrise.sdsc.edu/**

Pictures of Your Planet
If you are like me, the Earth is one of your favorite planets in the entire universe. But what do you do when you meet an alien who pulls out a wallet and starts showing you photos of his home planet? Invite him over to your computer, fire up your web browser, and point it to "Planet Earth Images and Movies". Never again will you have to let a foreigner one-up you when it comes to civic pride.

## Federal Geographic Data Products

This web page is the manual of Federal Geographic Data Products, a government program that attempts to create a cohesive geographic resource system available to all areas of government on the Internet.

**Web:**
**http://info.er.usgs.gov/fgdc-catalog/title.html**

## Geographers' Resources

If you are a professional geographer or a geography student, you will enjoy this site. There are lots of links to educational resources, research publications, maps, images, geographic data sources, as well as information about organizations and professional associations.

**Web:**
**http://www.utexas.edu/depts/grg/virtdept/resources/contents.html**

## Geographic Information and Analysis Laboratory

The Geographic Information and Analysis Laboratory (GIAL) server at the University of Buffalo is a multipurpose resource center for the study of geography. This page has links to many kinds of geographical resources and information.

**Web:**
**http://www.geog.buffalo.edu/GIAL/**

## Geographic Information Systems

A geographical information system (GIS) is a computer system used to manipulate information that is related to specific geographical locations. For example, satellite photos showing patterns of vegetation might be part of a GIS. There are many different types of GISs, and a lot of information available on the Net. Here is a good place to start looking.

**Web:**
**http://www.geo.ed.ac.uk/home/giswww.html**

## Geography Departments Worldwide

This site has a search engine that allows you to search geography department resources all over the Net. You can narrow your search by research field, so you could look up more specific resources, such as who is studying human geography in Bangladesh or remote sensing in Switzerland. You can access resources in many countries and in many different fields of geographical research.

**Web:**
**http://geowww.uibk.ac.at/links/geo-search.html**

## Geography Talk and General Discussion

Imagine what life would be like if there was no geography. There would be no road maps to have to re-fold. There would be no grueling hours of having to memorize the capitals of third world countries. And worse, there would be no map showing what hills and dales you have to go over to get to Grandma's house. In fact, geography is so important that you can find a lively discussion about it in Usenet. Go hang out with the people who know the planet like the backs of their hands.

**Usenet:**

**bit.listserv.geograph**

## Geography-Related Web Sites

Here are lots of sources of geographical information on the Net. Maps, data, products—a good selection of resources for the geographically inclined.

**Web:**

**http://www.delorme.com/links**
**http://www.geog.le.ac.uk/cti/geosub.html**

## Global Land Information System

The Global Land Information System (GLIS) is an interactive computer system developed by the U.S. Geological Survey (USGS). Scientists can use GLIS to find all kinds of information about land surfaces all over the Earth.

**Web:**

**http://edcwww.cr.usgs.gov/glis/glis.html**
**http://edcwww.cr.usgs.gov/webglis**

## Great Globe Gallery

One of the most interesting and difficult problems for cartographers is how to represent all or parts of the Earth (which is three-dimensional) on a flat surface. I recently read a cartography textbook (just for fun), and I was amazed at how many decisions and tradeoffs there are in making a map. The overall general principle is: if you want to go into outer space and look down, you can see the real thing. Anything else is, in some way, a compromise and there are many, many ways to construct an image of the Earth. Here, in one place, is a magnificent collection showing many ways in which our globe can be represented on a computer screen.

**Web:**

**http://hum.amu.edu.pl/~zbzw/glob/glob1.htm**

### *Look What I Found on the Net...*

```
Newsgroup: bit.listserv.geograph
Subject: Impact of a 3 Meter Rise in Oceans on Maps

> This is probably a question to which most of you already know
> the answer, but I don't even know where to look.  If the
> global warming people are correct in their views, and there
> is a rise in sea-level of 3 meters, where in the world would
> maps change the most? The least?

Find a topographic map (showing altitude and depth) of the
regions in which you are interested, and search for all areas
that are under 3 meters in height.  They will probably be under
water.

Good luck.
```

## Interactive World of Maps

It's getting harder and harder to get away with the excuse, "I would have been there sooner, but I got lost." Why? Because there are now interactive street guides on the Net that will allow you to access lots and lots of detailed maps. You can save a map, add your own points of interest to it, and mail it to someone else. You can also get city-to-city driving directions, as well as learn about the history of cartography and mapping symbols. Many of these maps have details right down to individual streets. Amazing. (Try it and you will see what I mean.)

**Web:**

**http://www.mapblast.com/**
**http://www.mapquest.com/**

## Land Surveying

Surveying is cool because there is so much land to go around, you will never run out. Also, when you survey, you get to use neat tools, talk about things other people don't understand, and generally swank around like you own the place. When it comes to being cool about mapping the Earth, surveyors really draw the line. To help you, here's where you can find lots of good information about surveying rules and regulations, state statutes, educational events and resources, professional organizations, and data sources. The Usenet group is for the discussion of the measurement and mapping of the Earth's surface.

**Web:**

**http://www.lsrp.com/mainind.html**

**Usenet:**

**sci.engr.surveying**

## Landform Atlas of the United States

Here is a great place to find a topographic map of any state within the United States. You can examine a selection of beautiful, high-resolution color maps. Take a look. I think you will really find them interesting, especially when you look at the state boundaries and see how they compare with the topography.

**Web:**

**http://fermi.jhuapl.edu/states/states.html**

**There once was a fellow named Randall,**
**Who had all the gals he could handle,**
**He'd whip out his browser,**
**A sure-fire arouser,**
**And show them the Landform**
**Atlas of the United States.**

## Local Times Around the World

You wake up in the middle of the night and look at the clock—it is 2:18 AM. You close your eyes and try to go back to sleep, but all of a sudden a thought comes into your head: what time is it in Bangkok? And you know—you just know—that there is no way you will get to sleep until you find out the answer to your question. Here's what to do. Go to your computer, fire up your Internet connection, and connect to the Local Times Around the World web site. In a few minutes, you will have satisfied your temporal curiosity and sleep, tired Nature's sweet restorer, will once again be yours.

**Web:**

**http://www.hilink.com.au/times/**

## Pathfinder Land Data Sets

This web page sponsored by NOAA and NASA offers satellite data sets of geographic information. The page also has links to archives, geography software to process the data sets, and video sequences from satellites.

**Web:**

**http://xtreme.gsfc.nasa.gov/**

## Perry-Castañeda Library Map Collection

This collection contains a large number of maps which you can access from anywhere on the Net. For example, using only two mouse clicks, I was able to call up a map that showed the exact location of the McMurdo research station on Antarctica (where, by the way, they have copies of my Internet books).

**Web:**

**http://www.lib.utexas.edu/Libs/PCL/Map_collection/Map_collection.html**

## United States Gazetteer

Here is a place to find information about any city or town in the United States. Just enter a city name or a zip code, and get useful information about that location: population, latitude and longitude, zip codes, as well as a colorful map you can save and customize. By the way, did you know there are two towns in the United States that are named after me? Harleyville, South Carolina (1990 pop. 633) and Harleysville, Pennsylvania (1990 pop. 7405). I bet if you check, you would find that the people in these towns are smarter, better looking, and more successful than the rest of general American population.

**Web:**

**http://www.census.gov/cgi-bin/gazetteer/**

## World Population Datasheet

Suppose you need to print brochures for a mass-mailing promotion to everyone in Burkina Faso. Where can you get the population data? Well, this site will show population estimates of many countries around the world, as well as other interesting statistics such as birth and death rates. In case you can't meet your brochure printing deadline, there are also population projections for the year 2025.

**Web:**

**http://dbdev.ciesin.org:8989/cgi-bin/wdb/wdbprb/fdf/PRBWDS/form**

## World's Highpoints

Here is an easy way to stay head and shoulders above your friends. Start with this web site, where you will find maps and graphs of the highest mountain peaks in the world. Select the mountain nearest you, pack your suitcase and walk to the top. Each individual mountain page at this site has additional links with information and climbing routes related to the particular mountain. Be sure to check out all the information before you leave, so you can plan where to stop for drinks and snacks along the way.

**Web:**

**http://www.inch.com/~dipper/world.html**

## Xerox Map Viewer

The PARC Web Map Viewer is an experiment in providing dynamic information retrieval via the Web. It allows you to zoom in and out of a map of the world and supplies many options that you can use to instantly make custom web maps of any location in the world.

**Web:**

**http://pubweb.parc.xerox.com/map**

**Stay away from "X-Rated".**

### *Look What I Found on the Net...*

(from the World Population Datasheet)

| REGION/COUNTRY | World | U.S. | Sweden |
|---|---|---|---|
| POPULATION 1995 [THOUSANDS] | 5,701,769 | 263,200 | 8,857 |
| CRUDE BIRTH RATE | 24.4 | 15.4 | 12.8 |
| CRUDE DEATH RATE | 8.9 | 8.8 | 12.1 |
| RATE OF NATURAL INCREASE [PERCENT] | 1.55 | 0.66 | 0.07 |
| POPULATION 2025 [THOUSANDS] | 8,312,025 | 338,338 | 9,570 |
| INFANT MORTALITY RATE | 61.6 | 8.0 | 4.8 |
| TOTAL FERTILITY RATE | 3.1 | 2.0 | 1.9 |
| LIFE EXPECTANCY AT BIRTH | 65.7 | 75.5 | 78.2 |

## Zip Codes of the U.S.

This simple Internet resource once saved my life. The details are classified, so I can't tell you the whole story, but I can explain how the system works. You enter any address within the United States, and the U.S. Postal Service delivers to your web program, free of charge, the postal code—zip code—to use for that address. By the way, "zip" stands for Zone Improvement Plan.

**Web:**
**http://www.usps.gov/ncsc/lookups/lookup_zip+4.html**

# GEOLOGY

## Ask-a-Geologist

Do you ever lie awake at night wondering whether all Texas lakes are man-made, or where you can find a good source of reservoir rock that is litharenite or sublitharenite? Thanks to modern technology, you can ask such questions of a real geologist. Whip off a letter to a geologist and eventually, someone somewhere will explain something that is geologically interesting. Check out this web site and find out how to submit a question.

**Web:**
**http://walrus.wr.usgs.gov/docs/ask-a-ge.html**

## Earth Science Data Directory

The Earth Science Data Directory (ESDD) is being developed by the U.S. Geological Survey as a system for readily determining the availability of specific earth-science and natural-resource data. It offers access to a USGS computer repository of information about earth-science and natural-resource databases.

**Web:**
**http://www.usgs.gov/gils/esdd/waisgate.html**

## Earthquakes

People talk a lot about earthquakes, but few people actually know much about them. Moreover, most people don't realize that earthquakes are not unusual. Every week, there are a number of earthquakes around the world, some of them large. This site contains a variety of information designed to allow anyone to keep up on how Mother Earth is shaking. Tune in at any time and you may be surprised what happened in the last week.

**Web:**
**http://www.seismo-watch.com/**

## Geological Image Library

The next time you are having a bunch of geology friends over for a rock party, leave this web site displayed on your computer screen. Simply type a keyword into a search engine and you will be rewarded with many beautiful images relating to geology. Once your friends wander over to the computer and start playing with this resource, they will become totally captivated, and you will be free to eat all the onion dip yourself.

**Web:**
**http://www.science.ubc.ca/~geol202/s/cgi-bin/gallery.cgi**

## Geological Time Machine

Here is a fast way to go back to the past without having your time machine run up your electricity bill. Explore an outline of the various eras starting from the Precambrian. Each era is broken down into smaller time periods, with information about each one. There is also information about the formation of the Earth, evolution, and how our planet has changed over the ages.

**Web:**
**http://www.ucmp.berkeley.edu/help/timeform.html**

**Feel lucky? Try "Contests".**

**Intrigue, Privacy, Secret Stuff...**

## Geological Time Scale

Here is a short, well-organized time scale charting the eras and events of the last 4600 million years. This is the best place I know to check when you need to find out if the Devonian era came before or after the Silurian (after), and in which time frame graptolites were dominant (the Ordovician).

**Web:**

**http://www.geo.ucalgary.ca/~macrae/timescale/timescale.html**

## Geology of Radon

Radon is a colorless, radioactive gas formed by the natural decay of radium. As a tool, Radon is primarily used in radiotherapy for treating cancer. However, radon also occurs naturally in areas where uranium-238 is present in the rocks and soil. Elements like uranium decay over long periods of time and, as they decay, the atoms transmutate. Eventually, uranium decays into other elements that produce radium. When radium decays, it forms radon. At the same time, a type of radiation called alpha particles is released. (An alpha particle consists of two protons and two neutrons.) Radon gas is itself radioactive because it also decays, emitting more alpha particles and forming polonium (another radioactive element). The problem is, if there is radon in your environment, you breathe it, whereupon it gets trapped in your lungs. When the radon decays, the radiation and the polonium can cause damage to the tissue and predispose you to developing lung cancer. This web site will give you detailed information: what is radon, where is it found and what can you do to reduce the risk of radon affecting your living environment?

**Web:**

**http://sedwww.cr.usgs.gov:8080/radon/georadon.html**

## Geology Talk and General Discussion

Geology is the study of the structure of the Earth and its surface. These are the places where the geologically inclined discuss technical matters, as well as topics of interest to non-scientists. Talk about rocks, fossils, the origin of natural formations, and so on. If you have a geological question (such as where to take your kids to look for fossils), you can post it here and see if an expert will answer you.

**Usenet:**

**sci.geo.geology**

**Listproc Mailing List:**

List Name: **geology**
Subscribe to: **listproc@cc.fc.ul.pt**

## Global Map of Earthquakes

As you move on to adulthood, it is not uncommon for your mother to experience fits of anxiety and despair because she fears for your safety. If you are about to make that big move from home (or if you moved out 30 years ago and your mother is still worried), take a look at these earthquake maps. Show your mother that where you live is nowhere near a fault line and, in no time at all, she will feel completely at ease. (Hint for anyone living on or near a fault line: download the picture ahead of time, and use a graphics program to remove any red lines that are close to where you live.) The map facilities at this site let you zoom around a graphical representation of the Earth, checking out all the recent quake action. The Usenet group is that place to talk with other people about what makes the Earth move under your feet.

**Web:**

**http://cires.colorado.edu/people/jones.craig/EQimagemap/global.html**

**Usenet:**

**sci.geo.earthquakes**

**Read the FAQs of life.**

## Hydrology Web

Hydrology is the study of water, its properties, distribution and movement across land. Hydrology encompasses a huge area of study, because the hydrologic cycle is so complex. (The hydrologic cycle refers to the entire process of water evaporating from the Earth's surface and eventually coming back down to Earth.) Moreover, water is present in several different physical forms (like rain, snow and ice) and travels in diverse patterns. For example, water can freeze into polar ice caps, where it will stay for millions of years. Or water can fall onto land where it immediately soaks into the ground, is utilized by plants, and runs off into rivers or soaks into the groundwater. Here is a collection of hydrology-related resources, which will give you a good background in the field of hydrology as well as links to related resources. If you'd rather talk than read, check out the Usenet discussion group.

**Web:**

**http://terrassa.pnl.gov:2080/EESC/resourcelist/hydrology.html**

**Usenet:**

**sci.geo.hydrology**

## Illustrated Glossary of Geologic Terms

This is a must-have for anyone interested in geology or for anyone studying geology in school: an illustrated glossary of geologic terms. Many of these terms have a link you can follow for more information, including pictures. While I was here, I read some interesting information about the various types of coral reefs, how they are formed, and how they adapt to neighboring land masses.

**Web:**

**http://www.public.iastate.edu/~geat/new_100/gloss.html**

**When life hands you a lemon, put it on your web page.**

### *Look What I Found on the Net...*

```
Newsgroup: sci.geo.geology
Subject: The Deepest?

>> Hi, does someone know the greatest depth humans have ever
>> reached?  The information I have is:

>>    Kola scientific borehole 10 km
>>    mine (South Africa)       3 km

>> However, I am not sure.  Also I want to know the following:

>>    Coal mine ?
>>    Oil drilling ?
>>    Geophysical survey ?

> "Geophysical surveys" have no direct depth measurement
> associated with data gathering.  The data are measurements of
> geological/geophysical aspects which are in turn analyzed and
> depths estimated.
>
> As such, to answer your question, the deepest measurement made
> via earth-directed geophysical exploration methods would be
> the diameter of the earth.

Shouldn't that be the radius?

Q: How far into the woods can you go?
A: Halfway.
```

**Find a friend in "People".**

## Mineral Gallery

This site will give you more than the recommended daily allowance of minerals. This is a great searchable database of information about gems and minerals of all types. When you find the mineral you are looking for, you will be presented with an image as well as lots of information, such as the mineral's appearance, its uses, details about its physical properties, and so on.

**Web:**

**http://mineral.galleries.com/**

**THE MINERAL GALLERY**

**You can find information about animals simply by interviewing people at a rock concert.**

**And you can learn about vegetables by talking to people who watch a lot of television.**

**But there is only one place to search for data about minerals. Use the Net to visit the Mineral Gallery.**

## National Geophysical Data Center

The National Geophysical Data Center (NGDC) manages environmental data in the fields of solar-terrestrial physics, solid earth geophysics, marine geology and geophysics, paleoclimatology and glaciology.

**Web:**

**http://www.ngdc.noaa.gov/**

## Rock Shop

The two biggest uses of rocks in our culture are (1) to stub your toe, and (2) to hold down paper on your desk. However, studying and collecting rocks can also be a lot of fun, providing entertainment for lapidary hobbyists and various species of rockhounds. If you like to run around looking for interesting rocks and minerals, take a look at this great site, where you will find interesting news and features about rock collecting, as well as a large selection of pictures.

**Web:**

**http://www.rockhounds.com/rockshop/table.html**

## Seismic Information

Here is a large collection of links to seismic information available on the Net. There are lots and lots of earthquake-related resources, so the next time you run into someone on the street who asks, "What's shaking?" you can invite him over and show him in person.

**Web:**

**http://www.geophys.washington.edu/seismosurfing.html**

## Smithsonian Gem and Mineral Collection

A collection of images and descriptions of different types of gems and minerals. This page presents you with a thumbnail picture of the images available, then you can select these to view the gem or mineral in more detail in a full-size image.

**Web:**

**http://galaxy.einet.net/images/gems/gems-icons.html**

**Happiness is a warm modem.**

## U.S. Geological Survey

The U. S. Geological Survey (USGS), a part of the United States Department of the Interior, is America's largest agency devoted to earth science. The USGS creates and provides (for free) an enormous amount of information relating to geology (rocks and soil), topography (lay of the land), and hydrology (water). There are lots of maps and databases, as well as many research analyses of natural resources.

**Web:**

**http://info.er.usgs.gov/**

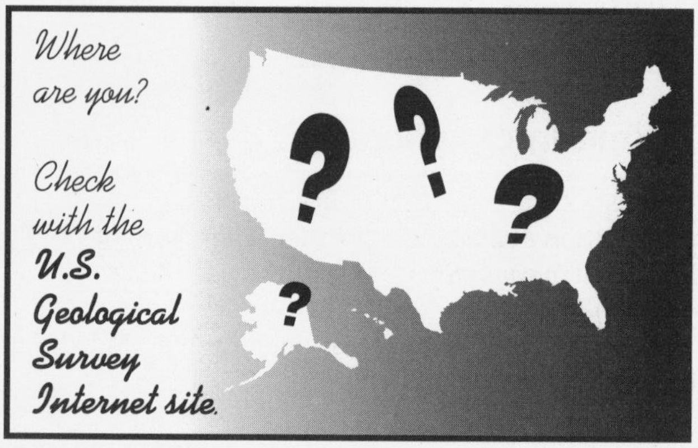
Where are you?
Check with the
U.S. Geological Survey Internet site.

## Virtual Cave

When I was younger, I spent a lot of time exploring the Colossal Cave in the Adventure game (the very first computer-based adventure game). However, I have never had a chance to explore a real cave. Now, however, I can visit the Virtual Cave whenever I want and look at pictures of all kinds of fascinating cave formations. So if—like me—you have always wanted to go spelunking (cave exploring), you can start by doing it over the Net. If you live in the U.S., you can also check with the United States Cave Directory to find out information about many of the public caves you can visit.

**Web:**

**http://www.goodearth.com/virtcave.html**

**Lost? Try a search engine.**

## Volcanology

It used to be that the only thing you could do with a volcano was to throw a virgin into it and hope that the gods were appeased. Now you can hook up all sorts of wires and gadgets to it, and use X-ray fluorescence to examine trace elements and aerial photographs to analyze pumiceous pyroclastic flow. These sites present detailed descriptions of several volcanoes and includes pictures and instructional material.

**Web:**

**http://covis.atmos.uiuc.edu/geosciences/instructional/geology/volcano.html**
**http://vulcan.wr.usgs.gov/home.html**
**http://www.geo.mtu.edu/volcanoes/**

### Volcanoes

What can you say about volcanoes and their almost magnetic attraction for us all? I could remind you that they are holes or cracks in the Earth's surface that release molten lava, ash or other products from underground magma chambers. (Now *that's* a word: "magma." Bet you can't say it ten times real fast.)

Anyway, I could wax eloquent about the runny volcanic outpourings and how they build basalt beds, or how the more viscous types of lava form steep-sided volcanoes, or how ash residue tends to build cone-like peaks. Or I could go on and on about how volcanoes erupt where one lithospheric plate is forced beneath another, or where two such plates diverge.

Yes, there is a lot to say about volcanoes and, if truth be told, they are among my favorite large-scale geological formations. Still, there is something unsatisfying about mere talk and, if you are like me, you will want some pictures, and that is where the Net comes in. Take a cruise to volcano web sites and I guarantee that you will find more than a few shots suitable for framing.

# GOVERNMENT: INTERNATIONAL

## African Governments

Africa is the second largest continent in the world, containing about 10 percent of the world's population. The people of Africa are divided into over 50 countries, which are further fragmented into various ethnic and tribal divisions. Africa's presence in the Net is severely hampered by the lack of a large-scale dependable telephone system. However, there are some African countries with Internet access. These web sites have links to such African governmental resources as exist on the Net.

**Web:**

**http://www.agora.stm.it/politic/africa.htm**
**http://www.lib.umich.edu/libhome/Documents.center/forafr.html**
**http://www.lrz-muenchen.de/~a2c0133/www/govt/africa.html**

## Asia Pacific Governments

The Asia Pacific region of the world consists of those Asian countries that border the Pacific Ocean (that is, most of what used to be referred to as the Orient). Today, the Asia Pacific region is considered to also contain Australia and New Zealand. The significance of this group of countries lies in their economic and political interdependence. To help you find information about the governments of these countries, here is a web site that contains a collection of useful links to resources from Asia Pacific countries.

**Web:**

**http://www.lib.umich.edu/libhome/Documents.center/forasia.html**

"Romance" is waiting for you.

## Australian Government

Okay, you don't always need instant access to a huge amount of information regarding all the different organizations and departments that comprise the government of Australia. But when you do, you'll be glad you have the Net. Imagine how embarrassing it might be to, say, lose the respect of your friends and co-workers just because you don't how to order a Zone Rebate Map from the Australian Taxation Office.

**Web:**

**http://gov.info.au/**
**http://www.nla.gov.au/oz/gov/**

## British Intelligence Organizations

If you have read any James Bond books or seen any of the movies, you would probably guess that the real British intelligence agencies are not exactly like the Secret Service for which Bond works. However, they are no less interesting. See for yourself by reading about MI5 (Military Intelligence 5: internal security and intelligence); MI6 (Military Intelligence 6: national security both internal and external); GCHQ (Government Communications Headquarters: intercepting and monitoring communications), SAS (Special Air Service: covert operations, especially counter-terrorism), SBS (Special Boat Service: naval-based covert operations).

**Web:**

**http://www.cc.umist.ac.uk/sk/**

## Diplomacy

In these days of modern times, the diplomacy game has shifted from fast forward into a post-cold war low speed business. This web site has information related to modern diplomacy. Read about multilateral negotiation and current diplomatic issues, explore links to other negotiation resources and find out about schools of diplomacy. (I wonder, how does a diplomacy student go about convincing a professor to raise his grade?)

**Web:**

**http://www.clark.net/pub/diplonet/**

## Embassies and Consulates Around the World

An embassy is the principle site of official representation of one country within another. Traditionally, embassies are located near the capital of the host country. For example, in the United States, most of the foreign embassies are in (or near) Washington, D.C. The head of the diplomatic mission is called an ambassador. In large countries, there may be other official diplomatic offices called consulates. For example, in the United States, there is a Canadian embassy in Washington, D.C., as well as consulates in various major cities around the country. Embassies and consulates provide a lot of useful information, and many of these offices around the world have their own web sites. Here is a collection of links to such sites.

**Web:**

**http://www.embpage.org/**

## Embassies in Washington, D.C.

When it's late at night and you are in the mood for a little political intrigue, take a look at these embassy-related links. You'll get the goods on the staff and resources of the Washington, D.C., embassy community, embassy web sites, press releases, commerce and trade information, as well as travel and tourism reports. Remember, when you're in Washington, D.C., you can't be too careful. Today's attaché to the assistant secretary for international trade regulations could be tomorrow's industrial spy.

**Web:**

**http://www.embassy.org/**

**Reach out and email someone.**

## European Governments

There are many governments in Europe, and sometimes it can be difficult to find the information you want. To help you, here are web sites that contain links to many different European governments and organizations. When I am looking for European information—especially from an official organization—I often start here.

**Web:**

**http://www.lib.umich.edu/libhome/Documents.center/foreur.html**
**http://www.lrz-muenchen.de/~a2c0133/www/govt/europa.html**

### European Governments

Sometimes when I have trouble sleeping, I get up in the middle of the night and read about the governments of Europe.

After a half hour, my mind is full of all kinds of information about legislative, executive and judicative branches, and I can return to bed for a quiet, peaceful sleep.

Truly, you can never be too rich, too skinny, or know too much about European governments.

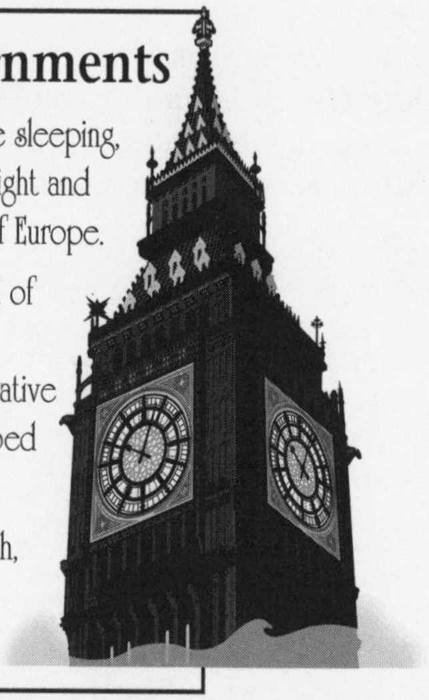

## European Parliament

The European Parliament is the only democratically elected international governing body in the world. The elected representatives exercise control over the member bodies at a European level. As such, the European Parliament is an important part of the European Union. Here is their official web site, which contains information about the organization, including its powers, responsibilities, organization and operation.

**Web:**

**http://www.cec.lu/europarl/europarl.htm**

## European Union

Interesting facts about the European Union: On May 9, 1950, the French Foreign Minister formally read a declaration in which he proposed the creation of an international European organization to manage the coal and steel industry. (At the time, coal and steel were crucial to the balance of European military power.) From this proposal, a series of institutions were formed that, many years later, resulted in the European Union. For this reason, May 9th is now celebrated as Europe Day. Here is something even more interesting. The European flag consists of a circle of twelve gold stars in a blue background. Why twelve stars? The flag was originally designed for the Council of Europe (a completely different organization, sort of like a United Nations for Europe). At the time the Council of Europe was formed, there was some controversy over how many sovereign countries there would be. So, instead of creating a flag with one star for every country, they decided on a flag with twelve stars, because the number "12" was thought to be a symbol of completeness and unity. Why? There are twelve months in the year; twelve constellations in the zodiac; and—in order to win the support of the Christian population of Europe—it was observed that Jesus had twelve apostles. (I am not making this up.) In 1986, the flag was adopted by the European Communities, which later passed it on to the European Union. (Actually, I have a reason which is even better. The number "12" has a large number of factors: 1, 2, 3, 4, 6, 12. This symbolizes that—although there is only one union—there are many divisions.) Finally, here is one last item of European Union trivia. The European anthem (official song) is the prelude to the last movement of Beethoven's Ninth Symphony, often called the "Ode to Joy". (Note to Americans: Beethoven was a European musician who, in some parts of the world, has enjoyed a popularity rivaling that of Elvis Presley.)

**Web:**

**http://eubasics.allmansland.com/**
**http://europa.eu.int**

**Usenet:**

**talk.politics.european-union**

**Spam is more than a food.**

## Governments of the World

There are well over 200 countries in the world, and each one insists on having its own government, resources, organization, culture, and even its own flag. This site has a lot of this type of information, organized by country, including links to other web sites. There is also a nice collection of links to various world organizations. (Hint: This is the place I go when an emergency arises and I need to find the web sites of the major political parties of Finland.)

**Web:**

**http://www.adminet.com/world/gov/**

## Intelligence Organizations

An intelligence organization is one devoted to gathering secret information usually, but not always, about an enemy. Such organizations employ many different methods, the most basic of which is spying. However, modern intelligence organizations go well beyond this traditional pastime, devoting much of their efforts to gathering massive amounts of data, monitoring of communications, industrial espionage and covert operations. Of cource, these guys do not want you to know anything about their operations or how deeply entrenched they are within the various branches of government. However, as one of my readers, you deserve to know everything. Enjoy.

**Web:**

**http://www.awpi.com/IntelWeb/countries.html**
**http://www.loyola.edu/dept/politics/intel.html**

## International Government Talk and General Discussion

The world of international government involves is a lot more than facts, figures and meetings. There are also opinions, power struggles, influence peddling and intrigue. If you would like to immerse yourself in a discussion of international affairs, join either of these mailing lists. Every day, there is some new turn of events to discuss, and there is no reason why everyone shouldn't know your interpretation of what's happening.

**Listproc Mailing List:**

List Name: **int-affairs**
Subscribe to: **listproc@mailer.fsu.edu**

**Listproc Mailing List:**

List Name: **iro**
Subscribe to: **listproc@listproc.bgsu.edu**

## International Organizations in Geneva

There are a *lot* of international organizations in Geneva, including a large portion of the United Nations. Many of these organizations are related to various governments. This web page provides a well-organized reference which allows you find and access information about many, many international organizations both public and private.

**Web:**

**http://geneva.intl.ch/geneva-intl/gi/egimain/edir.htm**

## International Relations and Security Network

The International Relations and Security Network is a large collection of information in several related areas: security and defense, peace and war, and international relations. This is an excellent site if you are looking for research material, or if you are interested in following current world issues and how they are developing. Hint: If you are a political science student and you need to come up with an essay fast, this is a great place to look for raw material.

**Web:**

**http://www.isn.ethz.ch/**

## Israeli Government

The State of Israel, a democracy, was founded on May 14, 1948. Israel is governed by the Knesset (a house of representatives), the members of which are elected by the entire country. Unlike other governments, the Prime Minister is directly elected by the people (as opposed to being the leader of the majority party). The Prime Minister appoints the members of the Cabinet. The head of state is the President, a largely ceremonial position, who is elected by the Knesset. This web site provides a lot of basic information about the Israeli government, as well as links to various departments and organizations.

**Web:**

**http://www.israel.org/gov/**

Are you one of those people who have to understand what is going on, everywhere, all the time? If so, you certainly can't depend on television, radio and newspapers.

You need the International Relations and Security Network.

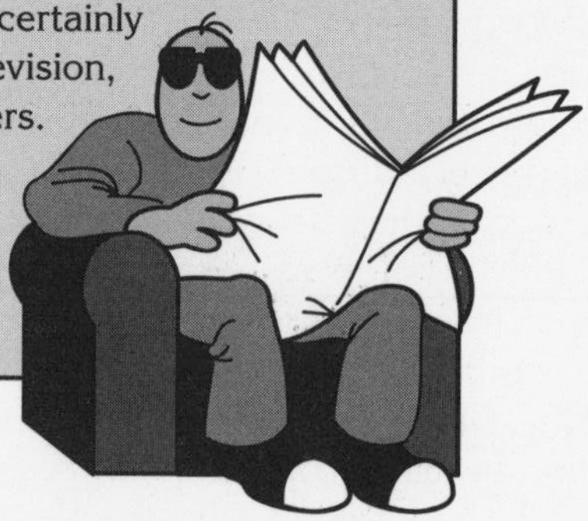

## Japanese Government

Japan consists of a chain of islands off the coast of east Asia, between the North Pacific Ocean and the Sea of Japan. Most of Japan's land mass consists of four main islands: Honshu (the main island where Tokyo is), Hokkaido, Shikoku and Kyushu. Together, all of Japan is only 143,000 square miles (370,000 sq km), smaller than the state of Montana. Japan's population of about 125,000,000 is slightly less than half that of the entire United States, making Japan the seventh most populated country in the world. (The top six are China, India, Russia, the U.S., Indonesia and Brazil.) There are eleven Japanese cities with a population of over 1,000,000. The largest, Tokyo, has well over 8,000,000 people, making it the fourth largest city in the world (after New York, Mexico City and Los Angeles). Japan's government is a mixture of modern post-World War II democracy and traditional institutions. The main components of national government are its legislative body called the Diet (consisting of the House of Councilors and the House of Representatives), and the Prime Minister (elected by the Diet) and the Cabinet (appointed by the Prime Minister). Although the Prime Minister is the chief executive, the head of state is the Emperor. (Technically, Japan is a constitutional monarchy.) On a regional level, Japan is divided into 47 prefectures, each of which elects its own governor and legislature. Even though Japan's government may look similar to that of other countries, its system is uniquely Japanese, built on a pronounced work ethic and a large degree of government-industry cooperation.

**Web:**

**http://jin.jcic.or.jp/navi/category_1.html**

## Latin American Governments

Latin America consists of the countries of America south of the United States, in which Romance languages are generally spoken (Portuguese in Brazil, French in Haiti, and Spanish just about everywhere else). The breadth of Latin America is huge, ranging from the border of the U.S. to the tip of South America not far from Antarctica. This web site contains links to government departments in many Latin American countries, offering a wide variety of information and resources.

**Web:**

**http://www.latinworld.com/government/**

## Middle East Governments

The Middle East refers to the area that includes most of southwest Asia and parts of northeast Africa. The countries in the Middle East are Israel, Syria, Jordan, Iraq, Iran, Lebanon and part of Turkey (Asia); Saudi Arabia, Yemen, Oman, United Arab Emirates, Qatar, Bahrain, Kuwait (the Arabian peninsula); and Egypt and Libya (Africa). This region was the site of the ancient civilizations of Mesopotamia and Egypt, as well as the birthplace of three of the world's major religions, Judaism, Christianity and Islam. In modern times, the Middle East has suffered from a great deal of turmoil and political unrest, much of it due to the tension between Israel and the Arab states, intra-Arab conflicts, and the fact that the region is sitting on a significant portion of the world's oil reserves. Here is a resource that contains links to such Middle East government sites as exist on the Net.

**Web:**

**http://www.lib.umich.edu/libhome/Documents.center/forme.html**

**The Net is waiting for you.**

**Check out a free online book.**

## National Parliaments

Want to see a magic trick? Pick a parliament, any parliament. Now look it up on one of these web pages and click with your mouse. Wait a few minutes. All of a sudden, you will see the web page for that organization. (Actually, it's not really magic—it's the Net.)

**Web:**

**http://www.gdn.org/flags.html**
**http://www.soc.umn.edu/~sssmith/Parliaments.html**

## NATO

NATO (the North Atlantic Treaty Organization) was formed on April 4, 1949, with the signing of the North Atlantic Treaty by twelve countries. Since then, other countries have joined and, today, NATO is a large, complex organization devoted to a voluntary security system in which the member countries share responsibilities. Today, NATO is a defensive alliance based on political and military cooperation. There are sixteen members: Belgium, Canada, Denmark, France, Germany, Greece, Iceland, Italy, Luxembourg, the Netherlands, Norway, Portugal, Spain, Turkey, the United Kingdom and the United States.

**Web:**

**http://www.nato.int/**

## North American Free Trade Agreement

The North American Free Trade Agreement (NAFTA) is an economic agreement signed by the U.S., Canada and Mexico in order to promote economic growth among the three countries. Here you can find the full text of the agreement, as well as resources to help you understand and work with the rules and regulations.

**Web:**

**http://www.i-trade.com/dir05/**
**http://www.sice.oas.org/trade/nafta/naftatce.htm**

## North Atlantic Assembly

North Atlantic Assembly is an inter-parliamentary organization that provides a forum for representatives from member countries to discuss issues of common concern. The primary purpose of the Assembly is to facilitate consensus building (as opposed to arguing with guns or money). The Assembly operates through five committees: Political, Defense and Security, Economic, Civilian Affairs, and Scientific and Technical. These committees act as both study groups and forums. The North Atlantic Assembly has a close working relationship with NATO, although there are no formal ties. The Assembly has delegations (who vote) from Belgium, Canada, Denmark, France, Germany, Greece, Iceland, Italy, Luxembourg, the Netherlands, Norway, Portugal, Spain, Turkey, the United Kingdom, and the United States. There are also associate delegations (who do not vote) from Albania, Belarus, Bulgaria, Czech Republic, Estonia, Hungary, Latvia, Lithuania, Poland, Romania, Russia, Slovakia and Ukraine.

**Web:**

**http://www.nato.int/related/naa/**

## Organization of American States

The Organization of American States (OAS) is the oldest regional organization in the world, having been established on April 30, 1948, by the United States and twenty Latin American republics. The purpose of the OAS is to promote cooperation among the countries of North and South America; to work toward peace and security; and to support economic, cultural and social development. Today, all 35 countries in North and South America belong to the OAS (although the current government of Cuba is not allowed to participate). This web site contains general information about the OAS, as well as the activities of its many departments and programs.

**Web:**

**http://www.latinworld.com/government/**

**Sv bndwdth. Dn't typ ny vwls.**

### *Look What I Found on the Net...*

```
(from the North American Free Trade Agreement)

PREAMBLE

The Government of Canada, the Government of the United Mexican
States and the Government of the United States of America,
resolved to:

STRENGTHEN the special bonds of friendship and cooperation...
CONTRIBUTE to the harmonious development and expansion of...
CREATE an expanded and secure market for the goods and services
REDUCE distortions to trade
ESTABLISH clear and mutually advantageous rules...
ENSURE a predictable commercial framework for business...
BUILD on their respective rights and obligations...
ENHANCE the competitiveness of their firms in global markets...
FOSTER creativity and innovation, and promote trade...
CREATE new employment opportunities, improve working conditions.
UNDERTAKE each of the preceding in a manner consistent with...
PRESERVE their flexibility to safeguard the public welfare
PROMOTE sustainable development
STRENGTHEN the development and enforcement of environmental laws
PROTECT, enhance and enforce basic workers' rights

HAVE AGREED as follows...
```

## Post-World War II Political Leaders

The history of the late twentieth century is really the end result of everything that has been happening since the end of World War II. And in that time, much of what happened was influenced and controlled by our political leaders. This web site offers an easy way to look up the political leaders of any country from 1945 to the present. I found some interesting patterns by reading through some of the lists. I also use this site when I need to find out the name of a political leader quickly.

**Web:**

**http://lgdx01.lg.ehu.es/~ziaorarr/00index.htm**

## Swiss Government

The official name for Switzerland is Confoederatio Helvetica (which roughly translates as "the Swiss Federation"). Switzerland has a long history of remaining neutral and, in fact, they are not even a member of the European Union. Switzerland itself is actually a union. It consists of a confederation of 23 different cantons. The country has four official languages: German (the first language of 63.7% of the people), French (19.2%), Italian (7.6%) and Romansh (0.6%). The remainder of the people, 8.9%, speak another language. The country is an interesting one, and they have a lot of information on the Web. In fact, the ancestor of the Web (called the World Wide Web) was invented in Switzerland.

**Web:**

**http://ethz.ch/swiss/Switzerland_Info.html/**
**http://heiwww.unige.ch/switzerland/**
**http://www.admin.ch/**

## United Kingdom Government

The United Kingdom—England, Scotland, Wales and Northern Ireland—is a constitutional monarchy. The hereditary monarch (currently Queen Elizabeth II) acts as the head of state, carrying out largely ceremonial duties. The parliament consists of an elected House of Commons and a non-elected House of Lords. The Prime Minister is the leader of whichever party holds a majority in the House of Commons. The Prime Minister appoints the Cabinet, the members of which are chosen from among the members of the House. Here is a web site that contains links to selected British government organizations. (What I am waiting for is an online version of Prince Charles's diary.)

**Web:**

**http://www.open.gov.uk/index/figovt.htm**

## United Nations

On January 1, 1942, during World War II, representatives of 26 countries signed the "Declaration by United Nations", in which they promised to continue fighting together against the Axis (the bad guys). The name "United Nations" was coined by U.S. President Franklin Roosevelt. On June 26, 1945, the United Nations as we know it was established with the signing of the "United Nations Charter". In 1945, the U.N. had 51 member countries. Today, there are 185. The United Nations oversees a great many international organizations such as the Security Council, the General Assembly, the International Court of Justice, the United Nations Childrens Fund (Unicef), the World Health Organization, the World Bank, and so on. Overall, the U.N. has 54,000 employees—about the same as Disney World + Disneyland.

**Web:**

**http://www.un.org/**
**http://www.unsystem.org/**

**Usenet:**

**alt.politics.org.un**

## United Nations Security Council

The United Nations Security Council is the body of the United Nations with the responsibility of maintaining international peace and security. Unlike the General Assembly—which has a representative from every country and is not always in session—the Security Council has a limited number of members and functions continuously. The Security Council has fifteen members: five permanent members (the United States, China, France, Russia and the United Kingdom) who have veto power over all decisions, and ten elected members who change from time to time. Here are some resources with information about the Security Council, as well as the various documents they create.

**Web:**

**http://www.un.org/Overview/Organs/sc.html**

**Get in step by reading "Dance".**

## U.S. International Aid

USAID (United States Agency for International Development) is an independent government agency that provides foreign assistance and humanitarian aid to "advance the political and economic interests of the United States". Read about their goals and studies: regional information, population and health information, economic growth studies, and global environmental issues. I'm trying to get a government grant to send me on an all-expense paid trip to the south of France. The only problem is showing how such a trip would be in the economic interests of the United States.

**Web:**

**http://www.info.usaid.gov/**

## World Government

Do you think that we would be better off with one large world government, rather than a whole bunch of countries continually arguing with one another (not to mention clogging up the Olympics and the United Nations)? Here are some resources that you can use to explore and learn about the idea of world government. In the old Superman comics, Superman came from the planet Krypton, which was much more advanced than the Earth. In particular, the Kryptonians had one large world government. (And look where they are today.)

**Web:**

**http://www.bath.ac.uk/~adsjrc/eu/eu-main.html**
**http://www.webcom.com/~worldgov/**

## World Rulers

Once you start collecting all the names, it's amazing how many people have at one time or another ruled a country. And where else can you go when you need to find out the name of the first president of Nigeria? This is a great site that has a huge amount of well-organized information. For example, you can pick up a nice list of all the presidents of the United States, as well as the governors of any particular state. Or perhaps you would like to know who the Governor General of Canada was when you were born, or when the various General Secretaries of the Hungarian Socialist Workers' Party took office. (By the way, the first president of Nigeria was Benjamin N. Azikiwe; the Governor General of Canada when I was born was Vincent Massey; and there were four different General Secretaries of the Hungarian Socialist Workers' Party.)

**Web:**

**http://www.geocities.com/Athens/1058/rulers.html**

**"Animals and Pets" are people too.**

### *Look What I Found on the Net...*

(from the preamble to the Charter of the United Nations)

WE THE PEOPLES OF THE UNITED NATIONS DETERMINED

to save succeeding generations from the scourge of war, which twice in our lifetime has brought untold sorrow to mankind, and

to reaffirm faith in fundamental human rights, in the dignity and worth of the human person, in the equal rights of men and women and of nations large and small, and

to establish conditions under which justice and respect for the obligations arising from treaties and other sources of international law can be maintained, and

to promote social progress and better standards of life in larger freedom...

# GOVERNMENT: UNITED STATES

## Budget of the United States Government

Have you ever wondered exactly how much money the government spends? Well, now you can find out. The entire budget of the United States federal government is on the Net. (That is, at least the parts of the budget that aren't deadly secrets like funding for clandestine operations.) Here is an interesting statistic: In 1994, the Department of Defense spent $1,610,490,000. The estimate for 1997 is $1,463,800,000 (a decrease of $146,690,000).

**Web:**

**http://www.access.gpo.gov/su_docs/budget96/budget001.html**

## Cap Web's Guide to Congress

Information about the Senate, House of Representatives, Library of Congress, congressional support agencies, the Constitution, all rolled up with a legislation search facility.

**Web:**

**http://policy.net/capweb/congress.html**

## Census Information

How many cool male Internet authors live on the north side of any given street in any given city? The Census Bureau can't tell you if the authors are cool, but they do know the rest. They also store financial data on state and local governments and schools, poverty in the United States, and housing changes.

**Web:**

**http://www.census.gov/**

**Express yourself. Make a web page.**

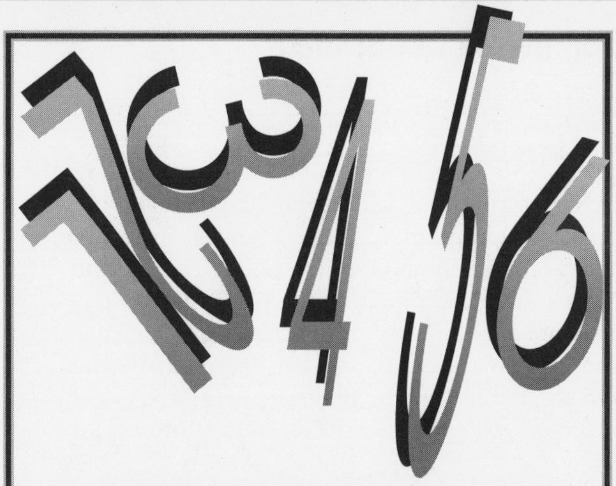
23456

**Need some numbers?**

Check out the *Census Information* Server.

## CIA

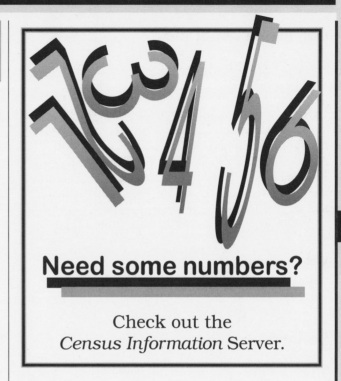

The Central Intelligence Agency (CIA) was formed in 1947 by the passage of the National Security Act. The CIA's role is to concern itself with intelligence and counterintelligence activities outside the United States, and to coordinate activities with the FBI (Federal Bureau of Investigation) relating to domestic counterintelligence. If you would like to experience a little of the mystery and intrigue of the CIA—without having them start a file on you—visit their web site, where you can learn more about the agency and take a virtual tour of the parts of their operation they are willing to discuss. While you are here, be sure to check out some of the CIA's publications, such as the "Factbook on Intelligence" and the "CIA World Factbook". The Usenet group is for the discussion of the CIA. You are probably safe to say anything you want because, after all, the United States is a free country and no government agency would ever dare monitor a Usenet discussion group. (Ha, ha.)

**Web:**

**http://www.odci.gov/cia/**

**Usenet:**

**alt.politics.org.cia**

## Commerce Department

The U.S. Department of Commerce was started in 1903 and, since then, has continually changed to keep in step with current economic conditions. Today, the DOC has many agencies, some of which you might be surprised to find in this department. For example, here you will find NOAA (National Oceanic and Atmospheric Administration), NIST (National Institute of Standards and Technology), the Patent and Trademark Office, and the National Weather Service. For links to all of these government agencies, and more, check out the DOC's main Internet site.

**Web:**

**http://www.doc.gov/**

## Congress

Senators are elected for only six years, while representatives are elected for an even shorter two-year term. However—like General MacArthur and adult children without jobs—they can return. If you would like to check up on your elected representatives, here is all the information you need to find them, send them email, connect to their web pages, and generally see what they are doing (at least when they think you are looking).

**Web:**

**http://lcweb.loc.gov/global/legislative/house.html**
**http://lcweb.loc.gov/global/legislative/senators.html**

## Congressional Committee Assignments

In Congress, a *lot* of power rests with committees, sub-committees, and the people who lead them. Here are the resources you need to find out exactly who is sitting on which committee, and what they are supposed to be doing.

**Web:**

**http://lcweb.loc.gov/global/legislative/housecomm.html**
**http://lcweb.loc.gov/global/legislative/jtcomm.html**
**http://lcweb.loc.gov/global/legislative/senatecomm.html**

Department of Commerce

*What could be more romantic than soft lighting, romantic music, a bottle of fine wine, and a direct link to the U.S. Department of Commerce?*

*So the next time your hot date starts to cool off, go back to your place, fire up your Internet connection and tap into the* ***Department of Commerce*** *web site. Before you know it, your social life will perk up like a ferret on a caffeine binge.*

## Congressional Quarterly

A newsletter that offers the latest dirt—or rather, news—from Capitol Hill. The information is nonpartisan and in-depth, so it offers good coverage and analysis.

**Web:**

**http://pathfinder.com/CQ**

## Economic Conversion Information Exchange

Even though the cold war is over, there are still a lot of people and companies devoted to making things that kill, snoop and destroy. The Office of Economic Conversion was established by the U.S. Department of Commerce and Department of Defense in order to provide information about "defense adjustment and conversion". Perhaps, one day, all the schools will get plenty of funding, while the U.S. Department of Defense has to have a bake sale to raise money for its web site.

**Web:**

**http://netsite.esa.doc.gov/oeci/**

## Executive Branch

Never again will you have to hotfoot it around the Net looking for information about the President and his minions. The Library of Congress has compiled a web page that covers resources pertaining to the executive branch of the federal government and its various departments, as well as independent executive agencies.

**Web:**

**http://lcweb.loc.gov/global/executive/fed.html**

## FBI

The Federal Bureau of Investigation (FBI), created in 1908, is a division of the United States Department of Justice. The FBI investigates various violations of federal law such as kidnapping, bank robbing, sabotage, espionage and civil rights violations. If you have ever been in a United States post office, you may have seen the pictures on the wall of desperate and suspicious-looking individuals. These are fugitives that are being pursued by the FBI. However, you don't have to go into the post office to see these pictures. At the FBI web site, you can check out the list of the "Ten Most Wanted Fugitives" and see if you happen to know any of them. You can also root around the web site and learn a lot about the FBI. The Usenet group is for the discussion of the FBI and its operations and politics.

**Web:**

**http://www.fbi.gov/**

**Usenet:**

**alt.politics.org.fbi**

## Federal Government Information

Don't take the politicians' word. Look up government data yourself and make your own decisions. Information is categorized by source (for example, Government Accounting Office). Choose a source, then a document.

**Web:**

**http://www.wcs-online.com/usgovdoc/**

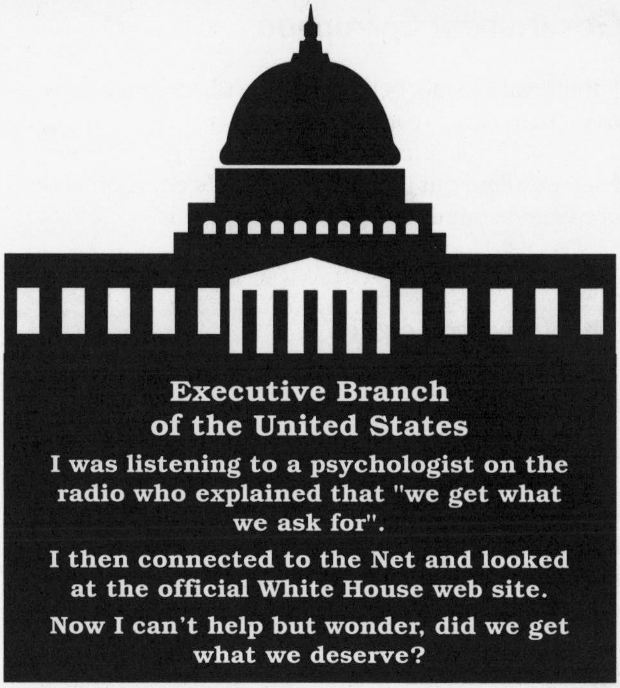
Executive Branch
of the United States
I was listening to a psychologist on the radio who explained that "we get what we ask for".
I then connected to the Net and looked at the official White House web site.
Now I can't help but wonder, did we get what we deserve?

## Federal Register

Documents from the Federal Register and information on how to gain full access to the daily U.S. Federal Register via the Internet. Documents include proclamations, executive orders, and so on.

**Web:**

**http://cos.gdb.org/repos/fr/fr-intro.html**

## FedWorld

An enormous resource for scientific, technical, and other information provided by the federal government. FedWorld is taxpayer-supported through the National Technical Information Service (NTIS). It is an easy-to-use system that offers information on a wide variety of subjects.

**Web:**

**http://www.fedworld.gov/**

## General Accounting Office

Reports from the General Accounting Office (GAO) on budget issues, investment, government management, public services, health care, energy issues, and virtually every other area of government on which the GAO may have reported.

**Web:**

**http://www.gao.gov/**

## Government Corruption

I don't want to talk behind anyone's back, but rumor has it that there is corruption in government. I thought if you were going to hear it, you should get the news from me. Find out the details of what's going on in the nooks and crannies of the political system.

**Web:**

**http://www.epic.org/fcg/**

## Government Information Sources

Here are lots of sources of U.S. federal government information. From this site, you can get to just about anything within the U.S. government, as long as it is on the Net.

**Web:**

**http://www.law.vill.edu/fed_agency/fedwebloc.html**
**http://www.nttc.edu/gov_res.html**

## Housing and Urban Development

Descriptions of the mission and functions of the Department of Housing and Urban Development (HUD): reports, news, research findings on violence issues, and links to other federal, commercial, and educational servers. Enjoy the window dressing, but keep your hands on your First Amendment rights.

**Web:**

**http://www.hud.gov/**

## Infomine

Have you been looking for a specific government resource and you don't know where to find it? Here is a database of federal, state and local government resources that you can search by subject, keyword or title.

**Web:**

**http://lib-www.ucr.edu/govpub/**

### Government Corruption

Corruption is in the eyes of the beholder and–for people in government service–it is all too often the case that the I's have it. Check out the **Government Corruption** site, and see what your friends on the Net have to say about the government's tendency to confuse the ideas of "mine", "yours", and "ours."

## Inspectors General

Information about the Federal Offices of Inspectors General, the fine folks who are responsible for auditing, investigating and inspecting government agencies. Their goal is to decrease fraud, waste and abuse, and they have the web page to prove it.

**Web:**

**http://www.nara.gov/ig/**
**http://www.sbaonline.sba.gov/ignet/**

## Justice Statistics

Statistics on topics relating to the U.S. Department of Justice, including crimes, victims, drugs, prisons, courts, sentencing, and much more. There is a lot of interesting information here and, in my opinion, it speaks highly of the United States that such information is made accessible, for free, to anyone in the world. In many other countries, information like this is kept secret, not broadcast on the Internet.

**Web:**

**http://www.ojp.usdoj.gov/bjs/**

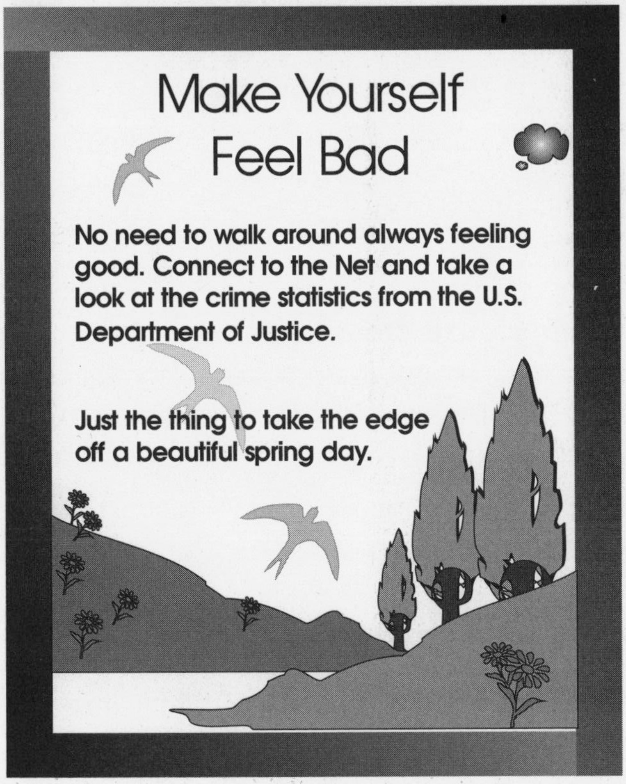
Make Yourself Feel Bad
No need to walk around always feeling good. Connect to the Net and take a look at the crime statistics from the U.S. Department of Justice.
Just the thing to take the edge off a beautiful spring day.

## Justices of the Supreme Court

The Supreme Court is the highest federal court in the United States and has jurisdiction over all the other courts in the nation. The Supreme Court consists of judges—a chief justice and eight associate justices—all of whom are nominated by the President and confirmed by the Senate. The Supreme Court has two main duties: to interpret acts of Congress, and to determine whether federal and state statutes conform to the United States Constitution. If you want the scoop on those people currently serving on the Supreme Court, check out this web site. It has a list of the justices, along with biographical data and their pictures (in case you run into one of them in the supermarket). You will also find a lengthy and fascinating collection of each judge's opinions for the court: important majority opinions, important concurring opinions, and selected dissenting opinions.

**Web:**

**http://www.law.cornell.edu/supct/justices/fullcourt.html**

## Legislative Branch

Keep up with what's going on in the U.S. legislative branch of the government. The Library of Congress has put together a nice selection of resources pertaining to Congress, including links to web pages of various members of Congress and notations on the members' voting records.

**Web:**

**http://lcweb.loc.gov/global/legislative/congress.html**

## National Archives and Records Administration

The U.S. National Archives and Records Administration is the agency that oversees the management of all the records of the federal government. (And you thought it was a big job just keeping your room tidy.) Here you will find a wealth of information including: historical records, the Federal Register (the daily record of the government), genealogical data, links to the presidential libraries, the official U.S. Government Manual (which contains just about *everything* under the American sun), and much more.

**Web:**

**http://www.nara.gov/**

## National Performance Review

The government is trying hard to get you in on the action—at least they'd like you to think so. The National Performance Review has a more interactive site which includes not only information, but an actual "toolkit to help reinvent government" so you can do your own part in making everything run as smooth as well-oiled baby.

**Web:**

**http://www.npr.gov/**

## Social Security Administration

The Social Security Administration Office Support System Information Server (OSS-IS) offers data on monthly benefits, current operating statistics, history of benefits paid, and income data on the aged.

**Web:**

**http://www.ssa.gov/**

## State Department

The United States maintains diplomatic relations with about 180 countries as well as many international organizations. The Department of State is the principal foreign affairs agency of the U.S government. As such, it has two broad mandates: to represent U.S. policies and interests abroad, and to gather information used to create foreign policy. The head of the State Department—the Secretary of State—is the fourth in line of presidential succession (after the Vice President, the Speaker of the House, and the President Pro Tempore of the Senate).

**Web:**

**http://dosfan.lib.uic.edu/**

## U.S. Government Talk and General Discussion

Blah, blah, blah. Everyone talks and talks about the government, but where do you go for serious discussion? Try this mailing list, devoted to the issues involving trust in government. After all, in the United States, government is by the people and for the people. Trust, or lack thereof, is an important factor in the political world.

**Listproc Mailing List:**

List Name: **gov-trust**
Subscribe to: **listproc@u.washington.edu**

## White House

Here is the official Internet site for the White House. If you have nothing to do, you might want to connect and see who is living there.

**Web:**

**http://www.whitehouse.gov/**

## White House Press Releases

Find out the official word on the activities and goings-on at the White House and related U.S. agencies. If you want, you can even subscribe to the mailing list and get a free daily summary. Just the thing to give your son or daughter for a graduation present. (After all, who wants a car?)

**Web:**

**http://library.whitehouse.gov/PressReleases.cgi**

**Majordomo Mailing List:**

List Name: **wh-summary**
Subscribe to: **majordomo@reeusda.gov**

**Don't forget to email your mother.**

### *Look What I Found on the Net...*

(from the archives of the United States State Department)

[The following is excerpted from a speech given by the U.S. Secretary of State at the John F. Kennedy School of Government, Harvard University, January 18, 1996.]

...This is not the end of history, but history in fast-forward. Eight decades ago, when this century's first Balkan war ended, it took an international commission to piece together what had happened. Now, images of violence in Sarajevo are beamed instantly around the world. Six decades ago, it took several years for the Great Depression to become a global disaster. Now, an economic crisis in Mexico can disrupt the global economy in the blink of an eye.

In this time of accelerated change, American leadership must remain constant. We must be clear-eyed and vigilant in pursuit of our interests. Above all, we must recognize that only the United States has the vision and strength to consolidate the gains of the last few years, and to build an even better world...

# HEALTH

## Acne and Eczema

Acne is an condition in which the sebaceous glands become inflamed, generally due to the clogging of skin pores. Acne is characterized by blackheads, pimples and cysts which appear on the face, neck, chest, arms and back. Eczema is an inflammatory condition in which the skin develops redness and itching. There may also be a watery discharge which can become encrusted and scaly. These web sites offer detailed information about the causes and treatment of acne. The Usenet group is for the discussion of acne and eczema. The mailing list is for sufferers of eczema and for health professionals who treat eczema.

**Web:**

**http://victorvalley.com/health%26law/hlaw-apr/skin.htm**
**http://www.housecall.com/databases/ami/convert/000873.html**

**Usenet:**

**alt.skincare.acne**

**Listserv Mailing List:**

List Name: **eczema**
Subscribe to: **listserv@sjuvm.stjohns.edu**

## Addictions

Academic and scholarly discussion of addictions, including food disorders, sex, codependency, nicotine, and other addictions. Not intended for alcohol and drug addiction discussion.

**Listserv Mailing List:**

List Name: **addict-l**
Subscribe to: **listserv@listserv.kent.edu**

Can't **stop** the music?
That's okay.
Can't **stop** something else?
You may have a problem.
If so, try the
Addictions mailing list.

## AIDS

AIDS (acquired immune deficiency syndrome) and the HIV (human immunodeficiency virus) family of viruses that cause it are important medical topics. There is lots of AIDS information on the Net, including Usenet discussion groups.

**Web:**

**http://www.teleport.com/~celinec/aids.shtml**
**http://www.thebody.com/**

**Usenet:**

**misc.health.aids**
**sci.med.aids**

## American Dental Association

Here it is, your guarantee against boredom: the official Internet site of the American Dental Association. Here you will find the Dental News Digest as well as all kinds of information relevant to the practice of dentistry: news articles, details about dental associations, dental legislative news, journal previews, a dental event calendar, and directories of dental societies. Now, if I could only find a way to prevent tartar build-up on my cat's teeth.

**Web:**

**http://www.ada.org/**

## Aromatherapy

Aromatherapy is the therapeutic use of scented essential oils derived from plants. The oil can be put into a vaporizer, applied to the skin by massage, or put into a bath. If you are not sure where to start, check out these resources. You will learn how to pick out appropriate oils and how to use them in conjunction with massage, baths or vaporizers. You can also read about the interesting history of aromatherapy. The Usenet group is for the discussion of aromatherapy or for asking questions.

**Web:**

**http://www.halcyon.com/kway/**
**http://www.healthy.net/clinic/therapy/aroma/**

**Usenet:**

**alt.folklore.aromatherapy**

## Arthritis

"Arthritis" means inflammation of one or more joints of the body. Symptoms include pain, redness and stiffness, which can range from mild to severe. Although people talk about arthritis as if it is a single disease, there are actually many different types of arthritis. The two most well-known are osteoarthritis, a degenerative disease that sometimes accompanies aging, and rheumatoid arthritis, an auto-immune disease most commonly affecting women. In general, most types of arthritis, as well as many other auto-immune conditions, fall under the branch of medicine known as rheumatology. Here are some good web resources that will give you more detailed information about arthritis, how it is treated, what research is being conducted and much more. The Usenet groups offer a place for arthritis sufferers, medical personnel, or supportive family and friends to talk about arthritis.

**Web:**

**http://www.arthritis.org/**
**http://www.pslgroup.com/arthritis.htm**

**Usenet:**

**alt.support.arthritis**
**misc.health.arthritis**

## Attention Deficit Disorder

Information about Attention Deficit Disorder (ADD), including its diagnoses, questions to ask, articles, and other resources relating to ADD.

**Web:**

**http://www.seas.upenn.edu/~mengwong/add/**

## Birth Control

Here is where you can find out everything you always wanted to know about birth control (but never bothered to ask). You can find general information about all methods of contraception (including abstinence). Learn about drugs, contraceptive devices, useful statistics, family planning, and much more.

**Web:**

**http://gynpages.com/ultimate/**
**http://www.ppfa.org/ppfa/lev2bc.html**

Birth control: When you care enough not to send the very best.

## Centers for Disease Control

The Centers for Disease Control and Prevention (CDC) is an agency of the United States Department of Health and Human Services. (The CDC was originally established in 1946 as the Communicable Disease Center.) The CDC offers national programs for the prevention and control of communicable diseases, conducts research and directs quarantine activities when necessary. At their web site they offer information about communicable diseases, health risks, injuries and disabilities, and prevention guidelines. They also have a nice selection of tips for people who are planning to travel outside the country. Take some time to read the information here. You will learn a lot.

**Web:**

**http://www.cdc.gov/**

## Children Who Require Special Health Care

A mailing list dedicated to children with special health care needs and their families, as well as pediatric health care in general.

**Listserv Mailing List:**

List Name: **cshcn-l**
Subscribe to: **listserv@nervm.nerdc.ufl.edu**

## Children's Mental Health

If you have a family or if you work with children, this is a good place to visit to read factsheets that cover important topics such as depression, lying, children of alcoholics, lead exposure, learning disabilities, teen suicide and teen pregnancy.

**Web:**

**http://www.aacap.org/web/aacap/factsFam/**

## Depression

Depression is more than being bummed out because someone else ate the last of the ice cream. Depression is a psychological disorder characterized by a persisting general unhappiness often accompanied by other symptoms such as sleep disturbances, lack of appetite, lack of concentration, suicidal thoughts, problems with work or family life, and feelings of emptiness and worthlessness. This web site is an excellent source of information about depression and the treatment of depression. It has information about medical and psychological treatments for depression as well as a lengthy list of Usenet support groups. If you want to talk to someone online, try the IRC channel or post to the Usenet group. The mailing list is for sufferers of depression as well as friends and family. On the Net, someone is always home.

**Web:**

**http://www.execpc.com/~corbeau/**

**Usenet:**

**alt.support.depression**

**Majordomo Mailing List:**

List Name: **walkers**
Subscribe to: **majordomo@world.std.com**

**Majordomo Mailing List:**

List Name: **walkers-digest**
Subscribe to: **majordomo@world.std.com**

**IRC:**

**#asd**

## Diabetes Talk and General Discussion

Need the latest info about diabetes? Will new immune-desensitizing therapies provide a much-needed preventative measure or even a cure? Read all about the management, treatment, and research of diabetes. Talk with other diabetics who share their experience, tips, and opinions.

**Usenet:**

**misc.health.diabetes**

## Epilepsy and Seizure Disorders

Epilepsy is a chronic condition in which the normal electrical functions of the brain are disturbed in such a way as to produce seizures. Epilepsy can also produce other neurological symptoms affecting consciousness, movement or sensation. Epilepsy is a common condition, and in most cases, there is no known cause. Here is a lot of useful information about epilepsy, including a FAQ (frequently asked question list).

**Web:**

**http://www.efa.org/**

## First Aid Online

Information about first aid supplies, as well as hints on what first aid to use for common conditions and injuries: blisters, burns, frostbite, breathing difficulties, choking, fainting, bruising, puncture wounds, ears/eyes/nose problems, poisoning, bites, sprains, fractures and shock.

**Web:**

**http://www2.vivid.net/~cicely/safety/**

## Good Health Web

The Good Health Web is a collection of links to health-related Internet resources. Here you will find information about organizations, news, discussions, FAQs, mailing lists, and a library of health topics.

**Web:**

**http://www.social.com/health/**

## Headaches

It could be one of those dull, throbbing ones. Or it could be a sharp, aching one. Or maybe it starts slow when the back of your neck is tense and works its way up until it feels like your eyeballs will pop out. If you have personal or professional interest in headaches of any sort, this is a mailing list that will interest you. Discussion covers the physical, emotional, social, and economic impact of recurring headaches.

**Listserv Mailing List:**

List Name: **headache**
Subscribe to: **listserv@shsu.edu**

A B C D E F G H I J K L M N O P Q R S T U V W X Y Z

## Smoking Addiction

The phrase "the only way to break a bad habit is to drop it" was invented by someone who never had to quit smoking. It's a habit that is hard to break whether you quit altogether or try to taper off. Find support from other people recovering from their addiction to cigarettes or from people who have already recovered.

**Usenet:**

**alt.support.non-smokers**
**alt.support.stop-smoking**

## Snakebites

In North America, snakes are not nearly as dangerous as most people believe. North American snakes seldom bite humans, and even when they do, the bites are rarely fatal. However, if you do get bitten by a snake, you may be in need of some hard information quickly. If so, here is the place to look. If you happen to be bitten by a snake in a different part of the world, catch the first plane for North America, and then check this site. (By the way, unless you are in a movie, it is never a good idea to suck out the venom with your mouth.)

**Web:**

**http://io.datasys.swri.edu/PATC/snakbite.html**

## Stress

Stress, stress and more stress. I'm so tired of stress I could scream. But when I'm tired of screaming and I want the real lowdown, I turn to the Stress Internet site. Here is information on the history of stress, the reasons and biological basis for stress, the physiology of stress, how to manage stress, and hints on how to relax. (My hint is to stop reading about stress.)

**Web:**

**http://www.foobar.co.uk/users/umba/stress/**

## Stuttering

It's not painful or fatal, but it's certainly frustrating. Researchers and clinicians are continually working toward a solution to the problem of stuttering, and one helpful tool is networking on the Internet. Discussion of projects, procedures and theories are a few of the things relating to stuttering on this list.

**Listserv Mailing List:**

List Name: **stutt-l**
Subscribe to: **listserv@vm.temple.edu**

## Suicide Prevention

Sometimes life is frightening and miserable, and even though the pain won't last forever, it's still hard to deal with. If you feel like you've had all you can take and you're not sure what to do next, try getting in touch with the Samaritans. This is not a religious organization, but a group of people who want to give you a place to reach out to, confidentially. Their charity has been offering emotional support by phone, personal visits, and snail mail for 40 years, and now they are offering help electronically. Members of their staff are trained volunteers.

**Mail:**

**jo@samaritans.org**
**samaritans@anon.penet.fi**

## Typing Injuries

I have a good friend (who happens to be the wife of my lawyer) who injured her forearm by typing too much. Such injuries are common and more bothersome than most people realize—until it happens to them. The best treatment is to rest. However, most people, including my friend, want to keep on typing. (I remember when she only wanted to keep on truckin'.) Anyway, if you have or are developing a typing injury, here is a great place to look for information. By the way, I avoid such injuries by taking frequent breaks and doing the yoga "reverse namaste" pose. (Put your hands behind your back, fingers pointed up, and press with your palms together gently. Breathe slowly and think pure thoughts. After a while, it gets easy and feels great.)

**Web:**

**http://www.cs.princeton.edu/~dwallach/tifaq/**

**Listserv Mailing List:**

List Name: **sorehand**
Subscribe to: **listserv@itssrv1.ucsf.edu**

**Majordomo Mailing List:**

List Name: **rsi**
Subscribe to: **majordomo@world.std.com**

**Stay connected.**

**Typing Injuries**

I was minding my Ps and Qs. I thought I had it down to a T, but I missed my Q.

"O no," I said. "I KO'd my wrist".

"R U OK?" she asked.

"Y do U ask?"

"B-cause, A typing injury can B painful. B careful."

"G," I said, "now I C Y. OK."

## U.S. Department of Health and Human Services

The DHHS web server provides information on the mission, programs, organization, initiatives, activities, and impact of the DHHS on the health and well-being of the American public. In addition, this server provides access to information and resources made available by the various organizations that comprise DHHS.

**Web:**

**http://www.os.dhhs.gov/**

## Women's Health

Women have a number of special health considerations. Here is a large collection of links to resources related to women's health. There is lots and lots of information here. Read about pregnancy, birth and midwifery, breast cancer, menopause, osteoporosis, rape and sexual assault, abortion, safe sex, fertility, sexual harassment, AIDS, sexually transmitted diseases, mental health, pap tests, and much, much more.

**Web:**

**http://www.femina.com/femina/health**

## World Health Organization

Here is the Internet site for the World Health Organization (WHO), which operates under the auspices of the United Nations. The goal of WHO is the "attainment by all peoples of the highest possible level of health". What do they mean by health? "A state of complete physical, mental and social well-being—and not merely the absence of disease or infirmity—in which each person in the world has at least two Harley Hahn books."

**Web:**

**http://www.who.ch/**

# HERBS

## Algy's Herb Page

You don't have to hop all over the Net just to find good herb information. This site has loads of links relating to ornamental herbs, culinary and medicinal herbs, recipes, news and discussions.

**Web:**

**http://www.algy.com/herb/herb.html**

## Chinese Herbs

If you are interested in herbs, you will enjoy reading about Chinese herbs and how they are used in traditional healing. This web site offers information for students of Chinese herbology as well as practitioners. The mailing list is for the discussion of Chinese herbs and related health issues.

**Web:**

**http://acupuncture.com/Herbology/HerbInd.htm**

**Majordomo Mailing List:**

List Name: **herb**
Subscribe to: **majordomo@geog.hkbu.edu.hk**

## Culinary Herbs

When I cook, I like to use a variety of fresh herbs to season my meal. They taste great, they are economical, and they are easy to use. Here is a FAQ (frequently asked question list) that will help you learn about using herbs in your cooking and growing your own culinary herbs.

**Web:**

**http://sunsite.unc.edu/herbmed/culiherb.html**

## Garlic

I love garlic. I have a recipe for garlic and parsley spaghetti topped with a smoked garlic tomato sauce that is fantastic. (1: Buy ready-made garlic and parsley spaghetti. 2: Buy ready-made smoked garlic tomato sauce. 3: Cook spaghetti. 4: Warm sauce in microwave. 5: Combine spaghetti and sauce.) Garlic is good for more than cooking, though. You can use garlic to promote health. Garlic contains a large amount of organic sulfides and other nutritious compounds and is reported as being useful as an antibiotic, anti-carcinogen, antioxidant, as well as reducing atherosclerosis (at least in lab animals). This web site will tell you all about the wonders of garlic from a scientific and historical point of view, including the effective dosages and formulations for ingesting this wonder herb.

**Web:**

**http://essentialgarden.com/faq/garlic/**

## Growing Herbs

Herbs are great for so many things. You can eat them, make decorations out of them, and use them as medicine (or even as a recreational activity provided you don't inhale). Learn how to grow your very own herbs. This guideline will tell you about the care and feeding of common garden herbs.

**Web:**

**http://etcs.ext.missouri.edu/publications/xplor/agguides/hort/g06470.html**

## *Culinary Herbs*

Would you like to meet some
of my favorite friends?

Basil, curry, sage, chives, saffron, cilantro, rosemary, thyme, bay leaves, mint, tarragon, dill, garlic, lemon grass, horseradish, fennel, anise, parsley, ginger, borage, horehound, marjoram, oregano, caraway, savory and chamomile.

Why not invite them over to
dinner sometime?

## Henriette's Herbal Homepage

When I want to get the latest dirt on the world of herbs, I like to go check with Henriette. Here you will find a great archive of postings taken from various herbal newsgroups. While you are here, you can find herb FAQs, pictures, software and a database of plant names.

**Web:**

**http://sunsite.unc.edu/herbmed/**

## Herb Directory

This is a nice collection of herb information. Each herb has a link to a page detailing various aspects of the plant: mythology or origin of the herb, detailed description of the appearance, what type of soil and lighting the herb requires, pests and diseases common to the herb, cultivation, companion planting, propagation methods, bloom time and color, harvesting, various uses of the herb, and other applicable notes.

**Web:**

**http://hortweb.cas.psu.edu/vegcrops/herbs.html**

## Herb Elektra

Get out the wheelbarrow and load up on lots of herb links. This site has information about growing and cultivating herbs, cooking with herbs, herbs and health, and identifying herbs.

**Web:**

**http://www.cruzio.com/~mswaine/Nancyville/HerbElektra.html**

## Herb List

It's always good to know about herbal healing properties. For example, if you have a big publishing deadline, and your editor will not allow you to sleep or have fun, it is nice to know that gotu kola helps alleviate mental fatigue and rose hips fight stress. You can learn these helpful facts and more at this web site.

**Web:**

**http://people.delphi.com/janruh/herbs1.htm**

## Herb Magick

When you are trying to get through life, you don't necessarily have to stick with "the known" reality most people agree on. For instance, you can utilize some herb magick to make life go your way. These web resources have basic information about getting started with herbs, as well as more esoteric information about the magickal properties of various woods and plants. Don't have a spellbook? No need to worry. You can find sample spells online. Bad with plants? It doesn't matter. After all, you don't need a green thumb when you have a magick wand.

**Web:**

**http://www.indy.net/~apl/Astralite/pantry.html**
**http://www.ipcc.com/market/newage/oils.htm**

## Herb Talk and General Discussion

Things that grow and things that don't, plants that heal and plants that won't, little herbs that stink and flower, have their merit and their power. Here's the place where people go, to talk about the herbs to grow, for cooking, eating, dying blue, to give as gifts, for healing, too.

**Usenet:**

**alt.folklore.herbs**

## Herb List

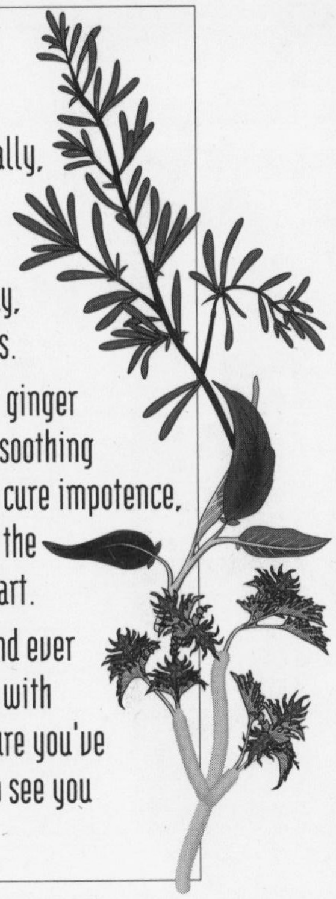

You probably know that, historically, certain herbs have been used for medicinal purposes. However, before you use an herb in this way, be sure you understand its effects.

For example, tradition holds that ginger helps fight a cold, chamomile is soothing to the nerves, sarsaparilla helps cure impotence, and hawthorn berries strengthen the muscles and the nerves to the heart.

So, guys, if your wife or girlfriend ever brings you chamomile tea mixed with sarsaparilla and ginger, make sure you've got plenty of hawthorn berries to see you through the night.

## Herbal Forum

Join this interactive forum relating to herbs. Fill out a form asking a question about herbs. Reload the page and see if anyone else is around to talk about it. Chat about herbs, share information or just meet fellow herb lovers.

**Web:**

**http://frank.mtsu.edu/~sward/HERBBOARD/herbboard.html**
**http://naturalnet.com/wwwboard/wwwboard.html**

## Herbal Hall

Here is an excellent site for herbalists, gardeners, botany lovers and anyone else interested in herbs. This page is loaded with articles, news and links to related sites.

**Web:**

**http://www.crl.com/~robbee/herbal.html**

A B C D E F G H I J K L M N O P Q R S T U V W X Y Z

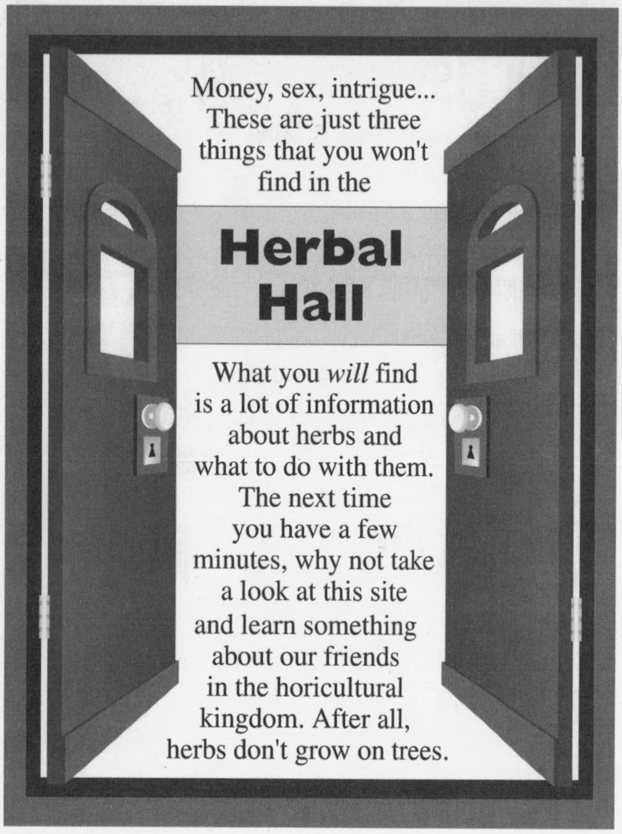
Money, sex, intrigue...
These are just three
things that you won't
find in the
Herbal
Hall
What you *will* find
is a lot of information
about herbs and
what to do with them.
The next time
you have a few
minutes, why not take
a look at this site
and learn something
about our friends
in the horicultural
kingdom. After all,
herbs don't grow on trees.

## Herbal Healing

If you are interested in herbs for their nutritional and medical healing properties, take some time to browse these resources. Read the medicinal herbs FAQ which answers questions about herbal healing, specific herbs, disorders that are helped by herbs, and much more. Or check out the Herb Research Foundation, a non-profit research and educational foundation which focuses on using herbs for health.

**Web:**

**http://sunsite.unc.edu/herbmed/mediherb.html**
**http://sunsite.unc.edu/herbs/**

## Herbal History

Herbs have been used as healing adjuncts for thousands of years. This article traces the history of herbs and their uses from ancient times to modern times.

**Web:**

**http://www.theriver.com/danith/hhistory.html**

## Herbal Smoking Mixtures

A great deal of the herbal information I have read talks about making ointments, tinctures or teas out of herbs. However, there are some herbs you can smoke (as if you didn't know). This site has information about smoking various herbs: which herbs are safe to smoke, how you prepare herbs for smoking, herbs for ceremonial usage, and herbs for medicinal usage. Hint: If you ever want to be president of the United States, make sure not to inhale.

**Web:**

**http://www.teleport.com/~howieb/smoking/smoke1.html**

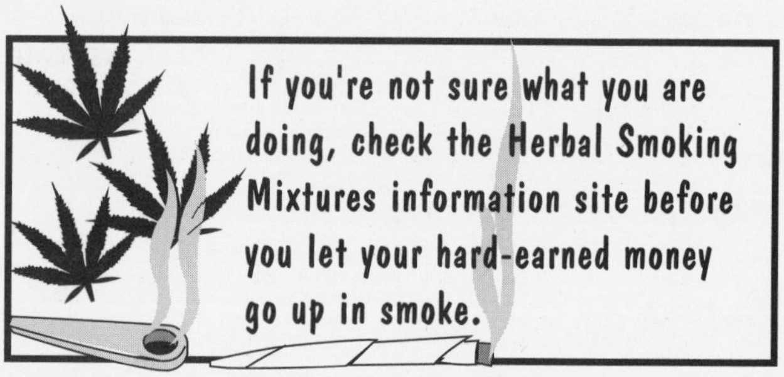
If you're not sure what you are doing, check the Herbal Smoking Mixtures information site before you let your hard-earned money go up in smoke.

## Herbnet

For lots of information about herbs, Herbnet is the place to go. In addition to a collection of links to herbal resources, there is a great deal of information about print publications and journals, herb and seed sources, societies and associations, botanical gardens and herbalism schools.

**Web:**

**http://www.herbnet.com/**

## Herbs and Spices

When you are looking for the real dirt on herbs and spices, have a look at this web page, which offers a lengthy index of various herbs for cooking and medicinal purposes. Learn how to cook with herbs, read historical and geographical information, see pictures and recipes, or get tips on how to grow your own herbs.

**Web:**

**http://www.teleport.com/~ronl/herbs/herbs.html**

## Herbs Mailing List

Commune with other herb lovers and gardeners. This mailing list is a great place to discuss medicinal and aromatic herbs.

**Listserv Mailing List:**

List Name: **herb**
Subscribe to: **listserv@trearnpc.ege.edu.tr**

## Medicinal Herbs

The Medicinal Herb Garden is located on the campus of the University of Washington in Seattle. It provides a great resource for anyone interested in herbs, and is a pleasant place to visit. This Internet site has lots of information about the many herbs that grow in the garden, as well as a photo tour. Just the thing to share with that special someone in your life.

**Web:**

**http://www.nnlm.nlm.nih.gov/pnr/uwmhg/**

## Modern Herbal

In 1931, Mrs. M. Grieve wrote an herbal reference detailing the properties, folklore and cultivation of many hundreds of plants. In the book, Mrs. Grieve described how to use plants for healing, cooking, and even for cosmetics. She called her book "A Modern Herbal". Although it is not modern any longer, the book is still a fantastic resource for anyone interested in herbs. Here is a hypertext version of Mrs. Grieve's wonderful reference.

**Web:**

**http://www.botanical.com/botanical/mgmh/mgmh.html**

## Pictures of Herbs

Herbs are sometimes hard to identify, and if you are putting them in your mouth, it's not a good idea to make a mistake. This archive can help. It has a collection of pictures of herbs in various stages of growth.

**Web:**

**http://www.rt66.com/hrbmoore/HOMEPAGE/**

## Plants and Cancer Treatments

Herbs are sometimes used in conjunction with chemical treatments for cancer. Herbs can help alleviate some of the side effects that occur during the treatment of cancer, and some herbs have been noted to work against the cancer itself. This site has information about various herbs that complement the cancer treatment process. You can find a list of herbs with their pictures, descriptions, histories and what they are generally used for. Each herb also is accompanied by information about the relevant medical compounds it contains with details about the chemical makeup and pharmacology of the compound.

**Web:**

**http://biotech.chem.indiana.edu/botany/**

# HISTORICAL DOCUMENTS

## American Historical Documents

Many people have heard about the important American historical documents. But few people have had the opportunity to look at the actual texts. Here is your chance. Take a look at the Unites States Constitution, Amendments to the Constitution, Annapolis Convention, Articles of Confederation, Bill of Rights, Charlottetown Resolves, Continental Congress Resolves, Japanese and German surrenders, M. L. King's "I Have a Dream" speech, inaugural addresses, the Monroe Doctrine, Rights of Man, treaties, and more.

**Web:**

**http://history.cc.ukans.edu/carrie/docs/docs_us.html**
**http://www.rci.rutgers.edu/~snash/amhist.html**

NOTHING TO DO?
Download a copy of the American Constitution and change all the parts you don't like.

## Canadian Constitution Act

Most people think of Canada as a large country sitting quietly in the northern portion of North America, waiting patiently for winter. But believe me, Canada has seen its share of political action. And it all started in 1867 when the British parliament passed the British North America Act (also known as the Constitution Act), the legislation that created the independent country of Canada. The original country consisted of only four provinces: Ontario (Upper Canada), Quebec (Lower Canada), New Brunswick and Nova Scotia. It is interesting to read this document and compare it to the United States Declaration of Independence and the United States Constitution. The differences in the personalities of the two countries really show.

**Web:**

**http://insight.mcmaster.ca/org/efc/pages/law/cons/Constitutions/Canada/English/ca_1867.html**

## Constitution of the United States of America

The Constitution of the United States is not only an important historical document, but an inspiration to people all over the world. At this site, you can look at the constitution and its amendments (the first 10 amendments being the Bill of Rights). You can also search for a particular phrase, and look at other, related information.

**Web:**

**http://lcweb2.loc.gov/const/constquery.html**

## Council of Trent

The Council of Trent was an ecumenical council of the Roman Catholic church. It was convened in 1545 by Pope Paul III to address the problems of the Protestant Reformation. The Council of Trent met sporadically until 1563, when it was concluded by Pope Pius IV. Throughout its active years, the Council of Trent was a major figure in the Catholic Reformation. The reforms—which covered topics such as the Mass, the clergy, sacraments, scripture, relics, education and feasts—formed a basis for modern Catholicism. Here are the texts and transcripts of the Council of Trent's canons and decrees.

**Web:**

**http://history.hanover.edu/early/trent.htm**

## Declaration of Arms, 1775

On July 6, 1775, the representatives of the "United Colonies of North-America" met in Philadelphia and issued a document called "Declaration of the Causes and Necessity of Taking Up Arms". These guys were sick up and fed with the way they were being treated by Great Britain, and this document is the explanation as to why they were rebelling. The document did not mince words. For example, the declaration refers to the members of the British parliament as "stimulated by an inordinate passion" for power, and describes them as being blinded "by their intemperate rage for unlimited domination". Sound familiar?

**Web:**

**http://grid.let.rug.nl/~welling/usa/causes_text.html**

## Declaration of Sentiments

In 1848, the first Women's Rights Convention was held in Seneca Falls, New York. The convention was convened by Elizabeth Cady Stanton and Lucretia Mott, who presented the Declaration of Sentiments, a document based on the Declaration of Independence. This declaration, however, was a list of grievances denouncing the inequality between men and women in the areas of education, religion, employment, property rights, marriage, family and voting. Almost 150 years later, the Declaration of Sentiments still makes for interesting reading. Note: After the Declaration of Sentiments was presented, another 71 years passed before American women were given the right to vote under the 19th Amendment to the U.S. Constitution.

**Web:**

**http://www.rochester.edu/SBA/declare.html**

**Get the latest dirt in "Archeology".**

## Emancipation Proclamation

In the United States, the expression "Lincoln freed the slaves" is commonly used as an all-purpose rejoinder in certain sticky social situations, such as when your boss tells you to work overtime without extra pay, or when your mother forces you to clean up your room. But just how did Lincoln free the slaves? At the time of the Civil War, Lincoln was president of the Union (the northern states), leading them against the Confederacy (the southern states). On September 17, 1862—possibly the bloodiest day of the Civil War—the Battle of Antietam in western Maryland ended with combined losses of over 23,000 men. Lincoln used the occasion to issue the Emancipation Proclamation, which declared free all slaves in states still in rebellion against the Union. The slaves were not actually freed until April 9, 1865, when the Union won its final victory against the Confederacy. If any of this interests you, take a few minutes to look at the actual proclamation (and at the fine print contained therein).

**Web:**

**http://www.nps.gov/ncro/anti/emancipation.html**

The next time your teacher or your boss tries to tell you what to do, download the Emancipation Proclamation and mail them their own personal copy.

## English Bill of Rights

The English established their Bill of Rights in 1689. This document lessened the power of the throne and gave more power to the subjects of England. The Bill of Rights elevated the political stature of Parliament over that of the crown, gave civil and political rights to English subjects and stated that no Roman Catholic would rule England. The Bill of Rights was accepted by William III and Mary II after the Glorious Revolution which ousted James II from the throne. You can read about this document that created a significant turning point in the history of England.

**Web:**

**http://www2.dmatrix.com/rody/documents/EnglishBill.html**

## European Texts and Documents

Have you ever worried that you might run out of important historical documents to read? Well, relax. You are causing yourself unnecessary strain. There are lots of wonderful documents only a mouse click away. These sites, for example, have many European historical documents dating from Medieval times to the present. As long as you have the Net, you will never run out of important European documents.

**Web:**

**http://history.hanover.edu/europe.htm**
**http://library.byu.edu/~rdh/eurodocs/**

## Federalist Papers

Between 1787-1788, a series of 85 political essays—now called "The Federalist Papers"—was published in New York. The series was initiated by Alexander Hamilton in order to persuade New York to approve the Federalist Constitution (which they eventually did). Hamilton wrote most of the essays, the others being written by James Madison and John Jay. As they were written, the essays were published in newspapers and were read widely. (Compare to what you see in modern newspapers.) Even today, the Federalist Papers are acclaimed for their high literary quality and well-developed cogent arguments.

**Web:**

**http://www.teachersoft.com/Library/history/federalist/contents.htm**

**Don't get fooled.**
**Read**
**"Consumer Information".**

## Gettysburg Address

From 1861 to 1865, the United States was embroiled in a civil war between the northern states (Union) and the southern states (Confederacy). There were many causes of the war, but the primary reasons for conflict were fundamental disagreements over slavery and federal control of individual states. Approximately halfway through the war, a turning point occurred in the city of Gettysburg, Pennsylvania. On July 1, 1863, General Robert E. Lee (military commander of the Confederacy) attempted to invade the North, but after battling for three days, the Southern troops were routed. Many thousands of men were killed in those three days. On November 19, 1863, President Abraham Lincoln made a speech at the dedication of the new Civil War cemetery in Gettysburg. His beautiful and oft-quoted words expressed Lincoln's grief for the fallen soldiers and describes the principles for which the men died. Ironically, in the speech Lincoln says, "The world will little note, nor long remember, what we say here...", but in fact, the Gettysburg Address is one of the most famous speeches in American history. What American does not recognize the words "four score and seven years ago" and "government of the people, by the people, and for the people"? At this web site, you will find various drafts of the Gettysburg Address. It is a short, powerful speech, and it shows us why Lincoln is considered one of the great American presidents of all time.

**Web:**

**http://www.loc.gov/exhibits/G.Address/ga.html**

## Historical Document Archive

An archive of historical documents, including the Magna Carta, the U.S. Bill of Rights, Lincoln's Second Inaugural Address, the Monroe Doctrine, the Mayflower Compact, the Emancipation Proclamation, and many others.

**Web:**

**http://grid.let.rug.nl/~welling/usa/othertexts.html**

**Do a backup.**

## Historical Documents Talk and General Discussion

Countries create important documents—such as constitutions, bills of rights, treaties, declarations, and so on—to solve problems. However, most of the time, the signing of the document is only the beginning, not the end. All important documents deserve discussion and interpretation, over and over. For example, in the United States, there is a continuous debate over the meaning of certains parts of the U.S. Constitution. If you enjoy discussing such matters, this is the Usenet group for you. Here you will find a forum for all types of historical topics.

**Usenet:**

**soc.history**

## Joint Declaration of Peace

Ireland has a long, complex history of unrest. In modern times, the main issue is that the Protestants in Northern Ireland (the Unionists) want to be associated with England, while the Catholics (the Republicans) want all of Ireland to be a completely independent country. The situation, however, dates from the 12th century, when Pope Adrian granted control of Ireland to the King Henry II of England. This initiated a continuing Anglo-Irish conflict that worsened in the 16th century when England tried to impose Protestantism on the Irish population, which was largely Catholic. In 1800, English control was underscored by the Act of Union, which formally unified the English and Irish parliaments. This legislation created a great deal of political unrest in Ireland, resulting in a series of Home Rule bills, providing for increased Irish control of the country. These bills resulted in great animosity on both sides of the controversy (pro-British and pro-independence). On April 24, 1916 (Easter Monday), a small group of Irish patriots in Dublin led an assault on the British. The "Easter Rising", as it came to be called, lasted only six days before it was put down by British troops. However, it laid the groundwork for the independence of southern Ireland, as well as further decades of violence, unrest and political turmoil. After the Rising, the extreme nationalist political party Sein Fein ("Ourselves Alone") won most of the seats in the 1918 General Election, and the Irish Republican Army (IRA) was formed to fight the British administration. For years, the IRA led a hit-and-run assault on the British and as a result, in 1921, a treaty was negotiated dividing the country into two mostly self-governing areas: Northern Ireland (also called Ulster) and Southern Ireland (the Irish Free State). In 1937, the people of Southern Ireland passed a referendum declaring themselves completely independent, and in 1948, the Republic of Ireland Act officially recognized the country—now called the Republic of Ireland or Eire—as being separate from the British Commonwealth, bringing an end to hundreds of years of direct British influence. However, this did not bring an end to the violence and unrest. Northern Ireland, now a part of the United Kingdom, has a Protestant majority that generally favors the union with Britain. However, the Catholic minority in Northern Ireland would prefer to be part of the south, and there are still many people in both countries who are willing to fight for a completely unified and independent country. In 1993, a document was created as a new starting point in the peace process. This document, the Joint Declaration of Peace, was signed on December 15, 1993, by John Majors, the Prime Minister of England, and Albert Reynolds, the Taoiseach (Prime Minister) of the Republic of Ireland. If you would like to read the Joint Declaration (which is actually quite easy to understand), here is a web site that contains the full text.

**Web:**

**http://pwaldron.bess.tcd.ie/dclrtn.htm**

## Maastricht Treaty

On February 7, 1992, the Treaty on European Union was signed, formally acknowledging the intentions of a number of European countries to form a political, monetary and social union. The treaty is generally known as the Maastricht Treaty, named after the city of Maastricht in southeast Holland where the meeting and signing took place. (The name is pronounced Mas'-trikt.) On November 1, 1993, the Maastricht Treaty was ratified, establishing the European Union (EU). The treaty is a complex document, but the main goals of the EU can be summarized as follows: (1) to create an economic and monetary union under the control of one central European bank; (2) to create a unified European market in which a single currency is used everywhere; (3) to ensure the unrestricted movement of people within the Union; (4) to create a common foreign and security policy; (5) to ensure cooperation among the member states with respect to justice and law enforcement; (6) to establish a European coal and steel community; (7) to establish a unified European atomic energy community; and (8) to strengthen the powers of the European Parliament. Although it all sounds simple (at least in principle), the European Union is actually a continuing work in progress, and many of the goals of the Maastricht Treaty have not yet been implemented completely. If you would like to read the actual treaty, to see the original intentions of the signatory countries, here is the web site at which the document can be found.

**Web:**

**http://europa.eu.int/en/record/mt/top.html**

## Question:
### What do the following people have in common?

His Majesty The King Of The Belgians,
Her Majesty The Queen Of Denmark,
The President Of The Federal Republic Of Germany,
The President Of The Hellenic Republic,
His Majesty The King Of Spain,
The President Of The French Republic,
The President Of Ireland,
The President Of The Italian Republic,
His Royal Highness The Grand Duke Of Luxembourg,
Her Majesty The Queen Of The Netherlands,
The President Of The Portuguese Republic,
Her Majesty The Queen Of The United Kingdom Of Great Britain And Northern Ireland

**Choose the correct answer. All of these people...**

(A) have four or more Harley Hahn books.
(B) were unable to get a job in the private sector.
(C) have hosted at least two Tupperware parties.
(D) signed the Maastricht Treaty in order to establish a European Union

## Magna Carta

Feudalism was a political and social system in Western Europe that developed in the late 9th century and lasted until the rise of absolute monarchies. The feudal system centered upon the ownership of land and manors. The lord of the manor would allow peasants (serfs) to utilize his land for farming and for living. In exchange, the peasant was bound by an oath of fealty to pay money or to perform servile labor for the lord. Within the feudal system, the king owned all land. Under the king was a hierarchy of nobles (for example, barons) who would hold land granted by the king. Under the high nobles were lesser nobles who controlled land granted by the high nobles, and so on, each landowner swearing fealty to the noble above him (not unlike multilevel marketing). During the reign of King John (1199-1216) the barons revolted. They did so because of their strong opposition to the King's abuse of the feudal custom by encroaching on baronial privileges in order to raise money. To settle the rebellion, King John put his seal on the Magna Carta which guaranteed rights to the subjects of England and generally precluded the excessive use of royal power. The Magna Carta is an interesting document to read, as it lays out what various members of the feudal system could and could not do.

**Web:**
**http://portico.bl.uk/access/treasures/magna-carta.html**

## Native American Treaties

In the late 1700s through the late 1800s, there were many treaties signed between the United States government and various Native American (Indian) tribes. Many of these treaties were to have long-lasting effects, some to the present day. I found it fascinating to read some of these treaties. In addition, I was surprised how many well-known names of places are derived from Indian tribal names.

**Web:**
**http://www.colorado.edu/libraries/govpubs/native.htm**

**"Fun" is fun.**

**FAQs are cool.**

## Treaties

Over the centuries, many treaties have been signed for many different reasons. However, all treaties have the same basic purpose: to create an agreement between states or countries to act in a civilized manner according to recognized guidelines. The devil, of course, is in the details. This site has a great collection of treaties you can examine and study. People have been fighting and making peace for a long time. What is remarkable is how we keep repeating the same mistakes (and solutions).

**Web:**
**http://law.house.gov/89.htm**

## Treaty of Guadalupe Hidalgo

For some years before 1846, there was tension between Mexicans and Americans living in the region that later became the state of Texas. In 1846, upon the annexation of Texas by the United States, a war broke out between the United States and Mexico. The Mexican War continued until 1848, when the Treaty of Guadalupe Hidalgo was signed. This treaty granted the United States possession of the provinces and territories of Texas, New Mexico, California and other significant portions of the southwest. In return, the United States was to pay Mexico $15 million and assume $3.25 million in American claims against Mexico. The U.S. also recognized prior land grants in the southwest and offered citizenship to any Mexicans living in the area. Clearly, this document was instrumental in defining the territory of modern day America. Here is the text if you would like to read it for yourself.

**Web:**
**http://www.monterey.edu/other-sites/history/treaty.html**

## Treaty of Paris

On September 3, 1783, about two years after the conclusion of the American Revolutionary War, the Treaty of Paris formally ended the hostilities. The Treaty of Paris recognized the independence of the 13 colonies and set forth what territory the British would cede: the Americans received huge territories in North America; the Spanish received Florida and regained West Indian properties; and France regained St. Lucia, Tobago, Senegal, Gorée, and East Indian properties.

**Web:**

**http://w3.one.net/~mweiler/ushda/paris.htm**

## United States Bill of Rights

On December 15, 1791, the Bill of Rights became law in the United States. The Bill of Rights is a set of 10 amendments made to the U.S. Constitution (adopted in 1787). The Bill of Rights sets out various freedoms that all citizens of the United States are guaranteed. For example, the first part of the Bill of Rights guarantees freedom of religion, freedom of speech, freedom of the press, freedom of assembly, and freedom to petition the government. This is one of the most important documents in American history, and if you have never read it, you may want to spend some time seeing exactly what it contains.

**Web:**

**http://lcweb2.loc.gov/const/bor.html**

## United States Declaration of Independence

On July 4, 1776, the Declaration of Independence was adopted by the Thirteen Colonies as an announcement of their separation from Great Britain and their creation of the United States of America. The Declaration of Independence portrays what the Americans considered an ideal government and lists particular grievances that went unanswered for too long. The American Revolution lasted for eight years and finally ended with the United States keeping their independence and their territories. Now you can get your own personal electronic copy of the Declaration of Independence from this web site. (And if you have an irresistible surge of patriotism, you can print a copy for yourself and add your signature to the list at the end.)

**Web:**

**http://lcweb2.loc.gov/const/declar.html**

**Web, web, web...**
**sleep, eat...**
**web, web, web...**

### *Look What I Found on the Net...*

```
(from the Treaty of Paris, ending the American Revolution)

Article 1:

His Britanic Majesty acknowledges the said United States, viz.,
New Hampshire, Massachusetts Bay, Rhode Island and Providence
Plantations, Connecticut, New York, New Jersey, Pennsylvania,
Maryland, Virginia, North Carolina, South Carolina and Georgia,
to be free sovereign and independent states, that he treats with
them as such, and for himself, his heirs, and successors,
relinquishes all claims to the government, propriety,
and territorial rights of the same and every part thereof...
```

A B C D E F G H I J K L M N O P Q R S T U V W X Y Z

## Universal Declaration of Human Rights

On December 10, 1948, the General Assembly of the United Nations adopted the Universal Declaration of Human Rights, a document based on the U.S. Bill of Rights, France's Declaration of the Rights of Man, and England's Magna Carta. The Universal Declaration of Human Rights was created to set a standard for human rights that all countries should meet. It stresses the dignity and worth of humanity, equal rights for men and women, and freedom as a right for everyone. The document was written primarily by René Cassin, a French public official who later (in 1968) won the Nobel Peace Prize for his efforts in promoting human rights. The Universal Declaration of Human Rights is inspiring and well worth a look.

**Web:**

**http://www.un.org/Overview/rights.html**

## Versailles Treaty of 1919

Over the centuries, there have been many treaties signed in Versailles. The most famous, however, is the treaty signed in 1919 that helped bring World War I to a close. Four world leaders—the "Big Four"—negotiated the treaty: President Wilson (United States), Premier Clemenceau (France), Prime Minister Lloyd George (Britain), and Premier Orlando (Italy). The treaty called for many actions, most of which were geared to strip Germany of its military, political and economic powers. The treaty's main resolutions placed limits on German armed forces, put into place a method for Germany to make enormous reparations, restored various cities and territories to their rightful owners, demilitarized the Rhineland, and created the League of Nations. Unfortunately, the terms of the Treaty of Versaille were so punitive as to create enormous unrest in the German population. In the 1920s, the German economy suffered through a terrible decline and, combined with the resentment over the Treaty of Versailles, the economic suffering created an atmosphere in which Hitler was able to rise to power. What were the actual details of this treaty? Here is a web site that contains the text, so you can read it for yourself.

**Web:**

**http://ac.acusd.edu/History/text/versaillestreaty/vercontents.html**

# HISTORY

## American Civil War

If you are a Civil War buff, you'll love this great collection of Civil War web links. Learn about historic sites, military parks, museums, plantations, battlefields, calendars, documents and flags.

**Web:**

**http://www.cwc.lsu.edu/civlink.htm**

## American Memory Collection

The Library of Congress has put together these "scrapbooks" of American history and culture. Flip through and look at Civil War photographs, portraits of literary figures, artists and celebrities, photos of rural America, and hear sound recordings of speeches that were delivered around the World War I era.

**Web:**

**http://rs6.loc.gov:8080/ammem/amtitle.html**

## American Studies

This is a great place to argue about who discovered America, because you can be sure these people know what they are talking about. And with American Studies there aren't as many dates to remember because the history is much shorter. Come dwell on the past with other scholars of American Studies and discuss issues relating to your field.

**Listserv Mailing List:**

List Name: **h-amstdy**
Subscribe to: **listserv@uicvm.uic.edu**

Do you like snappy dialog? What about intellectual stimulation, daring discussions and invaluable tidbits of fascinating information?

All that, and more, is waiting for you on the American Studies mailing list.

And what country could be better to study?

America—a place where even squares can have a ball.

## Ancient Mediterranean

This mailing list provides a forum for debate, discussion, and the exchange of information by students and scholars of the history of the ancient Mediterranean cultures.

**Listserv Mailing List:**
List Name: **ancien-l**
Subscribe to: **listserv@ulkyvm.louisville.edu**

## Ancient World Cultures

I find it fascinating to explore ancient world cultures. For instance, when I want to take a break, I love to pour a fresh glass of carrot juice, sit in my special relaxation chair, and read about the formation, by Amenhotep IV, of a new Egyptian monotheistic religion dedicated to the worship of the sun. Or about how, in 750 A.D., Irish monks established early Medieval art, of which survives the glorious illuminated "Book of Kells". There is a lot to know, so you had better get started now. Check out these web sites to learn about various ancient world cultures, and to find out who were the movers and shakers in the last couple of millennia.

**Web:**
**http://eawc.evansville.edu/**
**http://members.gnn.com/shickman/ancient.htm**

## Anglo-Saxon Discussion

This is a mailing list for scholars and others interested in the culture and history of England in the later Middle Ages and early medieval periods.

**Listserv Mailing List:**
List Name: **ansax-l**
Subscribe to: **listserv@wvnvm.wvnet.edu**

### Eighteenth Century Resources

You can't live in the past–unless you are on the Net–in which case you can visit the eighteenth century whenever you want.

## Classical Studies

Classical Studies (the Classics) encompass the Greek and Roman civilization and their direct antecedents. This area of study includes the Greek and Latin languages as well as their literature, art, architecture and archaeology. For discussion, see the Usenet group. For the FAQ (frequently asked question list), see the web site.

**Web:**
**http://www.lib.ox.ac.uk/internet/news/faq/archive/classics-faq.html**

**Usenet:**
**sci.classics**

## Eighteenth Century Resources

Travel back in time, back to the 18th century: a kinder, gentler time before the invention of cellular phones, fax machines and pizza delivery. Instead of doing cool things like playing video games and watching talk shows, people of the 18th century had to be more culturally advanced and make great literature, art, architecture, music and philosophy. Explore the past. Right now.

**Web:**
**http://www.english.upenn.edu/~jlynch/18th/**

## Feudal Terms

Feudalism was a form of social organization common in Western Europe from the fall of Charlemagne's empire (9th century) to the rise of the absolute French, Spanish and English monarchies (14th century and later). An exact definition of feudalism is hard to give, but you won't go far wrong if you think of it as a system characterized by three main characteristics: strict social classes, law based on local customs, and land holding dependent upon a fee. If you want to read or talk about things feudal, you will need the proper vocabulary, so here is an online glossary with a large number of feudal words, from "abbey" to "witen".

**Web:**
**http://history.cc.ukans.edu/history/subject_tree/e3/gen/feudal-terms/**
**http://www.arts.cuhk.hk/LocalFile/feudalterm.html**

## Gulf War

Information on Operation Desert Storm: the countries and world leaders involved, lists of military units deployed, glossary of military unit terms, military equipment used such as helicopters, tanks, artillery, chemical weapons, and aircraft.

**Web:**
**http://www.nd.edu/~aleyden/contents.html**

## Hiroshima

It was the summer of 1945. The Allied forces which had defeated Germany now turned their full attention toward Japan and its massive war machine. Although the war in Europe was over, the Japanese had more than 2,000,000 soldiers and 9,000 kamikaze suicide bombers ready to fight to the death. It was estimated that a full-scale invasion of Japan would kill over 500,000 American servicemen as well as many millions of Japanese. On July 26, the United States, Britain and China warned Japan to surrender unconditionally or face "prompt and utter destruction". Japanese officials stalled for time and scoffed at the demands. In response, U.S. President Harry Truman gave the order to drop an atomic bomb on Japan. On August 6, an atomic bomb was dropped on the bustling city of Hiroshima. Three days later, a second bomb was dropped on the city of Nagasaki. On August 10, 1945—overruling the desires of its military leaders who wanted to keep fighting—Japan finally surrendered. The dropping of the two bombs ended the war, saved millions of lives, and ushered in a new and terrifying era of human history.

**Web:**
**http://www.sva.edu/salon/HiroshimaProject/**

## Historian's Database and Information Server

HNSource is the central information server for historians, located at the University of Kansas. This system allows users to browse through a wide variety of information resources related to the historical discipline.

**Web:**
**http://history.cc.ukans.edu/history/**

## Historian's Newsletter

A newsletter for historians and anyone else interested in history. Remember, those who do not repeat history are doomed to study it.

**Listserv Mailing List:**
List Name: **histnews**
Subscribe to: **listserv@ukanvm.cc.ukans.edu**

## Historic American Speeches

The text of many historic American speeches and addresses, including some of those given by Washington, Jefferson, Martin Luther King, Lincoln, Kennedy, and others.

**Web:**
**http://pubweb.acns.nwu.edu/~doetting/douglass.htm**

### Historic American Speeches

Here is my favorite historic American speech:

"Fourscore and seven years ago our fathers brought forth on this continent a new nation, conceived in liberty and dedicated to the proposition that all men should use the Net. Innocent peoples, innocent nations are being cruelly sacrificed to a greed for power and supremacy, by not ensuring that everyone has a copy of *The Internet Complete Reference*. I know not what course others may take; but as for me, give me a Harley Hahn book or give me death!

(Don't believe it? Connect to the Net and check it out for yourself.)

## Historical Sounds and Speeches

The Vincent Voice Collection of historical sounds and speeches contains many sound files of famous speeches, including some from John F. Kennedy, Richard Nixon, Teddy Roosevelt, Babe Ruth, Betty Ford, and many more.

**Web:**
**http://web.msu.edu/vincent/**

## History Archives

Archives of history material, including articles, bibliographies, databases, software, images, papers, newsletters, and diaries. Historical subjects include diplomacy, ethnicity, military, maritime, political, scientific, women, and many more.

**Web:**
**http://ihr.sas.ac.uk/ihr/ihr0101.html**

## History Talk and General Discussion

The great thing about history is that you never run out of it. Every minute there is more history made and that just means there is more to memorize when you are in school. Stop in on the Net, and hang out with the people who love to dwell on the past.

**Usenet:**
**soc.history.moderated**

**Listserv Mailing List:**
List Name: **history**
Subscribe to: **listserv@ukanvm.cc.ukans.edu**

## Holocaust Discussion

This list not only covers the Holocaust itself, but also related topics such as anti-semitism, Jewish history in the 1930s and 1940s, and any topics with related themes in the history of World War II and Germany. The web site has articles and other information geared toward remembrance of the Holocaust.

**Web:**
**http://remember.org/**

**Listserv Mailing List:**
List Name: **holocaust**
Subscribe to: **listserv@listserv.arizona.edu**

**Forget the sitter, check out the "Kids" section.**

### *Look What I Found on the Net...*

```
Newsgroup: soc.history.moderated
Subject: Why Did Civilization Start Where It Did?

Actually, the origin of civilization is a highly debated
subject.  The earliest civilizations -- Mesopotamia, Egypt, and
the Indus -- developed in river valleys.

In the case of Mesopotamia, as the region became more and more
arid, people from the dry areas moved into the valleys of the
Tigris and Euphrates rivers.  There they found water, swamps and
fertile soil.  They also found conditions that could only be
solved by organizing and by using large numbers of people on
irrigation and drainage projects.  Out of this situation came
civilization, because the people who conquered the river valleys
needed protection from floods and foes, as well as record
keeping, housing for increasingly large numbers, and steady
supplies of food and goods.

In other words, civilization arose out of necessity.  Once
civilization developed, it attracted a more or less steady
stream of settlers from the mountain and desert periphery --
settlers who brought new blood, new languages, and new
technologies.  The result was, in comparative terms, rapid
development...
```

## Hyperhistory

If you have some time to explore the Net, I suggest visiting this site. It has massive charts that show various historical and cultural happenings (science, politics, medicine, religion and more) juxtaposed so you can see how various events relate to one another. For example, did you know that the year the Pope announced that Catholics could not practice birth control was the same year that Martin Luther King and Robert Kennedy were assassinated? Were you aware that the Berlin Wall was constructed in the same year that Yuri Garagin became the first man in space? And I bet you didn't know that Mussolini and Hitler formed the Rome-Berlin Axis around the same time Margaret Mitchell was writing "Gone with the Wind". This world history chart has lots of great information about people, events and history, and includes some cool maps.

**Web:**
**http://www.hyperhistory.com/**

## Medieval History

Never mind that people were dirty, smelly, poor, and ate rotten food. Medieval history is cool because people got to fight with swords. Anyone who studies the culture and history of the medieval era can tell you that people were very different back then, as is evidenced by their politics, art, philosophy and religion. Scholars and students of the Middle Ages (476 - 1453 A.D.) discuss this period in history.

**Web:**
**http://www.georgetown.edu/labyrinth/labyrinth-home.html**

**Listserv Mailing List:**
List Name: **mediev-l**
Subscribe to: **listserv@ukanvm.cc.ukans.edu**

## Mystery of the Maya

Explore the mystery of the Mayans, masters of mathematics and calendrics, who built their cities without metal tools, animals or the wheel. Get information about their civilization as well as photographs of pyramids, hieroglyphs and other artifacts.

**Web:**
**http://www.nfb.ca/E/4/2/maya.html**

## Renaissance

What a creative time in history the Renaissance was. Beautiful art, architecture and clothing are just a few of the things that originate from that time period. If you can ignore the plague, you can almost imagine it would be a great time in which to live. Scholars, students, and historians exchange information on the history of the Renaissance in the form of letters, papers, announcements of meetings and debates.

**Listserv Mailing List:**
List Name: **renais-l**
Subscribe to: **listserv@ulkyvm.louisville.edu**

## Revisionism

Revisionism is the act of changing the way people view a commonly accepted doctrine or series of events. For example, within a movie, a person may be portrayed as a popular hero when, in fact, he was not at all liked during his time. There are many styles of revisionism. Revision can occur from people feeling nostalgic and making "the old days" into a more romantic, endearing time than it was. Revision can also occur when people want to heighten or lessen, for whatever reason, the emotional impact of events from the past. This Usenet group is a forum in which you can talk about revisionism in any form.

**Usenet:**
**alt.revisionism**

## Spanish and Portuguese History

Spice up your mailbox with some discussion on Spanish and Portuguese historical studies. Most of this list is in English, but postings in Portuguese, Spanish or Catalan are welcome. This list is for both students and scholars.

**Listserv Mailing List:**
List Name: **espora-l**
Subscribe to: **listserv@ukanvm.cc.ukans.edu**

## This Day in History

Fill your mind with some trivial thoughts by finding out who was born and who died on this day in history. You never know when an important event or holiday is coming up for which you need to dress appropriately. Don't be caught unaware.

**Web:**
**http://www.historychannel.com/today/**

## Twentieth Century USA

The history of 20th century America is rich with interesting events. Here is a collection of links to web sites that cover important aspects of the last hundred years in the United States. Explore Prohibition, the Nixon era, the Cuban missile crisis, various wars, the women's rights movement, and much more.

**Web:**

**http://www.msstate.edu/Archives/History/USA/20th_C./twenty.html**

## Vietnam War

The Vietnam War was a long, drawn-out affair, stretching from 1957 to 1975. In Washington, D.C., on the Vietnam Veterans Memorial, you can see the names of 58,153 dead serviceman, and over 300,000 more were wounded. As terrible as these numbers are, they are small compared to the dead and injured in Vietnam itself and in neighboring Laos and Cambodia. To anyone growing up in the Sixties, Vietnam was "The War". More than an actual conflict, it was a metaphor for the great mid-century life crisis that America and the world was to experience. It's hard to explain, even generally, what happened and why it was important. Suffice it to say that the Vietnam War finally convinced just about everyone that armed conflict is not a good way to settle differences. And by 1975, America finally started to realize that looking your enemy square in the face was most likely to lead you to a reflection of yourself.

**Web:**

**http://www.bev.net/computer/htmlhelp/vietnam.html**
**http://www.shss.montclair.edu/english/furr/vietnam.html#texts**

**Usenet:**

**alt.war.vietnam**
**soc.history.war.vietnam**

**Listserv Mailing List:**

List Name: **vwar-l**
Subscribe to: **listserv@ubvm.cc.buffalo.edu**

**History buffs: join the Renaissance mailing list and see what other people have to say about art, beauty, architecture, and all the other things that people used to do before there was television.**

## Vikings

Here is a web site dedicated to the Vikings. This page includes lots of information about the Viking era (793-1050): texts, manuscripts, reference material, runic fonts, the AEsir cult, ships, music, exhibitions, food and drink, museums, and much more.

**Web:**

**http://control.chalmers.se/vikings/viking.html**

**Vikings**

Who: Scandinavian warriors.

What: Raiding coastal communities; exploring new lands.

Where: The coasts of the British Isles and Western Europe; Greenland and North America.

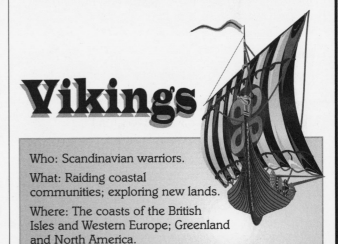

When: Eighth to eleventh centuries.

Why: Overpopulation and dissension at home; quest for trade and adventure.

What stopped them: Introduction of Christianity into Scandinavia; creation of kingdoms in Norway, Denmark and Sweden; European states became strong enough to repel invaders.

## War

Whenever you have more than one person on the planet at the same time, there is always the chance that you are going to have a war. This sort of behavior has been going on for centuries and no amount of naps or "time-outs" is going to solve the problem. Historians and history lovers gather around the Usenet campfire to talk about anything relating to war. The web page has links to lots of war resources around the Net.

**Web:**

**http://www.cs.usm.maine.edu/~burns/war.html**

**Usenet:**

**soc.history.war.misc**

## World War I

The Net has a great deal of information on World War I. Here are some of the resources that will help you learn just about anything you need about this time period. The mailing list is a forum for military history in general, World War I specifically, and the period from 1900 to 1920.

**Web:**

**http://info.ox.ac.uk/departments/humanities/rose/war.html**
**http://www.lib.byu.edu/~rdh/wwi/**
**http://www.pitt.edu/~novosel/ww1.html**
**http://www.worldwar1.com/**

**Listserv Mailing List:**

List Name: **wwi-l**
Subscribe to: **listserv@ukanaix.cc.ukans.edu**

**Want to waste some time? Try "Cool, But Useless".**

## World War II

World War II was the most important conflict of the twentieth century. Here are some good starting points to explore the war and its aftermath. The mailing list and Usenet groups are for military and history buffs to discuss the history, strategy, technology, politics and sociology of World War II.

**Web:**

**http://fiddle.ee.vt.edu/proto/Arts/Humanities/History/20th_Century/World_War_II/**

**Usenet:**

**soc.history.war.world-war-ii**

**Listserv Mailing List:**

List Name: **wwii-l**
Subscribe to: **listserv@ubvm.cc.buffalo.edu**

## World War II Propaganda Posters

Have you ever wondered what would inspire thousands and thousands of people to voluntarily march off to a big war far from home? Here's one of the answers: massive government propaganda. Examine these posters that were commissioned by government agencies to stir up the patriotism and sentiment of the American people during World War II. The posters, which are beautifully crafted (some by famous artists such as Norman Rockwell and Thomas Hart Benton), encourage men and women to enlist in the armed services, women to join the work force, and everyone to work hard, conserve resources, and keep secrets from the enemy.

**Web:**

**http://www.openstore.com/posters/**

# HOBBIES

## Antique Talk and General Discussion

Capture the past by collecting antiques and vintage items. Learn to restore your old Victrola, music box, or clock. Find out where you can get issues of the Charlie Chaplin comics. Buy, sell, and trade.

**Usenet:**

**rec.antiques**

## Archery

You don't have to wear a green outfit and tights to fit in here. You do have to have a passion for nocking an arrow onto a taut bowstring, pulling the string to its absolute limit, then letting go and seeing the arrow sink smoothly into your target. Archery is great for so many things—hunting, competition, relaxation—and they are all covered in this group.

**Usenet:**

**alt.archery**

## Auctions

If you like auctions, this is the place for you. Links to more auction-related Internet sites than you would ever have believed exist. Cars, boats, real estate, collectibles, computers, art, wine—it's all here, waiting for the highest bid.

**Web:**

**http://www.syspac.com/usaweb/auction.html**

## Audio Talk and General Discussion

A real audio system will make your living room windows bulge. Take the squeak out of your tweeter and the growl out of your woofer with a few helpful hints from the folks who know audio. High-fidelity, high-end, and professional audio are some of the topics covered.

**Usenet:**

**rec.audio.high-end**
**rec.audio.misc**
**rec.audio.pro**

## Autograph Collecting

To many people, an autograph is just someone signing their name. For example, suppose you are eating in a restaurant, and you see someone famous like the President of the United States or Bart Simpson or Denis Thatcher walk in. If you're like most people, you grab a napkin, casually saunter over, and ask Mr. Famous Person for an autograph. Later, you take the napkin home with you, show it around to a few friends, and then throw it out. A serious autograph collector, however, would do it all differently. He or she would use a special piece of paper, not a napkin, and afterward, the autograph would be carefully cataloged and stored. Moreover, real collectors don't collect autographs willy-nilly. They tend to concentrate in certain areas, and build their collection by requesting specific autographs, often by mail. If you would like to learn more about this fascinating hobby, take a look at these autograph-related resources on the Net. (By the way, the story in the restaurant is true. All three of the celebrities were there, and I was able to get three great autographs for my collection. I specialize in "Men Who Live With Forceful Women".)

**Web:**

**http://mail.bcpl.lib.md.us/~ddavison/autos.html**

**Usenet:**

**alt.collecting.autographs**

**The Net cares.**

*Look What I Found on the Net...*

```
Newsgroup: rec.antiques
Subject: The Best Stores

> Someone wanted to know if it was really so awful for an
> "antique" store to have collectibles in it.  It seems to me
> that if you think the definition of antique is elastic, the
> definition of "collectible" is even more so, since it can be
> stretched to cover everything from Depression glass to
> cheap toys made last week.

A friend of mine has a rule:

If you smell potpourri when you walk in the door of a place
that says it's an antique shop, turn around and walk out.
```

## Clocks and Watches

Here are lots of great resources for anyone interested in horology (the science of measuring time and the art of making timepieces). These resources offer information about collecting clocks and watches, timepiece repair, the history of timekeeping, antique timepieces, and trading. The mailing list and Usenet group are forums in which you can talk about horology any time, day or night.

**Web:**

**http://glen-ellyn.rice.iit.edu/~clocks/clocks/clocks.html**

**Usenet:**

**alt.horology**

**Listserv Mailing List:**

List Name: **clocks**
Subscribe to: **listserv@listserv.syr.edu**

Don't be late.
Check out clocks, the Internet's most timely mailing list.

## Coins and Money

It can be a lot of fun to collect various types of money. The web site has some useful and interesting resources for people interested in collecting coins and banknotes. The **numism-l** mailing list is not a collector's list. It is for discussing coin topics relating to antiquity and the Middle Ages (up to c.1454). The **biblionumis-l** list is devoted to literature having to do with numismatics.

**Web:**

**http://www.coin-universe.com/**

**Listserv Mailing List:**

List Name: **numism-l**
Subscribe to: **listserv@univscvm.csd.scarolina.edu**

**Majordomo Mailing List:**

List Name: **biblionumis-l**
Subscribe to: **majordomo@netcom.com**

## Collecting Talk and General Discussion

Is there anyone who doesn't collect anything? (I, for example, collect Internet books.) Collecting seems to be part of our nature as human beings. Thus, if you are human, there is a place in this discussion for you. Use your imagination: anything that can be quantified or categorized is fair game. The **.cards** newsgroup is for those who collect trading cards, both sport and non-sport.

**Usenet:**

**rec.collecting**
**rec.collecting.cards.discuss**
**rec.collecting.cards.non-sports**

## Doll Collecting

There are lots and lots of doll collectors on the Net, and lots and lots of doll stuff to enjoy. Even if you can't tell the difference between a Cabbage Patch Baby Surprise and the Barbie Neptune Fantasy 92 (from the Bob Mackie series), you can still enjoy bopping around, looking at dolls and doll-related discussion.

**Web:**

**http://www.cascade.net/dolls/links.html**

**Usenet:**

**alt.collecting.barbie**
**rec.collecting.dolls**
**rec.crafts.dollhouses**

## Drums and Marching

You've seen those rowdy children who sit in the middle of the kitchen floor and beat pots and pans together. What you may not know is that these very same children grow up to be in the drum corps, where they can make lots of noise and people praise them instead of sending them to their rooms. Join high-spirited marching bands as they talk tech and tell the world why their group is better than your group.

**Usenet:**

**rec.arts.marching.drumcorps**
**rec.arts.marching.misc**

## Drums and Marching

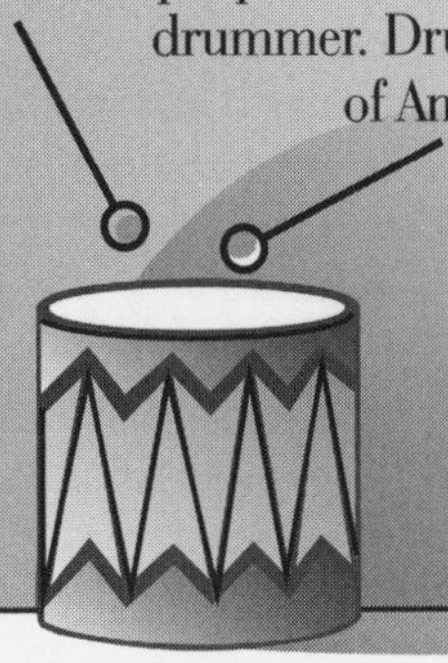

You may not know it, but there are a whole lot of people who march to someone else's drummer. Drum corps competition is one of America's fastest growing leisure time activities. What better way could anyone find to spend a sunny, weekend afternoon?

## Gold Prospecting

Gold has, since antiquity, had a profound effect on people, often affecting their behavior to the point of irrationality. To a scientist, gold has some unique properties. Among the metals, gold is the most malleable (easily shaped) and ductile (able to be stretched). Compared to other common materials, gold is very dense (19.2 times as dense as water), an excellent electrical conductor, and will not rust, corrode or tarnish. For example, when a treasure of gold coins is recovered from a sunken ship, the coins are as bright and shiny as the day they were minted, even if they were immersed in sea water for hundreds of years. Which brings us to the more interesting properties of gold. It can make otherwise normal human beings act as complete loonies. True, gold is valuable, but not as valuable as, say, platinum (which is actually denser). And there are other precious metals (silver, palladium and rhodium) that are also important enough to be commonly traded as commodities. However, the allure of gold is unmatched in the psychology of mankind. Would you like to explore this irrational craving firsthand? You can. Here are some resources to help you get started with recreational gold prospecting. Start small, and with perseverance, you may soon work yourself up to a fully qualified fanatic. In the meantime, you can have a lot of fun.

**Web:**

**http://www.dnai.com/gold/**
**http://www.klws.com/gold/gold.html**

## Guns

Discussions and information about shooting sports, training, personal defense, gun laws, weaponry, and other topics related to firearms in general. And before you get on your high horse about weapons and gun control, I want you to remember that it isn't guns that kill people: it's bullets traveling at high velocity.

**Web:**

**http://www.teleport.com/~dputzolu/**

**Usenet:**

**rec.guns**

## Juggling

I can juggle three oranges. So when I tell you that juggling is a great way to make friends and influence people, you know I'm telling the truth. Join the group and learn how to keep none of your eggs in one basket.

**Web:**

**http://www.hal.com/services/juggle/**

**Usenet:**

**rec.juggling**

## Kites and Kiting Resources

Did you know that in Thailand, kiting is a major sporting event with teams, rules and even umpires? Kiting competition involves fighting between kites that are controlled by teams of up to twenty players. Whether you are a serious kiter or just like to fly kites for fun, these web sites will have something for you. Find kite reviews, stories, tips on flying, general information, event guides, and even graphic images of single, dual, and quadline kites. When the wind isn't blowing, stay home and talk about kites on Usenet ot IRC.

**Web:**

**http://www.latrobe.edu.au/Glenn/KiteSite/Kites.html**
**http://www.mathcs.emory.edu/~kml/kites/kites.html**
**http://www.win.tue.nl/win/cs/fm/pp/kites/**

**Usenet:**

**rec.kites**

**IRC:**

**#kites**

A B C D E F G H I J K L M N O P Q R S T U V W X Y Z

## My Trip to Kite Land

The other night, I was researching kites on the Internet. However, it was so late and I was so tired, that it was all I could do to drag myself to bed, where I fell asleep immediately.

All of a sudden, I found myself in Kite Land, flying around a wonderful blue sky, zooming from one small fluffy white cloud to another.

Within a few minutes, I was joined by a large flock of brightly colored kites, who led me through a tunnel into a mountain cavern where the King of Kite Land sat on a splendid throne.

"Welcome visitor," he said. "You are my honored guest." He wagged his tail and a servant brought out a large covered tray. "You will join me in a feast," said the King of Kite Land. The servant removed the cover of the tray, revealing the largest marshmallow I had ever seen.

For a good half hour, the King and I gorged on marshmallow. Finally he said, "The feast is over. You must now leave Kite Land," whereupon I suddenly woke up in my own bed, my stomach full of marshmallow and my mind spinning from my wonderful trip to Kite Land.

Now, if I could only find my pillow.

## Living History

History seems so exciting in retrospect, much more exciting than it probably was when it was happening. (How interesting is *your* life?) Relive history by joining others who find delight in reenacting historical periods or events. Remember, those who remember history are fated to repeat it.

**Usenet:**

**alt.history.living**

**Wow, free software.**

## Magic

Even after seeing the cut-up tie trick or the lady and the tiger a hundred times, you still can't figure them out. Brush up on your magic and learn some trade secrets. Learn how to make your little brother disappear or how to change that pesky IRS auditor into a pen and pencil set. You don't have to sell your soul to the devil, you just have to be more clever than the rest of us.

**Web:**

**http://www.daimi.aau.dk/~zytnia/faq.html**
**http://www.onramp.net/~pulcher/faqs/magic.html**

**Usenet:**

**alt.magic**

## Model Building

If you like building and enjoying models, there are lots of people on the Net to talk with. The best place to start is with the Usenet discussion groups for modeling enthusiasts: **.rockets** is for model rockets; **.scale** for the building of scale models; **.railroad** for all types of model railroads; and the **.rc** groups for radio controlled devices.

**Usenet:**

**rec.models.railroad**
**rec.models.rc.air**
**rec.models.rc.land**
**rec.models.rc.misc**
**rec.models.rc.water**
**rec.models.rockets**
**rec.models.scale**

## Nudity

Naturists are cool because they never have to iron their clothes. Sense the freedom and vitality of the human body unfettered by fabric. Nudists and naturists discuss the meaning, the legality, and the public's opinion of being naked. If you are looking for a hot game of strip poker, you are bound to be disappointed.

**Usenet:**

**rec.nude**

## Origami

In the 6th century, the secret of paper was carried by Buddhist monks from China to Japan. The Japanese soon integrated paper into their culture. Traditional designs were passed down orally, from one generation to the next. Creative paper folding with non-traditional designs was popularized by Akira Yoshizawa, starting in the 1930s. Modern origami (from the Japanese words for "fold paper") is a pastime enjoyed all over the world. Origami is a wonderful hobby to explore, and the Net is the place to start learning. Read about all facets of origami including bibliographies, folding techniques, display ideas and materials.

**Web:**

**http://www.datt.co.jp/Origami/**

**Listserv Mailing List:**

List Name: **origami-l**
Subscribe to: **listserv@nstn.ns.ca**

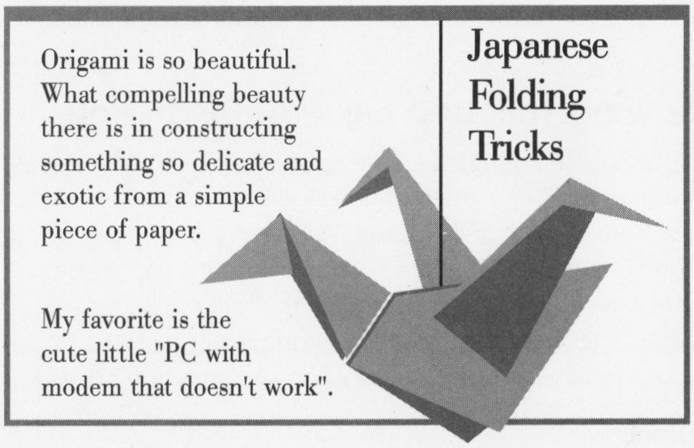
Japanese Folding Tricks
Origami is so beautiful. What compelling beauty there is in constructing something so delicate and exotic from a simple piece of paper.
My favorite is the cute little "PC with modem that doesn't work".

## Postcards

Postcards were designed so that people who go on vacation could quickly and easily torture all those friends or family members who didn't get to go. Connect with other postcard collectors and discuss the history of picture postcards, information on research activities or find people with whom you can exchange postcards by mail.

**Listserv Mailing List:**

List Name: **postcard**
Subscribe to: **listserv@idbsu.bitnet**

## Puppetry

Like to be in control? Maybe you should take up puppetry as a safe outlet. Get information about puppets, puppeteers, and puppet troupes. Read about the Puppeteers of America organization, see a list of festivals and guilds, or read about the history of puppetry. For those people who like to also work with their hands, there are patterns for making paper and cloth puppets. The mailing list is for performers and historians to discuss history and theory of puppet performance, tradition and innovation.

**Web:**

**http://www-leland.stanford.edu/~rosesage/puppetry/puppetry.html**

**Usenet:**

**rec.arts.puppetry**

**Majordomo Mailing List:**

List Name: **puptcrit**
Subscribe to: **majordomo@jefferson.village.virginia.edu**

## Puzzles

What's a six-letter word for the best place to participate in a discussion over the Net? Drive your friends wild with an endless supply of puzzles, quizzes, and problems. Open yourself up for a little brain teasing, or be merciless and create a puzzle that hardly anyone can solve. (!tenesU :rewsnA)

**Web:**

**http://www.scit.wlv.ac.uk/university/scit/maths/puzzle.htm**

**Usenet:**

**rec.puzzles**
**rec.puzzles.crosswords**

## Railroad

Who's been working on the railroad, all the live-long day? And what has Dinah been doing in the kitchen? Join the railroad fanatics and discuss real and model trains.

**Web:**

**http://www-cse.ucsd.edu/users/bowdidge/railroad/rail-home.html**

**Listserv Mailing List:**

List Name: **railroad**
Subscribe to: **listserv@cunyvm.cuny.edu**

## Rock Collection

They're not friendly or cuddly, but you don't have to feed and water them and they don't make any noise. If you are into long-term commitment without the emotional sloppiness, rocks make perfect friends. Get together with other collectors to exchange ideas and share tips on gem, mineral, and fossil hunting and collecting.

**Web:**

**http://www.rahul.net/infodyn/rockhounds**

**Majordomo Mailing List:**

List Name: **rocks-and-fossils**
Subscribe to: **majordomo@world.std.com**

## Roller Coasters

You are utterly terrified, screaming. Your heart is pounding and you think you might vomit. You love every minute of it and want more, more, more. You are addicted to roller coasters. It's okay, because you are not alone. Frenzied coaster fans review the best amusement parks and the top roller coasters in the country as well as discuss accidents and safety.

**Usenet:**

**rec.roller-coaster**

## Rubber Stamps

For people who like to stamp designs onto paper using colored inks. Stamping resources, a list of people on the Net who like stamping, information about stores and conventions, reviews and tips, stamp artwork, and a glossary. For a little more interactive action, there is a mailing list for those who like to talk about stamping as much as they like actually doing it.

**Web:**

**http://www.calweb.com/~mcfadden/rubber.html**
**http://www.xmission.com/~jmabunga/stamp.htm**

**Majordomo Mailing List:**

List Name: **rubberstampers**
Subscribe to: **majordomo@list.genie.com**

Rocks are our friends, and who couldn't use more friends? The **Rock Collection** resources will help you appreciate all that is hard, small and intriguing. After all, why should a piece of Annabergite be a mere hunk of hydrated nickel arsenate, when it can be a full-fledged member of your extended family?

## Sewing Archives

Get supply information, peruse the antique sewing machine guide, and trade tips, techniques and patterns with sewing buffs and professionals. Also includes pointers to historical costuming and textile-related books, and much more material about sewing, fitting, and pattern drafting.

**Web:**

**http://studentweb.tulane.edu/~dmui/sewing.html**

## Sewing Talk and General Discussion

Your bobbin is tangled and your darts are crooked. Needle little advice? Ask questions, get answers, give answers, learn new sewing shortcuts. Whether you're a pro or someone who can't stitch your way out of a paper bag, you'll be able to gain insight on the theory and practice of sewing. (And remember, sewing is not just for women; it just seems that way because men don't do it.)

**Usenet:**

**alt.sewing**

## Skateboarding Talk and General Discussion

If you can't skateboard there, why bother going? Maybe because your law firm doesn't like it when you jump the ramp into the office, sliding your briefcase into the receptionist's hands before doing the slalom between all the associates' desks. Beyond that, there's no sense in ever getting off your board. Discover all the clever things you can do with wheels under your feet.

**Usenet:**

**alt.skate-board**

## Skating Talk and General Discussion

Some people look like they were born with wheels or blades on their feet. The rest of us are like pigs on ice. Hockey, figure skating, and rollerblading are the mainstay of this group. Discuss trivia, learn new competition rules on routines and dance music, and discuss the physical rigors of being a skater.

**Usenet:**

**alt.skate**

## Society for Creative Anachronism

Step back in time to the Middle Ages, where chivalry lives and everyone's lives are ordered by the rising and setting of the sun. Watch people dress up in metal and hit each other with sticks. Experience the grace and beauty of period costuming. Discover the festivity of a real medieval feast. Members and friends of the SCA discuss how it feels to live life in the modern Middle Ages.

**Web:**

**http://www.sca.org/**

**Usenet:**

**alt.heraldry.sca**
**rec.heraldry**
**rec.org.sca**

The *Society for Creative Anachronism* is all about living simply, using the tools and customs from a bygone era. See how much fun it can be living in the Middle Ages with an Internet account.

## Stamp Collecting

If you like to collect stamps, these stamp collecting resources could be just the ticket for you! Check out the mailing lists to horse trade for stamps or just chat with other collectors and hobbyists.

**Web:**

**http://www.execpc.com/~joeluft/resource.html**

**Usenet:**

**rec.collecting.stamps**

**Listserv Mailing List:**

List Name: **stamps**
Subscribe to: **listserv@psuvm.psu.edu**

## Steam Locomotives

In their day, steam locomotives were large, noisy, powerful vehicles that opened vast frontiers and provided the Industrial Revolution with large-scale dependable transportation. Today, these locomotives are gone from day-to-day use, but not forgotten. Many still survive, and steam locomotive hobbyists around the world share information with one another on the Net.

**Web:**

**http://www.arc.umn.edu/~wes/steam.html**

## Trading Cards

A forum for people interested in collecting, speculating, and investing in baseball, football, basketball, hockey, and other trading cards or memorabilia. Discussion is open to anyone and "wanted" and "for sale" lists are welcome.

**Listserv Mailing List:**

List Name: **nonsport-cards**
Subscribe to: **listserv@listserv@aol.com**

**Listserv Mailing List:**

List Name: **sports-cards**
Subscribe to: **listserv@listserv.aol.com**

## Treasure Hunting

Treasure is good. Imagine a great fantasy scenario in which you are walking along the beach and stumble across a barnacle-encrusted chest. You break it open and out tumble thousands of gold coins. Then a thousand federal agents come racing toward you waving paper and red tape. Wait, strike that last part. This is a fantasy. If you like treasure hunting, read all about hunts, shipwrecks and metal detecting. There are also some great stories and legends.

**Web:**

**http://www.treasure.com/**

## Unicycling

Forget the romance of a bicycle built for two. In fact, forget two wheels, period. Unicycling may not catch on as an energy-saving way to commute to work, but it sure is fun. Unicycling enthusiasts have put together a FAQ list, mailing list, pictures and animation. Now, if they could only come up with a unicycle built for two.

**Web:**

**http://www.unicycling.org/**

**Majordomo Mailing List:**

List Name: **unicycling**
Subscribe to: **majordomo@winternet.com**

## Woodworking

While it isn't the most forgiving medium, wood is rich in texture and color. Rev up your chainsaw or sharpen your chisel. Whatever your approach, the wood will yield to your skilled handling of the blade. Your neighbors will probably prefer the chisel approach, but if you use a chainsaw, they probably won't complain. At least not to your face.

**Web:**

**http://www.cs.ruu.nl/wais/html/na-dir/woodworking/faq/faq.html**

**Usenet:**

**rec.woodworking**

**Listserv Mailing List:**

List Name: **woodwork**
Subscribe to: **listserv@vmb.ipfw.indiana.edu**

### WOODN'T IT BE GREAT?

*Wood is so cool–and organic too. There is something about a nicely shaped piece of wood that can turn on just about anybody. (I call it the Pinocchio factor.) Join the folks on* **rec.woodworking** *and see what's happening wood-wise.*

## World War Reenactment

If your domestic life is too mild for your tastes, strike up a little war action the safe way by becoming a living-history enthusiast and reenacting World Wars I and II. This site has information to get you started or, for old-timers, an outlet for talking about old battles and battle wounds.

**Web:**

**http://www.reenactor.net/**

# HOME MAINTENANCE

## Ask the Builder

Okay, so you bought a house. In the words of the banker and real estate agent who encouraged you to go deep into debt, you are now a "homeowner". Here is a secret. It won't be long until you find out that it is actually the home that owns you. And, within a short time, you will be devoting as much energy to fixing a faucet and replacing a cabinet as you used to put into choosing which wine to have with dinner. But never fear, help is available. Here is a library of answers to commonly asked home maintenance questions. After all, just because all your weekend time is spent fixing things you never used to care about doesn't mean you can't know what you are doing.

**Web:**

**http://www.askbuild.com/cgi-bin/library**

## Books That Work

If you are too proud to ask for advice or help around the house, you can safely gain assistance without anyone ever knowing. Utilize these Books That Work. You'll find lots of interesting articles and hints about problems with home repair, landscaping, gardening, automotive and real estate.

**Web:**

**http://www.btw.com/**

## Controlling Pests

Information about how to be inhospitable to those tiny pests who just love to make themselves at home in your home. If it moves, it's on the Net.

**Web:**

**http://www.enforcer.com/**
**http://www.homecom.com/orkin/**
**http://www.nj.com/yucky/getrid/**

## Decorating a Country Home

Decorating a country home has its own special challenges. You are probably starting with an old house, a house that has many hidden traps and idiosyncrasies. What would be a relatively minor task in a newer house—such as replacing a cabinet—can turn into a big project faster than you can say "unforeseen lateral expansion". In addition, you probably want to have your house blend well with the nearby scenery and topography. Finally, there always seems to be so much to do, but only a limited amount of money in the decorating budget. If you have a country house—or if you simply like looking at them—you will enjoy this web site containing lots of articles and pictures documenting how various country houses have been redecorated and renovated. Turning your country house into a showplace is not for the faint at heart. One of the people quoted in an article put it thus: "We have never stopped working on the place."

**Web:**

**http://homearts.com/cl/toc/00cldec1.htm**

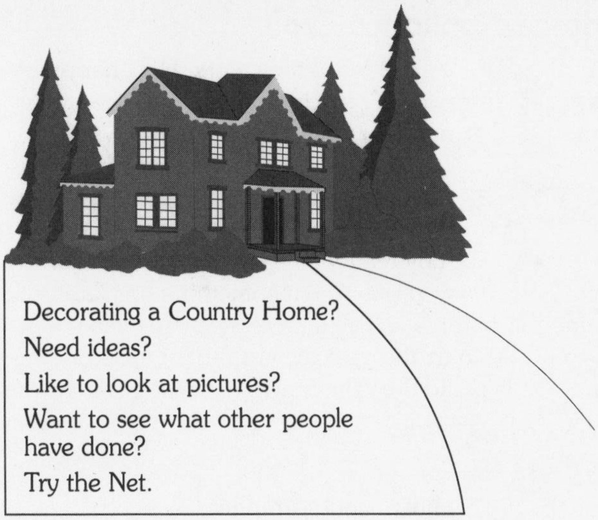
Decorating a Country Home?
Need ideas?
Like to look at pictures?
Want to see what other people have done?
Try the Net.

## Feng Shui

Feng Shui is an ancient tradition that involves the orientation and placement of objects and buildings. Originating in China, Feng Shui is now popular with people who are in search of a more spiritually harmonious living environment. Check out the talk about Feng Shui on Usenet.

**Usenet:**

**alt.chinese.fengshui**

## Handyman Hints

People who are trying to get rich quickly like to talk about using OPM: other people's money. I think it is far more valuable to learn from OPE: other people's experience. Eventually, you can probably learn to fix almost anything. However, it is certainly a lot easier to learn from other people. This mailing list is devoted to an ongoing discussion of everything you need to be the handiest man or woman in the house. Subscribe to the list, and you can read what other people are saying about tools, new products, techniques, design tips, working with a contractor, and on and on.

**Majordomo Mailing List:**

List Name: **handyman-hints**
Subscribe to: **majordomo@cedar.cic.net**

## Home Appliance Clinic

Appliances are great when they work. How happy life is when your washing machine actually washes, your dryer really dries, and your refrigerator knows how to stay cool. The best way to achieve such contentment is to choose good appliances in the first place (either new or used). If you are thinking of buying a home appliance, start by reading the knowledgeable words of advice at this web site. And if something breaks, check here first, before you call for a repairman. Even if you don't want to fix the machine yourself, understanding the problem and the solution will go a long way toward helping you stay in control.

**Web:**

**http://www.phoenix.net/~draplinc/**

## Home Environmental Hazards

If you spend much time watching TV or listening to the radio, you are bound to hear about home environmental hazards: radon, asbestos, lead, hazardous waste, contaminated water, formaldehyde and so on. It's enough to make you feel a tad uneasy. Is your home sweet home a castle of happiness, or a slow-but-sure death trap that will end up subjecting the members of your family to a slow, painful and expensive death? I understand your discomfort, and I know the cure. It's the same cure that always works in such cases. Find out the truth, so you can make informed decisions.

**Web:**

**http://www.hsh.com/pamphlets/hazards.html**

## Home Front Tips

You're waiting for your wife or husband to get ready to leave the house, and you still have a few minutes to kill—not long enough to start a new project, but you don't want to sit around doing nothing. Here's what to do. Connect to the Home Front web site and scan the list of home maintenance questions and answers. If you like puttering around the house, fixing and improving, I guarantee there will be something here to pique your interest. So sit down, find something interesting, and before you know it, you will hear a voice behind you saying, "Will you turn off that computer already? It's time to leave."

**Web:**

**http://www.capitalonline.com/homeofweek/rooneymain.html**

**When you own your own home, you are never far from the front lines. There's always something that needs to be fixed, serviced or replaced.**

**Learn from the pros by reading the *Home Front Tips*.**

## Home Improvement Warehouse

Here is a web site guaranteed to make you feel inadequate. For example, there is a wonderfully ambitious list of 10 important projects that you could be doing right now. (Sort of like Martha Stewart singing "If I Had a Hammer".) Or read the step-by-step instructions showing how to manage a major project (like putting in a new floor), and realize that some people actually know what they are doing. At the same time, you can't help but realize that just about anything major around the house is going to take more time, cost more money, and create more aggravation than you planned. Still, if you flounder around like an ignorant lummox, it can only be worse. Check with the experts before you start, and at least you'll have a chance.

**Web:**

**http://www.lowes.com/**

## Home Repair Talk and General Discussion

It's midnight and the shower is creating a tsunami in the upstairs bathroom. The emergency plumber is out on a hot date and can't stop by. What do you do? Find out on these home fix-it discussion forums where handy people talk about home improvement, repairs, electricity, plumbing, and carpentry. These people really know their widgets, gadgets and whatchacallits.

**Usenet:**

**alt.home.repair**

**Listserv Mailing List:**

List Name: **homefix**

Subscribe to: **listserv@vm3090.ege.edu.tr**

## How-To Center

It's like having an uncle in the handyman business. Just select a project, and with the click of a mouse, you will have sensible, down-to-earth advice on what to do and how to do it. Projects range from small, anybody-can-do-it activities (such as installing a light fixture) to large ambitious events (such as remodeling a bathroom or building a log cabin). So the next time you want to fix that leak in the bathroom, check with the Net before you go off half-caulked.

**Web:**

**http://www.hometime.com/pc1.htm**

## Illustrated Tool Dictionary

It is well known in the home maintenance world that a man is only as good as his tools, and a neighbor is only as good as the tools he can lend you. This resource is great: an encyclopedia of tool information, written for a normal person. If it wasn't for this resource, you would be reduced to asking advice from the tool nerds who hang around the hardware store. You know the ones I mean. You find them at the hardware store on Saturday afternoons, standing around talking about reciprocating saws and spiral design auger bits. You have to wait patiently to get their attention. Then they make you feel like a goober when you ask a question, after which you have to listen to them dispense esoteric advice with a supercilious attitude that would put a stereo salesman to shame. Later, when you get home, you find out what they told you was all wrong anyway. Never again. From now on, the Net will take care of you. Check with this site *before* you go to the store.

**Web:**

**http://homecentral.com/Tools/**

**Need a pickup? Try "Energy" (or "Cars and Trucks").**

**Get into "Mischief".**

## Joist Span Calculator

Joists here and joists there, joists are everywhere. Make sure you have your joists the right distance apart or when your contractor friends come over and see what you've done they will be snickering behind your back and making jokes about you down at the neighborhood lumberyard. Enter all this joist information and let the computer calculate where your joists should be.

**Web:**

**http://www.btw.com/applets/span_calc.html**

## Paint Estimator

It's bound to happen. You've taken on the weekend painting project and here it is Sunday night at midnight and you are still at it. The really annoying thing is that you have about two feet of wall space left to cover and you've run out of paint. If you had used the paint estimator, you would be tucked cozy into bed dreaming of freshly painted homes. All you had to do was enter in the dimensions of your room and the calculator would tell you exactly how much paint you needed to buy.

**Web:**

**http://www.btw.com/applets/paint_calc.html**

**Don't get backed into a corner. Use the Paint Estimator *before* you start.**

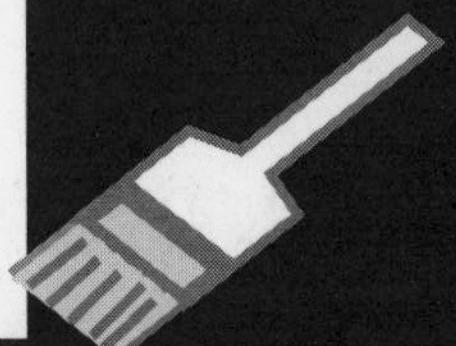

A B C D E F G H I J K L M N O P Q R S T U V W X Y Z

## Plumbing

Spend some time teaching yourself about the ins and outs of common household plumbing problems, and I guarantee you will be the most popular person on the block. After all, the neighbors may fawn over the guy who used to be a professional football player, or the fellow who can imitate a chicken laying an egg, but when the plumbing breaks, there is no one more in demand that someone who knows his pipes. Here are some great resources to help you understand plumbing: from the basics (such as how to change a washer or freshen up a garbage disposal) to advice on large ambitious projects involving construction, renovation and restoration.

**Web:**

**http://www.faucet.com/faucet/**
**http://www.plumbnet.com/**
**http://www.theplumber.com/faq.html**

## Toilet Repair and Maintenance

Okay, let's get this straight. Toilets are *not funny*. And when I tell you that this is the best tutorial about toilets on the Net, you are not to laugh. You are to proceed to this web site immediately, and teach yourself more about toilets than most people learn in a lifetime. You will find lots and lots of useful information about toilet repair and maintenance. Learn how these useful devices work, how to fix them, and how to maintain them. If nothing else, be sure to read the emergency advice about what to do when the toilet overflows. (Read it now, *before* it happens.) At the very least, you'll save yourself some real money. At best, you'll find a brand new hobby.

**Web:**

**http://www.vni.net/~kayk/toc.htm**

**On the Net, there is always someone to talk to.**

## Woodworking

Wood is really a mass of plant tissue called xylem, formed within the plant from a thin layer (the cambrium) that lies between bark and the stem. Xylem has two primary functions: to conduct water throughout the plant and to provide structural support. Softwood comes from coniferous (evergreen) trees, and has a uniformly nonporous appearance. Hardwood comes from deciduous (leaf-losing) trees that produce xylem with a great many vessels, giving the wood a complex, non-uniform appearance. When wood is freshly cut, it contains a lot of moisture and, before it can be used, it must be dried (seasoned)—either in a kiln or by the action of the sun. This description, though accurate, fails to capture that magic inherent in a beautiful piece of wood. And talking about xylem and cambrium—though interesting to a botanist—doesn't even hint at the enormous utility of wood: a substance that is an integral part of just about every culture in the world. If you are one of the people who appreciate wood for what it is and what you can do with it, there are many useful resources on the Net. To get you started, here are some well-organized web sites that will point you to a massive amount of woodworking and wood-related information. In addition, I have included a web site that offers a summary of various woods and their properties. This will help identify and appreciate some of the more exotic varieties of wood that you would not normally see in a lumber yard. For discussion, you can talk on IRC, follow the ongoing give and take on Usenet or join a mailing list.

**Web:**

**http://theoak.com/**
**http://www.intac.com/~rpm/Woods.html**
**http://www.iucf.indiana.edu/~brown/hyplan/wood.html**

**Usenet:**

**rec.woodworking**

**Majordomo Mailing List:**

List Name: **woodworking**
Subscribe to: **majordomo@theoak.com**

**IRC:**

**#woodworking**

# HUMANITIES AND SOCIAL SCIENCES

## Aboriginal Studies Archive

The Australian Institute of Aboriginal and Torres Strait Islander Studies maintains material in the Aboriginal Studies Electronic Data Archive. An online catalog gives brief details of material held at the Institute.

**Web:**

**http://coombs.anu.edu.au/SpecialProj/ASEDA/ASEDA.html**

## Anthropology Resources

Anthropologists study human beings: their origins and behavior, as well as their cultural, physical and social development. Here are some great collections of anthropological resources, suitable for students as well as serious researchers.

**Web:**

**http://dizzy.library.arizona.edu/users/jlcox/first.html**
**http://www.nitehawk.com/alleycat/anth-faq.html**

## Communications

Don't just talk—communicate. Can't? This'll help. Lotsa links here. Lotsa stuff for the ubiquitous communications student, as well as his or her teachers. Cool. (Although I think I really want to go into broadcasting.) Like, it's great. On the Web, nobody knows if you have nothing to say.

**Web:**

**http://www.fau.edu/divdept/commcatn/resource.htm**
**http://www.uark.edu/depts/comminfo/www/ACA.html**

**Should You Be a Communications Major?**

If you want prestige, go to medical school.

If you want money, study business and finance.

If you want respect, become a nuclear physicist.

If you want intellectual stimulation, take philosophy or math.

But if you want prestige, and money, and respect, and intellectual stimulation...

## Coombspapers Social Sciences Server

A large repository of social science and humanities papers, offprints, departmental publications, bibliographies, directories, abstracts of theses, and other material.

**Web:**

**http://coombs.anu.edu.au/**

## Demography and Population Studies

This page keeps track of leading information facilities of value and significance to researchers in the field of demography. It includes links to census information, social science data services, population studies, databases, and many web servers of interest to demographers.

**Web:**

**http://coombs.anu.edu.au/ResFacilities/DemographyPage.html**

## Evolution of Humans and Primates

Some days it's hard to believe that humans might have evolved from primates. Then on a very bad day you will encounter some Neanderthal whose vocabulary is limited to grunts varying only in pitch and perhaps resonance. On those days it's easy to believe in the theory of evolution. Get together with people who spend their days contemplating the anthropological aspects of the evolution of humans and primates.

**Usenet:**

**sci.anthropology.paleo**

## Generation X

The term "Generation X" refers to the post-Baby Boomer Americans born between 1961 and 1981. (The name came from a book by Douglas Coupland.) Before they were named, nobody talked much about the Gen Xers. Now just about everyone has something to say. On the Net, you can visit Generation X web sites, read a FAQ (frequently asked question list), and participate in a Usenet discussion group. Pretty soon, they'll have their own logo.

**Web:**

**http://www.mindspring.com/~tag/**
**http://www.ungh.com/asg-x/**

**Usenet:**

**alt.society.generation-x**

## Humanities Hub

A fabulous collection of links relating to anthropology, theology, cultural studies, dictionaries, architecture, women's resources, sociology, European studies, film and media, gender studies, philosophy, languages and many other humanities resources.

**Web:**

**http://www.gu.edu.au/gwis/hub/hub.home.html**

## Humanities Online

If you are in involved in the humanities in any way, this site can be your virtual home. Reviews of books and software, announcements, job information, teaching material, as well as lots of links to humanities-related resources around the Net—it's all available and as close as your nearest Internet connection.

**Web:**

**http://h-net2.msu.edu/**

## Leisure Studies

Leisure studies—often combined with recreation studies—is the examination of how people spend their leisure time. This is a huge discipline involving many different areas of study such as tourism, sports, outdoor recreation, parks and other public facilities, stress reduction, exercise, resource allocation, and so on. Rest assured, no matter what you do for fun, someone, somewhere, is studying it. If you are a leisure studies student or researcher, the Net has lots of resources to help you. In fact, using the Net to find the information you need will save you so much time, you won't know what to do with it all.

**Web:**

**http://www.geog.ualberta.ca/als/als1.html**
**http://www.hbs.gu.edu.au/lswp/home.htm**

**Listproc Mailing List:**

List Name: **leisurenet**
Subscribe to: **listproc@gu.edu.au**

The Humanities Hub
When you were a kid, you used to hang out at the playground.
When you were a teenager, you used to hang out at the mall.
When you were a student, you used to hang out at the cafeteria.
But now you're a social scientist. Time to start hanging out at the Humanities Hub.

## Lexicon of the Humanities

From time to time, as you work in the humanities, you will encounter an unfamiliar word. However, there is no need to get out of your chair in search of a dictionary. Just connect to the Net and check with this lexicon, where you will find glossaries and quotations relating to the various humanities.

**Web:**

**http://www.sil.org/humanities/**

## Paradigms

Do you think if you studied the social and cultural patterns of the entire world's population long enough that eventually you could predict the future? And then if you could do that, you could rule the entire world. What a job that would be. It would mean you could get all the free ice cream you wanted. Get a jump on the crowd by checking out the discussion about paradigms.

**Usenet:**

**alt.society.paradigms**

## Perseus Project

Do you feel nostalgic for the good old days of ancient Greece? Are you disgruntled and dissatisfied because you missed out on hearing the readings of epic poets and watching the original Olympics? Well, on the Net, you *can* live in the past. Check out this ancient Greek gathering place, and enjoy the art, archaeology and images.

**Web:**

**http://www.perseus.tufts.edu/**

## Popular Culture

Just because something is popular doesn't necessarily mean it's good. However, some people enjoy going along with the crowd, and other people enjoy studying the people who enjoy going along with the crowd. No matter which category you fall into, I think you will enjoy this site. It contains a great collection of resources for people who study the popular culture in a scholarly fashion.

**Web:**

**http://www.mcs.net/~zupko/popcult.htm**

### Popular Culture

I usually don't answer the phone while I am writing, but for some reason the machine didn't pick up.

"Uh... hello... you don't know me," she said, "but I wonder if you could email me something witty so I can graduate?"

"Say that again."

"I'm a student, and I've read all your books and I think they're great, and all I have to do is finish one last project for my course and I can graduate."

"What course?"

"Modern American Humorists Who Write Internet Books," she said.

I thought about it. "Must be an easy course."

"Independent study," she replied. "I chose it 'cause of the short reading list. So, can you help me?"

"What do you need?" I asked.

"I need to send you email and have you write back a witty message."

"No problem," I said.

"Great. Now I can finish my project and graduate."

"Congratulations. What's your degree?" I asked.

"Popular culture. I'm majoring in Dick Van Dyke with a minor in Lucy. Bye. Gotta go now."

Imagine that. A student studying my books in a college course. I have finally arrived.

Norman Mailer, eat your heart out.

## Population Studies

There are several sources of information on the Net for population studies. Take a look at publications, a data archive, research projects and other population resources linked to this site.

**Web:**

**http://www.psc.lsa.umich.edu/**

## Social Science Information Gateway

Research in the social sciences has never been so easy. No matter what topic you are looking for, you can scan down this long list of links and make your selection. You can also look for resources by keyword in order to narrow down your search. This is an invaluable web page for anyone interested in social science.

**Web:**

**http://www.tc.cornell.edu/Edu/ArtSocGateway/**

## Social Sciences Resource Guides

Internet resource guides for education, anthropology, bisexuality, business, economics, geography, government, journalism, law, library, social science, and women's studies.

**Web:**

**http://www.sscl.uwo.ca/explore/socsci.html**

## Social Work

During the Great Depression, the United States government, along with private, state and local social organizations, began to help people who were in need of some type of assistance. This evolved into today's large network of people and agencies devoted to helping individuals and families who are facing poverty, alcoholism, drug abuse, and other physical, mental and social problems. If you are a social worker or a student of social work, here are some resources you will find useful. These sites have information about mailing lists, social work schools and organizations, resources for mental health care professionals, child abuse prevention, international social work and much more.

**Web:**

**http://www.colostate.edu/Depts/SocWork/lists.html**
**http://www.geocities.com/Athens/5767/swcafe.html**

**Don't click here.**

## Society and Underwear

What is wrong with a society that is so repressed about underwear that we all have to wear it under our clothes? There is some really neat underwear in existence and it's a shame that we can't show it off in public. Read about the effects of underwear on society and if you want to read these newsgroups wearing only your underclothes, your secret will be safe with me.

**Usenet:**

**alt.society.underwear**

### It's What's Underneath That Counts

The mark of a real man (and most real women) is what they wear under their clothes. Your friends on the Net recognize how important such things are and are all ready to discuss the intimate details in the **alt.society.underwear** Usenet group. To get you started, I will tell you what I am wearing under my clothes at this very moment. I am wearing... oh, sorry... I'm out of room. Maybe in the next edition.

## Sociology Resources

The difference between a sociologist and a voyeur is that a sociologist gets paid to watch people. There are lots of sociology resources on the Net and one nice collection is at the Virtual Library. This list of links will take you to institutions, specialized resources and related fields.

**Web:**

**http://www.w3.org/hypertext/DataSources/bySubject/Sociology/Overview.html**

## Sociology Talk and General Discussion

We've all heard the rumors—that sociology is one of those fluffy topics that people are required to take in college. Well, I am here to tell you that it's not so. Get into the hard-core science of sociology, and talk down and dirty with people who know their people.

**Usenet:**

**sci.sociology**

## U.S. National Endowment for the Humanities

The United States National Endowment for the Humanities (NEH) is a United States government agency that offers grants for projects in history, philosophy, languages and other areas of the humanities. If you are a humanities scholar, take a look at the NEH's web site, where you can learn about the NEH, their grants, and find out how to apply for a grant of your own. Every year, the NEH awards millions of dollars. There is no reason why some of this money shouldn't be supporting your research.

**Web:**

**http://www.neh.fed.us/**

## Voice of the Shuttle

Here is a huge collection of links and resources for the humanities, social sciences, and many other related (and not really related but put here anyway) areas of study.

**Web:**

**http://humanitas.ucsb.edu/**

# HUMOR AND JOKES

## Atheism Satire

The Surgeon General's priest warns that reading this newsgroup could be hazardous to your spiritual health. But it's so much fun that it doesn't really matter. Put off your eternal damnation tomorrow for hours of chuckles today.

**Usenet:**

**alt.atheism.satire**

## Best of Usenet

Don't spend hours searching through thousands of newsgroups looking for the funny stuff. Someone has already done the dirty work for you. If you are in the market for humor, you can find lots of laughs with one-stop shopping by checking out the group that claims to have the best of what Usenet has to offer. The **alt.humor.best-of-usenet** group has the funny stuff and **alt.humor.best-of-usenet.d** is where you can talk about the funny stuff.

**Usenet:**

**alt.humor.best-of-usenet**
**alt.humor.best-of-usenet.d**

## Bible in Pig Latin

If you are not afraid of being struck by lightning or plagued by locusts, check out this version of the bible translated into Pig Latin. It is the 319th translation of the entire bible, and is based upon the King James version.

**Web:**

**http://www.well.com/user/earl/Ible-bay.html**

## Bootsie Report

Experience life from an outlandish Bootsie point of view. Teetering on the edge of credibility, Juan Bootsie writes reports of his adventures and encounters with famous people in a fun and lively manner that will make you want to quit your job, stick a press badge in your hat band and take off in search of the newsmakers. Read the Bootsie reports to get a piece of the action without having to leave your seat.

**Web:**

**http://www.webcom.com/~hamlet/juan.html**

## British Humor

England has a long tradition of world-famous comedians: Prince Charles, Margaret Thatcher, and Neville Chamberlain, among others. If you are a fan of British "humour," tune in to this newsgroup and discuss your favorite TV shows, performers, movies and personalities.

**Usenet:**

**alt.comedy.british**

Nothing is funnier than **British Humor**

(except maybe their food, or the weather, or the royal family, or. . . )

### *Look What I Found on the Net...*

(from the Bible in Pig Latin)

```
1:1  In-ay e-thay eginning-bay Od-gay eated-cray e-thay
heaven-hay and-ay e-thay earth-ay.

1:2  And-ay e-thay earth-ay as-way ithout-way orm-fay, and-ay
     oid-vay; and-ay arkness-day as-way upon-ay e-thay ace-fay
     of-ay e-thay eep-day. And-ay e-thay Irit-spay of-ay Od-gay
     oved-may upon-ay e-thay ace-fay of-ay e-thay aters-way.

1:3  And-ay Od-gay aid-say, Et-lay ere-thay e-bay ight-lay:
     and-ay ere-thay as-way ight-lay.

1:4  And-ay Od-gay aw-say e-thay ight-lay, at-thay it-ay as-way
     ood-gay: and-ay Od-gay ivided-day e-thay ight-lay om-fray
     e-thay arkness-day.

1:5  And-ay Od-gay alled-cay e-thay ight-lay Ay-day, and-ay
     e-thay arkness-day e-hay alled-cay Ight-nay. And-ay e-thay
     evening-ay and-ay e-thay orning-may ere-way e-thay irst-fay
     ay-day.
```

A B C D E F G H I J K L M N O P Q R S T U V W X Y Z

## Canadianizer

See how your favorite web pages will look after they have been Canadianized. Type a URL into this form and you will jump directly to a modified version of the page complete with Canadian slang.

**Web:**

**http://www.io.org/~themaxx/canada/can.html**

## Canonical Lists

Need that joke for a special occasion? Check out the **rec.humor** archives where you can find not only canonical lists of jokes, but the canonical list of canonical lists. Blonde jokes, answering machine messages, lawyer jokes, things that are politically incorrect, and a list of people in need of a good, hard caning. The archives go on and on.

**Web:**

**http://www.cs.caltech.edu/~adam/USENET/rec.humor.faq**

## College Humor

College humor has certainly come a long way since Max Shulman and Dobie Gillis. (Who?) Join the discussion and hear some real, honest-to-god stories, rumors, and anecdotes, some of which might even be true.

**Usenet:**

**alt.folklore.college**

## Comedy Talk and General Discussion

I love jokes, so I am encouraging everyone to choose comedy as a career. Sure, the world will have to make do with fewer new inventions, scientific discoveries and medical miracles, but we will all be laughing too hard to notice. Comedy is an addiction and when people are not listening to it or watching it, they are talking about it on Usenet.

**Usenet:**

**alt.comedy.british**
**alt.comedy.british.blackadder**
**alt.comedy.firesgn-thtre**
**alt.comedy.slapstick.3-stooges**
**alt.comedy.standup**
**alt.comedy.vaudeville**
**alt.tv.comedy-central**

## Contemporary Humor

Humor isn't just for fun. Some people study it or actually make a living out of it. This list has a dual purpose—to entertain, but to also provide a body of contemporary humor for people who take their jokes seriously. And who knows, you may find out why the chicken really did cross the road.

**Listserv Mailing List:**

List Name: **humor**
Subscribe to: **listserv@uga.cc.uga.edu**

### *Look What I Found on the Net...*

```
Newsgroup: alt.folklore.college
Subject: Early Birds

> Someone here just did a poll on virginity at the University of
> Pennsylvania.
>
> The results:
>     Over 50% of incoming freshman are virgins.
>     Less than 20% of outgoing seniors are virgins.
>
> What does this mean?

It means that if you're into virgins, come and get it fast
during freshman orientation.
```

A B C D E F G H I J K L M N O P Q R S T U V W X Y Z

## Cruel Site of the Day

Humor isn't always pretty—but someone has to do it. The Cruel Site of the Day is one of the places you *must* know about. Every day (well, not every day, but most days... well, some days anyway) there is a new link to a bizarre site on the Net. The site might be serious, it might be a parody, or it might be so strange as to defy classification. What is always true, however, is that you are sure to find someone to laugh at. When you have some extra time, check out the Cruel Site archives ("Our Cruel Heritage") for some guaranteed bad-taste-meets-the-Net humor-in-a-box.

**Web:**

**http://www.cruel.com/**

## Fifty Fun Things for Non-Christians to Do in Church

If your mom makes you go to church and you just don't want to, here's a list of things you can do that will probably make her decide it's better for you to sleep in on Sunday mornings. There are fifty ideas, so you can do a different one every Sunday and you won't run out of new things for nearly a year.

**Web:**

**http://freethought.tamu.edu/library/humor/church_fun.html**

## Find-the-Spam

You can never been too rich, too thin or have too much Spam. Play Find-the-Spam and test your powers of observation. All you have to do is find the Spam, not eat it, so it's not such a difficult task.

**Web:**

**http://sp1.berkeley.edu/findthespam.html**

## Firesign Theater

Firesign Theater, an American comedy and satire group from the 1970s, has a cult following all their own. Join these Usenet groups to discuss whatever-happened-to-so-and-so, as well as upcoming appearances by ex-FST members and a host of trivia questions. Read the regularly posted FAQ list and find out if we really are all bozos on this bus.

**Usenet:**

**alt.comedy.firesgn-thtre**
**alt.fan.firesign-theatre**

### Don't Crush That Modem, Hand Me the Browser

Firesign Theater is one of the highest achievements of modern American theater. However, you need to have just the right type of warped mind to appreciate it. Fortunately, I do; and so can you.

Tune in to the FST Usenet groups and join George Tirebiter, Ralph Spoilsport and Nick Danger back on the Internet (which is already in progress...)

## Funny People

Usenet has a whole set of newsgroups devoted to the worship and discussion of various famous people and their work. Humor, of course, is well represented. Join the disciples and discuss your favorite humorists.

**Usenet:**

**alt.fan.bill-gates**
**alt.fan.dave_barry**
**alt.fan.dice-man**
**alt.fan.goons**
**alt.fan.jay-leno**
**alt.fan.letterman**
**alt.fan.mel-brooks**
**alt.fan.monty-python**
**alt.fan.penn-n-teller**
**alt.fan.pratchett**
**alt.fan.wodehouse**
**alt.fan.woody-allen**

## Giggles

It's fun to let yourself go and collapse into a fit of giggles. I won't tell. In fact, you can do it now. Nobody is watching. Go ahead. Or if you want, you can save it for when you join this list and see all the funny jokes, stories and anecdotes people have to share. You can even post some yourself as long as what you send is not copyrighted and is related to humor.

**Listserv Mailing List:**

List Name: **giggles**
Subscribe to: **listserv@listserv.vt.edu**

## Humor Archives

Where do you go when you need a good laugh, and you can't find your old high school yearbook? To the Net, of course. Here are some Internet resources that will lead you to enough jokes, humor and overall silliness to supply the entire Peruvian army.

**Web:**

**http://www.synapse.net/~oracle/Contents/HumorArch.html**
**http://www.ugcs.caltech.edu/~nathan/humor.html**

## Humor Mailing List

Why go out into the cold cruel world in order to hunt down humor, when you can have it come directly to your electronic mailbox? Subscribe to the **humor-l** mailing list, and you will be able to distract your co-workers by laughing as you read your mail. Then, you can forward the best jokes to all your friends, so they will see what a terrific sense of humor you have and appreciate how lucky they are to know you.

**Listproc Mailing List:**

List Name: **humor-l**
Subscribe to: **listproc@cornell.edu**

## Humorous Text Filters

Text filters that turn your text into Swedish chef talk, Jive, Pig Latin, and Valley Girl.

**Web:**

**http://emoryi.jpl.nasa.gov/ftp/misc/filters**
**http://gumbo.tcs.tufts.edu/chef/**
**http://www.cs.utexas.edu/users/jbc/home/chef.html**

## Imprudent Wit and Verbal Abuse

Some days when things are going great and you just need someone to bring you back down to earth, help is just a few keystrokes away. This site features a variety of insults from sharp-tongued and quick-witted famous people. If you are going to be verbally abused, it might as well come from someone interesting.

**Web:**

**http://www.iaehv.nl/users/roberth/**

## Interactive Top Ten List

If you are tired of passively hearing about other people's Top Ten lists, then rejoice: you can participate in making your own. Fill in a form with your entry, submit it and wait to see if yours is selected and put on display. Fame could be just around the corner for you.

**Web:**

**http://downtime.stanford.edu/topten/**

## Jokes

This is the most important place on the entire Internet: the joke-telling Usenet group. Anyone may post a joke about anything (although truly tasteless jokes are best sent to **alt.tasteless.jokes**). Beginners note: The **.d** newsgroup is for the discussion of jokes or for requests (such as "Does anyone have the canonical list of Hillary and Beavis jokes?"). The **rec.humor** group is for jokes only.

**Usenet:**

**rec.humor**
**rec.humor.d**

### *Look What I Found on the Net...*

```
Newsgroup: rec.humor
Subject: Poetry

Mary had a little skirt
Split right up the sides,
And every time she wore that skirt
The boys could see her thighs.

She also had another skirt
Split right up the front,
But she never wore that one.
```

A B C D E F G H I J K L M N O P Q R S T U V W X Y Z

## Jokes and Fun Archive

It's that awkward silence that always makes you want to find a hole to crawl into. Never again will you have to suffer the embarrassment of being speechless. Just whip out the clever remark you got from this archive of jokes, anecdotes and funny stories.

**Web:**

**http://mars.superlink.net/~zorro/humor.htm**

**The Net is immortal.**

## Jokes, Moderated

This moderated group is to **rec.humor** what Compuserve is to the Internet: there is Someone in Charge. All jokes are submitted to a moderator who posts the ones he thinks are funny. What this means is that, unlike **rec.humor**, you don't have to wade through a whole lot of junk, silliness, and bad jokes. It also means that you have to put up with irritating messages that are tacked on to the end of each joke, as well as regularly posted draconian ukases, setting out rules and regulations. Still, this newsgroup is one of the most popular on the entire Usenet (in our estimation, coming between **rec.arts.erotica** and **alt.sex.bondage**).

**Usenet:**

**rec.humor.funny**

### *Look What I Found on the Net...*

```
Newsgroups: rec.humor.funny
Subject: Advice for the Young Bride

[The following is an excerpt from what -- supposedly -- is a an
article from The Madison Institute Newsletter, Fall Issue, 1894]

                    INSTRUCTION AND ADVICE
                           FOR THE
                         YOUNG BRIDE

To the sensitive young woman who has had the benefits of proper
upbringing, the wedding day is, ironically, both the happiest
and most terrifying day of her life.  On the positive side,
there is the wedding itself, in which the bride is the central
attraction in a beautiful and inspiring ceremony, symbolizing
her triumph in securing a male to provide for all her needs for
the rest of her life.  On the negative side, there is the
wedding night, during which the bride must pay the piper, so
to speak, by facing for the first time the terrible experience
of sex...

...Clever wives are ever on the alert for new and better methods
of denying and discouraging the amorous overtures of the
husband.  A good wife should expect to have reduced sexual
contacts to once a week by the end of the first year of marriage
and to once a month by the end of the fifth year of marriage...
```

## Miss Netters' Advice Column

She is the Miss Manners of the Internet. Have a question about how to deal with shameless users who propagate chain letters or whether to answer unsolicited talk requests from potential studly hunks of nerdflesh? Ask Miss Netters for her advice on netiquette.

**Web:**

**http://www.ugcs.caltech.edu/~mnetters/**

## Monty Python

Monty Python's Flying Circus was a British comedy group that flourished in the early 1970s. The members were (in non-alphabetical order) John Cleese, Terry Gilliam, Graham Chapman, Terry Jones, Eric Idle and Michael Palin. Notice there was no person named "Monty Python". (It's a joke, son.) Monty Python became so successful that even today, long after the group has stopped performing, they are still popular, mostly among young college students who think they are discovering something new, and aging baby boomers who believe that relaxed jeans are God's way of telling them that it's okay to slow down. In all, Monty Python created 47 television shows, 5 movies, 16 record albums and 16 books. (You know—except for the television, movies and records—that's the same as me.)

**Web:**

**http://www.pythonline.com/afmp/**

**Usenet:**

**alt.fan.monty-python**

**IRC:**

**#montyp**

**Nothing to do?**

Download some Monty Python skits and put on a show for your friends.

## Onion

The Onion is the online version of a satirical college newspaper based in Madison, Wisconsin. The Onion is funny—very funny. (And goodness knows, anyone living in Madison can use a good laugh.) The writing is first-rate, providing a wonderful parody of the ubiquitous self-conscious weakly written style championed by today's mainstream newspapers and magazines. If you have ever had occasion to read newspapers and magazines from earlier in the century (say, before television), you cannot help but notice the difference between what our grandparents used to read and what passes for writing today. In an age when watching an entire uninterrupted 60-second commercial is considered an extreme test of one's power of concentration, it's hard to believe that there used to be a time when daily newspapers published articles with paragraphs that routinely contained more than two sentences. The reason I mention this is because I find the Onion to be the perfect antidote to the banal and diluted output of our current print media. Now that "lowest common denominator" is considered to be a desirable goal by writers and publishers alike, reading the Onion is, in my opinion, the perfect way to pass the time until something better comes along. Also, it's funny. (And goodness knows, anyone living in Madison can use a good laugh.)

**Web:**

**http://www.theonion.com/**

**Want to send some fan mail?**

**Read "People:**

**Famous and Interesting".**

## Oracle

You send in any question you want to the Usenet Oracle. After a short wait, you receive your response. Great, you say, the wondrous powers of omnipotent wisdom are at my disposal whenever I want. Then you notice a catch: in return for answering your question, the Oracle sends *you* a question to answer. "Why not?" you say. "Maybe the Oracle is overworked this week, and it is really quite a compliment to be asked for my opinion." Then you notice that whenever you ask a question, you are sent one in return. Eventually you catch on, "Why, we are all just answering..." Well, we're sure you don't need our help to figure it out (especially if you have ever sold Amway products). The Usenet Oracle is a time-honored tradition. Read the best of the Oracle's answers in the moderated group **rec.humor.oracle**. The **.d** is non-moderated and is for an open discussion of the Oracle's wisdom.

**Usenet:**

**rec.humor.oracle**
**rec.humor.oracle.d**

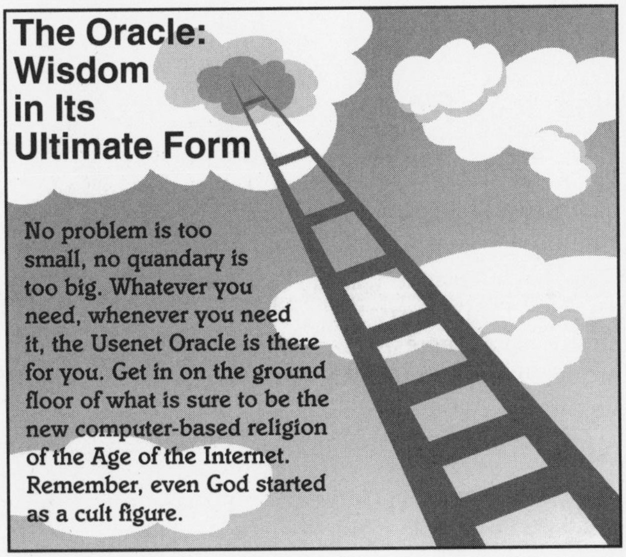
The Oracle: Wisdom in Its Ultimate Form
No problem is too small, no quandary is too big. Whatever you need, whenever you need it, the Usenet Oracle is there for you. Get in on the ground floor of what is sure to be the new computer-based religion of the Age of the Internet. Remember, even God started as a cult figure.

## Project Galactic Guide

A large and humorous guide to everything real and unreal in the galaxy, written in the style of Douglas Adams' "Hitchhiker's Guide to the Galaxy".

**Web:**

**http://web.cs.city.ac.uk/pgg/guide.html**

## Puns

It has been said that puns are the lowest form of humor. The people who read this newsgroup either haven't heard or they just don't care. I have to warn you, if you want to read these puns you need to make sure you have a strong constitution. This is not for the weak or hesitant. These punsters take their word play seriously.

**Usenet:**

**alt.humor.puns**

## Shakespearean Insults

Each time you connect to this resource a different insult is thrown at you in perfect Shakespearean style. Examples: "Thou clouted knotty-pated maggot-pie," "Thou jarring plume-plucked measle," "Thou errant toad-spotted pignut," or "Thou dankish bat-fowling pumpion."

**Web:**

**http://alpha.acast.nova.edu/cgi-bin/bard.pl**

## Swifties

The brainchild of Edward Stratemeyer, Tom Swift began as a fictional character who later became immortalized for his dramatic mannerisms. Today, a "Swifty" is a particularly stylized pun.

**Web:**

**http://www.scripps.edu/pub/dem-web/misrael/TomSwifties.html**

**Join the fun—now.**

## Tag Lines Galore

You can wow all your friends by having thousands of tag lines at your fingertips. At this site you will find a line covering almost any topic. The listings are sorted in alphabetical order and by topic.

**Web:**

**http://www.brandonu.ca/~ennsnr/Tags/**

## Tasteless (and Dirty) Jokes

Don't read this newsgroup unless you want sickening, tasteless, repulsive, humiliating, insulting jokes and stories (many of which are silly, but—like Congressmen—you get what you pay for). Don't you dare post anything that is not tasteless. And don't you dare complain that anything in this newsgroup offends you. You have been warned... now check it out.

**Usenet:**

**alt.tasteless.jokes**

### Tasteless Is in the Mind of the Beholder

The best thing about tasteless jokes is that, if you have enough of them, you will be able to offend just about anyone. Personally, I feel everyone should be offended once a week, just on general principles. So the next time you want to provide a public service, spend some time reading the **alt.tasteless.jokes** discussion group, select the most obnoxious jokes you can find, and then use them to offend as many people as possible. After all, no man is an island: we all have a social responsibility to make sure that the social fabric rips once in a while.

**The Net loves poetry.**

**Wow, free software.**

## Ten Commandments for C Programmers (Annotated)

The annotated edition of this humorous document for C programmers.

**Web:**

**http://www.tc.umn.edu/nlhome/g408/ande0870/cten.html**

## Wall O' Shame

These are news stories, old posters and documents, letters, advertisements, and anything else we should be ashamed of or embarrassed by. Contributions welcome.

**Web:**

**http://web.milk.com/~wall-o-shame/**

## Web Soap Opera

If you can't get enough daytime drama, spend a little time reading As the Web Turns. This is the story of Bob, an Information Systems Director, his fiery Latina wife, a construction worker named Brick and a few other characters who wander in and out of Bob's daily existence. Don't worry that you might be getting in on the story late. There are back issues you can browse through while you are waiting for the next part of the story to come out.

**Web:**

**http://www.metzger.com/soap/**

## Why?

A funny collection of questions like "If a cow were to laugh, would milk come out her nose?" and "If nothing ever sticks to Teflon, how do they get Teflon to stick to the pan?"

**Web:**

**http://www.qns.com/~robinson/quizme/whyaskwy.html**

# INTERNET

## Announcements of Internet Services

Keep informed with what is happening on the Internet. In this moderated newsgroup you will find announcements for interesting resources as they are made available, and keep up on the new and latest Internet technology.

**Usenet:**

**comp.infosystems.announce**

## Coolest Hostnames

Cool is as cool is named. The vanity trend of the Internet is to have an interesting hostname registered. See how fun and bizarre people can be with their domain names.

**Web:**

**http://homepage.seas.upenn.edu/~mengwong/coolhosts.html**

People talk a lot about the Internet and exaggerate a great deal. However, one thing that is not well understood is that the Net is older than most people think. In my mind, I tend to think of the Net as dating back only a short time to the publication of Ed Krol's seminal book (The Whole Internet User's Guide and Catalog). However, the Net actually started back in the mid-1970s with the first experimental packet switching network done under the auspices of ARPA (the U.S. Advanced Research Projects Agency). When you get a few moments, take a look at the Internet Timeline. It will give you a perspective on the Net and allow your feelings of where you are in the course of human events to be all the more meaningful.

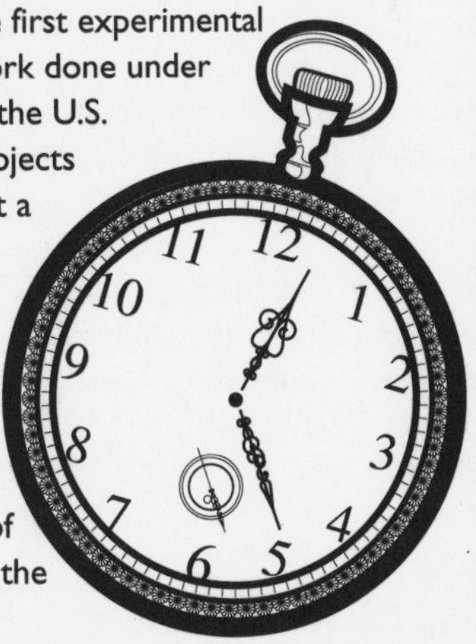

## Domain Name Registration

Within any type of Internet address, the name of the computer is called the domain name or, more simply, the domain. For example, in the address **president@whitehouse.gov**, the domain is **whitehouse.gov**. In **http://canada.gc.ca/**, the domain is **canada.gc.ca**. Have you ever wondered how these names are assigned? There are two systems. Outside the United States, all addresses end with a two-letter country code. In our second example, for instance, the two-letter country code is **ca**, indicating that this is a Canadian domain. The United States uses a different system. There is a country code (**us**), but it's not used much. Instead, most people use an older system that was devised before the Internet became international. The last part of the domain—called the top-level domain—is a three-letter code. The most common of these top-level domains are **com** (commercial), **edu** (educational), **gov** (government), **org** (non-profit organizations) and **net** (network providers). If you have used the Net much, you will have noticed that the **com** top-level domain is also used for miscellaneous addresses that don't fit into another category. So how do you register a domain? You can either have your Internet service provider (ISP) do it for you, or you can do it yourself. In the U.S., most of the registration is done by the InterNIC Registration Services. For assistance, connect to their web page and read the help information. If you are outside the U.S., I have included a second web site (also maintained by the InterNIC) that contains links to other registration organizations.

**Web:**

**http://rs.internic.net/help/other-reg.html**
**http://rs.internic.net/rs-internic.html**

## Freenets

One of the great things about the Internet is that things are free. Sometimes even access itself is free. Find links to various freenets as well as articles on how to get a network up and running and network communities. There is a great deal of information here.

**Web:**

**http://www.usask.ca/~scottp/free.html**

## Historical Timeline of the Internet

Here is a timeline that shows the history of the Internet from the 1956 Russian launch of Sputnik (which may have triggered it all), through the Arpanet (1969), UUCP (1976), Usenet (1979), DNS (1984), IRC (1988), gopher (1991), the World Wide Web (1992), and on and on.

**Web:**

**http://www.euregio.net/d/branchen/present/HIT.html**

## Internet Conference Calendar

This site lets you search a database of information about upcoming conferences, symposia, courses and workshops related to the Internet and various computer technologies. Search by specific events, by date or by location. Now, when your spouse makes you take a vacation, you can check ahead of time for something interesting to do so you won't be bored.

**Web:**

**http://www.automatrix.com/conferences/**

## Internet Drafts

Examine the up-to-date collection of working documents of the Internet Engineering Task Force. Most of these documents relate to technical aspects of the Net, but there are also general interest articles. These draft documents are working proposals, created by the people who are planning the future of the Net and circulated within the Internet community for general comment.

**Web:**

**http://www.ietf.cnri.reston.va.us/1id-abstracts.html**

## Internet Fax Server

The Internet Fax Server is an attempt to make it possible to send free faxes to many different parts of the world through Internet mail. The recipient's name and fax number are converted to an electronic mail address within the remote printing domain, and the mail message is routed via the Internet to a computer near the destination. The receiving computer converts the mail message into a fax and transmits it through the local telephone network to the recipient's fax machine.

**Web:**

**http://linux1.balliol.ox.ac.uk/fax/faxsend.html**

## Internet Media Coverage

The Internet is the talk of just about every town on the map. This Usenet group is devoted to a discussion of how the Internet is covered in the mass media. Discuss new software releases, Internet service providers, legal aspects of the Net, and much more. One day, perhaps, we will live long enough so that reporters will stop writing Internet stories that contain the words "surfing" and "cyber".

**Usenet:**

**alt.internet.media-coverage**

## Internet News

The Internet changes so fast that literally no one can keep up on what's happening. However, if you would like to keep in touch, here are some places that can help. You can check every week, every day, or even every hour, and you will find lots and lot of news articles. In particular, you will find coverage of all the companies that are doing business related to the Net.

**Web:**

**http://www.cnet.com/**
**http://www.iworld.com/**

## Internet Radio Shows

Here are web sites for radio shows that discuss the Internet. Check here for information about when the shows are on the air. With some shows, you can even listen right over the Net. The Nettalk show is co-hosted by a friend of mine, Rick Broadhead, who is the co-author of the all-time best-selling Canadian Internet book. (Modesty prevents me from telling you the name of the all-time best-selling Internet author from Canada.) The other show is Internet@Night, hosted by Tony Reynolds. Tony is a cool guy (I know because I have been a guest on his show), who knows what he is talking about. His show is always worth listening to.

**Web:**

**http://www.nettalk.com/**
**http://www.night.net/**

## Internet Service Providers

An Internet service provider (ISP) is a company or organization that provides access to the Internet. For example, if you have a computer at home, you access the Net by having your computer connect to an ISP. The web page contains a list of public Internet service providers. If you need to find an ISP for a particular area, this is a good place to look. (If you do not already have access, ask a friend to help you by looking at the list to find out what providers serve your area.) For discussion about Internet access, you can read the Usenet groups.

**Web:**

**http://thelist.iworld.com/**

**Usenet:**

**alt.internet.access.wanted**
**alt.internet.services**

**Internet Service Provider**

Once you are on the Net, you become dependent on your Internet service provider (ISP). Unfortunately, many people don't appreciate how important this relationship really is.

A good ISP can make a big difference to making your time on the Internet comfortable and satisfying, so don't make the mistake of choosing your ISP as casually as you might choose a university, or an employer, or a spouse.

Do your homework now, and you'll avoid a lot of regret later.

## Internet Statistics

Have you ever wondered how many computers are connected directly to the Internet? Or how many countries are on the Net? All this information, and more, is available at these web sites. Be aware, there is a *lot* of exaggeration among people who don't know what they are talking about and who haven't read the real statistics. Thus it is common to hear that there are tens and tens of millions of computers or people on the Net. The real truth is, no one knows exactly how big the Net really is. The "size" of the Net depends very much on how you define what you are measuring. For example, a "host" is a computer on the Net. However, technically, there are different ways to define a host. By one definition, there were (for example) 9.5 million hosts on the Net in January 1996. By another definition, there were 1.7 million hosts on the Net in January 1996. So when someone asks how many computers are on the Net, it's hard to know exactly what to tell them. What I can tell you for sure is (1) the Net is very important to humanity, and (2) it is large and growing faster than anyone can understand.

**Web:**

**http://www.cc.gatech.edu/gvu/user_surveys/**
**http://www.nlm.nih.gov/publications/staff_publications/rodgers/internet_course/growth.html**
**http://www.nw.com/zone/WWW/top.html**

## Internet Talk and General Discussion

The next best thing to being on the Internet is talking about being on the Internet. Get your fix of Internet topics by checking out the Usenet groups where anyone who thinks they are anyone chats about issues relating to the Internet.

**Usenet:**

**alt.internet**
**alt.internet.talk.haven**
**alt.internet.talk.of.the.town**

**The Net loves poetry.**

## Look What I Found on the Net...

```
                (from Internet Growth Statistics)

Note: It became much harder to gather accurate statistics after the completion of
privatization of the Internet in April 1995. The information below ends before this
event; the indicated growth trends have continued to the present.

-------

Here is a graph (in logarithmic scale) showing the growth of
the Internet.  The "@" characters show an estimate of the number
of hosts (that is, computers connected to the Internet).

          ^
          |
4,852,000 |                                                       @@
3,212,000 |                                                      @
2,056,000 |                                                     @
          |                                                    @
1,313,000 |                                                   @@
  890,000 |                                                  @
          |                                                 @
  535,000 |                                                @
          |                                               @
  313,000 |                                             @
          |
  130,000 |                                           @
          |
          |                                          @
   56,000 |                                         @
          |
   28,174 |                                       @ @
          |
          |
          |
          |
          |
    5,089 |                                     @
          |
          |
    1,961 |                                   @
          |
    1,024 |                               @
          |
      562 |                             @
          |
          |
      213 |                         @@
          |
          |
          |
       63 |              @
          |           @
       35 |      @
          |
       23 |     @
       13 |  @
          |
          |
          |
        4 |@
          +------------------------------------------------------->

  year    70  72  74   76  78  80  82   84  86  88   90  92    95
```

## InterNIC Information Services

When you hear people talk about the Net, you will often hear references to "they". For example, how do they keep all the computer addresses straight? Or, do they have any place where I can search for someone's name? Have you ever wondered, who are "they"? Well, in the United States, "they" are the InterNIC (Internet Network Information Center). The InterNIC consists of two separate projects: Directory and Database services (administered by AT&T), and the Registration Services (administered by Network Solutions). Although—thank goodness—there is no central Internet authority, the InterNIC does provide some important centralized services.

**Web:**

**http://www.internic.net/**

## IP Address Resolver

This resource will determine the IP address of an Internet site and send you a mail message with the address. Useful for people who don't have access to the **host** or **nslookup** commands.

**Mail:**

**dns@grasp.insa-lyon.fr**
Body: **site [site name]**

> **Do you need to know the numeric (IP) address of a particular Internet site? Use the IP Address Resolver.**

## Net Happenings

Be on the super-sharp—thin as the blade of a razor—cutting edge of the latest happenings in Net resources. Net Happenings is an ambitious mailing list whose purpose is to distribute "announcements of interest" to people who use the Net. You can subscribe to the mailing list, or you can read the postings (and archives) on the Web.

**Web:**

**http://socrates.ro.cc.mn.us/docs/nh.html**
**http://www.gene.cinvestav.mx/mail/nethap/**

**Listserv Mailing List:**

List Name: **net-happenings**
Subscribe to: **listserv@lists.internic.net**

> ### Net-Happenings
>
> Okay, we all know that the world is just chock full to the Plimsoll line with fanatics. What is really great is when you can get some of that extreme energy working for you without having to do anything for yourself.
>
> Enter Net-Happenings. Simply subscribe to the mailing list and your box will fill up with the latest info on more new and interesting Internet resources than you can shake several sticks at.
>
> Even if you only subscribe for a little while, I guarantee that you will be impressed with all the new stuff on the Net. In fact, *I* am impressed (and *I* am hard to impress).

## Scout Report

Stay on top of what is happening in the Net world, by getting weekly lists of the latest cool Net sites. Experience the luxury of having someone else do the hard part while you get to have all the fun.

**Web:**

**http://rs.internic.net/scout_report-index.html**

**Majordomo Mailing List:**

List Name: **scout-report**
Subscribe to: **majordomo@lists.internic.net**

## Web Talk and General Discussion

Would you like to talk about the Web? Goodness knows there is a lot to say. The Usenet groups are for ongoing discussions about various aspects of the Web. The **advocacy** group is for opinion. The **announce** group is for announcements. This is a good place to let people know about a new web site. The **misc** group is for everything else related to the Web. For talking in real time, try the IRC channel.

**Web:**

**comp.infosystems.www.advocacy**
**comp.infosystems.www.announce**
**comp.infosystems.www.misc**

**IRC:**

**#www**

A B C D E F G H I J K L M N O P Q R S T U V W X Y Z

## Whois

Would you like to find out who is in charge of a particular Internet domain? Use the InterNIC's Whois service. Just enter a name, and their computer will check their database and show you the public information.

**Web:**

**http://rs.internic.net/cgi-bin/whois/**

# INTERNET: DEVICES, GIZMOS AND THINGAMAJIGS

## Ant Farm

There's nothing like the feeling of having your own personal ant farm sitting close by. All day, as you are working, you can glance over and see the ants being industrious, running back and forth carrying things and generally doing whatever it is ants do. If you've always wanted to have your own ant farm, but felt too guilty about confining live things in a small narrow area, here's the next best thing: a picture of a live ant farm. Now, whenever you need to take a small breather from the hustle and bustle of daily life, peek in on the hustle and bustle of the daily ant life. Whenever you want to see what's new, simply reload the web page and you will get an updated picture.

**Web:**

**http://sec.dgsys.com/antfarm.html**

## Antarctica Live

Would you like to see a picture of Antarctica right now? This web site shows you a recent picture of the view outside Mawson Station (on the eastern side of Holme Bay, perched on a horseshoe-shaped outcrop of rock). Mawson Station has been in continuous operation since February 1954, and now you can visit whenever you want.

**Web:**

**http://www.antdiv.gov.au/aad/exop/sfo/mawson/video.html**

## Cameras on the Net

Feeling lonely and out of sorts? This web site will allow you to view some interesting people, places and things around the world. If you are stuck in a cubicle, check out the views of exotic lands. If you are stuck in an exotic land, look for a cubicle. There are a large number of cameras on the Net, and these collections of links are great places to look for great places to snoop.

**Web:**

**http://www.cris.com/~jdholley/wcc/**
**http://www.earthcam.com/**
**http://www.intertain.net/~cameras/**

**Cameras** on the Net

Now, for a change, *you* get to be Big Brother. Use one of the cameras on the Net to see what someone else is doing.

## Dr. Atomic's List of Devices on the Net

I don't want to distract you from your work, but you should look at this web site. It has a large collection of links to cameras and other devices connected to the Net. Just take five minutes and look for something interesting. If your boss complains, tell him I said it was okay.

**Web:**

**http://www.phoenix.net/~dratomic/cambot.html**

## Fatso the Cat

Fatso is a cat that lives in a building housing a collection of artist's studios in Rhode Island, United States. The story is that Fatso has a radio transmitter on his collar. As he moves from place to place, his location is picked up by a special receiver and relayed to a computer. You can check Fatso's current location by visiting this web site. The question is: does Fatso really exist? Okay, so you see a picture of a cat moving from one place to another. Do you really believe there is a cat in Rhode Island walking around? Like all important questions about life, you need to answer this one for yourself.

**Web:**

**http://www.ids.net/~as220/where_is_fatso.html**

## Giraffe Cam

I used to have a pet giraffe, but the neighbors kept complaining that he was looking over the fence into their sunbathing area. So I told him, "You'll have to stop looking or we'll need to make other arrangements." Well, he made other arrangements. He got a job as a White House press secretary. (He was the only job applicant who was not afraid to stick his neck out.) When I miss my giraffe, I connect to the Giraffe Cam at the Cheyenne Mountain Zoo in Colorado, where I can see happy-go-lucky giraffes frolic to and fro in the cool mountain air.

**Web:**

**http://www.cmzoo.org/buttons/live12.html**

## Go Watch a Mountain

Look up. What do you see? If you see a wall of a cubicle, it's time to take a break. Connect to this web site and sneak a quick peek at beautiful Mount Hood in Portland, Oregon. At night, you can see the lights of Portland. Who needs an office with a window when you can look at such a beautiful view whenever you want?

**Web:**

**http://www.teleport.com/~peekpa/pittockcam.html**

## Hot Tub on the Net

Everybody has fantasies about having a computer environment advanced enough to coordinate launching a space shuttle. And everyone has fantasies about being able to sink into an exquisitely monitored hot tub in which you can bubble your cares away. But who would ever think to put the two together? Someone whose two favorite things are the Internet and his new hot tub. Check out the status of an actual hot tub and read the documentation on this hot tub project. The hot tub seats eight, so if you know the magic password you may get invited over.

**Web:**

**http://hamjudo.com/cgi-bin/hottub**
**http://hamjudo.com/hottub_notes.html**

*Hot Tub on the Net*

One of my favorite pastimes is relaxing in my hot tub admiring a spectacular ocean view.

However, I don't always feel like sitting in the water. Sometimes, I just don't want to get wet.

So, instead of jumping in my tub, I connect to the Hot Tub on the Net.

It's not exactly the same experience, but it's fast and easy, and I don't have to take off my clothes.

## Iguana Cam

If you want a pet, but you don't want to get into serious commitment, the Net will provide a substitute. Any time you want, you can connect to this web page and look at Dupree the Iguana. Here is a secret. You can pretend that Dupree is really *your* iguana. Just invite your friends over and say, "Hey, do you want to look at a picture of my iguana?" They'll never know the difference.

**Web:**

**http://iguana.images.com/dupecam.html**

## Interactive Model Railroad

This is really cool. You can play with a pair of model trains in Germany. All you have to do is select a train and a destination, and press a button to make the train leave the station. Watch the train zoom around the track. As it moves, the web page will display the IP number (official address) of the person's computer that is currently controlling the train. If you want, you can even type a message for other people to read. I love this. I can not only control the train, but everyone who is watching knows that the commands came from *my* computer.

**Web:**

**http://marconi.w8upd.uakron.edu/users/search/ interact.html**

## Jacobs Field

Did you know that, right now, you could be experiencing the thrill of seeing Jacobs Field in Cleveland (the home of the Cleveland Indians baseball team)? Here is a camera that is pointed toward the stadium. Take a look and maybe you will be lucky enough to see the Cleveland Indians playing ball. Isn't this a great way to spend a Saturday afternoon? Don't you think it would be great fun to sit around your computer with a bunch of friends, drinking beer and eating potato chips, watching the view of the baseball stadium change every few minutes? (Actually, it's almost as exciting as a real baseball game except there are no commercials.)

**Web:**

**http://www.xa.com/jregal/webcam.htm**

## Jukebox Controller

Here is a company that has a jukebox, filled with various CDs, that you can control. Connect to the web site and choose the next song. You won't be able to hear it yourself, but people far removed from you will have to listen to whatever *you* choose. Go ahead, make their day.

**Web:**

**http://www.dvsystems.com/songlist.html**

## Los Angeles Traffic Conditions

Do you drive in Los Angeles? If so—or if you intend to visit—think about this: as you drive, you are making a small contribution to the overall traffic pattern. That is important because people all over the world are looking at that traffic pattern right now on the Web. Take a look. See the cool color-coded map that shows you where the traffic is moving and where it's stuck. Try again during rush hour and see the pattern change. Aren't you glad you're not there?

**Web:**

**http://www.scubed.com/caltrans/la/la_big_map.shtml**

### THE PERFECT RELAXATION TECHNIQUE

When I feel the need to relax, I use the Net to check the traffic flow on the Los Angeles freeway system.

I look at every colored dot on the map and imagine tens of thousands of cars, slowing down, speeding up, making noise and emitting exhaust.

Within a few minutes, I am completely relaxed and ready to get back to work.

## New York Views

I love New York in June, how about you? The good news is, you don't have to wait until June to see some hot New York action. Check out these Big Apple cameras now, and look at the plaza at Rockefeller center as well as a view of the Manhattan skyline from the Empire State Building. If you are lucky while you are looking out from the Empire State Building, you may see a kid drop a penny.

**Web:**

**http://www.ftna.com/cents.cgi**
**http://www.realtech.com/webcam/**

## Office Snooper

The office has a camera that relays pictures to the web. Watch the man as he sits at his desk. Watch the man as he talks on the phone. Watch the man as he moves around in his chair. Wow. And it gets even better. Use your web browser to move the camera so you can get different views. Type a message for the man to read. Wow. (Now get back to work.)

**Web:**

**http://38.246.215.4/cgi-win/andycam.exe**

## Refrigerator Status

I'm sure that, before you go to bed every night, you check to make sure that the door of your refrigerator is closed. Well, now you have another fridge to check. This one is connected to the Net and, whenever you want, you can check its status: temperature, light, and whether or not the door is closed.

**Web:**

**http://hamjudo.com/cgi-bin/refrigerator**

## Seismo Cam

I love Southern California, but I realize that not everybody wants to live here. After all, most people probably wouldn't enjoy frolicking on the beach all year round, or sitting in the hottub at night looking at the stars. I understand that. However, if you aren't here in person, you can at least be here in spirit. Check out the Seismo Cam: a gadget that broadcasts a regularly updated picture of a seismograph (a device that records the movement of the earth). Most of the time, nothing interesting will happen. But, if there is an earthquake in Southern California, the needle on the seismograph will move, making a wiggly line. It's almost as good as being here in person.

**Web:**

**http://www.knbc4la.com/seismo/**

## Talking Machine

In the outside world, talk is cheap; on the Net, it's free. And now you can talk and talk to someone you don't even know. Go to this web page and type in a message. Whatever you type will be relayed to a voice synthesizer in a particular office. Someone may actually be listening. Who knows? This is your chance to say something profound, provocative or witty to some guy you don't even know. And remember, there is absolutely no chance of a reply. You won't even know if anyone heard what you typed. It's so existential, it goes way beyond cool.

**Web:**

**http://www.inference.com/~hansen/talk.html**

## Telerobot

When I was a kid, I made my own robot out of various things I found around the house: a few old radio parts, three tin cans, a pair of knitting needles and my brother. It was a great robot, and I could make it do anything I wanted just by hitting it. Now, you can have almost the same experience on the Net. Connect to this web site at the University of Western Australia. The robot is complex and it may take you a while to make it do everything you want. Don't complain. I'm still trying to understand my brother.

**Web:**

**http://telerobot.mech.uwa.edu.au/**

Talking Machine
I bet, right now, that you have something wonderful to say. Don't you? (Of course you do.)
Well, if you can't find anyone who will listen, why not use the Talking Machine?
Send your words onto the Net and let them emerge in an office somewhere in another part of the world.
Remember, if something is worth saying, it's up to you to say it.

## Temperature in Boulder, Colorado

Just think. Right this minute, there is a computer in Boulder, Colorado, that is ready to tell you the temperature outside University of Colorado at Boulder's Engineering Center. Just connect to this web site and check it out. (This web site comes in handy if you are planning a trip to the Colorado University Engineering Center, and you are wondering what to wear.)

**Web:**

**http://www.cs.colorado.edu/htbin/temp**

## Things on the Net

Stuff is good. However, having too much stuff in your house is not good. But now, thanks to the Net, you can have access to other people's stuff. This web site has links to lots of devices that are connected to the Net: cameras, machines, robots, gadgets, screen captures, pagers, and lots more.

**Web:**

**http://marconi.w8upd.uakron.edu/users/search/interact.html**

## Vending Machines

The rage started with being able to check the Coke machine from the Internet. Things got out of control with the invention of CU-SeeMe. Check out coffee machines, temperature gauges, light sensors and a geiger counter without leaving your seat. "Spy cameras" have been set up in offices and pointed out windows so you can even have a view.

**Web:**

**http://www-cse.ucsd.edu/users/bsy/iam.html**

## Wave to the Cats

Sometimes when I am working at my desk and my cat walks by outside, I will give him a friendly wave. (As a man, I know how important it is to work on important relationships.) However, I know that some people are not fortunate enough to have their very own cat. If you like the idea of waving at cats, connect to this web site. You can wave at one of a group of cats (or if none of the cats happen to be in the room, you can wave at a person). All you have to do is select the style of wave you want to perform, and with a click of a button, you will be waving to Paul's cats in a friendly fashion.

**Web:**

**http://hogwild.hamjudo.com/cgi-bin/wave**

## Webcam Talk and General Discussion

So you've visited some of the webcams on the Net (places where you can view an automatically updated image of something or other), and you have decided to create a webcam of your own. Good idea: I bet there are a lot of people who would love to look at wherever you decide to point your camera. However, the details of setting up a camera and connecting it to the Net can be a bit tricky, so if you need help, try this Usenet group. This is the place where people discuss video cameras and how to connect them to computers. Stick to it and, before long, everyone in the world will be able to watch your pet cactus plant grow in real time.

**Usenet:**

**rec.video.desktop**

### Make Your Own Webcam

A Webcam is a camera that broadcasts pictures over the Web.

Here's my idea.

Get a camera of your own, connect it to your computer, and create a Webcam. Then point the camera at your desk, so people all over the world can watch you as you work. (Be sure your Harley Hahn books are in the background, so everyone knows you have good taste.)

Then, once you become famous all over the world, sell your life story to a tabloid newspaper for a huge sum of money.

You may have doubts, but both Prince Charles and ex-Princess Diana are following my plan and—any day now—they are going to clean up big time.

# INTERNET: HELP

## E-Mail Access to Internet Resources

Although most people on the Net use a web browser, there are many people in the world who only have access to electronic mail. If this is the case for you, you should know that it is possible to access most of the resources on the Internet by mail. To start, send mail to the address below and read the document that will be sent to you. By the way, this document is translated into many different languages aside from English.

**Mail:**

**mailbase@mailbase.ac.uk**
Body: **send lis-iis e-access-inet.txt**

## Glossary of Internet Terms

The computer and Internet industry is flooded with all sorts of terms that you may or may not be familiar with. If you ever run across a term and you don't know what it means, look it up in this glossary of Internet terms.

**Web:**

**http://www.matisse.net/files/glossary.html**

Many of the Internet's resources are available by electronic mail, so there is no need to be left out just because your Internet connection is slow or inadequate. **E-Mail Access to Internet Resources** will show you what to do to keep up with the Net-Joneses, even if they have their own personal high-speed direct connection and all you have is an e-mail account with a six-hour lag time. Soon, you will be able to do anything they can (only slower). Hint: These services are perfect if you have the type of job where they give you e-mail access to the Net, but won't let you get at the good stuff.

## Internet Help Talk and General Discussion

If you are new to the Net, there are certain Usenet groups where you can go to ask questions about using the Net. The **newbies** group is for general comments and questions about the Net. The **news** group is for discussion about learning how to use Usenet.

**Usenet:**

**alt.newbies**
**news.newusers.questions**

**Want to get starry-eyed? Try "Romance" (or "Astronomy").**

## Internet User Guides

This site has a large collection of help files and user guides relating to the Net. Learn about the Internet, read special documents for PC and Macintosh users, and browse through material about Unix, Perl and C/C++ programming.

**Web:**

**http://ug.cs.dal.ca:3400/newbie.html**

### Mr. Know-It-All

**Remember Bullwinkle the Moose in his guise as Mr. Know-it-all, the Isaac Asimov of cartoon-land? Well, you too can be a pedant. All you need do is investigate the Internet User Guide. Once you memorize everything in this collection, you will have more facts and ideas at your fingertips than there are tea leaves in China in a month of Sundays. (Well, something like that anyway...)**

## IRC Guides

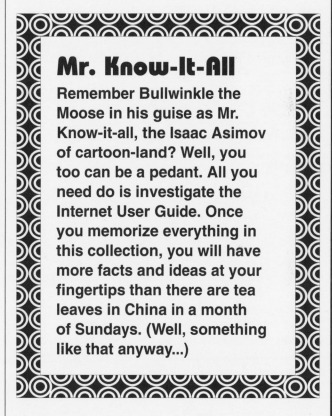

IRC is a fun way to chat and make new friends. Get help learning the general commands, read the FAQ, and get some quick reference help. You will also find information on related Usenet groups, mailing lists, primers, manuals and archive sites.

**Web:**

**http://mistral.enst.fr/~pioch/IRC/IRCprimer/IRCprimer1.1/IRCprimer1.1.html**
**http://urth.acsu.buffalo.edu/irc/WWW/ircdocs.html**

A B C D E F G H I J K L M N O P Q R S T U V W X Y Z

## IRC Help

Has IRC got you scratching your head? Help on any aspect of IRC is available here. You can use the Helper bot to ask a question such as "What is a bot?" or "What is a client?" and there are many help topics available that you can list or search.

**IRC:**
**#irchelp**

## IRC Questions

Once you immerse yourself in IRC, you are going to have a great many questions about all the commands you can use. FAQs (frequently asked question lists) are available, but it's nice to know that there is a more interactive option. Post your questions on this Usenet group and, not only may you get the answer, but you will meet some interesting people in the process.

**Usenet:**
**alt.irc.questions**

## Jargon File

The Jargon File is a legendary work that sounds like it should be dull: a collection of words and technical terms—definitions and examples—used with computers and the Internet. However, the Jargon File is anything but dull. It is not only exquisitely written, it is witty, comprehensive and accurate. In addition, there are also well-written essays discussing the hacking community and its customs. Out of all the dictionaries in the world, this one is probably the most fun.

**Web:**
**http://www.ccil.org/jargon/jargon.html**

## John December's Internet Web Text

Here is a well-organized web-based guide to Internet resources. You will find orientation guides, tools, hints, and links to other related sites. The flexible presentation allows you to teach yourself whatever you want at your own speed.

**Web:**
**http://www.december.com/web/text/**

### JARGON

**We are what we think, and we think with the words that we manage to scrape up off the sidewalk of life and somehow implant in non-volatile memory. The Jargon File is a wonderful resource that has, to coin a phrase, stood the test of time. In other words, someone smart and witty wrote it and it's a lot of fun to read. Take a few moments and check it out. If nothing else, you will see the human side of the techno-nerd part of our culture that is all too often hidden behind the glamour and the heartache of life in the technical/computer/rational fast lane.**

## Listserv User Guide

Do you only put "subscribe" or do you add your name, too? And when you want to unsubscribe do you say "signoff" or "unsubscribe"? Getting on mailing lists is sometimes tricky. Getting off mailing lists is usually trickier. This guide is a nice thing to have at your fingertips. It gives all the commands for subscribing and unsubscribing, for getting archives, and setting list options. And you don't even have to subscribe to anything to get it.

**Web:**
**http://www.earn.net/lug/notice.html**

## Web Tutorial for Beginners

If you are new to the Net, here is an easy-to-follow guide to help you learn about the Internet and the Web. (If you are a woman, pretend that I am sitting beside you, holding your hand. If you are a man, pretend that your mother is holding your hand.)

**Web:**
**http://www.gactr.uga.edu/exploring/toc.html**

# INTRIGUE

## Cloak and Dagger

Find out what is going on in the world's intelligence services. This site includes information about special operations forces and counterterrorist units.

**Web:**

**http://www.abdn.ac.uk/~u01ded/candd/candd.html**

Don't look now but they are out to get you. Really. Better read all about conspiracies before it's too late.

## Conspiracies

The world (or so they say) is full of many amazing conspiracies of all kinds: AIDS being a government plot, Russia's operational Star Wars system, secret wars, what really happened at Waco, the final analysis of the JFK assassination, and much more.

**Web:**

**http://www.paranoia.com/~fraterk/conspire.html**
**http://www.uc.edu/~TAYLORRM/**
**http://www.webcom.com/~conspire/**

**Stay away from "X-Rated".**

## *Look What I Found on the Net...*

The Top 20 Listserv Mailing Lists

| Subscribers | List Name | Description |
|---|---|---|
| 488,205 | dispatch | Computer-related news |
| 102,436 | shareware-dispatch | New shareware |
| 72,903 | in-touch | News about Windows 95 |
| 40,771 | techlink | Technology information |
| 38,036 | tidbits | Newsletter for Mac Users |
| 36,838 | tourbus | Interesting Internet resources |
| 35,561 | pc-games-new | New shareware: PC games |
| 31,473 | ms-windows3x-top | Top shareware: Windows 3.x |
| 29,283 | scout-report | New Internet resources |
| 24,176 | ms-windows-all--new | New shareware: Windows |
| 21,569 | netgir-l | Netgirl forum newsletter |
| 21,343 | ms-windows3x-new | New shareware: Windows 3.x |
| 20,450 | dos-new | New shareware: DOS |
| 20,243 | eol-dispatch | Entertainment gossip |
| 18,257 | new-list | Announce new mailing lists |
| 17,434 | inbusiness | Business and the Internet |
| 16,352 | weeks-worth | Online newsletter |
| 15,700 | pc-games-top | Top shareware: PC games |
| 15,358 | online-l | News about online services |
| 14,235 | omri-l | News: eastern Europe, Soviet.. |

## Conspiracy Talk and General Discussion

Don't look behind you. Don't say anything out loud. Just act natural. Okay, are you ready? There is a big conspiracy. It involves the government (particularly the CIA), the media and big business. I can't tell you the details here. This Usenet group is the only safe place to talk. See you there.

**Usenet:**

**alt.conspiracy**

## Crime and Killers

If English is your first language, this page may seem a little strange because the headings are in German. (However, if the Allies had lost World War II the whole Net would be in German, so I'm certainly not going to complain.) Examine this large list of links to web sites with information about famous criminals and their exploits: Bonnie and Clyde, Al Capone, Lizzie Borden, Elisabeth Bathory, Ted Bundy, Jack the Ripper, the Mafia, Marquis de Sade, the Unabomber, and lots more.

**Web:**

**http://ourworld.compuserve.com/homepages/kmedeke/geheimbn.htm**

## Disinformation

As they say in Brooklyn, "Dis information is not easy to come by." But, if you have a Net connection, you can get disinformation whenever you want. Try this collection of links that will lead you to sources about revolutionaries, propaganda, censorship, counterculture, media double-talk and counterintelligence.

**Web:**

**http://www.disinfo.com/**

## JFK Assassination

The whodunit of all whodunits. Just when you think you've seen all the JFK conspiracy material, someone compiles a whole bunch more. At these web sites, you will find articles galore about every aspect of every assassination theory. New evidence is emerging all the time (from somewhere), so don't get left behind on this very important historical controversy. For up to the minute, late-breaking information, as well as lots of discussion, you can always take a peek at the Usenet group.

**Web:**

**http://rmii.com/~jkelin/fp.html**
**http://www.indirect.com/www/vista/jfk.html**

**Usenet:**

**alt.conspiracy.jfk**

### *Look What I Found on the Net...*

```
Newsgroup: alt.conspiracy
Subject: Schools and Politics

> Schools are left wing brainwashing centers.  Most colleges
> were started by Christians, but were completely taken over by
> the far left a long time ago.  They are politically correct
> institutions where it is not allowed to question the views of
> the leftists.

There is much truth in this statement.  However, just because
the "left" is often wrong does not mean that the "Christians"
are always right.

There is a big difference between Left-Right politics and
Evolutionist-Creationist "science".  I would agree that
left wing politicians (and the professors who still spout their
illogical theories) are way off base, but this doesn't prove
anything, one way or the other, about science, religion or
"truth".
```

## Lincoln Conspiracies

The Statute of Limitations has probably run out on the assassination of President Abraham Lincoln. But that certainly doesn't mean that people don't want to continue with the conspiracy theories involving the event. That puts Abe in good company with Elvis and JFK. Don't wait to hear the news from the National Enquirer—learn the latest conspiracy theories relating to Abraham Lincoln from Usenet.

**Usenet:**

**alt.conspiracy.abe-lincoln**

## Mafia

Whatever else you say about the Mafia, at least you have to admit they understand the importance of Family Values. If you want to learn even more about this collection of underground criminal societies, here are some good places to start. First, you can read articles by a veteran New York reporter who has been writing about organized crime for over ten years. Second, you can look at some interesting information about the Cosa Nostra. (Literally, Cosa Nostra—another name for the Mafia—means "our thing".)

**Web:**

**http://home.pacific.net.sg/~seowjean/LaCosaNostra/lacosanostra.html**
**http://www-leland.stanford.edu/~jercap/**

## Mind Control

This is a really freaky site. It has brain scans of people with implants in their heads. Learn how "they" (the government) have been conducting mind control experiments on unfortunate individuals. Explore links to other mind control sites, and learn just how sinister the people in charge really are. If you still have the free will to carry on a discussion, try the Usenet group.

**Web:**

**http://www.designr.com/designr/MK-resistance/**

**Usenet:**

**alt.mindcontrol**

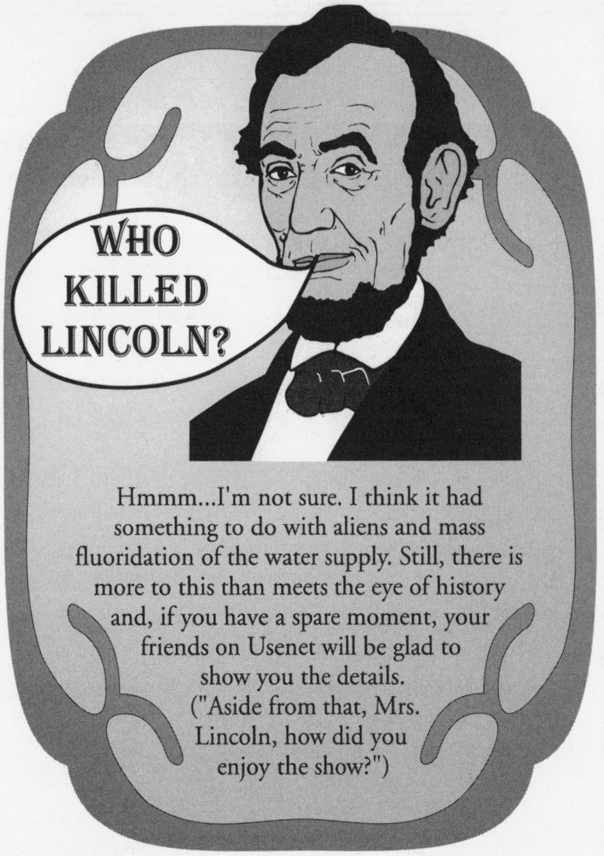
WHO KILLED LINCOLN?
Hmmm...I'm not sure. I think it had something to do with aliens and mass fluoridation of the water supply. Still, there is more to this than meets the eye of history and, if you have a spare moment, your friends on Usenet will be glad to show you the details.
("Aside from that, Mrs. Lincoln, how did you enjoy the show?")

## Parascope

Parascope is a magazine that reports on weird stuff going on all over the place. The different sections cover conspiracies and cover-ups, UFO stuff, and paranormal weirdness. There is also documented evidence such as declassified government documents, analysis of covert actions and propaganda campaigns. If your friend in the next office has been telling you about the CIA's links to a Contra cocaine ring that is trying to cover up the Roswell Incident, so the Vietnamese informants who are influencing our elections won't be discovered, this is the place to check it all out.

**Web:**

**http://www.parascope.com/**

**Feel lucky? Try "Contests".**

## *Look What I Found on the Net...*

Newsgroup: alt.mindcontrol
Subject: Satan a Figment?

>> Before I chose to believe in the "children's story" about
>> Jesus saving mankind through His blood, I was a loser with no
>> hope. I was a drunk, lost everything and was going nowhere
>> fast. I was miserable and lonely.
>>
>> Then some caring person had the guts to tell me what made
>> their life a joy: Jesus. I asked Him into my life and I have
>> been transformed by this living Jesus -- whom you call
>> a fairy tale -- into someone who loves life, has a wife and
>> three kids and a successful business of my own.

> I have to say this, and I'm sorry if it offends. What saved
> you wasn't "God" or Jesus. You saved you. No one forced you
> to stop drinking. No one forced you to change your outlook.
> No one did that but you.
>
> All too often people chalk it all up to their religion when
> they perform the miracles. Don't brush it off as someone
> else's doing. It was no God. It was no "son of God". It was
> you. Don't go around telling people that God did that to you
> or for you unless you are willing to consider yourself
> helpless and manipulatable, and you accept the other side of
> that coin, that "God" put you into the alcohol as well. Would
> you really like to pin that on your savior as well?

I did the Bible thumper thing, and it almost destroyed my family. I believed that God would deliver me from drinking and drugs, etc. All that happened was that I went on one hell of a dry drunk for 3 years.

AA helped me get sober and clean. It was there that I found a Higher Power of my own understanding. I give credit to myself, as well as to the God of my understanding.

Why do we have to seek a God outside of ourselves? If God is within us, working to help us grow spiritually, He helps us to save ourselves. Faith in any god we choose to believe in gives us the strength and ability to free ourselves from any type of bondage.

## Secret Messages

Fortune cookies are mostly unsatisfying because it takes so little to find out what the messages say. Now, if you want a real challenge, you should try intercepting and decoding messages from real spies. In fact, go right now to read up on these numbers stations over which secret messages are broadcast.

**Web:**

**http://itre.uncecs.edu/radio/numbers.html**
**http://www.access.digex.net/~cps/numbers.html**
**http://www.ibmpcug.co.uk/~irdial/conet.htm**

## Sources Journal

Here is an electronic journal with news articles about the intelligence community. Read reports about information, disinformation and what passes for intelligence within the secret parts of the government. This web site has facts that someone, somewhere, doesn't want you to know. Your job is to find this information and tell all your friends.

**Web:**

**http://www.dso.com/Sources/**

## Spies

Wouldn't it be fun to be a spy? You could pretend to be any kind of person you want and cleverly infiltrate other governments and risk your life for people who don't even know or care one bit about what you are doing. If this idea appeals to you, check out this page on spies. Read a detailed description by Chinese warrior/philosopher Sun Tzu (500 B.C.) about why spying is useful. Explore links to security resources, security services, Usenet groups, industrial and military intelligence, spy publications and U.S. intelligence agencies.

**Web:**

**http://www.kimsoft.com/kim-spy.htm**

**Intrigue, Privacy, Secret Stuff...**

**They're in every country.**
**Every government uses them.**
**We love them when they are on our side. We vilify them when they work for the enemy.**
**Spies. They're everywhere.**
**Learn all about them on the Net.**

## Taylorology

In 1922, one of Hollywood's top movie directors, William Desmond Taylor, was shot to death in his home. The killing was never solved and remains Hollywood's most fascinating murder mystery. Taylorology is a lengthy newsletter devoted to analyzing and reprinting source material pertaining to the crime and its coverage in the press.

**Web:**

**http://www.vuw.ac.nz/dlis/courses/847/lisweb94/janine/txtinjo/taylor.html**

**Usenet:**

**alt.true-crime**

## Terrorism

Here are two complementary web resources. First, a great collection of links with information about many different terrorist groups. Here you can find detailed information about the terrorist organizations: who they are, their location, their purpose, and their patterns of operation. The other web site is run by the Bureau of Diplomatic Security at the U.S. State Department. Read about the cases the Bureau is actively investigating, and learn about how you can pick up a huge lump of reward money by helping them capture a terrorist.

**Web:**

**http://www.heroes.net/**
**http://www.site.gmu.edu/~cdibona/group.html**

## Truth Is Redacted

Redaction is obscuring part of a document or picture so as to make it impossible to see some of the information. For example, when you see a picture with someone's eyes blocked out, that is redaction. Many government agencies use redaction to hide sensitive and private information from the general public. In the United States, the Freedom of Information Act and the Privacy Act have numerous loopholes that allow government departments to redact information. This site is dedicated to exploring the "real story" and wresting the "truth" from those who would hide it. Read about famous crimes, and examine information that may lead you to believe that the official story is not as complete as "they" would like you to believe. (The night after I looked at this site for the first time, I had a dream that I was playing "Truth or Dare" with Lee Harvey Oswald.)

**Web:**

**http://www.redacted.com/**

## Unsolved Mysteries

Do you like unsolved mysteries? Here is a whole list of mysteries just waiting for someone like you to solve. Look at pictures of fugitives and missing persons. Then read about the crime or the disappearance. Now, keep a sharp eye open. As you walk around, look at everyone you meet. You never know when *you* will recognize someone and solve a mystery. (And if you have any spare time, you can help me track down the person who ate the last low-fat chocolate cupcake.)

**Web:**

**http://www.unsolved.com/home.html**

## Vigilante Talk and General Discussion

Just like the way of the Old West, vigilantism has its popularity in some circles of people who are fed up with going through "routine channels". Whether you agree or disagree with taking the law into your own hands, you can at least discuss the philosophy and see heated debates on the subject.

**Usenet:**

**alt.vigilantes**

## Waco

If you didn't get enough of the Waco news on television, take a look at this compilation which offers a list of Texas Branch Davidian members, a timeline, and a copy of David Koresh's manuscript Exposition of the Seven Seals.

**Web:**

**http://www.neo.com/ucalpress/whywaco/**

**My other joke is funny.**

### *Look What I Found on the Net...*

```
Newsgroup: alt.vigilantes
Subject: 493125

The money has been transferred.

3 targets have been terminated.

W.M., H.H., and L.N. are still active.

C.H. was terminated at 1700.

Maintain silent running.

-- 493125
```

# JOBS AND THE WORKPLACE

## About Work

Here is a snappy, snazzy site, all about work. I guarantee that you will find something here to interest you. Are you looking for your first job? Are you retired? Are you out of work? Do you work at home? Would you like to start a business and become an entrepreneur? Or do you work for a large company? There are slots of articles, discussion areas, as well as links for related resources around the Net.

**Web:**
**http://www.aboutwork.com/**

About Work
Work, work, work.
Find it. Keep it. Change it. Create it.
Work, work, work.
Dress right. Act right. Talk right. Think right.
Work, work, work.
There's more to it than most people think. Learn from the Net.

## American Indian Work Issues

Sometimes there are special issues an American Indian has to address with respect to work and employment. Explore employment problems faced by American Indians, including cultural conflict, the culturally appropriate workplace, and other barriers that affect individuals as well as the American Indian population as a whole.

**Listserv Mailing List:**
List Name: **nat-work**
Subscribe to: **listserv@vm1.cc.uakron.edu**

## America's Job Bank

If you live in America, this web site can help you find a job just about anywhere in the country. America's Job Bank is a free service provided by the U.S. Department of Labor and the various state Employment Service offices. The intention is that all of the listings—from all of the state and federal Employment Service offices—should be gathered in one main database. Here it is. Use it and see what you find. There is no cost: the whole thing is funded by the unemployment insurance taxes paid by employers.

**Web:**
**http://www.ajb.dni.us/**

## Bad Bosses

Are you mad at your boss? This web site lets you vent your frustration by reading and submitting jokes and stories about annoying bosses. If you are looking for a place to complain about your manager, supervisor or employer, look no further. Read true stories that will make you realize that things could always be worse.

**Web:**
**http://www.myboss.com/**

## Biological Sciences

If you have a shiny new biological sciences degree in your hand and can't decide what to do with it, consider turning to Usenet to supplement your job search. Post your qualifications and requirements to this Usenet group and see if anyone takes the bait.

**Usenet:**
**bionet.jobs.wanted**

## Career Mosaic

Career Mosaic is an online employment guide with information about employers, companies and job opportunities. Through a colorful interface, it presents information about where employers are, what they specialize in, and what's important to them.

**Web:**
**http://www.careermosaic.com/**

## Career Net

Working means more than getting a job. Working means keeping yourself educated, understanding where your industry is going, and (of course) learning how to use the Internet effectively at your job. This web site will show you resources for every state in the United States and all the provinces in Canada, as well as several other countries. There are thousands of links to jobs and helpful career resources such as bibliographies, publications, resource evaluations, event calendars, and so on. If you happen to be without a job right now—or you are thinking about moving on to something better and more rewarding—I suggest you spend some time browsing around this web site.

**Web:**

**http://www.careers.org/**

## Contract Labor

More and more people are working from contract to contract. Aside from the cachet of getting to call yourself a "consultant", you will find that life is a lot more fun and challenging without fringe benefits. Here is the place to offer your services, look for a contract job, or swap experiences. (For hourly contracts, see **alt.sex.wanted**.)

**Usenet:**

**misc.jobs.contract**

MEMO MEMO MEMO

### Contract Labor

Would you enjoy working (1) for more money per hour, (2) with less supervision, (3) with more control over your destiny?

Would you be willing to work without (1) job security, (2) benefits, (3) a steady income?

If you answered "Yes" and "Yes", you may be ready for contract labor.

Let's talk about it on the Net.

## Education-Related Jobs

So you spent the first part of your life sitting in a classroom, waiting patiently for the bell of freedom to ring? And now you're trying desperately to get back into a classroom, so you can contribute and make a difference (while being underpaid and under-appreciated). Here is an Internet site that has everything—and I mean everything—all in one place.

**Web:**

**http://www.usjobnet.com/**

## Entry Level Jobs Offered

There's an old riddle: What does an arts graduate say to a computer science graduate? The answer is, "Would you like fries with your order?" Here is a newer riddle: What does a person who doesn't know how to use the Net say to a person who does? The answer is, nothing. Because the person who knows how to use the Net is too busy working at a satisfying and lucrative job. Okay, so we all have to start somewhere, and if you are ready for an entry-level job, this is the Usenet group for you. Check out the jobs that offer you no place to go but up, and talk to the people who really care whether or not you want fries.

**Usenet:**

**misc.jobs.offered.entry**

## E-Span

E-Span provides a database that you can search for available jobs. In addition, you can also send your resumé to a special database which is available to employers. This site is a good place to look when you are wide open to where and for whom you want to work, and you would like to spend some time exploring possibilities.

**Web:**

**http://www.espan.com/**

**Find a friend in "People".**

## Higher Education Jobs

This site contains the job listings from the current issue of The Chronicle of Higher Education. Here is the place to look for faculty and research positions, as well as jobs for administrators and executives. There are also listings for academic-type jobs outside of colleges and universities (such as in museums, galleries, research facilities, social service organizations, and so on). It is a good idea to check this site regularly, as new jobs are posted every week.

**Web:**

**http://chronicle.merit.edu/.ads/.links.html**

## Job Hunt

Some days the classifieds just don't have what you are looking for. Well, there are lots and lots of job-related resources to check on the Net. This well-organized web site makes it easy to track down the resources that might help you.

**Web:**

**http://rescomp.stanford.edu/jobs.html**

## Job Information Center

Here's a great place to go if you are searching for a job. You can get advice on careers and job searching, links to Usenet groups, and listings of available job opportunities, including international and government jobs.

**Web:**

**http://www.tvpress.com/vpjic.html**

## Job Talk and General Discussion

Before you send away for instructions on how to make money at home stuffing envelopes, maybe you should check it out with your friends on the Net. Just as important, don't start your job hunt without finding out which companies allow their employees to wear long hair and earrings. If you need a job, have a job, or are offering a job, this Usenet group is the place to talk and trade tips about employment, the workplace and careers.

**Usenet:**

**misc.jobs.misc**

### *Look What I Found on the Net...*

```
Newsgroup: misc.jobs.misc
Subject: Internet Project

Help make me an Internet Millionaire.

Please send just $1.00 cash, check or money order, and in return
receive, by email ONLY, one of the following:

1.  World's Best Salsa Recipe.

2.  How To Meditate, Relax and Live Longer.

3.  Over 1000 Internet Sites to Advertise FREE or for a Small
    Fee.

4.  How To Make a Woman Scream...With Pleasure.
    (Just the introduction and first chapter on this one.)

Send your request to:

X. Xxxxx
Box xxxxxx
Xxxxxxx, Texas

Be sure to include your e-mail address with your request.

And THANKS for participating in this important Internet Project.
```

## Jobs for College Students and Graduates

There are so many career resources around the Net that you might never even have to leave the house to go to the employment agency. These sites have loads of links for college graduates and students. Look for a job and read useful information about resumés, interviewing, negotiating and more.

**Web:**

**http://www.att.com/college/jobs.html**
**http://www.collegegrad.com/**

## Jobs Offered

Nothing to do all day? Perhaps you might like a job. Here are two general announcement forums for all types of employment.

**Usenet:**

**biz.jobs.offered**
**misc.jobs.offered**

## MedSearch America

The medical field is vast. Whether you are looking for a job as a brain transplant specialist or merely a chrono-synclastic-infundibulum technician, MedSearch America is there to help you (at least in America).

**Web:**

**http://www.medsearch.com/**

## Occupational Medicine

Occupational medicine focusing on the treatment of injuries and conditions arising from work, and how to prevent such problems. If you are an occupational therapist, or if you are involved in a related area—of which there are many—you may enjoy participating in the Usenet discussion group devoted to this area of medicine.

**Usenet:**

**sci.med.occupational**

## Occupational Safety and Health Administration

The Occupational Safety and Health Administration (OSHA) is an agency of the United States Department of Labor. OSHA's purpose is to "save lives, prevent injuries and protect the health of America's workers". Here is the official OSHA web site, at which you will find general information about the agency and its programs and services. You can also read useful publications (such as factsheets about safety and health) and press releases, and access pertinent data and statistics.

**Web:**

**http://www.osha.gov/**

## Online Career Center

This web site is a commercial enterprise. However, the employers pay to advertise their jobs, but you can search the listings for free. Simply type a keyword that describes the job you want and browse through the results. This is an effective way to use the Net to quickly see if anything is available in your area.

**Web:**

**http://www.occ.com/**

## Repetitive Stress Injuries

A repetitive stress injury (RSI)—also called a cumulative trauma disorder—is a medical condition caused by chronic stress to one or more parts of the body. The most common causes of RSIs are: repetitive motion, working in an awkward position, using an unbalanced force, and not resting enough. In the workplace, the common RSIs are carpal tunnel syndrome (a wrist condition often caused by too much typing), chronic back pain, tendonitis and—everyone's favorite—"stress". Here are some web sites that have a wealth of information about RSIs, in and outside of the workplace. For discussion, you can read the Usenet groups. There is a lot you can do about workplace injuries caused by ongoing conditions, but before you can make a difference, you need to understand the real problems. The Net is a good place to start.

**Web:**

**http://ctdnews.com/site_index.html**
**http://www.engr.unl.edu/ee/eeshop/rsi.html**

**Usenet:**

**misc.health.injuries.rsi.misc**
**misc.health.injuries.rsi.moderated**

## Repetitive Stress Injuries

Every day, you do the same type of work—again and again and again.

Before you know it, something hurts. Don't worry about it, people tell you. It will go away.

But it doesn't.

Every day, you do the same type of work—again and again and again.

You hurt more, and it doesn't go away.

It's time to find out about repetitive stress injuries.

## Resumés

Here is a Usenet group to which you can post your resumé. My advice is, post to this group if you want, but don't stop there. There are various web sites to which you can also send a resumé. One thing that may help you is to look at other people's resumés. Reading what other people write can give you good ideas about how to present yourself in the best possible manner.

**Usenet:**

**misc.jobs.resumes**

## Riley Guide

The Riley Guide is a great resource for learning how to use the Internet to find a job. Explore a comprehensive collection of information and tips explaining how the Net can help you get what you want. The guide is also useful for employers who want to learn how to use the Net to fill job openings.

**Web:**

**http://www.jobtrak.com/jobguide**

## Scientific Research

Scientists are like Sherlock Holmes. They spend their days looking for clues, gathering information and putting it together to solve the mysteries of the universe. If you have a career in scientific research or if you want one, examine all the issues relating to the topic by checking out this Usenet group. Researchers discuss their current projects, funding and job opportunities, as well as posting requests for information.

**Usenet:**

**sci.research.careers**

## Sexual Harassment on the Job

If you have a problem with sexual harassment on the job, you are not alone. Before you get too upset, check with the Net where you will find lots of relevant information: a list of hotline telephone numbers you can call for help and advice, a guide on how to handle difficult situations, as well as lots of information, opinion and discussion on this complex and volatile topic.

**Web:**

**http://www.aracnet.com/~dawn/Psych/sexualhar.shtml**
**http://www.cs.utk.edu/~bartley/other/9to5.html**
**http://www.feminist.org/911/sex.html**

## Telecommuting

Telecommuting (or teleworking) refers to working at home as part of a regular job with an established company. Of course, some people have always worked at home, and home-based businesses are nothing new. What is new is that, with telecommuting, many people who traditionally would have worked in an office environment with lots of other people, are now working at home. As you might imagine, this creates a variety of problems as people need to readjust to the logistical and social consequences of being oneself. Here are some telecommuting resources that can help you. For discussion, you can participate in the Usenet group.

**Web:**

**http://grove.ufl.edu/~pflewis/commute.html**

**Usenet:**

**alt.support.telecommute**

## Women in Science and Engineering

Woman to woman, share your experiences, tips, and feelings about science and engineering, especially when it comes to jobs. For biologists, there is the **women-in-bio** group. For science and engineering in general, there is **wisenet** (the Women In Science and Engineering Network). Get it? W.I.S.E.NET... Oh, never mind. Silly acronyms are for men, anyway.

**Usenet:**

**bionet.women-in-bio**
**info.wisenet**

## Workplace Safety

Everyone agrees that workplaces should be safe. However, workplace safety depends on many different factors, some of which are difficult to control. This web site has an organized collection of links to many occupational and workplace safety resources around the Net: read about chemical safety, commercial resources, conferences, construction safety, electrical safety, fire safety, emergency management, ergonomics, and much, much more.

**Web:**

**http://turva.me.tut.fi/~oshweb/**

# JOURNALISM AND MEDIA

## Computer-Assisted Reporting and Research

How can you use computers to help you research and report the news? Here are some mailing lists devoted to that very subject. Subscribe to these lists and you will be able to hang out with working journalists, journalism teachers, news librarians, researchers, as well as various nattering nabobs of negativism. The **carr-l** list is for the discussion of general computer-assisted reporting and research. The **nicar-l** list is for the discussion of the activities of the National Institute for Computer-Assisted Reporting and for general computer-assisted reporting topics.

**Listproc Mailing List:**

List Name: **nicar-l**
Subscribe to: **listproc@lists.missouri.edu**

**Listserv Mailing List:**

List Name: **carr-l**
Subscribe to: **listserv@ulkyvm.louisville.edu**

### *Look What I Found on the Net...*

```
Newsgroup: info.wisenet
Subject: Why Men Are the Way They Are

Sports metaphors in the workplace bother me a lot.

Not long ago, a male friend of mine was telling me about his
high school football days, and how part of training involved
fighting on demand.  If the coach didn't like a player's
performance, he would pick another player and assign them to
fight.  Literally.  Just beat the crap out of each other until
someone couldn't fight anymore.  In most cases, the boys
involved were friends; certainly, they were teammates.

I listened and marveled at what VERY different youths we'd
experienced, and how very differently we might see the world,
or life, as a result...
```

## Email the Media

Do you like to sound off? Have you ever thought about writing a letter to the editor? If so, you'll love this site. First, choose a publication from among a large list of magazines, newspapers and periodicals. Next, use the handy web-based interface to create your own personal letter. Then, with a click of the mouse button, your letter will be emailed to the appropriate address. (And, since you are one of my readers, your letter will, no doubt, be published quickly, with the full respect it deserves.) In order to test the service, I sent a letter to Time magazine. The letter began as follows: "Dear Editor: I never thought I would be writing one of these letters to a magazine such as yours. I am, by trade, a writer and, to tell you the truth, I always believed that the first-hand personal accounts I read in your magazine were invented by your editors. However, the experience I had last week showed that such experiences can happen to people like me, and I felt that I just had to share the details with your readers. It all started when the young widow next door asked me if I would help her carry in her groceries. She was wearing a low-cut blouse, a tight, very short miniskirt, and black high-heeled pumps. As I deposited the groceries on the kitchen table, she asked if I would like to visit and have a drink while she changed into something more comfortable..." (So, anyway, that's the beginning of what I sent as a test of this web site. I don't have room for the whole thing here, so if you would like to find out how the story ends, you will have to find the back issue of Time magazine in which the letter was published.)

**Web:**

**http://www.searcher.com/media.html**

## Environmental Journalist's Resources

This site is put together by the Society for Environmental Journalism, an organization devoted to helping journalists better inform the public about environmental issues. Expect to find links to environmental resources, environmental journalism organizations and newsletters. If you write about the environment, this is a web site with which you should be familiar.

**Web:**

**http://www.sej.org/**

## Gonzo Journalism

In the tradition of Hunter S. Thompson, gonzo journalism is the method of reporting in which the journalist is a participant in the series of events or story being reported on. Follow the discussion about Thompson and the concepts of gonzo journalism.

**Usenet:**

**alt.journalism.gonzo**

**Bedtime for Gonzo**

Fear and Loathing on the Internet

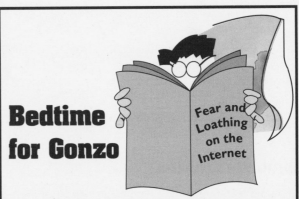

Is there anyone who has read "Fear and Loathing in Las Vegas" and not felt Hunter Thompson to possess that spark of outrageous genius which is all too rare? Too bad, then, that the spark fanned into a dull flame that attenuated and died years ago, regretted by all. In its place, we have the legacy of Gonzo journalism, a largely mythical school of creation in which the writer is immersed in the events about which he is reporting. Still, as you might guess from reading this book, I firmly believe that irreverence is as irreverence does and that the spirit of Gonzo lives. So, if you are one of the atavistic intellectual hold-outs from the '70s, take some time and visit your friends in **alt.journalism.gonzo**. And if you happen to be reading this in a bookstore, buy this book or I will be forced to rip your lungs out.

**Happiness is a warm modem.**

## Investigative Journalist Resources

The web page has a collection of resources and tips on how investigative journalists can use the Net in their work. Would you like to know all about their tricks? Learn how to find people on the Net, how to find an expert when you need one, how to hunt down facts, and how to find mailing lists and databases relevant to your research. If you happen to be an investigative reporter or editor, you can join the mailing list to participate in an ongoing discussion among the professionals.

**Web:**

**http://www.vir.com/~sher/julian.htm**

**Listproc Mailing List:**

List Name: **ire-l**
Subscribe to: **listproc@lists.missouri.edu**

## Journalism Criticism

The media is taking a lot of heat for its sensational tendencies. Take a close look at the criticism offered by the Usenet community about various journalists and the general media.

**Usenet:**

**alt.journalism.criticism**

## Journalism Mailing Lists

For long-term discussion, nothing on the Net works better than a mailing list. Here are several lists in which people discuss various aspects of journalism. The **spj-l** list is for a general discussion of journalism, **journet** is for journalism education, and **magazine** is for topics related to magazine publishing.

**Listserv Mailing List:**

List Name: **journet**
Subscribe to: **listserv@qucdn.queensu.ca**

**Listserv Mailing List:**

List Name: **magazine**
Subscribe to: **listserv@vm.its.rpi.edu**

**Listserv Mailing List:**

List Name: **spj-l**
Subscribe to: **listserv@psuvm.psu.edu**

## Journalism Resources

Journalists spend their time collecting and publishing information, so it makes a lot of sense that the Net would be a wonderful tool for a working reporter or researcher. Here are some collections, where you can find many, many resources. When you get a spare moment, I suggest that you explore, looking for those places that can help you. As you know, one of the most valuable possessions a journalist can have is a list of reliable sources. The time you spend creating such a list of Internet resources for yourself will be repaid many times over.

**Web:**

**http://www.it-kompetens.se/journ.html**
**http://www.online-journalist.com/**

## Journalism Student Resources

Are you young? Are you interested in journalism? Would you be willing to work long, impossible hours performing mundane tasks for little or no money? If you answered yes to all of these questions, you may be in line for a journalism internship. Well, here's a great place to find information about being an intern on a newspaper, magazine, television station or radio station. If you are a journalism student, you will find the Usenet group a useful discussion group.

**Web:**

**http://www.daily.umn.edu/~mckinney/**

**Usenet:**

**alt.journalism.students**

## Journalism Talk and General Discussion

Throughout the Net, journalists of varying size, shape and paycheck are discussing every aspect of journalism. Join the discussion. If you know what you are doing, contribute. If you don't know what you are doing, ask. If you don't know how to ask, just sit there and read what everyone else has to say (so you can report on it later).

**Usenet:**

**alt.journalism**
**alt.journalism.freelance**
**alt.journalism.moderated**
**alt.journalism.objective**
**alt.journalism.print**

## *Look What I Found on the Net...*

Newsgroup: alt.journalism
Subject: Tricks Journalists Use

> Are there any seasoned journalists or journalism students who
> can help me? I've been "enlisted" to take over a journalism
> course, but my background is in English, not journalism.
>
> I'd like to send the students out and have them dig deep into
> some campus issues... I'd like them to see that there are ways
> to trap an interviewee into answering something...

I think you are underestimating the amount of preparation and investigation that goes into an expose interview and overestimating the importance of questioning technique.

Let me give you one example from my personal experience. When Michael Jackson and Lisa Presley were allegedly married in May 1994, in the Dominican Republic, I knew in my gut it was a hoax.

I did a half-program broadcast on August 15. I said I only had questions about the holes in the story, but not the answers. It took another 16 months of painstaking investigation, before I was able to sit in front of the Justice of the Peace and ask him for an on-camera interview.

I did not tell him of the evidence we had. Nor did I lie. He was blinded by the belief that he had gotten away with the hoax and could safely talk about the subject.

Step by step, the on-camera interviewer fed him the story he had already told the world. Date, place, time. We showed him the official records he had signed, and he happily confirmed his pivotal role in performing and recording the ceremony.

Then we showed him the proofs that he and Michael Jackson and Lisa Presley and their "witnesses" were really somewhere else at those exact moments: solid documentary evidence, as well as highly credible eye-witnesses. All our questions were simple: "Please help us understand this apparent discrepancy..."

We had records that proved none of the "wedding party" ever went closer than four hundred kilometers to the place the wedding supposedly took place...

We were about to show him the [incriminating] photo when he attacked us and tried to wreck the camera and grab the cassette. His 300-pound assistant locked us in the office, and his secretary was screaming, "Give him the gun." It was only the fact that the producer and sound man were experts in Aikido that allowed us to literally punch our way out with the tape.

No trick questions in the world would have nailed this guy. It was the slogging and brilliant work of a hard-working producer -- following the trail I laid out for him -- that got the evidence.

## Media Watchdogs

Here are the web sites for two of the principle media watch organizations in the United States. One group is Accuracy in Media (AIM), a conservative media watch organization. The second group is Fairness and Accuracy in Reporting (FAIR), a liberal media watch organization. The goal of each group is the same: to monitor and criticize writers, broadcasters and commentators who expound viewpoints with which the group disagrees.

**Web:**
**http://www.aim.org/aim.html**
**http://www.igc.org/fair/**

## Music Journalism Talk and General Discussion

Forget the blood and gore. Don't bother with the evening news and prime time telling of current events. Go for the glitz and the glory by following the music scene. Not only will you be able to wear rad clothes, but you can talk to cool rock stars and actually get paid for it. When you are a rich and famous music journalist and hosting your own show on MTV, you can say you got your start on the Internet.

**Usenet:**
**alt.journalism.music**

## News Media

As Mark Twain once said, "Everybody does something about the news, but nobody talks about it." Here's your chance to prove him wrong. Join the discussion, and talk, talk, talk to your heart's content about those wonderful people and organizations that help us to tune in, turn off, and drop names.

**Usenet:**
**alt.news-media**

## Newslink

Newslink is a web site featuring many resources related to journalism and the news. Read about news sources, hot news sites, links to newspapers, magazines, radio and television stations, other journalism resources, and much, much more. There are also feature articles reprinted from the American Journalism Review.

**Web:**
**http://www.newslink.org/**

## Photojournalism

Every day, you see pictures in the newspaper, but for every picture you see, probably more than a hundred were taken and discarded. A photojournalist—someone who specializes in taking pictures for newspapers and magazines—has to be trained in photography and modern technology, and must conjure up immense amounts of patience and endurance to produce that one picture that may make it onto the page. The web site will lead you to a collection of photojournalism projects on the Net, as well as links to resources for photojournalism, regular journalism and photography. Even if you are not a photojournalist, you will find a great many interesting photos to enjoy. The Usenet group is for discussion of general issues about photojournalism and related topics.

**Web:**
**http://www.intac.com/~jdeck/index2.html**

**Usenet:**
**alt.journalism.photo**

## Press Photographers' Mailing List

A press pass is a license to barge in where you are not wanted. If you're lucky you can snap pictures of famous movie stars and world leaders. If not, you end up doomed to take pictures of the winners of the Blizzard County 94th Annual Chili Cook-Off. This mailing list is sponsored by the National Press Photographers Association and offers a forum in which photographers, photo and graphics editors, designers, educators and students can discuss this noble profession.

**Listserv Mailing List:**
List Name: **nppa-l**
Subscribe to: **listserv@cmuvm.csv.cmich.edu**

If you have an interest in pictures and journalism, you'll find the Press Photographers' mailing list interesting and useful.

After all, anyone can get the picture. But it takes someone real special to get paid for it.

**Stay connected.**

## Pulitzer Prize

The Hungarian-born American publisher Joseph Pulitzer (1847-1911) was not only a highly successful businessman, he was also a visionary. Before he died, Pulitzer endowed the Graduate School of Journalism at Columbia University, as well as an annual series of prizes (awarded by Columbia University) for achievements in American journalism, letters, drama and music. Over the years, the Pulitzer Prizes have become some of the most prestigious and certainly the most well-known awards for American writers. (I myself had to turn down several such awards, as I was too busy working on this book to attend the ceremony.) Here is the official site for the Pulitzer Prizes, where you can look at a list of current and previous winners, and a history of the prizes.

**Web:**
**http://www.pulitzer.org/**

## Radio and Television Companies

Here is a huge collection of links to the web sites of broadcasting companies around the Net. When you need to find a particular media company, radio station, television station or network, this is a good place to start.

**Web:**
**http://www.searcher.com/links.html**

## Reporter's Internet Survival Guide

Got a deadline? Need a quick source? Don't panic. Here's a hotlist to take reporters and journalists quickly to information sources and current news stories. When the people around you are letting you down, you can always find people on the Internet who know the real story.

**Web:**
**http://www.qns.com/~casey/**

## Reporters Network

The Reporters Network is an organization formed to promote the use of the Internet by working journalists. This web site contains a database of journalists who can register for free. If you are looking for a journalist, you can search by entering a location or a specialty. (I find this resource invaluable whenever I need to make out the guest list for a party.) If you are a working journalist, you can join the organization, which will provide you with Internet-related services, such as an email forwarding service and web space.

**Web:**
**http://www.reporters.net/**

## Television News Talk and General Discussion

Television news shows have only a short time each day to present the most recent current events. Moreover, each story cannot be more than a minute or two, and many stories last only seconds. This means that, every day, people at each news show have to decide what gets on the show and what is left out. This makes the actual choices very important, so it is no surprise that just about everyone has an opinion as to how good or bad a particular news show is at portraying the day's events. If you would like to discuss television news shows and related topics, there is a Usenet group devoted to this small, but important part of the popular culture.

**Usenet:**
**alt.tv.news-shows**

**Lost?**
**Try a search engine.**

# KEYS AND LOCKS

## Guide to Lock Picking

This page is Ted the Tool's Guide to Lock Picking. Start out by learning how a key opens a lock, and then build on your knowledge to learn about pin columns, scrubbing, and analytic thinking about lock-picking.

**Web:**
**http://www.lysator.liu.se/mit-guide/mit-guide.html**

## History of Locks

Take a historical tour of locks through the ages. There are lots of cool pictures of old locks and the different uses to which locks were put in ancient times. Read interesting factual tidbits such as Catherine the Great collected locks, and Marie Antoinette's husband—King what's-his-name XIV—was a locksmith. If you like locks, you will enjoy these brief, interesting historical articles.

**Web:**
**http://www.schlagelock.com/halllock.html**

## Impressioning

As we go through life, it is handy to be able to make a good impression. However, if you want to be a locksmith, "impressioning" will do more than earn you the kindness of strangers, it will win you the admiration of everyone in your social circle (especially if you hang around with teenage boys). Impressioning is a technique used to create a key to fit a lock without taking the lock apart. You insert a key blank of the correct type and size. Turn the key to bind the pins and then wiggle it. This will produce small but noticeable marks on the shaft of the key in those places where the pins bind. Withdraw the key and carefully file down the shaft where you see marks. Repeat this process until you have a key that raises each of the pins to the shear line, opening the lock, or until someone comes along to open the lock with a real key. Does this sound like a good way to spend your spare time? Then check out this web site where you will find a primer on the theory and practice of impressioning: a skill that every young person should master early in life.

**Web:**
**http://www.cs.swarthmore.edu/~weiler/locks/impressioning.html**

## Lock Picking for You

I bet you would just love to be able to get into places where you are not supposed to be. Of course, as one of my readers you are scrupulously honest with a well- developed sense of ethics. However, wouldn't if be fun to know how to pick locks, just in case you have to some day? (For example, what would happen if the Queen of England came to visit one day and accidentally locked herself in the pantry?) Enjoy this short guide to lock picking. With a little knowledge—and a lot of practice—you will soon be a useful, important member of society, respected by all and worshipped by every male teenager you meet.

**Web:**
**http://rtt.colorado.edu/~jnmiller/lock_pick.index.html**

## Lock Talk and General Discussion

Do you need the name of a book that will show you how to get into a locked, keyless automobile? How about a reference on safe-cracking? Or an electronic copy of The MIT Guide to Lockpicking, by Ted the Tool? Or are you an amateur locksmith with a picky problem? Check with the lock and key set for all your needs. Just don't tell anyone where you found out about it.

**Usenet:**
**alt.locksmithing**

## Locksmithing and Security Terminology

You can't tell the players without a program. If you want to understand keys and locks, you have to master the basic terminology. Here it is.

**Web:**
**http://www.locknet.com/terms.htm**

## Locksmithing FAQ

This is the FAQ (frequently asked question list) for the **alt.locksmithing** Usenet group. This FAQ has lots of information about locksmithing. In particular, there are answers to common questions about lockpicking. Read advice on picking various types of locks, buying or making lockpicking tools, duplicating keys that say "Do Not Duplicate", opening a Kryptonite-style lock, and so on. You can also find out where to learn about lock picking and locksmithing, learn useful terminology, see a short discourse on ethics, and much more.

**Web:**
**http://www.indra.com/archives/alt-locksmithing/**

## Look What I Found on the Net...

(from the Locksmithing frequently asked question list)

---

How can I make my own picks and tension wrenches?

You can file or grind picks out of spring steel. It is best to use spring steel -- sources include hacksaw blades, piano wire, clock springs... In a pinch, safety pin steel, or even a bobby pin can be used...

---

Where can I get the "MIT Guide to Picking Locks"?

Mattias Wingstedt has converted the Guide to HTML and made it available on the Web at:
http://www.lysator.liu.se/mit-guide/mit-guide.html

---

What are "pick guns" or "automatic pickers" and do they work?

A "pick gun" is a manual or powered device that uses a vibrating pin to try to bounce the pin tumblers so there are spaces at the shear line so the plug can rotate. They are not a panacea, aren't always effective, and the Net seems to feel that these are no substitute for a little skill with a pick and learning how locks work...

---

Can the Club be picked? Is the Club any good?

[Note: The "Club" is a widely advertised automobile anti-theft device that you use to lock the steering wheel when you leave your car.]

"I used to have a Club, purchased on the recommendation of a coworker. The first time I tried picking it, it took me approximately 30 seconds, using the cap of a Papermate Flexgrip pen for tension, and a bent jumbo paper clip to rake the pins. With practice, I was able to reliably pick every Club device I encountered in 5-30 seconds using these tools."

However, it doesn't really matter, no car thief is going to pick it, they are going to cut the soft plastic steering wheel with a hacksaw or bolt cutters and slip the Club off.

---

Here are some of the things collected about locations and availabilities (most are from alt.locksmithing). We do not endorse any of these, but feel that you can get information by reading.

*(continued on next page)*

*(continued from previous page)*

PADLOCK SHIM PICKS. Open padlocks in seconds! Our new padlock shim pick's unique design makes it so successful that it is frightening! Simply slide the shim down between the shackle and the lock housing, twist and the lock is open. Works best on laminated type padlocks (the most popular type) but will open almost any type of padlock -- including the popular 3 number combination type...

PICK GUN. Picks locks FAST. Open locks in less than 5 seconds. Specifically designed for tumbler locks. Insert pick into key slot, then just pull trigger. Throws all pins into position at one time. Lock is then turned with tension bar. Used extensively by police and other government agencies...

PRO-LOK "CAR KILLER" KIT. Over the years we have had thousands of requests for a multi-vehicle opening kit. We are now able to offer the most complete kit that we have ever seen. This kit of tools will open over 135 automobiles, both domestic and foreign, on the road today. The opening procedure for each vehicle is diagrammed and explained in the instruction manual...

TUBULAR LOCK PICK. This tool is an easy and reliable method for picking tubular locks, as found on commercial vending machines, washers, dryers, etc...

HOW TO GET IN ANYWHERE, ANYTIME (video tape). Nearly two full hours of on-site techniques to get in any building, beat any lock, open any safe, enter any car...

TECHNIQUES OF BURGLAR ALARM BYPASSING. Alarms covered include: Magnetic Switches, Window Foil, Sound and Heat Detectors, Photoelectric Devices, Guard Dogs, Central Station Systems, Closed-Circuit Television and more...

TECHNIQUES OF SAFECRACKING...

HIGH SPEED ENTRY: INSTANT OPENING TECHNIQUES (video tape)...

THE COMPLETE GUIDE TO LOCK PICKING by Eddie the Wire. The very best book ever written on how to pick locks...

CIA FIELD-EXPEDIENT KEY CASTING MANUAL. How to make a duplicate key when you can keep the original only a short time...

HOW I STEAL CARS: A REPO MAN'S GUIDE TO CAR THIEVES' SECRETS (video tape). How to open and enter practically any modern automobile and how to start them without the key...

---------------------------------------------------------

**Reach out and email someone.**

## Murphy's Laws of Locksmithing

You have probably heard of Murphy's Law: "Anything that can go wrong, will." Although locksmithing requires specialized skills and a great deal of practice, locksmiths are not immune to unintended mishaps and accidents. Here is a witty collection of aphorisms that express the spirit of Murphy's Law applied to locksmithing. For example: "Parts that are difficult to install will freely fall out on their own," and "The number of witnesses available is directly proportional to the skill you demonstrate." Actually, now that I think of it, these sayings also apply to writers. For instance, in my experience, it is very difficult to install new vowels into a paragraph, and yet, they are always the first letters to fall out of a book and onto the floor of the library.

**Web:**

**http://www.jfbdtp.com/Murphy.html**

## Picking Locks and Opening Safes

You can pick your friends, and (if you read the information at the site) you can learn how to pick locks. But here is something that can be even handier. Suppose the Pope comes over to your house and accidentally locks himself into a safe for which no one has the combination. (This actually happened to me once.) You will be glad that, at a moment's notice, you can connect to the Net and find out all kinds of useful ways to open a locked safe. Learn about using sound, drilling, punching, grinding and burning. Of course, this might take a while, so be sure to have some reading material in the safe for visitors. (In my case, it worked out okay, as the safe contained my entire collection of Superman and Donald Duck comics, most of which the Pope hadn't already read.)

**Web:**

**http://ginch.dial.umd.edu/users/gasman/text/misc/chem3.txt**

# KIDS

## 365 TV-Free Activities for Kids

The kids are getting bored. Do not turn on the television. Do not rent a video. Instead, connect to this wonderful children's web site that specializes in things that you can do with your kids. There are so many great activities. Spend the whole day with your children, playing, learning and having fun. (Then, when they fall asleep, you can watch TV.)

**Web:**

**http://family.starwave.com/funstuff/activity/tvtoc.html**

**Use the Net to help you create a TV-free zone in your house.**

## 4 Kids Treehouse

The 4 Kids Treehouse is a huge collection of children's resources from all over the Net. Pick a section that interests you and explore. You'll find all kinds of stuff such as cartoons, music, television, science, social studies, government, history, and online books.

**Web:**

**http://array.4kids.com/~4kids/**

**"Romance" is waiting for you.**

## Ant Fun

This site is all about ants. There are facts about ants (did you know there are over 10,000 species of ants?), ant quotes ("Ants do not bend their ways to empty barns, so no friend will visit the place of departed wealth"), puzzles and word games relating to ants, and jokes about ants ("What kind of ants have trunks?" Answer: eleph-ants). Basically, here is lots and lots of ant stuff for kids.

**Web:**

**http://www.timetrend.com/anthill/fun.htm**

## Astronomy Picture of the Day

Every day, there is a different astronomy picture placed on this web page. Along with the picture you will find description information as well as links to other related places. If you like astronomy, this is a great place to visit every day when you get home from school.

**Web:**

**http://antwrp.gsfc.nasa.gov/apod/astropix.html**

## Banyan Tree Friends

If you like poetry, try the Banyan Tree Friends web site. You'll find poetry written by schoolchildren around the Net. Browse by last name of author, school, grade or state, or you can do a quick click to see the last ten poems submitted. You can also submit your own poems if you want to share them with other kids. By the way, a banyan is a type of fig tree that grows in the tropics. Banyan trees have a great many aerial roots (roots that branch off the trunk and branches). The aerial roots develop into new tree trunks allowing the tree to grow and spread widely. Thus, the name "Banyan Tree Friends" refers to the hope that friendship and poetry will spread widely via the Net (and this web page).

**Web:**

**http://sashimi.wwa.com/~uschwarz/poetry/btf000.html**

## Bee-Eye

Did you ever wonder what the world looks like from a bee's point of view? Now you can know. Click on a shape or an image and see how it would look to a bee.

**Web:**

**http://cvs.anu.edu.au/andy/beye/beyehome.html**

## Best Sites for Children

Here is a supermarket of children's Internet sites. The list covers all the basics and is arranged by subject. Find links to animals, art, the environment, astronomy, history, fun, safety, stories and much more.

**Web:**

**http://www.cochran.com/theosite/ksites.html**

**Best Sites for Kids**

Of course, you want what's best for your kids.
Start them with the Best Sites for Kids.
In a few weeks, they'll be teaching you how to use the Net.

## Camp Internet

It may not always be summer, but on the Internet, you can always go to camp. Camp Internet is an online learning environment organized like a summer camp. Camp Internet is based in Southern California and has lots of free resources for kids and parents to visit. There are also a variety of activities that you can have fun with in your own home.

**Web:**

**http://www.rain.org/campinternet**

## Carlos's Coloring Book

I love this site. You can use your web browser to color pictures according to your own tastes. For example, I colored Santa Claus with a green mustache and a pink reindeer. This is a great place to play. And after you are finished coloring, you can save your work to a file on your own computer. (I saved my Santa, so I can have something to show important editors when they visit.)

**Web:**

**http://www.ravenna.com/coloring/**

## Children's Stuff

Here is a nice collection of Internet children's resources: stories, poems, pictures, magazines, movie clips, cartoons, museums and lots of other fun sites.

**Web:**

**http://www.comlab.ox.ac.uk/oucl/users/jonathan.bowen/children/**

## Contests for Kids

Enjoy this collection of links to contests that are related to or about kids. (I am thinking of having a Harley contest. Whoever can think of the best idea for a Harley contest gets a free, autographed book.) Lots of these contests are sponsored by commercial companies that are giving away free stuff in drawings or scavenger hunts for publicity. Still, fun is fun. Just remember, if you have to type in your name and address, you are going to end up on someone's mailing list.

**Web:**

**http://fly.hiwaay.net/~garson/sweep_kids.htm**

## Cyberkids Magazine

This is an online magazine made by kids for kids. Visit the reading room and the art gallery. Listen to music compositions by other children. Read messages from kids around the world. There is lots to do at this web site.

**Web:**

**http://www.cyberkids.com/**

## Demo of the Day

Here is a cool place to visit. Every day you will see a new demonstration that you can do for yourself to show you something interesting. (Well, something that an adult thinks is interesting.)

**Web:**

**http://nyelabs.kcts.org/demo/demo.html**

### Interesting Projects for Young Children

The Demo of the Day web site has ideas for interesting projects that you can do with your youngsters. Not only will your kids have fun and get to make a mess, but somebody (whose name I won't mention) might learn something interesting by accident.

## Dinosaurs

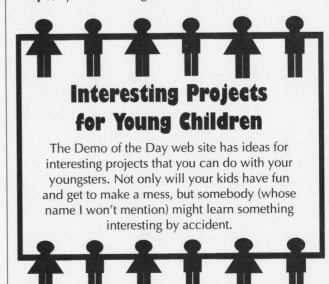

Do you like dinosaurs? Of course you do, everyone likes dinosaurs. Here is a web site that will show you lots of dinosaur stuff. Take a look at the dinosaur pictures and exhibits. Then take a tour and find out what the Earth was like before life existed.

**Web:**

**http://rs6000.bvis.uic.edu/museum/exhibits/Exhibits.html**

## Droodles

A droodle is a cross between a riddle and a doodle. Look at a picture and try to figure out the riddle within the image. Check out the droodle of the week, as well as an archive of past droodles. (In case you get stumped, the correct answers are available.) If you feel creative, you can contribute by sending in your own droodle.

**Web:**

**http://www.webonly.com/droodles/**

## Global Show-N-Tell

Show and Tell does not have to be limited to just your classroom. Take a look at this exhibition of artwork and home pages of children around the world. You will also find links to other children's projects and exhibitions, so you can do lots of exploring.

**Web:**
**http://www.manymedia.com/show-n-tell/**

## Her Online

This is an online zine specially designed for girls. There are interviews and reports on various inspiring girls around the world, such as a 13 year-old girl who raises guide dogs for the blind. Look for articles having to do with keeping fit and looking good, famous people (such as musicians and actors), fashion, sports, art, gardening, school, books, television and more.

**Web:**
**http://www.her-online.com/room.html**

## Heroes

We all need someone to inspire us. My heroes, for example, are Isaac Asimov, P.G. Wodehouse, Freddy the Pig, Carl Reiner and Perry Mason. Here is a web site that will let you find out about various types of heroes. There are buttons on the page you can press for the type of hero you want to read about: a teacher hero, an artist hero, a business hero, a writer hero, and so on. This is an interactive site, so you can tell the people who maintain the site about your favorite hero, and send in text and pictures and they might add them to the page. Or you can sign the hero guest book and write about your hero there for everyone else to see.

**Web:**
**http://myhero.com/**

**Spam is more than a food.**

Help your kids bring out
the best in themselves,
by helping them find
a real live hero to admire.

## iKids

This site has lots of really, really silly stuff. (You have to see it to believe it.) Here are some examples. Visit Camp Click-a-lot where you can see the fake stuff going on in camp and create a letter to mail home. Check out the Ask Ed column: wonderful explanations from a guy who knows what he is talking about. Read the Emoticomics: a comic strip that has various emoticons (smileys) talking to one another. Or visit Switcheroos where you can put various body parts together to make a monster. Bored? The Web time machine will take you back to various eras and show you what it is to be a scientist in 1634, a dictator in 47 B.C. or a pilot in 1935. This site is great: lots of original content along with some links to other fun stuff. I love it.

**Web:**
**http://www.iguide.com/kids/**

## KidPub

Are you a kid who likes to write stories? Here is the place for you. Send in your stories and they will be put on the Web, so anyone in the world can read them. You can then tell your friends to look on the Web for your story. Later you can check back, and see how many people have looked at your story since it was put on the Web. I like to check the site once in a while, just to find something interesting. Many of the stories are well-written and fun to read. Some of the stories are especially thought-provoking, and argue a high degree of natural talent.

**Web:**
**http://www.en-garde.com/kidpub/**

## Kid's Internet Delight

Kid's Internet Delight (KID) is a gathering of links to a great many Net resources that children might enjoy. Explore dinosaurs, sports, space, games, museums, animals, fossils, stories and much, much more.

**Web:**

**http://www.clark.net/pub/journalism/kid.html**

## Kids Space

The name tells it all: a place for kids (under 16) to hang around on the Net. Here you will find lots of activities just for kids: pictures, stories, movies, penpals, web pages by kids, and more. If you are new to the Net, there is a lot of help, specially designed just for kids. Finally, for teachers and parents, there are facilities for schools from all over the world to participate in the fun, as well as extra information to help you use the Net with your kid. If you have kids, if you teach kids, or if you are a kid, this is a place you will want to visit.

**Web:**

**http://plaza.interport.net/kids_space/**

## Kids Talk and General Discussion

Clubhouses and playhouses are always fun because they are great places to hang out and be yourself with no parents allowed. There is a place like that on Usenet, where you can talk about anything you want and it's just for you—so, parents, no peeking.

**Usenet:**

**alt.kids-talk**

**NO ADULTS ALLOWED!**

**Kids, would you like to talk to other kids around the world?**

**Join the discussion on the alt.kids-talk Usenet group.**

**It's for kids only. No parents, teachers or any other adults are allowed.**

## Kidstuff

This is a kids web site created by a large magazine publishing company. In spite of the commercial overtones, there are lots of interesting things here as well as a great deal of original content. For example, you can read special kids' editions of magazines (such as Sports Illustrated and Time). You can also visit Underwater World (lots of underwater and ocean things to read), and take a tour which will show you how cartoons and animation work. This is a good place to visit when you are bored.

**Web:**

**http://pathfinder.com/kids/**

## Knot Tying

Here are two great web sites that can teach you all about tying knots. You will find diagrams showing you exactly how to create some really cool-looking knots. Have you ever wondered, why are there so many different knots? It's because there are many different uses for knots. For example, the knot you would use to tie down a tent or a tarp would be different from the knot you use to tie a boat to the pier. Once you learn about different knots—and when to use each one—you will find your knowledge useful in many situations. As a matter of fact, after spending some time practicing your knots, I bet you will be walking around looking for something to tie up. In case you get serious about knots, I included a web site that contains links to many other related resources all over the Net.

**Web:**

**http://www.geocities.com/Yosemite/2158/**
**http://www.netg.se/~jan/knots.htm**

## Library for Kids

Kids, whip out those school reports with style. This online library helps you get fast information on art, drama, literature, chemistry, computers, space, biology, games, sports, history, math, geology, physics and other subjects.

**Web:**

**http://www.npac.syr.edu/textbook/kidsweb/**

## The Library for Kids (Sort Of)

When you're a kid, going to the library can be a lot of fun. You can hide in the back room with a friend and look at the "art" books. You can write secret messages on a piece of paper, and hide them in a book for someone to find later. Best of all, you can sit at a table with your friends and tell secrets about someone else, and laugh so much the librarian will have to keep coming over and warning you to be quiet.

"ART"
"ART"
"ART"

So what happens when a bunch of adults get government money and donations to create a kids' library? Just what you think: They create an online resource which is just how adults think a kid should do research.

So here is my advice. Use the **Library for Kids** for research (it does have a lot of useful stuff), and get your work done as fast as possible. Then go to the real library where you can have some fun. (When you go, be sure to take this book with you, so everyone will know how smart you are.)

## Lite-Brite

Have fun making pictures with this online Lite-Brite. Select colors and make a design to submit, or you can just view the gallery of pictures made by past visitors.

**Web:**

**http://asylum.cid.com/lb/lb.html**

## National Wildlife Federation Kids Stuff

This site is put together by the National Wildlife Foundation. There are games, riddles and facts about animals. For example, honey bees make a total of 10 million trips between their hives and flowers for each pound of honey they make. (And you only have to make one trip to the supermarket to buy all the honey you want.) Take an educational (but fun) tour of water, wetlands, endangered species and U.S. public lands, and visit other fun science sites.

**Web:**

**http://www.nwf.org/kids/**

## Neat Science Demonstrations

Here is a nice collection of science demonstrations you can do at home by yourself or at school (with a teacher around to make sure you don't have more fun than is absolutely necessary).

**Web:**

**http://sln.fi.edu/tfi/activity/act-summ.html**

## Paper Airplanes

Paper airplanes are so cool. They are fun to make, the materials cost next to nothing, you can throw them at other people, and if they blow up in mid-air the government doesn't force you to hold an expensive investigation. Each month, this web site offers a different paper airplane that you can make for yourself. There are diagrams showing how to fold the paper as well as a picture of what the airplane should look like when it is completed. (Hint: When you are finished and the airplane is ready, see if you can talk your little sister into being a flight attendant. Tell her she gets to watch you fly the plane, and she has to make you a sandwich whenever you want.)

**Web:**

**http://pchelp.inc.net/paper_ac.htm**

## Papermaking

Have you ever made your own paper? Here are instructions to show you how to take old newspapers and recycle them into brand new paper. The instructions start out: "Making recycled paper is messy." I'm convinced. I would walk a mile out of my way to do something messy.

**Web:**

**http://www.edu.cuhk.hk/~johnson/extra/paper.html**
**http://www.nbn.com/youcan/paper/paper.html**

**The Net is waiting for you.**

A B C D E F G H I J K L M N O P Q R S T U V W X Y Z

**Papermaking**

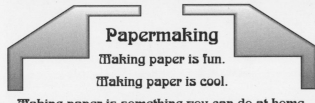

Making paper is fun.
Making paper is cool.
Making paper is something you can do at home.
So go make some paper.
(And then use it to write a note to someone you love.)

## Preschool Pages

Here are some web sites designed especially for preschoolers, with colorful pictures and simple writing. One web site has pictures of various animals with some writing about each animal, as well as stories. The other site is for parents and teachers of preschoolers. You will find seasonal activities, craft ideas, preschool projects, printable pages of worksheets, music activities, kids cooking activities, and more.

**Web:**

**http://www.ames.net/preschool_page/**
**http://www.intex.net/~dlester/pam/preschool/preschoolpage.html**

## Stories by Kids

Read stories that are written and illustrated by children. These stories are good for young readers and are written about exciting and adventurous subject matter.

**Web:**

**http://www2.northstar.k12.ak.us/schools/upk/books/books.html**

**Check out a free online book.**

**Get in step by reading "Dance".**

## String Figures

String figures—such as those created when you play the traditional Cat's Cradle game—are patterns made from a loop of string which you wind around your fingers. You can make such figures by yourself or with another person (by passing the loops back and forth). Most of the time you only need your fingers, but sometimes, with more complicated patterns, you also have to use your feet or mouth. One of these sites is the home of the International String Figure Association. Visit it and learn about the background of string figure games. In addition, I have included some web sites that have lists of string figures, along with diagrams and step-by-step instructions for making the patterns.

**Web:**

**http://www.ece.ucdavis.edu/~darsie/string.html**
**http://www.isfa.org/~webweavers/isfa.htm**
**http://www.zia.com/hac/String/**

## Sugar Bush

Sugar Bush has stories by kids that are displayed in large type to make them easy to read. Many of the stories have links in them that give you interesting information about characters in the story. There is also a collection of craft projects, as well as a treasure hunt section where you have to find the answers to questions by looking at other web pages. This is a good place for youngsters to get started on the Net.

**Web:**

**http://intranet.ca/~dlemire/sb_kids.html**

## Uncle Bob's Kids' Page

Uncle Bob has a handle on where the cool kid stuff is on the Internet. This kids' page has links to stuff that's fun, educational, cultural and informative.

**Web:**

**http://gagme.wwa.com/~boba/kids.html**

## Wendy's World of Stories for Children

This wonderful, charming site—created by a wonderful, charming woman—has a collection of stories for children: poetry, myths, fairy tales, fables, campfire stories, and original stories and poems. Some of the stories are illustrated; all are great for younger kids or for anyone who enjoys children's stories. Parents: This is a great site to visit with your kids. Help them learn how to read by exploring Wendy's World of Stories together.

**Web:**

**http://www.wendy.com/children/stories.html**

Wendy's World of Stories for Children

Reading and listening to stories is an important part of our culture. So take your kids to Wendy's World of Stories for Children, where they will learn and enjoy themselves at the same time.

It's a win-win-win-win activity.

(Your kids win, because they will have a great time while they are practicing their reading or listening to a story. You win, because you will enjoy spending pleasant hours reading with your children. Wendy wins, because she is able to help children and parents around the world enjoy stories. And I win, because after you all have such a good time, you are bound to want to rush out and buy lots of copies of this book for your friends.)

**"Animals and Pets" are people too.**

**Express yourself. Make a web page.**

## White House Tour for Kids

Would you like to take a kids tour of the White House? Learn about this famous building (the home of the U.S. President and his family). Read about its history, the President, children of various Presidents, White House pets, and so on. You can also send a letter to the President and tell him your ideas. Note: Enjoy yourself writing the President if you want, but please understand that nobody really reads the letters. In fact, nobody even reads the letters that are sent to the President's regular email address. (Actually, I think you would be better off writing a letter to Santa Claus and leaving it where your parents can see it accidentally.)

**Web:**

**http://www.whitehouse.gov/WH/kids/html/**

## Wild Weather

This page is created by a TV weatherman in order to explain weather to kids. The topics include clouds, temperature, pressure, radar, tornadoes, hurricanes, lightning and forecasting. Have you got a weather question? Send a note to the weatherman. In addition, the are resources for teachers who want to teach their kids about weather.

**Web:**

**http://www.whnt19.com/kidwx/**

## Yucky Stuff

This is called "The Yuckiest Site on the Internet". (To tell you the truth, I know of other, more yucky sites, but I can't mention them in a family book.) Actually, the material here is only yucky if you don't like bugs. If you do, come right in and visit Worm World and Cockroach World. I bet you'll learn something interesting.

**Web:**

**http://www.nj.com/yucky/**

# LANGUAGE

## Acronyms

Here is a resource that should be in everyone's bookmark list. You specify an acronym, and a program looks it up in the master list and tells you what the acronym means. You can also search the list of meanings for a particular word or expression. If you have a friend who thinks he knows everything, ask him what MOTSTJHTBHWIGH means.

**Web:**

**http://www.ucc.ie/info/net/acronyms/**

## Alternative Dictionaries

Here are words you will never see in a regular dictionary: slang that is used around the world. This web site is the home of a collaborative project to compile slang words and expressions from every country and culture on the Net. For example, suppose you are in Quebec and someone says to you "Accouche qu'on baptise". Or let's say you are on the east coast of Scotland and a fellow comes up to you and asks if you are a Weedjie. Whatever are they talking about? The list of languages is huge, and the coordinator welcomes anyone around the world who would like to add to the collection of words. Hint: If you find yourself working too hard, remind yourself (as they say in Holland) not to buffelen, or you may become besodemieterd zijn.

**Web:**

**http://www.notam.uio.no/~hcholm/altlang/**

**Alternative Dictionaries**

When you study a language in school, you learn how to speak "properly".

However, when you visit a foreign country, you find there are a lot of common words you are never taught in school.

School is fine, but to prepare yourself for life in the street, you need the Alternative Dictionaries.

## American Sign Language

When I was younger and living in Berkeley, I studied ASL (American Sign Language) for a semester, and I found it to be the most beautiful language I have ever seen. If I could pick a second language in which to be fluent, it would be ASL. (Unfortunately, I am not one to pick up second languages. For over 10 years, the Canadian government tried to get me to learn French, and they failed miserably.)

**Web:**

**http://home.earthlink.net/~masterstek/ASLDict.html**
**http://www.gbdi.com/asl/links.html**
**http://www.vuw.ac.nz/~nzsldict/**

**Listserv Mailing List:**

List Name: **slling-l**
Subscribe to: **listserv@yalevm.ycc.yale.edu**

## Arabic

If Arabic is on your list of things to learn before retirement, you are in luck. Download audio lessons, films, music and pictures. Or if you don't have time for a multimedia experience, check out some vocabulary and nifty-looking Arabic fonts.

**Web:**

**http://babel.uoregon.edu/Yamada/fonts/arabic.html**
**http://fas-www.harvard.edu/~munson/arabic2.html**
**http://philae.sas.upenn.edu/Arabic/arabic.html**

## British-American Lexicons

Although it seems as if the English and the Americans speak the same language, there are a lot of words that are used differently in each country. For example, an Englishman who has had a little too much to drink may think nothing of eating a chip butty. An American wouldn't know a chip butty if it bit him in the face. To help you avoid unnecessary confusion—or, perhaps, create some intentional confusion of your own—here is a list of British-American lexicons to fill the transatlantic gaps in your vocabulary.

**Web:**

**http://pages.prodigy.com/NY/NYC/britspk/dictlink.html**

A B C D E F G H I J K L M N O P Q R S T U V W X Y Z

## Chinese

Here is a large list of resources relating to the Chinese language, including information about how to view and listen to Chinese on the Net.

**Web:**
**http://www.webcom.com/bamboo/chinese/**

## Colibri

Colibri is an electronic newsletter, produced at Utrecht University in the Netherlands, for people interested in the fields of natural language processing, speech processing and logic. Colibri publishes short announcements about upcoming events, jobs and other notes of interest. The web site also contains links to resources related to these areas of study, as well as information about conferences, organizations, software, dictionaries, research, and so on.

**Web:**
**http://colibri.let.ruu.nl**

## Computation and Language E-Print Archive

This is a fully automated electronic archive and distribution server for papers on computational linguistics, natural language processing, speech processing, and related fields.

**Web:**
**http://xxx.lanl.gov/cmp-lg/**

## Cyrillic Alphabet

The Cyrillic alphabet is used to write Russian and certain other Slavic languages. The name comes from St. Cyril who—along with his brother St. Methodius—was said to have introduced this alphabet in their missionary work among the southern Slavs. Here is a great resource that can help you learn to read the Cyrillic alphabet, as well as understand something of its role in history and culture.

**Web:**
**http://solar.rtd.utk.edu/friends/cyrillic/cyrillic.html**

### *Look What I Found on the Net...*

(from a paper in the Computation and Language E-Print Archive)

This paper discusses the processes by which conversants in a dialogue can infer whether their assertions and proposals have been accepted or rejected by their conversational partners.

It expands on previous work by showing that logical consistency is a necessary indicator of acceptance, but that it is not sufficient, and that logical inconsistency is sufficient as an indicator of rejection, but it is not necessary.

I show how conversants can use information structure and prosody, as well as logical reasoning, in distinguishing between acceptances and logically consistent rejections, and relate this work to previous work on implicature and default reasoning by introducing three new classes of rejection:

-- implicature rejections
-- epistemic rejections
-- deliberation rejections

I show how these rejections are inferred as a result of default inferences, which, by other analyses, would have been blocked by the context...

## Czech

Here is information about the Czech language (spoken in the Czech Republic) as well as an English-Czech dictionary. Mluvite anglicky? Dekuji.

**Web:**

**http://ww2.fce.vutbr.cz/bin/ecd**
**http://www.muselik.com/czech/czau.html**

## Dutch

Slip off your wooden shoes and cozy up to the keyboard for some discussion of Dutch language and literature. The Usenet group is moderated; the IRC channel isn't. The web site has a short course in Dutch which covers pronunciation and grammar.

**Web:**

**http://www.gospelcom.net/dutchcourse.html**

**Usenet:**

**bit.lang.neder-l**

**IRC:**

**#dutch**

## Eastern European Languages

Would you like to learn basic words and phrases in an Eastern European language? Just select a language and you will be shown a small but useful list of the words in that language. Although the vocabulary is limited, you can at least learn enough to stay out of trouble. The word lists are available in Albanian, Croatian, Estonian, Latvian, Polish, Russian, Slovak, Bulgarian, Czech, Hungarian, Lithuanian, Romanian, Serbian and Slovenian. As they say in Lithuanian, "Nesuprantu".

**Web:**

**http://www.cusd.claremont.edu/~tkroll/EastEur/**

## English

The sun may have set on the British Empire, but their language lives on around the world. Here are a variety of interesting resources relating to the English language. To discuss English, try Usenet and the mailing lists. Interesting true fact: More Harley Hahn books are written in English than in any other language.

**Web:**

**http://ebbs.english.vt.edu/hel/hel.html**
**http://gs213.sp.cs.cmu.edu/prog/webster**
**http://www.comenius.com/**

**Usenet:**

**bit.listserv.words-l**

**Listproc Mailing List:**

List Name: **hel-l**
Subscribe to: **listproc@ebbs.english.vt.edu**

**Listserv Mailing List:**

List Name: **words-l**
Subscribe to: **listserv@uga.cc.uga.edu**

## English and Modern Language Graduate Students

Next to the language of love, English and the modern languages are the most handy languages to know. On this mailing list, graduate students exchange academic and professional information about English and the modern languages.

**Listproc Mailing List:**

List Name: **e-grad**
Subscribe to: **listproc@listproc.bgsu.edu**

### *Look What I Found on the Net...*

```
Newsgroup: bit.listserv.words-l
Subject: Linguistic Terminology

> "Rhetorical device", "linguistic phenomenon", what's the deal
> with sullying the name of linguistics this way?  I guess it's
> called metonymy.  Of course, for you guys everything is
> metaphor, right?

A man's reach should exceed his grasp, or what's a meta phor?
```

## Esperanto

Esperanto is a language invented by the Polish doctor L.L. Zamenhof in the late 19th century. His idea was that if everyone spoke the same language, we would all get along better, and war would be much less likely. The idea of an artificial language is not uncommon: hundreds of such languages have been proposed in the last few centuries. Perhaps one of the most interesting was Solresol, developed by Jean Francois Sudre (1866). Its vocabulary was based on the notes of the musical scale, making it possible to sing as well as speak the language. Esperanto is the most well-known and successful artificial language. Because it is based on the European Romance languages, Esperanto is difficult to learn for people with a completely different mother tongue (Chinese, Japanese, Russian, and so on). However, as languages go, Esperanto is straightforward and sensible, and there are many enthusiasts around the world who enjoy speaking and promoting the language.

**Web:**

**http://www.webcom.com/~donh/esperanto.html**
**http://wwwtios.cs.utwente.nl/esperanto/hypercourse/**

**Usenet:**

**alt.uu.lang.esperanto.misc**
**soc.culture.esperanto**

**Listserv Mailing List:**

List Name: **esper-l**
Subscribe to: **listserv@vm3090.ege.edu.tr**

**IRC:**

**#Esperanto**

## Foreign Language Dictionaries

Dictionaries to translate words from one language to another. For example, if you speak English, there are dictionaries to translate words to and from Spanish, French, Russian, Swedish, Chinese, Japanese and many more.

**Web:**

**http://math-www.uni-paderborn.de/HTML/Dictionaries.html**

## Foreign Languages for Travelers

Are you going to visit a foreign country where it would help if you knew some of the most important words in their language? Just specify which language you already speak and which language you want to learn. You will then see a list of choices for phrases you can learn: basic words, numbers, shopping, travel, directions, places, times and dates. You can see a list of countries where the foreign language is spoken as well as links to related resources. There are over 20 languages here. One of them is bound to interest you.

**Web:**

**http://www.travlang.com/languages/**

## French

French is a member of the family of Romance languages, and thus has much in common with Spanish, Italian, Portuguese and other such languages. However, French has a distinct personality, a certain *je ne sais quoi* that makes it unlike any other language. French is the 11th most widely used language in the world. Of course, French is spoken throughout France, but you also find the language in parts of Belgium and Switzerland, as well as in areas that were formerly under French control, such as Algeria and French Polynesia (including Tahiti). There is also a form of French spoken in the province of Quebec in Canada, as well as a creole version used by Cajun speakers in the south-central United States. There are many reasons why you might want to learn French. (What I like best is being able to read the menus in snooty restaurants.) The web sites I have chosen will help you find a large variety of French-related resources. The mailing lists are for ongoing discussion.

**Web:**

**http://etext.lib.virginia.edu/french.html**
**http://hapax.be.sbc.edu/**
**http://library.adelaide.edu.au/guide/hum/french/**
**http://web.culture.fr/**

**Listproc Mailing List:**

List Name: **francais**
Subscribe to: **listproc@gac.edu**

**Listproc Mailing List:**

List Name: **frenchtalk**
Subscribe to: **listproc@listproc.net**

You know, it's funny. As a young lad in Canada, I studied French for 10 years, and I still can't speak it fluently. And yet, in France, young children hang around in the street with no education whatsoever speaking the language like natives. Perhaps they have access to the **Foreign Language Dictionaries**.

## Gaelic

Gaelic is the English word used to describe Irish Gaelic, Manx Gaelic, and Scottish Gaelic, the three languages that form one half of the Celtic language family group. These sites offer examples of spoken Gaelic, a short history of the Celts, mailing list archives, lists of Gaelic books and tapes, Irish National Radio news, and links to many other Celtic-related topics and resources. The mailing list will allow you to experience Gaelic interactively.

**Web:**

**http://futon.sfsu.edu/~jtm/Gaelic/**
**http://sunsite.unc.edu/gaelic/gaelic.html**

**Listserv Mailing List:**

List Name: **gaelic-l**
Subscribe to: **listserv@irlearn.ucd.ie**

## German

Sprechen Sie Deutsch? Brush up on your German by asking questions, reading posts and practicing in this Usenet group. Discussion is held in both English and German. If you're up to a real-time test, try your skill on the IRC channels. For reference, you can find German/English dictionaries on the Web.

**Web:**

**http://www.leo.org/cgi-bin/dict-search**
**http://www.lib.ua.edu/dict6.htm**

**Usenet:**

**alt.usage.german**

**IRC:**

**#german**
**#germany**

## Hawaiian

The Hawaiian language only has five vowels and twelve consonants, out of which twelve letters (a, h, i, k, l, m, n, o, p, t, u, and w) are represented here. By choosing a specific letter, you can see a selection of Hawaiian words beginning with that letter and their English translation.

**Web:**

**http://bookweb.cwis.uci.edu:8042/Books/Moon/glossary.html**

Maui

Going to Maui soon? Perhaps a copy of the Hawaiian dictionary would help you. It really helps to be able to talk to the natives in their own language when you need to say, "Can I please have a condo that does not overlook the parking lot?"

## Hindi

In India, Hindi is spoken by about 480 million people (180 million as a mother tongue, 300 million as a second language). Hindi is an especially expressive language. A poet writing in Hindi can use simple words to convey sophisticated emotional overtones. There are also many beautiful Hindi songs which are loved by people around the world. (In English, of course, we have our own lovely songs, such as "Satisfaction" and "Rudolf the Red-Nosed Reindeer".) Here are some Internet resources to help you learn about Hindi and the cultures in which it is spoken.

**Web:**

**http://philae.sas.upenn.edu/Hindi/hindi.html**
**http://www.cs.colostate.edu/~malaiya/hindiint.html**

## Icelandic

Icelandic—the official language of Iceland—is a Scandinavian language that is the purest descendent of Old Norse. Here are some Internet resources for learning about the language and the country in which it is spoken. To practice, use IRC. Hint to guys: If you are traveling in Iceland, and you meet a beautiful, young woman, here is the right thing to say: " Þú ert engill af himni ofan. Ég hef aldrei seð yndislegri konu. Getur pabbi þinn lúbarið mig?"

**Web:**

**http://islandia.nomius.com/people/language.html**

**IRC:**

**#iceland**

## Italian

Is there anything more beautiful than listening to someone in love speak Italian? Actually, even when Italians are arguing they sound kind of cool. If you are learning to speak and read Italian, here are some resources that can help. To help you learn how to read Italian, I have included a web site with selections from Italian literature.

**Web:**

**http://www.eat.com/learn-italian/**
**http://www.willamette.edu/~tjones/languages/Italian/Italian-lesson.html**

**IRC:**

**#italia**

## Japanese

Is your kanji a bit weak? Or do you just need a bit of help with pronunciation? These resources will help you with Japanese vocabulary and pronunciation. So the next time you go out for sushi, you won't have to just point at the menu and say, "I'll have that thing." You can ask for raw tuna with such a good accent, the fish will sit up and bow to you.

**Web:**

**http://www.missouri.edu/~c563382/**
**http://www.ntt.jp/japan/japanese/**

**Usenet:**

**sci.lang.japan**

## Language IRC Channels

Here are a few IRC channels where you can meet new friends and talk in different languages. Whether you are a native speaker or a student of a second language, IRC is the place to be.

**IRC:**

**#espanol**
**#francais**
**#france**
**#italia**
**#russian**
**#turks**

## Languages of the World

Here are some collections of information about the various languages spoken by humans and other animals. If you are interested in any particular language or country, I guarantee you can find information that will astonish you. For example, did you know that in the United States, there are 191 languages, 164 of which are living, 26 of which are extinct, and one that is a second language only with no mother tongue speakers?

**Web:**

**http://www.sil.org/ethnologue/ethnologue.html**
**http://www.willamette.edu/~tjones/Language-Page.html**

## Latin

Latin is the language spoken by the ancient Romans (although the Latin we learn today has been modified throughout the years). Latin is important for three main reasons. First, many ancient documents and books are written in Latin. Second, Latin is the basis of our modern Romance languages (such as French, Spanish, Italian and Portuguese). Finally, Latin is important to the traditions and liturgy of the Roman Catholic Church. Here are some Latin resources that will help you learn and appreciate the language.

**Web:**

**http://ccat.sas.upenn.edu/jod/AG/allgre.contents.html**
**http://pw2.netcom.com/~nemesise/latin.html**
**http://www.compassnet.com/mrex/index2.htm**
**http://www.nd.edu/~archives/latgramm.htm**

**Talk, talk, talk.**
**In any language.**
**At any time.**
**Now.**
**On IRC.**
**Be there or be square (in several languages at the same time).**

## Linguistic Talk and General Discussion

You won't find any puns, anagrams or palindromes here: the Usenet group is where scholars of linguistics hang out to discuss the scientific and historical study of human language. Get in on some hot and heavy discussion of Latin declensions or a quick and dirty comparison of Frisian to Old English. To help you participate in the discussion, I have included a web site that contains the FAQ (frequently asked question list) for the Usenet group, as well as another site that contains information about the many linguistic mailing lists on the Net.

**Web:**

**http://www.ling.rochester.edu/lists.html**
**http://www.tezcat.com/~markrose/langfaq.html**

**Usenet:**

**sci.lang**

## Linguistics

Linguistics is the study of human speech. Linguistics concerns itself with various areas: the structure of languages, the history of languages, how languages relate to one another, and the purpose of language within a culture. To understand the structure of languages, study grammar (rules describing how words and their components are combined), phonetics (how sounds are produced, combined and represented) and morphology (the structure and form of words). These web sites will help you find a large variety of linguistic resources on the Net.

**Web:**

**http://www.emich.edu/~linguist/**
**http://www.emich.edu/~linguist/datasources.html**
**http://www.ling.rochester.edu/linglinks.html**

## Lojban

Lojban is an artificial language based on logic, and designed to be used for clear communication (especially with computers). Lojban is unambiguous, genderless, and easy to learn. Here is a place on the Net to find lots of information about what I can only describe as a very strange language (mostly because humans are anything but clear, logical and unambiguous). What does Lojban look like? Here is an example: ".i mi pacna lenu lemi vo panzi baco'a xabju lo jecta noi ra sepajni ji'u le skari be lera skapi be'o na.e le selkai be leranuntarti" ("I have a dream that my four little children will one day live in a nation where they will not be judged by the color of their skin but by their character.")

**Web:**

**http://xiron.pc.helsinki.fi/lojban/**

## Middle English

After the Norman Conquest (in 1066), the use of Anglo-Saxon—the native language of England—was diminished significantly in favor of French, which became not only the official language, but the language of polite society. Anglo-Saxon was depressed into an illiterate dialect which underwent rapid and radical changes, emerging in a new form that we now call Middle English. The period of Middle English lasted from 1100 to 1500 (give or take a day or two). If you are interested in Middle English, here is a resource from which you look at a nice collection of literature. My favorite work is "The Harley Lyrics", transcribed from Manuscript Harley 2253 from the British Museum MS. Here is a direct quote: "Middelerd for mon wes mad / vnmihti aren is meste mede".

**Web:**

**http://etext.lib.virginia.edu/mideng.browse.html**

**Stop working: it's time to cruise.**

## Pronunciation in the American South

Unless you grew up in the United States, don't even think about trying to understand this web site. It's full of a great many colloquial pronunciations common in the southern part of the United States. The words are there somewhere, but unless you are from the South (or have watched a great many Andy Griffith reruns), you may not get it. For example, to truly appreciate modern American culture, you need to be able to understand statements like: "Lawd willing and the crik don't rise, I sho do hope that thuh President don't get us kilt by sum farn gummit. He's a nice enough feller, but he can lilac a dawg."

**Web:**

**http://ua1vm.ua.edu/~crispen/word.html**

## Roget's Thesaurus

In 1852, Peter Mark Roget published the first edition of his "Thesaurus of English Words and Phrases", on which he had been working for 50 years. Throughout successive editions—which were supervised by Roget, his son, and later his grandson—what we now call the Roget's Thesaurus has become a standard reference work of the English language. The purpose of the Roget's Thesaurus is simply stated: you use it when you know the meaning of a word but do now know the word. Roget arranged all the words in the English language and their idiomatic combinations, not in alphabetical order as in a dictionary, but according to the ideas they express. If you care at all about writing, please take some time to become familiar with this classic reference and how to use it. Treating a Roget's Thesaurus as if it were nothing more than a dictionary of synonyms is like using a collection of Mozart CDs as a paperweight.

**Web:**

**http://humanities.uchicago.edu/forms_unrest/ROGET.html**

### Roget's Thesaurus

Do you need a word? A specific word with a particular **shade** of meaning?
Use the online Roget's Thesaurus, and you'll have the exact word you need promptly, immediately, quickly, soon, before long, shortly, instantly, forthwith, summarily, immediately, briefly, speedily, directly, before the ink is dry, in no long time, and before you can say "Jack Robinson".

## Russian

Here is a collection of resources for students and aficionados of the Russian language and Russian literature. If you want to talk, there are people waiting on IRC. To help you translate words, I have included a web site that provides an online English-Russian dictionary.

**Web:**

**http://www.elvis.msk.su/cgi-bin/mtrans**
**http://www.pitt.edu/~cjp/rslang.html**

**IRC:**

**#russian**

## Serbian

It has been said that Serbian is one of the easiest languages to learn to write because it is so phonetic. See if this is true, by brushing up on your Serbian as well as the Cyrillic and Latin alphabets.

**Web:**

**http://www.umiacs.umd.edu/research/lpv/YU/HTML/jezik.html**

## Slovak

As early as the 11th century, Slovakia was associated with Hungary. Following World War I, the Slovaks separated from Hungary and joined the Czechs (from Bohemia) to form Czechoslovakia. From 1939 to 1945—thanks to the invading Germans—the Slovaks and Czechs were "declared" independent of one another. After the war, they rejoined to reform Czechoslovakia. Finally, however, on January 1, 1993, the Slovaks separated for the last time and formed their own country, Slovakia. Throughout it all, they managed to create and maintain their own language, Slovak, which is now the official language of their country. If you plan to visit, here is a nice glossary of Slovakian words to make your trip a pleasant one.

**Web:**

**http://www.eunet.sk/slovakia/.dict/tourdict.html**

## Spanish

Learn basic words, numbers and pronunciation in Spanish. The Waterloo web site will even conjugate Spanish verbs for you. (Boy, I could have used this when I was in high school.)

**Web:**

**http://csgwww.uwaterloo.ca/~dmg/lando/verbos/con-jugador.html**
**http://www.willamette.edu/~tjones/Spanish/lesson1.html**

## Word Detective

Enjoy the online version of a column in which the writer answers about words and their origins. If you enjoy learning about language and words, you will like this site. Here are some examples. (1) One guy wrote a letter because he and his girlfriend had been having an argument about whether to say "have your cake and eat it too" or "eat your cake and have it too". (2) Another person asked if "busting someone's chop" and "busting someone's hump" is the same thing. (3) A third reader who mentioned the term "old fogey" wanted to know if there were such a thing as a "young fogey". (4) And finally, there is a link to an answer to the question "Aside from 'angry' and 'hungry', what well-known English word ends in 'gry'?" By the way, the answers to these questions are (1) It doesn't matter. (2) No. (3) Yes, but people don't use the expression. (4) There are no other common words that end in "gry". The whole thing is a hoax.

**Web:**

**http://www.users.interport.net/~words1/**

**Usenet:**

**alt.fan.word-detective**

## Word-a-Day

If someone calls you a "wowser" and you don't know whether to feel congratulated or insulted, then you might need to improve your vocabulary by checking out these word-a-day sites. Impress your friends and co-workers. Don't be caught verbally unaware.

**Web:**

**http://www.randomhouse.com/jesse/**
**http://www.wordsmith.org/awad/**

# Word–a–Day

**We all know that having a big vocabulary is essential if you want to know a lot of words. Still, there is no royal road to knowledge, and if you want to know a lot of words you are just going to have to know a lot of words. The easy way is to subscribe to the Word-a-Day mailing list and soon, you too, will be able to tergiversate with the best of them.**

es·ta·mi·net
con·duc·to·met·ric
con·es·to·ga
apo·neu·ro·sis

## Wordbot

Wordbot is a robot assistant that reads a web page full of text and inserts links to every word that can be defined in a particular online dictionary. Once the page has been processed, a definition is only a mouse click away. If you see a word you do not understand, click on the symbol next to the word and Wordbot will give you the definition. For instance, suppose you are learning English. You can have Wordbot process a web page for you and then look up any word you don't understand. This is also useful if you are reading something that is highly technical. The Wordbot is *very* cool.

**Web:**

**http://www.cs.washington.edu/homes/kgolden/wordbot.html**

A B C D E F G H I J K L M N O P Q R S T U V W X Y Z

# LAW

## Computers and the Law

The world of computers and the Internet has raised many legal issues: some of them brand new, some of them novel variations of existing legal doctrine. This web site contains a wealth of information related to legal issues and computing, especially the Internet. If you have heard about a famous case involving the Net, you can probably find the details here.

**Web:**

**http://www.eff.org/pub/Legal/**

## Copyrights

A copyright protects the writings of an author against copying. In this sense, "writings" refers not only to books and printed publications, but to software, music, recordings, movies, and so on. In most cases, copyright is automatically vested in the creator of the work, although the legal rights can be assigned or sold to someone else. For example, I own the copyright to this book, which I license to my publisher. To help you understand copyright and its nuances, here is a collection of Internet copyright resources. In addition, I have included the web site for the United States Copyright Office, which will allow you to access official U.S. information regarding works registered for copyright since 1978.

**Web:**

**http://lcweb.loc.gov/copyright/rb.html**
**http://www.benedict.com/**
**http://www.law.cornell.edu/topics/copyright.html**

**Usenet:**

**misc.int-property**

## Criminal Justice and Popular Culture

The Journal of Criminal Justice and Popular Culture offers film reviews and essays on criminal justice and popular culture.

**Listserv Mailing List:**

List Name: **cjmovies**
Subscribe to: **listserv@albany.edu**

The criminal justice system—like health care reform and soap on a rope—makes a small but indelible contribution to our popular culture. To follow this connection regularly, subscribe to the **cjmovies** mailing list and read the *Journal of Criminal Justice and Popular Culture*. (The article I am waiting for is "Favorite Barbecue Recipes of the O.J. Simpson Defense Team.")

## Federal Communications Law Journal

The Federal Communications Law Journal is the official journal of the Federal Communications Bar Association, published in association with the Indiana University School of Law. The journal publishes articles dealing with issues related to communications and information, both American and international. If you are interested in broadcasting, telephony, the Internet or intellectual property, you will find this journal useful and interesting. For example, I enjoyed reading an article analyzing how certain broadcasting licenses are awarded in the U.S.

**Web:**

**http://www.law.indiana.edu/fclj/fclj.html**

## Information Law Papers

Among other things, lawyers are notorious for being hard to get in touch with. If you just have to have law information at your fingertips fast and in an easy-to-read fashion, connect to the Center for Information Law and Policy at the Villanova Law School. Among the resources available are electronic living wills, documents on network and computer law, and search warrants.

**Web:**

**http://ming.law.vill.edu/**

## International Criminal Justice Info

In spite of what most people think, the bulk of crime in the world is not confined to small portions of Los Angeles. There is crime all over the world, and as a Net person, you have access to lots of information related to this popular global pastime. Here it is—enjoy.

**Web:**

**http://www.acsp.uic.edu/**

## International Law Students Association

Law students interested in international law can check out information about the International Law Students Association and get links to a library with online texts, law journals, documents about international law and related resources.

**Web:**

**http://www2.magmacom.com/~dbell/**

## International Trade Law

This web site is devoted to international trade law. Find information about sales of goods and services, protection of intellectual property, carriage of goods, insurance, payment mechanisms, agency, limitation periods, and other areas of international law.

**Web:**

**http://itl.irv.uit.no/trade_law/**

## Law Firms

There are a large number of law firms on the Net, and here is a list of many of them. Don't be surprised if, soon, being on the Net is a prerequisite to running a law practice. I can tell you that all of my lawyers are on the Net. (Now, if I can only get them to use PGP, so we can send secret stuff by email.)

**Web:**

**http://www.law.indiana.edu/law/v-lib/lawfirms.html**

## Law Resources

This is a useful collection of law resources divided into sections: commercial law, defense funds, human rights, institutes, intellectual property, international trade, law firms, legal agencies, libraries, newsletters, Supreme Court, and more.

**Web:**

**http://www.io.org/~jgcom/librlaw.htm**

## Law Schools

The great thing about going to law school is that, when you graduate, you will be in a profession that is so popular that people like to tell lots of jokes about it. So, before you commit yourself to one school or another, make sure you do enough research on the Net to make sure that your school is worthy of joking about. To help you, here is a list of many, many law schools, all of which have a presence on the Internet. For more interpersonal research, you can join the law school mailing list.

**Web:**

**http://www.law.indiana.edu/law/v-lib/lawschools.html**

**Usenet:**

**bit.listserv.lawsch-l**

## Law Talk and General Discussion

It's Saturday night and you are anxious to discuss freedom of religion, libel and the concept of invasion of privacy with someone. When you have no place to go and you are just itching to talk law, check out Usenet, where you will find lawyers, law students and lawyer wannabes chatting about legalities.

**Usenet:**

**misc.legal**
**misc.legal.moderated**

## Lawtalk

Lawtalk, a service provided by the law school at Indiana University, offers links to information about the amendments to the U.S. constitution, business and personal finance law, criminal law and civil law.

**Web:**

**http://www.law.indiana.edu/law/lawtalk.html**

## Legal Domain Network

The Legal Domain Network is a web site that provides access to law-related Usenet groups. When you use this service, you can read what is in the discussion groups, but you can't post articles of your own (probably for legal reasons).

**Web:**

**http://www.kentlaw.edu/lawnet/lawnet.html**

## Patents

A patent protects the right to use an invention. In the United States, there are three main types of patents: Utility Patents (machines, processes, etc.), Design Patents (design for an manufactured article), and Plant Patents (new varieties of plants). With respect to computers, patents are issued not only for new hardware, but for specific software and computer algorithms. To help you understand patents and how they work, here are some useful resources, including the web site of the U.S. Patent and Trademark Offices.

**Web:**

**http://www.law.vill.edu/~rgruner/patport.htm**
**http://www.uspto.gov/web/patinfo/toc.html**
**http://www.wnspat.com/primpatp.html**

## Supreme Court Rulings

With Project Hermes, the United States Supreme Court makes its opinions and rulings available in electronic format within minutes of their release.

**Web:**

**http://www.law.cornell.edu/supct/**

## Trade Secrets

There's little that is more pleasurable than hearing a secret that you aren't supposed to hear. If you like secrets, especially trade secrets, take a look at the trade secrets resources on the Internet. You can get information on unfair competition, trade secret protection programs, investigations, nondisclosure and confidentiality agreements, inevitable disclosure doctrines, how to protect intellectual property rights and information on computer software and anti-trust guidelines.

**Web:**

**http://www.execpc.com/~mhallign/**

### *Supreme Court Documents*

Have you ever been in the situation of being introduced to the man or woman of your dreams, getting into a wonderful conversation, and then all of a sudden having that person turn you down like a bedspread because you have no knowledge of recent Supreme Court rulings? Fortunately, this all-too-common occurrence need not happen to you. All you need to do is take the simple precaution of checking on the Net for new Supreme Court opinions every day when you get up. Never again will you lose out on the relationship of a lifetime because of poor preparation.

## Trademarks

A trademark is a word, name or symbol used to distinguish the source of specific services or goods. Trademarks do not have to be registered. However, if you do register a trademark, you have more protection against people using it for their own products. Here is official information from the United States Patent and Trademark Offices, as well as some other trademark-related resources you will find useful.

**Web:**

**http://www.cvfn.org/business/bus/trade.html**
**http://www.fplc.edu/tfield/Trademk.htm**
**http://www.naming.com/naming/icclasses.html**
**http://www.uspto.gov/web/trad_reg_info/toc.html**

## Virtual Law Library

When you are looking for law information on the Net, here is a great palce to start. The Virtual Law Library contains a long list of links to online legal information. This resource offers topical and alphabetical listings of organizations, including a list of United States government law resources.

**Web:**

**http://www.law.indiana.edu/law/v-lib/lawindex.html**

# LIBRARIES

## Archiving Talk and General Discussion

An archiver must be farsighted. If he does his job correctly, no one will know for a long time and, unfortunately, it often seems as if no one cares. However, if he does his job poorly, the material he is working with will be lost or destroyed, and by the time anyone notices, it will be too late. Truly, we owe a lot to these quiet, skillful workers who labor away in obscurity just so that, years from now, our cultural descendants will have access to the information that we generate today. If you have an interest in archiving, here is a mailing list on which you can correspond with your peers.

**Listserv Mailing List:**

List Name: **archives**
Subscribe to: **listserv@miamiu.muohio.edu**

Of course you have a special place in your bookcase for all your Harley Hahn books. (Well, I do, anyway.) But how can you sleep at night, worrying that the books may be slowly degenerating (like all the old Superman comics in that box in the garage)? Not to worry. Subscribe to the **archives** mailing list and pick up the fine points of archiving your valuable works of art. Never again will you lie awake all night, concerned for the safety of your first editions of *How to Write Beautiful Programs for the IBM System\360* or *Unconventional Medicine Explained.*

Harley Hahn
Harley Hahn
Harley Hahn

## Carl System

Carl is a computerized network of library systems. Search for keywords from any of five databases (library catalogs, current articles, information databases, other library systems, library and system news).

**Web:**

**http://www.carl.org/carlweb/**

## Cataloging Talk and General Discussion

It's not a job that most people envy—cataloging and keeping track of all those books. It takes someone with patience, perseverance and a good sense of organization. Those are the kind of people who hang out in this Usenet group. Check out the raging debates over the modality and paradigms of cataloging. The mailing list is for the discussion of automated methods of cataloging.

**Usenet:**

**bit.listserv.autocat**

**Listserv Mailing List:**

List Name: **autocat**
Subscribe to: **listserv@ubvm.cc.buffalo.edu**

## Circulation Control

Anyone who has worked in a library knows how much can go wrong when it comes to circulation. Considering how many books are shuffled back and forth every day, it's an exemplary library system where few problems arise, and it's understandable why librarians often look stern. They are the scholarly version of the military's drill sergeant. This mailing list deals with issues related to circulation control in libraries, including shelving, reserve room operations, and stack maintenance.

**Listserv Mailing List:**

List Name: **circplus**
Subscribe to: **listserv@idbsu.bitnet**

A B C D E F G H I J K L M N O P Q R S T U V W X Y Z

## College Libraries

So many backpacks to search, so little time. College librarians have to keep up with the ebb and flow of students who race in and out, who move and change addresses, forget to turn the books in, forget to pay fines, and get an occasional mean streak and decide to make off with the only copy of the 1952 version of a textbook on human sexuality. This list serves as a forum for discussing issues relevant primarily to college librarians and staff who hold down the fort at four-year undergraduate institutions.

**Listproc Mailing List:**

List Name: **collib-l**
Subscribe to: **listproc@willamette.edu**

## Dental Librarians

It's amazing that such a small portion of the body, like your mouth, can have a whole library devoted to it. This discussion group is intended for librarians, educators, and persons who have an interest in dental and oral health information issues and wish to exchange information and ideas. Next time you are lying helpless in the dental chair with someone's hands stuck in your mouth, you can think how lucky you are that such a great resource exists.

**Listserv Mailing List:**

List Name: **dentalib**
Subscribe to: **listserv@usc.edu**

**NEED TO FIND THE BEST PLACES TO READ ABOUT GINGIVITIS AND THE MORE OBSCURE BRANCHES OF THE TREGEMINAL NERVE? NO NEED TO FEEL DOWN IN THE MOUTH. THE *Dental Librarian mailing list* AWAITS YOU.**

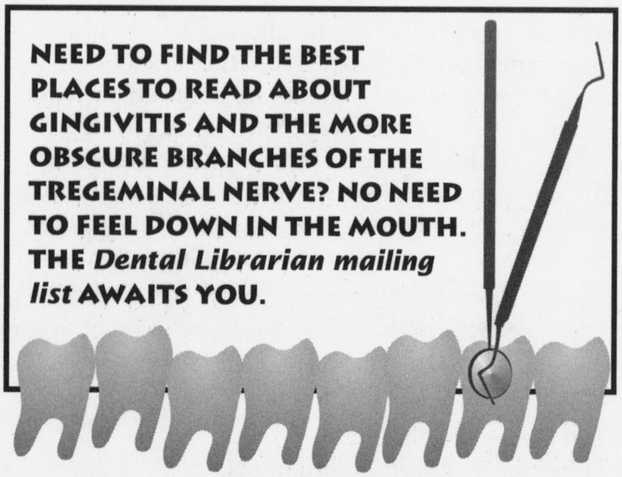

## Dewey Decimal System

The Dewey Decimal system for the classification of non-fiction library material was developed in 1876 by an American librarian named Melvil Dewey. Dewey created the classification scheme based on his understanding of human knowledge in Europe and the United States. Although the Dewey Decimal System has undergone modifications, the main design has proved remarkably enduring for well over one hundred years, and is used widely throughout North America and Europe. The name "Decimal System" comes from the idea that all knowledge is divided into ten major categories, numbered "000" through "900". Within a category, sub-categories are assigned a specific three-digit number. More detailed specification is expressed by extra numbers following a decimal point. For example, the social sciences all lie within the 300 division, economics is 330, labor economics is 331, and career information is 331.702. This web site contains a useful hypertext list of all the main Dewey Decimal categories and sub-categories. This is a great place to look up the meaning of a particular number, or to search for the number that describes a particular type of information.

**Web:**

**http://www.colum.edu/colum/library/deweysum.html**

## Digital Library Projects

There are many people around the world working to build digital libraries on the Web. This resource is a collection of links related to such efforts. Find information about various projects, hardware and software, tools for storing and managing data, intellectual property and copyrights, new technologies, SGML (Standard Generalized Markup Language) as well as other useful resources.

**Web:**

**http://www.texshare.edu/TexShareServices/Professional/digital.html**

**Do a backup.**

## Government Document Issues

Besides whitewashing, the government is well-known for its paperwork and production of triplicates and quadruplicates resulting in the deforestation of small third world countries. All these documents have to go somewhere, so they end up at Federal Depository Libraries. What happens to them after that is up to the librarians. Topics discussed on this list are the electronic dissemination policies of the Government Printing Office, census documents and Freedom of Information Act issues.

**Listserv Mailing List:**

List Name: **govdoc-l**
Subscribe to: **listserv@psuvm.psu.edu**

## Hytelnet

Hytelnet is a program that presents library resources on an easy-to-use menu interface. When you choose a resource, Hytelnet will show you how to access the resource, or even connect you to it automatically. Executables for various machines, as well as source code, are available.

**Web:**

**http://library.usask.ca/hytelnet/**

### Hytelnet

(1) Hytelnet is a library-inspired service that points to lots of stuff.

(2) Librarians love information.

(3) Hytelnet gives you access to lots of information.

(4) Therefore, if you use Hytelnet, librarians will love you.

## Image Databases

Computers are a great help in the library system, not only for keeping track of things, but for storage of material as well. Photographs, artwork and more can be scanned and stored in a digital format. Get in on the discussion of hardware, software, copyright legality and other aspects of image databases in library systems.

**Usenet:**

**bit.listserv.imagelib**

## Internet Public Library

There are lots of interesting bits of information at the Internet Public Library. This great collection includes reference material, information on youth services and services for librarians and information professionals, and an education division. Librarian services include reviews, professional development, on-the-job resources, and weekly news.

**Web:**

**http://ipl.sils.umich.edu/**
**http://www.bibliomania.com/**

## Librarian's Resources

Put together as only librarians and library students know how, here are some lists of library-related sites. There is lots of information here for librarians and other information experts.

**Web:**

**http://www.ex.ac.uk/~ijtilsed/lib/wwwlibs.html**
**http://www.library.nwu.edu/.nul/libresources.html/**

## Libraries Around the World

Librarians work hard to collect, maintain and make available massive amounts of information. As you might expect, there are a great many libraries around the world that have web sites. This resource collects the links to such web sites. As such, it is a great place to start when you are looking for a particular library. Browse through the list, and you will be impressed as to how many libraries are on the Net. Truly, librarians are among the leaders of the information revolution.

**Web:**

**http://sunsite.berkeley.edu/Libweb/**

## Library and Information Science

If there is anything in the world that you want to know, ask a librarian. Library and information science turns ordinary mortals into oracles of facts. Even if they don't know it off the tops of their heads, librarians will know where to find what you are looking for. See discussion on librarianship from a technical and a philosophical point of view.

**Usenet:**

**bit.listserv.lis-l**

**Listserv Mailing List:**

List Name: **libres**
Subscribe to: **listserv@listserv.kent.edu**

**The Net is immortal.**

## Library of Congress

The Library of Congress was established as a legislative library for the Congress of the United States. The core of the original library was the personal collection of Thomas Jefferson, who might truly be called the father of the library. Today, the Library of Congress has grown to encompass many, many information-related activities (including the U.S. Copyright Office). The library holds 532 miles of bookshelves in three principal buildings. Although all the storage areas are closed to the public (you tell them what you want and they fetch it for you), the services of the library are available, free of charge, to anyone over high school age. The Library of Congress is not only the research arm of the U.S. Congress, it is recognized as the United States' national library, and its collections are considered the most comprehensive record of human creativity and knowledge in the world (although they do not have a full set of Harley Hahn books). The Library of Congress has many, many programs and services, a lot of which are accessible via the Internet. If you have anything to do with research, here is one Internet site with which you should be familiar.

**Web:**

**http://lcweb.loc.gov/**

### *Look What I Found on the Net...*

```
Newsgroup: bit.listserv.lis-l
Sender: Library and Information Science Student Discussion Group
Subject: Join the Army.....

... We must demand that librarians are paid what they are worth.
 We have spent tens, even hundreds of thousands of dollars on
our education.  We should earn money that is indicative of our
levels of education and time spent in the field.  It is really
frustrating to me that I am earning more money working as a temp
(doing secretarial stuff) than I was earning working in my
library.  Granted, I was a circulation clerk, but it still was a
hard decision.  I feel like I have lost my touch on the pulse of
the public library...
```

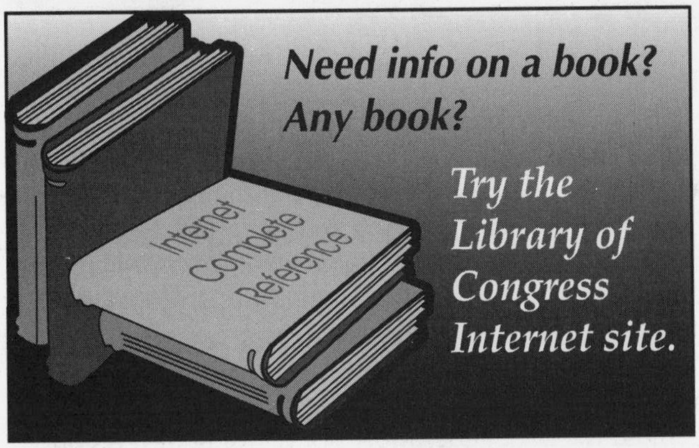
Need info on a book?
Any book?
Try the
Library of
Congress
Internet site.
Internet
Complete
Reference

## Library of Congress Classification System

The Library of Congress Classification System was developed in the nineteenth century as an aid in classifying the vast resources of the United States Library of Congress. The system uses the letters of the alphabet to represent 26 main categories. The categories are divided into sub-categories, each of which is given a two-letter code. To further refine a specific classification, a number is appended to the two-letter code. For example, the social sciences all lie with the letter H, commerce is assigned the code HF, business uses HF5001 to HF6002, and vocational guidance and career development would lie within the specific range HF5381 to HF5386. The Library of Congress Classification System is updated continually and is more detailed than most people realize. The current version actually runs to some 48 volumes with over 13,000 pages. Most people, however, only need the categories, sub-categories and important classifications. This well-organized web site has all this information in an easy-to-use format. (Alternatively—if you need a romantic present for that special someone in your life—for a modest fee you can purchase a printed outline of the system directly from the Library of Congress.)

**Web:**

**http://www.geocities.com/Athens/8459/lc.html**

**Join the fun—now.**

## Library Policy Archive

If you administer a library, you will find this resource interesting and useful. It is a collection of library policy statements on many different topics. In particular you can find the American Library Association's Freedom to Read statement and the ALA Library Bill of Rights.

**Web:**

**http://www.eff.org/pub/CAF/library/**

## Library Resources

Access to many Internet library-related resources, including lists, articles, newsletters, archives, electronic journals, and library catalogs.

**Web:**

**http://nysernet.org/staff/jowens/library.html**

## Public Library Internet Access

If you work in a public library, each page at this site has an annotated listing of links that will be of interest to you. There are guides on how to obtain funding for Internet access for your library, information on how to implement Net access, lists of online libraries, hints on how to build a library web page, examples of library pages, as well as other librarian-related resources. The information at this site is well-organized, and easy to understand with useful annotations. (You can tell it was prepared by a librarian.)

**Web:**

**http://recall.lib.indiana.edu/~caingram/IF/**

## Web Mailing List for Librarians

This is a mailing list formed to discuss issues relating to creating and managing web servers and clients that are based in libraries. Topics cover not only staff usage of the resources, but also access to patrons.

**Listserv Mailing List:**

List Name: **web4lib**
Subscribe to: **listserv@library.berkeley.edu**

# LITERATURE

## African-American Literature

African-American literature reflects the characteristics and heritage that form the cultural underpinnings of the modern black community in the United States. These web sites contain links to a great deal of information about African-American writers, especially women writers. Read about Maya Angelou, Octave Butler, Alex Haley, Derek Walkout, Booker T. Washington, Alice Walker and many more authors who have helped create the rich canon of modern-day African-American literature. If you would like to participate in an ongoing discussion, you can join the mailing list.

**Web:**

**http://www.acsu.buffalo.edu/~aniebo/library.html#write**
**http://www.netdiva.com/written.html**

**Listserv Mailing List:**

List Name: **afamlit**
Subscribe to: **listserv@listserv.kent.edu**

## American Literature Talk and General Discussion

Would you like to join a discussion of topics and issues in American literature? The **amlit-l** mailing list will allow you to participate in a worldwide community of American literature buffs.

**Listserv Mailing List:**

List Name: **amlit-l**
Subscribe to: **listserv@umcvmb.missouri.edu**

## Australian Literature

As J. Wellington Wimpy used to say, "I'll gladly pay you Tuesday for a comprehensive list of Australian writers today." Well, today, all Wimpy would have to do is get access to the Internet, and he would be able find all the information about Australian writers that he could stomach. Spend some time at this comprehensive web site, and you will never again complain that Australian literature is under-represented on the Net. There is lots and lots if information about Australian writers, aboriginal writers, conferences, calls for papers, reviews and criticisms, poetry, literary magazines, and much more.

**Web:**

**http://www.vicnet.net.au/~ozlit/ozlit.html**

## Beat Generation

The Beat generation refers to a number of American writers and artists who were popular in the 1950s. Among this group were novelists William Burroughs and Jack Kerouac (writer of the seminal book On the Road), and poets Allen Ginsberg and Lawrence Ferlinghetti. The Beat generation were the grandfathers of the 1960s, so their work is particularly relevant to our life today (seeing as the 1960s was an abrupt watershed in twentieth century culture). Visit the web site and read about many of the literary people who defined the Beat generation. For ongoing discussion, you can read the Usenet group.

**Web:**

**http://www.charm.net/~brooklyn/**

**Usenet:**

**alt.books.beatgeneration**

## Classics

If you are looking for something old to go with your something new, borrowed and blue, you can easily find something on the Net. Here are some databases, information on classical antiquity, Roman law, Latin language, links to museums, college classics departments, classical organizations and journals. The mailing list is for discussions about classics, classical literature, and Latin in general.

**Web:**

**http://www.dla.utexas.edu/depts/classics/links.html**

**Listserv Mailing List:**

List Name: **latin-l**
Subscribe to: **listserv@psuvm.psu.edu**

## Contemporary Literature of the Americas

Contemporary American literature is best considered as a variety of separate movements, all based on modern American culture. Read about the various genres, such as African-American, Asian-American, Gay and Lesbian, Latino/Chicano, Native American and women's literature. The resources include bibliographies, Net resources such as links to related web sites, as well as mailing lists and Usenet groups for ongoing discussion.

**Web:**

**http://sawfish.lib.utexas.edu/~vicky/contemplit/contemporarylit.html**

## Dutch Literature Mailing List

This moderated group offers a change of scenery with its concentration on the Dutch language and literature. You'll find yourself swept up in the culture and atmosphere of the Netherlands.

**Usenet:**

**bit.lang.neder-l**

## English Renaissance Literature

Renaissance literature refers to work created around the time of the sixteenth century (1485-1603). (The most famous Renaissance writer, of course, was Shakespeare, 1564-1616.) Use this web site to explore the world of English Renaissance literature. Learn about Shakespeare, Walter Raleigh, Thomas More, Thomas Campion, Christopher Marlowe, John Davies and other authors. Read bibliographical information, essays, articles and excerpts from their work.

**Web:**

**http://www.alchemyweb.com/~alchemy/englit/renlit/**

## Gothic Literature

A Gothic novel is one inspired by the English genre of fiction popular in the 18th and early 19th centuries. Gothic novels are characterized by an atmosphere of mystery and horror in a pseudo-medieval setting. Fans of Gothic literature have expanded the original definition somewhat, but the basic characteristics still remain. Here are some collections of Gothic literature resources. If you like Gothic, there is a lot to read on the Net.

**Web:**

**http://www.cse.ogi.edu/~dhouse/Gothic/goth-lit.html**
**http://www.siue.edu/~jvoller/gothic.html**

How we love Gothic literature and all its magic, mystery and chivalry. If you are an 18th century person trapped in a 20th century body, check out the **Gothic Literature web site** and spend some time in the past.

## *Look What I Found on the Net...*

```
Newsgroup: alt.books.beatgeneration
Subject: A Jolly Old Soul Indeed

Last spring I read Jack Kerouac's "On The Road", and I'm
currently reading "The Dharma Bums". I love these books
because...well...for lack of a better way to put it, they
make me feel good.

As I've thought about this I've decided that it's kinda ironic.
Here we have two books showing a guy who seems to live life to
its fullest. Whenever I read a little of Kerouac I look at the
whole world differently. Everyone I see becomes potentially
"mad" or "beat". Everything seems much more glorious.

How is it that such a wonderful feeling could come from a man
who suffered from alcoholism and drank himself to death? I was
told that "Big Sur" is much darker than the two books I'm
familiar with.

I guess Jack was just one happy-sad guy.
```

## Jewish Literature

The expression "Jewish literature" seem innocuous enough. However, even a cursory glance into the literature reveals a variety of work that almost surpasses human understanding. When you consider that, within the family of Jewish literature, Woody Allen must somehow co-exist with Rabbi Shuley Boteach (a noted Chabad scholar), you can only wonder how so many types of people can arise from the same roots. Go figure.

**Web:**

**http://omni.cc.purdue.edu/~royald/jewish.htm**
**http://www.utexas.edu/students/cjso/Chabad/chabad.html**

## Literary Calendar

If you have ever wondered what happened in the world of literature on a particular day, this web site can tell you. Select any day of the year, and you will find out all the interesting literary events that occurred on that day. Of course, the first thing you have to do is put in your birthday. I did and I found out that the most interesting thing that happened on my birthday was that, in 1940, F. Scott Fitzgerald died of a heart attack in Los Angeles at the age of 44. (By the way, my birthday is December 21, and money is always in good taste.)

**Web:**

**http://www.yasuda-u.ac.jp/LitCalendar.html**

## Literary Theory

It's one thing to read literature. It's another thing to be able to understand it so well as to appreciate the underlying principles and forces that drive the creation and expression of the literary arts. This web site is host to a list of links to literary theory resources around the Net. You can find information on classical, enlightenment, romantic, 19th and 20th century literature, as well as contemporary literary theory. There is also information on related journals, zines, Usenet groups, conferences, and calls for papers.

**Web:**

**http://humanitas.ucsb.edu/shuttle/theory.html**

## Literature Mailing Lists

The Internet has many mailing lists devoted to literature and its relatives, writing and books. Here is a long list of such mailing lists, in an easy to understand form. If you want to talk about literature, I guarantee that you will find something here to interest you.

**Web:**

**http://tile.net/listserv/literature.html**

## Literature Resources

Literature and related resources abound on the Net. To help you find what you need (and some interesting places to browse), here are some web sites I find particularly useful, as they offer comprehensive collections of literary resources. You can start with these sites and spend all day cruising the Net for things literary. Just about everything you need to get started on a hot search of the literature is here somewhere.

**Web:**

**http://www.rust.net/~rothfder/weblit.html**
**http://www.vmedia.com/shannon/litweb.html**

## Literature Talk and General Discussion

If you like to talk about literature, there are many people on the Net ready to accommodate you. Here are several general discussion groups that are good places to start (one of which is for children's literature).

**Usenet:**

**bit.listserv.literary**
**rec.arts.books**
**rec.arts.books.childrens**

## Modern British and Irish Literature

Wrap yourself up in a thick cable-knit sweater, grab a cup of tea, some biscuits, and settle down to discuss literature of Britain and Ireland. Any literature from 1895 to 1955 is considered an acceptable topic in this forum.

**Listserv Mailing List:**

List Name: **modbrits**
Subscribe to: **listserv@kentvm.kent.edu**

## Mysteries

Curling up with a mystery and a cup of hot cocoa is a great way to spend the night—especially a dark and stormy night. And some people just can't get enough. This web site is a substantial guide to mysteries and crime fiction on the Net. The mailing list was formed to give mystery lovers a place to talk about their passion for the genre. The list was named after Dorothy L. Sayers, one of the great mystery writers of the century. Check out the IRC channel if you want to meet mystery lovers online.

**Web:**

**http://www.db.dk/dbaa/jbs/homepage.htm**

**Listserv Mailing List:**

List Name: **dorothyl**
Subscribe to: **listserv@kentvm.kent.edu**

**IRC:**

**#Mystery**

## Nancy Drew

You were a rare girl if, while growing up, you did not idolize Nancy Drew, girl detective. Inevitably, someone has taken Nancy Drew and turned her into a scholarly project by analyzing the history and symbology of these delightful teen mysteries.

**Web:**

**http://sunsite.unc.edu/cheryb/nancy.drew/ktitle.html**

## Native American Literature

Explore the culture of Native Americans through their literature. Scholars and other people interested in Native American literature share thoughts on book reviews, articles about poetry and fiction, and offer criticism and information on new publications or conferences. Inclusive in the term "Native American" are indigenous peoples of the United States (including native Alaskans and native Hawaiians), Canada and Mexico.

**Listserv Mailing List:**

List Name: **nativelit-l**
Subscribe to: **listserv@cornell.edu**

### *Look What I Found on the Net...*

```
Newsgroup: bit.listserv.literary
Subject: Cliff Notes

> I was just wondering what the general consensus is on
> Cliff Notes.
>
> We are doing Hamlet in my literature class, and my teacher
> preferred that I didn't buy Cliff Notes because they include
> commentaries that aren't always accurate.  I bought them
> anyway and have only been reading them for the summaries.
>
> My question is: do you think using commentaries promotes not
> thinking about the plays for yourself, or do you think that
> they are helpful and not damaging to the studying and thought
> process?

I don't think anything is particularly damaging about Cliff Notes.

However,  I think the fun of reading Shakespeare involves making
writing your own summary and your own interpretation.  The only
supplementary material needed at high school and lower division
levels is, maybe, a guide to Elizabethan world view and
language.
```

## LITERATURE: AUTHORS

### Austen, Jane

Jane Austen (1775-1817) was an English novelist known for her witty, satiric novels portraying the social lives of the upper classes. Her stories, which uniformly ended in happy marriages, celebrated the virtues of reason and intelligence (as opposed to passion and impulse).

**Web:**

**http://uts.cc.utexas.edu/~churchh/janeinfo.html**

### Author, Author!

If you are looking for information on your favorite author, start here. This is a collection of author home pages on the web. There are also links to literature pages and various libraries.

**Web:**

**http://www.li.net/~scharf/author.html**

**Quick, turn the page.**

### *Look What I Found on the Net...*

```
Newsgroup: alt.books.bukowski
Subject: Ham on Rye

> "Women" is better, in my opinion.  More visceral and less
> crafted, written in the manner in which Bukowski's best work
> is seemingly done.
>
> From the spirit of the morning after you have lost the job you
> hated anyways, woken up with sore hands and spilled liquor all
> over your torn shirt, and with some dog you've never seen
> before looking at you from the floor by the couch, trying to
> figure out who you are and, well, you get the picture.
>
> Roll on, Hank.

I disagree.  Sure, "Women" is a great book, and I must admit
I read it in a day (I just couldn't put it down), but "Ham on Rye"
is the sort of book that shows Bukowski at his greatest.
It combines all his greatest qualities: his humor, his humanity,
his sense of tragedy, in one little book.

I don't think "Women" contains this range and depth.  It is
much more shallow -- Bukowski goes all out for jokes and not
much else.  I don't think "Women" is the tour de force that
"Ham on Rye" undoubtedly is.  "Women" is a muted Bukowski.
A Bukowski that has much, much more hiding under the surface.

I urge you to disagree with me.

P.S. Am I right in assuming that you are a woman?  Perhaps I
just can't empathize with the opposite gender well, but I would
have thought that "Women" would be sort of offensive. Am I
mistaken?
```

## Author Talk and General Discussion

Take a look and see if your favorite author is on this list. If so, there are a lot of people on the Net who share your enthusiasm. These are some of the Usenet groups devoted to discussing the work and personality of specific well-known authors. It can be a lot of fun to talk to people all over the world about the books you enjoy so much.

**Usenet:**

**alt.books.bukowski**
**alt.books.chesterton**
**alt.books.cs-lewis**
**alt.books.george-orwell**
**alt.books.h-g-wells**
**alt.books.isaac-asimov**
**alt.books.kurt-vonnegut**
**alt.books.phil-k-dick**
**alt.books.toffler**
**alt.fan.heinlein**
**alt.fan.philip-dick**
**alt.fan.tolkien**
**alt.fan.wodehouse**
**rec.arts.books.tolkien**

## Baum, L. Frank

Lyman Frank Baum (1856-1919) was an American writer of juvenile stories, the most famous of which are the fourteen Oz books. The first book, The Wonderful Wizard of Oz, was made into the movie The Wizard of Oz, starring Judy Garland as Toto. After the death of Baum, the Oz books series was continued by R. P. Thompson.

**Web:**

**http://rrnet.com/~djamund/books/baum/**
**http://www.literature.org/Works/L-Frank-Baum/wizard/**

**The Net loves poetry.**

## Bierce, Ambrose

Ambrose Bierce (1842-1914?) was an American journalist and author, known for short stories that demonstrate a distillation of satire, savagery and horror. The latter part of Bierce's life was suffused with a sense of weariness and sadness, much of which can be evidenced in his most well-known book, The Devil's Dictionary, a work that is especially popular among people who confuse cynicism with wit, and irony with insight.

**Web:**

**http://hydra.tamu.edu/~baum/bierce.html**
**http://nti.uji.es/CPE/ed/0.0/bierce/**
**http://www.creative.net/~alang/lit/horror/bierce.sht**

## Brönte Sisters

The Brönte sisters, Emily (1818-1848) and Charlotte (1816-1855) were English novelists. The sisters led a lonely childhood in a remote area of English countryside, which no doubt contributed to their remarkably imaginative novels: Wuthering Heights (Emily), Jane Eyre (Charlotte), and so on. An interesting fact—rarely mentioned by modern literary critics—is that the Bröntes come between "bronco" and "brontosaurus" in the dictionary.

**Web:**

**http://www.sbbs.se/hp/cfalk/bronteng.htm**

**Majordomo Mailing List:**

List Name: **bronte**
Subscribe to: **majordomo@world.std.com**

## Carroll, Lewis

Lewis Carroll (1832-1898) was the pseudonym of Charles Lutwidge Dodgson, an English writer and mathematical lecturer at Oxford University. Carroll is remembered for his sophisticated children's books (Alice's Adventures in Wonderland, and Through the Looking Glass), as well as his nonsense verse (The Hunting of the Snark).

**Web:**

**http://www.cstone.net/library/alice/carroll.html**
**http://www.students.uiuc.edu/~jbirenba/texts.html**

## Conrad, Joseph

Joseph Conrad (1857-1924) is among the great novelists of the English language. Conrad was born to Polish parents (his original name was Teodor Jozef Konrad Korzeniowski) in the Russian-dominated Ukraine and did not even learn to speak English until he was an adult. Although writing was difficult for Conrad, and English was his fourth language—after Polish, Russian and French—his work shows a style and mastery that is almost unmatched in modern times. Conrad's most well-known works are the novel "Lord Jim" and the short story "Heart of Darkness" (which inspired the movie "Apocalypse Now"). His work is imbued with a sensitivity to the nuances and ambiguities of what normal people call life, and what English teachers refer to as "the human condition".

**Web:**

**http://www.tc.cornell.edu/~krose/sources/darkness.txt**
**http://wcarchive.cdrom.com/pub/obi/Joseph.Conrad/**
**http://www.cp-tel.net/~miller/BilLee/quotes/Conrad.html**

## Dickens, Charles

Charles Dickens (1812-1870) is perhaps the most famous English novelist of all time. Blessed with an extraordinary gift of satirical humor, melded with the ability to bring his readers both to laughter and to tears, Dickens managed to arouse the conscience of his audience while capturing the popular imagination of his time. More so than any other English novelist, Dickens had the ability to tell a story. Within his many novels (Oliver Twist, Great Expectations, A Christmas Carol, and so on), Dickens created the most marvelous gallery of characters in English fiction. When I was an undergraduate, I had a friend named Ralph who liked to read Dickens to relax. Now, you don't know Ralph, but believe me, the fact that Dickens could write stories that, a hundred years later, could interest a guy like Ralph, really says something.

**Web:**

**http://hum.ucsc.edu/dickens/**
**http://lang.nagoya-u.ac.jp/~matsuoka/Dickens.html**

**Listserv Mailing List:**

List Name: **dickns-l**
Subscribe to: **listserv@ucsbvm.ucsb.edu**

## Doyle, Arthur Conan

Arthur Conan Doyle (1859-1930) was a Scottish doctor and novelist who is famous all over the world for his Sherlock Holmes stories and novels. Although the detective Holmes and his companion Dr. Watson are two of most famous characters in literature, Doyle was more than a mystery writer; he also wrote historical romances. Following the premature death of his son in the First World War, Doyle became excessively enamored of spiritualism, proving that even a mind capable of the most exact, logical reasoning is prey to human weakness. Personally, the Sherlock Holmes stories are some of my very favorites; I love to read them over and over.

**Web:**

**http://watserv1.uwaterloo.ca/~credmond/sh.html**

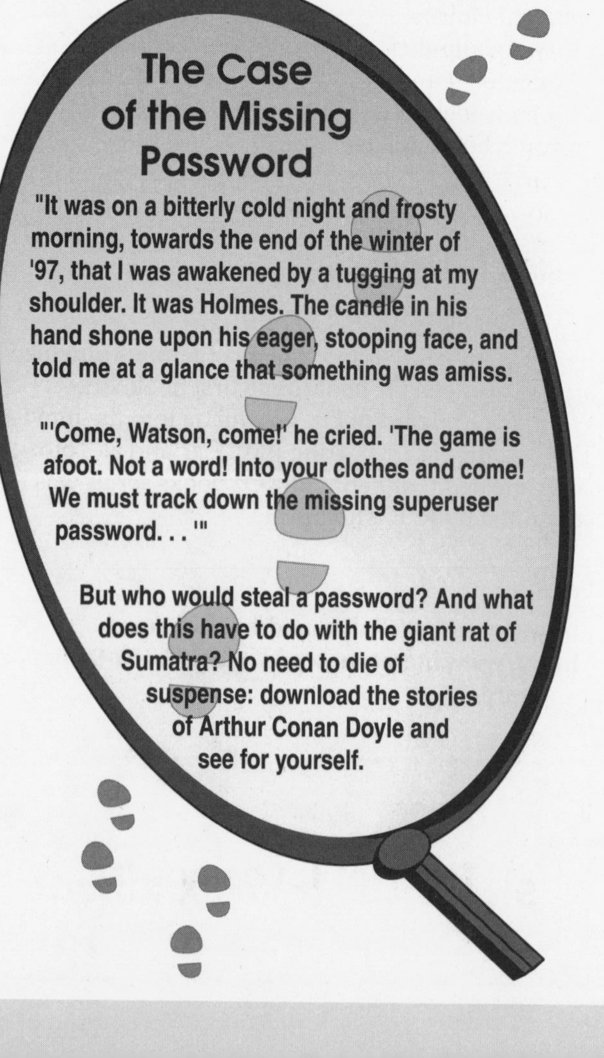
The Case of the Missing Password
"It was on a bitterly cold night and frosty morning, towards the end of the winter of '97, that I was awakened by a tugging at my shoulder. It was Holmes. The candle in his hand shone upon his eager, stooping face, and told me at a glance that something was amiss.
"'Come, Watson, come!' he cried. 'The game is afoot. Not a word! Into your clothes and come! We must track down the missing superuser password. . . '"
But who would steal a password? And what does this have to do with the giant rat of Sumatra? No need to die of suspense: download the stories of Arthur Conan Doyle and see for yourself.

## Faulkner, William

William Faulkner (1897-1962) was an American novelist from Mississippi. His greatest writing was based on the legends and history of the Southern United States, as well as the characteristics of his own family. His most famous works (such as the novel "The Sound and the Fury") are set in the town of Jefferson in the mythical county of Yoknapatawpha (pronounced just as it looks). In 1949, Faulkner was awarded the Nobel Prize for literature.

**Web:**

**http://www.mcsr.olemiss.edu/~egjbp/faulkner/faulkner.html**

## Hemingway, Ernest

Ernest Hemingway (1899-1961) was an American novelist who lived in France when it was cool to be an American in Paris. Hemingway's writing is known for its plain, stark, tough, brutal, primitive—dare I say it?—masculine style. His first important book (The Sun Also Rises) became a success by capturing the post-World War One disillusion of the so-called "lost generation". (And this was years before anyone had heard of Generation X.) Hemingway's novels deftly resonate with the universal themes of Man's struggle against Nature, Man's struggle against other men, and Man's struggle (when no one is looking) against women. In 1954, Hemingway was awarded the Nobel Prize for literature. In 1961, after a long illness, he killed himself.

**Web:**

**http://www.ee.mcgill.ca/~nverever/hem/pindex.html**

**Majordomo Mailing List:**

List Name: **heming-l**
Subscribe to: **majordomo@mtu.edu**

**Stay away from "X-Rated".**

## Hesse, Hermann

Hermann Hesse (1877-1962) was a German-born Swiss novelist and poet. His work revolves around the recurring theme that artists are estranged from the society in which they live and, hence, suffer from a spiritual loneliness. Perhaps his best known novels are Siddhartha (1922) and Steppenwolf (1927). As he grew older, Hesse's novels became more analytical and—to the chagrin of undergraduate English students forced to write long essays on exams in order to pass mandatory literature courses—more symbolic. In 1946, Hermann Hesse was awarded the Nobel Prize for literature.

**Web:**

**http://www.empirenet.com/~rdaeley/authors/hesse.html**

**Listserv Mailing List:**

List Name: **hesse-l**
Subscribe to: **listserv@ucsbvm.ucsb.edu**

## Lovecraft, H.P.

Howard Phillips Lovecraft (1890-1937) was an American writer of fantasy and horror tales that catapulted him into that rarefied area occupied by writers who have managed to generate a cult following. Lovecraft is best known for his "Cthulhu" mythos—an imaginary world inhabited by a variety of strange, bizarre beings. Lovecraft is also known for the huge volume of his personal correspondence.

**Web:**

**http://www.primenet.com/~dloucks/hplpage.html**

## Mansfield, Katherine

Katherine Mansfield (1888-1923) was a New Zealand-born English author who was a superb writer of short stories. Her stories—a favorite of Women's Studies teachers everywhere—were deceptively simple, able to bring out emotion in even the roughest, toughest raised-on-TV-and-violence readers. Although the average man on the street might not know it, Mansfield's work was heavily influenced by Chekhov (the Russian, not the one on Star Trek). After Mansfield's untimely death from tuberculosis, her husband edited and published her poems, her letters, and her scrapbook (don't even ask).

**Web:**

**http://www.buffnet.net/~starmist/kmansfld/kmansfld.htm**

## Katherine Mansfield

If you are a woman who likes literature and needs someone to look up to, take a break and read some of Katherine Mansfield's stories.
(I was particularly touched by "The Doll's House.")

## Milton, John

John Milton (1608-1674) was an English poet best known for "Paradise Lost". The theme of this epic poem is Man's fall from grace. More specifically, Milton describes Satan's rebellion against God and the expulsion of Adam and Eve from the Garden of Eden. A later work, "Paradise Regained", describes in detail how Jesus overcame Satan's temptations (just in case you were wondering how it turned out). When he was 44 years old, Milton went blind and, for the rest of his life, had to dictate his work (including the Paradise poems). A sonnet he wrote about blindness—and how it need not stop anyone from serving God—is one of the most beautiful poems I have ever read. It ends, "...They also serve who only stand and wait."

**Web:**
**http://www.urich.edu/~creamer/milton.html**

## Parker, Dorothy

Dorothy Parker (1893-1967) was an American humorist, drama critic (for Vanity Fair) and book critic (for the New Yorker). However, what she was best known for was her role as critic of humanity, starting with herself and working sideways. Her humor, quips and light verse virtually define the idea of irony (at least for the twentieth century). She was the only female member of the Algonquin Round Table—a group of New York-style witty bon vivants that included her wistfully just-beyond-reach paramour Robert Benchley. Have you ever been bothered by someone, and then had the experience of thinking of the perfect comeback—smooth and subtle, with exactly the right amount of graceful reproach—only six hours too late? Dorothy Parker could do it perfectly and in real time.

**Web:**
**http://www.empirenet.com/~rdaeley/authors/parker.html**

## Poe, Edgar Allan

Edgar Allan Poe (1809-1849) was an American poet, short story writer and critic. Poe is considered to be one of America's most skillful and intelligent writers. Poe is best known for (1) inventing the idea of the detective story; (2) creating a universe within his writing that was both beautiful and grotesque; and (3) being a witty and intelligent critic who often wrote about the craft of writing. In addition, Poe also distinguished himself by (4) getting kicked out of both the University of Virginia and West Point.

**Web:**
**http://www.cstone.net/~wmm/VIRGINIA/people/Poe/**

## Pratchett, Terry

Terry Pratchett (1948-) is a well-known author of humorous, fantasy-based science fiction novels. His Discworld series—19 books and counting—has a huge cult following (well, a good-sized cult following) around the world. He also has the distinction of having his own Usenet discussion group, something even Zsa Zsa Gabor was never able to achieve.

**Web:**
**http://www.lspace.org/**

**Usenet:**
**alt.fan.pratchett**

## Rice, Anne

Anne Rice (1941-) is well-known among contemporary literary aficionados for her work in two main genres: vampire and horror stories, and bondage erotica. Anne Rice is actually a non-de-plume: her real name being Howard Allen O'Brien (I am not making this up). Rice's first novel Interview With the Vampire (1973) was extremely popular among American teenagers of all ages. Indeed—in spite of the fact that she managed to write the entire book in five weeks—it was so successful within the mainstream vortex of popular American culture as to be hailed as an "event", almost before the ink on her first royalty statement was dry.

**Web:**
**http://www.personal.psu.edu/users/l/m/lms5/aboutar.html**

**Listserv Mailing List:**
List Name: **annerice**
Subscribe to: **listserv@psuvm.psu.edu**

## Shakespeare, William

William Shakespeare (1564-1616) was an English playwright and poet, considered to be the greatest dramatist of all time. Shakespeare wrote a large variety of plays: histories, tragedies, romances and comedies, and his skillfulness and insight were developed to such a high degree as to almost defy description and analysis. That, of course, never stopped anyone, and today, in just about every high school and university in the world, there is an active Shakespeare industry, carefully discussing, memorizing, studying and generally taking apart just about everything that Shakespeare ever wrote. Although Shakespeare never wrote a made-for-TV movie or a vampire book, his plays are still performed frequently all over the world (even though he is dead and is, therefore, not entitled to any of the royalties).

**Web:**

**http://ipl.sils.umich.edu/reading/shakespeare/shakespeare.html**
**http://library.utoronto.ca/www/utel/rp/authors/shakespe.html**
**http://the-tech.mit.edu/Shakespeare/works.html**
**http://www.gh.cs.usyd.edu.au/~matty/Shakespeare/**

### A Hint About Shakespeare

What can you say about Shakespeare? Truly, he was a happening dude for his day. Of course, there are ugly rumors that he didn't really write his own plays, that they were all done by someone else who happened to have the same name. In fact, if you take the soliloquy from Macbeth and run it through the **Unix tr** command you will find a secret message that says "This was really written by Shakespeare."

But don't believe me. Shakespeare's work is available for free on the Net. Download your favorite play or poem and perform your own analysis.

## Tolkien, J.R.R.

John Ronald Reuel Tolkien (1892-1973) was a South African-born English novelist and scholar. Tolkien, a professor of Anglo-Saxon and English Literature at Oxford University, published a children's book called The Hobbit in 1937, in which he created a fantasy world populated by cute pseudo-human creatures. Later (1954-1956) Tolkien published a trilogy, The Lord of the Rings, in which he enlarged this world into a more fully populated Middle Earth, complete with good guys, bad guys, war, adventure, intrigue and masterly storytelling. The trilogy centers around the activities of a hobbit named Frodo, who sets off on a heroic quest of epic proportions, pitting Good against Evil in a series of adventures that surely must rank among the greatest inventions of English literature. (We are talking major Allegory City here.) I know what you are wondering: after all those adventures was Frodo successful? Well, just in case you haven't read all 1,518 pages, I don't want to ruin the ending for you. Let's just say the Force was with him.

**Web:**

**http://www.csclub.uwaterloo.ca/u/relipper/tolkien/rootpage.html**

## Twain, Mark

Mark Twain (1835-1910) was an American writer and humorist, who single-handedly ushered in the phenomenon of Modern American Literature. "Mark Twain" was actually a pseudonym for Samuel Langhorne Clemens. At one time, Clemens was one of many Mississippi river pilots, among whom it was common to use the call "mark twain" to indicate a water depth of two fathoms. Twain's novels and stories are of such enduring value that they are enjoyable even to school children who are forced to read real literature (by English teachers who teach to support themselves while they are finishing their own novels). Twain's most famous characters, Tom Sawyer and Huckleberry Finn, are brilliant but folksy creations, as genuinely American as apple pie, baseball and complaining about Congress.

**Web:**

**http://web.syr.edu/~fjzwick/twainwww.html**

**Listserv Mailing List:**

List Name: **twain-l**
Subscribe to: **listserv@yorku.ca**

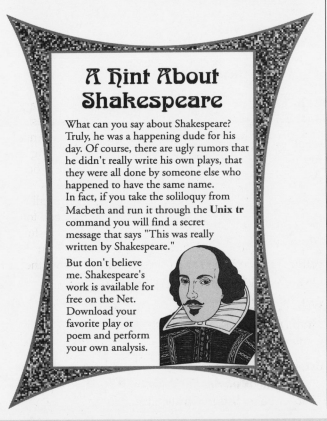

## Virgil

Virgil (70-19 B.C.) was a Roman poet: the dominant figure in all of Latin literature. His most important work is an epic poem called the Aeneid. Considered to be one of the greatest masterpieces of world literature, the Aeneid takes place after the fall of Troy, describing the adventures of a young fellow named Aeneas (the son of Venus, no less) as he wandered from one place to another; goofing around with Queen Dido in Carthage, having adventures left and right, and finally moving to Italy so his descendants could found Rome. Virgil's perfect mastery of poetic expression has earned him the number one spot in the Poets Hall of Fame, Pastoral Division.

**Web:**

**http://ccat.sas.upenn.edu/~joef/vergil/home.html**

## Wells, H.G.

Herbert George Wells (1866-1946) was an English author and social critic, who had a long and varied career as a writer. He is best known for his fantastic stories (what would now be called science fiction), such as The Time Machine, The Invisible Man, and The War of the Worlds. As Wells aged, his style moved from scientific fantasy to realism to pessimism. Wells was a lot more than a novelist, however. Before he started to write he taught biology, and later he wrote the well-received "The Outline of History" and co-wrote "The Science of Life"—truly the Isaac Asimov of his day.

**Web:**

**http://www.literature.org/Works/H-G-Wells/**

*P.G. Wodehouse was called "the best living writer of English prose". (That was when he was alive, of course.) Take a look at the Wodehouse archives and see what you're missing.*

## Wodehouse, P.G.

Pelham Grenville Wodehouse (1881-1975) was an English writer of novels, short stories, plays, and song lyrics. Wodehouse (pronounced "Woodhouse") is the creator of a great many enduring characters, including Bertie Wooster and his valet Jeeves, Mr. Mulliner, Lord Emsworth and the Empress of Blandings, and Stanley Featherstonehaugh ("Fanshaw") Ukridge. Wodehouse is unique in that, over a long and successful career, he consistently demonstrated a level of skill that would be difficult to overpraise. He is, by far, my favorite author and, if you have never read any of his books, my advice to you is go out and buy one right now. If you happen to be reading this in a bookstore, it should be the work of a moment for you to pick up a Wodehouse book on the way out. Everything he created was uniformly pleasant and well-written: the best human nature has to offer. If you have not met Wodehouse, you have not led a full life.

**Web:**

**http://bushrat.jpl.nasa.gov/tak/wodehouse.html**
**http://www.acm.org/~mscully/pgw.txt**
**http://www.serv.net/~camel/wodehouse/**

**Usenet:**

**alt.fan.wodehouse**

## Yeats, William Butler

William Butler Yeats (1865-1939) was an Irish writer who is considered to be one of the greatest poets of the twentieth century. Yeats wrote many short plays (such as The Countess Cathleen) and was one of the founders of the Irish National Theatre Company. As a young man, Yeats wrote a great deal of love poetry. As he grew older, he began to infuse his work with more and more complex symbolism (sort of like real life only more interesting). In 1923, Yeats was awarded the Nobel Prize for literature.

**Web:**

**http://www.humanities.mcmaster.ca/~student3/yeats.htm**

**Express yourself.**
**Make a web page.**

# LITERATURE: COLLECTIONS

## Ancient Greek Literature

The literature of the ancient Greeks forms one of the pillars of modern Western civilization. Very few people, of course, can read ancient Greek. However, many surviving works have been translated into modern English, and these web sites will help you access a great many texts. Read the work of Aeschylus (tragedy), Aesop (fables), Aristophanes (comedy and satire), Aristotle (philosophy and science), Epictetus (philosophy), Euripides (tragedy), Herodotus (history), Homer (epic poetry), Plato (philosophy and science), Sophocles (tragedy) and Thucydides (history).

**Web:**

**http://alcor.concordia.ca/~hellas/literature.html**
**http://www.lapis.ece.uvic.ca/~nkouroun/greek/Literature.html**

## Anglo-Saxon Tales

In the movie "Annie Hall", Annie (Diane Keaton) is trying to decide on an adult education course to take. Alvy Singer (Woody Allen) advises her, "Just don't take any course where they make you read Beowulf." So who was this Beowulf guy, anyway? In the middle of the 5th century, after the withdrawal of the Romans, Germanic tribes from Europe overran England, bringing the Anglo-Saxon language—also known as Old English—with them. Anglo-Saxon was used increasingly until the Norman invasion (William the Conqueror in 1066 and all that), after which time French replaced Anglo-Saxon as the most important language in England. Anglo-Saxon literature is a rich area of scholarship, perhaps best known for an epic poem named Beowulf. Beowulf was written in the 8th century and can be considered the epitome of Anglo-Saxon literature. The poem begins and ends with the funeral of a great king (Beowulf), the story being told against the background of an impending disaster. Beowulf is a Scandinavian hero who, in the course of the poem, destroys a monster named Grendal and Grendal's mother, as well as a fire-breathing dragon. If you ask me what I think of the poem Beowulf, I would have to tell you frankly I have trouble understanding all the nuances. However, I did like "Annie Hall".

**Web:**

**http://humanitas.ucsb.edu/shuttle/eng-med.html**
**http://wcarchive.cdrom.com/pub/obi/Anglo-Saxon/**

### *Anglo-Saxon Literature*

In the fifth and sixth centuries, the Angles and the Saxons joined with the Jutes and headed over to England to see what they could dig up in the way of territory to conquer. Armed only with a few weapons, their wits, a tradition of bravery, and a boxful of copies of *The Internet Complete Reference*, they managed to take over much of what we now call England, including the house in which ex-Princess Diana used to entertain her male friends. One of the more important results of this invasion was the establishment of a culture that eventually led to a large number of works of literature, including Beowulf, The Seafarer, Widsith, Deor's Lament, and Walt Disney's Comics and Stories. If you want to download some Anglo-Saxon material for your next party, the Net will oblige with a nice selection of free literature.

## British Authors

This is a well-organized collection of links to help you find web sites devoted to various British authors. All you need to do is select the time period in which you are interested, and you will see a list of resources to explore. For an ongoing discussion of British literature, you can join the mailing list.

**Web:**

**http://lang.nagoya-u.ac.jp/~matsuoka/UK-authors.html**

**Listserv Mailing List:**

List Name: **eng-lit**
Subscribe to: **listserv@cfrvm.cfr.usf.edu**

## Chinese Literature

Here is a collection of Chinese literature, including novels, poetry, and classics. Help is available if you want to find out how to read Chinese characters over the Net.

**Web:**

**http://www.cnd.org/Classics/**

## Electronic Books

There are many, many books available to read for free on the Net. Although it is not always as comfortable to read books on your computer screen as it is on paper, there are some advantages to using an electronic version. For example, it is easy to search the entire text for a particular word or phrase. And, once you have the text, you can manipulate it with a regular editing program or word processor. When you have some time, take a look at some of the literature available on the Net. I bet you will find something enjoyable.

**Web:**

**http://masala.colorado.edu/internet/library.html**
**http://wcarchive.cdrom.com/pub/obi/**
**http://www.cs.cmu.edu/Web/books.html**
**http://www.lib.ncsu.edu/staff/morgan/alex/alex-index.html**

## English Server

A web site dedicated to the sharing of texts in English and other languages. Titles include autobiographies, plays, essays, hypertexts, jokes, novels, poems, speeches, short stories, and other items of interest.

**Web:**

**http://eng.hss.cmu.edu/**

## Fairy Tales

A fairy tale is a legendary story involving imaginative characters and unusual adventures. Use the Net to enter the wonderful world of childhood magic. There are lots of fairy tales for you to read to children and enjoy on your own.

**Web:**

**http://wcarchive.cdrom.com/pub/obi/Fairy.Tales/**
**http://www.ece.ucdavis.edu/~darsie/tales.html**

## French Literature

French literature is a rich, varied world of taste, style and content. Here are some resources to help you find French books—old and new—as well as other commentaries and other writing.

**Web:**

**http://humanities.uchicago.edu/romance/french/#lit**
**http://web.cnam.fr/ABU/**
**http://www.lm.com/~kalin/author.html**

## German Stories

If you are a fan of German literature, you will enjoy this collection of 19th century German stories and poems, most of which have English translations available. Aside from the stories and poems, there are wonderful old illustrations. The collection is limited but well worth your time.

**Web:**

**http://www.fln.vcu.edu/menu.html**

## Gothic Tales

Do you like Gothic literature? Here is a collection of dark, bloody gothic and horror stories. Read material from classic authors such as Virginia Woolf, Edith Wharton, H.P. Lovecraft, and Edgar Allan Poe.

**Web:**

**http://www.cascade.net/gothic.html**

## Hypertext Fiction

When you use the Web, you jump from one place to another by using your mouse to click on "links". This type of information is called hypertext. Well, people use hypertext not only to create general web pages, but to write stories as well. Imagine a story containing links. As you read, you choose which links you want to follow, effectively choosing in what order you will read the various parts of the story. Imagine no longer: hypertext fiction is here and you can try it now.

**Web:**

**http://www.duke.edu/~mshumate/hyperfic.html**

## Italian Literature

This web page has links to many works of Italian poetry, literature, and theater, including titles such as La Divina Commedia, I Sonetti, Dei Sepolcri, and others; narratives including I Promessi Sposi, Pinocchio, Una Giornata, and many others.

**Web:**

**http://www.crs4.it/HTML/Literature.html**

## Latino Literature

The literature of Latin America is rich and complex, invloving many different writers and cultures. Here are some web resources to help you explore the world of latino literature and its cultural associations.

**Web:**

**http://latino.sscnet.ucla.edu/research/lite.html**
**http://www.mercado.com/arte/lit/lit.htm**
**http://www.ollusa.edu/alumni/alumni/latino/latinoh1.htm**

## Literature Collections Talk and General Discussion

The oldest and most renown collection of literature on the Net is Project Gutenberg. This mailing list is for a discussion of issues related to this ambitious project.

**Listserv Mailing List:**

List Name: **gutnberg**
Subscribe to: **listserv@postoffice.cso.uiuc.edu**

### *Look What I Found on the Net...*

(from a fairy tale archive on the Net)

Living Like a Pig
(a tale from India)

One day, a guru foresaw in a flash of vision what he would be in his next life. So he called his favorite disciple and asked him what he would do for his guru in return for all he had received. The disciple said he would do whatever his guru asked him to do.

Having received this promise, the guru said, "Then this is what I'd like you to do for me. I've just learned that when I die, which will be very soon, I'm going to be reborn as a pig. Do you see that sow eating garbage there in the yard? I'm going to be reborn as the fourth piglet of its next litter. You'll recognize me by a mark on my brow. When that sow has littered, find the fourth piglet with a mark on its brow and, with one stroke of your knife, slaughter it. I'll then be released from a pig's life. Will you do this for me?"

The disciple was sad to hear all this, but he agreed to do as he had promised.

Soon after this conversation, the guru did die. And the sow did have a litter of four little pigs. One day, the disciple sharpened his knife and picked out the fourth little pig, which did indeed have a mark on its brow. Just as he was about to bring down his knife to slit its throat, the little pig suddenly spoke. "Stop! Don't kill me!" it screamed.

Before the disciple could recover from the shock of hearing the little pig speak in a human voice, it said, "Don't kill me. I want to live on as a pig. When I asked you to kill me, I didn't know what a pig's life would be like. It's great! Just let me go."

## Middle English

Middle English refers to the dialects of English spoken from about 1100 to 1500 A.D. This web site is a valuable reference for students, researchers and fans of Middle English literature. You can not only find the texts of many works, but information and commentary about important authors such as Chaucer, Gawain, Langland, Julian, Kempe and Malory. Even if you have absolutely no interest in Middle English, take a few moments to browse this site. I think you will find it interesting to take a look at a Middle English text, just to see what the language looked like. If you do get interested, you will find translations of many of the texts into modern English.

**Web:**

**http://www.alchemyweb.com/~alchemy/englit/medlit/**

**Middle English**

*As soon as I finish this book, I'm going to start my next project: translating the complete set of James Bond stories into Middle English, making changes where appropriate.*

*("...The name is Gawain, Sir Gawain...")*

## Project Gutenberg

The father of modern printing is considered to be Johann Gutenberg, the first person to use movable type. Before Gutenberg, printing required creating a separate solid block for each page. The most famous book produced by Gutenberg—and possibly the first book printed in Europe—was an edition of the Bible printed in the year 1456 (or thereabouts). Project Gutenberg is devoted to making works of literature available, for free, in electronic format. There is a lot to choose from, so I have listed several web sites, where you can select fiction by author or title, as well as non-fiction by subject.

**Web:**

**http://www.promo.net/pg/ev/list/author.html**
**http://www.promo.net/pg/ev/list/list.html**
**http://www.promo.net/pg/lists/subject.html**

## Secular Web

The Secular Web—which contains a literature archive—is maintained by a group called the Internet Infidels. The Infidels promote the philosophy of secularism: the belief that morality and education should not be based on religion. If you are religious, I understand that this philosophy may be in direct contradistinction to everything you believe (or have been taught). However, the books and articles at this site all resonate around the idea that people can actually think for themselves and should be able to choose to accept or reject important ideas on their own merit. Take an look and see what you think.

**Web:**

**http://freethought.tamu.edu/freethought/**

## Short Stories

The definition of a short story is a work of fiction that you can read at one sitting. Here is a limited, but worthwhile collection of short stories: fun to read when you have the urge to explore something new.

**Web:**

**http://www.bnl.com/shorts/**

## Victorian Literature

The study of Victorian literature covers the work of nineteenth century English writers. The Victorian era (named for Queen Victoria, who reigned from 1837 to 1901) was rich in cultural, scientific and social development. In particular, England was blessed with an outpouring of literature, much of which is popular to this day. Many of the great Victorian writers are as famous today as they were in their own time: Charlotte Brontë, Emily Brontë, Elizabeth Barrett Browning, Robert Browning, Thomas Carlyle, Lewis Carroll, Charles Dickens, George Eliot, Rudyard Kipling, Dante Gabriel Rossetti, Alfred Tennyson, W.M. Thackeray, Anthony Trollope and Oscar Wilde. If you have never read any Victorian literature, why not give it a try? (I suggest Oscar Wilde's book, The Picture of Dorian Gray.) If you are a serious scholar or even just a literary buff, there are a great many Victorian literature resources on the Net. I have selected the Victorian Women Writers Project, and—for general browsing and research—a web site containing a large collection of links to Victorian literature resources around the world.

**Web:**

**http://humanitas.ucsb.edu/shuttle/eng-vict.html**
**http://www.indiana.edu/~letrs/vwwp/**

## Western European Literature

There is lots of literature on the Net, but it is not always so easy to find what you want. Here is a web site that will help you find literature in a large number of European languages: Catalan, Danish, Dutch, Finnish, French, German, Italian, Norwegian, Old Norse, Portuguese, Provençal, Spanish and Swedish. Select the language in which you are interested, and you will be shown a selection of resources to explore.

**Web:**

**http://www.lib.virginia.edu/wess/etexts.html**

## Women and Literature

Experience the remarkable writing of women in literature. This site archives numerous women authors, including notables such as Louisa May Alcott, Jane Austen, Emily Brontë, and Sylvia Plath.

**Web:**

**http://sunsite.unc.edu/cheryb/women/wlit.html**

# LITERATURE: TITLES

## Aeneid

Aeneas, son of the goddess Aphrodite and a Trojan shephard named Anchises, is a mythical hero of Troy and Rome. After the Trojan war, Aeneas travels overseas to found a city. The story of the Aeneid begins seven years into the voyage when Aeneas encounters a dreadful storm at sea. Written by the poet Virgil around the year 29 B.C., the Aeneid is an epic tale full of godly boasting, adventures at sea, murder, suicide, and passionate tales of whirlwind love and romance.

**Web:**

**http://www.ilt.columbia.edu/academic/digitexts/vergil/aeneid/title.html**

**Intrigue, Privacy, Secret Stuff...**

*Look What I Found on the Net...*

```
          (from an archive of Victorian literature)


               From "Sonnets from the Portuguese",
        published in 1850 by Elizabeth Barrett Browning...

                           XLIII

   How do I love thee ? Let me count the ways.
   I love thee to the depth and breadth and height
   My soul can reach, when feeling out of sight
   For the ends of Being and ideal Grace.
   I love thee to the level of everyday's
   Most quiet need, by sun and candle-light.
   I love thee freely, as men strive for Right;
   I love thee purely, as they turn from Praise.
   I love thee with the passion put to use
   In my old griefs, and with my childhood's faith.
   I love thee with a love I seemed to lose
   With my lost saints,--I love thee with the breath,
   Smiles, tears, of all my life !--and, if God choose,
   I shall but love thee better after death.
```

**My other joke is funny.**

## Aesop's Fables

Aesop was born a slave around the year 620 B.C. and raised himself from servility to a position of high renown. His reputation was that of a great thinker and philosopher, and he eventually came to be widely admired. Aesop was hired by King Croesus of Lydia as a diplomat in order to try to establish peace between the various republics of Greece. Aesop reconciled the citizens by telling his wise fables. You probably know of many of these fables that have short but memorable morals such as "Familiarity breeds contempt" or "It is easy to be brave from a safe distance." Here is a nice collection of the fables of Aesop. They are engaging for children and thoughtful for adults. Try some.

**Web:**

**http://attila.stevens-tech.edu/~soh1/aesop.html**
**http://www-unix.oit.umass.edu/~cushing3/aesop/**

## Alice's Adventures in Wonderland

What people commonly refer to as the story of Alice in Wonderland is actually two different books: "Alice's Adventures in Wonderland" and the sequel "Through the Looking Glass". These stories are clever tales written by Lewis Carroll about a young girl named Alice who has strange adventures in a surrealistic place. In the first story, Alice enters Wonderland by following a rabbit down a hole. In the second story, she begins her journey by climbing through a looking glass (mirror). If you have children—or if you ever were a child at one time—I suggest that you set aside a few hours and read these stories to someone smaller than yourself. (Even though it's possible that you may enjoy the stories even more than the children.)

**Web:**

**http://www.cstone.net/library/alice/aliceinwonderland.html**
**http://www.cstone.net/library/glass/alice-lg.html**
**http://www.literature.org/Works/Lewis-Carroll/alice-in-wonderland/**
**http://www.literature.org/Works/Lewis-Carroll/through-the-looking-glass/index.html**

## Anne of Green Gables

Lucy Maud Montgomery (1874-1942) was a Canadian novelist who wrote a series of books about a red-haired, green-eyed, freckled orphan named Anne. Montgomery's first book, Anne of Green Gables (1908), was so popular that she ended up writing an entire series using Anne as her central figure. In 1935, Anne of Green Gables was made into a motion picture and, in recent years, a popular TV series. Moreover, even today, the books themselves are still enjoyable.

**Web:**

**http://www.cs.cmu.edu/Web/People/rgs/anne-table.html**
**http://www.inform.umd.edu:8080/EdRes/ReadingRoom/Fiction/AnneofGables**

## Arabian Nights

The Arabian Nights are a collection of fairy tales originating in Persia, Arabia and Asia. Originally the tales were not intended for children, but were told by bold and dramatic entertainers who made their living telling stories. The stories were passed on orally until the 14th-16th centuries when they were translated into French and English and were finally written down. The most well-known tale of the Arabian Nights is that of Aladdin and his lamp. The lamp, when rubbed, brought forth a genie who would do Aladdin's bidding. Another well-known hero and adventurer of the Arabian Nights was Sinbad, who had seven amazing sea voyages. At this web site you can read all the stories of the Arabian Nights, including the adventures of Aladdin and Sinbad.

**Web:**

**http://www.teachersoft.com/Library/lit/lang/contents.htm**

**Read the FAQs of life.**

## As a Man Thinketh

James Allen, a 19th-century English philosopher, believed that "A man is literally what he thinks, his character the complete sum of all his thoughts." When Allen wrote As a Man Thinketh, he intended the small book to motivate people to explore the idea that they are responsible for their own success, that each individual is created by his or her thoughts.

**Web:**

**http://wiretap.spies.com/Gopher/Library/Classic/thinketh.txt**

Go ask Alice,
I think she'll know.

## Call of the Wild

Jack London (John Griffith London, 1876-1916) was an American author. He did much of his early writing as a newspaper correspondent for the Klondike rush or the wars of his era. His fictional stories were adventurous and romantic. They were engaging because the characters and settings were so realistic, based on his travels and experiences. "The Call of the Wild", written in 1903, is one of his Klondike stories. The tale is about a dog named Buck who is dragged into the frozen Yukon as a companion to greedy men hunting for gold. If you like dog stories, you'll love "The Call of the Wild".

**Web:**

**http://wiretap.spies.com/Gopher/Library/Classic/callwild.txt**

## Canterbury Tales

Geoffrey Chaucer (c. 1340-1400) was an English poet who wrote the Canterbury Tales, a 17,000-line poem about a group of pilgrims traveling to see the shrine of St. Thomas à Becket at Canterbury. The Tales are fascinating because Chaucer is a master storyteller who creates characters that are full of life. The Canterbury Tales is an unfinished work, but shows a delightful slice of 14th-century English life.

**Web:**

**http://etext.virginia.edu/CT.html**

## Civil Disobedience

Henry David Thoreau (1817-1862) was an American essayist and poet who believed in "living deep and sucking out all the marrow of life". His best-known book is Walden. Thoreau's essay "Civil Disobedience" emphasizes the idea of passive resistance against social organization.

**Web:**

**http://www.cs.indiana.edu/statecraft/civ.dis.html**
**http://www.gonix.com/mr/fund-doc/civil.dis**

Here is my favorite quote from Civil Disobedience, by Henry David Thoreau. (Actually, when we used to hang around the pop stand after school, I usually called him "Hank"):

"I heartily accept the motto, 'That government is best which endorses Internet books'; and I should like to see it acted up to more rapidly and systematically. Carried out, it finally amounts to this, which also I believe — 'That government is best which makes sure that all of its citizens have a copy of *The Internet Complete Reference* and other Harley Hahn books' and when men are prepared for it, that will be the kind of government which they will have."

A B C D E F G H I J K L M N O P Q R S T U V W X Y Z

## Communist Manifesto

The Communist Manifesto was written by Karl Heinrich Marx (1818-1883) and Friederich Engels (1820-1895). Written in 1848, the Communist Manifesto demonstrated Marx and Engel's view of the class struggle and the need to strengthen the solidarity of the working people.

**Web:**

**http://ccwf.cc.utexas.edu/~thurmy/Philosophy/The_Communist_Manifesto**

## Connecticut Yankee in King Arthur's Court

In 1889, Mark Twain wrote A Connecticut Yankee in King Arthur's Court. It's the story of a man who is whacked in the head with a crowbar and upon waking, finds himself transported to the realm of Camelot where he is almost immediately chased up a tree by a knight eager for a jousting opponent. Read the book online and find out what happens to this stranger in a strange land.

**Web:**

**http://wiretap.spies.com/Gopher/Library/Classic/yankee.mt**

## Discourse on Method

Rene Descartes (1596-1650) was a French philosopher and scientist who originated Cartesian coordinates, Cartesian curves and founded analytic geometry. His essay, "Discourse on Method", contains his reasoning and explanations of the idea *cogito, ergo sum* ("I think, therefore I am").

**Web:**

**http://www.teachersoft.com/Library/phil/descarte/contents.htm**

**Find a friend in "People".**

**Happiness is a warm modem.**

## Divine Comedy

Dante Alighieri (1265-1321) was an Italian poet who was exiled from Florence during a time of political unrest. While he was banished from his homeland, he wrote Commedia (the original name of his poem, which was later called Divina Commedia). The poem tells about the poet's journey through Hell, Purgatory and Heaven and is highly imaginative, with characters such as the poet Virgil and Beatrice, the embodiment of ideal love.

**Web:**

**http://www.crs4.it/~riccardo/DivinaCommedia/DivinaCommedia.html**

**http://www.ilt.columbia.edu/projects/dante/**

## Dracula

Bram Stoker (1847-1912), an English novelist, is best known for the creation of the vampire Count Dracula. The story of Dracula is one that has stayed popular since it was written in 1897 and has inspired many movies, television shows, books and campfire stories.

**Web:**

**http://fs1.clarkson.edu/edu/lit/books/Books/dracula.html**

**http://www.literature.org/Works/Bram-Stoker/dracula/**

The Net wants you to relax, so if you need a break, why not use your web browser to read Dracula?

## Fanny Hill

John Cleland (1709-1787) was an English novelist, noted for writing "Fanny Hill: Memoirs of a Woman of Pleasure" (1750). Considered the first great pornographic work in English, "Fanny Hill" has been repeatedly banned for its frank sexual descriptions. In the early 1960's, it was declared obscene in the United States. Later, on an appeal, in 1966, the U.S. Supreme Court ruled that the book was, indeed, not obscene. The story relates the adventures of a girl named Frances (Fanny) Hill, who was born in Liverpool to a poor family. At the age of 15, Fanny becomes a destitute orphan after her parents die from smallpox. She hears glamorous stories about life in the big city of London and decides to travel there to seek her fortune. On her second day in town, she meets an older woman who introduces Fanny to a life of prostitution. Then, things get interesting.

**Web:**

**http://web.inter.nl.net/hcc/C.Verburg/fanny.htm**

## Far From the Madding Crowd

Thomas Hardy (1840-1928) was an English novelist and poet. His book Far From the Madding Crowd, written in 1874, was one of his more successful creations and gave him a prominent place among contemporary novelists. Hardy's work is characterized by using somber and rugged settings to portray man's struggle against nature and his own inner passion.

**Web:**

**http://www.teachersoft.com/Library/lit/hardy/crowd/contents.htm**

**Get in step by reading "Dance".**

## Fictional Character Talk and General Discussion

What do Nancy Drew, Sherlock Holmes, James Bond, and Winnie the Pooh all have in common? First, they each embody a particular aspect of coolness. Second, they are fictional characters who have their own Usenet groups. On the Net, you get the respect you deserve.

**Usenet:**

**alt.books.nancy-drew**
**alt.fan.holmes**
**alt.fan.james-bond**
**alt.fan.pooh**

## Flatland

"Flatland", written by Edwin Abbot, is a mathematical story, in which a "person" who lives in Flatland tells us what life is like in his world. Flatland is completely two-dimensional—that is, the whole world exists on a flat surface. Although this seems impossible to imagine, Abbot is such a good writer (and mathematician) that he makes the whole thing understandable and plausible. The most interesting thing is that "Flatland" is a lot more than a mathematical book; it is actually an extremely well-executed social commentary. If you have even the slightest skill in mathematical thinking, I suggest that you take a look at "Flatland". It will expand your thinking in more ways than one.

**Web:**

**http://www.isu.edu/~harrdavi/fl_cover.html**
**http://www.teachersoft.com/Library/lit/abbott/contents.htm**

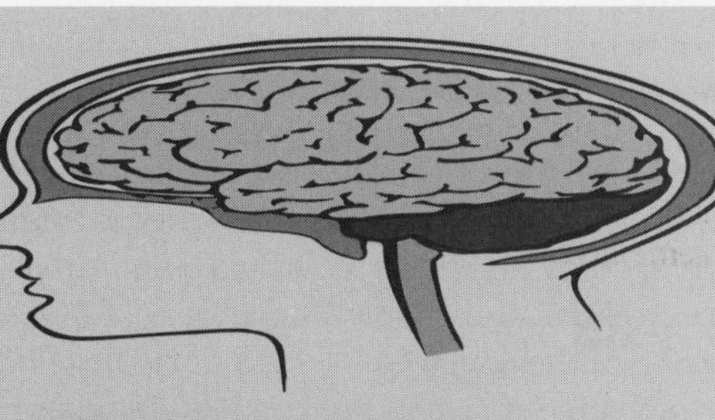

**Want to expand your mind? Read Flatland.**

"Animals and Pets" are people too.

## Frankenstein

Mary Wollstonecraft Shelley (1797-1851) was an English author who was married to the poet Percy Bysshe Shelley. Her most notable work was the horror novel Frankenstein which has remained popular to this day. Frankenstein has been adapted to many stories, books, television shows and movies.

**Web:**

**http://www.umich.edu/~umfandsf/other/ebooks/frank10.txt**

## Gift of the Magi

"The Gift of the Magi" was written by O. Henry, which was a pseudonym of William Sydney Porter (1862-1910), an American short-story writer. His short and simple stories are known for being carefully crafted and for having surprise endings. "The Gift of the Magi" does not stray from the pattern. It's a bittersweet tale of love and sacrifice.

**Web:**

**http://www.america.net/christmas/magi.html**

## House of the Seven Gables

Nathaniel Hawthorne (1804-1864) was an American novelist and short-story writer. His work is often characterized by an eerie occult flavor and displays the eccentricities of the New Englanders of his time. The House of the Seven Gables is a dark psychological book which takes place in Puritan New England.

**Web:**

**http://www.tiac.net/users/eldred/nh/sg.html**

## Hunting of the Snark

"Just the place for a Snark!"—With these words begins Lewis Carroll's poem "The Hunting of the Snark". The poem has been a favorite of many people for years, because of its delightful nonsense and whimsical word play. Carroll wrote the poem in 1876, proving that nonsense is not an exclusive product of the twentieth century.

**Web:**

**http://www.cstone.net/library/snark/snark.html**

## Invisible Man

Herbert George Wells (1866-1946), best known as H.G. Wells, was an English author whose early books were noted for being replete with fantasy and pseudo-science. Into his early work, Wells often inserted his philosophies and political beliefs. The Invisible Man was written in 1897 and is about a man whose tinkering and experiments turned him invisible.

**Web:**

**http://www.literature.org/works/H-G-Wells/invisible-man/**

## Jabberwocky

Jabberwocky is a poem written by Lewis Carroll, and is included in his book Through the Looking Glass. It is hard to explain why so many people like this poem (especially computer and math majors). Read it through for yourself—it is only seven verses—and I bet you will like the way it sounds, even if you don't understand what it means.

**Web:**

**http://www.inslab.uky.edu/~bmgold00/jabberwocky.html**

Feel lucky? Try "Contests".

## Lewis Carroll

If you have never read Lewis Carroll's poem Jabberwocky, download it now and take a look. It is a strange piece of writing, but no more strange than Carroll himself.

Carroll lived in England from 1832 to 1898. He was, of course, the author of *Alice's Adventures in Wonderland* (1864) and *Through the Looking Glass* (1871). At the age of 18, he entered Oxford University, where he stayed the rest of his life, teaching mathematics to several generations of students.

Carroll (whose real name was Charles Lutwidge Dodgson) was, throughout his life, more comfortable in the company of children than adults. He often gave children's parties, and took them to the theater and on boating trips. (All before the days when such activities would land you in the pages of *The National Enquirer*.)

At first, the poem Jabberwocky seems like nonsense, but look at it carefully. It scans (mostly) and it rhymes (sort of). The more you read it, the more you get a feeling it must mean something.

And it does. In 1885, Carroll wrote the first stanza into his scrapbook, along with an explanation of what it means. The strange words are actually Anglo-Saxon. As such, the first stanza can be loosely translated into modern English as follows:

"It was evening, and the smooth active badgers were scratching and boring holes in the hill side. All unhappy were the parrots, and the grave turtles squeaked out."

The pursuit of knowledge notwithstanding, it seems to me that, in certain cases, we are better off being ignorant of the real meaning of a poem (as well as the personal habits of its author).

## Jungle Book

Rudyard Kipling (1856-1936) was an English author whose stories and poems were full of the life and romanticism of India and English imperialism. The Jungle Book, written in 1894, is one of a collection of children's stories involving a boy named Mowgli and talking animals, with whom Mowgli shares aventures.

**Web:**

**http://www.literature.org/Works/Rudyard-Kipling/jungle-book/**

## Legend of Sleepy Hollow

Washington Irving (1783-1859) was an American author and diplomat who wrote essays and short stories. One of his most famous stories is The Legend of Sleepy Hollow in which the headless horseman is a significant character.

**Web:**

**http://www.sci.dixie.edu/DixieCollege/EBooks/sleepy.html**

## Moby Dick

Herman Melville (1819-91) was an American author who spent much time on a whaling vessel. He and a companion fled the hardships of the boat, but after escaping were captured by cannibals. Melville was not eaten, fortunately, or we would not be able to read his great novels such as Moby Dick (sometimes called The Whale). Melville wrote Moby Dick in 1851, but it was not well received in his lifetime. The book is full of symbolism related to Melville's philosophy and ideas about eternal truth.

**Web:**

**http://www.princeton.edu/~batke/moby/**

**Make Your Own Literature**

Herman Melville labored for years writing *Moby Dick* and now you can read the whole thing for free anytime you want, just by using a web browser. Better yet, download your favorite chapters and make changes. For example, use your word processor and replace every instance of "Dick" with "Harley".
You are now reading *Moby Harley*!

**Don't forget to email your mother.**

A B C D E F G H I J K L M N O P Q R S T U V W X Y Z

## Oedipus Trilogy

Sophocles (c. 496-406 B.C.) was a Greek tragic poet who was an innovator in the history of drama, introducing ideas such as expanding the chorus and introducing scene paintings. The Oedipus Trilogy centers around a young man named Oedipus who was divined to murder his father and marry his mother. I don't want to spoil it for you by telling you how the story turns out.

**Web:**

**http://www.teachersoft.com/Library/lit/sophcles/contents.htm**

**Whatever else you say about Oedipus, you have to admit he *was* nice to his mother.**

## On Liberty

John Stuart Mill (1806-1873) was an English philosopher and economist. His writing primarily explored political ideas and philosophies. He was a strong advocate of political and social reform such as the emancipation of women and the development of labor organizations.

**Web:**

**http://wiretap.spies.com/Gopher/Library/Classic/liberty.jsm**

## Paradise Lost

John Milton (1608-1674) was an English poet who wrote a great deal of work about religious ideas and philosophy and was a strong voice in various church reforms. Paradise Lost is an epic poem about Satan's rebellion against God, and the story of Adam and Eve in the Garden.

**Web:**

**http://www.literature.org/Works/John-Milton/paradise-lost/**

## Peter Pan

James Matthew Barrie (1860-1937) was a British playwright and novelist. In 1904, he wrote the popular tale about Peter Pan, the boy who would never grow up. The story of Peter Pan is popular today in cartoons and film. Enjoy this story about Peter, Wendy, Captain Hook, the Lost Boys and their adventures in Never Never Land.

**Web:**

**http://www.teachersoft.com/Library/lit/barrie/contents.htm**

## Scarlet Letter

Nathaniel Hawthorne (1804-1864) was an American novelist and short-story writer. The Scarlet Letter—which gives a grim portrait of Puritan society—is the story of a woman who is branded by her community as an adulteress and forced to wear a red "A" on her clothing.

**Web:**

**http://www.teachersoft.com/Library/lit/hawthorn/scarlet/contents.htm**

### Understanding Your Editor

One day, you may be faced with having to write a book. If so, you will find that one of the great privileges of writing is being able to work with editors. However, you may also find that your editors have only a rudimentary idea of how to deal with writers. If so, show them how to download a copy of The Strange Case of Dr. Jekyll and Mr. Hyde. You may not know it, but that story is actually a metaphor for author/editor relations. I am sure that you will find the story to be useful in many ways, especially if you are trying to understand your husband or wife. (I use it to look for hints on how to negotiate for higher royalties.)

A B C D E F G H I J K L M N O P Q R S T U V W X Y Z

## Scarlet Pimpernel

The Scarlet Pimpernel is an adventure novel written in 1905 by Baroness Emmuska Orczy (1865-1947), a Hungarian-born English writer. The novel takes place during the Terror just after the French Revolution. The Scarlet Pimpernel is a dashing hero who, in disguise, spends his time saving French aristocrats from the guillotine by helping them escape from their captors. When the Pimpernel is not running around saving people, he hides out in his secret identity, which is the mild-mannered Sir Percy Blakeney, an Englishman who seems more interested in dressing stylishly than having adventures. Does any of this remind you of Superman and Clark Kent? This is a great story; you will love it. In fact, the story is so good it was made into four different movies (two for television) as well as a cartoon, "The Scarlet Pumpernickel", starring Daffy Duck. (By the way, "Scarlet Pimpernel" is the common name for Anagallis arvensis: a vine-like plant with small red flowers.)

**Web:**

**http://www.teachersoft.com/Library/lit/orczy/contents.htm**

## Song of Hiawatha

Henry Wadsworth Longfellow (1807-1882) was an American poet who wrote sentimental, moralizing verse. His famous poem "Song of Hiawatha" was based on legends and stories of North American Indian tribes and was named after the semi-legendary chief of the Onondaga tribe.

**Web:**

**http://www.teachersoft.com/Library/poetry/longfellw/contents.htm**

## Strange Case of Dr. Jekyll and Mr. Hyde

In 1886, Robert Louis Stevenson wrote The Strange Case of Dr. Jekyll and Mr. Hyde. It took Stevenson only three days and nights to write the novel about a man who created a potion that upon drinking would turn him into his evil self. The framework of the story came to him in a dream.

**Web:**

**http://www.bibliomania.com/Fiction/stevensn/drjekyll/**

## Time Machine

In 1895, H.G. Wells wrote his future-thinking book, The Time Machine. It's a fantastic tale of a man who creates a machine with which he travels through time and visits the distant future. I am amazed at how well Wells was able to describe such a machine and cleverly contemplate the meaning and the mechanics of time travel. The book is relatively short and well worth the time.

**Web:**

**http://wiretap.spies.com/Gopher/Library/Classic/timemach.txt**

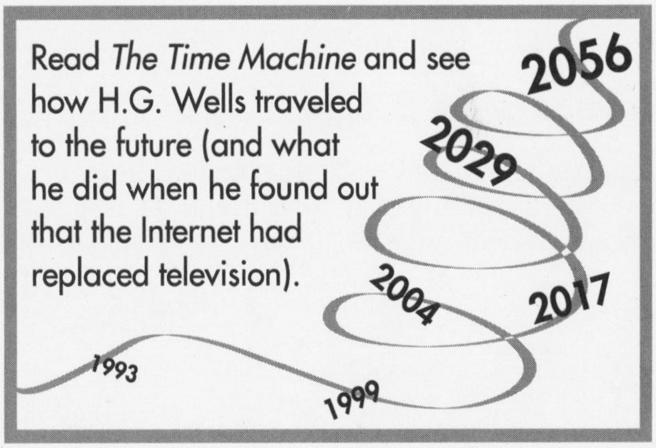
Read *The Time Machine* and see how H.G. Wells traveled to the future (and what he did when he found out that the Internet had replaced television).
2056
2029
2004
2017
1993
1999

## Tom Sawyer

Mark Twain was a great teller of tales, and he did not skimp on The Adventures of Tom Sawyer. Mark Twain spent his boyhood in Hannibal, Missouri, and used that setting as a backdrop for the various adventures of the young energetic rascal Tom Sawyer.

**Web:**

**http://www.literature.org/Works/Mark-Twain/tom-sawyer/**

Why not take a few minutes and download TOM SAWYER? Then spend the rest of the afternoon reading it. (You can tell your boss that I said it was okay.)

## Uncle Tom's Cabin

Written by Harriet Beecher Stowe in 1852, Uncle Tom's Cabin is a novel about slavery that was originally published as a serial in an abolitionist paper. When Uncle Tom's Cabin was made into a novel, it was extremely popular and sold more than 300,000 copies in its first year (almost as much as this book). Uncle Tom's Cabin was seen by many as a major piece of Unionist propaganda preceding the American Civil War.

**Web:**

**http://www.teachersoft.com/Library/lit/stowe/contents.htm**

## Voyage of the Beagle

Voyage of the Beagle is Charles Darwin's story of his voyage on a ship named the Beagle. During this voyage, Darwin gathered evidence for his theory of evolution which he later described in The Origin of Species.

**Web:**

**http://www.literature.org/Works/Charles-Darwin/voyage/**

## War of the Worlds

In 1898, H.G. Wells wrote a novel about a Martian invasion of Earth. On October 30, 1938, the American actor and producer Orson Welles put on a radio dramatization of The War of The Worlds that scared the daylights out of a great many credulous Americans.

**Web:**

**http://www.fourmilab.ch/etexts/www/warworlds/warw.html**

**Don't leave home without this book.**

**Stay connected.**

## Wonderful Wizard of Oz

The Wonderful Wizard of Oz is the first of 14 novels written by L. Frank Baum in the Oz series. This book is about the adventures of a young girl from Kansas who is caught in a tornado and whisked off to a strange land full of witches, Munchkins and other bizarre characters.

**Web:**

**http://www.literature.org/Works/L-Frank-Baum/wizard/**

Spare time? Take a look at *The Wonderful Wizard of Oz,* L. Frank Baum's marvelous satire of the Clinton White House.

## Wuthering Heights

In 1847, Emily Brönte published her story "Wuthering Heights", a beautiful, passionate tale of romance between Catherine Earnshaw and the savage rebel Heathcliff.

**Web:**

**http://www.inform.umd.edu:8080/EdRes/Topic/WomensStudies/ReadingRoom/Fiction/WutheringHeights**

**http://www.literature.org/Works/Emily-Bronte/wuthering/**

# MAGAZINES

## Business and Finance Magazines

Calvin Coolidge said, "The business of America is business." I say, "The business of America is everybody's business." The Net is standing ready, twenty-four hours a day, to help you mind your own as well as everyone else's business. One good way to keep up with how the world of money is shaking out is to read financial magazines online. Try these: Advertising Age, Forbes, Fortune and Money.

**Web:**

**http://www.adage.com/**
**http://www.forbes.com/forbes/current/**
**http://pathfinder.com/fortune/**
**http://pathfinder.com/money/**

## Cars, Trucks and Motorcycle Magazines

If it's got an engine and you can drive it, it's cool. I guess I don't have to tell you that. What I do want to tell you is that there is a nice selection of magazines online for aficionados of cars, trucks and motorcycles. No need to drive to the store just to keep up on what's moving. Check the Net: Car and Driver, Hemmings Motor News and Motor Trend.

**Web:**

**http://www.caranddriver.com/hfm/**
**http://www.hmn.com/**
**http://www.motortrend.com/**

## Children's Magazines

Magazines for children are great. By tuning into mainstream culture as they are growing up, kids can not only enjoy themselves and act like grown-ups, they can prepare themselves for being good citizens and consumers later in life. The Net is always ready to help. Take a look at these online versions of kid's magazines: American Girl and Sports Illustrated for Kids.

**Web:**

**http://www.pleasantco.com/ag/ag.cgi**
**http://pathfinder.com/SIFK/**

## Collector's Magazines

Collecting is great. Nothing can surpass the thrill you get when you finally add a rare item to your personal collection. And it's a lot of fun to go to conventions and talk with people who collect the same sort of stuff as you. If you like collecting, there are some magazines on the Net you may enjoy. Check out their web sites and see what you think: Autograph Collector, Collecting, Collecting Toys and Goldmine.

**Web:**

**http://www.odysseygroup.com/acm.htm**
**http://www.odysseygroup.com/collect.htm**
**http://www.kalmbach.com/toys/collectingtoys.html**
**http://www.krause.com/goldmine/**

## Computer Magazines

The world of computing moves fast and furious and takes no prisoners. So how do you keep up? One way is to read computer magazines. (I like to read PC Week.) Here are some magazines that have a lot of online information and articles: Byte, Computer Life, MacUser, MacWeek, PC Computing, PC Magazine and PC Week.

**Web:**

**http://www.byte.com/**
**http://www.zdnet.com/complife/home/home.html**
**http://www.zdnet.com/macuser/**
**http://www.macweek.com/**
**http://www.zdnet.com/pccomp/**
**http://www.pcmag.com/**
**http://www.pcweek.com/**

## Entertainment Magazines

Something new is always going on in the world of entertainment and *you* need to keep up. There's only one good way. Connect to the Net and read some online entertainment magazines. After all, we are all part of the popular culture and, as such, we have a civic obligation to make sure we know what's happening in the world of television, film and music. Start here: Axcess, Comedy, Details, Entertainment Weekly, Premiere and Vibe.

**Web:**

**http://www.axcess.com/**
**http://www.earthchannel.com/comedymg/**
**http://www.swoon.com/j_mag_rack/01_details/details.html**
**http://www.premieremag.com/hfm/**
**http://pathfinder.com/ew/**
**http://pathfinder.com/vibe/**

A B C D E F G H I J K L M N O P Q R S T U V W X Y Z

## Entertainment Magazines

It's not enough to simply watch television and go to the movies. In order to keep up with your social responsibilities, you must also take an interest in the people behind the images.

To quote from the Handbook of Personal Responsibility:

"As a citizen of our modern world, you are required to care about the lives of the actors, directors and producers to whom we owe so much. Moreover, you must be familiar with all the new movies and shows, as well as the personal philosophy of every movie star whose films gross over $50,000,000 a year."

However, many people find it difficult to maintain the vast amount of knowledge necessary to discharge their civic responsibility. That is why the Net is such a godsend.

Each morning when you wake up, and each night before you go to sleep, all you have to do is spend a few minutes reading the entertainment magazines on the Net. This simple plan will enable you to keep up on all the important news, fulfilling yourself as a human being and setting a proper example for young people everywhere.

## Family and Parenting Magazines

Raising children can be lots of fun (so they say). Still, it really doesn't take up enough of your time. If you are like most parents, your kids don't really keep you all that busy and you spend a lot of time sitting around bored. Well, the next time you have some spare time, you can read about parenting on the Net. Here's a magazine to start you off: Smart Kid.

**Web:**
**http://www.smartkid.com/**

**Don't click here.**

## Fashion Magazines

Here is my easy, two-step plan to always stay in fashion. (1) Every day, spend at least a half hour reading one of these fashion magazines on the Net. This will develop your knowledge and sense of fashion. (2) Wherever you go, make sure you have a Harley Hahn book under your arm. That way, no matter what you wear, people will always know you have good taste. The Net is your fashion friend. The reading starts here: Elle and Glamour.

**Web:**
**http://www.ellemag.com/hfm/**
**http://www.swoon.com/j_mag_rack/02_glamour/glamour.html**

## Food, Wine and Cooking Magazines

I bet you understand the pleasure of the table: the sensual aroma of good food, the added pleasure of a great wine, and the company of congenial friends with which to share your culinary experiences. Great experiences start with great planning, and here are some magazines to help: Bon Appetit, Epicurious, Gourmet and Smart Wine.

**Web:**
**http://www.epicurious.com/b_ba/b00_home/ba.html**
**http://www.epicurious.com/a_home/a00_home/home.html**
**http://www.epicurious.com/g_gourmet/g00_home/gourmet.html**
**http://smartwine.com/**

## Gossip Magazines

Not only is talk cheap, talking about other people is essential to your health. That's why medical scientists consider gossip magazines an integral part of a well-balanced intellectual diet. Tell me the truth—when I mention Diana, Wills, Lisa Marie, Liz, Madonna, Roseanne, Barbra, Fergie and Keanu, do you know who I mean? Of course you do. So don't waste any more time. Connect right now to this online version of the grandmother and grandfather of gossip—National Enquirer and People Magazine—and see what the rich and famous are doing while you and I are busy working and paying taxes.

**Web:**
**http://www.nationalenquirer.com/**
**http://pathfinder.com/people/**

## Health and Fitness Magazines

There are lots of ways to keep fit. I swim in the ocean, practice yoga, run along the beach, and play with my cat. However, if you don't have the time to work out every day, you can use Plan B, a little-known but highly effective way to stay slim, trim and energetic. Simply use the Net to read health and fitness magazines. Give it a try for six months and see what happens. Start here: Muscle Media 2000, Prevention, Runner's World and Thrive.

**Web:**

**http://www.mm2k.com/**
**http://www.prev.com/**
**http://www.runnersworld.com/**
**http://pathfinder.com/thrive/**

## Hobby Magazines

Hobbies are a great way to pass the time and enjoy your spare hours. Moreover, it's also fun to read about your hobby. Here are a few hobby magazines with web sites that I think you might enjoy. If these are publications you already like, take a few minutes and try out the online versions: FineScale Modeler, Knitter's, Model Railroader and Wood.

**Web:**

**http://www.kalmbach.com/fsm/finescale.html**
**http://www.xrx-inc.com/knitters/knitters.html**
**http://www.kalmbach.com/mr/modelrailroader.html**
**http://woodmagazine.com/**

## Home and Garden Magazines

When you need some ideas for making your home and your garden as comfortable and attractive as possible, the Net is ready to help. Here are some magazines whose web sites contain lots of useful information to help you turn an ordinary domicile into your own personal castle: Country Living, Good Housekeeping and This Old House.

**Web:**

**http://homearts.com/cl/toc/00clhpc1.htm**
**http://homearts.com/gh/toc/00ghhpc1.htm**
**http://pathfinder.com/TOH/**

## Home Maintenance Magazines

Taking care of your home can be a lot of fun. Moreover, if you didn't have all those projects to take up your spare time, you would just be sitting around bored every weekend. Still, as one of my readers, I would never let you get bored. If you ever do get caught up around the house and find yourself with nothing left to fix, adjust or replace, the Net has something for you—articles about home improvement. Enjoy: Popular Mechanics.

**Web:**

**http://popularmechanics.com/popmech/homei/2HHIFMP.html**

## Magazine Collections

How many magazines are there on the Net? Lots and lots and lots (and lots). Here are some web sites that collect links to online magazines. If the magazine you want is on the Net, you'll find it here. If you can't find what you want, maybe you need to start your own.

**Web:**

**http://www.ecola.com/news/magazine/**
**http://www.enews.com/monster/**

***There is always something to read on the Net. Check the Magazine Collections and see what's new on the Internet newsstand.***

## Magazine Talk and General Discussion

This is better than going to the newsstand, because you don't have to take off your fuzzy slippers and leave the house. Check out zines, newsletters and magazines from your computer. Read contents and summaries of electronic and printed publications and find out how to get them.

**Usenet:**

**rec.mag**

## Men's Magazines

Don't let the springtime of your life turn into a cold, empty summer. Use the Net to stay up on what's current in the world of men. Fashions change, tastes evolve, attitudes go in and out of style, but you can be there on the electronic cutting edge, gamely following where only the cool, brave and the bold dare to tread. Men's magazines on the Net. Check them out now: FHM, GQ and P.O.V.

**Web:**

**http://www.erack.com/fhm/**
**http://www.swoon.com/j_mag_rack/03_gq/gq.html**
**http://www.povmag.com/**

## Music Magazines

It's fun to listen to music, but keeping up on the music industry is a lot more than fun, it's positively groovy. Here are some magazines that you can read online to check out what your favorite musicians are doing and to see what's hot and selling: Addicted to Noise, Billboard and Puncture.

**Web:**

**http://www.addict.com/ATN/**
**http://www.billboard-online.com/**
**http://www.teleport.com/~puncture/**

## News and Politics Magazines

There are two ways to keep up on the news and on what is happening in the political world. First, you can get your news from radio or television. However, you will only hear snippets of information. An alternative is to read a news magazine that takes a more long-term view and has more analyses. When you get a chance, here are some magazines to explore. Some are news, some are politics, some are politics masquerading as news: Christian Science Monitor, George, Mother Jones, The Nation, Time, U.S. News & World Report and Washington Post.

**Web:**

**http://www.csmonitor.com/**
**http://www.georgemag.com/**
**http://www.mojones.com/**
**http://www.thenation.com/**
**http://pathfinder.com/time/**
**http://www.usnews.com/**
**http://www.washingtonpost.com/**

## Outdoors Magazines

I have to confess, I'm a typical masculine outdoorsy kind of guy. Why, I think nothing of waking before sunrise, going for a five-mile tramp across freshly ploughed country fields, coming back to chop a cord or two of wood, and then sitting down to a good old-fashioned breakfast: stacks and stacks of homemade hotcakes and real maple syrup. Yup, I sure do love all that stuff. But you know what I like even more? Sitting inside a nice cozy house, with my cat in my lap and a cup of hot chocolate in my hand, using my computer to browse outdoor magazines on the Net. Want to join me? Here they are: National Geographic, Scuba Diving and Sports Afield.

**Web:**

**http://www.nationalgeographic.com/ngs/mags/ng_online/ngm_splash001.html**
**http://www.scubadiving.com/**
**http://sportsafield.com/**

## Photography Magazines

If you have ever taken a college-level photography course, I bet you have mixed feelings. On the one hand, you love photography. On the other hand, there is a good chance that any native love you have for the art was beaten out of you by a cynical academic loudmouth teacher. You know the type I mean. A fellow who teaches because he couldn't make it as a real photographer, and who constantly criticizes his students' work to alleviate his unconscious feelings of inadequacy. Well, photography is a great art, and the Net wants you to get back into it. Here's a good place to start, an online photography magazine: Photo District News.

**Web:**

**http://www.pdn-pix.com/**

## Popular Culture Magazines

We all need some good fun once in a while, and what could be more enjoyable than popular culture? You know, all the things that people do, watch and talk about when they are not working? Here are some popular culture magazines, with stuff to think about and stuff to look at: Life and Omni.

**Web:**

**http://pathfinder.com/Life/lifehome.html**
**http://www.omnimag.com/**

## POPULAR CULTURE MAGAZINES

I like popular culture so much that I create some whenever I get a chance. But I can't help but wonder, if popular culture is cultured, how could it be so popular?

Maybe we should just read the popular culture magazines and leave the deep questions to the philosophers.

### Science Magazines

More than anything, science is a way of thinking about life and exploring the nature of our universe. I believe that people gain so much in their life when they train their minds to be rational, knowledgeable and informed. If you enjoy reading about science and new discoveries, I think you'll like these magazines: Discover, Popular Science and Scientific American.

**Web:**

**http://www.enews.com/magazines/discover/**
**http://www.popsci.com/**
**http://www.sciam.com/WEB/webfeature.html**

### Sports Magazines

No matter what sports are your favorites, there is something for you on the Net. So when your significant other tells you to get away from that television and do something else for a change, tell her (or him) that you are going to turn off the TV and spend some time using the computer. Then connect to the Net where you can read sports magazines all day long: Ski, Sports Illustrated, Tennis and Yachting.

**Web:**

**http://www.skinet.com/ski/**
**http://pathfinder.com/si/**
**http://www.tennis.com/**
**http://www.yachtingmag.com/**

### Travel Magazines

Sometimes, when I have been working hard for days on end, I like to just browse a travel magazine and read about exotic places. If you need ideas for your next trip, or if you love to read about traveling, here are some magazines I know you will enjoy. Get ideas about places to visit, things to do, planning a trip, and much more by reading these magazines: Conde Nast Traveler, and Travel and Leisure.

**Web:**

**http://travel.epicurious.com/travel/g_cnt/home.html**
**http://pathfinder.com/Travel/TL/**

### Women's Magazines

Let me tell you something. Even men can enjoy woman's magazines. My chief researcher brings in a woman's magazine from time to time and leaves it in the bathroom. At first, I used to ignore the magazine, but, well... I love to read and when I'm sitting around bored I'll read just about anything. So I started reading about fashion, celebrities and relationships. And then one day I found myself taking one of those tests ("What type of person is *your* ideal mate?") and I knew I was hooked. If you are a woman, here are some magazines to enjoy. If you are a man, my advice is, don't get started: Cosmopolitan, Ladies Home Journal, Mademoiselle and Redbook.

**Web:**

**http://mmnewsstand.com/static/products/105/index.html**
**http://www.lhj.com/**
**http://www.swoon.com/j_mag_rack/04_mlle/mlle.html**
**http://homearts.com/rb/toc/00rbhpc1.htm**

**Reach out and email someone.**

A B C D E F G H I J K L M N O P Q R S T U V W X Y Z

# MATHEMATICS

## Alan Turing

Alan Turing, the man who brought you the Turing Test, the most popular after-dinner pastime of pre-television families of the early 1950s, has a site devoted to his life and work. Read his chronology, family origins and information about his early life. Discover who inspired him in his work and read about the Turing Machine, Turing's codebreaking work, early computer technology, his arrest, trial and eventual suicide.

**Web:**

**http://mrh.slip.netcom.com/**
**http://www.wadham.ox.ac.uk/~ahodges/Turing.html**

## Algebra Assistance

It's a total bummer when you are working on an equation at three o'clock in the morning and you have nobody to ask for help. Never again will you be left mathematically stranded. With this Usenet group, you will always have a place to turn. Too bad you can't take the computer in with you when you have a test.

**Usenet:**

**alt.algebra.help**

Need help with your Algebra?
Try alt.algebra.help.
If anything goes wrong, tell your teacher that you can't hand in your homework because your dog ate the modem.

## American Mathematical Society

The American Mathematical Society was establishing in 1888 in order to promote mathematical research. Since then, the mathematical world has changed more than anyone in 1888 could have imagined. However, the AMS is still around serving its thousands of members. On this Internet site, you will find information about conferences, journals, education, as well as links to many other math sites around the Net.

**Web:**

**http://e-math.ams.org/**

## Calculus Graphics

This is a collection of graphical demonstrations for first year calculus. It includes sections on derivatives and differentials, computing the volume of water in a tipped glass, Archimedes' calculation of pi, and a bouncing ball.

**Web:**

**http://www.math.psu.edu/dna/graphics.html**

## Calculus Software

When I was a kid, one did not talk about calculus in polite society. I had to learn to differentiate and integrate the same place everyone else did—in the street. Today you can enjoy these once-forbidden arts in the privacy of your own home. Connect to the Net and go wild. (Just remember, if your parents find out what you are doing, you didn't learn about it here.)

**Web:**

**http://wuarchive.wustl.edu/edu/math/software/msdos/adv.calculus/**
**http://wuarchive.wustl.edu/edu/math/software/msdos/calculus/**

## Chance Server

What exactly is a snowball's chance in hell? Check in at the Chance Server and you might find out. Get the Chance News, a bi-weekly report with popular news items that can be used in classroom settings to make teaching statistics and probability fun. (Not that it isn't normally fun, of course.) Teaching aids are also available.

**Web:**

**http://www.geom.umn.edu/docs/snell/chance/**

## The Monty Hall Problem and the Chance Server

There is an old probability problem: You are a guest on the "Let's Make a Deal" TV Show. The host, Monty Hall, shows you three doors. Behind two of them are goats; behind the third is a brand new car. You choose one of the doors but, before it is opened, Monty Hall–who knows what is behind each door–opens one of the other doors and shows you a goat. Then he asks, "Do you want to stick with your original choice, or do you want to switch?"

As strange as it seems, the best choice is to switch; it will actually improve your odds of winning. Now this is counterintuitive, and for a long time I thought that switching doors would make no difference whatsoever. However, I was wrong (and my first degree was a math degree!). I found out I was wrong by reading an article about the "Monty Hall Problem" on the **Chance Server**. The article made me think about my assumptions and, after recasting my reasoning, I was able to come to the correct conclusion.

When you have a spare moment, spend some time with the **Chance Server**, and learn how and why so many people misunderstand probability and odds-making.

(By the way, here is how I solved the Monty Hall Problem: Imagine there are 100 doors. Behind one door is a car, behind the other 99 doors are goats. As in the original problem, choose one door, but do not open it. Next, imagine Monty–who knows what is behind each door–opening 98 of the remaining 99 doors and showing you they hid goats. When he asks, do you want to keep your original door, or switch to the one remaining closed door, the choice should be obvious.)

## Chronology of Mathematicians

Find out who came before whom by reading this lengthy list of mathematicians organized chronologically from 1700 B.C. to modern times. There are also links to some of the mathematicians who have available biographical information.

**Web:**

**http://aleph0.clarku.edu:80/~djoyce/mathhist/chronology.html**

:-)

## Computer Algebra Information

Look no further for information about computer algebra. At this site you can find a list of conferences, job opportunities, an overview of software systems and packages, an educational archive, newsletters, address lists and bibliographies. And you thought it was going to be another boring Saturday night.

**Web:**

**http://www.can.nl/**

## Electronic Journal of Combinatorics

When I was a young mathematical sprout of a lad, I helped one of my professors with his combinatorics research. We were looking for Balanced Incomplete Block Designs of order 35 (7x5), handy things to have if you have to arrange a duplicate bridge tournament. I wrote a program to intelligently search all possible combinations looking for the BIBDs, and we actually found some. Since then, I have turned my attention to other matters, but it's comforting to see that the combinatoric scholars of the world are still as busy as mathematical beavers. Here's a web site that will allow you to see what they are doing.

**Web:**

**http://ejc.math.gatech.edu:8080/Journal/**

## Electronic Journal of Differential Equations

The Electronic Journal of Differential Equations web server is dedicated to all aspects of differential equations, integral equations, and functional differential equations and their applications. (Just don't forget to add the constant.)

**Web:**

**http://ejde.math.swt.edu/**

## Electronic Sources for Mathematics

This page links many mathematical resources on the Internet. It has links to electronic journals and zines, archives sites, and the home pages of other organizations such as the American Mathematical Society.

**Web:**

**http://www.math.upenn.edu/MathSources.html**

## Electronic Transactions on Numerical Analysis

When I was an undergraduate math and computer science student, we had to pick an area of concentration. I ended up with two, one of which was numerical analysis (analyzing and creating algorithms for numerical computation). I liked it a lot because I got to use my math instincts while I was writing programs. If you are a numerical analysis buff, you can keep up on the state of this most important mathematical art by using the Net to access an electronic numerical analysis journal. (Hint: If epsilon is too big, divide it by an order N polynomial, and then wave your hands to make it go away.)

**Web:**
**http://etna.mcs.kent.edu/**

## Geometry Center

The Geometry Center at the University of Minnesota is dedicated to computing and visualizing geometric structures, and facilitates communication among mathematicians, and between mathematicians and the public.

**Web:**
**http://www.geom.umn.edu/**

## History of Mathematics

Get the real story of mathematics, the one your teachers never told you. Read these well-researched essays on various topics in the history of math as well as the biographies of several hundred mathematicians. Contemplate those yet-unsolved questions about prime numbers and whether Konigsberg burned his bridges behind him.

**Web:**
**http://www-groups.dcs.st-and.ac.uk/~history/**

## Hub Mathematics and Science Center

Take a few mathematicians and scientists, network them together, and suddenly you have The Hub, a service designed to help math and science researchers efficiently utilize telecommunications opportunities. The Hub offers a quarterly newsletter full of Internet usage tips and Internet and telecommunications resources. The Hub can also help you publish reports or requests for proposals.

**Web:**
**http://ra.terc.edu/HubHome.html**

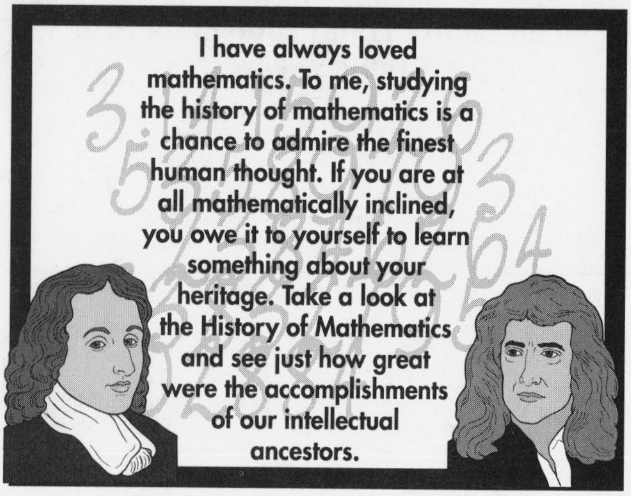
I have always loved mathematics. To me, studying the history of mathematics is a chance to admire the finest human thought. If you are at all mathematically inclined, you owe it to yourself to learn something about your heritage. Take a look at the History of Mathematics and see just how great were the accomplishments of our intellectual ancestors.

## Logic Talk and General Discussion

(1) The Internet is important to the human race. (2) Before you can use the Internet, you must learn how it works. (3) *The Internet Complete Reference* is the best Internet book ever written. Therefore, it follows that (4) anyone who has not bought *The Internet Complete Reference* has not fulfilled his or her obligation as a human being. For more complex questions of logic, read this Usenet group, in which you will find discussions of mathematics, philosophy and computation.

**Usenet:**
**sci.logic**

## Math and Philosophy

Do you agree that even Frege can be faulted for insufficient tenacity in giving up his program after Russell's discovery of the eponymous paradox? Or do you think that ramified type theory, contextual definition of class abstracts, the doctrine of acquaintance, and the theory of proposition identity are just so much hot air? Sit in with people who really understand who shaves the barber (if the barber shaves everyone who does not shave himself). Just be careful to behave yourself: someone may prove that you do not really exist.

**Usenet:**
**sci.philosophy.tech**

## Math Articles

Here is a well-designed collection of hundreds of short articles on many different topics in mathematics. The articles are easy to read and informative. This is a good place to browse.

**Web:**

**http://www.seanet.com/~ksbrown/**

## Mathematical Association of America

The Mathematical Association of America is an organization of college and university mathematics teachers with the goal of advancing the mathematical sciences. This web page has links to math preprints, publications, career opportunities and other math resources on the Internet.

**Web:**

**http://www.maa.org/**

## Mathematical Quotations Server

The next time you are going to a hot math party, be sure you are well equipped with some good icebreakers, like quotes by your favorite mathemeticians. Quotations are sorted alphabetically so you can browse through them or you can do a fast search by keyword.

**Web:**

**http://math.furman.edu/~mwoodard/mquot.html**

## Mathematical Research

Keep abreast of what is happening in the world of mathematics. Just the place to send your new proof of Fermat's Last Theorem that *does* fit in the margin of a book.

**Usenet:**

**sci.math.research**

### *Look What I Found on the Net...*

```
Newsgroup: sci.philosophy.tech
Subject: Is This Finite or Infinite?

> Well, then, if you're an ambitious logician, try your hand at
> describing the anaphoric construction (and finding the
> indirect quotation) in this example:
>
>     John didn't catch a fish, and he didn't eat it.

This is easy:  Quantify over concepts, and define the relation
of things falling under (singular or natural kind) concepts.
Then proceed to say that there is no object X falling under the
concept of fish, such that John caught X, or John ate X.

(Note that this analysis works for unicorns just as well.)

As for the scope of indirect quotation, it is implicit in the
intentional aspect of John's sporting and alimentary failure --
since to catch X is to succeed in seeking that X comes in one's
possession.  Again, all of this is exceedingly well known from
intensional logic.
```

## Mathematics FAQ

Math fans and trivia buffs need to look at the mathematics FAQ. Get information about Fermat's Last Theorem, prime numbers, special numbers, unsolved or famous problems, formulas and mathematical oddities.

**Web:**

**http://daisy.uwaterloo.ca/~alopez-o/math-faq/**

## Mathematics Problems

Flabby gray matter is unacceptable. Wrap your brain around some of these math problems and keep your mind alert and active. There are lots of puzzles, questions and things over which you can ponder while you are lying in bed at night.

**Web:**

**http://www.civeng.carleton.ca/Problems/**
**http://www.mathpro.com/math/mathCenter.html**

## Mathematics Resources

If you are looking for something mathematical, here are a few good places to start: collections of Internet mathematical resources relating to research, math organizations, publications, software archives, as well as a great many interesting articles and novelties.

**Web:**

**http://euclid.math.fsu.edu/Science/math.html**
**http://www.ama.caltech.edu/resources.html**

## Mathematics Servers

There are a large number of mathematical resources on the Net. Here is a good place to start looking for what you want: a collection of links to university math departments, math organizations and math web sites on the Internet.

**Web:**

**http://www.cs.fsu.edu/projects/group2/math.html**

## Mathematics Talk and General Discussion

This is a general discussion of things mathematical. Now, you might think that unless you are specifically working on a particular research problem or you have a question, talking about math is a waste of time. What you are forgetting is that, traditionally, the most beautiful and intelligent women have always been attracted to the mathematically inclined. Remember, a man who knows his numbers is a man you can count on.

**Usenet:**

**sci.math**

### Mathematics

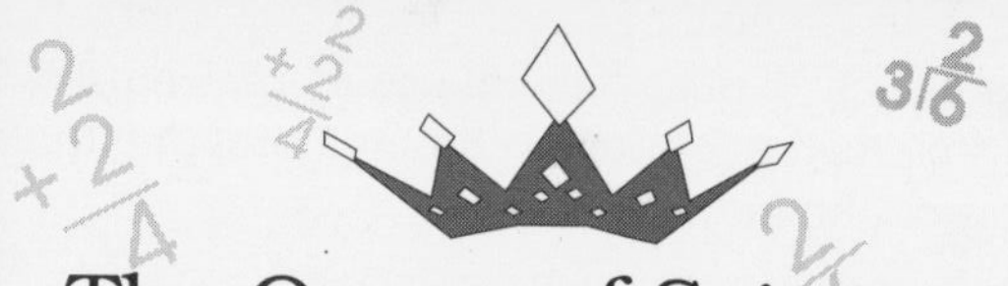

### The Queen of Sciences

What do you do when it's two in the morning and you need to remember all the characteristics of a vector space? You could go down to the all-night convenience store and ask the guy behind the counter. Or, you could call directory assistance and hope that the operator would know. But, if all else fails, why not send a request to the **sci.math** and let the Net help you?

(By the way, while I was researching this book, I came across a new proof for Fermat's Last Theorem that is more complete and easier to understand than Andrew Wiles' proof. His proof is long and cumbersome and runs into trouble in attempting to bound the order of a cohomology group which looks like a Selmer group for $Sym^2$ of the representation attached to a modular form. My proof moves directly to elliptic curve theory and is much simpler. All in all, it is a marvellous proof but, unfortunately, there is not enough space here to write it down. What I can do, instead, is remind you that the largest known prime—which is also the largest known Mersenne prime—is $2^{859433}$-1.)

## Nonlinear and Linear Programming

Nonlinear and linear programming are used to optimize mathematical quantities, subject to various constraints and relationships. With linear progamming, the relationships are expressed as a series of linear equations. With nonlinear programming, generalized functions, not necessarily linear, are used instead. Both nonlinear and linear programming are part of operations research and, as such, are discussed in the **sci.op-research** Usenet group. Here are the FAQs (frequently asked question lists) from this group, explaining these branches of mathematics.

**Web:**

**http://www.mcs.anl.gov/home/otc/Guide/faq/linear-programming-faq.html**

**Web:**

**http://www.mcs.anl.gov/home/otc/Guide/faq/nonlinear-programming-faq.html**

## Numerical Analysis

It's amazing how many people still don't know a Tchebyshev polynomial from a fourth-order Runge-Kutte algorithm. Join the discussion with people who want more out of life than the simple L2 norm that seems to satisfy a whole world of mathematically disadvantaged social scientists.

**Web:**

**http://www.nada.kth.se/nada/na/resnumanal.html**
**http://www.netlib.org/na-net/na_home.html**

**Usenet:**

**sci.math.num-analysis**

## Operations Research

Operations research is the study of how to use mathematics to make decisions when the problem at hand is complex, and you have to decide how to balance various factors to optimize particular criteria. (If there is significant uncertainty in the outcome, you can say you are doing systems analysis and ask for more money.) Here is a collection of resources devoted to operations research and related activities.

**Web:**

**http://mat.gsia.cmu.edu/**

**Usenet:**

**sci.op-research**

## Pi (3.4159...)

Here are some Internet sites celebrating the charm and elusiveness of pi: the irrational number that expresses the ratio of the circumference to the diameter of any circle. Would you like to see pi to many, many digits? Would you like to have your very own program to calculate pi? Would you like to experience pi in ways that normal people have never imagined? It's all here, waiting for you on the Net. (By the way, you may be wondering, is pi my favorite transcendental number? No, I have to admit that my favorite is *e*. However, I wouldn't kick pi out of bed for eating mathematical crackers.)

**Web:**

**http://gryphon.ccs.brandeis.edu/~grath/attractions/gpi/**
**http://www.ccsf.caltech.edu/~roy/pi.html**
**http://www.cs.umu.se:80/~mnlebs/pi/pi.html**

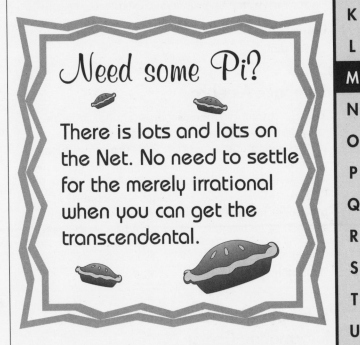

*Need some Pi?*

There is lots and lots on the Net. No need to settle for the merely irrational when you can get the transcendental.

## Society for Industrial and Applied Math

The Society for Industrial and Applied Mathematics provides information about activities and issues of interest to applied and computational mathematicians, engineers, and scientists who use mathematics and computers.

**Web:**

**http://www.siam.org/**

## Square Root of 2

When you've almost got it figured out and everyone keeps interrupting your thinking space, it's really aggravating. There's no sense in starting over again, trying to recalculate the square root of 2. It's already been done: to a million digits.

**Web:**

**http://cossc.gsfc.nasa.gov/htmltest/gifcity/sqrt2.1mil**

## Statistics

When you need a fuzzy clustering algorithm right away and the resident statistician has gone to the 7-11 for a 6-pack of Jolt cola, where do you turn for answers? Try the Net: just the place for people who are approximately right, some or all of the time.

**Web:**

**http://www.math.yorku.ca/SCS/StatResource.html**

**Usenet:**

**sci.stat.math**

## Symbolic Algebra

The invention of symbolic computational programs has added a whole new set of tools to the arsenal of the practicing mathematician. This group discusses such tools, as well as the related mathematical issues. Talk about Mathematica, Maple, Macsyma and Reduce. (My goodness, is Reduce still around? I remember using it back in the mid-1970s. Oh, how symbolic algebra makes one feel old.)

**Usenet:**

**sci.math.symbolic**

## Symbolic Mathematical Computation Information Center

SymbolicNet focuses on the areas of symbolic and algebraic computation known as computer algebra. SymbolicNet hopes to automate mathematical computations of all sorts. This web page is the home page of this organization and has links to many resources and documents relating to this area of mathematics.

**Web:**

**http://symbolicnet.mcs.kent.edu/**

# MEDICINE

## AIDS

Learn about AIDS (Acquired Immune Deficiency Syndrome) and the HIV virus. By reading the Usenet group or joining one of the mailing lists, you can keep up to date on the medical treatments of AIDS, including the AIDS daily summary from the Centers for Disease Control and Prevention (CDC) National AIDS Clearinghouse. For lots of online information, see the web sites.

**Web:**

**http://planetq.com/aidsvl/**
**http://www.who.org/newsletters/WHONewsletters.html**

**Usenet:**

**sci.med.aids**

**Listserv Mailing List:**

List Name: **4acure**
Subscribe to: **listserv@health.state.ny.us**

**Listserv Mailing List:**

List Name: **gap**
Subscribe to: **listserv@listserv.syr.edu**

**Majordomo Mailing List:**

List Name: **aids**
Subscribe to: **majordomo@wubios.wustl.edu**

**Majordomo Mailing List:**

List Name: **cdcsumms**
Subscribe to: **majordomo@queernet.org**

**There's no place like your home page.**

## Allergies

Sneezing, coughing, runny nose, itchy eyes, funny red bumps and a general miserable feeling—these are a few of the symptoms of allergies which plague millions of people around the world. Find out more about this aggravating condition. On the mailing list, doctors, scientists, researchers and those who suffer from allergies gather to discuss causes and treatments for allergy conditions. The web site and Usenet group are nothing to sneeze at either.

**Web:**

**http://www.ability.org.uk/allergie.html**

**Usenet:**

**alt.med.allergy**

**Listserv Mailing List:**

List Name: **allergy**
Subscribe to: **listserv@tamvm1.tamu.edu**

## Anatomy Teaching Modules

Some days there are just not enough cadavers to go around. Not to worry. Learn anatomy online with these teaching modules. They come complete with information text as well as images.

**Web:**

**http://www.rad.washington.edu/AnatomyModuleList.html**

## Anesthesiology

The web site has a collection of resources related to anesthesiology. The mailing list is for ongoing discussion among anesthesiologists and other professionals.

**Web:**

**http://gasnet.med.yale.edu/**

**Listserv Mailing List:**

List Name: **anest-l**
Subscribe to: **listserv@ubvm.cc.buffalo.edu**

Subscribe to the *anesthesiology* mailing list and find out what happens when the lights go out.

## Atlas of Hematology

Blood, blood and more blood. Vampires and other fans of hematology can browse these pictures of blood smears, lymphoma, bone marrow metastasis, platelets, anemia and other interesting things that go bump in your arteries.

**Web:**

**http://pathy.fujita-hu.ac.jp/pathy/Pictures/atlas.html**

## Biomedical Engineering

If you ever find medical imaging too boring, these are the places to be: signal processing, biomedical engineering—your cup will runneth over.

**Web:**

**http://www.me.su.oz.au/research/biomed/biomed.html**

**Usenet:**

**sci.engr.biomed**

## Brain Tumors

Whether you are a patient, a family member, or a professional interested in tumors, this forum is for the discussion of issues relating to this condition. The web site has lots of medical information about various tumors in adults and children.

**Web:**

**http://www.oncolink.upenn.edu/disease/brain/**

**Listserv Mailing List:**

List Name: **braintmr**
Subscribe to: **listserv@mitvma.mit.edu**

*Look What I Found on the Net...*

```
Newsgroup: sci.engr.biomed
Subject: The Physiology of Being Turned On

When women are turned on they can experience anything from
being mildly dizzy to nauseous (and almost vomiting) in extreme
cases.

What released chemical in the body is causing this? Are there
any references for the physiology of being turned on?

Why doesn't this seem to happen to men?
```

## Breast Cancer

These web pages have lots of information about breast cancer, including information for health professionals and links to other cancer servers and resources. If you would like to talk to other people, there are also mailing lists you can join.

**Web:**

**http://nysernet.org/bcic/**
**http://www.nabco.org/**

**Listserv Mailing List:**

List Name: **brca-l**
Subscribe to: **listserv@nervm.nerdc.ufl.edu**

**Listserv Mailing List:**

List Name: **breast-cancer**
Subscribe to: **listserv@morgan.ucs.mun.ca**

## Cancer

Health and clinical information related to cancer and cancer research. There is lots and lots of cancer information on the Net, as well as the Usenet group for serious discussion of a medical nature.

**Web:**

**http://www.gretmar.com/webdoctor/oncology.html**
**http://wwwicic.nci.nih.gov/**

**Usenet:**

**sci.med.diseases.cancer**

## Chronic Fatigue Syndrome

It's no fun being tired all the time. You miss the end of movies, you can't get enough speed up to slide into home plate, and it's hard to make it across the intersection before the DON'T WALK sign lights up. Join in the discussion of chronic fatigue syndrome or check out the web site for information about this condition.

**Web:**

**http://www.alternatives.com/cfs-news/index.html**

**Usenet:**

**alt.med.cfs**

**Listserv Mailing List:**

List Name: **cfs-l**
Subscribe to: **listserv@list.nih.gov**

**Listserv Mailing List:**

List Name: **cfs-med**
Subscribe to: **listserv@list.nih.gov**

**Listserv Mailing List:**

List Name: **cfs-news**
Subscribe to: **listserv@list.nih.gov**

**The Net: open 24 hours a day.**

## Clinical Photograph Library

Whether you are a doctor, a medical student or just someone who likes to look at scary medical photos, this site is bound to have something you will find interesting. Clinical photographs are available, some with correlating radiographs and EKGs. These are pictures of accidents, traumas and other health problems, and should not be viewed close to mealtime.

**Web:**
**http://www.njnet.com/~embbs/photo/photo.html**

## Crohn's Disease and Colitis

Intestinal disorders are painful and debilitating. Sufferers of Crohn's disease and colitis can find support and information on this newsgroup. On Usenet, patients, friends and family members participate in technical discussions about health as well as personal discussions about how these diseases affect their lives. The web site will lead you to a variety of useful and interesting online resources.

**Web:**
**http://www.ccfc.ca/**

**Usenet:**
**alt.support.crohns-colitis**

**Do a backup.**

## Cryonics Frequently Asked Questions

Cryonics is the practice of freezing a recently deceased person in the hope that one day science will be able to cure the dead person's malady and restore him or her to life. This collection of documents deals with many of the issues involved in cryonics, including such gems as the question of whether it's better to freeze the whole body or just the head.

**Web:**
**http://www.lib.ox.ac.uk/internet/news/faq/sci.cryonics.html**

## Cystic Fibrosis

Cystic fibrosis is not just a medical issue. It's also a holistic and personal issue. Welcome to the discussion group that covers all these categories. You can get information on the latest medical advances as well as therapeutic and nutritional treatments. This is also a place for CF patients to share their frustrating encounters with the medical-industrial complex, or with bias in school or at work.

**Web:**
**http://www.ai.mit.edu/people/mernst/cf/**
**http://www.ccff.ca/~cfwww/**

**Listserv Mailing List:**
List Name: **cystic-l**
Subscribe to: **listserv@yalevm.cis.yale.edu**

### *Look What I Found on the Net...*

```
Newsgroup: sci.med.dentistry
Subject: Need Stories About Jaw Wiring

I am looking for humorous anecdotes about patients who have had
their jaws wired shut, especially for the purpose of weight
control.

Please email me direct at: xxxxx.ucla.edu

Thank you,
Xxxxxxx Xxxxxxxxx, D.M.D.
```

## Dentistry

Long in the tooth or down in the mouth, everyone is welcome to this discussion on dentists, materials and dental techniques. Whether you need help deciding if implants are better than a bridge or just want to read humorous stories about people who have had their jaws wired shut, nothing is more exciting and breathtaking than modern dentistry.

**Web:**

**http://www.discover.net/corporate/smiledoc/**

**Usenet:**

**sci.med.dentistry**

**Listproc Mailing List:**

List Name: **dentalma**
Subscribe to: **listproc@listproc.net**

## Dermatology

If it's itchy or scratchy or blotching or peeling, it's probably a matter for the dermatologist. This list is moderated and is open to physicians who practice dermatology (the people who really know that beauty is only skin deep). For online information, see the web sites.

**Web:**

**http://biomed.nus.sg/nsc/skin.html**
**http://www.rrze.uni-erlangen.de/docs/FAU/fakultaet/med/kli/derma/bilddb/db.htm**

**Listserv Mailing List:**

List Name: **derm-l**
Subscribe to: **listserv@yalevm.cis.yale.edu**

## Digital Imaging

Join discussions of the technical details of digital imaging and communications as practiced in bio-engineering and medicine. When you are not talking, there are some interesting digital imaging resources for you to check out on the Web.

**Web:**

**http://www-sci.lib.uci.edu/HSG/MedicalImage.html**
**http://www.largnet.uwo.ca/med/i-way.html**

**Usenet:**

**alt.image.medical**

## Emergency Medicine

What do you do when you have an emergency medical situation and you don't have a first aid book? Take a look at this information for professionals in the area of emergency medicine and primary home care. These sites have a radiology and photograph library, national physician job listings directory, an EKG of the month and an EKG file room. Browse the interesting cases on file, complete with photographs and diagnosis discussion. This won't help you in your medical emergency, but at least it will keep your mind occupied while help is on the way.

**Web:**

**http://gema.library.ucsf.edu:8081/**
**http://www.njnet.com/~embbs/**

## Endometriosis

Read discussion on all aspects of endometriosis, with emphasis on coping with the disease and its treatment. Anyone is welcome to participate in the discussion whether or not they actually have the disease. This list offers a convenient way to exchange information and promote discussion of current treatments, research, and educational literature, and the web sites offer additional background information.

**Web:**

**http://www.ability.org.uk/endometr.html**
**http://www.ivf.com/endoassn.html**
**http://www.ivf.com/endohtml.html**

**Listserv Mailing List:**

List Name: **witsendo**
Subscribe to: **listserv@listserv.dartmouth.edu**

## Forensic Medicine

Forensic medicine is the specialty dealing with medicine and the law. There are many aspects of forensic medicine involving highly technical information in a variety of disciplines. Here is a list of related resources on the Internet to help you find what you need.

**Web:**

**http://www.shadow.net/~nfstc/links.html**

## Hippocratic Oath

Hippocrates was a physician in ancient Greece, who was born on the island of Cos around 465 B.C. (He lived at the same time as the famous historian Herodotus). The Hippocratic Oath is a pledge, attributed to Hippocrates, that doctors take at the outset of their career. Traditionally, the original Hippocratic Oath is taken by doctors upon the awarding of their M.D. degree. However—in these days of modern times—tradition is not always acceptable. For example, it is certainly politically expedient to ignore the fact that the original oath obliges physicians to refuse to give abortions. Perhaps even more restrictive is the promise "With purity and with holiness I will pass my life...". Not to worry, there are brand new versions of the Hippocratic Oath, much more up to date and specifically designed to harmonize with the best of modern medical tradition.

**Web:**

**http://qlink.queensu.ca/~3ec17/hippoc.htm**

## History of Medicine

The web page of the National Institute of Health's History of Medicine Division. This page has links to articles and online exhibits, including a searchable database of over 60,000 images.

**Web:**

**http://wwwoli.nlm.nih.gov/databases/olihmd/**

## Immunology

Having no immune system is like going away on a vacation and leaving all the doors and windows open. Diseases such as chronic fatigue syndrome, lupus, candida, hypoglycemia, and others manifest themselves in the immune system and wreak havoc on all the other systems in your body. Find out information about specific conditions on the Net.

**Web:**

**http://rehd.med.upenn.edu:1025/**
**http://www.hooked.net/users/sadams/**

### Immune System Talk

You can take my word for it. The immune system is where it's at--medically speaking--in the 21st Century. I predict that all kinds of conditions will be treated by modifying the immune system and that desensitization by oral ingestion of particular substances will become the modality of choice for many illnesses that are being treated today by drugs. For example, certain types of arthritis will be treated by eating chicken soup (or at least the collagen by-products). I further predict that one day some smart fellow is going to take a close look at those homeopathic remedies that actually work, put them together with current immune system theory and treatment, and snarf a Nobel prize for him- or herself. In the meantime, there is no need for you to be out in the ether. You can follow what the specialists are saying by subscribing to the immune system mailing list.

## Infertility

If at first you don't succeed, try try again. If you still don't succeed, check out the resources on the Net to see if you can find something that will help. Discussion and information covers the causes, solutions and treatments for infertility in both men and women.

**Web:**

**http://www.ihr.com/infertility/**

**Usenet:**

**alt.infertility**
**misc.health.infertility**

## Medical Education

If you are involved in a medicine, your education never stops. From your first day in anatomy lab to the last time you pick up a medical journal, there is always something new to learn. Here are some Internet resources—including help in finding medical education software—to help make the job easier.

**Web:**

**http://dpalm2.med.uth.tmc.edu/**
**http://www.med.virginia.edu/med-ed/otherMedEd.html**

## Medical Libraries

Discussions regarding the care and feeding of medical libraries (and medical librarians).

**Usenet:**

**bit.listserv.medlib-l**

## Medical Physics

Here is the forum for medical physicists (those nice people who give you radiation therapy). Do they really glow in the dark or is that just an old wives' tale?

**Web:**

**http://www.snm.org/**

**Usenet:**

**sci.med.physics**

## Medical Software

These web sites will help you find software useful to medical and health science professionals, researchers and students. There is a large variety of medical software on the Net, so it is worth looking to see if you can find what you need.

**Web:**

**http://cac.psu.edu/~sxb41/Med/med_soft.html**
**http://mediswww.cwru.edu/internet/medres/software.html**

## Medical Students

One would think that med students wouldn't have time to hang out on the Internet because they are always in a classroom somewhere with their hands thrust deep into some formaldehyde-soaked cadaver examining its medulla oblongata and vermiform appendix. But as addictive and distracting as the Internet can be, it's not surprising to find a place where medical students from around the world can gather to discuss anything relating to being a med student—labs, study habits, diseases, residencies, exhaustion, and overwork. The web sites offer a collection of information about various issues medical students might face.

**Web:**

**http://www.ama-assn.org/mem-data/special/ama-mss/ama-mss.htm**
**http://www.amsa.org/**
**http://www.s2smed.com/**

**Usenet:**

**bit.listserv.medforum**

**Listserv Mailing List:**

List Name: **medstu-l**
Subscribe to: **listserv@unmvma.unm.edu**

## Medical Use of Drugs

The PDR is fine for looking up standard reference information, but sometimes you will need to do a little research and see what is new with some particular drug. Here is a good web resource to help you, as well as a Usenet discussion group.

**Web:**

**http://pharminfo.com/drg_mnu.html**

**Usenet:**

**sci.med.pharmacy**

## Medicine Talk and General Discussion

Here is the agora of the Usenet medical community. Need to find out the etiology of kidney stones? Need to find out what "etiology" means? This is the place for you. General, free-flowing talk on everything medical. (Does anyone have a cure for a chrono-synclastic infidibulum?)

**Usenet:**

**sci.med**

## Medworld

Medworld is a fabulous resource: an exquisitely designed web site with all manner of medical resources. You could spend hours and hours here, just wandering around. Put this one on your medical bookmark list, and check back often to see what's new.

**Web:**

**http://www-med.stanford.edu/medworld/**

## Mood Disorders

These mood disorder web sites offer access to FAQ files on the drugs Prozac and Effexor, a hypertext FAQ on depression, other resources relating to depression, the writings of Ivan Goldberg, and links to other related resources including a server devoted to adult Attention Deficit Disorder.

**Web:**

**http://avocado.pc.helsinki.fi/~janne/mood/**
**http://www.fairlite.com/ocd/**

## Nursing

These Internet resources are all about nursing: research, practice, education, publications, professional communications, and, on Usenet, lots of discussion.

**Web:**

**http://www.communique.net/~nursgnt/**
**http://www.wp.com/InterNurse/**

**Usenet:**

**alt.npractitioners**
**bit.listserv.snurse-l**
**sci.med.nursing**

**When I was in medical school, I would sometimes sleep overnight in a spare room in the nurses' dormitory, when I was on call in a nearby hospital. Aside from that, I know very little about nursing, so when I need some pertinent info, I check with the *nursing* site (and so should you).**

NURSE

### *Look What I Found on the Net...*

```
Newsgroup: bit.listserv.medforum
Subject: Halfway Through Step 2


Man, does this test suck or what?  I can't believe how long the
items are.

I finished every single book of Step 1 before the 10-minute
warning, and today I was struggling.  Well, I finished Book 1
14 minutes before time, but with Book 2, I was 20 seconds under
the wire, and I didn't get a chance to give any significant
amount of thought to the last few questions.

And what's with all these vitamin/nutrition and ob/gyn
infectious questions?

If I read about one more person who comes in for a health
maintenance exam, or one more person with jugular venous
distension and bibasilar crackles, I'm going to scream!
```

## Occupational Medicine

Need to pick out a back-friendly chair or an ergonomic keyboard? The Usenet discussion on occupational medicine will be just what the doctor would have ordered if he had thought of it. For a lot of immediate information, try the web sites.

**Web:**

**http://ctdnews.com/**
**http://www.osha.gov/**

**Usenet:**

**sci.med.occupational**

## Oncology

Not just for medical people, these Internet resources offer a variety of information for patients, friends and family of patients as well as for any medical field relating to cancer, including gynecology, pediatrics, and veterinary medicine.

**Web:**

**http://cancer.med.upenn.edu/**
**http://cancerguide.org/**

**Listproc Mailing List:**

List Name: **ncinet**
Subscribe to: **listproc@lists.acs.ohio-state.edu**

**Listserv Mailing List:**

List Name: **cancer-l**
Subscribe to: **listserv@wvnvm.wvnet.edu**

## Online Medical Multimedia Texts

Informative medical texts, created using pictures and images in order to be accessed online. Here you can find material on a variety of subjects. Good for teaching, learning or checking into the latest information in a particular area.

**Web:**

**http://indy.radiology.uiowa.edu/Providers/Textbooks/MultimediaTextbooks.html**

## Organ Transplants

One of the miracles of modern medicine is the ability to replace various body parts as needed. Of course, it's not that simple, but as the years go by the process becomes more advanced. The mailing list and Usenet group offer a means for organ transplant recipients, family members, and anyone interested in transplant issues to discuss their thoughts and experiences on the subject. The web sites provide information of a medical and emotional nature.

**Web:**

**http://www.cis.ohio-state.edu/hypertext/faq/usenet/medicine/transplant-faq/top.html**
**http://www.gen.emory.edu/medweb/medweb.transplant.html**
**http://www.infi.net/~donation/**

**Usenet:**

**bit.listserv.transplant**

**Listserv Mailing List:**

List Name: **trnsplnt**
Subscribe to: **listserv@wuvmd.wustl.edu**

## Paramedics

If you have been eating an apple a day but you still need help, you may not be able to get the doctor to come over; however, the paramedics are always available. Join the discussion with paramedics and other emergency-oriented workers. The web site has pictures and information about emergency and rescue workers.

**Web:**

**http://www.catt.citri.edu.au/emergency/**

**Usenet:**

**misc.emerg-services**

**"Fun" is fun.**

## Pharmacy

What a pickle. You have to bring something to the local PTA potluck and you forgot the recipe for methylenedioxyamphetamine. Ask a pharmacist. Or maybe you just need a pharmacist joke. (Did you hear about the pill counter who married the bean counter? They had a son who became a CPA, but would only work one hour before or three hours after meals.) Find out why pharmacy is the new glamour profession of the '90s.

**Web:**

**http://members.aol.com/pharmtimes/**
**http://pharm.cpb.uokhsc.edu/pharmacy/pharmint.html**
**http://www.cpb.uokhsc.edu/pharmacy/pharmint.html**
**http://www.ns.net/~ryan/**

**Usenet:**

**sci.med.pharmacy**

**IRC:**

**#pharmacy**

## Politics and Medicine

Talk is cheap, but medical care is not. What happens when an irresistible force (health care reform) meets an immovable object (the health care industry)? Join the ongoing debate and share your story of Uncle Willie and his gallbladder operation or check out the web sites for some late breaking news.

**Usenet:**

**talk.politics.medicine**

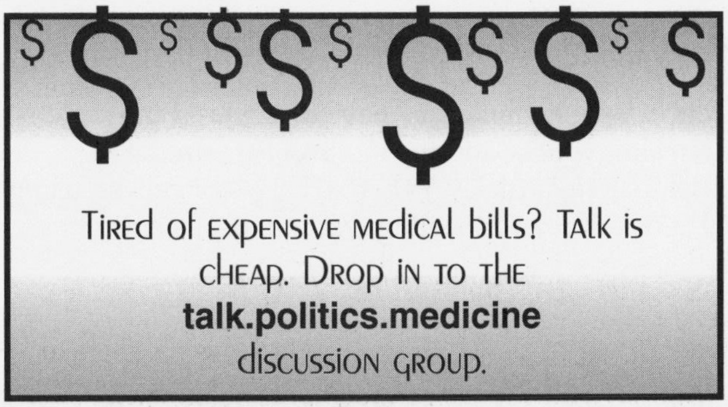
Tired of expensive medical bills? Talk is cheap. Drop in to the
talk.politics.medicine
discussion group.

## Radiology

Radiology is the medical specialty that deals with all kinds of imaging: radiographs (X-rays), CAT scans, IVPs, and so on. The Usenet group is for ongoing discussion among radiology professionals. The web site is the home of the Radiological Society of North America, where you will find a lot of useful resources.

**Web:**

**http://www.rsna.org/**

**Usenet:**

**sci.med.radiology**

## Schizophrenia

Look into this unmoderated discussion list devoted to schizophrenia research. This is a place for researchers and medical professionals to explore this mental illness, facilitate collaborations between investigators, and foster discussion on published and unpublished findings and ideas.

**Majordomo Mailing List:**

List Name: **schiz-l**
Subscribe to: **majordomo@list.pitt.edu**

## Telemedicine

Telemedicine means using electronic signals to transfer medical information from one place to another. In other words, clinical consulting via computer networks: new technology for the world's second oldest profession.

**Web:**

**http://www.telemed.org/**

**Usenet:**

**sci.med.telemedicine**

## Virtual Hospital

See this remarkable multimedia medical database that is available 24 hours a day. Multimedia textbooks and teaching files, lectures, clinical references, and medical history are just a few things offered here.

**Web:**

**http://vh.radiology.uiowa.edu/**

A B C D E F G H I J K L M N O P Q R S T U V W X Y Z

Do you know someone
who needs a doctor,
but not right away?
Tell them to wait while
you connect to the
Virtual Hospital and
teach yourself everything
you need to know.

## Virtual Library of Medicine

The Virtual Library of Medicine is an ambitious project to make massive amounts of useful medical information available over the Net. Here you will find various types of medical information and resources: plain text, multimedia textbooks, patient simulations, practice guidelines, journals, and on and on—organized in several different ways to make it easy to find what you want.

**Web:**

**http://vh.radiology.uiowa.edu/Providers/Providers.html**

## Webdoctor

Whatcha gonna do when you need some medical info on the Net, and you're not sure where to look? Try Webdoctor: the place for busy doctors to find what they need in a hurry. (There are also special resources for rural physicians.)

**Web:**

**http://www.gretmar.com/**

# MEDICINE: ALTERNATIVE

## Acupuncture

Acupuncture is used to treat quite a variety of problems. If you are thinking of having an acupuncture treatment, you might want to read this brief overview of the process, a partial list of ailments and conditions treated by acupuncture, guidelines for selecting an acupuncturist and a bibliography of interesting reading material.

**Web:**

**http://www.acupuncture.com/**

## Alternative Medicine Resources

Tired of legal drugs and poor bedside manner? Drop in to the alternative medicine forum where alternative-oriented people share alternative medical tips, alternative home remedies, and alternative approaches to healing. (If you can't make it, send an alternate.)

**Web:**

**http://www.pitt.edu/~cbw/altm.html**
**http://www.talamasca.org/avatar/alt-healing.html**

**Usenet:**

**misc.health.alternative**

Alternative Medicine
My philosophy is that it is better to not get sick in the first place. Still, if you do, it's nice to know that you have a forum in which you can discuss the types of things that you can only whisper about at the doctor's office. So, next time you need to know how many leeches to use to cure brain cancer, check with your friends on misc.health.alternative.
Remember the old saying about an apple a day...

## Alternative Methods of Healing

Lots of people think they have discovered the secrets of health, vitality and the foolproof treatment of disease. Read articles on herbal cures for cancer, using light or oxygen for healing, vitamin usage and other articles on alternative methods of healing.

**Web:**

**http://www.livelinks.com/sumeria/health.htm**

## Ayurvedic Medicine Talk and General Discussion

In Sanskrit, *ayurveda* means "laws of health," and is the name of one of the four sacred Hindu texts. Ayurvedic medicine is based on Indian traditions more than 3,000 years old. Read this Usenet group and learn about this ancient healing art and how it is practiced today.

**Usenet:**

**alt.health.ayurveda**

## Cannabis and Medicine

Cannabis (marijuana) is one of the most popular intoxicating drugs in the world. The most common use of marijuana is to induce a sustained sense of well-being and mild euphoria (the technical term is "getting high"). However, there are a number of medical conditions for which cannabis can be used as an effective treatment: cancer chemotherapy symptoms, certain types of loss of appetite, chronic glaucoma, muscle spasms, menstrual cramps, certain AIDS symptoms and moderate chronic pain. Read about these treatments as well as related information about government and legal issues.

**Web:**

**http://www.foobar.co.uk/users/ukcia/medicine.html**
**http://www.norml.org/medical/**

## Chiropractic

It's good to be informed on all aspects of medical treatments. When I was in medical school at the University of Toronto, I used to go to the local chiropractic school's public clinic to be treated. These Internet sites offer you an introduction and history of chiropractic, an overview of the profession and treatment, links to education and licensing information, and other chiropractic resources.

**Web:**

**http://ssi.syspac.com/~ezikmun/**
**http://www.mbnet.mb.ca/~jwiens/chiro.html**
**http://www.panix.com/~tonto1/dc.html**

## Complementary Medicine

A list of alternative forms of medicine that some people choose to use in addition to regular medicine. Find a huge list of topics such as acupuncture, diet and nutritional therapy, biofeedback, rolfing, aromatherapy, cryogenic medicine, shiatsu and many more.

**Web:**

**http://galen.med.virginia.edu/~pjb3s/ComplementaryHomePage.html**

## Herbal Medicine

Herbs have been used in healing for thousands of years, with their popularity occasionally rising and falling. However, there is a lot more to using herbs than knowing enough to give valerian to your lawyer to calm him down. Before you start messing around with your body chemistry, spend a little time on the Net and learn something about the herbs you propose to take. To help you, here are some resources that offer particularly useful information.

**Web:**

**http://frank.mtsu.edu/~sward/MEDFAQ/**
**http://users.vnet.net/shae/altheal/herbs.html**

## Holistic Healing

Going to the doctor is no fun. Everyone is wearing a uniform, it's all sterile and rigid, and various people take turns poking you with sharp instruments. Experience a gentler alternative to medicine in the form of holistic concepts and methods of living, which are reported to be a more natural way of dealing with the hairpin turns on the road of life. A variety of holistic topics are discussed, such as states of consciousness, meditation, healthy diet, herbs, vitamins, rolfing, and massage.

**Web:**

**http://www.holistic.com/~holistic/**

**Listserv Mailing List:**

List Name: **holistic**
Subscribe to: **listserv@siucvmb.siu.edu**

## Homeopathy

Homeopathy is a popular form of alternative medicine based on remedies that contain tiny amounts of active ingredients. Find out more about it on the Net: where you can get a FAQ, information about mailing lists and Usenet groups, contacts in the U.S., U.K. and other parts of the world, a useful bibliography, and medical resources links.

**Web:**

**http://www.dungeon.com/~cam/homeo.html**

## Massage Therapy Talk and General Discussion

In the last 25 years, massage therapy and bodywork have taken the place of what used to be referred to as "getting a rubdown". Today, registered massage therapists undergo specialized training including many hours of practice. For some people, having bodywork done is an emotional, transcendent, healing experience. For others, a rubdown is a rubdown. Still, almost everybody likes to be touched, and giving or receiving a massage is high up on most people's lists of enjoyable activities. I myself have had many massages from various types of practitioners, both professional and amateur. What do I think of massage? When it's good, it's really good; and when it's bad, it's still pretty good. This Usenet group is for discussion of massage in all its forms. (The group is *not* for soliciting people to massage you.) If you are interested in massage, I think you would enjoy reading the FAQ (frequently asked question list) for this group, which you can find at the web site. Here you will find a good basic introduction to massage. You will also learn about various types of massage as well as topics of interest to massage professionals.

**Web:**

**http://www.ii.uib.no/~kjartan/backrubfaq/**

**Usenet:**

**alt.backrubs**

**Spam is more than a food.**

**Unconventional treatments and schools of thought are more in vogue than ever. If you want to follow what is happening in the netherworld of medicine, subscribe to the holistic mailing list.**

## Mind and Imagery Therapy

This is an online version of an imagery magazine called Atlantis. It has information about mental imagery for health professionals and for regular people, techniques, articles and a bibliography on imagery. Learn about breath techniques, mantra meditation, and so on.

**Web:**

**http://www.electriciti.com/atlantis/**

## Music Therapy

Virtually everyone responds to music. We all know that the right music at the right time can be soothing, energizing, inspiring or entertaining. Music therapy practitioners use music and rhythm to alleviate various medical and social conditions. In the United States, certified music therapists must complete an approved college curriculum (including an internship) and then pass a national board examination. These web sites provide a lot of information about music therapy: what it is, its philosophy and history, what conditions are treated by music therapists, and so on. There is also information explaining the profession and what sort of training is required.

**Web:**

**http://falcon.cc.ukans.edu/~memt/mt.html**
**http://ukanaix.cc.ukans.edu/~dirkcush/mt.html**
**http://www.namt.com/namt/**

## Osteopathy

Osteopathy is a system of medicine descended from the teachings of Andrew Taylor Still (1828-1917). Osteopaths receive medical training similar to regular doctors, with the addition of special courses in tissue manipulation. Where a regular doctor is known as an M.D., an osteopath uses the designation D.O. (Doctor of Osteopathy). In the United States, osteopaths are licensed to practice medicine by using drugs and surgery. However, they tend to have a more generalized and natural approach to healing that they use along with their manipulation techniques. A large portion of osteopaths are engaged in primary care (family medicine).

**Web:**

**http://www.concentric.net/~Ericdo/**

## Relaxation Techniques

People complain about stress, but think how much less satisfying relaxation would be if there were nothing to relax from. In fact, what good would these sites be if it weren't for stress? So stop what you are doing right now and contemplate the stress in your life, and how lucky you are that stress provides you with an excuse to fall apart and utilize the relaxation resources available on the Net. (Note: I have chosen these sites carefully to provide a variety of approaches to relaxation. One of them will suit you.)

**Web:**

**http://www.ari.net/jec/gtower/gtower.html#mm1**
**http://www.cns.net/consortium/relax.html**
**http://www.gasou.edu/psychweb/mtsite/smpage.html**
**http://www.shsu.edu/~counsel/shortr.html**

***Relaxation Techniques***

**All stressed out and nowhere to go?**

**The Net will take care of you.**

**Visit one of the Relaxation Techniques sites, and soon you'll be cruising through life as cool as a virtual cucumber.**

## Rolfing

Rolfing is a complex system of bodywork in which a practitioner makes structural changes in the body of the client. Rolfing is named after its inventor, the American biochemist and physiotherapist Ida P. Rolf (1896-1979). Within the body, the muscles, tendons, ligaments and organs are surrounded by thin, tough sheets of tissue called fascia. This tissue is arranged in "fascial planes" that run throughout the body, providing a framework for movement and posture. A rolfer is specially trained in understanding the nature of the fascial planes and manipulating them along with the musculature. (Note: I spent four years in medical school, and I don't remember learning anything about the fascial planes. Later I found out that the only people who really understand them are rolfers and plastic surgeons.) Rolfing is carried out in a series of treatments (usually ten) in which the rolfer uses his hands, arms and even elbows to manipulate the soft tissue of the client. I can sum up the entire experience (I have been rolfed a lot of times) as follows: (1) It can hurt. (2) It can be expensive. (3) It is absolutely wonderful and is definitely worth doing.

**Web:**

**http://www.rolf.org/**
**http://www.teleport.com/~amrta/rolfing.html**

## Shiatsu

Shiatsu is a traditional form of Japanese medicine in which the practitioner uses his palms and thumbs to apply pressure to various points on the body, the same points that are recognized and stimulated during acupuncture. A shiatsu treatment can be a lot like acupuncture using pressure instead of needles (in which case it is sometimes described as acupressure), or it can be more like a massage that concentrates on the various points. A session with a skilled shiatsu practitioner is usually an enjoyable experience, leaving one with a pleasant feeling of relaxation and comfort.

**Web:**

**http://www.doubleclickd.com/shiatsu.html**
**http://www1.tip.nl/users/t283083/e_index.htm**

# MEN

## At-Home Dad

Fathers, if you stay at home with the kids, here is a newsletter for you. At-Home Dad focuses on fathers who, for whatever reason, are the primary homemaker. After all, by their nature, men are less nurturing than women and a little help is always welcome. For an ongoing discussion of male homemaking, you can participate in the Usenet group.

**Web:**

**http://www.parentsplace.com/readroom/athomedad/newslett.html**

**Usenet:**

**alt.support.househusbands**

## Backlash

Backlash is a magazine that rallies the troops against various unfair political beliefs. In particular, I am including the magazine here because Backlash comes out strong against male stereotypes. My advice is to visit this site and explore the Sexism section, where you will find features, news and regular columns written from the male point of view.

**Web:**

**http://www.backlash.com/**

## BlokeNet

Do you like irony? Can you stand British-oriented irony aimed in the face of just about everybody? Try BlokeNet: a not-for-your-sensitive-90s-man online zine. BlokeNet is for guys who lust after women, drink beer, eat meat and participate in unhealthy activities (that is, for just about every man within 100 miles of this book). This is not the place to visit if you are going to be offended by male-pig-oriented fashion tips for women (wear short skirts and have breast augmentation) or by real but politically incorrect advice (women should not be impatient with men who are slobs and want to spend lots of time in a pub). No siree, Bob. This is a place for people who are ready to enjoy silly man stuff with a British accent.

**Web:**

**http://ourworld.compuserve.com/homepages/Top_Bloke/**

## Crisis and Grief of Men

You don't have to flounder around when it comes to dealing with sadness, grief or a crisis that feels too big to be handled alone. On the Net, you can read articles about how to handle your own grief or how to help other people deal with their problems. This site also offers a regular column about the differences between genders with respect to healing.

**Web:**

**http://www2.dgsys.com/~tgolden/**

## Fathers

Whether you are a single father or a father in a traditional family, there are resources on the Net that will interest you. These sites have lots of information on parenting, rights of fathers, at-home dads, things to do with the kids and lots more. Join the mailing list and talk to other online dads.

**Web:**

**http://aipnet.com/workshop/**
**http://www.cyfc.umn.edu/FatherNet.htp**
**http://www.fathermag.com/contents.html**
**http://www.parentsplace.com/readroom/frc/**
**http://www.pitt.edu/~jsims/singlefa.html**

**Listserv Mailing List:**

List Name: **father-l**
Subscribe to: **listserv@tc.umn.edu**

## Friends of Choice for Men

View the idea of "choice" from a man's point of view. The Friends of Choice for Men promote the idea that men should not be forced into fatherhood. This organization works for the equality between men's and women's reproductive rights. The Friends of Choice for Men offer articles, stories and other resources that promote choice for men.

**Web:**

**http://www.nas.com/c4m/**

## Hair Loss

This site gives information on various methods of treating hair loss. You can read about various treatment agents, a male pattern baldness FAQ (frequently asked question list), patterns of hair loss, personal experiences, shampoo reviews, alternative treatments, drugs that contribute to hair loss, and on and on. (Men, listen to me. When you try to cover your bald spot by combing the hair on the side of your head over the top, you're not really fooling anyone. Trying to look younger than your real age is a game you can only lose. Want my advice? Forget about trying to look younger than you really are and learn to be gracious about getting older.)

**Web:**

**http://www2.xstar.com/baldspot.htm**

## Man's Life

A Man's Life is an online magazine devoted to men. You will find news and a variety of articles. Read about women (relationships, being a sex object, how to get a woman), family (relating to your kids, relating to your dad) and fashion (picking out cool clothes, wearing hats, dressing for sex). They also cover interesting topics from the male point of view, such as health, fitness, outdoors, food, pets, goofing off, sports, money, home repairs. The articles are fun and lighthearted, and provide a pleasant way to pass the time.

**Web:**

**http://www.manslife.com/**

## Men in the Justice System

Here is a variety of links that relate to the role men play in the justice system. You will find information on court bias against men, statistics about men in the justice system, and links to specific state or international court systems.

**Web:**

**http://www.vix.com/pub/men/criminal/justice.html**

## M.E.N. Magazine

M.E.N. stands for Men's Evolvement Network. This magazine was created to offer information, support and advocacy for men. Various nationally recognized authors have written stories and articles dealing with conflicts with children, grief, love, child abuse recovery, divorce and other related men's issues. While you are here, check out the calendar of events to see if there are any conferences you would like to attend.

**Web:**

**http://www.vix.com/menmag/**

## Men's Health

Men have health concerns all their own, and here are some web sites that address the issues. Read about prostate cancer, urinary tract infections, vasectomies, self-care, sex and more. You can also enjoy informative articles about men's health and related topics.

**Web:**

**http://www.malehealthcenter.com/**
**http://www.menshealth.com/**

### *Look What I Found on the Net...*

(from an editorial in the online Fathering Magazine)

Fathers Are Important

A U.S. government survey found that the most important factor predicting whether a child will grow up to commit a violent crime is not social class, not race, and not educational level or cultural background.

The absence of a father in the home is the most significant predictor of a later conviction for a violent crime.

## Men's Health

Men, let's face it. The health care system is not always going to take care of us the way we need. We have special problems and health considerations that the female-centric medical establishment doesn't always recognize.

The first step to maintaining our health is to become knowledgeable about our bodies and how they work. Then we need to learn about men's health issues and how they affect us.

The Net can help.

## Men's Internetwork

An interesting site maintained by a men's movement organization. Read news relating to the men's movement, stories and articles in the writer's gallery, the Men's Manifesto and the Father's Manifesto. You will also find links to other sites dealing with equality between men and women.

**Web:**
**http://www.webcom.com/~tmi.com/**

## Men's Issues

Check out this great collection of men's issues resources. These pages cover topics such as attitudes toward men, domestic violence, employment, fatherhood, health, history of men's movements, romance and relationships, the justice system and much more. You will also find reviews of books and links to information about various men's organizations.

**Web:**
**http://www.contact.org/usmen.htm**
**http://www.msn.fullfeed.com/~rschenk/hotspots.html**
**http://www.vix.com/men/**

## Men's Mailing Lists

Talking and sharing feelings is not just for women. Here are some mailing lists that offer a great place for men to talk about anything at all: current issues, legislation, book reviews, news, scholarly articles or just chatter. These lists are safe zones for men where everyone is encouraged to participate.

**Listserv Mailing List:**
List Name: **mensig-l**
Subscribe to: **listserv@mizzou1.missouri.edu**

**Listserv Mailing List:**
List Name: **talk-man**
Subscribe to: **listserv@tamvm1.tamu.edu**

## Men's Rights

This mailing list and Usenet discussion group offers a chance for men to talk actively about men's rights and issues. While all men's rights discussion on Usenet is fair game for anyone reading and posting, the mailing list offers a chance for men to talk without worrying about flame wars with people who have radically opposing viewpoints.

**Usenet:**
**alt.mens-rights**

**Majordomo Mailing List:**
List Name: **mens-rights-l**
Subscribe to: **majordomo@world.std.com**

### Men's Rights

*The definitive speech on men's rights was delivered by Rob Petrie on October 24, 1961 (The Dick Van Dyke Show, episode #5: "Washington vs. the Bunny"):*

"A man is a man, even if he is a husband, and at no time, as a man or as a husband, should he ever be his wife's puppet. I have to do what I think is right. A man shouldn't sacrifice his self-respect just to keep peace in the home. All right, a woman's opinion should be weighed and considered, but in the final analysis, a man has to do what he thinks is right, or he is no man."

The implications of this speech are still being debated. Join the discussion on the Net.

## Men's Talk and General Discussion

Okay men, this is the place where we can talk about whatever we want without having to worry about being sensitive or politically correct. For the purposes of this book, I will say that in the men's discussion group we talk about work, relationships, feminism, health, and other such topics. (But I'm sure you know what we *really* discuss.)

**Usenet:**

soc.men

## National Coalition of Free Men

A non-profit organization, the National Coalition of Free Men sponsors this site which discusses sex discrimination and has links to other sites that may be of interest to men. Read news, letters and see the calendar of events.

**Web:**

http://www.ncfm.org/

### *Look What I Found on the Net...*

```
Newsgroup: soc.men
Subject: Need Examples of Feminist Weirdness

> I'm looking for examples of really weird, bizarre feminist
> thought.  Not the garden-variety man-bashing and double
> standards, but stuff that is really OUT there: bizarre
> conspiracy theories, goddess worship, menstrual worship,
> performance art, fractured historical "herstory," etc.
>
> This is for a planned web page on feminist weirdness...

                    (reply from a man)

Ah, the voice of equality speaks.  So this web site is going to show
the negative side of feminism?

Of course, it will be accurate since you will check the
sources.  This way, no one can say it is a lie. Unless, of
course, you try to state that it is reflective of all feminism.
That would be a lie.

And if feminists decide to create a web site showing only the
"bad" side of the men's movement (like how its very name is
sexist, how it deals only with a certain group's rights and
ignores others), that will be okay, wouldn't it?

                    (reply from a woman)

Hey, sweetcakes, man-bashing and double standards?  That's WAY
out there already.  You want something weirder than that?

How about the stories men tell women to try to "get a little"?

Or how the same men explain it when they get home?

Or maybe how some men focus on woman-hating topics, spending all
their energy trying to find an acceptable reason to hate the
gender they want to love?
```

## P.O.V.

P.O.V. ("point of view") is the online version of a guy's magazine. Of course there are men's magazines, but this one is for *guys*. Read about careers, finances, and various topics of general interest. I saw an article about guys who brew their own beer. (You see what I mean? Real men don't brew their own beer, but real guys do.) The site also features a collection of web links for guys. Hot patootie, bless my soul.

**Web:**

**http://www.povmag.com/**

## Self-Help for Men

If things are not going your way, do a little reading that will inspire, comfort or assist you in problem-solving. Read these articles and archives of self-help resources for men. There are also links to other self-help sites.

**Web:**

**http://avalon.dash.com/ftx/ftx.html**
**http://www.well.com/user/selfhelp/artindex.htm**

## Twelve Steps for Divorced Fathers

Divorced fathers often need support. Being separated from your wife and children is a tough situation. If you are having a bad time, check out this site. The twelve-step program is based on the famous Alcoholics Anonymous model and, as such, involves a good deal of believing in God. However, if that's okay with you, the program might help. Give it a try.

**Web:**

**http://www.spacelab.net/~mission/**

## What Women Find Attractive in Men

The title says it all. Women leave notes about what they find attractive in men and you (the men) can read them. If you really care about what women want, this is a good place to start learning.

**Web:**

**http://www.itsnet.com/~bug/guys.html**

# MILITARY

## Armed Forces of the World

These web sites are great sources of information about various military organizations around the world. You can find links to defense forces, journals, documents, maps, military bases, military reserves, research centers and intelligence organizations. For example, I was able to learn how the Israeli military forces follow a doctrine of "speed, initiative and audacity". You can also find a lot of interesting information (such as the fact that Cyprus has four aircraft and eight helicopters even though they don't have an air force or a navy). Hint: If you are a student looking for a topic in which to write an essay, here are some wonderful sources of information.

**Web:**

**http://members.aol.com/rhrongstad/private/milinksr.htm**
**http://www.cfcsc.dnd.ca/links/milorg/**
**http://www.iaw.on.ca/~awoolley/lwformil.html**

## Chemical and Biological Warfare

We hear a lot about chemical and biological warfare, but not many people really understand it. These web sites can help you appreciate the power of these types of weapons and how they work. Learn about substances such as nerve gas, mustard agents, tear gases and hydrogen cyanide, as well as handy tips for protecting yourself should it become necessary. You can also explore a large number of related resources, including some official government web sites. There are links to storage and disposal facilities, research facilities, articles and treaties, and much, much more.

**Web:**

**http://members.aol.com/tomhun8054/bioweps.html**
**http://www.opcw.nl/chemhaz/chemhome.htm**

**FAQs are cool.**

## Contemporary Military Conflicts

Stay current with serious military activity by visiting the web site whenever you need to know what is happening where. Select the part of the world in which you are interested, and you will find links to news and information about the countries in conflict in that area. You can find out the latest news as well as read about the origins of the conflict, military aggressions, and the organizations and activist groups who are involved in helping to resolve the situation.

**Web:**

**http://www.cfcsc.dnd.ca/links/wars/**

**The Net cares.**

## Disarmament Talk and General Discussion

Discussion and monthly digests of military and political strategy, technology, sociology, and peace activism involved in accelerating disarmament of nuclear, conventional, and chemical weapons. **disarm-d** provides monthly digests of selected mail discussions that are posted to **disarm-l**. It also includes essays, papers, reviews, and excerpts from important publications.

**Listserv Mailing List:**

List Name: **disarm-d**
Subscribe to: **listserv@uacsc2.albany.edu**

**Listserv Mailing List:**

List Name: **disarm-l**
Subscribe to: **listserv@uacsc2.albany.edu**

### *Look What I Found on the Net...*

(from the "What Women Find Attractive in Men" web site)

What do I find attractive in men?

Someone who is tall, generous, confident, funny, comfortable not being in control of the relationship, and will let me be.

Someone who isn't afraid to show his emotions, and who has values similar to mine.

Someone who isn't into strip bars, pretty models and porn (unless we watch it together).

He has to support me, and see men and women as equals, but accept that women are better drivers than men.

He has to kill the spiders for me, and be a vegetarian.

He must be ready for me to keep my maiden name should we marry, and be willing to pass my name, not his, on to our children.

He has to take paternity leave if his job allows it, and be willing to take on a greater share of the housework.

He has to wish my mother happy birthday and happy Mother's Day when required, and bring her a small gift.

He can't be possessive or try to keep me from my busy lifestyle.

Foot rubs are necessary once per week, and he has to be concerned with my sexual satisfaction.

Moreover, he has to have as much energy as me, have a positive outlook, and try his hardest at everything.

I expect near perfection, and accept nothing less than the best.

Oh, and if anyone doubts that such a man exist, I already found him (except that he isn't a vegetarian, but he's from England, so that makes up for it).

## Medieval Armor

These web sites have lots of information about armor. Visit one site and you can read about armor construction (how-to info), and look at pictures of armor. You will also find an armor glossary, and an area where you can share messages, links and references with other armor enthusiasts. The other web site has pictures of basic armor of the Middle Ages, including horse armor, as well as pictures of various weapons from the Middle Ages (bows and arrows, swords, spears, axes and so on).

**Web:**

**http://darkstar.swsc.k12.ar.us/~davidc/**
**http://www.hipark.austin.isd.tenet.edu/medieval/armour/main.html**

## Military Academies

A military academy is a school or college that provides a full-time military living environment for young men and women while they are following a regular academic program. Traditionally, one of the main purposes of a military academy is to train future officers for the armed services. In the United States, there are a great many military academies for students of all ages. The most well-known academies are the three college-level schools: the Military Academy at West Point, New York; the Naval Academy at Annapolis, Maryland; and the Air Force Academy at Colorado Springs, Colorado. There is also the Coast Guard Academy in New London, Connecticut, and the Merchant Marine Academy in Kings Point, New York. These web sites contain links to a great many military academies throughout the United States. If you would like to discuss life in a military school—especially if you are a cadet—you may enjoy participating in the Usenet group.

**Web:**

**http://vax1.rain.gen.mo.us/~kemper/amcsus2.htm**
**http://www.artsci.wustl.edu/~jrdorkin/military.html**
**http://www.geocities.com/Athens/7429/milcollege.html**

**Usenet:**

**alt.military.cadet**

## Military Brats

Children who grow up in a military family have lives that are just a tad different than the children of civilians. This Usenet discussion group is for talking about growing up in a military family, whether you are currently in such a family or whether you grew up in one. If you have problems, you may want to talk to other people who understand your situation.

**Usenet:**

**alt.culture.military-brats**

## Military History

Both pages have lots and lots of great links to pages about military history. You can find information on military history from ancient times to present day. I am not sure what else to say except that if it's on the Net, you are bound to find it here.

**Web:**

**http://www.cfcsc.dnd.ca/links/milhist/**
**http://www.olcommerce.com/cadre/milhist/**

## Military Magazines

These magazines are for people interested in the military culture. I have selected these sites to provide an interesting variety. On one web site, you will find the online edition of Soldiers, the official magazine of the U.S. Army. Read news and features about the U.S. Army and its soldiers. I found the articles interesting, even though I have no connection at all with the Army. The other magazine, Military Review, has been published since 1922. It is a forum for the discussion of military affairs. This magazine focuses on the art and technique of modern warfare. If you are serious about military science, you will enjoy the articles, especially if you are into hardcore strategy and planning.

**Web:**

**http://www-cgsc.army.mil/cgsc/milrev/milrev.htm**
**http://www.redstone.army.mil/soldiers/**

**My other joke is funny.**

**Military Academies**

**Are you thinking of going to a military academy (or sending your son or daughter to one)? Check with the Net first. Just about every military academy in the United States has a web site.**

## Military Medals

This site has a great collection of medals from the United States as well as other countries. You can see medals and ribbons (such as the Medal of Honor or the Purple Heart) as well as rank insignia. If you enjoy reading about medals, you will find some real curiosities here, such as a collection of fictitious Star Trek ribbons and information about certain rare medals (such as the USMC Brevet Medal, only 23 of which were ever awarded).

**Web:**

**http://users.aol.com/gman755/medals/medals2.html**

## Military Police

This site is an Internet home for MP (Military Police) officers around the world. Look for information about military police, reunions, MPs in the news, articles about MPs and their service, as well as links to related sites around the Net. The Usenet group is for MPs from all over the planet to hang out and talk about MP stuff.

**Web:**

**http://www.primenet.com/~burchel/milpol.html**

**Usenet:**

**alt.military.police**

**Wow, free software.**

## Military Secrecy

What words come to mind when you think about the military? Of course you think of soldiers, guns, tanks, and so on, but high up on anyone's list is secrecy. Personally, I love finding out stuff that I am not supposed to know, and if you are like me at all, you will appreciate this web site devoted to military secrecy. The emphasis is on the American military, but they have enough secret stuff to keep you busy reading for a long time. Find out about classified government programs, how much funding they received, various secret locations (such as Area 51), information about various test sites, and much, much more. One of the most interesting documents is the National Security Administration (NSA) employee handbook. For example, I found out that any NSA employee who is planning a personal trip outside the United States must fill out a form describing his or her plans 30 working days before the trip and have the trip approved before being allowed to go. If you like secrets, there is enough information at this web site to keep you busy for a long time.

**Web:**

**http://www.portal.com/~trader/secrecy.html**

## Military Talk and General Discussion

The military is a lot more important and more powerful than most people realize. Moreover, there are lots of important military topics that bear discussion: military science, weapon design and deployment and, of course, politics. There are a number of Usenet groups devoted to ongoing discussions of military topics. Here are the places you can talk about the latest military technology, the various armed services around the world, life in the service, military urban legends, and much more.

**Usenet:**

**alt.folklore.military**
**sci.military**
**sci.military.moderated**
**sci.military.naval**

## Military Terms and Acronyms

Have you ever encountered a military term that you didn't understand? It's not surprising—there are literally tens of thousands of such terms and nobody knows them all. If you are interested in any aspect of the military, here is a useful tool that can save you a lot of running around. It is a file containing more than 20,000 military terms and acronyms. The data is stored in WinHelp (Windows help file) format. (This may be the first time the Windows help program will actually give you some useful information.)

**Web:**

**http://www.jcave.com/~bandorm/megaterm/megaterm.htm**

**Get into "Mischief".**

## Military Uniforms

Military uniforms are fascinating. Examine this web site and you will see what I mean. You can look at pictures of European military uniforms from the early 19th century and from the Burgoyne Expedition (1777). The early 19th century images cover armies from Austria, Britain, Denmark, France, Greece, Italy, Prussia, Russia, Saxony, Spain and Sweden. The Burgoyne section has uniforms of British, German and American soldiers. Note: John Burgoyne (1722-1792) was a British general who was a hero in the Seven Years War, a worldwide conflict that was fought from 1753-1763 in Europe, North America and India. Burgoyne was elected to Parliament (1761) and led troops during the American Revolutionary War. Later, he became a playwright and was known by the nickname "Gentleman Johnny".

**Web:**

**http://www.nypl.org/research/chss/subguides/milhist/costnypl.html**

## *Look What I Found on the Net...*

```
Newsgroup: sci.military.moderated
Subject: Why Are There No Robot Ground Troops?

>> Pardon me if this has been addressed before, but why are
>> there no robot ground troops?
>>
>> Is it just the reluctance of the various militaries?
>> Squeamishness? Or have robots not been sufficiently developed?

> Current robotics technology limitations make this unfeasible.
>
> 1. Robots are really really expensive.
> 2. Robots are really really delicate and mechanically fussy.
>
> The U.S. military has currently fielded unmanned robot
> observation drone planes (used in the Gulf War).  That's about
> all for now.

To me, this poses some moral questions.

1. Wouldn't the ability to fight wars without exposing troops to
   danger make the price of the military option too small?

2. Who would be responsible for war crimes committed by such a
   robot?

It seems that a device built to seek out people and kill them
without human supervision should be classified as a weapon of
mass destruction.
```

## Military Vehicles

If you are into testosterone-laced fighting machines, here is a list of web sites that will get your motor running. There are lots of pictures of various types of military vehicles from the United States and other countries. Read about vehicles such as the M1 Abrams Main Battle Tank, the AH-64 Apache Attack Helicopter or, my personal favorite, the HMMWV or Humvee (a super-cool jeep with a thyroid condition). Watch and listen to video clips, sounds and animations, and read factsheets about various military crafts. The Usenet discussion group is for people who like to talk about military vehicles.

**Web:**

**http://sorex.tvi.cc.nm.us/~rhernend/tanks.htm**
**http://www.jmu.edu/rotc/gallery.html**
**http://www.militarycity.com/library.htm**

**Usenet:**

**sci.military.vehicles**

## Mine Warfare

A mine is a bomb that is placed in a specific location in such a way that it will explode when some person or piece of equipment sets it off. Some mines—called land mines—are designed to be buried in the ground so that, when you walk on them and press on a sensor, they will explode. If you are lucky, you are maimed. If you are unlucky you die. Other mines—such as naval mines—are deployed in water, on or below the surface. These mines have sonar or magnetic sensors that make then useful for blowing up warships and other marine vessels. These web sites offer a wide variety of information about the various types of mines (of which there are many). Learn about how and why mines are used, as well as countermeasures that are sometimes effective and ways in which mines can be detected. Look at pictures, read the facts, and be glad you live in a safe place.

**Web:**

**http://faramir.mece.ualberta.ca/landmine/links.html**
**http://vricl4c.vrinet.com/infonet/minecd.html**
**http://www.ae.utexas.edu/~industry/mine/**

## Selective Service System

The United States Selective Service System (SSS) is an independent agency that is part of the executive branch of the federal government. The job of the SSS is twofold. (1) In case of emergency, the SSS is to deliver untrained manpower to the U.S. Department of Defense. (2) At the same time, the SSS is to administer an alternative service program for conscientious objectors. Basically, the SSS works by forcing all young men to register so the organization can keep track of them in case they are needed to serve in the military. In the aftermath of the Vietnam War the program was suspended, but in 1980 (during the last year of Jimmy Carter's presidency), the registration requirement was reinstated. Right now, in the United States, the law says that all men between the ages of 18 and 26 are required to register with the Selective Service System. (You can get the form in any post office.) When a young man turns 18, he must register within 30 days of his birthday. In the event of an emergency that required a military draft, a lottery would be held to choose who has to go. Priority would be given to those who are currently 20 years old. For more information—some of it astonishing—check the web page. By the way, young women are not required (or allowed) to register. This rule was upheld by the Supreme Court in 1981.

**Web:**

**http://www.sss.gov/**

## Siege Warfare

The neighboring castle has really been bothering you and now you feel that you should spend the weekend laying siege to it. The problem is, you just don't know where to start. Talk to the people who really know their siege warfare and can give you useful information on siege towers, sappers, ballistas, battering rams, catapults, and more. Get technical with the physics and mechanics of siege weapons or discuss the military strategies of attack and defense.

**Listserv Mailing List:**

List Name: **siege**
Subscribe to: **listserv@morgan.ucs.mun.ca**

## Special Operations

You have probably heard of the Green Berets and the Rangers (Army), the SEALs (Navy) and the Air Commandos (Air Force). These are all examples of special operations units (sometimes called special forces): highly trained groups of men who respond with speed, skill and authority to high-risk situations. Most countries with a significant military force have such groups, and in the United States there are actually a great many special operations units. This web site contains lots and lots of links to information about the various special operations units. These men train for years to be able to carry out jobs that most people wouldn't even think are possible.

**Web:**

**http://members.aol.com/tomhun8054/tom.html**

**SPECIAL OPERATIONS**

The most highly trained military men are those in "special operations".

Use the Net to find out what these guys do. I bet you will be impressed.

## Technology Insertion

The Department of Defense likes to keep its war-fighters informed. We think that's a great idea, too. It keeps them from drag racing through quiet suburban neighborhoods. The DoD has put together a great deal of information on wireless communication, asynchronous transfer modes, and communication technology in general.

**Web:**

**http://www.disa.atd.net/**

## United States Armed Forces

These are the official web sites of the main branches of the United States armed forces: the Air Force, Army, Coast Guard, Navy and Marine Corps. Each of these sites is independent, and the information varies from one page to the next. In general, though, you can find out a lot about each of the services, including what they do and how to join. I find visiting these sites interesting, as they show how the various branches of the U.S. armed services have distinct personalities and ways of looking at the world. If you need any information at all about part of the U.S. military, one of these web sites is a good place to start. You can read about what each service does, its history, recruiting policies (including various careers), retirement information, alumni organizations, news and press releases, upcoming public events, and much more.

**Web:**

**http://www.af.mil/**
**http://www.army.mil/**
**http://www.dot.gov/dotinfo/uscg/**
**http://www.navy.mil/**
**http://www.usmc.mil/**

## U.S. Department of Defense

This web site is the official Internet public visiting area of the United States Department of Defense (DoD). You will find lots of cool information about the DoD, what they do and who runs the show. (I know it's hard to believe that such information can be cool, but check it out yourself and you will see what I mean.) This is the place to look for links to all the organizations within the Department of Defense, such as the Secretary of Defense, the Joint Chiefs of Staff, and the various branches of the military. If you are American, take a few minutes to explore this site. These guys spend a lot of money, so you might as well have an idea of what they are doing.

**Web:**

**http://www.dtic.dla.mil/defenselink/**

**Check out a free online book.**

## Vietnam Veterans

The American involvement in the war in Vietnam lasted from 1961-1973, with most of the troops being deployed in the late 1960s. Although it may be hard to believe, in 1969 there were well over 500,000 American troops in Vietnam—about four percent of all the men in America. In other words, in 1969, about one out of every twenty-five American males was in Vietnam. It is no surprise then that, almost thirty years later, there are a lot of resources on the Net devoted to Vietnam veterans. If you fought in Vietnam, this web site has a large collection of resources in which you may be interested, including veteran organizations, support groups and information about reunions. For veterans and their families, the Usenet discussion group is a good place to talk. Note: The Vietnam Veterans Memorial is a monument in Washington, D.C., containing the names of all the servicemen and women who were killed or presumed missing in the Vietnam War. The memorial is a tall V-shaped black granite wall, measuring 493 feet (150 meters) long. Along the long, black surface are inscribed 58,000 names. This is a good image to keep in mind the next time you hear someone talk about starting a war. (Interestingly enough, out of 58,000 names, you will find very few belonging to the politicians and older Americans who supported the war—although their sons are well-represented.)

**Web:**

**http://grunt.space.swri.edu/vetorgs.htm**

**Usenet:**

**soc.veterans**

## War

Let's face it, war has been given a bum rap. Okay, so lots of people die, and many more suffer in horrible ways. Yes, families are broken, and people are changed for the worse permanently. And, I guess, it is true that all kinds of property is damaged and destroyed, and huge amounts of money and resources are funneled away from social productive uses and into a military machine. But, don't fall into the trap of assuming these are all *negative* things. Listen to some of the war discussion in Usenet and make up your own mind.

**Usenet:**

**soc.history.war.misc**

## Women in the Military

This site is devoted to women and the military: women who are currently in the service, retired from active duty, or even thinking about joining. Read about life after joining the military, family life and child care, women in combat, harassment issues, women who served in war zones, military humor and more.

**Web:**

**http://www.militarywoman.org/homepage.htm**

# MISCHIEF

## April Fools

The Ides of March is the least of the Internet's worries. The first day of April is the time when tricksters all over the world unleash their clever plots of lighthearted deceit. April Fools' pranks have been developed into an art form and are brought together in the form of archives which you can view from the safety of your own home.

**Web:**

**http://cac.psu.edu/~mxs233/fools.html**
**http://sunsite.unc.edu/dbarberi/april-fools.html**
**http://www.freezone.com/flash/marchissue/fool.html**
**http://www.zia.com/holiday1/april-fools-day/**

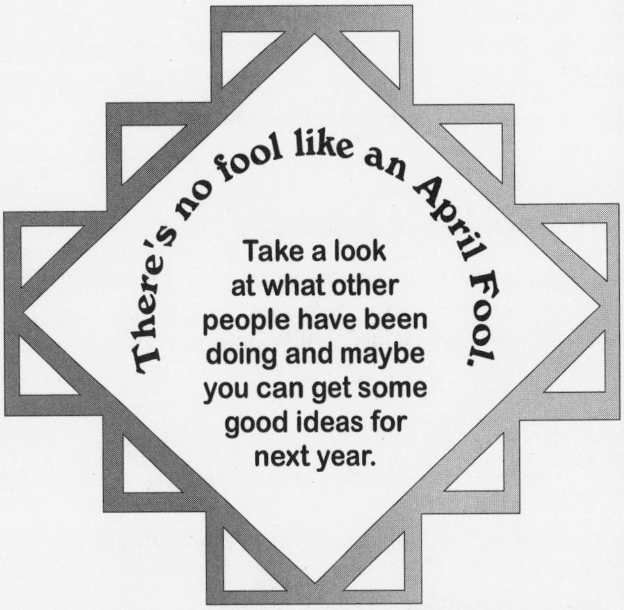
There's no fool like an April Fool.
Take a look at what other people have been doing and maybe you can get some good ideas for next year.

A B C D E F G H I J K L M N O P Q R S T U V W X Y Z

A B C D E F G H I J K L M N O P Q R S T U V W X Y Z

## Avenger's Page

It's not nice to get even, but if you just have to do it, you might as well do it the best way you can. The Avenger's Handbook is a collection of postings from the **alt.revenge** Usenet group. It has everything you need to know to get revenge, except a listing of bail bondsmen in your area.

**Web:**

**http://www.cs.uit.no/~paalde/Revenge/**
**http://www.flashback.se/archive/revenge_FAQ.html**

## Backyard Ballistics

This web site is dedicated to all the wonderful ways in which you can propel objects into the air in your own backyard. Learn about spud guns and spudzookas, air cannons, matchstick rockets, aussie mortar, the annual "Pumpkin Chunkin" contest and much more.

**Web:**

**http://www2.csn.net/~bsimon/backyard.html**

## Big Book of Mischief

Enjoy information on how to make explosives, tennis ball cannons and carbide bombs, how to open locks, and other vital information for the budding soldier of fortune. (For amusement only. You are on your honor not to actually do any of this stuff.)

**Web:**

**http://www.ripco.com:70/1/text/tbbom**

## Canonical List of Pranks

Never again will you have to worry about running out of tricks to play on people. Get the canonical list of pranks and drive everyone around you crazy.

**Web:**

**http://k2.scl.cwru.edu/~mcw6/fool/pranks.htm**
**http://math.lfc.edu/thomason/Humor/Lists/pranks.html**
**http://www.cs.indiana.edu/hyplan/ameiss/humor/pranks.html**
**http://www.lehigh.edu/~sjb3/pranks3**

## Do-It-Yourself Atomic Bomb

This file outlines the history and development of the atomic bomb and explains nuclear fusion and fission and the mechanism of an atomic bomb, along with a handy diagram of such a bomb. Although you might think that such information isn't all that practical, what else can you do to use up any extra plutonium you may have laying around the house?

**Web:**

**http://www.cyberus.ca/~sgi/atomic.txt**

## Hack Gallery

Hack Gallery is a compendium of Interesting Hacks To Fascinate People (IHTFP) at MIT. The word "hack" refers to a clever, benign, and ethical prank which is challenging and amusing for the perpetrators. The gallery offers a large list of hacks sorted by topic, location, and the dates when they were perpetrated. There is also a FAQ, book list, and a "best of" hack list.

**Web:**

**http://fishwrap.mit.edu/Hacks/Gallery.html**

**The Hack Gallery**

BEEP...
GULP

Looking for a nice trick to play on someone? Try the MIT Hack Gallery for inspiration.

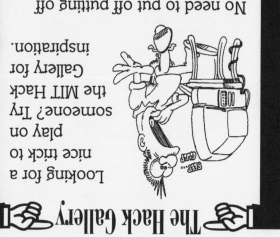

No need to put off putting off that special someone. The master hackers of the world have perpetrated all kinds of pranks and hoaxes and there is no reason why you can't join their ranks.

## How to Ruin Someone's Life

This file is old, but faithful. Are you interested in horrible things you can do to other people? Read about how you can make someone absolutely miserable by canceling their credit cards, phone cards and memberships to local businesses, by sending in magazine subscriptions in their name, putting personal ads in the newspaper, and so on. Some of these ideas are highly creative; all of them are downright awful.

**Web:**

**http://www.roadrunner.com/~plewis/Jason/mis/ruin.txt**

## Mischief Talk and General Discussion

The **alt.shenanigans** is the Usenet home for discussion of all manner of practical jokes ("shens"). I particularly like reading all the stories of jokes that people have played on unsuspecting victims. This is also a good place to ask for a suggestion when you feel a burning need to put someone in their place. The web page is the home page for **alt.shenanigans**, where you can find archives of interesting shens as well as a FAQ.

**Web:**

**http://www.xmission.com/~mgm/shenanigans/**

**Usenet:**

**alt.shenanigans**

## Practical Jokes

For serious enjoyment, what could be more good clean fun than embarrassing your friends and neighbors by making them look foolish? The dribble glass and plastic vomit are child's play. On the Net, you can read about lots and lots of ideas, techniques, and experiences with practical jokes. Make your loved ones say "uncle", and make your uncle say, "bork, bork, bork",

**Web:**

**http://humor.ncy.com/type/practical_joke/**
**http://www.lysator.liu.se:7500/jokes/practical.html**

## Prank Phone Calls

When you are sitting around with nothing to do, visit this site devoted to the art of prank telephone calls. Here you will find links to other prank call pages, information about the Jerky Boys (kings of the prank phone call), and tips about specific types of prank calls (such as 101 zany ways to phone in a pizza order).

**Web:**

**http://www.scruz.net/~knielsen/prankcall/**

## Pranksta's Paradise

Visit this nice collection of pranks and practical jokes, where you can read about various activities involving cars (inside and outside), homes (yours and others), the telephone, computers and partying (drunks, the bathroom, and so on).

**Web:**

**http://www.voicenet.com/~mika/**

## Revenge Talk and General Discussion

Landlord got you pissed? Teacher rapped you with a ruler? Your ex-SO (significant other) won't return your only copy of The Little Prince? Don't get mad, get even. Join the pros and find out just how smelly a fish in the ventilation duct can be. (Federal regulations require us to remind you of the ancient Chinese saying: "Before you set out for revenge, be sure to dig two graves.")

**Usenet:**

**alt.revenge**

## Telemarketer Torture

Do you hate telemarketers (people who call you trying to sell something)? Here is a list of horrible things you can do to annoy and torment telemarketing people when they make an uninvited phone call to your home. The suggestions are in the form of a game. Each thing you can do to torture a telemarketer has a point value. After the call, you can add up the points to determine your score.

**Web:**

**http://www.izzy.net/~vnestico/torment**

## Terrorist's Handbook

A few of the techniques and methods employed by people who use terror as a means to achieve their social and political goals. The web page is the entry point for a hypertext version of The Terrorist's Handbook which allows you to easily follow links between the sections of your interest. It includes sections on buying explosives and propellants, acquiring chemicals, explosive recipes, impact explosives, low order and high order explosives, ignition devices, projectile weapons, rockets and cannons, pyrotechnics, a list of suppliers, and even more. (Note: This is for your amusement. Only a fool would actually do any of this stuff.)

**Web:**

**http://www.bonn.citynet.de/people/jens/anarchy/thb/thb_title.html**

### Stuff You Are Not Supposed to Know About

Whether you are planning to blow up the World Trade Center, or merely explode a few small devices in your backyard, the **Terrorist's Handbook** is an invaluable guide to having a good time. Where else can you get such wonderful ideas about how to use up all that extra ammonium triiodide left over from last year's revolution?

## Trolling

Trolling is the slang for fishing around for flames (emotional complaints) on a Usenet discussion group. Trolling is practiced by people who invade Usenet groups and try to start flame wars, by posting stupid questions or comments, or by deliberately making provocative remarks. The trollers originally started out in the **alt.syntax.tactical** group. You may sometimes find them there, or in **alt.bigfoot** or **alt.flame**. The FAQ (frequently asked question list) explains how to deal with trolling, not how to do it. (But if you read the FAQ, you'll know how to do it.)

**Web:**

**http://digital.net/~gandalf/trollfaq.html**

**Usenet:**

**alt.syntax.tactical**

## Trolls, Media Hacks and Pranks

Here is a great list of pranks that have been played on the media and the public at large. (For example, have you heard the urban legend that a guy dressed in scuba gear was found dead in the aftermath of a forest fire? Presumably, he was swimming in a lake when an air tanker scooped him up with a load full of water and then dumped him on the fire.) Read about posting fake flyers around a town, tabloid talk-show hoaxers, the Good Times virus hoax, the "Microsoft Windows for Macintosh" prank, and the "911 Chatline" (see the news release for a 900 number that allows you to listen in on 911 lines in various parts of the country). Maybe this page will inspire you to acts of greatness. If so, there is no need to mention you read about it here.

**Web:**

**http://www.lycaeum.org/~sputnik/Hacks/**

**Read a zine today.**

# MONEY: BUSINESS AND FINANCE

## American Stock Exchange

A daily online market summary, provided by AMEX (the American Stock Exchange, based in New York). This resource includes a list of AMEX companies, information on options and derivatives, late-breaking market news, as well as the blueprints for the secret rumpus room in the basement of Bill Gates's new mansion.

**Web:**

**http://www.amex.com/**

## Asia, Inc. Online

Here is an online magazine devoted to Asian business and finance. You will find a variety of useful information on world financial markets, Asian business news, technical commentaries, and so on. You will also find a directory to help you locate Asian business resources on the Internet. Lots and lots of information in an easy to use package.

**Web:**

**http://www.asia-inc.com/**

## Bank Page

Finally, no more waiting in line at the bank. Find links to various banks on the Net and information about electronic money, non-U.S. banking, government-related banking institutions, credit cards, thrifts and credit unions.

**Web:**

**http://www.moneypage.com/**

## Business Headlines

Wondering whether to sell or buy, have a party or jump out the window of the men's washroom on the 44th floor? Don't be hasty. Read the headlines and summaries of the latest business news before making a decision.

**Web:**

**http://www.cnnfn.com/**

### Asia Online

Doing business in Asia is a lot different from doing business in Fargo, North Dakota. For example, it rains a lot more in Asia and the food is spicier. On the other hand, chances are that a Fargo businessman isn't going to be insulted just because you ran afoul of some local oriental custom and offered a beer to his wife with your left hand.

So, before you even think about doing business with your Asian cousins, check out the Asia, Inc. Online web site. Before you can say:

*"O-genki desu ka. The Little Nipper desu. Uchi no obasan wa kuruma no shita. Tomato wa arimasu ka. Kono hon wa subarashi."*

you will be in business in a big way (thanks to this book and proper research).

## Business Information Resources

A large collection of pointers to business information resources on the Net. Here you can read business magazines and journals, find out about opportunities and business services on the Net, see some entrepreneurial resources and much more.

**Web:**

**http://www.eotw.com/business_info.html**

### Business Headlines

Need to stay current with matters financial? The Business Headlines will help you keep up on those who keep up while you are sleeping.

A B C D E F G H I J K L M N O P Q R S T U V W X Y Z

## Business Information Server

The Dun & Bradstreet business server has articles on marketing your business globally, strategic business planning, tactical marketing, effective research, and a series of tutorials to help the small business owner.

**Web:**

**http://www.dnb.com/**

## Business Talk and General Discussion

The world of business and finance is huge, and there is a lot to talk about. This is the place to do all that talking: the Usenet group devoted to general business discussion.

**Usenet:**

**alt.business.misc**

## Commerce Business Daily

The Commerce Business Daily is a special publication that announces invitations to bid on proposals requested by the U.S. government. This information is updated every business day.

**Web:**

**http://www.ld.com/cbd/today/**

### Commerce Business Daily

Would you like to serve humanity and make money at the same time? Why not do business with the U.S. government? (You couldn't find a nicer group of people anywhere.) Take a look at the Commerce Business Daily and you just may find your path to life, liberty, and the pursuit of financial happiness.

## Commercial Use of the Internet

Greed is good. Money is the root of all evil. So which is it? (Hint: It depends on whether you are cross-posting mass advertising across Usenet groups.) Find out strategies for using the Internet in your commercial ventures. Includes statistics, informational lists, and links to various commercial sites.

**Web:**

**http://www.netrex.com/**

## EDGAR Mutual Funds

Want to see what is happening in the world of mutual funds? Get fast information on a huge selection of various mutual funds—find out what's been going on in the past months or just the last few days.

**Web:**

**http://edgar.stern.nyu.edu/mutual.html**

## Entrepreneur Talk and General Discussion

Tired of being manacled to that creaking metal desk with the file drawer that always sticks? Take charge of your life: own your own business. See the pitfalls and glories that await you, the entrepreneur.

**Usenet:**

**misc.entrepreneurs**

### Your Own Business

**What could be more fun than running your own business?**

**Why let someone else worry about health care, liability insurance, meeting the payroll, and making a profit, when you can do so yourself?**

**(Of course, there are drawbacks as well.)**

**If you are starting your own business, make sure to read misc.entrepreneur. There are a lot of people just like you.**

$$$$$$$$$$$$

## FinanceNet

FinanceNet is a U.S. government resource with massive amounts of information relating to money. For example, would you like to find out how much American civil servants are paid? Just display the Federal Pay Scales. This is a must-have resource for anyone who wants to know about the U.S. government. You will also find links to many U.S. state and local resources. What a great place to take your potential best girl or guy for a first date.

**Web:**

**http://www.financenet.gov/**

## Global Trade Center

Spaghetti, falafel, salt from the bowels of distant countries—these are all things you can get through international trading without having the local supermarket as a go-between. If you like to do things the hard way, risking money and perhaps life and limb, get into a little international trading. The Tradezone offers information and links for businesses interested in exploring international trade.

**Web:**

**http://www.tradezone.com/tz/**

## Idea Futures

Gambling is the most fun when you are playing with someone else's money. If you like to break a sweat, but only a little, try playing with some idea futures. Start with a certain number of shares in your betting pool, climb into your think tank, and win or lose as the gods of speculation will have it.

**Web:**

**http://if.arc.ab.ca/IF.shtml**

If you think investing in futures is easy, try it on paper before you lose your money betting on the real thing. Play with the **Idea Futures** web site and practice, practice, practice. If you are lucky, you'll escape with enough money to invest in a couple of Harley Hahn first editions.

## Importing and Exporting

Trading is fun because you can get rid of all the stuff you don't need anymore and get cool new stuff that somebody wants to get rid of and that makes everyone happy. Make people happy all over the globe by reading up on the import-export business. You might even end up with more stuff than you know what to do with. The **.only** group is moderated.

**Usenet:**

**alt.business.import-export.computer**
**alt.business.import-export.food**
**alt.business.import-export.only**
**alt.business.import-export.raw-material**
**alt.business.import-export.services**

## Industry Net

When you want the goods on the industrial and manufacturing sectors of the world, take a look at Industry Net. The forms at this web site will let you pick topics you are interested in, then when you log in, the computer will give you the industry news relating to your interests. You have to register, but membership is free.

**Web:**

**http://www.industry.net/**

## International Accounting Network

The life of an accountant is truly exciting: all those numbers to punch, calculator tapes flying, phones ringing, deadlines to meet, and clients to bail out of jail. As if that's not enough, accountants also have the International Accounting Network, which offers details about accounting conferences, accounting mailing lists and archives, lists of accounting organizations around the world, accounting research and journals, software and educational resources. Nothing but fun.

**Web:**

**http://anet.scu.edu.au/ANetHomePage.html**

## Investor Channel

This site offers an in-depth look at companies that are publicly trading on stock exchanges around the world. Get snapshots, full reports, the latest news releases and the current closing quotes of listed companies.

**Web:**

**http://www.wimsey.com/Magnet/**

## Japanese Business Studies

The times are more civilized, and international business is a little safer than it used to be because nowadays people leave their swords at home when they come to the bargaining table. This is not to say that negotiations can't get brutal. As the saying goes, "The pen is mightier than the sword," and that especially holds true for signing contracts. Japan scholars, students, government and business researchers, and executives devote themselves to discussion regarding Japanese economy and business systems.

**Listserv Mailing List:**
List Name: **japan**
Subscribe to: **listserv@pucc.princeton.edu**

## Marketing Discussion

There are lots of different facets of marketing and, on the Net, there are lots of mailing lists—discussion lists, that is—which you can join to talk to people. Each list is devoted to its own particular slice of the economic pie. Here is a resource to help you choose which mailing list is best for you.

**Web:**
**http://www.bayne.com/wolfBayne/htmarcom/mktglist.html**

## Multilevel Marketing Talk and General Discussion

The great pyramids are not just in Egypt. Learn all about the "trickle-up theory" and hear stories of why multilevel marketing is the greatest money-making scam, er... scheme ever. Don't settle for a rattling car and a rental home. Sell Amway so you can drive a Rolls Royce and own a yacht. These folks can show you how.

**Usenet:**
**alt.business.multi-level**

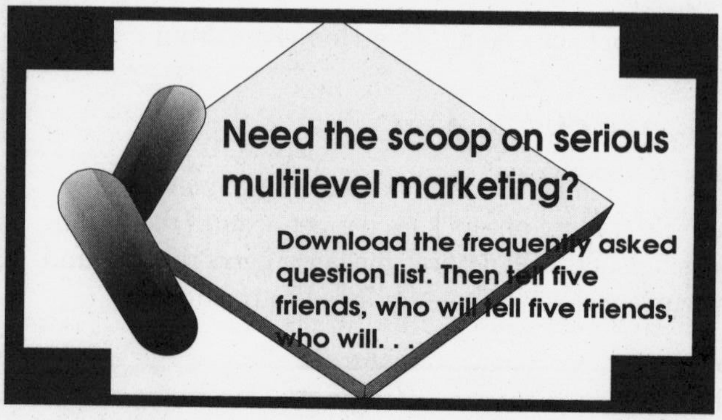
Need the scoop on serious multilevel marketing?
Download the frequently asked question list. Then tell five friends, who will tell five friends, who will. . .

## Mutual Fund Quotations

If you have any money in a mutual fund, and you like to torture yourself by checking its value every chance you get, this is the site for you. Just specify the ticker symbol (official abbreviation) for your fund, and you will get a nice graph showing how the NAV (net asset value) has been changing. Now that I think of it, you could also use this information to check out various funds before investing.

**Web:**
**http://networth.galt.com/www/home/nav/netnav.htm**

## Mutual Funds

If I were smarter, I would probably be buying stocks and bonds (and losing all my money). Instead, I put my savings into a mutual fund and let someone else do the driving. This mutual fund resource provides useful, focused content and has original material with references to other valuable Internet resources.

**Web:**
**http://www.brill.com/**

## Mutual Funds Phone Numbers

Need to call a mutual fund? I do it all the time. When you need to call, the phone number will surely be here. This web page is a huge list of phone numbers for many mutual funds.

**Web:**
**http://www.cs.cmu.edu/~jdg/funds.html**

## Non-Profit Organizations

These days the fastest way to see money come pouring in is to operate a non-profit business. The only problem is that you can't keep all the money. Learn about forming non-profit organizations, how to be a wise donor, tips on fund raising, annual reports of non-profit organizations, and philanthropy in general.

**Web:**
**http://www.nonprofits.org/**

## Publicly Traded Companies

There's no need to sneak around looking for information about your favorite publicly traded company. Now you can get all the financial details you need straight from the Net. As long as you have your web browser and a connection, you are empowered. Listen up, all you publicly traded companies: you can run, but you can't hide.

**Web:**

**http://www.csn.net/natcorp/traded.html**

They Can Run, But They Can't Hide.

Yes, it's true. Even though a worldwide corporation may be larger than one of Bill Gate's erotic fantasies, the suits in charge can't hide from you as long as you have the Net. At any time, while the accountants and lawyers are sleeping, you can log in, load down, and tune up to the latest info on Publicly Traded Companies.

Projections
Wholesale Revenue
Retail Revenue
Cost of Goods Sold
Operating Expenses
Research & Development
Your company name here

## Real Estate Research and Data

When you are into real estate, you don't just tromp around in the woods or traipse through people's homes. You have to do paperwork, research, and learn laws and banking regulations. Real estate researchers and students gather to discuss research problems, data gathering, and other matters that relate to the roll-up-your-sleeves-and-get-down-to-it parts of real estate.

**Listserv Mailing List:**

List Name: **re-forum**
Subscribe to: **listserv@utarlvm1.uta.edu**

## Real Estate Talk and General Discussion

It's just like a Monopoly game, except you use real money and the bail is higher if you end up in jail. Learn tips on acquiring real estate: how to choose a good agent, perks for first-time homebuyers, and how to avoid the rental property blues.

**Usenet:**

**alt.real-estate-agents**
**misc.invest.real-estate**

## Security APL Quote Server

Watch your stack of money rise and fall as the minutes pass. The APL Quote Server states the current S&P 500 Index and offers a graphical representation of the Dow Jones Industrial Average and the daily volume at the New York Stock Exchange. The news is updated from Wall Street approximately every fifteen minutes, so you will have that much of a head start if you have to leave town.

**Web:**

**http://www.secapl.com/cgi-bin/qs**

## Small Business Administration

Running your own business can be a delight or a hassle, depending on how you approach it. It helps to have as much information at your fingertips as possible. The Small Business Administration is now online, and you can read about business development, government contracting, minority business, and financial assistance.

**Web:**

**http://www.sbaonline.sba.gov/**

**REAL ESTATE REALITY**

**Isn't it great? All you have to do is spend some money and you can own your very own piece of an actual planet (Earth).**

**I love real estate because it brings out the best in people; and some of the best real estate people hang out in misc.invest.real-estate.**

**Remember, though, talking on the Net is no substitute for experience: the smart way is to "walk the dirt, smell the dirt and feel the dirt". (Fortunately, there's no shortage of dirt.)**

SOLD!

## Small Business Resource Center

A large collection of online reports and links relating to small businesses. If you are starting your own business—or if you would like to enhance what you already have—there will be something here to help you.

**Web:**
**http://www.webcom.com/~seaquest/sbrc**

## Stock Market Data

The next time your therapist tells you to take stock in yourself, you will know where to look. Here is a resource that can help you find stock information for just about any security you can imagine. (And who wouldn't like to imagine more security?)

**Web:**
**http://www.stockmaster.com/**

## Stock Market Timing

Just like with sex, in the stock market, timing is everything. Don't be caught with your pants down. Read these weekly technical analyses of the stock market along with the online recommendations.

**Web:**
**http://www.firstcap.com/**

FINANCIAL SECTION

**Stock Market Timing**

Stock market timing is a technique that attempts to determine the underlying trends of the market in order to decide when to buy and when to sell. (This is the opposite of buying stocks and holding them for a very long time.)

The market is so complex as to be well beyond the understanding of any human being, but that doesn't mean you can't find some useful patterns.

If you are interested in trying to beat the averages, don't forget to check with the Net first.

## Technical Aspects of Investing

This is where money and math collide. Flying formulas, staggering statistics, and profitable predictions abound to provide the basis for economic decision-making. How do you know when to buy a mutual fund? What good is a regression analysis? Take part in the discussion and learn how to buy and sell by the numbers.

**Usenet:**
**misc.invest.technical**

## Trade Statistics

Black market traders, investors, and exporting gurus will all be interested to hear what the Foreign Trade Division says about U.S. International trade statistics. Scoot back off the edge of your seat. The waiting is over. Point your web browser to the U.S. Bureau of Statistics and get all the numbers you need.

**Web:**
**http://www.census.gov/ftp/pub/foreign-trade/www/**

## Wall Street Net

While everyone else is getting their hands grubby going through various newspapers, searching for the latest news, you can be sitting pretty with the information all laid out in front of you. Wall Street Net brings you the latest on what is happening in the world of corporate debt and equity financing. See their archival data, which includes SEC filings and prospectuses on transactions that have occurred in the last twelve months.

**Web:**
**http://www.netresource.com/wsn/**

# MONEY: PERSONAL FINANCE

## American Homeowners Foundation

Homeowners: now you can get all sorts of tips from the American Homeowners Foundation. Topics cover buying and selling your home, remodeling, fire safety, home pricing, a mortgage calculator and real estate links.

**Web:**
**http://homes.inresco.com/Bcorgs_ahf.html**

## Common Tax Preparation Errors

Every spring, Americans get the chance to bring themselves closer to achieving Tax Preparation Perfection. In order to hasten you on your path of Enlightenment, the folks at Ernst and Young have created a list of the 25 most common tax preparation errors. Use this as a checklist to see if you can save money, or at the very least, keep yourself out of federal prison.

**Web:**

**http://www.ey.com/us/tax/25error.htm**

## Currency Converter

The Koblas Currency Converter is simple to use. You select the desired country and all the other countries' currencies will be converted relative to the one you selected. The name of the currency will appear as part of your selection.

**Web:**

**http://bin.gnn.com/cgi-bin/gnn/currency**

## Estate Planning

Estate planning is important for everyone. If you die without a will, the government has a great many rules that will determine what happens to all your money, property and possessions (that is, your estate). There is no guarantee that what eventually happens will be what you want. However, if you make up a will ahead of time, there is much more chance that your wishes will be followed. Moreover, proper estate planning can often save your heirs a great deal of inheritance tax. If you are married, or if you have children, you absolutely must have a will. Let me tell you a personal observation. I don't plan on dying any time soon, and I don't even like to think about death. However, I did have a will made and, once it was done, I felt good about it. It brought me peace of mind. Just do it and you will see what I mean. Here are some resources that can help you understand estate planning. In addition, you can read the text of the wills of various famous people, such as Elvis Presley, Jerry Garcia and Richard Nixon.

**Web:**

**http://www.ca-probate.com/links.htm**

### Estate Planning

If you don't plan your estate, the state or province in which you live will plan it for you.

The Net has lots of estate planning information to help you decide what's best for you and your family.

## Getting the Most From Your Money

Don't let anyone ever call you cheap. As one of my readers, you have excellent judgment and, of course, that extends to money matters as well. Some people may think you are frugal, but let those people throw their money away. You and I can find the bargains and get the most for our dollars. So, to help you, here are a few good places to look for tips, hints and Internet resources that can help you spend your money wisely. If you would like to talk to other people about living frugally, check out the Usenet group.

**Web:**

**http://www.best.com/~piner/frugal.html**
**http://www.stretcher.com/**

**Usenet:**

**misc.consumer.frugal-living**

## Homebuyer's Fair

Buying a house is a little different than running to the corner market to pick up an extra package of hot dog buns. Get answers to questions about buying a home, learn information about mortgages and how to avoid "junk fees". You can even view images of homes for sale.

**Web:**

**http://www.homefair.com/**

**"Sex" is not a four-letter word.**

## Household Budgeting

Sometimes it seems that, no matter how much money you make, it is never enough. Well, that's true for two reasons. First, probably no one ever makes enough money in the sense that there is always something else to buy. However, the second reason is more important: many people simply do not know how to budget their money wisely. Realize that budgeting well is something that you have to learn (and practice). At first, living with a budget may seem like an imposition. But once you get used to it (if you created a good budget for yourself), you will find that spending and planning within your means is a comfortable way to live. One of the web sites contains lots of useful information to help you understand and plan a household budget. The other site allows you to take a self test in order to evaluate your "spending personality".

**Web:**

**http://www.netxpress.com/users/hadap/budget.html**
**http://www.ns.net/cash/selftest/selftest.html**

## Insurance Information

Insurance is something we buy, hoping that we will never use it. There are many types of insurance, and you can't always depend on the salesman to make sure you understand everything. Here are some useful consumer tips that could end up saving you money (and time) when it comes to understanding your insurance needs.

**Web:**

**http://www.iii.org/consumer.htm**

**Do you want to ruin your day?**

**Use the Mortgage Calculator and find out how much you are *really* paying for your house.**

## Investment Talk and General Discussion

Mutual funds, IRAs, discount brokerages, margin terms—do you sometimes feel like your head is going to spin around? Learn everything you need to know about investments and handling money. Make your money work for you.

**Usenet:**

**misc.invest**
**misc.invest.canada**
**misc.invest.commodities**
**misc.invest.emerging**
**misc.invest.fixed-income**
**misc.invest.forex**
**misc.invest.funds**
**misc.invest.futures**
**misc.invest.index-futures**
**misc.invest.options**
**misc.invest.stocks**
**misc.invest.stocks.penny**

## Money News

Money talks—and talks and talks and talks. There is a lot of money news in the world and it is not always easy to keep up. Here is where the Net is great. Check out these web sites regularly for the latest consumer-oriented financial news. Keep up on what is happening with mutual funds, airfare wars, investment scams, smart cards, credit card debt, and more.

**Web:**

**http://cnnfn.com/yourmoney/**
**http://www.usatoday.com/money/mfront.htm**

## Mortgage Calculator

If you have your eye on that choice piece of property down the road and you want to see just how bad the mortgage will bite into your wallet, put this mortgage calculator to work. Simply enter the buying price, the interest rate, and a few other pieces of information. A program will give you a fully amortized schedule or a brief summary of what you will be paying in principle and interest, your monthly payments, and what you should be earning to be able to afford the house.

**Web:**

**http://ibc.wustl.edu/mort.html**

## Mortgages

If you are contemplating a mortgage, find out lots of information about interest rates, mortgage companies, rate trends and loan programs from this web page. Not only will you learn interesting things that will help you make a better decision, but you can also utilize an online mortgage payment calculator, see historical interest rates and read consumer tips and information.

**Web:**

**http://www.dirs.com/mortgage/**

## NETworth

Money markets, stocks, bonds, mutual funds—if your vault is getting overcrowded, maybe you need to invest. Arm yourself with a load of information before making investments with the help of this free investing service.

**Web:**

**http://networth.galt.com/**

## Personal Finance Center

Create a good personal finance system for yourself or perfect the one you already have. On the Net, you can find newsletter excerpts, columns, and links to information relating to personal finance.

**Web:**

**http://gnn.com/meta/finance/**

## Personal Finance Tips and Resources

It was so much easier when you were a kid. Your biggest money worry was trying to figure out how to break the piggy open without anybody noticing. Now there's all this tax stuff, deductions and annuities, investments and exemptions. At least people on the Net are making it a little easier to sort out all the information. Find great tips and resources that can help you manage your personal finances.

**Web:**

**http://www.thegroup.net/green.htm**

## Planning for Retirement

Here's a simple but effective way to save for retirement. Throughout your life, set aside 10% of every paycheck. No matter what happens, always set aside the 10%, and never ever use the money for anything else except retirement savings. Now, in the course of a lifetime, it is certain that financial emergencies will arise and, when they do, you are going to be tempted to "borrow" from your retirement money. The key to accumulating wealth is to resist that temptation. Every month, even before you pay your bills, set aside the 10%. If you learn to live on 90% of your income, you won't notice much difference day-to-day, but over the years, you will build up a significant nest egg. What should you do with your retirement money? If you are more than 10 years from retirement, invest the money safely in the stock market using, for example, a growth oriented mutual fund, or a fund that tracks the S&P 500. Retirement planning is an important issue, and there are lots of resources on the Net that can help you. To get you started, I have picked out a few good web sites. These resources are especially helpful if you live the United States. However, please remember what I said: no matter where you live, no matter what you do for a living, save 10% of everything you take in and invest it wisely. I want to ensure that, when you retire, you will have enough money to buy all the Harley Hahn books you ever need.

**Web:**

**http://www.awa.com/softlock/tturner/401k/401k.html**
**http://www.bookpageweb.com/kiplinger/**
**http://www.ssa.gov/**

## Selling by Owner

Have you decided you don't need a real estate agent? If so, check out the advice offered here about selling your house on your own. Topics cover hiring a lawyer, advertising and how to have a successful open house.

**Web:**

**http://www.crocker.com/byowner/articles.html**

## Tax Preparation

Ah, the glorious month of April. The birds rejoice at the dawn of spring. Earthworms happily aerate the soil to stimulate new growth. A delicate breeze blows. And you are stuck inside doing your taxes. Isn't life cruel? Try to make it as painless as possible by planning ahead. Get handy instructions and forms available at this web site, then go catch some rays.

**Web:**

**http://www.el.com/ToTheWeb/Taxes/**
**http://www.irs.ustreas.gov/prod/forms_pubs/**
**http://www.scubed.com/tax/**

Tax Forms
Yes, you really can get tax forms–American and Canadian–and all kinds of tax information for free over the Internet . There is a *lot* of stuff here, including the entire tax code (all 22 megabytes), so what are you waiting for?

## Teaching Kids About Money

It is important that children understand money. But how do you know what to teach them and when? The Net can help. Check these web sites to articles about many useful topics such as children's allowances and teaching good spending habits. Explore by yourself and then invite the kids to join you. After all, if you make sure that your kids understand money and how to use it, you will be providing them with valuable knowledge that will last a lifetime.

**Web:**

**http://pages.prodigy.com/kidsmoney/**
**http://www.parentsoup.com/library/mon003.html**

## Timesharing

Timesharing is an option for those who would like to have a vacation home without having to pay for the whole thing alone. Get timeshare tips, a brief history of timesharing, read a newsletter or browse the classifieds.

**Web:**

**http://www.timeshare-users-group.com/**

# MOTORCYCLES

## Antique Motorcycles

Visit the web site of the Antique Motorcycle Club of America, a non-profit organization dedicated to the restoration and exhibition of antique motorcycles. Find out information about the various chapters as well as a schedule of events. If you like antique motorcycles, you may as well join the club. As I always say, Harleys only get better as they get older.

**Web:**

**http://ww1.comteck.com/~amc/**

## British Motorcycles

A list for the discussion of British motorcycles. You don't have to be British, in Britain, or even know anyone British as long as you are talking about British motorcycles.

**Majordomo Mailing List:**

List Name: **brit-iron**
Subscribe to: **majordomo@indiana.edu**

## European Motorcycles

If you want to fill your mailbox with lots of interesting conversation about European motorcycles, get on this mailing list right away. Talk to people all over the world about your common interests. The web site corresponds to the mailing list and contains the mailing list archives as well as links to other cool European motorcycle resources.

**Web:**

**http://www.micapeak.com/euro-moto/**

**Listproc Mailing List:**

List Name: **euro-moto**
Subscribe to: **listproc@mom.isc-br.com**

## Harley Owners Group

There's something so lovable about a Harley. Maybe it's because they are so sexy, powerful and have lots of thrust. Or maybe it's that air of exotic mystery and charisma. Or maybe they're just good motorcycles. If you're a Harley fan, check out this site, which has art, technical information, pictures and stolen bike information.

**Web:**

**http://www.magicnet.net/mni/hog.html**

Harley Owners Group
Experts agree, there's nothing like having a Harley in your life. If you're lucky enough to own one, join the group.

## Helmet and Bike Laws

Helmets are important when you are riding a motorcycle. For this reason, many jurisdictions require a helmet as well as other safety protection. Here are resources that you can use to check out motorcycle safety requirements in the U.S. and Canada: helmets, eye protection, headlights during the day, and so on.

**Web:**

**http://www.cyberstation.net/~drider/bikelaws.htm**
**http://www.motorcycle.com/mo/mcads/mcruss/helmet.html**

## Motorcycle Camping

Have you ever gone camping with your motorcycle? If so, you will appreciate this practical information: choosing bags that work well with your bike, what gear to pack in your limited space, tips on how to best pack your bike and tie it all down, and so on.

**Web:**

**http://mom.isc-br.com/WL/camping.html**

## Motorcycle Maintenance

If you enjoy working on your own bike, these web sites have a lot of information you will find useful. Read the tips on repair, maintenance and tune-ups for many popular brands of bikes. You will not only save money, but you can get your motorcycle running just the way you want it, as well as have the satisfaction of being just that much closer to the machine. (My philosophy is that everyone should have at least one good relationship in their life.)

**Web:**

**http://owatonna.ll.net/spider/mtools.htm**
**http://www.hut.fi/~pastori/bikerepair.html**

## Motorcycle Online Magazine

While it's not as convenient as a paper magazine sitting in the bathroom, this electronic motorcycle magazine is spiffy and worth a look. It features news stories, video and photo archives, a virtual museum, a U.S. events database, sneak previews of next year's motorcycle models, and links to services offered by commercial parties and manufacturers.

**Web:**

**http://motorcycle.com/motorcycle.html**

## Motorcycle Racing

What a rush it is to be racing at high speeds with nothing between you and the air except a flimsy little jumpsuit that will disintegrate upon impact with the asphalt. Motorcycle racing enthusiasts discuss road racing from the racer's point of view as well as the pit crew's.

**Majordomo Mailing List:**

List Name: **race**
Subscribe to: **majordomo@thumper.lerc.nasa.gov**

## Motorcycle Reviews

A large collection of motorcycle and accessory reviews written by readers of the Usenet **rec.motorcycles** groups and based on their own experiences. New reviews are always welcome. Includes some motorcycle pictures.

**Web:**

**http://rmr.cecm.sfu.ca/RMR/**

## Motorcycle Safety

Riding a motorcycle is inherently more dangerous than, say, driving a car or running around the house with a spoon in your mouth. As part of learning how to ride a motorcycle, it is important to develop an appreciation for safety and good habits. These web pages can help you enjoy your cycle while minimizing the chances of an accident or injury.

**Web:**

**http://www.coffey.com/~glwidup/home.htm**
**http://www.tiac.net/users/emax/MSF/aboutMSF.html**

## Motorcycle Talk and General Discussion

Anything named "Harley" is bound to be sexy. No doubt that is why so many people love their motorcycles. If you just can't live without something hard and powerful, these Usenet groups are the places to be.

**Usenet:**

**alt.motorcycles.harley**
**rec.motorcycles**
**rec.motorcycles.dirt**
**rec.motorcycles.harley**
**rec.motorcycles.racing**

**Listproc Mailing List:**

List Name: **motolist**
Subscribe to: **listproc@mom.isc-br.com**

**The Net is immortal.**

## Motorcycle Tips

Riding a motorcycle calls for a lot more skill and stamina than riding around in a car. These web sites are full of tips that will make your driving experience more pleasant and enjoyable. Read about shock absorbers, teaching new riders to lean, dumping bikes, tire pressure, how to cool down when riding in hot weather, braking methods, stopping distances and so on. This is stuff that everyone should know, so do take some time to check it out.

**Web:**

**http://home.earthlink.net/~jamesdavis/DISCUSS.html**
**http://www.ironbutt.com/25tips.html**

## Motorcycling in the Rain

Riding a cycle safely in the rain calls for a great deal of skill and judgment. The Wetleather web site is based on a mailing list devoted to issues related to riding in the rain, specifically in the northwestern part of the United States and adjacent areas in Canada. Wetleather people gather together for camping, riding and lots of fun. Check out the calendar of events, ride reports, pictures of Wetleather members racing and then join the list.

**Web:**

**http://mom.isc-br.com/wetleather/**

**Listproc Mailing List:**

List Name: **wetleather**
Subscribe to: **listproc@micapeak.com**

### *Look What I Found on the Net...*

```
Newsgroup: rec.motorcycles
Subject: Cleaning a Bike

Your bike can be as clean as you want, and it'll always look
dirty.
```

## Regional Motorcycle Mailing Lists

When you want to discuss motorcycle topics with people all over the world, join a mailing list. This site has a comprehensive list of motorcycle mailing lists around the Net, including regional lists which allow you to interact with motorcycle enthusiasts close to home.

**Web:**
**http://mom.isc-br.com/WL/mmlo.txt**

## Scooters

Oh, the indignity of it all. Your boss hog is in the shop for repairs and you have to motor around on this little scooter in the meantime. Accept your fate gracefully along with other motor scooter fans, and talk about the care and maintenance of scooters.

**Usenet:**
**alt.scooter**

## Short Bikers

Riding a motorcycle can be a lot of fun, but most bikes are made for people of average height and above. If you are a short motorcycle rider, there are special riding techniques you can practice. This web page will point you in the right direction, and offers a list of bikes, with leg measurements, that are suitable for shorter riders. You can also join a mailing list and explore the web sites of other short bikers. My feeling is, if your legs are long enough to reach the ground, you're tall enough.

**Web:**
**http://www.calweb.com/~trouble/short/shortindex.html**

## Sidecars

A sidecar is not something you see every day. The last one I saw was racing down the highway attached to a motorcycle driven by a young man in a leather jacket. The sidecar was loaded down with a plump blonde woman in her seventies who was also wearing a leather jacket and a long scarf that was trailing out behind her. Sidecars must be cool.

**Web:**
**http://www.sidecar.com/**

**It takes a certain type of person to attach a sidecar to his motorcycle. If you would like to hobnob with such people, check out the *Sidecars* Internet resources. It takes all types to make a world, and nowhere is this more true than in the world of motorcycles. After all, one of the first lessons we learn in life is we can't all have Harleys.**

## Stolen Motorcycles

Stealing a bike is like someone taking your baby. Don't sit still for it. Utilize this web site dedicated to listing descriptions and photos of stolen motorcycles.

**Web:**
**http://www.dorsai.org/~pweinman/**

# MOVIES

## Asian Movie Talk and General Discussion

Experience the unique flavor of Asian movies. Fans and critics discuss action, adventure, horror and other genres of the Asian silver screen.

**Usenet:**
**alt.asian-movies**

## Box Office

Visit the web site for the print magazine Box Office. Read reviews of films, lists of new movies, interesting facts about the movie industry (such as which films are making the most money), and info about films in the works. There are also advance reviews from film festivals, as well as articles and interviews with film stars and directors.

**Web:**
**http://www.boxoff.com/**

## Cam's Movie Zone

What's on at the movies? Pop a little popcorn, grab a cold drink, and point your web browser toward Hollyweb. Read reviews, articles, movie and video picks, history, and find out the top money-makers in the industry.

**Web:**

**http://www.noord.bart.nl/~marb/**

## Cinema Chat

You can only spend so much of your life watching movies—sometimes you need to take a break. So what can you do for a change? Connect to IRC and talk about movies. After all, life is short, so why waste it?

**IRC:**

**#cinema**
**#movies**

### CINEMA CHAT

Do you want to talk about the movie you just saw - that new musical comedy about the Dewey Decimal System?

If so, join the people on IRC who love to talk about films.

## Cinema Mailing List

If you are interested in any aspect of the film world, you may want to join this mailing list. It is devoted to a general discussion of the film world. Feel free to talk about anything you want—film making, directing, screenwriting, critiquing, acting, watching—even politics—as long as you remember the people who participate in this list are serious film buffs.

**Listserv Mailing List:**

List Name: **cinema-l**
Subscribe to: **listserv@american.edu**

## Cinema Space

Film study is more than good popcorn and a comfortable seat. Learn more about cinema and the "new media" by reading scholarly articles and papers of a critical and philosophical nature. Cinema Space is the name of a journal put out by the film studies program at U.C. Berkeley. Film clips are also available.

**Web:**

**http://cinemaspace.berkeley.edu/**

## Cult Movies Talk and General Discussion

No matter how bad they get, no matter how outlandish they are or how far away from their origins they evolve, you will go see the hundredth remake of a film. There are a few movies that have a cult following and fans feel so strongly about these films that they will see them at all costs. These newsgroups cover cult movies in general and some in particular like the Evil Dead movies and Rocky Horror Picture Show.

**Usenet:**

**alt.cult-movies**
**alt.cult-movies.evil-deads**
**alt.cult-movies.rocky-horror**

## Directors Guild of America

In the movie industry, there are two types of people. Those who will admit that "they really want to direct", and those who already are directors. Once you become a director, you get to join the Directors Guild of America (DGA). Even better, you can visit the official web site and remind yourself that you *belong*. However, even if your talent has not yet been properly recognized and you are still waiting for that big break, you can visit the web site whenever you want and read interviews with famous directors. What I found most inspiring was the letter of welcome from the President of the DGA in which he explains that the DGA strives to help directors "strengthen their ability to develop meaningful and credible careers". Wow. (And I'm hard to impress.) My only question is, where can I find such a cool organization for writers?

**Web:**

**http://dga.org/dga/**

## Film and TV Studies Mailing List

Who knew there was so much to film and television? It's not just a matter of whether you enjoy it or not. There are all sorts of academic things involved, like post-post-structuralist theory and pedagogical, historical and production issues to think about. This is a list for students, teachers and theorists who are interested in more than a good shoot-em-up flick or comedy.

**Listserv Mailing List:**

List Name: **screen-l**
Subscribe to: **listserv@ua1vm.ua.edu**

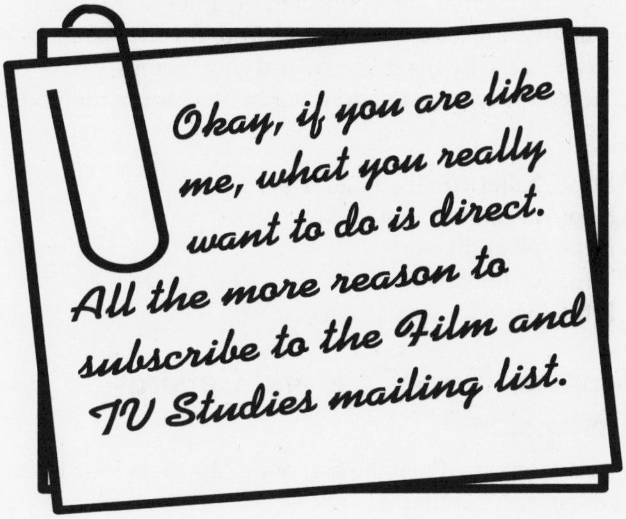
Okay, if you are like me, what you really want to do is direct. All the more reason to subscribe to the Film and TV Studies mailing list.

## Film Festivals

Has anyone noticed that, as life reluctantly drags itself out of the twentieth century, there are more and more film festivals? I bet if Mickey Rooney and Judy Garland were to make a movie today, there would be a big scene in which Mickey would say, "Hey wait, why don't we put on our own film festival?" Ya see, George, there are so many of these things that a beginner just doesn't know where to start. No problemo. Just connect to the Net and check out this great list of film festivals around the world. Wait, I have an idea—how does this sound to you? The Harley Hahn Film Festival: Woody Allen movies, The Rocky Horror Picture Show, Sleepless in Seattle, When Harry Met Sally, and a special screening of Summer School with Mark Harmon showing up to answer questions from the audience. Sounds great to me. Let's have a meeting.

**Web:**

**http://www.laig.com/law/entlaw/filmfes.htm**

## Film, Television and Popular Culture

Scholars don't just study old stuff like dead languages and crumbling tombs. Some of them just watch movies and television. Now that is a fun way to be a scholar. Sit around with other people who study film, television and popular culture, and the use of media in teaching. Read reviews of books, films and documentaries, announcements of grants, conferences and jobs, see course outlines, class handouts and syllabi, and participate in discussions on film history.

**Listserv Mailing List:**

List Name: **h-film**
Subscribe to: **listserv@h-net.msu.edu**

## Film.com

This is a great site for film buffs and casual movie fans alike. There are lots of reviews for new releases as well as for previous new releases (back to 1991). Want to know when a new film will be released? Check the release calendar, by name or by date.

**Web:**

**http://www.film.com/**

## Filmmaking and Reviews

Don't you hate it when you're sitting in a dark theater enjoying popcorn soaked in an obscene amount of butter and the hero of the flick has just been blown 30 feet into the sky by a car bomb when suddenly the guy behind you says, "Plastique does not have that sort of structured explosive radius. How unrealistic." Unfortunately, not everyone views movies in the same way. For some, film is art. For others, it is pure entertainment. It can also be a business or communications media. For amateur filmmakers, these Usenet groups offer sources of help and a way to connect with other filmmakers and learn about new equipment and techniques.

**Usenet:**

**bit.listserv.film-l**
**rec.arts.movies.production**

## Girls on Film

Girls on Film is a collection of articles written by four women who review movies and talk about movie stars. You can not only read their reviews, you can also enjoy some extra-special stuff about each of the four women (Lise, Sibyl, Andrea and Clare). If you are looking for profound, in-depth analyses, well... I guess you'll just have to judge for yourself. In the meantime, there are lots of archives of fun, lighthearted reviews through which you can browse. (Sibyl liked La Cage Aux Folles much more than The Birdcage; Clare and Andrea thought Mission Impossible was predictable, but it's worth the money because you get to see Tom Cruise.) I like this site. Girls may be girls, but as we all know, some are better at it than others.

**Web:**
**http://www.girlsonfilm.com/**

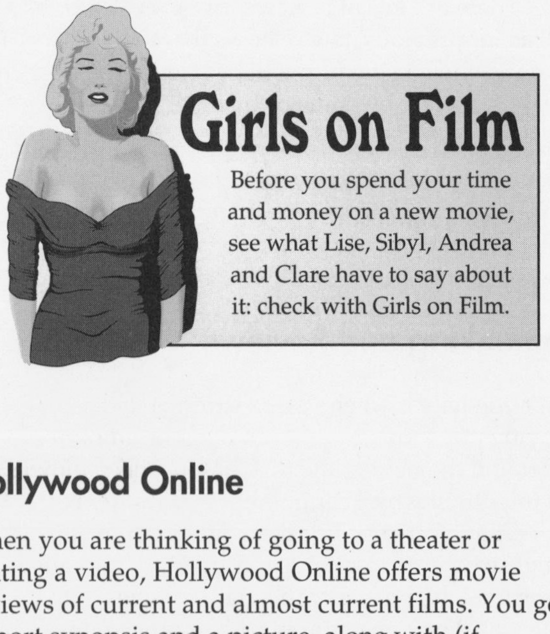
Girls on Film
Before you spend your time and money on a new movie, see what Lise, Sibyl, Andrea and Clare have to say about it: check with Girls on Film.

## Hollywood Online

When you are thinking of going to a theater or renting a video, Hollywood Online offers movie reviews of current and almost current films. You get a short synopsis and a picture, along with (if available) a long review, extra pictures, sound clips and a link to the movie's web site. There are also chat rooms where you can talk to other movie fans. Why even go out? It's a lot easier—and cheaper—to make some popcorn and just sit home reading and talking about movies.

**Web:**
**http://www.hollywood.com/**

## Horror Movie Mailing List

Love a movie that scares you out of your wits? You're not alone. Join with other fans of horror films in this mailing list forum and talk about all your favorites.

**Listserv Mailing List:**
List Name: **horror**
Subscribe to: **listserv@iubvm.ucs.indiana.edu**

## Internet Movie Database

It's a horrible feeling when you are trying to think of a movie title and you just can't remember it. That never has to be a problem if you connect to the Internet Movie Database. Now you can search for your favorite (or most hated) movie by the title, cast and crew names, cast character name, genre and other more obscure methods.

**Web:**
**http://ballet.cit.gu.edu.au/Movies/**
**http://cezanne.daum.co.kr/cynema/**
**http://uk.imdb.com/**
**http://us.imdb.com/**
**http://www.leo.org/Movies**

## Monster Movie Talk and General Discussion

I love monsters. Even the bad ones. Monsters inevitably cause massive amounts of chaos, destruction, explosions and a variety of property damage, but that doesn't make them all bad. They are bound to be good for the economy in that they keep people employed—construction workers, for instance. Check out the Usenet group devoted to the discussion of monster movies and get the real lowdown on Godzilla's family history.

**Usenet:**
**alt.movies.monster**

## Movie Index

Previews are fun. They're like lots of little movies and often are better than the actual feature movie. Plan now for that hot date: pop some popcorn, pull up some chairs and download lots of movie previews. Not only can you impress your date with your taste in movies, but also with your technological prowess. This site has movie pictures, posters, videos and information about the casts and films.

**Web:**
**http://movieweb.com/movie/**

## Movie Reviews

It's a terrible situation when you are bored and you want to go to a movie and you've never heard of any of the movies that are at the theater. If you are looking for a good movie and need a recommendation, check out the movie reviews offered here.

**Web:**

**http://www.service.com/PAW/thisweek/movie_reviews.html**
**http://www.sfgate.com/ea/film/#critics**

**Usenet:**

**rec.arts.movies.reviews**

## Movielink

If you are in the United States, this site allows you to find out about movies playing in your local area (if you happen to live in one of the many cities that are covered). If Movielink has your city listed, you can find movie times and theater locations. This is the place that I go to when I need to find out what's playing and when. However, even if your city is not listed, you can read the synopses of movies and (if available) look at posters and previews.

**Web:**

**http://www.movielink.com/**

## Movies and Filmmaking Talk and General Discussion

Movies are fun to watch from the audience, but don't you wonder what it would be like to be in on the action? You can at least get in on the talk. Discuss movies and the making of movies from a creative or technical point of view. Fans and filmmakers frequent these Usenet groups.

**Usenet:**

**alt.movies.branagh-thmpsn**
**alt.movies.chaplin**
**alt.movies.hitchcock**
**alt.movies.independent**
**alt.movies.indian**
**alt.movies.joe-vs-volcano**
**alt.movies.kubrick**
**alt.movies.silent**
**alt.movies.spielberg**
**alt.movies.tim-burton**
**alt.movies.visual-effects**
**alt.music.scorsese**
**rec.arts.movies**
**rec.arts.movies.current-films**
**rec.arts.movies.lists+surveys**
**rec.arts.movies.local.indian**
**rec.arts.movies.misc**
**rec.arts.movies.movie-going**
**rec.arts.movies.past-films**
**rec.arts.movies.people**
**rec.arts.movies.production**
**rec.arts.movies.tech**

### *Look What I Found on the Net...*

```
Newsgroup: alt.movies.monster
Subject: Willard

> Is Willard a rat or a man?
> I have money riding on this.

Willard is the name of a movie about a guy named Willard, who
just happens to be a mad doctor who was kicked out of the
military, and now uses mind control to have rats commit murders
for him.
```

## Mr. Showbiz

Mr. Showbiz is packed to the brim with movie industry buzz. It reviews the latest movies, and offers feature articles about the films and the stars. When you're tired of reading, you can enjoy some of the crazy time-wasters. For example, I enjoyed the "plastic surgery lab" (where you can modify your favorite stars), an awesome crossword puzzle, and some trivia games. This is a really, really cool site that can keep you busy for a long time.

**Web:**
**http://www.mrshowbiz.com/**

## Science Fiction Movie Talk and General Discussion

Movies of the science fiction genre are getting better all the time. Special effects are more creative and technically seamless, and the movie ideas are more outlandish. Discuss current science fiction movies as well as the more classical versions of the last few decades.

**Usenet:**
**rec.arts.sf.movies**

If God really wanted us to live in the real world, why did he give us science fiction movies? (For that matter, why did he give us this book?)

## Stargazer's CinemaSite

If the view outside your window is crummy, take a look at the hottest male stars of the cinema. Fans of these hot bodies should come armed with drool buckets, wet wipes and a safety cover for the keyboard. For those less-visually inclined, follow links to other interesting movie sites and some behind-the-scene information.

**Web:**
**http://www.geocities.com/cgi-bin/main/Hollywood**

## Weird Movie List

This is a long, alphabetical list of weird movies, including descriptions. The list is getting old, but it is irreplaceable. Where else can you find a quick plot summary of "The Brain that Wouldn't Die", "The H-Man" (probably the best blob movie ever made), "She Devils of the SS", and "Terror Creatures From the Grave"? Even a casual glance through this list will convince you that Plan 9 From Outer Space is not the worst film ever made—not by a long shot.

**Web:**
**http://wiretap.spies.com/Gopher/Library/Media/Film/weird.movi**

WEIRD MOVIES

The only thing better than weird movies is reading about weird movies. If you think that the best things on film are the ones that make you scratch your head (or other parts of your anatomy), then this resource is for you. No need to feel left out when people at parties discuss films. Take a look at the Internet's weird movie list, and you will be more popular than a dog at a flea convention.

# MUDS: GENERAL INFORMATION

## Cardiff's Mud Page

When you are looking for something fun to do, check out Cardiff's Mud Page. It has mud lists and information galore, so you will never lack for fun ways to spend the day when you could be doing something important like winning a Nobel Prize for medicine.

**Web:**

**http://paladin.cm.cf.ac.uk/User/Andrew.Wilson/MUDlist/**

## History of Muds

Muds have an intriguing history that demonstrates some of the most important qualities of the Net and of shared reality experiences. Once you become a serious mudder, you will enjoy knowing how muds got started, and how they developed. These two web sites are good places to start. In the future, all young children will be required to study the history of muds in school. You and I might as well start now.

**Web:**

**http://www.ludd.luth.se/mud/aber/articles/history.html**
**http://www.shef.ac.uk/uni/academic/I-M/is/studwork/groupe/t1.html**

## Macintosh Mudding Resources

If you are a Mac user, I want you to know about this site. It is a great place to find resources that are scattered all over the Net: mud clients, servers and utilities, as well as links to a nice selection of mud resources, including some for beginners. If you need a mud client, look here first. Not only will you find links to the download locations, but comprehensive commentary that makes it easy to decide which program might be best for you.

**Web:**

**http://www.eden.com/~hsoi/mud/**

## Moo Library

New to the worlds of moo? Here's a web page that will help you out. Read these tutorials, FAQs, command reference sheets, research papers and other moo-related documents. There are also links to various moos, so once you feel ready you can start exploring.

**Web:**

**http://lucien.berkeley.edu/moo.html**

## Mud Admin Talk and General Discussion

As a player, if you think it's an inconvenience when your mud crashes, think how it would be if you were in charge of the machine that crashed it. Learn the ins and outs of being an administrator of a mud. How do you start a mud, and when you get it started, how in the world do you keep it going?

**Usenet:**

**rec.games.mud.admin**

## Mud Announcements

What's new? What's passed away? Every Friday, get the latest word on what mud sites are up and running and which ones have been put to pasture. Did you lose your favorite mud? Ask around here—someone will know the answer.

**Usenet:**

**rec.games.mud.announce**

### Muds in the News

The best thing about Muds is that they keep so many people away from real life, where they would otherwise get bored and cause trouble. (Just see how much trouble is caused by all the people who don't use Muds.)

So, for all you Mudders, be sure to tune in to rec.games.mud.announce and find out what's new and exciting. Wouldn't it be awful to telnet to your favorite Mud and find out that everyone else has moved to Mars?

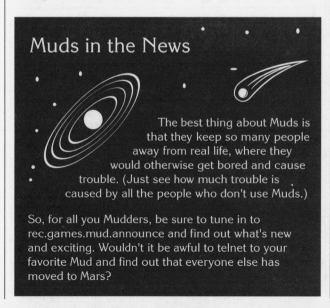

## Mud Area Building

The information at this web site is specific to building areas on a mud. You will find programs than can help you (such as "Make Zones Fast"), sample areas that you can study, lots of tips, links to other resources, as well as a mailing list devoted to creating mud areas. Hint: Before you start to code your mud areas, plan them out using graph paper.

**Web:**

**http://www.concentric.net/~rainman/build.shtml**

## Mud Building

Building a mud can be a lot of fun, but it will take you a great deal of time and involve you in a lot of technical details. Here are some resources that can help: lots of tips on building a mud, writing good descriptions and designing interesting objects. There are also links to related resources, such as various pre-built zones and pieces of code you can modify for your own use.

**Web:**

**http://www.goodnet.com/~esnible/mudinfo.html**
**http://www.vuw.ac.nz/who/Jamie.Norrish/mud/building.html**

**New to Mudding?**

**Try Mud Information. No point being more disoriented than is good for you.**

## Mud Clients

These are two of the best mud clients for Unix systems: TinyFugue and **tintin++**. For Windows, I have also included a web site that has an archive of Winsock mud clients. A good client can make a big difference. My advice is to experiment until you find a program you really enjoy using.

**Web:**

**http://fly.ccs.yorku.ca/mush/tf.html**
**http://www.port8zero.com/tintin++/**
**http://www.rahul.net/galen/client.html**

## Mud Dictionary

Like all great areas of human culture (art, music, science) mudding has a specialized vocabulary. When you encounter a word or term you do not understand, this web site is a great place to look for help. Lots and lots of definitions of words that are commonly used on muds and by mud players. Hint: The dictionary is not all that big. I suggest that you just read through the whole thing, especially if you are a beginner.

**Web:**

**http://www.eskimo.com/~hmcom/mud/wholedict.html**

## Mud Documents

An interesting selection of information about muds, including a history of muds, inter-mud communication, a mud survey, and a paper on social virtual reality in the real world.

**Web:**

**http://www.cis.upenn.edu/~lwl/mudinfo.html**

## Mud Information

Here is a large selection of information all about muds and the culture surrounding them, including research articles, clients, ftp sites, mud lists, and descriptions of various muds.

**Web:**

**http://www.utopia.com/talent/lpb/muddex/**

## Mud List

Are you bored out of your skull? Or perhaps you just have some responsibility you would like to avoid. No problem. Here's a list of all the Internet muds you will ever want to play. The site is well-organized and has lots of distractions to keep you busy not only with muds, but with documents designed to help you learn about muds.

**Web:**
**http://www.absi.com/mud/mud_home.html**

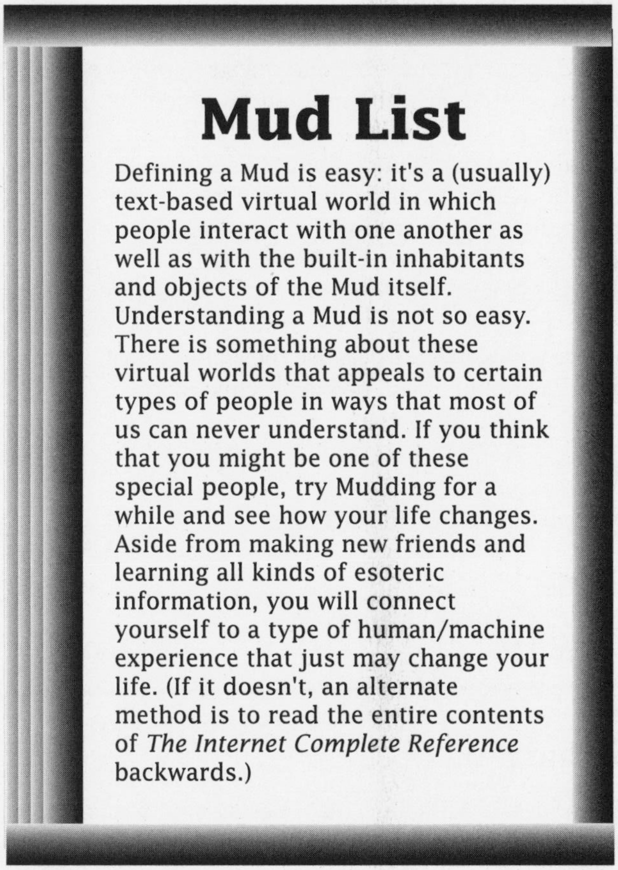

# Mud List

Defining a Mud is easy: it's a (usually) text-based virtual world in which people interact with one another as well as with the built-in inhabitants and objects of the Mud itself. Understanding a Mud is not so easy. There is something about these virtual worlds that appeals to certain types of people in ways that most of us can never understand. If you think that you might be one of these special people, try Mudding for a while and see how your life changes. Aside from making new friends and learning all kinds of esoteric information, you will connect yourself to a type of human/machine experience that just may change your life. (If it doesn't, an alternate method is to read the entire contents of *The Internet Complete Reference* backwards.)

## Mud Mailing List

If you like to talk about mudding as much as you like to actually play on a mud, then you will love this mailing list. For players and admins alike, this list offers a place to announce new muds and clients, talk about servers and programming tips or mudding in general.

**Listserv Mailing List:**
List Name: **mud-l**
Subscribe to: **listserv@vm.ege.edu.tr**

## Mud Talk and General Discussion

Immerse yourself in the wonders of muds: text-based virtual realities that provide you with an exciting realm in which to socialize or play adventure games. Find out what mudding is all about, but be warned: the Surgeon General has declared mudding to be addictive.

**Usenet:**
**alt.mud**
**rec.games.mud.misc**

## Mud Tutorial

If you have never used a mud before, this tutorial can help you get started. It explains how to connect to a mud, and what to do once you get there. This particular example uses a TinyMud for demonstration, but many of the ideas and concepts will work for all beginning mudders. (In addition, you might want to read the chapter on muds in my book *The Internet Complete Reference.*)

**Web:**
**http://www.cwrl.utexas.edu/moo/mudhandouts/beginning.html**

## Mush Documents

Enter the interactive social environment of mushs and create your own little corner of the world. Part of the charm of mushs is that anyone can do basic environmental programming. Read the tutorials that show you how to do this. There is also information on mush ethics, clients, and general startup help.

**Web:**
**http://www.cms.dmu.ac.uk/AUG/articles/mushmanual/html_manual/manual.html**

**The Net is waiting for you.**

# MUDS: SPECIFIC TYPES

## Apocalypse Mud

This is a very popular DikuMud with lots of extras, different races and character classes. There are chit-chat channels as well as great places to explore. Give it a try.

**Telnet:**

Address: **sapphire.geo.wvu.edu**
Port: **4000**

## Deep Seas Mush

A mush with an underwater theme. Refreshingly unique if you are looking for a change from hack-n-slash medieval muds. Explore caves, ocean floors, and whirlpools. This is a great place to go for those of you who can't just run down to the beach for a quick snorkel break.

**Telnet:**

Address: **muds.okstate.edu**
Port: **6250**

**Are you bored with mudding above ground?
Try the Deep Seas Mush and explore an underwater world.**

## Deeper Trouble Mud

If you like the flavor of the J.R.R. Tolkien books, then you might like to try Deeper Trouble. This is a fantasy mud based on the works and flavor of Tolkien.

**Telnet:**

Address: **alk.iesd.auc.dk**
Port: **4242**

## DikuMud Talk and General Discussion

A DikuMud is a text-based role-playing virtual reality. Slay a dragon, save a princess, drink a magic potion that will kill you (these are all optional, of course). If you love excitement, adventure, and fantasy, find out what DikuMuds are all about.

**Usenet:**

**rec.games.mud.diku**

## Genocide Mud

Tired of cutesy monsters and quests that make you storm around an entire mud environment for a few meager points? And what about those whiners who are always complaining about PK'ers (player killers) and how big and mean and nasty they are? Well, enough is enough. Go to Genocide, one of the most intense player-killing muds ever. You won't find a single monster. All you do is run around and kill other players. It might be hard for a new person to get started on Genocide because the action is fast, but if you like to kill, it will be worthwhile to learn your way around the system.

**Web:**

**http://www.shsu.edu/~genlpc/**

**Telnet:**

Address: **genocide.shsu.edu**
Port: **2222**

## Island Mud

Island is a unique mud that boasts about being "the world's most literate mud". Imaginative and well-designed, Island sets out to entertain and amuse you. Try it out. It's better than television.

**Telnet:**

Address: **teaching4.physics.ox.ac.uk**
Port: **2093**

**Happiness is a warm modem.**

## LambdaMoo

A large and popular virtual reality with more varied sections and interesting objects than you'll ever be able to explore. Players are allowed to program and create their own sections.

**Telnet:**

Address: **lambda.parc.xerox.com**
Port: **8888**

## Looney Mud

When you get tired of medieval fantasy or serious role-playing, try something really wacky, like Looney Mud. You'll start off at Sesame Street where you can chat with other players or can go off to maim small defenseless animals. Join a silly guild like the Animators Guild which uses a paintbrush as a magical way of gaining extra powers.

**Web:**

**http://looney.com/**

**Telnet:**

Address: **looney.com**
Port: **8888**

## LPMud Talk and General Discussion

Hack it, slash it, just make sure you clean up afterward. LPMuds are text-based virtual realities where you can puzzle out a quest for advancement in the game or you can just find monsters to kill. Discover the adventurer within you. If you are already a hard-core mudder and want to set up your own, check out the Usenet groups to get tips on how to start. The web site has an LPMud FAQ.

**Web:**

**http://www.imaginary.com/LPMud/lpmud_faq.html**

**Usenet:**

**alt.mud.lp**
**rec.games.mud.lp**

**Express yourself.**
**Make a web page.**

### *Look What I Found on the Net...*

```
Newsgroup: rec.games.mud.lp
Subject: Are Muds Appropriate for Kids?

> I have a very bright 11 year old who just discovered muds,
> and I don't quite get them.  Could someone please tell me if
> they are suitable for kids?

I have three children, two of which play muds regularly.
One child is 8, the other is 13.  Of course, I have immortal
characters on the muds they play.  I also take other
precautions.

The 13 year old is usually okay on his own.

The 8 year old always plays a male character (helps to
avoid the sexual advances).  I give her a list of players to
whom it is okay to talk.  If I catch her talking to others,
I change her password, and she may no longer return there (until
she proves she can follow rules).

Finally, I watch her: who she is talking to and what she is
doing.  If there is something I don't like, I make her leave.
On a whole we have had good experiences with her mudding, and
she enjoys it.
```

## Lua-uhane Mud

A wonderful Hawaiian mud with a fantasy theme. Populated by friendly folks who don't bother themselves with the politics and rules of player-killing. Morality rules on the player-killing issues. Killers become evil, which gives all good and neutral players license to gang up on them and kill them. Stealing is allowed, but so is revenge.

**Telnet:**

Address: **linus.actioninc.com**
Port: **4000**

## Mars Base Alpha 4 Mud

Mars Base Alpha 4 is a great place for those with outerspace fantasies. A basic talker-type mud, Alpha 4 is good for people who want a relatively mild environment. No obscenities are allowed except in the Smoking Room and non-harassment rules are strictly enforced.

**Web:**

**http://jumper.mcc.ac.uk/~mba4adm/**

**Telnet:**

Address: **jumper.mcc.ac.uk**
Port: **3214**

## Masquerade Mud

When you can't come out in the sunlight, sometimes sitting around in the house waiting for the night can get a little lonely. If you are a creature of the night or are a creature-of-the-night-wannabe, check out Masquerade, a White Wolf-style mud.

**Telnet:**

Address: **bashful.cc.utexas.edu**
Port: **9999**

**Join the fun—now.**

## Medievia Diku

Looking for a highly populated mud? Try this medieval-themed fantasy mud. Medievia allows for multi-classing and some player-killing in restricted areas. It's a heavily modified mud with ansi color. On Medievia you will encounter clan wars and a variety of environments, such as a watery zone called Atlantis and the catacombs with thousands of randomized rooms.

**Web:**

**http://medievia.netaxs.com:8080/**

**Telnet:**

Address: **medievia.netaxs.com**
Port: **4000**

## Meridian Moo

This moo is focused on travel and creating virtual worlds. Registered users are expected to create something. Code uses ascii art to illustrate rooms and includes lots of on-screen maps.

**Telnet:**

Address: **sky.bellcore.com**
Port: **7777**

## Necromium Mud

Here is a mud with a medieval theme where the motto is "Where death is a way of life". When you first join this mud, you get taken on a 15-minute tour of the game, instead of having to go to a mud school or being totally left to flounder around trying to figure out what to do. Thus, if you are new to mudding, this is a good place to start (as long as you like death).

**Telnet:**

Address: **necromium.com**
Port: **4000**

## Nightmare Mud

Nightmare is a high-energy mud with a variety of classes and races. Work your way up to be a High Mortal so you can beat up on the really studly monsters. Nightmare has high coding standards, so it's visually colorful and the settings are unique and imaginative.

**Web:**

**http://www.imaginary.com/LPMud/Nightmare**

**Telnet:**

Address: **nightmare.winternet.com**
Port: **1701**

## Nuclear War Mud

Taste a little bit of the dark future on Nuclear War. You begin your new life in a laboratory. Roam through the dilapidated city, deserted villages and slums. Join a gang of hackers, jetscreamers, inquisitors or undergrounders. This is an imaginative, futuristic environment and makes a nice change of pace.

**Web:**

**http://www.astrakan.hgs.se/nuke/**

**Telnet:**

Address: **nuclearwar.astrakan.hgs.se**
Port: **4080**

## Pern Mush

PernWorld is a mush based on the Dragonriders of Pern novels written by Anne McCaffrey. The timeline of the mush is after "All the Weyrs of Pern" and after the end of Threadfall for all time. If you are a fan of McCaffrey, dragons or just plain fantasy, enter Pern and have a look.

**Web:**

**http://www.loach.org/~pern/pern/**

**Telnet:**

Address: **pern.mccr.org**
Port: **4201**

### *Look What I Found on the Net...*

(from the Nightmare mud)

```
> look

Monument Square in Praxis [n, s, e, w]

From the center of Monument Square leads the two main roads of
the famous adventuring town of Praxis.  Monument Square was once
known as Krasna Square, but that name was changed when a
monument was erected in the square dedicated to those who helped
make Praxis what it is today.

Several major establishments occupy the corners of the square:
Lars' Pub on the southwest corner, Talimar Hospital on the
northwest corner, the town hall on the southeast corner, and the
Monastery of Praxia on the northeast corner.  None of them have
entrances accessible directly from the square, though you can
see entrances to all of them off of one or both of the streets
they occupy.

Gas lamps light the square and both the town's streets.  The
sounds of a busy adventuring town are all about.  A magic portal
to Newbieland, and a magnificent monument are here.

> w

Boc La just west of Monument Square [e, w]
You are standing outside of the sometimes rowdy, and certainly
always interesting Lars' Pub.  Boc La Road runs east towards
Monument Square and west through the western residential zone of
Praxis.  The walls of the local hospital run along the northern
side of Boc La Road.
```

### Phidar Diku

A hack-n-slasher with a fantasy/medieval theme. Beyond the usual classes included in a fantasy theme, you can also choose to be a minotaur, drow, vampire, or amazon. You can even receive Internet email while you are here.

**Web:**
**http://www.traveller.com/~phidar/**

**Telnet:**
Address: **phidar.traveller.com**
Port: **9000**

### Post Modern-Culture Moo

Talkers and wanderers will like this moo. Visit the Theatro de Saturnalia, a carnival, religion room, gardens, a desert, or the House of Fiction. A magic tour bus makes it easy for new ones to get a guided tour. This is a good environment for talking or exploring, but not role playing or building.

**Telnet:**
Address: **hero.village.virginia.edu**
Port: **7777**

### Sprawl Multimedia Environment Moo

The folks at SenseMedia call this a "woo". It's a moo environment based on ChibaMoo. Explore the moo on the web, jump to other moos, read stories in the collaborative fiction center, visit homes of the builder and read notes posted by inhabitants.

**Web:**
**http://sensemedia.net/sprawl/**

### Three Kingdoms Mud

Three Kingdoms has a hierarchy based on a human monarchy, so it achieves variety through guild selection instead of races. This mud is well-loved and full of life as evidenced by not only the traffic, but the high-spirited shouting that seems to be routine.

**Telnet:**
Address: **marble.confusion.net**
Port: **5000**
Address: **marble.pa.state.ky.US**
Port: **5000**

### TinyMud Talk and General Discussion

Some mudders consider adventuring and killing monsters barbaric. Imagine that. These social animals hang out on TinyMuds where social skill is a high art. If you are interested in chatting, making friends, or other socializing, you'll love TinyMuds (including mushs, muses, and moos).

**Usenet:**
**rec.games.mud.tiny**

## MUSEUMS

### Boston Science Museum

This museum has roots dating back to 1830, when six men formed the Boston Society of Natural History. This society collected natural history specimens and would display them in temporary halls until, in 1864, the society opened the New England Museum of Natural History. Eventually, this exhibition evolved into the Museum of Science. When I visited, I saw some great exhibits about fractals, electricity, archeology, as well as a collection of pictures taken with an electron microscope. (A flea under an electron microscope is pretty frightening.)

**Web:**
**http://www.mos.org/**

### Egyptian Art and Archeology

Egypt is cool. It's not often that most of us get to see big sand dunes, camels, pyramids and open street markets. In fact, if you haven't gotten to see any Egyptian artifacts, you just don't know what you are missing. Right this very minute you could be taking an online tour of Egypt and an exhibit of Egyptian artifacts. And you don't even have to get your shots to do it.

**Web:**
**http://www.memphis.edu/egypt/main.html**

### The Big Clue

In 1799, near Rosetta, Egypt, a French archeologist named Boussard excavated a black basalt slab, measuring three and a half feet by two and a half feet. On the slab was inscribed a decree in honor of the Pharaoh Ptolemy Epiphanes. This discovery was unique in that the same information was inscribed in three different languages: hieroglyphic (pictures), demotic (a late form of Egyptian cursive writing) and Greek. For the first time, there was a clue as to what the various hieroglyphic symbols meant.

By 1821, the French Egyptologist Jean François Champollion had used the Rosetta Stone to establish principles for deciphering the hieroglyphics. This work was so important that, to this day, many people consider Champollion to be the founder of the science of Egyptology.

If you would like to find out more about Egyptology and Egyptian Art, the University of Memphis, Tennessee, has a wonderful online site you can visit. After all, why should you go all the way to Egypt (or Tennessee for that matter) when you have the Net?

## Exploratorium

Science is fun. You can blow things up, stick things together, make things float and create loud noises that will guarantee you a trip to the principal's office. The Exploratorium in San Francisco creates an environment of hands-on fun learning and you can visit their home on the Net.

**Web:**

**http://www.exploratorium.edu/**

### THE EXPLORATORIUM

The Exploratorium is absolutely my favorite place in the San Francisco Bay Area (except for the offices of my publisher Osborne McGraw-Hill, in Berkeley, where they write the royalty checks). The next time you are in San Francisco, be sure to visit The Exploratorium, the greatest hands-on science museum in the world. There are hundreds of things to do and zillions of buttons to push. Before you go, get the lowdown by connecting to the Exploratorium's Internet facilities.

You can display all kinds of interesting pictures to give you a preview of what you will find at the museum. You can even try experiments, right in the privacy of your own computer.

(Hint for afterwards: When you are finished at the Exploratorium, go across the bay to Berkeley and drop into Osborne McGraw-Hill. Ask for my editor, Scott Rogers, and tell him that because you are a reader of this book, he must take you out to dinner.)

## Holocaust Museums and Memorials

From the time of Hitler's rise to power (1933) to the end of World War II (1945), the Germans, under Hitler's leadership, conducted a large-scale program to systematically persecute and exterminate the entire Jewish community within the German sphere of influence. This atrocity—today known as the Holocaust—resulted in the murder of about 6 million Jews, many of whom were sent to the infamous concentration camps: places whose sole purpose was to efficiently kill large numbers of men, women and children. The Jews were not the only people murdered in the Holocaust. The Germans also rounded up and killed homosexuals, Gypsies, Communists, as well as many Poles and other foreigners whose lands were overrun by the German military. The acts committed by Hitler, the Nazis and the German people during this time period are so gross as to challenge the imagination. Many people feel that such actions must never be forgotten, and that our society has much to gain by studying and understanding the Holocaust. Around the world, various Holocaust museums and memorials have been built. Here are the web sites for three of them: Yad Vashem in Israel, the United States Holocaust Memorial Museum in Washington, D.C., and the Simon Wiesenthal Center in Los Angeles.

**Web:**

**http://www.ushmm.org/**
**http://www.wiesenthal.com/**
**http://www.yad-vashem.org.il/**

## Italian Museums

Italy has many wonderful museums. If you like art, you will have a great time browsing through this collection of links to a great many Italian museums. (I enjoyed visiting the Leonardo da Vinci museum.) There are lots and lots of paintings and other works of art to enjoy in Italy, and the Web makes it easy to visit them.

**Web:**

**http://www.quipo.it/musei/musei.html**

Quick, turn the page.

## London Science Museum

The London Science Museum contains exhibits in the areas of science, the history of science, medicine, technology and industry. There are lots of fascinating things to learn about at this web site. For example, I read about genetically engineered mice. The first mammals ever patented were white mice that had been genetically altered to make them more prone to develop cancers. (The "oncomice" are used in cancer research.)

**Web:**

**http://www.nmsi.ac.uk/**

## Maritime Museums

A maritime museum collects exhibits and artifacts related to sailing and the sea. This web site has links to various maritime museums in North America. Visit the Jamestown Settlement (where there are three full-scale replicas of ships from 1607), Battleship Cove (where you can see the world's most complete collection of historic fighting ships), and many more fascinating online museums. Visiting a maritime museum makes you appreciate the achievements of shipbuilders throughout the ages. For example, the battleship U.S. Massachusetts (the "Big Mamie"), which was used during World War II, weighs over 46,000 tons, is longer than two football fields and is as tall as a nine-story building. If you like ships, there are many fascinating places to visit on the Net.

**Web:**

**http://www1.mhv.net/~omi/smith1.htm**

## Museum of Science and Industry

The Museum of Science and Industry in Chicago, Illinois, hosts this online collection of interesting exhibits. The exhibits change from time to time, so you can check every now and then and see what's new. This is a great place to visit with children.

**Web:**

**http://www.msichicago.org/**

## Museum Talk and General Discussion

These are the places where museum curators and other professionals gather to discuss their work. Talk about plans for new exhibits, problems, questions, answers, and whatever else arises in the lives of the people who set up and maintain museums around the world.

**Usenet:**

**bit.listserv.museum-l**

**Listserv Mailing List:**

List Name: **museum-l**
Subscribe to: **listserv@home.ease.lsoft.com**

## Museums and Galleries of Wales

Wales is a principality on the western peninsula of the island of Great Britain. Although Wales is part of the United Kingdom (along with England, Scotland and Northern Ireland), it has maintained its own distinct culture, including the Welsh language. This web site contains links to various Welsh museums on the web such as the Roman Legionary Museum, the Welsh Industrial and Maritime Museum and the Museum of Welsh Life. If you are planning a visit to Wales, I recommend you check this web site to get ideas for places you may want to visit.

**Web:**

**http://www.cf.ac.uk/nmgw/mainmenu.html**

## Museums, Exhibits and Special Collections

If you are not getting enough culture from television, try visiting some of the museums on the Net. You can hop around like a jet-setting socialite and visit museums all over the world. This web page has links to a diverse set of museums, exhibits and special collections that can be found on the Net.

**Web:**

**http://www.lam.mus.ca.us/webmuseums/**

## Museums on the Web

A collection of web links connecting museums and archives. This page offers pointers to such sights as the Hall of Dinosaurs, the Moscow Kremlin Online Excursion, the London Transport Museum, Native Vikings, and many other interesting destinations.

**Web:**

**http://www.icom.org/vlmp/**

**Strike up a conversation: try Usenet.**

## New Mexico Museum of Natural History

New Mexico is a state in the southwestern part of the United States, just north of the Mexican border. New Mexico Museum of Natural History has various online exhibits that you can visit on the Web. My favorite are the exhibits about mammals and dinosaurs. (If your kids like dinosaurs, bring them here.)

**Web:**

**http://www.aps.edu/htmlpages/NMMNH.html**

**The Net loves poetry.**

### *Look What I Found on the Net...*

```
Newsgroup: bit.listserv.museum-l
Subject: This Is Why I Love Working in a Museum

> Hello all.  The Deutsche Hygiene-Museum in Dresden is
> organizing an exhibit on the theme of "Sitting" (you read me
> right).  They have asked to borrow South Dakota's electric
> chair, of which we are the proud possessor.  Alas, we will not
> be able to lend, due to our own exhibition plans for it.
>
> Which leads me to my question: is there anyone out there who
> knows of an institution in the United States that has its
> state's electric chair?  The director of the museum asked for
> the names of other museums that might have such a thing, but I
> don't know of any.  I do believe, however, that we are not the
> only museum in the U.S. with an electric chair.

(reply #1)

The Old Jail Museum in St. Augustine, Florida, has one.  It's
quite nice as I recall.

(reply #2)

I believe the Wyoming Frontier Prison in Rawlins, Wyoming,
has one.

(reply #3)

The Louisiana State Museum has an electric chair in their
collection.  I was an intern there last summer, and they
threatened to put me in it.
```

## Oriental Institute Museum

For many of you, Chicago might be a little out of the way if you have the urge to make a quick trip to the Oriental Institute Museum. Now you can visit it on the Web. You'll have no hassle making airline reservations and finding a good hotel. All you have to do is connect to this site and you can get your fill of Oriental photographic archives and cultural information on temples, tombs, animals, clothing, combat, deities and industry from the Far East.

**Web:**

**http://www-oi.uchicago.edu/OI/MUS/OI_Museum.html**

## Royal Tyrell Museum of Paleontology

Joseph Burr Tyrell was an explorer for the Geological Survey of Canada. In the spring of 1884, Tyrell was leading an expedition to find coal deposits in an area in what is now the province of Alberta. During his explorations, Tyrell found the remains of a 70 million year-old dinosaur skull. The skull was from a genus of dinosaur that was later named Albertosaurus, and was the first specimen of that genus found in the world. The Royal Tyrell Museum of Paleontology is located near Drumheller in Alberta. The web page includes exhibits about fossils, continental drift, evolution, dinosaurs and the Ice Age. I looked at a page explaining the evolution of fish. If you get the chance, take a look at the Dunkleosteus. It makes a shark look like a house pet.

**Web:**

**http://tyrrell.magtech.ab.ca/**

**Oriental Institute Museum**

Are you interested in the languages, history and cultures of the ancient Near East?

Take the online tour of the Oriental Institute Museum and learn about:

Anatolia
Assyria
Cyprus
Egypt
Iran
Mesopotamia
Palestine
Syria

## Tower of London

Take a tour of the Tower of London, an ancient fortress that was once used as a royal residence, a jail and a repository for the Crown Jewels. Look at pictures of furniture in the tower, as well as armor that used to be worn by the guards. The Tower of London is the oldest palace, fortress and prison in Europe, and was built by William the Conqueror. The Lion Tower is where the kings kept animals. (Henry I had lions, Henry II had three leopards, an elephant and a bear. James I also had a bear.) This interesting web site will teach you about the various towers and their histories. Although history and museums can be kind of dull, I think you will like this tour—there are some interesting photos along with a lot of fascinating history.

**Web:**

**http://www.voicenet.com/~dravyk/toltour/**

# MUSIC

## A Cappella

Not everyone needs music to help them keep in tune or remember the beat (or drown out their voice). For some folks, they can sing sweetly without the accompaniment of musical instruments. That's what a cappella is all about. Find out more at the web site or talk about it on Usenet, with or without a musical instrument.

**Web:**

**http://www.casa.org/web_directory.html**

**Usenet:**

**alt.music.a-cappella**
**rec.music.a-cappella**

## Acid Jazz

Acid jazz is music style that is part jazz, 70s funk, hip-hop, and soul. This is the home page for acid jazz, with links to a mailing list, a mail archive, magazines, club information, and a regularly updated recording list.

**Web:**

**http://www.cmd.uu.se/AcidJazz/**

## Acoustic and Electric Bass

Music is just not the same without the rhythmic thumping and bumping of the bass. Whether you like your bass acoustic or electric, you can gather with other bass lovers and talk about how low you can go.

**Usenet:**

**rec.music.makers.bass**

## Afro-Latin

Discussion of music with an African and Latin American flavor. Music with a beat that just doesn't know when to quit—emotion, style and seduction—guaranteed to pick you up and drop you in a strange place, far away from real life.

**Usenet:**

**rec.music.afro-latin**

## Bagpipes

Archive files and discussion of any topic related to bagpipes, with all manner of Scottish, Irish, English, and other instruments discussed.

**Web:**

**http://pipes.tico.com/**

**Usenet:**

**rec.music.makers.bagpipe**

*Who hasn't heard a real Scotsman playing the bagpipes and not fallen in love with that sensuous, romantic, sophisticated sound that other, more euphonic musicians can only dream of?*

## Bands

If you've been looking for your favorite rock band on the Net and can't find them, check here. This site has a huge list of bands as well as information about rock, metal, death, thrash, and punk. There are links to magazines and other related sites.

**Web:**

**http://osiris.sund.ac.uk/cge/bandhome.html**

## Banjo Tablature

Africans brought the banjo all the way to America before 1688, just so people could go to bluegrass festivals and jam. It's true. Now that the banjo is well-established in American culture, it's time for you to practice up on your tablature. This web site has tablature helpers and information on MIDI players. Remember, the only way you can get to the Grand Old Opry is to practice, practice, practice.

**Web:**

**http://www.wsnet.com/~phil/banjo.html**

## Barbershop Quartets

Throw down your accordion, your bagpipes, your tin whistles, and join a barbershop quartet. More fun than a barrel of monkeys, able to leap octaves in a single bound, these singers are lively, energetic, and know how to have a good time. Check out their online organizations, calendar of events, FAQs, and other resource information.

**Web:**

**http://timc.pop.upenn.edu/**
**http://webpages.marshall.edu/~bennett7/hstation.html**

## Big Band

While you can't hear the snappy, lively big band sound through this Usenet group, you can at least talk about all your favorite bands and musicians, and the history of the music and era. The web site offers links to big band sites around the Net.

**Web:**

**http://www.musicsearch.com/genre/bigb.html**

**Usenet:**

**alt.music.big-band**

Big band music is a gift from the gods.

Follow **alt.music.big-band** and see what the people with good taste have to say.

## Bluegrass

A mailing list for issues related to the International Bluegrass Music Association, and bluegrass music in general, including but not limited to recordings, bands, individual performers, and live performances.

**Listserv Mailing List:**

List Name: **bgrass-l**
Subscribe to: **listserv@lsv.uky.edu**

## Blues

It's best played in tiny lounges with poor lighting. Maybe fill the room with some smoke. There is a true art to the mournful quality of the music. This is not just "crying in your beer" music. Explore the resources that bring the blues to life on the Net.

**Web:**

**http://badger.win.bright.net/bluesman/**

**Usenet:**

**bit.listserv.blues-l**

**Listserv Mailing List:**

List Name: **blues-l**
Subscribe to: **listserv@brownvm.brown.edu**

**Stay away from "X-Rated".**

## Bottom Line Zine

It's what you usually hear when you are stuck in a nightclub and the speakers are turned up way too loud. Or worse, you can feel it somewhere between your stomach and your heart. But any bassist with class will keep his or her bottom line where it's supposed to be. We're not sure where that is exactly, but it's bound to be someplace respectable. This electronic zine has articles and information for bassists.

**Web:**

**http://www.oulu.fi/tbl.html**

## Buying and Selling Music

Don't waste your time wandering the neighborhood looking for good garage sales at which to buy music and musical instruments. People all over the Net come to Usenet to buy and sell musical goods such as instruments and equipment, records, tapes, and CDs. Buying over the Net sure beats trying to get a piano home in the back seat of your car.

**Usenet:**

**rec.music.makers.marketplace**
**rec.music.marketplace**

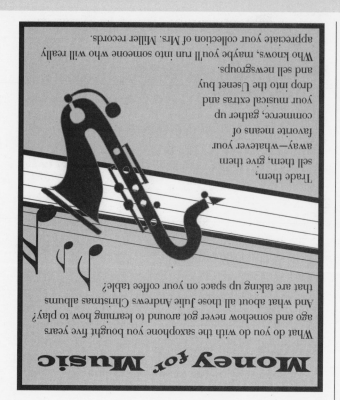

### Money for Music

What do you do with the saxophone you bought five years ago and somehow never got around to learning how to play? And what about all those Julie Andrews Christmas albums that are taking up space on your coffee table?

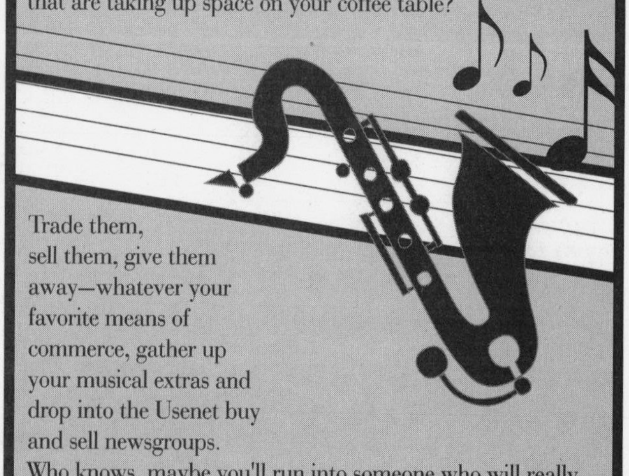

Trade them, sell them, give them away—whatever your favorite means of commerce, gather up your musical extras and drop into the Usenet buy and sell newsgroups. Who knows, maybe you'll run into someone who will really appreciate your collection of Mrs. Miller records.

## CDs

Collecting is a nice hobby to have, especially if you are goal oriented. How about collecting music CDs? They are thin and don't take up much space, they are cleaner than bugs, and you can use them as coasters if friends come over. Join in the Usenet discussion of music and CDs, including what's available, new releases, CDs wanted and for sale, and requests for information.

**Usenet:**

**rec.music.collecting.cds**

## Celtic Music

Music is something that the Celts do well. The soulful wail of the whistles and the primal beating of the drums would make just about anyone yearn to buy a plane ticket to Ireland. The proof is in the numbers. Fans of Celtic music are abundant on the Net and sponsor mailing lists and web pages with information about Celtic music magazines, live jam sessions, radio programs, and more.

**Web:**

**http://celtic.stanford.edu/ceolas.html**

**Usenet:**

**rec.music.celtic**

## Classical Music

The world of classical music is huge, with many composers and many styles of music. Here are some Internet resources for you to explore: web sites that will point you to all kinds of interesting and useful information, and discussion groups where you can talk to other people and ask questions.

**Web:**

**http://www.classical.net/**
**http://www.igc.apc.org/ddickerson/classical-music.html**

**Usenet:**

**rec.music.classical**
**rec.music.early**

**Listserv Mailing List:**

List Name: **classm-l**
Subscribe to: **listserv@brownvm.brown.edu**

## Complex Musical Arrangements

Complex times call for complex musical arrangements. Composers and music lovers discuss the construction, styles and history of music in relation to complex arrangement.

**Usenet:**

**alt.music.complex-arrang**

## Computers in Music Research

Forget sifting through dusty old archives of stained and smelly sheet music. Faster and more effective ways of conducting music research are being developed, and you can get in on the action along with musicologists, music analysts, computer scientists, and other people working on applications of computers in music research.

**Usenet:**

**comp.music**

## Concert Information

All dressed up and no place to go? This web page offers access to lists of concert schedules and information about where you can get tickets.

**Web:**

**http://www.wilma.com/**

## Country Music

If you don't get enough country music while riding in the pickup to and from the feed store, check out this site, which offers concert reviews, country radio stations, discussion groups, magazines, and fan club information. Love, marriage, divorce, truck driving, dogs, beer, intrigue—it's all just good old-fashioned American fun.

**Web:**

**http://www.tpoint.net/Users/wallen/country/country.html**

**Usenet:**

**rec.music.country.western**

I love you b-a-a-a-by!

## Country Music

There is something about the steady thump, thump, twang, twang of country music that is so reassuring. Country and western music serves up a heapin' platter of good ole' American culture at its finest: money, booze and bad love. Just the thing for tired Internet music lovers who have overdosed on bagpipes.

## Creative Internet Music Site

Creative Internet provides interactive worlds for music and television. You can check out the ultimate list of links that can be updated by visitors, vote in the polls, see the hottest links, and advertise your links on the free-for-all.

**Web:**
**http://www.cid.com/**

## Discographies

When you have a blind date with a girl and you know she likes a certain band, go to one of these discographies sites, find the band and memorize every song and album they have ever released (along with the dates they were released). On the date, talk is bound to turn to music and you can wow her with your knowledge of her favorite musical groups. I always say, plan for success.

**Web:**
**http://www.cgrg.ohio-state.edu/folkbook/discographies.html**
**http://www.teleport.com/~xeres/discog.shtml**

## Drums and Percussion

This is the part of the band that will never be able to sneak up on anybody. Read jokes, mailing lists, an encyclopedia of terms, and FAQs on how to make the kind of loud noises that people like.

**Web:**
**http://www.cse.ogi.edu/Drum/**

## Earfood

Music can be like a total food experience. At least that's what Earfood is trying to achieve. Gluttony of the aural sense. This site is fun and interesting, full of profiles, interviews, news releases and reviews of music artists. When you want the story behind the story, you can even get gossip about the music industry.

**Web:**
**http://www.tumyeto.com/tydu/music/earfood.htm**

## Early Music

Believe it or not, there really was music before rock and roll. And it was good music, too, but you can't do the Twist to it. If that doesn't bother you, you will probably love music from the Middle Ages and Renaissance. Early music lovers chat about records, books, performances, song texts, and translations as well as transcribing early music scores in electronic form.

**Listserv Mailing List:**
List Name: **earlym-l**
Subscribe to: **listserv@aearn.aco.net**

## Electric Music

The bad thing about electric music is that you can't play it during a power outage. So take advantage of the opportunity to download these audio files while the lights are still on. Do you think Ben Franklin had any idea that his little experiment would lead to this?

**Web:**
**http://www.hike.te.chiba-u.ac.jp/eem/**

## Electronic Music Talk and General Discussion

Composing and playing electronic music is mostly a solitary occupation: you spend a lot of time by yourself, with only a synthesizer, a computer, and some strange-looking audio equipment for company. However, when you want company there's no need to actually go and fetch a real live person. There are people enough on the Net ready to discuss whatever you want regarding electronic music, and *they* know what they are talking about.

**Usenet:**

**alt.emusic**
**bit.listserv.emusic-l**
**rec.music.makers.synth**
**rec.music.synth**

**Listserv Mailing List:**

List Name: **emusic-l**
Subscribe to: **listserv@american.edu**

## Ethnomusicology Research Digest

A periodical for professionals, librarians, and graduate students interested the field of ethnomusicology. (This is, of course, a subject of great global significance.)

**Web:**

**http://www.inform.umd.edu:8080/EdRes/ReadingRoom/Newsletters/EthnoMusicology/.WWW**

Who sang what, with whom, when? Go to the Net and cop some info from the **discography** archives.

## Filk

Filking is the clever, but nearly irreverent art of taking an existing song, gutting it, and making it into something new using the same music, but different words. Join the rowdy crowd around the campfire as they belt out the ballads.

**Usenet:**

**alt.music.filk**

**Feel lucky?**
**Try "Contests".**

### *Look What I Found on the Net...*

```
Newsgroup: alt.emusic
Subject: What Do You Call That Music?

> Hi!  I flew into this newsgroup hoping for an answer.  I am
> trying to find out what you call the music that sounds like
> you're on a different planet.
>
> Space music? Alternative? New Age?  I've searched and searched
> trying to find something.  I used to listen to it on the
> radio.  It was piped in through some satellite feed.
> Any suggestions?

Hmm... What does the music on this planet sound like?

The space age bachelor pad sounds of Esquevel?
Electronic experimentalists like SkyLab?
Disorienting media plunder like John Oswald?

We need a little more to work with here.  There are a lot of
planets out there.
```

A B C D E F G H I J K L M N O P Q R S T U V W X Y Z

## Film Music Talk and General Discussion

Discussions of the music used in movies and television, including music reviews, film composers, film music history and theory, and requests for information about film music.

**Listserv Mailing List:**

List Name: **filmus-l**
Subscribe to: **listserv@iubvm.ucs.indiana.edu**

## Folk Music

I think Tom Lerher put it best: "The reason most songs are so atrocious," he explained, "is that they were written by the people." Lerher is a tough act to follow, so I'll content myself with pointing out that the Net has lots of folk music resources, including a Usenet discussion group.

**Web:**

**http://pubweb.parc.xerox.com/digitrad**
**http://www.eit.com/web/folk/folkhome.html**

**Usenet:**

**rec.music.folk**

## Funk Talk and General Discussion

Opera makes you homicidal, classical puts you to sleep, and country music makes you want to get in a monster truck and plow over any small cars in your path. For a change, try some funk. Funk is based on the rhythmic innovations of James Brown. Discussion includes not only funk, but some rap, hip-hop, soul, R&B, and related varieties. Artists of the genre include Funkadelic, Parliament, and Earth, Wind, and Fire. Not only does funk sound good, you can dance to it, too.

**Usenet:**

**rec.music.funky**

## Grunge

This is definitely not your parents' music. Let your hair down, rip the sleeves off your shirt, and hang loose. Hang out with other angst-consumed rebels and discuss the grunge scene. If it's neat, clean, or prepackaged, it doesn't belong here.

**Listserv Mailing List:**

List Name: **grunge-l**
Subscribe to: **listserv@ubvm.cc.buffalo.edu**

Grunge
City

If you have to ask, don't even bother. But if you know and love grunge, you may want to subscribe to the **grunge-l** mailing list. Never again will you have to spend time in the real world without some grunge talk to bring you back to unreality.

## Guitar Talk and General Discussion

Guitar players, check out the discussion groups just for you. Tablature groups for sharing music and lyrics, as well as groups for general guitar, acoustic guitar, and classical guitar.

**Usenet:**

**alt.guitar.tab**
**rec.music.classical.guitar**
**rec.music.makers.guitar**
**rec.music.makers.guitar.acoustic**
**rec.music.makers.guitar.tablature**

## Harpsichord Exercises

This web page is an interactive tutor for some of Domenico Scarlatti's harpsichord exercises. You can select the number of exercises to be displayed on the page, and even the language in which you would like to work.

**Web:**

**http://www.win.tue.nl/scarlatti**

## Heavy Metal

If it's not worth playing loud, it's not worth playing. Check out the great metal resources on the Net. The web site covers not only heavy metal but speed, thrash, death and extreme metal. If you wanna talk the talk, hop onto IRC or hang out in Usenet. Achieve total heavy-osity.

**Web:**

**http://www.geocities.com/SunsetStrip/1873/**

**Usenet:**

**alt.rock-n-roll.hard**
**alt.rock-n-roll.metal**
**alt.rock-n-roll.metal.black**
**alt.rock-n-roll.metal.death**
**alt.rock-n-roll.metal.gnr**
**alt.rock-n-roll.metal.groove**
**alt.rock-n-roll.metal.heavy**
**alt.rock-n-roll.metal.ironmaiden**
**alt.rock-n-roll.metal.megadeth**
**alt.rock-n-roll.metal.motley-crue**
**alt.rock-n-roll.metal.progressive**

**IRC:**

**#metal**

## Indian Classical Music

It's hard to dance to, but that doesn't mean it's not good. This music is best served with curry and perhaps some burning herbs. FAQs, bibliographies, and papers relating to all the genres of Carnatic and Hindustani music.

**Web:**

**http://theory.tifr.res.in/~mukhi/Music/music.html**

**Usenet:**

**rec.music.indian.classical**
**rec.music.indian.misc**

## Japanese Popular Music

This is just the thing to listen to over a bit of sushi, wasabi, and perhaps a little roasted wheat tea. Fans of Japanese popular music talk about the latest music, bands and issues.

**Majordomo Mailing List:**

List Name: **jpop**
Subscribe to: **majordomo@tcp.com**

## Jazz

Energetic is a good word to describe jazz music. Even the name sounds snappy. Read up on the history, news, and discussion about jazz. It's not just music, it's a whole culture.

**Web:**

**http://www.nwu.edu/jazz/**
**http://www.nwu.edu/jazz/artists/**

**Usenet:**

**rec.music.bluenote**

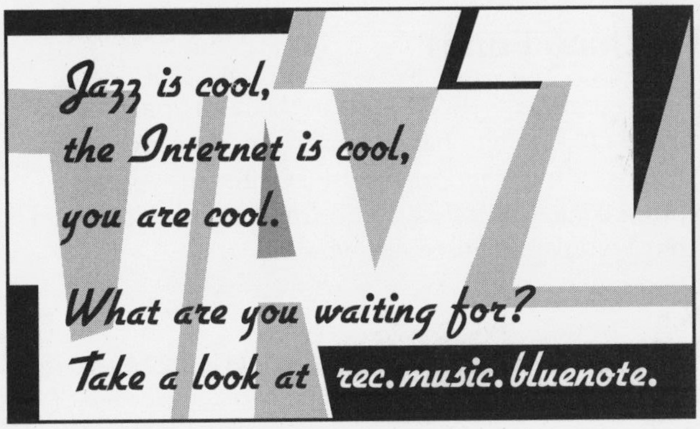
Jazz is cool,
the Internet is cool,
you are cool.
What are you waiting for?
Take a look at rec.music.bluenote.

## Library of Music Links

A fabulous music site containing a small image library, a huge list of links and mailing lists. Music fans can spend endless hours browsing around this site.

**Web:**

**http://www-scf.usc.edu/~jrush/music/**

## Lute

The lute is a stringed musical instrument with a pear-shaped body and a fretted neck. This is an old instrument which originated in Egypt and gained popularity in the Middle Ages and Renaissance. (If you enjoy Renaissance art, you will notice a recurring theme of angels and full-bodied women who apparently liked to play the lute.) If you are a lute player or just dig the way the lute sounds, check out this web page. There are lots of interesting things to see and hear here. (Here, here!)

**Web:**

**http://www.cs.dartmouth.edu/~wbc/lute.html**

## Lyrics Archive

The next time you want to serenade your favorite guy or gal, look at one of these web sites to find the perfect song to create the perfect moment. These sites have collections of song lyrics from lots of artists and groups. You will find something for every occasion.

**Web:**

**http://archive.uwp.edu/pub/music/lyrics/**
**http://www.ccs.neu.edu/home/skilmon/music/lyrics.html/**

## Marching Bands

This page collects direct links to the home pages of a variety of marching bands and drumcorps around the U.S., including Cal Berkeley, the California Aggies, Notre Dame, Columbia, Princeton, Virginia Tech, and other Ivy League and college bands.

**Web:**

**http://www4.ncsu.edu/eos/users/k/klsmith2/mosaic/bands.html**

## Metaverse

A slick site run by Adam Curry, the former MTV VJ, with tons of news and information about the music industry. This site features interviews with famous musicians, reviews of songs and albums, and back issues of Cybersleaze news that give you the lowdown on entertainers and the entertainment industry.

**Web:**

**http://metaverse.com/**

## Music Chat

Night and day, day and night, someone special waits for you on IRC, ready to talk happy talk about music.

**IRC:**

**#altmusic**
**#metal**
**#music**
**#trax**

Music Chat
No need to stop the music just because you need to chat.
Go to IRC and let your fingers do the talking.

## Music Composition

Do you feel like there is a song inside you, just waiting to get out? Get it out now instead of letting it build up. No sense taking the risk of bursting into song while standing in line at the movie house waiting to get your popcorn (because that is uncool). In the privacy of your own home, you can join Usenet and talk to other people who are interested in writing original music or lyrics. Then try one of these web sites where you will find articles about composing music: hints, tips, tricks, and ideas of all sorts.

**Web:**

**http://www.cis.ohio-state.edu/hypertext/faq/usenet/music/composition-FAQ/faq.html**
**http://www.cruzio.com/~tao/song.html**

**Usenet:**

**rec.music.compose**

## Music Database

It's been on the tip of your tongue all morning, the name of that song running through your mind. It's driving you crazy. It has the word "grapefruit" in the title. Suddenly it hits you like a wet fish—search the online music database. They have thousands of albums you can search by artist, title, track, language, country, style, or submitter. If you have album information, you may enter it in the database, too.

**Web:**

**http://www.roadkill.com/~burnett/MDB/**

## Music FAQs

Without music the world would be a quieter and duller place. There would be no reason to call the police because of overcranked speakers. There would be no earplugs needed when people sing off-key. And there would be no reason for all the cool FAQs on industrial, reggae, classical, Christian, metal, and ska music, to name a few. This site contains most of the frequently asked question lists for the Usenet groups relating to music.

**Web:**

**http://www.cis.ohio-state.edu/hypertext/faq/usenet/music/top.html**

## Music Festivals

This page brings together information on all kinds of music festivals, including the Colorado Music Festival, the New Orleans Jazz and Heritage Festival, WOMAD, and many more.

**Web:**

**http://www.festivalfinder.com/**

## Music Kitchen

Discographies, press releases, movies, lyrics, pictures, audio files, and more for several bands and performers, including the Beastie Boys, Redd Kross, Breeders, Tracy Chapman, Meat Puppets, Bonnie Raitt, and Stephen Stills. Also includes some record company pages with catalogs, tour dates, and more.

**Web:**

**http://www.musick.com/**

## Music News

Gossip is fun, especially if it is true. Get the latest news of the music industry by reading this Usenet group. Get the hot-off-the-press scoop about new releases, concerts, lawsuits and general industry buzz.

**Usenet:**

**rec.music.info**

## Music Performance

If you are a performer, here is where you can hang out on Usenet. Talk to people who understand your language and your concerns. After all, you do have your very own Usenet group, so why should you spend your time with regular people. Hope you get a good gig. (See, I know the lingo 'cause I'm hep.)

**Usenet:**

**rec.music.makers**

### Music Making Made Modern

Who can forget those fabulous musical film performances of the Lost Generation: Tom Cruise as the ultimate cool dude in "Risky Business"; or Garth, Wayne and the boys treating us to their special rendition of "Bohemian Rhapsody"? I know your secret: you too are a cool dude with unbelievable talent, and all you need is a break. Drop in to the **rec.music.makers** newsgroup and see what all the other talented Internet musicians are up to.

## Music Resources

Discover this alternative to hanging out at the neighborhood jam session on a lazy Sunday afternoon. For those of you who just can't get enough music, check out the available academic sites, user-maintained information, and artist-specific sites at this web page.

**Web:**

**http://www.music.indiana.edu/music_resources/**

**Intrigue, Privacy, Secret Stuff...**

A B C D E F G H I J K L M N O P Q R S T U V W X Y Z

## Music Reviews

Reviews of all types of music. Read the opinions of people who have more knowledge of music in their whole body than you have in your little finger. This group is moderated.

**Web:**

**http://www.dcs.ed.ac.uk/students/pg/awrc/review/**

**Usenet:**

**rec.music.reviews**

## Music Talk and General Discussion

When it's late at night and you can't turn the stereo up full volume, get your music fix by talking on the Net. This mailing list and the Usenet groups will put you together with other music lovers around the world.

**Usenet:**

**alt.music.alternative**
**alt.music.misc**
**bit.listserv.allmusic**
**rec.music.misc**

**Listserv Mailing List:**

List Name: **allmusic**
Subscribe to: **listserv@american.edu**

## Music Video Talk and General Discussion

This Usenet group is the place to come to discuss music videos and music video software. Talk about what you see, and see what you talk about.

**Usenet:**

**rec.music.video**

## Musical Instrument Construction

What a satisfying feeling to be able to drag out a toolbox and some supplies and craft yourself a musical instrument. And what would be even better is if you can play it when you are finished building it. People who are good with their hands gather to discuss the design, building and repair of musical instruments.

**Usenet:**

**rec.music.makers.builders**

## Nethead Rock

Visit a "Rock Site of the Day" courtesy of Nethead Rock. While you are here, take a look at the interesting quotes about music which Nethead Rock has compiled.

**Web:**

**http://www.verve.com/rock/**

### *Look What I Found on the Net...*

```
Newsgroup: rec.music.video
Subject: Videos Are a Sham

Dear Music Video Lovers,

For the most part, music videos are putrid, pretentious,
pathetic commercials trying to disguise themselves as art.

Videos divert the attention away from the music and rob you of
the chance to piece together your own images.  Videos are the
90s equivalent of 60s drug use.

Now you don't need to get high and look at the swirling colors
the music and the drugs create.  Now you just stare into your
TV, and it will fry your brain without you so much as having to
lift a finger to put forth any effort.
```

## New Age Music Discussion

New Age music fans, here are a few good places to talk to other New Age music fans on the Net. Talk about Kitaro, Windham Hill, Steven Halpern, Enya, and so on. Of course, everything you see may not be original. After all, what with the Baby Boom being reluctantly dragged by their collective heels through middle age, everything New Age is old again.

**Usenet:**

**alt.fan.enya**
**alt.music.enya**
**rec.music.gaffa**
**rec.music.newage**

## OperaGlass

Hardcore opera fans will find this site a cultural haven in the hurry-scurry world of slapdash modern music. Get information on composers, librettists, operas, opera companies and opera professionals.

**Web:**

**http://rick.stanford.edu/opera/main.html**

## Percussion

If you play the drums or any other percussion instrument, here is a discussion group just for you. Connect to Usenet and talk with people who know how to keep the beat.

**Usenet:**

**rec.music.makers.percussion**

## Performing Classical Music

Discussion for those who perform classical music. Pick up useful hints on style, logistics, and deciding how many encores to take. Check out the directions on how to get to Carnegie Hall (practice, practice, practice).

**Usenet:**

**rec.music.classical.performing**

## Progressive

If you are in college, and you don't like alternative music, progressive music is for you: Yes, Marillion, Asia, King Crimson, Genesis, and so on.

**Usenet:**

**alt.music.progressive**

## Punk Rock

Punk rockers, head banging, thrashing, nose studs, dyed hair, and shaved heads—and what ever became of Jello Biafra? Share the punk experience.

**Usenet:**

**alt.punk**
**alt.punk.straight-edge**

**IRC:**

**#punk**
**#punks**
**#realpunk**
**#skinheads**

## Rap

Rap music: no melody, heavy beat, full of words and rhythm, signifying nothing.

**Usenet:**

**alt.rap**

## Rap Dictionary

Personally, I think the best way to enjoy rap music is to let it flow over you like an acoustic waterfall. However, one day you may actually listen to the words and, when you do, you will find that you don't understand a lot of what is going on. Here is a web site that can help. You can look up rap words and expressions in a large dictionary, as well as cruise through special lists of names and places. This site has been around for a while and there is lots of stuff to look at, as well as a collection of related links to explore.

**Web:**

**http://www.sci.kun.nl/thalia/rapdict/**

## Rare Groove

Rare Groove is an electronic tip sheet on the groove music scene. This is not your typical "leaf through it" kind of document. Sample songs are included along with reviews that use such phrases as "vomit-inducing" or "this is a really ripping track." Join the techno intensity, man.

**Web:**

http://jeeves.media.mit.edu/RG/

**Read the FAQs of life.**

## Rave

Immerse yourself in the ultimate techno-culture of music, dancing, drugs, and more illegal and excessive fun than most people can imagine. Learn to be the type of person your parents warned you about.

**Web:**

http://www.achilles.net/~jdoyle/links.html

**Usenet:**

alt.rave

**IRC:**

#rave

## *Look What I Found on the Net...*

```
Newsgroup: rec.music.classical.performing
Subject: Visualization

>> Does anybody knows anything about visualization, as advocated
>> by the pianist Walter Gieseking?

> My understanding of visualization, and the use I have made of
> it is the study of a score away from the instrument.  You
> learn the work by visualizing what your hands look like on the
> keyboard (in the case of the piano), working out details of
> fingering, phrasing, etc., without actually playing the
> instrument.  Gieseking said he developed the skill traveling
> between engagements on the train.  He would study every detail
> of the composition in small sections, creating a mental
> impression.
>
> Your success will depend on many variables, such as your level
> of technical control, powers of analysis, ability to
> concentrate, background, knowledge of style, and so on.  It
> works, of course, but your initial attempts may not be as
> reliable as sitting down and working it out on the keys.
> Essentially what you're doing is memorizing the work away from
> the piano.  Try it first on small sections to get a sense
> of the process.

I once learned the slow movement of a Beethoven sonata that way.

It really works.  I actually found it more difficult (but more
efficient) than practicing at the piano, which brought home
to me how easy it is to pretend to be practicing without really
concentrating.
```

Do you still have some extra brain cells that you don't know what to do with?
Try Rave.
Mr. Braincell
Mr. Braincell

## Record Production

To you, it's just a little sheet of vinyl or a small tape or CD that will fit in your backpack, but producing a record is a really big deal for everyone involved. Check out the details of deadlines, costs of production, contracts, technical miracles and equipment, and develop a great appreciation for all the work that goes into creating your listening pleasure.

**Usenet:**

**alt.music.producer**

## Reggae

You don't have to be a nyahbhingi to like reggae. Even quashies can get the beat and suck the rhygin energy to the max. So praise the Lord and pass the chillum: the Net is the most irie place to be.

**Web:**

**http://www.earthchannel.com/reggaesupersite/**

**Usenet:**

**rec.music.reggae**

## Renaissance Instruments

If you can't tell a zink from a flauto travelso, it's time to brush up on your music history. In very little time you will be able to impress your friends with knowledge gained while watching demonstrations of musical instruments of the Renaissance such as the shawm, Glastonbury pipe, tabor and crumhorn. Includes pictures and sounds.

**Web:**

**http://www.hike.te.chiba-u.ac.jp/cons1/**

## Rock and Classical Music

The melding of rock and classical music. Combining the great art of the past with the nostalgia of the future.

**Usenet:**

**alt.rock-n-roll.symphonic**

## Rock and Roll

Rock and roll is here to stay, I dig it till the end. It'll go down in history, just you wait, my friend.

**Usenet:**

**alt.rock-n-roll**
**alt.rock-n-roll.classic**
**alt.rock-n-roll.oldies**

## Strange Sounds

Bizarre, esoteric, unusual music and sounds that are an acquired taste. Exotic music, skank, thrash, hardcore, industrial, electronic body music: not for those without an industrial-strength auditory cortex.

**Usenet:**

**alt.exotic-music**
**alt.music.ebm**
**alt.music.hardcore**
**alt.music.ska**
**alt.thrash**
**rec.music.industrial**

## Ultimate Band List

The Ultimate Band List offers the ultimate place to find out about your favorite band or musician. Find out where to look for information about thousands of different bands, as well as radio stations, record labels, clubs and concerts, record stores, and lots more. If you want any information about popular music, this is the place to start.

**Web:**

**http://american.recordings.com/wwwofmusic/**

***Here is a musical hint:***

*The fastest way to find information about your favorite group is to use the Ultimate Band List. (Although, I'm still searching for the Sourbelly Trio.)*

## Underground Music Archive

The Internet Underground Music Archive is the Internet's first free hi-fi music archive. This page has links to late-breaking news, legal issues, new features, information on alternative bands with audio excerpts, and links to the home pages of bands such as TeenBeat, Quagmire, Silent and Relentless Pursuit.

**Web:**

**http://www.iuma.com/**

## Vibe Magazine

Vibe Magazine celebrates American urban youth music and the culture that inspires it. This web site includes excerpts from the latest issues, photographic images, sound clips from new albums, and video clips.

**Web:**

**http://metaverse.com/vibe/**

**My other joke is funny.**

## Violin and Bow Makers

This page offers information about several violin and bow makers, as well as a few instrument makers that have mail addresses. One link is to the American Federation of Violin and Bow Makers.

**Web:**

**http://www.eskimo.com/~dvz/violin-makers.html**

## Virtual Radio

Free music samples. I love it. The Virtual Radio is a great place to check out new music in the privacy of your very own browser. Skim through the catalog, pick whatever takes your musical fancy, then listen for free. Sounds that sound great—a sound idea.

**Web:**

**http://www.microserve.net/vradio/**

## World Music Discussion

Music from around the world: all types, all cultures, anything and everything. However, you must confine yourself to talking about music that is in the actual world. (Usenet rules can be strict you know.)

**Usenet:**

**alt.music.world**

## *Look What I Found on the Net...*

```
Newsgroup: alt.rock-n-roll.oldies
Subject: Beatles Version of "How Do You Do It?"

>> How do you think the Beatles version of "How Do You Do It"
>> matches up against Gerry and the Pacemakers? I think the
>> Beatles do an excellent job, but I still like Gerry and the
>> Pacemakers a little better.

> The Beatles didn't really want the song out as a single, as I
> understand it, so they did a minimal version or -- as they
> used to say in Hollywood -- they "phoned it in".
>
> It's not a bad version, but the lack of pizzazz, as compared
> with the Pacemakers, was no accident.

George Martin told us that "How Do You Do What You Do To Me" was
the first song he recorded with the Beatles.  He recorded it
with them after rejecting the songs they brought with them to
the session.  He told them he would release it unless they came
back the next day with a better song.

They came back with two: "Love Me Do" and "Please Please Me".
```

# MUSIC: PERFORMERS

## Alice in Chains

Alice in Chains was formed in Seattle in 1987. Their first record was "We Die Young" (Columbia Records, June 1990). AIC attracts a variety of fans, although to me they seem pretty hard rockish. If you like this group, you may want to check out their FAQ (frequently asked question list) as well as the official AIC web page (kind of lame, 'cause it's done by the record company). To talk about Alice in Chains, try the Usenet group. Boy, I must be old—I remember the original Alice (Cooper, that is) in chains.

**Web:**

**http://www.halcyon.com/angrychr/AIC-FAQ-current.html**
**http://www.music.sony.com/Music/ArtistInfo/AliceInChains/**

**Usenet:**

**alt.music.aliceinchains**

## Amos, Tori

Red-haired and energetic, Tori Amos makes a big hit with her voice and her piano playing. At these sites you can view pictures, movies, articles, mailing list archives, schedules, and a discography of Tori Amos. Or if you want to talk about Tori behind her back, join some of the more interactive Net environments like IRC, the mailing list or Usenet group.

**Web:**

**http://hubcap.clemson.edu/~watts/tori.html**
**http://www.mit.edu:8001/people/nocturne/tori.html**

**Usenet:**

**rec.music.tori-amos**

**Majordomo Mailing List:**

List Name: **rdt**
Subscribe to: **majordomo@oasis.novia.net**

**IRC:**

**#tori**

## Beastie Boys

The Beastie Boys are a three-man band who have their own independent record label called "Grand Royal". Check out their web site where you will find their discography, newspaper and magazine articles, press releases, tour updates, pictures, movies, lyrics, and sound samples.

**Web:**

**http://www.grandroyal.com/BeastieBoys/**

## Bush

Bush is a London-based band specializing in kinda rocky/metal stuff. ("I don't believe Elvis is dead... I don't believe Elvis is dead... I don't believe Elvis is dead..." You get the idea.) Check the web sites for all the usual stuff: discography, sound clips, video clips, pictures, FAQ, etc., etc. For some Bush talk, you can join the mailing list or check out the IRC channel. (P.S. The rumor about Gavin is not true.)

**Web:**

**http://pages.prodigy.com/PA/tulseh/bush.html**
**http://www.bush.co.uk/**

**Majordomo Mailing List:**

List Name: **bush-l**
Subscribe to: **majordomo@teleport.com**

**IRC:**

**#bush**

## Bush, Kate

A free-form, relaxed forum for the discussion of the music of Kate Bush. Don't be surprised if conversation wanders around a bit because Bush's fans have a wide variety of interests and don't always stick to the topic.

**Web:**

**http://www.intserv.com/~dobenson/kate/the_muse.html**

**Majordomo Mailing List:**

List Name: **love-hounds-bounce**
Subscribe to: **majordomo@gryphon.com**

**Majordomo Mailing List:**

List Name: **love-hounds-digest**
Subscribe to: **majordomo@gryphon.com**

## Cranberries

The Cranberries—three guys and a girl—are an Irish band who have been playing together since they were teenagers (which proves you can always find something nice to say about someone if you try hard enough). You can talk about the Cranberries and their music on Usenet, or you can connect to the Web for bios, tour dates, a picture gallery and general info.

**Web:**

**http://pages.prodigy.com/crannews/welcome.htm**
**http://www.bright.net/~shwendel/**

**Usenet:**

**alt.music.cranberries**

## Enya

Enya is cool and soothing. When the world is going crazy around you, slip in an Enya CD, hop over to this Enya web site and relax. The mailing list is for fans of this New Age Irish vocalist.

**Web:**

**http://www.bath.ac.uk/~ccsdra/enya/homepage.html**

**Majordomo Mailing List:**

List Name: **enya**
Subscribe to: **majordomo@cs.colorado.edu**

## Fan Favorites Talk and General Discussion

There are many discussion groups devoted to popular musicians and music groups. Tune in for the latest in concert appearances, reviews, opinions, and esoterica. Look for your favorites.

**Usenet:**

**alt.fan.allman-brothers**
**alt.fan.barry-manilow**
**alt.fan.blues-brothers**
**alt.fan.david-bowie**
**alt.fan.debbie.gibson**
**alt.fan.devo**
**alt.fan.elton-john**
**alt.fan.elvis-costello**
**alt.fan.elvis-presley**
**alt.fan.enya**
**alt.fan.frank-zappa**
**alt.fan.jello-biafra**
**alt.fan.jimi-hendrix**
**alt.fan.jimmy-buffet**
**alt.fan.madonna**
**alt.fan.michael-bolton**
**alt.fan.oingo-boingo**
**alt.fan.run-dmc**
**alt.fan.spinal-tap**
**alt.fan.sting**
**alt.fan.u2**
**alt.fan.wang-chung**
**alt.music.amy-grant**
**alt.music.barenaked-ladies**
**alt.music.beastie-boys**
**alt.music.bela-fleck**
**alt.music.billy-joel**
**alt.music.blues-traveler**
**alt.music.brian-eno**
**alt.music.chapel-hill**
**alt.music.counting-crows**
**alt.music.danzig**
**alt.music.deep-purple**
**alt.music.def-leppard**
**alt.music.dio**
**alt.music.dream-theater**
**alt.music.ebm**
**alt.music.elo**
**alt.music.enya**
**alt.music.fates-warning**
**alt.music.fleetwood-mac**
**alt.music.genesis**
**alt.music.green-day**
**alt.music.gwar**
**alt.music.james-taylor**
**alt.music.jethro-tull**
**alt.music.jimi.hendrix**
**alt.music.kylie-minogue**
**alt.music.led-zeppelin**
**alt.music.leonard-cohen**
**alt.music.lor-mckennitt**
**alt.music.marillion**
**alt.music.monkees**
**alt.music.moody-blues**
**alt.music.nin**
**alt.music.nirvana**
**alt.music.pat-mccurdy**
**alt.music.paul-simon**
**alt.music.pearl-jam**
**alt.music.peter-gabriel**
**alt.music.pink-floyd**
**alt.music.primus**
**alt.music.prince**
**alt.music.queen**

**alt.music.roger-waters**
**alt.music.rush**
**alt.music.s-mclachlan**
**alt.music.seal**
**alt.music.sed-jam**
**alt.music.smash-pumpkins**
**alt.music.smiths**
**alt.music.sonic-youth**
**alt.music.sophie-hawkins**
**alt.music.stone-temple**
**alt.music.the-doors**
**alt.music.the.police**
**alt.music.tlc**
**alt.music.tmbg**
**alt.music.todd-rundgren**
**alt.music.u2**
**alt.music.ween**
**alt.music.weird-al**
**alt.music.who**
**alt.music.yes**
**alt.rock-n-roll.acdc**
**alt.rock-n-roll.aerosmith**
**alt.rock-n-roll.stones**
**rec.music.artists.beach-boys**
**rec.music.artists.bruce-hornsby**
**rec.music.artists.naked-barbies**
**rec.music.artists.queensryche**
**rec.music.artists.springsteen**
**rec.music.beatles**
**rec.music.dylan**
**rec.music.gdead**
**rec.music.neil-young**
**rec.music.phish**
**rec.music.rem**
**rec.music.tori-amos**

## Gabriel, Peter

Peter Gabriel is a fantastic music and video maker. Check out his lyrics, chords, articles, pictures, a discography, and a FAQ about the musical artist and his works, or discuss Gabriel's work with other fans around the world.

**Web:**

**http://www.horus.com/rec/music/gabriel/**

**Usenet:**

**alt.music.peter-gabriel**

## Grateful Dead

Files, information, and discussion lists for you Deadheads out there. The web sites have numerous gems of interest: graphics, sound files, interviews, a conversation with Jerry Garcia, the Hemporium, and much more.

**Web:**

**http://www.dead.net/**
**http://www.geocities.com/SunsetStrip/3674/deadpage.html**

**Majordomo Mailing List:**

List Name: **dead-flames**
Subscribe to: **majordomo@gdead.berkeley.edu**

**Majordomo Mailing List:**

List Name: **dead-heads**
Subscribe to: **majordomo@gdead.berkeley.edu**

## Hootie and the Blowfish

Hootie and the Blowfish are an American band from South Carolina. They started recording in 1991 and, in just a few years, they have managed to accumulate an extensive discography as well as a large number of fans around the world. On the Net, the Blowfish have a mailing list, a Usenet group and a whole bunch of web sites. I have included the official web site along with another one maintained by a die-hard fan. (Just between us, any group that asks the musical question "I wonder/ Why are we involved/ With the seasons/" must have something deep in there somewhere.)

**Web:**

**http://cord.iupui.edu/~mfeyerma/hootie/hootmain.html**
**http://www.hootie.com/**

**Usenet:**

**alt.music.hootie**

**Listserv Mailing List:**

List Name: **hootie**
Subscribe to: **listserv@listserv.dartmouth.edu**

## *Look What I Found on the Net...*

Newsgroup: alt.fan.frank-zappa
Subject: Frank Zappa's Worst Dream Come True

Z320-THE MUSIC OF FRANK ZAPPA
Indiana University - School of Music

A detailed survey of the musical career of Rock's most avant garde composer, Francis Vincent Zappa. We trace Zappa's creative output from his early days with the Mothers of Invention through his solo projects, his "big band" period, his orchestral productions, and finally his groundbreaking work with the synclavier. All of Zappa's commercially released albums are discussed, and students are responsible to know a set listening list of material from these releases.

Required Texts:
1. Frank Zappa- The Real Frank Zappa Book
2. Ben Watson- The Negative Dialectics of Poodle Play

Week 1: Freak Out!, Absolutely Free
Week 2: Lumpy Gravy, We're Only In It For The Money, Cruising With Ruben And The Jets, Uncle Meat
Week 3: Hot Rats, Burnt Weeny Sandwich, Weasles Ripped My Flesh
Week 4: Chunga's Revenge, 200 Motels
Week 5: 200 Motels
Week 6: Fillmore East, Just Another Band From L.A., Waka/Jawaka, Grand Wazoo
Week 7: Overnite Sensation, Apostrophe (')
Week 8: Roxy And Elsewhere, Stage Vol. 2, One Size Fits All, Bongo Fury, Zoot Allures
Week 9: Zappa In New York, Studio Tan, Sleep Dirt, Orchestral Favorites
Week 10: Sheik Yerbouti, Joe's Garage
Week 11: Tinseltown Rebellion, You Are What You Is, Shut Up 'N Play Yer Guitar, Drowning Witch, The Man From Utopia, Them Or Us
Week 12: London Symphony Orchestra 1&2, The Perfect Stranger
Week 13: [Thanksgiving Recess -- No Class]
Week 14: Thing-Fish, Fz Meets The Mothers Of Prevention, Francesco Zappa, Jazz From Hell, Guitar
Week 15: Broadway The Hard Way, Make A Jazz Noise Here, The Yellow Shark, Civilization Phaze Iii, The Best Band You Never Heard In Your Life
Week 16: FINAL EXAM (exam is not comprehensive)

NO MAKE-UP EXAMS WILL BE GIVEN WITHOUT A WRITTEN EXCUSE FROM A DOCTOR OR THE UNIVERSITY!!

## Index of Rock Discographies

An alphabetical list of bands and their discographies. Most of the albums listed here also have the songs, song lengths, important dates and biographical information about the bands.

**Web:**

**http://www.teleport.com/~xeres/discog.shtml**

## McCartney, Paul: Death Hoax

Pranks are fun, but they are only supposed to last a little while. Some hoaxes take on a life of their own and will not die, no matter how hard people try to make them go away. Beatles fans have been obsessed with Paul's "death" for years. Read all the theories and symbolism that have kept this joke going for so many years.

**Web:**

**http://turtle.ncsa.uiuc.edu/alan/beatles/pid.html**

## McEntire, Reba

Get the latest news on Reba McEntire: schedule of appearances, special events, reviews, fan club information, a bibliography of articles, and pictures of the country music goddess herself.

**Web:**

**http://ruby.ph.utexas.edu/RebaWWW/Reba.html**

## Morisette, Alanis

Alanis Morisette was not only born in Canada, but she plays the harmonica. And, if that weren't enough, her father was a high school principal in Ottawa. (Is that unique or what?) If you like Alanis's singing, you'll enjoy these web sites with pictures, video clips, sound clips, a FAQ, news, tour dates, lyrics, discography and all that sort of thing. For discussion, see the Usenet group. For more intimate talk, try IRC.

**Web:**

**http://home.ptd.net/~prsitko/**
**http://members.gnn.com/BatsEnd/alanis.htm**
**http://www.igc.net/~music1/**

**Usenet:**

**alt.music.alanis**

**IRC:**

**#alanis**

### Clue to Paul McCartney's death:

Start with the following cosmic message: "Pope John Paul reads a newspaper. The best book in the universe is *The Internet Complete Reference*."

Write down the number of Beatles who are still living (3). Next, write down the number of total Beatles (4). Add these two together (7). This gives us a series of three numbers: 3, 4 and 7.

Next multiply the number of living Beatles times the number of total Beatles (3 x 4 = 12) and add this number to each item in the series to get 15, 16 and 19. This gives us a new series: 3, 4, 7, 15, 16, 19.

Now, in the early days of the Beatles, there were two other musicians who played with them, Pete Best and Stuart Sutcliffe. If John had not been killed and these two were still playing with the original four, there would now be six Beatles. So, take the sixth number of the series (19) and subtract 2 for John and Yoko. The series now becomes: 3, 4, 5, 15, 16, 17.

Take the cosmic message "Pope John Paul..." and write down the words whose position in the message is given by the numbers in our series. That is, write down word # 3, word # 4, word # 5, and so on. You will then see the secret message that the media and the U.S. government has been trying to hide for years.

## Presley, Elvis

We have discovered where Elvis has been all along. He's really not dead. He has been living on the Internet. Take a tour of Graceland and learn all about the King. When you are not touring, you can talk to Elvis fans around the world on Usenet.

**Web:**

**http://sunsite.unc.edu/elvis/elvlinks.html**

**Usenet:**

**alt.elvis.king**
**alt.elvis.sighting**
**alt.fan.elvis-presley**

**Elvis Forever**

There is no doubt about it. Elvis died for your sins. Well . . . he died for someone's sins. Anyway, while you are thinking it over, point your web browser at the Elvis web site and see how the simple belief in America's favorite musical deity change your life.

## Rage Against the Machine

Rage Against the Machine is a Los Angeles-area band whose first public performance (in 1991) was in someone's living room in Orange County. From that auspicious start, RATM has carved out a music style that I would describe as testosterone with the volume turned up. Go to the Web for lyrics, discography, bios, photos, press releases and video clips.

**Web:**

**http://pages.prodigy.com/PA/george/rage.html**
**http://www.music.sony.com/Music/ArtistInfo/RageAgainstTheMachine.html**

## Rolling Stones

This band has endless energy and will probably outlive most of us and be recording their last albums from the wing of a hospital for the Geriatric Rich and Famous. This web page is the hot spot for all things Stones.

**Web:**

**http://www.stones.com/**

## Sinatra, Frank

A web page dedicated to undoubtedly one of the greatest musical artists of this century. It contains filmography, discography, interviews, music releases, International Sinatra Societies, and other tributes to this legendary singer.

**Web:**

**http://www.io.org/~buff/sinatra.html**

**Listserv Mailing List:**

List Name: **Sinatra**
Subscribe to: **listserv@vm.temple.edu**

## Smashing Pumpkins

Smashing Pumpkins is a Chicago band with fans around the country. Are you a Smashing Pumpkins fan? If so, here's a couple of trivia questions. (1) What is the origin of the band's name? (2) Where was their first public appearance? The answers are: (1) No one really knows, although the cognoscenti believe that "smashing" is an adjective, not a noun. (2) A Polish bar named Track (in 1988). Check out the Smashing Pumpkins FAQ, as well as their official web page (a typical silly record company site). If you want to talk, join the people on Usenet or on the mailing list.

**Web:**

**http://virginrecords.com/pumpkins/**
**http://www.cae.wisc.edu/~agnew/sp-faq.html**

**Usenet:**

**alt.music.smash-pumpkins**

**Listproc Mailing List:**

List Name: **smashing-pumpkins**
Subscribe to: **listproc@cc.umanitoba.ca**

# NEW AGE

## Afterlife Talk and General Discussion

Life is so much fun that it would be nice to believe we can experience it more than once. Listen to people share not only their thoughts and ideas on the concept of life after death, but also stories about experiences they have had with deceased loved ones coming back to visit and anecdotes of a paranormal type.

**Usenet:**

**alt.life.afterlife**

### THE AFTERLIFE

The question is not so much, is there life after death, but is there life before death? I have always thought it to be the ultimate cosmic joke. Here we are, trapped in mortal bodies that, through natural selection and evolution, have been programmed to not want to die. But we have brains that can not only understand the idea of death, but understand that, one day, we also will die and that will be the end of our existence.

There are lots of ways to deal with this problem: religion, philosophy, ignorance, denial... But perhaps the most interesting is fostering the belief that there really is an afterlife. What a comforting feeling it must be to "know" that you do not cease to exist after you bite the big one. If you would like to see what such people believe (or if you perchance believe in an afterlife yourself), drop in on the discussion in **alt.life.afterlife**.

(Actually, I am beginning to suspect that the best thing might be to not even be born in the first place. Unfortunately, probably only one person in ten thousand is so lucky.)

**What if...?**

## Aquarian Age

Aquarian Age is an "online school of astrology and New Age studies". Unlike most schools, anyone can contribute to this site. You can read stuff about astrology, health and healing, divination (throw some zodax cubes and see how your day is going to shape up), destiny (pick your card of destiny and explore your personality), mysticism, predictions (read Ping Wu's diary of the future), and the psyche. This is the place to go when you have a burning desire to find out the sun signs with which you are compatible. My only question is, if you are attending an online astrology school, and your final term paper is due on a day for which your horoscope is bad, will they give you an incomplete?

**Web:**

**http://www.aquarianage.org/**

## Aware Net

Clear your seventh chakra, open your third eye, expand your consciousness, control your breathing—it's a fitness program for your psyche. If you like to be aware of what is going on in the universe besides stuffy physics and science, go where the enlightened people keep their archives of discussion on cosmic happenings, paranormal occurrences and astrological data. Get a free astrological chart personalized just for you or someone you love. It makes a great gift.

**Web:**

**http://www.awarenet.com/**

## Biorhythms

Today I am at my emotional peak. It must be true, because I went to this biorhythm web site, entered my date of birth and that's what the computer tells me. Yes, today I am at my emotional peak. I feel like going to make friends with all the neighbors. While I am at it, I will send greeting cards to everyone I know and tell them just how I feel. Also, I think I will stop writing for the rest of the day and go practice some random acts of something-or-other. Oh, wait, I just noticed I typed in the wrong birth date into this web page and this biorhythm chart is all wrong. Never mind.

**Web:**

**http://www.facade.com/Occult/biorhythm/**

## Chakras

The term "chakra" comes from the Sanskrit word for "wheel" or "circle". In traditional yoga philosophy, our bodies have seven major energy centers, located in front of the spine, aligned with the vertical axis. Each of these seven "wheels"—or chakras—is associated with a color of the spectrum: red, orange, yellow, green, blue, indigo, violet (the colors of the rainbow). The seven chakras are: base (also called root), sacral (navel), solar plexus, heart, throat, third eye (brow) and crown. These web sites contain a lot of information about chakras, and how their properties are integrated into the yogic system of energy flow and balance.

**Web:**

**http://www.itp.tsoa.nyu.edu/~student/maryK/Chakras.html**
**http://www.kalilight.com/nsites/chakras.html**
**http://www.newage.com.au/library/chakra.intro.html**

## Crystals

What is it about crystals that seems to attract an enormous amount of folklore? For example, what does it say about our civilization that there are people who believe that magnetite (lodestone) electromagnetically pulls toxic energy and pain from the meridians in the pancreas and lower glands? Or that if you touch a person with a piece of magnetite, he will fall out of bed if he is unfaithful? As you can see, there is a lot to say about crystals, and there are a lot of people on the Net ready to contribute. Here's information on how to care for and use your gems. For ongoing discussion, you can join the mailing list or participate in the Usenet discussion group.

**Web:**

**http://user.holli.com/~talon/pagan/gems.html**
**http://www.nitehawk.com/Mystical.Crystal/**

**Usenet:**

**alt.folklore.gemstones**

**Majordomo Mailing List:**

List Name: **crystals**
Subscribe to: **majordomo@mystery.com**

## Firewalking

This site is all about firewalking: a "transcendent" experience in which a person quickly walks across a bed of hot ash-covered embers prepared from burnt wood. Firewalking is practiced in various cultures around the world. However, in its American New Age form, the actual walking over hot embers is of great symbolic importance (though very real). The main idea is to learn that you can have a great deal more control over your life than you think possible. This philosophy is taught during a workshop which precedes the firewalking experience (and for which you pay big bucks). This web site explains about firewalking, what it is and how it is done. Look at pictures, read book excerpts and explore other information. In the spirit of intellectual fairness, you may want to take a look at the discussion of firewalking in the FAQ (frequently asked question list) for the **sci.sceptics** Usenet group (for which I have also included a web site).

**Web:**

**http://heartfire.com/firewalk/homefire.html**
**http://www.cis.ohio-state.edu/hypertext/faq/usenet/skeptic-faq/faq.html**

## Lucid Dreams

Having a lucid dream is sort of like directing your own movie except that it's a whole lot cheaper and you don't have to deal with unions. Lucid dreams are those in which you are totally aware of what is going on and you can control the outcome. Read about other people's dreams, share some of your own, and discover ways to improve your technique. It's fun, and best of all, it's free.

**Web:**

**http://www.lucidity.com/LucidDreamingFAQ2.html**
**http://www.valleynet.net/~astral/lucid.html**

**Usenet:**

**alt.dreams.lucid**

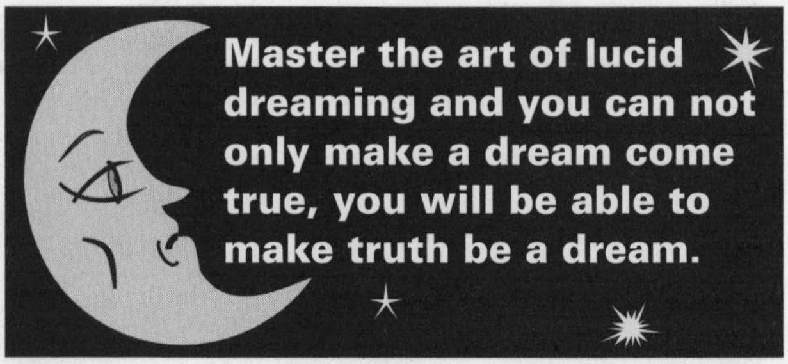
Master the art of lucid dreaming and you can not only make a dream come true, you will be able to make truth be a dream.

## Masters, Extraterrestrials and Archangels

Quench your burning desire to know all about ascended masters, extraterrestrial beings, and other spiritual higher-ups. Read about and see pictures of such notables as Maitreya, Serapis-Bei, Melchizedek, Khutumi, Michael and Ballerian.

**Web:**

**http://www.spiritweb.org/Spirit/masters-ets-angels.html**

## Meditation Talk and General Discussion

Close your eyes, breathe deep, relax. Clear your mind of all thoughts, free your body of all tension and float off to a world of pure spiritual essence. Explore the many methods of meditation, whether through yoga, visualization, traditional and philosophical processes, or by using more modern means. These Usenet groups will give you information on the history and technique of all types of meditation.

**Usenet:**

**alt.meditation**
**alt.meditation.quanyin**

## Mysticism Talk and General Discussion

It's a dark and stormy night, and during the dinner party someone brings up the subject of mysticism and begins telling about the seven layers of consciousness, time and the concept of becoming God. Then someone asks you what you think about the difference between the subconscient and the superconscient. Much to your embarrassment, the only response you can stammer is: "Anyone for dessert?" Raise your consciousness to a more mystical level by reading this Usenet group and never be caught with your aura down again.

**Usenet:**

**alt.consciousness.mysticism**

**I've never met a high-speed Internet connection I didn't like.**

### *Look What I Found on the Net...*

```
Newsgroup: alt.meditation
Subject: Where Does the Deception Lie?

> I recall an article in Yoga Journal where they quote
> Yogananda's description of "levitation" as involving hopping
> in the early stages.

I am not aware of this reference to hopping or whether it has
anything to do with what Transcendental Meditation teaches.
Yogananda did refer to saints who were able to levitate.  In
fact, he tells a story of a Christian monk who could not perform
his chores at the monastery because he could not stay on the
ground.

I should add that Yogananda repeatedly cautions the devotee to
avoid all psychic manifestations that are part of spiritual
unfoldment.  They are maya and easily divert the devotee from
the goal.  When Brother Bhaktananda, one of Yogananda's most
advanced disciples, was asked about levitation, he gave the
above warning, and then commented that it was better to devote
all of your spiritual energy to meditation and take the
elevator.
```

## New Age Information

Once I was in a bookstore and this man came up to me and showed me a calendar with the pictures of the Northern Lights on it. He began talking about Earth entering a photon belt and how certain unnamed lords of light and dark would be doing something or other. What do you say when this happens? If I had read this web site, I would have known, because there is a great deal of information on the photon belt as well as Nostradamus, Urantia, vegetarianism, Mayan prophesies and other New Age stuff. Oh, well.

**Web:**

**http://www.iinet.com.au/~bertino/newage.html**

## New Age Magazines

A New Age calls for new magazines. Here are two online publications: "Light" in which you can read about tarot, astrology, numerology, mind expansion and spirituality; and "Cougar WebWorks", which features articles on health, lifestyle, networking, drumming, dancing, travel tales and prophecies.

**Web:**

**http://www.he.net/~cougarww/**
**http://www.ili.net/~jjarrell/**

## New Age Talk and General Discussion

In this Usenet group, New Age believers encourage awareness, positive thinking, and healing with the mind, as well as offering information on many other topics. The talk covers a wide range of doctrines and philosophies. If you like to talk about religion, philosophy and the New Age movement, you are sure to never get bored here.

**Usenet:**

**talk.religion.newage**

**Find a friend in "People".**

## Numerology

Numerology is the study of the occult significance of numbers. According to this belief system, specific numbers are assigned to the letters of the alphabet. You can add up the digits that correspond to the letters in someone's name, and derive a single digit that is supposed to resonate with their personality. However, serious numerology is not that simple, because the personality is divided into various parts, each of which has a different number. In addition, there are also ways to take a birth date into account when analyzing a name. Here are some web sites that will introduce you to numerology and the significance of numbers. If you are wondering what the world of numbers has in store for you, analyze your own name. I used one of the web sites to analyze my cat's name and date of birth. I found out that he is "drawn to all that is beautiful, luxurious and expressive" which, as anyone who knows him will confirm, is certainly true.

**Web:**

**http://www.kaiwan.com/~mcivr/numbers.html**
**http://www.spiritlink.com/num1.html**
**http://www.sun-angel.com/interact/numquest/numquest.html**

## Reincarnation

Reincarnation refers to the rebirth of a soul from one body into another body or lifeform. Many old cultures believe in reincarnation as part of their religion. However, New Age people appreciate the idea of reincarnation from a somewhat different perspective. These web sites contain information about reincarnation from the point of view of Western culture. Read about karma, personal experiences, transpersonal hypnotherapy, simultaneous lifetimes, pre-birth memories, interesting historical tidbits, and much, much more. On a personal note, I once underwent a past-life regression session in which I discovered that, in a previous lifetime, I had been a person who underwent a past-life regression session in which I discovered that, in a previous lifetime, I had been a person who...

**Web:**

**http://www.spiritweb.org/Spirit/reincarnation.html**
**http://www.users.interport.net/~crystal/reincarn.html**

## Spirit Web

Do you ever get the feeling that there is more going on around you than you realize? What is it with all these alien sightings and interactions with ghosts and people who say they channel voices from the great beyond? Do they know something you don't? You don't have to feel left out any longer. Get information on channeling, alternative healing, UFOs, light technology, Earth changes, out-of-body experiences, astrology and other subjects that really are out of this world.

**Web:**

**http://www.spiritweb.org/**

## Spiritual Healing

A web page devoted to spiritual healing, such as the study of auras, chakras, energy work, Reiki, shiatsu, and homeopathy. These methods are much easier to practice on your friends than a splenectomy, plus you can do these tricks at dinner parties and it won't make people throw up.

**Web:**

**http://www.spiritweb.org/Spirit/healing.html**

**Stay connected.**

### *Look What I Found on the Net...*

(from a Numerology web site)

Name Analysis: Harley Hahn

Expression = 1: The Expression number shows us who we truly are, what we came into this life already knowing...

You have an innate ability to get what you want and what you need for your survival. You are primarily concerned about developing the self and acquiring resources for your own enjoyment. Your independence and courageous determination to succeed make you a good leader, and your unique approach is sure to open the doors to brave new worlds and fascinating discoveries.

Soul Urge = 7: The Soul Urge number has also been called Heart's Desire and Spiritual Urge, our secret, innermost longing...

You are a philosopher by nature. Inside, you are calm, shy and reserved, preferring to live alone in your own perfect world of thoughts and intuitive analysis of life's deeper mysteries. You experience irritation and upset in noisy or chaotic environments, as your hearing is more sensitive than most people. You have a good ear for music and are probably drawn to complex and meditative melodies.

Persona = 3: The Persona number describes the way we appear to the outside world...

There seems to be a golden glow of optimism and joy around you wherever you go. You are witty and playful, and your idealistic nature irresistibly draws the little child out of everyone you meet. Ever creative and interesting to talk to, you are never long without people to cluster around your radiance. You enjoy dressing up and are very creative with accessories. You've got a style all your own, even if you don't follow fashion.

Spiritual needs call for spiritual methods. That's why I recommend you use your computer and modem to connect to the **Spiritual Healing** site.

## Tarot

You're minding your own business, laying your tarot cards out in a simple little Celtic Cross spread when all of a sudden the Nine of Swords pops up in a place where you least suspected. Now, what does that mean? Don't let it stump you. Tarot fans and experts talk about this classical form of divination in Usenet. Get help, advice and hear interesting ideas about spreads, card meanings and different versions of tarot decks.

**Web:**

**http://web.cps.msu.edu/~philpott/Tarot/tarot.basics.html**
**http://www.facade.com/Occult/tarot/**
**http://www.infi.net/~jacksn/**

**Usenet:**

**alt.tarot**

## Urantia

What if someone were to tell you they could help you consolidate knowledge and all world views to improve life for everyone on Earth? Would you want to do it? If you would jump at the chance, then check out this list that discusses the Urantia material and is a forum for both scientific and theological perspectives for enhancing understanding of oneself using the Urantia material as a guide.

**Listserv Mailing List:**

List Name: **urantial**
Subscribe to: **listserv@uafsysb.uark.edu**

# NEWS

## Arabic Newsstand

The Arabic Newsstand has links to daily, weekly and monthly news sources. Some of the sources are in Arabic, some in English, and some in both languages. Read news from prominent newspapers of the Arab world and keep up on what is happening in Saudi Arabia, Kuwait, Bahrain, Lebanon, Jordan, United Arab Emirates, Palestine and Qatar. There are also Arab papers from countries such as the United States, Canada, Australia and the United Kingdom.

**Web:**

**http://www.liii.com/~hajeri/newsstand/arab-news.html**

## Australian News

Whenever I am itching for some news about Australia, I always go to this web site, because they have links to lots and lots of Australian news sources, including notices on the latest natural disasters. Just the thing if you are planning a little jaunt down under.

**Web:**

**http://www.aaa.com.au/Australian_News.html**

## Central European News

Visit this web site for news about central Europe and Russia. This is a spiffy online newspaper where you can read about business, politics and events of general interest. There is also a section called "Constitutions" that contains the constitutions of the Czech Republic, Poland, Hungary and Slovakia.

**Web:**

**http://www.ceo.cz/**

**Reach out and email someone.**

## Chinese News

China News Digest is a voluntary non-profit organization aimed at providing news and other information services to readers who are concerned primarily with China-related affairs. It offers both current news and an archive of previous global news, U.S., Canada, Europe, and Pacific regional news dating back many months, history, many scenic pictures from China, classic Chinese texts, and links to other news sites.

**Web:**

**http://www.cnd.org/**

## CNN Interactive

This is a great source of news information. CNN Interactive offers major news stories for the U.S. and the world, including sound clips and pictures. They also offer a compilation of articles for long-running stories and news events.

**Web:**

**http://www.cnn.com/**

## Daily Newspaper Email Addresses

Would you like to send email to a newspaper? Here is a large list of mail addresses of contacts and reporters for daily newspapers around the world. This list includes mail addresses in Canada, Czech Republic, Europe, Germany, Namibia, Poland, U.K., and a very large United States section. Send in your news tip today.

**Web:**

**http://www.helsinki.fi/~lsaarine/part2.html#DAILY**

Anyone can write a letter to the editor, but who do you know who can send an email message to *all* the editors at the same time? Well, now you can. Just check the list of addresses for daily newspapers, send off an important message, and soon it will be spam city, worldwide.

## Daily Sources of Business and Economic News

A large collection of links to free sources of daily news on the Internet. This page is divided into global news, regional news, national news, and links to specific general resources. It also offers newspaper, radio and television station email addresses.

**Web:**

**http://wuecon.wustl.edu/~lsaarine/news.html**
**http://www.helsinki.fi/~lsaarine/news.html**

**News, News and More News**

**Okay, so you are glued to your computer and fastened to the Net. Still, there is no need to miss the news. All you need is a web browser and you can make sure that no event whatsoever escapes your attention.**

## Drudge Report

I'm not sure how to describe this. It's a web site created and maintained by a weird guy (and I mean that as a compliment of the highest order), who collects a bunch of news information. He also takes news stories and sort of follows them, processes them, and spits them out in a Drudge Report. I don't know exactly what he does, but he does it with skill and pizzazz. When the going gets tough, the tough get their news from Matt Drudge.

**Web:**

**http://www.lainet.com/~drudge/**

## Electronic Newsstand

This comprehensive web site offers easy access to a wide range of interesting information and articles provided by U.S. and worldwide magazine publishers. Electronic Newsstand provides a window into the worlds of politics, science, business, foreign affairs, arts, travel, food and sports.

**Web:**
**http://www.enews.com/**

## German News

Here's the German news, the whole German news, and nothing but the German news (in German). But how important is this to the world at large? Can we learn anything about the Germans by studying their news? There is an old German proverb that says, "A country can be judged by the quality of its proverbs." Right. I couldn't have put it better myself.

**Web:**
**http://www.welt.de/**

## India News Digest

This mailing list collects and distributes news relating to the Indian subcontinent, with the most emphasis being given to India. Join this list and receive a daily email message with a summary of current Indian news.

**Listserv Mailing List:**
List Name: **india-l**
Subscribe to: **listserv@indnet.bgsu.edu**

## Irish Times

Take a look at the online version of the Irish Times. This newspaper provides you with daily news, sports, opinion, foreign news and stories on finance. You have to provide your own favorite pub brew.

**Web:**
**http://www.irish-times.com/**

**Marla leaves Donald for a handsome Internet author!!** Special Inside

**The Electronic Newsstand**

**How many times** have you held up the line in the supermarket reading the *National Enquirer* while everyone else encourages you to either buy it or move on? On the Net, you can take your time. Just connect to the *Electronic Newsstand* and browse till you're full. No, you won't find the *Enquirer*, but you will find a lot of other interesting items; certainly enough to keep you occupied when you should be working.

President consumes 32 million MacBurgers in effort to boost economy, and gains 576 lbs. as a result.

## Islamic News Talk and General Discussion

This Usenet group contains news, thoughtful articles and discussion about the world of Islam. This group is moderated and comes in a digest format.

**Usenet:**
**bit.listserv.muslims**

## Jerusalem Post

Find out what's going on in Jerusalem. News articles from the Jerusalem Post are on the Net. News, columns, and opinions are what you will find on the site, and the information is in English.

**Web:**
**http://www.jpost.co.il/**

## Los Angeles Times

The online version of this well-known southern California newspaper has all the typical newspaper stuff you would expect as well as lots of local information. Actually, the online site seems much better than the print version of the newspaper. If you register (for free), you can customize the site for the news you want.

**Web:**
**http://www.latimes.com/**

## MSNBC

MSNBC is an news-oriented cable TV and web site created by a partnership between Microsoft and the NBC television network. There is lots of news: world, commerce, sports, science, technology, life, opinion, weather as well as some local news. As you travel through MSNBC, you will find various interactive resources and Internet links scattered throughout. You can also personalize this site with local information, traffic reports, specific stock quotes, customized news, and so on.

**Web:**

**http://www.msnbc.com/**

## New Century News

This is an unusual news site. Their objective is to create a "homestyle" newspaper. Toward this end, the creators of this site collect an interesting selection of news pages from all over the Net. So, in one sitting, you might read diverse sections of newspapers from Toronto, Chicago, New Jersey, Tampa Bay, San Jose, and so on. The sections of interest offered are news, money, sports, people, kids, travel/entertainment, fun, marketplace, and more. Spend some time here and you will end up wandering through some interesting areas of our news culture that you otherwise would not have seen. Whether or not this qualifies as homestyle depends on your own personal definition of "home".

**Web:**

**http://www.newcentury.net/**

## New York Times

You can read the main guts of the New York Times for free (but you do have to register). There is a great selection of news here. I have so much fun looking around that I don't see how anyone would have time to look anywhere else. You can find a bit of every type of news: current events, cybertimes, politics, business, editorial, op-ed, arts and leisure, travel, real estate, classified ads, trivia and the famous crossword puzzle. There are also forums in which you can discuss news and events.

**Web:**

**http://www.nytimes.com/**

### New York Times

**If everyone who subscribed to the print version of the New York Times were to read the web site instead, we would save enough trees every year to re-populate the entire New Jersey rain forest.**

**(However, we would run out of electrons by 1999.)**

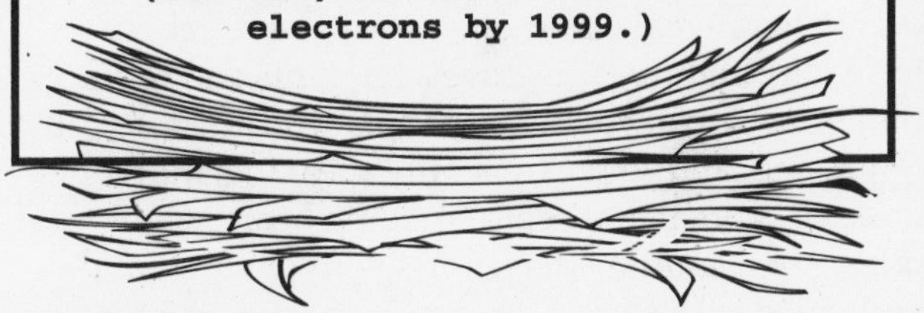

### *Look What I Found on the Net...*

(from the Islam FAQ, posted to bit.listserv.muslims)

In Islam, a woman has the basic freedom of choice and expression based on recognition of her individual personality. First, she is free to choose her religion. The Qur'an states: "There is no compulsion in religion. Right has been made distinct from error." (2:256)

Women are encouraged in Islam to contribute their opinions and ideas. There are many traditions of the Prophet which indicate women would pose questions directly to him and offer their opinions concerning religion, economics and social matters.

A Muslim woman chooses her husband and keeps her name after marriage. A Muslim woman's testimony is valid in legal disputes. In fact, in areas in which women are more familiar, their evidence is conclusive.

## Nikkei Net

Nikkei (Nihon Keizai Shimbun) is a Japanese news service founded in 1876. Today, Nikkei serves as the primary business information source for corporate executives and decision-makers throughout Japan. It publishes the Nihon Keizai Shimbun and four other newspapers—including the English-language Nikkei Weekly—with a combined circulation of 4 million. Nikkei is an employee-owned company that serves "no special interest beyond a desire to present objective news". This web site is the English edition of the Nikkei news service, dealing primarily with news summaries of business in Asia.

**Web:**
**http://www.nikkei.co.jp/enews/**

## OneWorld News

This is world news with a slant toward "global justice". The articles offer a global perspective. Although the coverage can be a bit superficial, they do a good job of highlighting important events around the world—events that relate to stories that don't always make the news. You can read about humanity and freedom issues, migrants and refugees, underdeveloped countries, people who are politically oppressed, and so on. Generally speaking, the stories are well written, not at all "bleeding heart". OneWorld offers some multimedia reports with pictures, audio, and video, as well as a discussion area to which you can post messages. The news service is part of a larger project called OneWorld Broadcasting Trust whose goal is to "create greater global understanding through broadcasting".

**Web:**
**http://www.oneworld.org/news/**

## Online Newshour

Newshour is a news and politics show hosted by Jim Lehrer on PBS (the Public Broadcasting System in the United States). This site is the online version of the show. You can find transcripts and screen shots of interviews, debates and discussions. You can also submit questions—which might be asked of guests on the show—and listen to audio clips.

**Web:**
**http://www1.pbs.org/newshour/**

## Pakistan

These discussions, in digest format, offer a huge amount of information on the latest news about Pakistan. The newsletters offer timely and thoughtful articles, poems, news of politics and the social environment in Pakistan.

**Web:**
**http://alumni.caltech.edu/~mughal/pns/pns.html**

**Usenet:**
**bit.listserv.pakistan**
**bit.listserv.pns-l**

## Pointcast Network

To use the Pointcast news service, you have to download their special software. However, it is free (because they advertise you to death with animated images). What is nifty about Pointcast is you can personalize the environment and get lots of up-to-date news and stock quotes as well as your local weather. The news comes from reliable sources such as the New York Times, Time magazine, People magazine, Money magazine, Reuters, Business Wire, and so on, so you know that everything you read is true(!). What I like is that you can customize your display to track news in a particular industry. This makes it easy to keep up on one area of the business world. (Here is a hint on what to do if the ads drive you crazy. Always read Pointcast with your window maximized. You will find that almost all of the ads are in a particular spot on the screen [such as the top right-hand corner]. Cut yourself a piece of cardboard that you can tape to the side of your display and flip down to cover the ad area whenever you are using Pointcast. I made such a cardboard device, which I call my "Pointcast filter", and it makes the experience of using Pointcast a great deal more pleasant. You may think that you can ignore the ads, but once you cover them up, you will realize that they were a lot more distracting than you thought.)

**Web:**
**http://www.pointcast.com/**

**Do a backup.**

## Positive Press

This is a really cool idea: a site with only upbeat news, featuring human interest stories and news items from various newspapers, journals and periodicals. This is not the place to find hardcore current events data. This is the place to have some great stuff that's all happy. Read stories about people overcoming difficulties, new breakthroughs in medicine and technology, new records being set, and so on.

**Web:**

**http://www.positivepress.com/**

## Reuters News

Reuters is a news agency founded by the German entrepreneur Paul Julius Reuter in 1851. The agency was based on Reuter's determination to "come up with solutions for his clients". For example, in 1850, Reuter used carrier pigeons to deliver closing stock prices, closing the only gap in the telegraph system connecting Berlin and Paris. The Reuters news agency prides itself on offering objective news services and, toward that end, they established the Reuters Trust to make sure Reuters is never owned by a particular interest group or faction. The online Reuters site is not fun. This is hardcore news without the cutesy lifestyle stuff. You can read lots of basic news—international, U.S., U.S. politics, business, and sports—and you can customize the site to suit your tastes.

**Web:**

**http://www.reuters.com/reutersnews/**

## Russian News

A daily digest from the Open Media Research Institute, this is a fabulous way to keep up on what is happening in Russia and related areas of the world. You can read the news on the Web, or subscribe to the mailing list and get a free update every day.

**Web:**

**http://citm1.met.fsu.edu/~glenn/russia/maillist.html**

**Listserv Mailing List:**

List Name: **omri-l**
Subscribe to: **listserv@ubvm.cc.buffalo.edu**

Positive
Press

Tired of reading about bad stuff? There are lots of good things happening in the world if you know where to look. I suggest spending some time reading the Positive Press.

Start with a daily dose of five minutes, and slowly work your way up to a half hour. Within a few weeks, you will be so happy that people will travel long distances just to shake your hand.

## South African News

If you are interested in finding out the details of what is happening in South Africa, here is the place to do it. Daily updates compiled from South African press agencies. You can find out a lot more by reading these summaries than you can from any regular newspaper.

**Web:**

**http://pantheon.cis.yale.edu/~jadwat/anc/**

## Swedish News

This site has news in both Swedish and English. If you want to keep up on what is new and exciting in Sweden, look no further. There are links to many, many Swedish news sources, including daily newspapers, magazines, radio and television. There is also a weather section which is handy during the winter, when you can cheer yourself up by looking at what the Swedes deal with day after day.

**Web:**

**http://www.it-kompetens.se/swedish/media.html**

**"Fun" is fun.**

A B C D E F G H I J K L M N O P Q R S T U V W X Y Z

## Time Daily

If you are a news junkie, this is a must-see site: daily news briefs from Time magazine. There is a good overview of each news story, and most of the stories also have a picture. At the end of many articles, there is a button you can press to search for more information about the person or place featured in the story.

**Web:**

**http://pathfinder.com/time/daily/**

## Today's News

Don't let the paperboy wake you up at five in the morning when he throws the newspaper at the front door. Instead, just check the computer over a cup of hot coffee and browse important news stories at your leisure. These news stories will give you an overview of the day's events so you'll have something to talk about during lunch time.

**Web:**

**http://www.infi.net/~opfer/daily.htm**

TODAY'S NEWS IS ON THE NET AND READY FOR YOU RIGHT NOW. (TOMORROW'S NEWS WILL BE AVAILABLE IN JUST A FEW MINUTES.)

## USA Today

Tired of recycling? Stop getting the newspaper and just get your news online. It's clean, it's neat and best of all you don't have to store a bunch of newspaper around the house until recycling day. USA Today has lots of interesting news and entertainment online. There's so much interesting stuff to read here, you might have to have a second cup of morning coffee just to get through it all.

**Web:**

**http://www.usatoday.com/**

## Washington Post

As you expect, you will find the latest U.S. and international news at this web site. What's nice is that you will often find Internet resources tucked away in the appropriate spots. (For example, I saw some great resources to help kids with their homework.) There is an unbelievable amount of stuff here: all types of news, including classifieds. There is also a special area for college students with trivia, news, and diversions such as Yenta the Matchmaker, who will help you find your true love.

**Web:**

**http://www.washingtonpost.com/**

## World News Sources

I'm warning you. Don't visit any of these sites unless you have plenty of time. There is so much news in the world of news that you will be distracted for hours. (And that's not news.)

**Web:**

**http://newo.com/news/**
**http://www.deltanet.com/users/taxicat/e_papers.html**
**http://www.discover.co.uk/NET/NEWS/news.html**
**http://www.stack.urc.tue.nl/~haroldkl/**

## World Statesman

This is an unusual news site with lots of good information here for thinking people (such as you and me). The emphasis is on news and opinions from world leaders and important political figures. There are letters, statements made to the press, responses to questions, and other written documents from important people. Most of the articles are lengthy, thoughtful, and written in response to specific issues. For most articles there is also a comprehensive background essay to give you an overview of the issues.

**Web:**

**http://www.kenpubs.co.uk/worldstatesman/**

# OCCULT AND PARANORMAL

## Astral Projection

It gets boring being in the same old body all the time. Try something new. Dust off the ol' astral body and try cruising around the neighborhood or perhaps just fly off to another country and see the sights. It's liberating, enlightening, and best of all, it's free. This astral projection web site will give you some handy tips on how to get out of your body.

**Web:**

**http://www.valleynet.net/~astral/astral.html**

Tired of moving SLOW in the FAST LANE? Try
Astral Projection.

## Astrology Charts

Don't wander through life wondering if you are going in the right direction. Use this interactive web page to learn exactly what your next move should be. Fill in the required information and the computer will whip out your astrological chart faster than you can say, "What's your sign, baby?"

**Web:**

**http://www.idirect.com/astrology**

**What if...?**

## Astrology Resources

Stars are more than just pretty lights you sit under at night. You can make wishes upon them, navigate ships by them, or record their positions to make up an astrological chart that you can consult for all your important decisions. Learn the basics of astrology, including its history and related topics like solar magnetism and etheric planets. If it's good enough for Nancy Reagan, it's good enough for...someone.

**Web:**

**http://www.magitech.com/pub/astrology/**
**http://www.spiritweb.org/Spirit/Astro/Overview.html**

## Astrology Talk and General Discussion

You've discovered that Uranus is in conjunction with your ascendant ruler, Jupiter. And as if that's not enough, Uranus also squares Mercury, your tenth house ruler, and you have four yods that are creating frustration and dissatisfaction in your life. What's a person to do? Besides calling the psychic hotline, you can post queries or hints to stargazers across the globe or even— depending on whom they know—across the universe.

**Usenet:**

**alt.astrology**
**sci.astrology.hindu**
**sci.astrology.misc**

## Channeling

The problem with people on the astral plane is that they have a hard time communicating with all the rest of us who are still hanging out on earth. That's where channeling comes in. Channelers have the great job of talking for these bodiless folks who still have a lot of things to say. Read stories, articles, and experiences relating to the process of channeling.

**Web:**

**http://www.execpc.com/~mholmes/chan.html**

**Usenet:**

**alt.paranormal.channeling**

## Chaos Magick

Chaos magick is a system of magick that is personal (as opposed to group-oriented), and non-traditional (as opposed to the "old ways" of traditional ritual). It does not have a particular belief system. Each "Chaote" (person who practices chaos magick) believes whatever suits him or her. Chaos magick recognizes no particular deity, theology or morality. "Nothing is True, and Everything is Permitted." This is a world view in which life is chance, random, accidental, chaotic and discordant. One of these web sites contains magick-related fonts, images, essays, software, spells and related links. The other site is a somewhat chaotic web page for the **alt.magick.chaos** Usenet group. (If you can make any sense of this information, you probably have the right chemistry to practice chaos magick.)

**Web:**

**http://www.crl.com/~tzimon/**
**http://www.io.com/~shub/amc.html**

**Usenet:**

**alt.magick.chaos**

## Ghosts and Hauntings

You don't have to wait for campfire stories to scare yourself silly. Tune in to this page where you will find some really creepy pictures of ghosts, descriptions of haunted places to visit and some scary stories. I recommend you leave all the lights on.

**Web:**

**http://www.best.com/~dijon/ghosts/**

**Ghosts and Hauntings**

Do you want to scare yourself silly? Do you believe in haunted houses? What about ghosts?

We're not talking Casper here. We're talking things that are so scary you will never get to sleep.

Check it out–
**if you dare.**

## Hermeticism

Hermeticism relates to alchemy and magick, as well as to the specific works of Hermes Trismegistus (the Egyptian god Thoth), who is the legendary author of various writings on astrology and magic. This site has lots and lots of resources relating to Hermeticism, including online versions of Hermes Trismegistus's writing. (What amazes me is that an ancient Egyptian god understood HTML.)

**Web:**

**http://www.necronomi.com/magic/hermeticism/**

## Inner Sanctum Occult Net

This site contains a collection of occult resources: an encyclopedia of magick and the occult, a web forum where you can discuss occult topics, an archive of files relating to the occult, as well as a huge list of other occult resources around the Net.

**Web:**

**http://www.inner-sanctum.com/**

## Lightful Images

If seeing is believing, then this will put you one step closer to believing that some really strange stuff is going on in the universe. Stuff that maybe you would rather not know. So maybe it's best if you didn't look at these pictures of aliens and other paranormal occurrences.

**Web:**

**http://www.spiritweb.org/Spirit/Images/**

## Magick

You never know when you will need to immediately lay your hands on the Hymn to Osiris in the Egyptian Book of the Dead or perhaps look up the definition for the word "utok" in the Dictionary of Ouranos Barbaric. Have access to more magick than you can shake a bag of runes at.

**Web:**

**http://www.nada.kth.se/~nv91-asa/magick.html**

## Magick Talk and General Discussion

The good news for witches in the '90s is that nobody gets burned at the stake anymore. Whatever brand of magick you like to practice, Usenet has something to offer you. Get information on solitary witches, rituals, equipment and supplies, ethics and the hardships faced by today's practitioners of magick.

**Usenet:**

**alt.magick**
**alt.magick.chaos**
**alt.magick.ethics**
**alt.magick.order**
**alt.magick.sex**
**alt.magick.tyagi**

## Near-Death Experience

It doesn't count if someone scares you so bad that you think you nearly have a heart attack. This Usenet group talks about real near-death experiences like actually going out of your body and wisping around the room in an ethereal form before being yanked back to consciousness. Read studies on the near-death concept as well as anecdotes from people who have had these experiences.

**Web:**

**http://www.mindspring.com/~scottr/end.html**

**Usenet:**

**alt.consciousness.near-death-exp**

**The name of the game is fast access.**

## Necronomicon

The original title of the Necronomicon was "Al-Azif". (Azif is an Arab word signifying a nocturnal sound, made by insects, which was thought to be the howling of demons.) The Al-Azif was written around the year 730 by Abdul Al-Hazred, a crazed and wandering poet from Yemen. In 950, the work was translated into what we now know as the Necronomicon by a Greek philosopher named Theodorus Philetus. Some people say the book is full of powerful spells by which you can raise the dead (in case your servants call in sick the night of a big dinner party); other people have their doubts. The document has a long history of suppression and destruction, and has been banned repeatedly. It is said that Abdul Al-Hazred met his death by being devoured by a monster in broad daylight. Even now, people say just looking at the Necronomicon will bring you bad luck. Still wanna read it?

**Web:**

**http://dorit.ihi.ku.dk/~otap/necro.html**

**Usenet:**

**alt.necronomicon**

## Occult and Magick Chat

Do you have your cauldron bubbling away and need a little advice about what to do if you run out of eye of newt? Hop onto IRC and talk to the folks who are into occult and magick. Maybe you can jump on the old broom and fly over to borrow a cup of mandrake root.

**IRC:**

**#babel**
**#magick**
**#omnet**
**#oto**
**#psimagick**
**#tarot**
**#thelema**

### *Look What I Found on the Net...*

```
Newsgroup: alt.magick
Subject: End of the World Party

Once again it's time to start planning for the annual End of the
World Party. This is an annual event invented by a bunch of drunks
in the backwoods of Oregon with nothing better to do...
```

A B C D E F G H I J K L M N O P Q R S T U V W X Y Z

## Occult Mailing List

No more will you wonder if the supernatural and existence-beyond-existence are real or just figments of your reality. Join the discussion about things hidden and esoteric, and learn about the history and theory of the occult.

**Listserv Mailing List:**

List Name: **arcana**
Subscribe to: **listserv@brownvm.brown.edu**

## Ouija

It's nice to know that at any time during the day if you have a question or problem, you can get a quick and easy answer from this web-based Ouija board. Think of a particular question you want to ask, close your eyes and let the mouse roam, clicking at random. The page will keep track of your choices and before you can say "Is this thing really working?" it will spit out an answer. While it may not solve all your problems, it's certainly cheaper than therapy.

**Web:**

**http://www.math.unh.edu/~black/cgi-bin/ouija.cgi**

## Out-of-Body Experiences

The best cure for indigestion is to just leave your body behind and let it work out the details for itself. Read up on astral projection, out-of-body healing, meditation, lucid dreaming, theories about higher realms, and tips on how to have an out-of-body experience.

**Web:**

**http://www.isl.net/~peterson/intro.html**
**http://www.lava.net/~goodin/astral.html**
**http://www.utu.fi/~jounsmed/asc/obe/faq/obe00.html**

**Usenet:**

**alt.oobe**
**alt.out-of-body**

**USING THE NET IS AN OUT-OF-BODY EXPERIENCE. YOUR BODY STAYS HOME, WHILE YOUR MIND GOES TO WORK.**

**If you have the questions, the Net has the answers.**

## Paranormal Investigation Committee

When in doubt, check out the home page for the Committee for the Scientific Investigation of Claims of the Paranormal (CSICOP). Read news and articles about skepticism and the scientific inquiry of paranormal events.

**Web:**

**http://iquest.com/~fitz/csicop/**

## Paranormal Phenomena Talk and General Discussion

The weird, the unexplained, the things that go bump in the night. I love stories, especially ones that give me goose bumps and make the hair stand up on the back of my neck. Read stories and theories about paranormal phenomena.

**Usenet:**

**alt.paranet.paranormal**
**alt.paranormal**

## Parapsychology

Remember all those nights you'd stay up late with friends, turn out the lights, and by the eerie glow of a flashlight you would tell ghost stories and creepy folk legends? None of that has changed, it's just that the scary stories get more complicated and sophisticated. Believers of the weird get together to talk about experiences, thoughts and questions such as ESP, out-of-body experiences, dreams and altered states of consciousness. The forum is not to debate whether psi exists, but to discuss the nature of it.

**Web:**

**http://eeyore.lv-hrc.nevada.edu/~cogno/para1.html**

**Listserv Mailing List:**

List Name: **psi-l**
Subscribe to: **listserv@vm.its.rpi.edu**

## Psi Phenomena Talk and General Discussion

You're sitting at the bus stop when a beautiful woman sits down next to you. The bus arrives and she stands up to get on board. She turns to look at you and without speaking you hear her say "Going my way?" You are astounded. Could it be that you read her mind? Or maybe she used psychic ability to put the thought in your head. Or maybe it's a lot of wishful thinking. Find out the scoop on psi phenomena so if this happens again, you will know just what to do.

**Usenet:**

**alt.paranet.psi**

## Scientific Theories Behind Paranormal Events

Ghosts, UFOs, poltergeists and other paranormal events are the stuff that makes urban folklore so rich. Skeptics and believers discuss scientific theories behind these paranormal phenomena.

**Usenet:**

**alt.paranet.science**

## Skeptic Bibliography

If you are more likely to say "bah, humbug" than "wowee" when it comes to astrology, paranormal events and fringe science, take a look at this lengthy bibliography of writings and resources that are mostly from a skeptical point of view.

**Web:**

**http://www.public.iastate.edu/~edis/skeptic_biblio.html**

## Skepticism

It's not easy being the bad guy, but someone has to do it. Take a look into this debunker's paradise and read skeptics' opinions on topics like UFOs, the Shroud of Turin, firewalking, faith healing, and, yes, even home schooling.

**Web:**

**http://www.xnet.com/~blatura/skeptic.shtml**

**Usenet:**

**bit.listserv.skeptic**
**sci.skeptic**

## I Think I Think (I Think), Therefore I Think I Am

You probably didn't expect to find intelligent, rational, educated thought in a section on Occult and Paranormal, but here it is. The skeptics have an annotated bibliography which will restore your faith in human reason. Before you cop out by saying, "It's all a value judgment and everyone is entitled to his or her own opinion," take a look at what the skeptics have to say and you may be surprised.

Thinking is generally a Good Thing™ and, like watching television and drinking coffee, using your intellect well can be habit forming. Having an open mind is great if you are undergoing brain surgery, but for fulfilling your birthright as a human being, nothing beats a good education and an understanding of how rational thought can be used to enhance our lives and stop other people from taking advantage of our emotional weaknesses.

## Spirit Web

If you are into anything remotely unusual, you will love this site. Read about meditation, channeling, light work, UFO phenomena, light technology, healing methods, reincarnation, out-of-body experiences, yoga, Vedic cultures, theosophy, great mysteries, astrology and more. Whenever I am looking for anything out of the ordinary, I check Spirit Web first.

**Web:**

**http://www.spiritweb.org/**

## Tantra and Sex Magick

In this age of recycling, everyone is making a great effort to make the most out of everything we use. We're not recycling material, but energy as well. Do you have a lot of sexual energy laying around that hasn't been put to good use? Check into tantra and sex magick. Utilize your sexual energy to create a better reality for yourself. They say it works. Start practicing now.

**Web:**
**http://www.tantra.org/**

**Usenet:**
**alt.magick.sex**

## Thelema

"Thelema" is a Greek word meaning "will" or "intention". However, "Thelema" is also the name of a spiritual philosophy that has been evolving over the last few hundred years. The basic tenet of Thelema is "Do what thou wilt shall be the whole of the Law." The earliest mention of Thelema was in the 16th century. However, the philosophy began to evolve rapidly in the early 1900s when a British occultist named Aleister Crowley (1875-1947) wrote "The Book of the Law". Crowley spent the rest of his life developing the philosophy of Thelema as it related to "The Book of the Law". (Historical note: Crowley wrote this book at urging of his wife who, it is said, was pestered by the Egyptian god Horus to get Crowley's attention while he and his wife were on their honeymoon in Egypt.) The basic idea is that "...each person has the right to fulfill themselves through whatever beliefs and actions are best suited to them (so long as they do not interfere with the will of others), and only they themselves are qualified to determine what these are." The web site gives a basic overview of Thelema as well as information about Crowley and the Stele of Revealing (the ancient Egyptian artifact through which the Law of Thelema was revealed to Crowley). You can also read the text of "The Book of the Law", look at a Thelemic calendar, find out about Thelemic organizations, and explore other, related resources. For talk, try the IRC channel.

**Web:**
**http://www.crl.com/~thelema/**

**IRC:**
**#thelema**

## Voodoo

Voodoo (also called Hoodoo or Vodoun) is a religious cult, practiced primarily in Caribbean countries, especially Haiti. Voodoo was created by West-African slaves who were forced by their Catholic masters to practice Catholicism. The Voodoo traditions grew from a syncretism (joining together) of Catholic beliefs with native African traditions. Voodoo recognizes a powerful supreme god who rules a large collection of local deities (some of whom act as guardians), saints and deified ancestors. These deities communicate with people through dreams, chants and possession. This web page is an excellent introduction to voodoo and its complexities. By the way, to create a zombie, you use black magic to kill someone, and then revive him in such as way that he no longer possesses a soul. The result is a pliant slave-like being. (Zombies, however, are only a small part of the voodoo tradition.)

**Web:**
**http://www.vmedia.com/shannon/voodoo/voodoo.html**

**You remind me of the man.**
**What man?**
**The man with the power.**
**What power?**
**The power of hoodoo.**
**Hoodoo?**
**You do.**
**Do what?**
**Remind me of the man.**
**What man?**
**The man with the power...**

# OPERATING SYSTEMS: OS/2

## Games for OS/2

OS/2 is not just a studly operating system. It's great for playing games, too. Check out the latest fun things you can do with OS/2 while nobody is looking.

**Usenet:**

**comp.os.os2.games**

## IBM Official OS/2 Web Sites

When you need the official word on Warp, turn to IBM's official OS/2 web sites. There are lots and lots of resources here: announcements and press releases, product information, service (including patches), support and OS/2 software to download. I have included one web site for OS/2 Warp and one web site for Warp Server.

**Web:**

**http://www.software.ibm.com/os/warp-server/**
**http://www.software.ibm.com/os/warp/**

## International OS/2 User Group

The International OS/2 User Group is a venerable organization, started in 1987. This is their official home page, containing a variety of OS/2 resources, including Pointers, the OS/2 User Group magazine.

**Web:**

**http://www.luna.co.uk/~os2ug/**

## Multimedia OS/2

Using multimedia under OS/2 is like having intimate relations on the back of a small car. It isn't necessarily easy, but it can work—if you do it right. Here is the place on Usenet where OS/2 people gather to discuss multimedia and how to do it well.

**Usenet:**

**comp.os.os2.multimedia**

## OS/2 Announcements

Announcements related to IBM's OS/2 operating system for PCs. If you maintain an OS/2 installation, you should read the Usenet group to keep up on what is happening and what is about to happen (maybe). The web site is a large collection of OS/2 happenings on the Net. It too is something you will want to check regularly.

**Web:**

**http://www.aescon.com/bestofos2/msgs/msgs.htm**

**Usenet:**

**comp.os.os2.announce**

## Keeping Up with the OS/2 Joneses

Okay, I admit it, I used to like OS/2 and hate Windows (3.1 that is). But since Windows 95 arrived, I have made The Big Switch and I am happy.

However, now that OS/2 has turned into a "legacy" system, there are still a lot of people who have to keep up on what IBM is doing. If you are one of these people (I won't mention any names, but you know who you are), don't run the risk of being left behind. Find out what's new and exciting by reading **comp.os.os2.announce**. (By the way, don't tell anyone, but I hardly even use DOS any longer...shh... it's a secret.)

## OS/2 Applications

Are you an OS/2 fan? Join the discussion where people around the world talk about various applications and how they run under OS/2.

**Usenet:**

**comp.os.os2.apps**

**Need to get the word out? Use the Net.**

A B C D E F G H I J K L M N O P Q R S T U V W X Y Z

## OS/2 Beta Releases

The days are long gone when a company would spend a lot of time checking a new product: getting rid of the last few bugs, re-writing the documentation, and preparing the technical people to support the software. Today, there is no extra time or extra money for anything. Instead of rehearsing carefully before inviting the audience and raising the curtain, the new custom is to release the unfinished software to your customers—as a "beta release"—and let them do the final testing for you. IBM is better than most companies at preparing properly, but there are still OS/2 betas that we must cope with and coddle. Here is the Usenet group in which such issues are discussed.

**Usenet:**

**comp.os.os2.beta**

## OS/2 Bugs and Fixes

Of course, all major software has bugs. However, now that the custom is to release operating systems as soon as possible (under the guise of beta testing), it should come as no surprise that a Usenet group devoted to discussing the bugs of anything is going to be a busy place. This group, set up to talk about OS/2 bugs, is no exception.

**Usenet:**

**comp.os.os2.bugs**

## OS/2 Chat

This is a IRC popular channel for discussing and exchanging information about OS/2. When it's two in the morning and you need some instant help, IRC may be your last resort.

**IRC:**

**#os/2**

## OS/2 Connect

OS/2 Connect is an online hypertext newsletter devoted to a worldwide audience of OS/2 users and enthusiasts. You can read OS/2 news, and find out about events in various countries. There are also links to a great many OS/2-related resources of all types. It is easy to spend a lot of time here.

**Web:**

**http://godzilla.eecs.berkeley.edu/os2/connect/**

## OS/2 Networking

OS/2 + Networking + not enough time + not enough money = 1 big headache. Through the years, networking with OS/2 has become a lot easier and a lot more powerful. However, there are still lots of details and lots of parameters to configure and lots of things that go bump in the night when you least expect them. So here are lots of network people to talk to who just may thank you for sharing.

**Usenet:**

**comp.os.os2.networking**
**comp.os.os2.networking.misc**
**comp.os.os2.networking.tcp-ip**
**comp.os.os2.networking.www**

COMPU BOOK

**OS/2 Networking**

If you run into an OS/2 networking problem, perhaps your friends on Usenet can help.

Remember, as long as you are on the Net, you are well connected.

## OS/2 Resources

Users and lovers of OS/2 will have lots to check out at these sites, which offer links to Usenet groups, other web pages, and support groups relating to OS/2.

**Web:**

**http://www.ccsf.caltech.edu/~kasturi/os2.html**
**http://www.mit.edu:8001/activities/os2/os2world.html**
**http://www.teamos2.org/~rsingh**

## OS/2 Setup

The OS/2 setup procedure is like the little girl who had a little curl right in the middle of her forehead. When it is good it is very very good, and when it is bad it is horrid. Don't despair, you are not alone. Stay tuned to the latest setup and installation issues by participating in the Usenet group of your choice.

**Usenet:**

**comp.os.os2.setup**
**comp.os.os2.setup.misc**
**comp.os.os2.setup.storage**
**comp.os.os2.setup.video**

## OS/2 Talk and General Discussion

Here are the general discussion groups devoted to OS/2. These are the places to talk about those topics that are not appropriate for discussion in more specific groups. ("Is it true that the Pope uses OS/2?") The **.advocacy** group contains more debate and controversial topics. ("Is it true that the Pope is thinking of switching to Windows NT?")

**Usenet:**

**comp.os.os2**
**comp.os.os2.advocacy**
**comp.os.os2.misc**

**Listserv Mailing List:**

List Name: **os2-l**
Subscribe to: **listserv@hearn.nic.surfnet.nl**

## OS/2 Web

OS/2 Web is a web-based magazine devoted to news. And news is what you get: lots and lots of news. My recommendation is to check with this site every few days, just in case something new has happened that you should know about.

**Web:**

**http://www.teamos2.org/os2web/**

**Over 95% of people check the "Trivia" section.**

## Programming in OS/2

Usenet discussion groups devoted to programming within the OS/2 environment. The **.porting** group is devoted to porting software from another system to OS/2. The **.oop** group is for object-oriented programming.

**Usenet:**

**comp.os.os2.programmer**
**comp.os.os2.programmer.misc**
**comp.os.os2.programmer.oop**
**comp.os.os2.programmer.porting**
**comp.os.os2.programmer.tools**

## Team OS/2

Like all good cults, Team OS/2 was started by evangelists and spread around the world. The original Team OS/2 members were IBM employees who were whipped into an institutional frenzy by management in preparation for the first release of Warp. Since then, Team OS/2 has expanded to include people (mostly non-IBMers) from all over the world. They interact electronically and have only one thing in common: their fanatical unswerving devotion to an excellent operating system. The Team OS/2 home page was designed to be a "one-stop source" for OS/2 information on the Internet. Well, I'm not ready to throw away my bookmark list, but this web site will get you through the night.

**Web:**

**http://www.teamos2.org/**

**Team OS/2**

**Want to join a cool organization just for OS/2 supporters? Participate in Team OS/2, a virtual OS/2 community on the Net.**

**Team OS/2 is free and there's no obligation. All you have to do is participate—and you belong.**

**OS/2: use it and you'll never have to worry about making the team.**

A B C D E F G H I J K L M N O P Q R S T U V W X Y Z

## Team OS/2 Help Desk

This is an enormous collection of help resources for OS/2. Team OS/2 (a worldwide users society) hosts this web site containing links to users groups, online magazines, tips and hints, lots of information, discussions, questions and answers, and much, much more. If you have a problem, check here first. There is a good chance someone else has had the same problem, and you will find the answer you need. If you want to get into serious OS/2 nerd stuff, you can join the mailing list.

**Web:**

**http://www.execpc.com/~lam/team_help.html**

**Listserv Mailing List:**

List Name: **teamos2help-l**
Subscribe to: **listserv@hearn.nic.surfnet.nl**

## Warp Online

Warp Online is an online web-based magazine covering the world of OS/2. The presentation is slick and the articles are not unlike what you expect from a print magazine. If you are in love with OS/2, you may want to check this site every month to see if there is anything of interest to you.

**Web:**

**http://www.warponline.com/**

## Warp Pharmacy

The Warp Pharmacy is a huge repository of OS/2 help information. You can think of this site as a huge FAQ (frequently asked question list) devoted to OS/2 questions and answers. The site is not supported by IBM; rather, it depends upon the participation of users (like you). One of my favorite resources is the one that allows you to look up a "symptom" and find a suitable solution.

**Web:**

**http://godzilla.eecs.berkeley.edu/os2/pharmacy/WarpPharmacy.html**
**http://www.atklab.yorku.ca/os2/pharmacy/WarpPharmacy.html**
**http://www.zeta.org.au/~jon/WarpPharmacy.html**

# OPERATING SYSTEMS: UNIX

## AIX

IBM's version of Unix, running on the RS/6000 and other platforms. The Usenet groups are for ongoing discussion; the web site contains archives, including back issues from AIXpert Magazine.

**Web:**

**http://www.developer.ibm.com/sdp/library/aixpert/aixpert.html**

**Usenet:**

**bit.listserv.aix-l**
**comp.unix.aix**

## DOS Under Unix

Now that DOS is kind of fading away, it's nice to know that it is still alive and well in the world of Unix. If you use DOS under Unix, I want you to know that there is a place for people like you: the DOS-under-Unix Usenet group.

**Usenet:**

**comp.unix.dos-under-unix**

## Emacs Text Editor

Emacs is more than a text editor. Emacs is even more than a full-scale, programmable working environment. Emacs is nothing less than a way of life (like baseball or religion). If you are an Emacs person—or if you want to be an Emacs person—here are some Internet resources that will help you on that long, twisted road to intellectual salvation.

**Web:**

**http://www.eecs.nwu.edu/emacs/emacs.html**

## FreeBSD

FreeBSD: A 32-bit multitasking Unix-like operating system for PC or Intel-based systems. FreeBSD is developed and maintained as a labor of love by hackers around the Net and is available for free and unlimited distribution. You will find the FAQs and current version of FreeBSD at the web sites. Hint: If you are looking for a free Unix-like operating system, you should also take a look at Linux.

**Web:**

**http://minnie.cs.adfa.oz.au/BSD-info/BSD.html**
**http://www.freebsd.org/**
**http://www.freebsd.org/FAQ/freebsd-faq.html**

## Linux

Linux: the free Unix clone, developed and maintained by Linus Torvalds and a gaggle of hackers around the Internet. Linux was written completely from scratch (using no "official" Unix code) for 386- and 486-based PCs. The world of Linux is huge and is one of the most important (and unsung) achievements in the history of operating system development. The newsgroups are for ongoing discussion; the web sites contain source code, documentation, and archives.

**Web:**

**http://pcola.gulf.net/~spatula/linux/**
**http://sunsite.unc.edu/pub/Linux/**
**http://www.leo.org/pub/comp/os/linux/**
**http://www.loop.org/linux/**

**Usenet:**

**alt.uu.comp.os.linux.questions**
**comp.os.linux**
**comp.os.linux.admin**
**comp.os.linux.advocacy**
**comp.os.linux.announce**
**comp.os.linux.answers**
**comp.os.linux.development**
**comp.os.linux.development.apps**
**comp.os.linux.development.system**
**comp.os.linux.help**
**comp.os.linux.misc**
**comp.os.linux.networking**
**comp.os.linux.setup**
**comp.os.linux.x**

### Emacs = Life

What is it about the Emacs working environment that seduces so many otherwise well-adjusted computer nerds? I'm not sure, but I do know that jumping into Emacs is one of the biggest, most significant intellectual commitments you will make in your life (and you won't even need a prenuptial agreement). Emacs creates a world of its own, from which you can edit text files, write and debug programs, read the Usenet news, and generally live high on the Unix hog. Moreover, the source for Emacs (it is written in the form of Lisp) is readily available, so you can look inside and customize it up the wazoo.

### Linux

Every now and then, some person gets an idea that takes on a life of its own and changes our culture. Such a person is Linus Torvalds, the original developer of the Linux operating system (now maintained by a large group of people around the Net).

Linux is one of those wonders–a professional-quality operating system put together entirely by volunteers–that makes you realize how important the Net really is to human affairs. In these days of no real Unix standard, Linux is the closest we have to a universal Unix. The wonderful thing is that, since no one is in it for the money, Bill Gates can't buy it.

(And I am *not* kidding.)

## Linux Chat and Support

Popular and friendly channels for discussing and asking questions about the Linux PC Unix operating system. The Linbot online bot offers help files, information on the latest kernel status, a short description of Linux, support availability information, and hardware and software requirements.

**IRC:**

**#linpeople**
**#linux**

## Mainframes and Large Networks

Unix is so different from Windows or OS/2 or MacOS. The latter are as clunky and slow as if they were designed for large computers, even though they run on small computers. Unix is fast and sleek and, although it was originally designed to run on a small computer, it runs even better on a large system. Here is the Usenet group devoted to discussing Unix as it is used with large (mainframe) computers and large networks.

**Usenet:**

**comp.unix.large**

## Questions and Answers About Unix

These are general Unix question and answer forums. Almost all questions should go to the **.questions** group. The **.wizards** group is only for real experts (stay away). You do not need to post a question to **.wizards** to make sure it is read by an expert—they read both groups.

**Usenet:**

**alt.unix.wizards.free**
**comp.unix.questions**
**comp.unix.wizards**

## Root Chatline

Talk on IRC with the guys and gals in charge: the ones who know the root password. Discussion is mostly technical: computer systems, languages, operating systems, programming, architectures, cooking with Jolt, and so on.

**IRC:**

**#root**

## SCO Unixware

SCO (Santa Cruz Operation) has a long history in the world of Unix. Today, they are still active, offering an entire product line based on their Unixware operating system.

**Web:**

**http://unixware.sco.com/**

**Usenet:**

**comp.unix.sco.misc**
**comp.unix.sco.programmer**

### SCO Talk

**Yes, there is a place on the Net for SCO bigots. Tune in to biz.sco.general and talk, talk, talk about ODT, Unix and (gasp) Xenix. Where else can you go when it's early Sunday morning and you need to find out just which EISA SCSI host adaptors are best supported under SCO Unix?**

**Stay connected.**

## Solaris

Get help from real experts from all over the world with Solaris, Sun's version of Unix. Solaris runs on Sun's Sparc computers as well as on PCs. There are fans, critics, experts, and newcomers, and they all seem to meet in this Usenet group. For more official assistance, check the official Solaris FAQ (frequently asked question list) at Sun.

**Web:**

**http://www.sun.com/solaris/solarisFAQ.html**

**Usenet:**

**comp.unix.solaris**

## Source Code to Unix Programs

One of the great things about Unix is there is a tradition of making source code available to the public. This Usenet group is the place for posting programs ready to download and compile.

**Usenet:**

**comp.sources.unix**

**Free Unix source code—**

**yours for the downloading.**

## Unix Administration

Surely, when the definitive book is written about the real heroes of the twentieth century, Unix system administrators are going to be right up there in Chapter 1. Running a Unix system is never easy and often surprising (in the same way that young children who are allowed to bring home strange animals are often surprising). When all else fails, read the documentation. Before it fails, read the FAQ (frequently asked question list) for the Usenet Unix sysadmin group.

**Web:**

**http://attila.stevens-tech.edu/~khockenb/comp-unix-admin.html**

**Usenet:**

**comp.unix.admin**

# RTFM

**Yes, rtfm is the longest word in the English language with no vowels. It's also the single most important word in the Internet/Unix community. Originally, R.T.F.M. was an acronym that meant "Read the F. . . . . Manual". (Sorry, I am not allowed to print swear words where your parents might see them.)**

**Today, rtfm has a more refined meaning: it represents the idea that before you ask a question, you should try to answer it yourself. On the Internet, you are expected to (1) read the FAQ (frequently asked question) list for a Usenet newsgroup before sending in a question for the first time, and (2) check with the Unix manual before asking a question about a Unix command.**

**FAQs are posted regularly to their respective Usenet groups and to news.answers. They are also available on the Web.**

**The Unix manual is a different story. All Unix systems should have a built-in command named man that will display the documentation for any Unix command.**

## Unix Chat and Help

Unix gurus chat, discuss, help, and argue everything and anything about the Unix operating system. This is a useful place to seek help when nobody else seems to have the answer or when you just can't wait for a Usenet reply.

**IRC:**

**#unix**

## Unix Internals

It's not generally well known, but Joseph Conrad wrote "Heart of Darkness" as an allegory about hacking in the Unix kernel. When you have a problem deep inside the bowels of Unix, ain't no one to call for tech support—you'll need your friends on the Net. This is not for the faint of heart.

**Usenet:**

**comp.unix.internals**

## Unix Manual

All Unix systems come with a built-in manual, documenting the commands and system calls. If you have access to a shell prompt, you can display information from the manual by using the **man** command. However, if you have a problem finding what you want, here is an online Unix manual you can access from anywhere on the Net. If you still have problems, try one of my Unix books: either *The Unix Companion* (published by Osborne McGraw-Hill) or *Harley Hahn's Student Guide to Unix* (published by McGraw-Hill College Division).

**Web:**

**http://www.softlab.ntua.gr/cgi-bin/man-cgi**

## Unix Programming Talk and General Discussion

So you want to be a Unix programmer, but you're spoiled by all the fancy DOS and Windows development systems. Well, you can still come here to talk with the experts on programming in Unix.

**Usenet:**

**comp.unix.programmer**

## Unix Reference Desk

If you are one of the lucky people who gets to use Unix, be sure you have access to a good amount of reference information. This site has a large amount of information on Unix applications, programming, various Unix systems, networking, security, Unix for PCs, Sun systems, X Window and more.

**Web:**

**http://www.eecs.nwu.edu/unix.html**

## Unix Security Talk and General Discussion

Tired of hackers getting into your system and setting up Trojan horses? Join **comp.security.unix** and find out how to prevent this and other minor irritations.

**Usenet:**

**comp.security.unix**

## Unix Shells

Do you still use the C-Shell, or even the Bourne shell? It's time to join the '90s and find out about the modern command-line interpreters, including bash (the Bourne Again SHell), the Tcsh, and the Zsh.

**Usenet:**

**comp.unix.shell**

## Unix Software and Source Code

One of the best things about Unix software—especially the vast amount of software available for free—is that the source code is often included with the programs. One of the worst things about Unix software—especially the vast amount of software available for free—is that you often need the source code to get things working the way you want. Anyway, source code or not, here are some Internet sites that contain lots and lots of free software.

**Web:**

**http://www.egr.msu.edu/DECS/Unix/Software/group.html**
**http://www.lame.org/~doc/warez.cgi**
**http://www.nova.edu/Inter-Links/software/unix.html**

**Want to really understand Unix? Go to the source (code, that is).**

## Unix Standards

Have you ever tried to make sense of the dizzying alphabet soup of Unix standards? If so, or if you're just interested, come here to find out about POSIX, ACE, and dozens of other standards both current and dead.

**Usenet:**

**comp.std.unix**

## Unix Talk and General Discussion

This is the place to talk about all kinds of general Unix topics that don't fit into a more specific group. The **.advocacy** group is for quiet sophisticated debate, searching for truth among the distractions of opinion. (In other words, the **.advocacy** group is for arguing.)

**Usenet:**

**comp.unix.advocacy**
**comp.unix.misc**

## Unix Vault

This page has a wealth of information about Unix online, with links to pages on specific versions of Unix, including AIX, A/UX, BSD, FreeBSD, Linux, and OSF/1 and others. This page also sports information about some Unix applications including Elm, the Z-shell, other Unix utilities, a complete set of Unix man pages online, and links to information about support groups, users groups, and other hot topics.

**Web:**

**http://www.nda.com/~jblaine/vault/**

**Get into "Mischief".**

## vi Reference Card

If you are a Unix person, using the **vi** editor is as close as you are going to get to perfection in this lifetime. The secret to remember is that **vi** is easy to use, but difficult to learn. (In fact, this is a good maxim to remember about Unix in general.) Here are some resources to help you learn **vi**. Once you know what you are doing, you can wait for a rainy day when there is nothing to do, and use these same **vi** summaries to brush up on the more esoteric commands.

**Web:**

**http://my.pages.de/vi-refcard.html**
**http://www.hsph.harvard.edu/SSH/Editors/ref_card**
**http://www.pica.army.mil/orgs/doim/ncmd/systems/vi.html**

# OPERATING SYSTEMS: WINDOWS AND WINDOWS 95

## Visual Tour of Windows 95

If you are new to Windows 95 (perhaps you are a Windows 3.x user who is upgrading), you will appreciate this web-based tour. Take all the time you want to teach yourself the basics. By the time you have looked at everything at this site, you will be comfortable with the Windows 95 interface and conventions.

**Web:**

**http://techweb.cmp.com/techweb/techweb/win95/1.htm**

## Win95 Glossary

In the beginning, there was the Word. And then, another Word, and another Word, and on and on. And finally, we found ourselves with a huge amount of technical terminology that only a nerd could understand. The next time you are reading about Windows and you encounter a word you don't understand, check the Win95 glossary: your permanent online nerd replacement.

**Web:**

**http://www.mcp.com/que/win95/glossary.html**

## Win95.com

I love this site. It's a collection of Windows 95 information and forums, a great place for browsing. Look through the Tips & Tweaks area, and I bet you will find something you don't already know. Do you have a problem? Join the Online Helpdesk: a forum in which you can leave questions for other people. Just scanning the previous questions will bring up a lot of interesting information. There are also live chat areas (using IRC) where scheduled get-togethers are held on specific topics. Check the schedule for upcoming events. In addition, you can find links to free software, other Win95 sites, and an online magazine.

**Web:**

**http://www.win95.com/**

## Windows 95 Annoyances

Once you get used to Windows 95, you will find that there are a number of small idiosyncrasies that annoy you. Well, they annoy everyone else, too. This site is a great collection of advice and procedures that you can use to make Windows 95 do what you want (some of the time anyway). I have found lots of great hints here. Hint: Don't visit this site unless you have a lot of time. I guarantee you will get distracted and spend half the night trying things.

**Web:**

**http://www.creativelement.com/win95ann/**

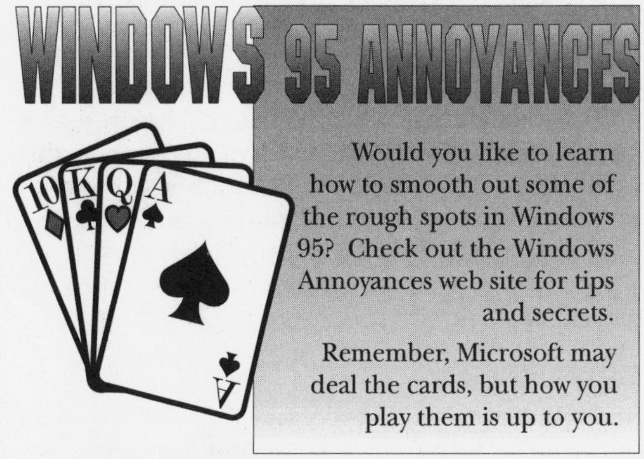
WINDOWS 95 ANNOYANCES
10
K
Q
A
A

Would you like to learn how to smooth out some of the rough spots in Windows 95? Check out the Windows Annoyances web site for tips and secrets.

Remember, Microsoft may deal the cards, but how you play them is up to you.

## Windows 95 Home Pages

There are many, many people around the world who have created their own web pages devoted to Windows 95. This is a collection of links to such pages. I find it fun to jump around the Net, visiting the various web sites and cruising for cool stuff. Actually, it's a long-standing tradition: getting your best girl, firing up your high-performance PC, and spending Saturday night cruising with the gang.

**Web:**
**http://www.planet-hawaii.com/global/win95.html**

## Windows 95 Official Web Site

Microsoft's official web site offers access to their Windows 95 resources on the Internet. This is a good place to look for the latest free programs and utilities, announcements, marketing info, and so on.

**Web:**
**http://www.microsoft.com/windows**

## Windows 95 Peer-to-Peer Networking

Did you know that you can configure your Windows 95 system to share files, directories and printers with other people over the Internet? You can let another person on the Net access your resources as easily as they access their own. All you have to know is how to configure the system properly. This web site contains instructions. Just think. A friend on the other side of the world can click on an icon and see your files. (If nothing else, this will teach you to choose your friends wisely.)

**Web:**
**http://www.windows95.com/connect/peercon.html**

## Windows 95 Question and Answers

This mailing list is dedicated to Windows 95 questions and answers. When you are completely stuck, and the possibility of useful tech support seems like a figment of Mr. Bill's overactive imagination, this mailing list is a godsend. Send in your question and you may get an answer from some kind soul somewhere on the Net. Of course, you have a responsibility, too. If you see a question you can answer, please do so and help someone else.

**Listserv Mailing List:**
List Name: **win95-l**
Subscribe to: **listserv@peach.ease.lsoft.com**

## Windows Announcements

This moderated Usenet group contains announcements related to the Microsoft Windows family of operating systems.

**Usenet:**
**comp.os.ms-windows.announce**

# Microsoft Windows Nostalgia

**Wasn't Windows great? Didn't you just love those GPF (General Protection Faults)? And don't you look back with nostalgia on so many of those fabulous UAEs (Unidentified Application Errors)?**

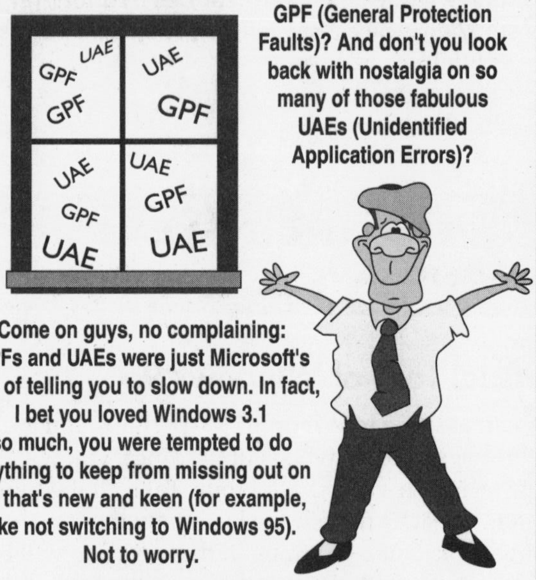
GPF UAE
UAE
GPF
GPF
UAE
UAE
GPF
GPF
UAE
UAE

**Come on guys, no complaining: GPFs and UAEs were just Microsoft's way of telling you to slow down. In fact, I bet you loved Windows 3.1 so much, you were tempted to do anything to keep from missing out on all that's new and keen (for example, like not switching to Windows 95). Not to worry.**

**Stay with Windows 3.1 and read comp.os.ms-windows.announce to see what you are missing.**

## Windows Applications Discussion

There is lots of discussion about the various types of applications that run under Windows 3.x and Windows 95. Look for the Usenet group that is closest to what you need to talk about.

**Usenet:**
**comp.os.ms-windows.apps.comm**
**comp.os.ms-windows.apps.compatibility.win95**
**comp.os.ms-windows.apps.financial**
**comp.os.ms-windows.apps.misc**
**comp.os.ms-windows.apps.utilities.win3x**
**comp.os.ms-windows.apps.utilities.win95**
**comp.os.ms-windows.apps.word-proc**

## Windows Developer Information

Items of interest to software and hardware developers for Microsoft Windows and Windows NT operating systems. Available information is from independent developers as well as from Microsoft.

**Web:**

**http://www.microsoft.com/DevOnly/**

## Windows Magazines

Here is a nice selection of online web sites maintained by various Windows magazines: PC World (all the Windows stuff gathered into one place), Windows magazine and WinUser magazine (completely online). If you like to keep up on Win95 news—especially developer issues—these are all good places to spend some time. I find skimming through these online magazine sites a lot more fun than reading the print versions.

**Web:**

**http://www.pcworld.com/workstyles/win95/**
**http://www.winmag.com/**
**http://www.WinUser.com/**

**When it's your turn to fix dinner, read "Cooking and Recipes".**

## Windows Networking Discussion

There are a variety of places to discuss Windows networking. First, there are a number of Usenet groups. It is a good idea to use the one that is most appropriate to your interests, although there is considerable overlap and cross-posting. Second, you can join the IRC channel for realtime networking talk.

**Usenet:**

**comp.os.ms-windows.networking.misc**
**comp.os.ms-windows.networking.ras**
**comp.os.ms-windows.networking.tcp-ip**
**comp.os.ms-windows.networking.win95**
**comp.os.ms-windows.networking.windows**

**IRC:**

**#win95-net**

## Windows News

Keep up on the latest news about the Windows family of operating systems, including the newest releases and upgrades. This is the official Microsoft news site, so you are getting the straight poop right from the horse's mouth.

**Web:**

**http://www.microsoft.com/windows/news.htm**

**Don't click here.**

### *Look What I Found on the Net...*

```
Newsgroup: comp.os.ms-windows.pre-release
Subject: Linux Is Booming Worldwide

>> STOP BUYING Microsoft Windows 3.1/ Windows95 and Windows NT.
>> If you do, you will lose a hell lot of money and will become
>> a slave of Microsoft...

I hope to outlive the great Microsoft dynasty.  If I do, when
they fall, everyone is invited over for a weenie roast.
```

## Windows Pre-releases

The life cycle of a Windows operating system goes like this: (1) Wait and wait a long time for a new version. (2) Beta release: use a beta version of the new operating system for a long time. (3) Go to 1. When we are in the throes of a beta, you can participate in these Usenet discussion groups to find out what everyone else is doing. These are also good places to send questions when something strange happens and you need some help.

**Usenet:**

**alt.windows95.beta**
**comp.os.ms-windows.pre-release**

## Windows Programming Articles

If you are a Windows programmer, you will appreciate this collection of articles written by a professional Windows 95 developer. Skim through and you will find lots of treasures relating to developing, designing, improving and debugging Windows applications. There are also links to various Windows programming sites around the Net.

**Web:**

**http://www.winmag.com/people/mheller/**

## Windows Programming Discussion

A large selection of newsgroups devoted to the topic of programming in the Windows environment. Topics cover general programming as well as more specific subjects like controls, graphics, memory management, multimedia, networking and tools.

**Usenet:**

**comp.os.ms-windows.programmer.controls**
**comp.os.ms-windows.programmer.graphics**
**comp.os.ms-windows.programmer.memory**
**comp.os.ms-windows.programmer.misc**
**comp.os.ms-windows.programmer.multimedia**
**comp.os.ms-windows.programmer.networks**
**comp.os.ms-windows.programmer.ole**
**comp.os.ms-windows.programmer.tools.mfc**
**comp.os.ms-windows.programmer.tools.misc**
**comp.os.ms-windows.programmer.tools.owl**
**comp.os.ms-windows.programmer.tools.winsock**
**comp.os.ms-windows.programmer.vxd**
**comp.os.ms-windows.programmer.win32**
**comp.os.ms-windows.programmer.winhelp**

## Windows Setup

The installation and configuration of Windows is supposed to be automatic and is supposed to work perfectly. However, once in a while, perhaps even too seldom to mention—I don't want you to think I am a complainer—something goes wrong. Thus, we have Usenet groups just for discussion of Window installations and other related miracles of modern life.

**Usenet:**

**comp.os.ms-windows.setup.win3x**
**comp.os.ms-windows.setup.win95**
**comp.os.ms-windows.win95.setup**

## Windows Talk and General Discussion

Join the talk about all aspects of Microsoft Windows. The **.advocacy** group is for controversial talk and debate. (The excitement is unbearable, so don't wait.)

**Usenet:**

**bit.listserv.win3-l**
**comp.os.ms-windows.advocacy**
**comp.os.ms-windows.misc**
**comp.os.ms-windows.win95.misc**

## Windows Video Discussion

If you have a special video adaptor in your PC, you may need some extra help getting everything working just perfectly with Windows. If so, this Usenet group is a good place to start.

**Usenet:**

**comp.os.ms-windows.video**

## Winsock

There are many people discussing various aspects of programming and using Winsock (Windows socket) applications (the types of programs you use as Internet clients). The web site contains the FAQ (frequently asked question list) for the **alt.winsock** Usenet group.

**Web:**

**alt.winsock**
**http://www.well.com/user/nac/alt-winsock-faq.html**

**Usenet:**

**alt.winsock**
**comp.os.ms-windows.apps.winsock.mail**
**comp.os.ms-windows.apps.winsock.misc**
**comp.os.ms-windows.apps.winsock.news**

# OPERATING SYSTEMS: WINDOWS NT

## Creating an Internet Site With Windows NT

Many people use a Unix machine as the gateway between their network and the Internet. But Windows NT will do the job nicely. This site will show you what you need to understand and do to use a Windows NT machine as your Internet gateway. My advice is to read everything first, and then plan carefully before you start.

**Web:**

**http://www.neystadt.org/winnt/site.htm**

## Internet Resources for Windows NT

Microsoft maintains this web page as a collection of links to many products, services and resources that support using the Internet with Windows NT. You will find developer tools, lots of Internet client programs, servers (such as would be used by an Internet service provider) as well as all kinds of utilities. Most of these products are shareware or freeware, not created by Microsoft. Thus, Microsoft asks you to "Please support the authors of these products by honoring the terms of the respective product-use agreements." You know, I never realized it before, but Microsoft really is a good corporate neighbor.

**Web:**

**http://www.microsoft.com/ntserver/tools/**

### *Look What I Found on the Net...*

```
Newsgroups: alt.warez.ibm-pc.apps, alt.winsock...
Subject: Winsock Registration Codes

[someone posts a message, looking for codes to use with pirated
software]

>>> Please post the registration codes for Winsock programs.
>>> Thanks.

[to which someone else replies]

>> Sure.  It's:
>>
>>        Name: IAmAnIdiot
>>    Password: AndCheapToo

[the original person then says...]

> Hey get the f*** out of this group!  This group is based on
> distribution of pirated software and/or cracking protected
> software.  I hope I haven't told you anything you don't
> already know.  There's a bunch of us cheap guys in this
> group, so if you don't condone it, don't f***ing post useless
> messages here.

[finally, two people explain what happened...]

Dear Clueless Jerk:
You crossposted to alt.winsock, that's why you're getting
flamed.  Keep it in the warez groups.

Do you really think you are only posting to ONE group?
Check the Newsgroups line.  You posted this to 29 groups, some
of which are NOT based on pirated software, but just the
opposite.  Before you tell us what "this" group is for, make
sure you are telling the right group.
```

## Introduction to Windows NT

Windows NT is unlike any other operating system. In particular, there are major differences between NT and Windows 95. If you are thinking about using NT—especially if you need to make a strategic decision for your company—this is a good document to read. I firmly believe that it is important to understand something about the architecture (design philosophy) of an operating system in order to know how and when to use it. The information here is for experts (or people who are supposed to be experts). Reading this won't turn you into a computer scientist, but it will help you understand the basic ideas and terminology, so you can make informed decisions.

**Web:**

**http://www.informatik.uni-stuttgart.de/misc/nt/intro.htm**

## Windows NT Drivers

There is nothing that can drive you crazy faster than not being able to find the right driver. This site is an absolute treasure: it is *the* place to look for information about the driver you want. Aside from information, you can possibly download various drivers, as well as request that a particular driver be emailed to you (if it is available). This is a great service and someone deserves an award. At the very least, Bill Gates should find the person who maintains this site and send him a free autographed picture.

**Web:**

**http://www.conitech.com/windows/winnt.html**

## Windows NT Internet Servers

This is Windows NT Server-City-to-the-Max: a collection of resources for finding and maintaining Window NT Internet servers of all types. If you have anything to do with providing Internet services using NT, this web site will help you find the software you need. The site is comprehensive and well-organized, and is a good place to start a search.

**Web:**

**http://www.intergreat.com/winnt/winnt.htm**

**Windows NT Internet Servers**

Windows NT makes a great platform on which to run Internet servers. But you do need to find the right software and learn how to install and configure it.

When you are ready to start serving, the Net is ready to help.

## Windows NT Magazine

This web site is maintained by Windows NT magazine. Although you can't read the contents of the magazine online, there is a wide variety of useful information, including a few of the most newsworthy articles. My advice is to visit here once in a while to see if any of the articles appeal to you. While you are at the site, explore a little. Be sure to visit the forums, where you will find discussion on many different technical topics.

**Web:**

**http://www.windowsnt-plus.com/sites/**

## Windows NT Official Web Site

Microsoft has two official web sites for the different versions of NT: server and workstation. You'll find all the stuff you would expect: general information, specs, answers to frequently asked questions, hardware and software requirements, support, training, software, and so on. There may be some controversy as to whether or not NT server and NT workstation are actually the same program, but Microsoft is certainly marketing them separately: the web sites are totally different.

**Web:**

**http://www.microsoft.com/ntserver/**
**http://www.microsoft.com/ntworkstation/**

**Do you have a code in the head? Try "Cryptography".**

## Windows NT Online Support From Microsoft

If you want to get someone knowledgeable at Microsoft to talk to you, be prepared to pay real money. However, you can access a great deal of high-quality support online by visiting this web site. There are lots of technical resources as well as troubleshooting guides, answers to the most commonly reported problems, and so on. You also have access to the NT software library, which contains drivers, patches (service packs), and so on.

**Web:**

**http://www.microsoft.com/NTWksSupport/**

## Windows NT Resources

This is a repository of a great many Windows NT resources. My advice is to look at the "Site Map". This will show you an outline of what is available. There are lots and lots of tools for users, developers and administrators. Take a look at this site and then put it on your bookmark list.

**Web:**

**http://www.ime.net/~peteb/**

## Windows NT Setup

Installing and configuring Windows NT can be tricky. Here are two Usenet discussion groups in which people share knowledge and tips about the best ways to install NT and to solve installation problems.

**Usenet:**

**comp.os.ms-windows.nt.setup.hardware**
**comp.os.ms-windows.nt.setup.misc**

## Windows NT Talk and General Discussion

Windows NT does not take prisoners. When it works, it's great, but when you have a problem, being able to talk to someone can be a lot of help. Here are a Usenet group and mailing list devoted to talking about NT. If you are a serious NT nerd (or administrator), you may want to participate.

**Usenet:**

**comp.os.ms-windows.nt.misc**

**Listserv Mailing List:**

List Name: **winnt**
Subscribe to: **listserv@listserv.optimedia.co.il**

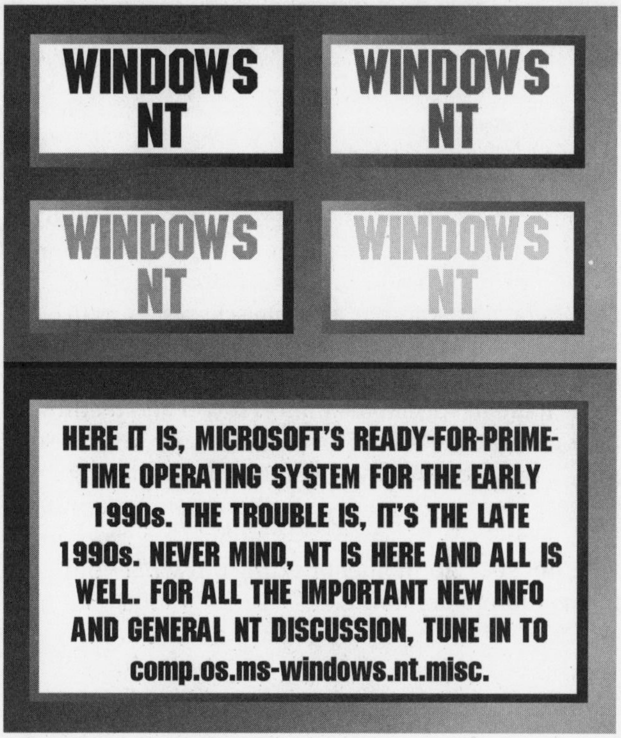
WINDOWS NT
WINDOWS NT
WINDOWS NT
WINDOWS NT
HERE IT IS, MICROSOFT'S READY-FOR-PRIME-TIME OPERATING SYSTEM FOR THE EARLY 1990s. THE TROUBLE IS, IT'S THE LATE 1990s. NEVER MIND, NT IS HERE AND ALL IS WELL. FOR ALL THE IMPORTANT NEW INFO AND GENERAL NT DISCUSSION, TUNE IN TO comp.os.ms-windows.nt.misc.

## Windows NT.net

Well, this is a strange one, probably worth looking at just so you can say you saw it once. It's a Windows NT information site—with a software database, some FAQs, and other assorted stuff—and the web pages are designed to mimic the NT graphical user interface (more or less the same as the Windows 95 GUI). If nothing else, this site demonstrates why we should be glad that the web doesn't use such a Windows interface. It would drive you bananas. (There's a good software search tool here, however.)

**Web:**

**http://www.windowsnt.net/**

## Windows NT-Related Web Sites

There are a lot of Windows NT sites on the Net, and sometimes it can be difficult to find the one you want. This is a large list of many sites which you can look up in alphabetical order. This is the place to come when you know the name of a Windows NT site, but you are not sure where it is. It's not an easy list to browse, but if you look under "M" (for Microsoft), you will see a nice list of Microsoft's NT resources.

**Web:**

**http://www.indirect.com/www/ceridgac/ntsite.html**

A B C D E F G H I J K L M N O P Q R S T U V W X Y Z

# ORGANIZATIONS

## Alumni Associations

If you graduated from a university, you are eligible to join an alumni organization. Alumni associations usually provide a number of services to their members. For example, at some schools, alumni members are allowed to use the university library. It is also common to be offered the chance to participate in special insurance, travel and credit card programs. Alumni associations also help the school itself, especially when it comes to raising money. Here is a web page that can help you find the Internet site for your association. Once you do, why not spend a moment finding out what your fellow alumni are doing?

**Web:**

**http://weber.u.washington.edu/~dev/others.html**

## America's Charities

What can you do with all that extra money you have lying around? Why not give it to a charitable organization? You may be able to use a tax deduction, but you can always used a few extra points with the Man (or Woman) Upstairs. Take a look at this web page, which has a list of charities that are just waiting for some free money.

**Web:**

**http://www.charities.org/**

**For some cool dreams, try sleeping with this book under your pillow.**

## ASPCA

The American Society for the Prevention of Cruelty to Animals (ASPCA) was founded in 1866 by Henry Bergh, an American diplomat. The ASPCA is modeled after England's Royal SPCA. The ASPCA's mission is to relieve pain, fear and suffering in animals. The ASPCA is involved with educating the public, law enforcement (removing animals from abusive owners), legislative action (lobbying for anti-cruelty laws), and animal care (collecting homeless animals and giving them food and medical treatment). This web site has information on pet care, government and legal issues, hot weather pet tips, press releases, an event calendar and information about the ASPCA.

**Web:**

**http://www.aspca.org/**

## Earth First

This environmentally friendly group discusses ways to put the Earth first. Read news about environmental causes, organizations, movements and alerts that are essential in saving the planet. The Usenet group covers all Earth-friendly topics.

**Web:**

**http://www.envirolink.org/orgs/ef/**

**Usenet:**

**alt.org.earth-first**

## Habitat for Humanity

Habitat for Humanity is a nonprofit Christian organization, founded in 1976 by Millard and Linda Fuller, that works toward providing housing for low-income families. The organization arranges to build or remodel low cost homes using a staff of primarily volunteers. These volunteers work with the partner families (the people who will end up owning the home) to build or remodel a house. When the home is finished, the intended family buys the home from Habitat for Humanity, at cost and with a no-interest mortgage. Habitat for Humanity does their work internationally. At this official web site, you will find information about the organization, a list of affiliates, current building projects, and profiles of habitat families.

**Web:**

**http://www.habitat.org/**

## Masons and Shriners

Freemasons (or masons) are members of a worldwide male, fraternal organization named the Free and Accepted Masons. The origins of Freemasonry are lost to antiquity. Some historians trace its roots back to the Middle Ages. Modern Freemasonry started in England in 1717 with the formation of the first Grand Lodge. Masons pass through levels of membership called "degrees". The three basic degrees are Entered Apprentice, Fellowcraft and Master Mason. Once a person attains the third degree, he is deemed to be a member of the Blue Lodge and is considered a full-fledged Mason. He is then entitled to join the Scottish Rite or the York Rite. Within these Rites, a Mason may advance in degree: in the Scottish Rite through 29 more degrees, in the York Rite, through 9 more degrees. Once someone has advanced to the highest degree (of either Rite), he can petition to join the Shrine—more formally, the Ancient Arabic Order of Nobles of the Mystic Shrine—at which point he is a Shriner. (When the Shrine was started in 1872 in New York, an Arabic theme was chosen, which is why Shriners wear red fezzes. Notice that the initials AAONMS form an anagram for "A MASON".) Shriners and Masons are well known for their charitable work and for their emphasis on moral development. They are also known for their elaborate rituals and secret traditions. (See, for example, the 1983 book Big Secrets by William Poundstone.) There is a huge amount of Masonic-related resources on the Net, mostly the web pages of various lodges. I have selected three good web sites, one of which contains a FAQ. For discussion, **alt.freemasonry** is for everyone, **alt.masonic.members** is for Masons only, **alt.masonic.demolay** is for members of Demolay (a Masonic-like organization for young men), and **alt.masonic.youth** is for members of all Masonic youth groups.

**Web:**

**http://freemasonry.org/**
**http://international.com/hiram/masfaq/faqtitl.html**
**http://shriners.com/**
**http://www.chrysalis.org/masonry/**

**Usenet:**

**alt.freemasonry**
**alt.masonic.demolay**
**alt.masonic.members**
**alt.masonic.youth**

## Mensa

Do you fancy yourself in the ranks of Adrian Cronauer, Marilyn Vos Savant, Geena Davis, and other smart people? If so, you should join Mensa so you can hang out on this elite list and talk about subjects that are calisthenics for your brain. Check out the official Mensa web site for information about the organization.

**Web:**

**http://www.mensa.org/**

**Usenet:**

**rec.org.mensa**

## National Center on Adult Literacy

The National Center on Adult Literacy is a good information resource for research and development in the field of adult literacy. They work with the Department of Education to help improve the quality of adult literacy across the United States. Get more information on NCAL at this site.

**Web:**

**http://litserver.literacy.upenn.edu/**

## National Child Rights Alliance

This organization, formed by survivors of child abuse and neglect, offers the youth bill of rights, many articles on children's rights, and a history of the NCRA.

**Web:**

**http:/www.ai.mit.edu/people/ellens/NCRA/ncra.html**

## National Institute of Standards and Technology

The National Institute of Standards and Technology (NIST) offers news, details of measurement services and laboratory programs, newsletters, budget information, factsheets, and industrial impact reports.

**Web:**

**http://www.nist.gov/**

## Nonprofit Organization Talk and General Discussion

Learn the ins and outs of running a nonprofit organization. Get ideas about raising money, hints on record keeping and how to start a nonprofit organization from scratch.

**Usenet:**

**soc.org.nonprofit**

## Peace Corps

Interested in making a difference in the world, but don't know where to start? Try the Peace Corps. Find information on joining, travel in foreign countries, and the perils and rewards of being a Peace Corps volunteer.

**Usenet:**

**alt.peace-corps**

**Listserv Mailing List:**

List Name: **pcorps-l**
Subscribe to: **listserv@cmuvm.csv.cmich.edu**

**Read a zine today.**

## Seniors Organizations

These are the official web sites of the American Association of Retired Persons (AARP) and the Canadian Association of Retired Persons (CARP). Both are nonprofit organizations dedicated to helping people over the age of 50. (The name "Retired Persons" is a misnomer, as you don't have to be retired to join.) The AARP is particularly helpful. You will find a lot of great information about retirement, housing, health, volunteer and community programs, and much more.

**Web:**

**http://www.aarp.org/**
**http://www.crm.mb.ca/scip/lifestyl/advoc/carp.html**

## *Look What I Found on the Net...*

```
Newsgroup: rec.org.mensa
Subject: Sample Test Questions for Mensa

(Here are the first five questions from a fifteen-question
sample Mensa test)

1. Which of the lettered designs best completes the following
   sequence?

      [o]    [.]    (o)

      A: (.)
      B: (o)
      C: [.]
      D: [o]

2. Sally likes 225 but not 224; she likes 900 but not 800; she
   likes 144 but not 145.  Does she like 1600 or 1700?

3. Only one other word can be made from the letters of
   INSATIABLE.   Can you find it?

4. Put the appropriate plus or minus signs between the numbers,
   in the correct places, so that the sum total will equal 1.

        0   1   2   3   4   5   6   7   8   9  = 1

5. What is the word coiled inside this circle?

                      T  P
                    I      U
                    A      N
                      L  S
```

## Service Organization Talk and General Discussion

Spending most of the day in front of the television is not the fastest way to feel fulfilled as a human being. Pull yourself out of the sofa and join a service organization. Check out this Usenet group to see which one would be right for you, or read the FAQ (frequently asked question list) at the web site.

**Web:**

**http://www.smartpages.com/faqs/service-clubs/general-faq/faq.html**

**Usenet:**

**soc.org.service-clubs.misc**

## Toastmasters

Join the club for people who love to make toasts. Hone your public speaking skills so you will be sought after when it comes time to do eulogies or partake in a celebrity roast.

**Web:**

**http://www.toastmasters.org/**

**Usenet:**

**alt.org.toastmasters**

## Unions

A labor union is an organization dedicated to serving the interests of a particular group of workers. Unions concern themselves with wages, working conditions, grievance resolution, health issues, and so on. These two web sites will lead you to a great many union-related resources on the Net.

**Web:**

**http://www.geocities.com/WallStreet/3088/labor.htm**
**http://www.unionweb.org/**

## United Way

Interested in charities? You can find out about the United Way on the Net. Look at this web site where you can find information about the United Way in America, Canada and Australia.

**Web:**

**http://www.clark.net/pub/pwalker/United_Ways_on_the_Internet/**

**The Net is immortal.**

### *Look What I Found on the Net...*

```
(from the FAQ posted to soc.org.service-clubs.misc)

What is a service club?

Service clubs are organizations which have been formed in many
parts of the world so that their members may volunteer to
perform valuable community services, as well as enjoy
fellowship, learn from knowledgeable speakers and interesting
programs which provide an insight into issues affecting the
local and global community, develop and exercise leadership
skills, expand business through professional networking, and
gain a sense of worthwhile accomplishment.

There are a wide variety of service clubs, with different goals,
focus, programs and memberships.
```

## Volunteers of America

Volunteers of America is a non-profit human service agency dedicated to helping people through volunteer efforts. Their web site will show you how you can become a volunteer, and will introduce you to the organization and its history. You can also read their online magazine, called Spirit. If you are interested in volunteering, you can find an affiliate office in your area.

**Web:**

**http://www.voa.org/**

## YMCA

When you are planning to travel around the world, it is nice to know that, like MacDonald's, there are places you can go to feel right at home. Check out the YMCA page and if you plan everything just right you can visit every one of the YMCA locations on your trip around the world.

**Web:**

**http://www2.interaccess.com/ymcaweb/**

# OUTDOOR ACTIVITIES

## Backcountry

An archive of backcountry-related resources, covering hiking, camping, and climbing. This web site contains trip reports, technical advice and tutorials, gear reviews and recommendations, places of interest, a gallery of some wonderfully scenic pictures, hiking club details, and links to other related pages. On Usenet you can discuss your hobby with other folks around the world.

**Web:**

**http://io.datasys.swri.edu/**

**Usenet:**

**rec.backcountry**

## Ballooning

When you need a break from the daily grind, hop into your hot air balloon and sail off into the blue. This web site has lots of information about ballooning, including resources and pictures.

**Web:**

**http://sunsite.unc.edu/ballooning/**

Would you like to get high
in a quiet, peaceful way?
Try ballooning.

## Boomerang World

A boomerang is a curved instrument—usually made of wood—that, when thrown in a particular manner, can be made to fly away and return. Boomerangs were invented in Australia. (In fact, the name "boomerang" is derived from "bumariny", a word from Dharuk, the Aboriginal language of southeast Australia.) Today, boomerangs are used around the world for fun, and there are various boomerang organizations and competitions. One of these web sites is a collection of boomerang-related links and information. The other site contains instructions to help you learn how to throw and catch. Hint: If you are left-handed, be sure to use a left-handed boomerang.

**Web:**

**http://ic.net/~tbailey/Boomerang.html**
**http://www.jcn.com/mx/how.html**

## Camping

There are various ways to go camping. Basically, you can either drive to the campground or you can walk (at least from a trail head). If you drive, there is a big dichotomy between those people who go car camping and those who have recreational vehicles (RVs). If you like to camp, here are some web sites that will be useful no matter what your *modus operandi*. In particular, you can read the various camping FAQs (frequently asked question lists). You can also use the Net to help you find a campground. For discussion, there are Usenet groups for general camping talk as well as groups for RV people.

**Web:**

**http://kendaco.telebyte.net/rlindber/rv/**
**http://www.campgrounds.net/**
**http://www.wrolin.com/campindx.htm**

**Usenet:**

**alt.rec.camping**
**alt.rv**
**rec.outdoors.camping**
**rec.outdoors.rv-travel**

## Climbing

Trapped indoors but ready to go climbing? Help ease the pain by checking out this great list of links. This web site has lots of places you can go on the Net to see pictures of climbing, information about climbing, in fact, just about everything about climbing and related activities. On Usenet you can find open discussion about climbing techniques, specific climbs, and competition announcements.

**Web:**

**http://www.cmc.org/cmc/rocklist.html**

**Usenet:**

**rec.climbing**

**Join the fun—now.**

## Fishing

Put an end to the stories about "the one that got away." Get tips on fishing and fly fishing. Images are available as well as archives to **rec.fishing** and **alt.outdoors.fishing**.

**Web:**

**http://www.geo.mtu.edu/~jsuchosk/fish/fishpage**

**Usenet:**

**rec.outdoors.bass**
**rec.outdoors.fishing**
**rec.outdoors.fishing.fly**
**rec.outdoors.fishing.saltwater**

## Great Outdoor Recreation Pages

Get out into the sunshine and fresh air. When you want to know where to go and what to do, take a look at all this great information. You'll find loads of stuff to read about things to do and places to visit: national parks, forests, wilderness areas, hiking, biking, fishing and climbing.

**Web:**

**http://www.gorp.com/**

## Hiking

Articles and guides about hiking and the great outdoors. Includes hiking songs, a snakebite guide, campfire lore, water filtering information, and other topics of interest to campers.

**Web:**

**http://www.teleport.com/~walking/hiking.html**

## Human-Powered Vehicles

Save the environment and get healthy at the same time. Human-powered vehicles could be the next trend in transportation. Learn to build and power these unique vehicles.

**Web:**

**http://www.ihpva.org/**

A B C D E F G H I J K L M N O P Q R S T U V W X Y Z

## Hunting

There are many aspects to hunting and a lot to discuss. Here are the resources you need to get started. The Usenet group **rec.hunting** is for discussion of any hunting-related topics. (Although, this is not the proper place to discuss the politics of gun control.) The mailing list is a mirror of the discussion group, so you only need to participate in one or the other. Finally, the web site is the official home for **rec.hunting**, where you will find links to many hunting resources around the Net, including the areas of ethics, firearms, conservation, bowhunting, organizations, vendors, useful articles (such as how to identify various types of ducks) and—assuming all goes well on your outing—recipes.

**Web:**

**http://helper.tamu.edu/STAFF/cbarnes/hunting/**

**Usenet:**

**rec.hunting**

**Listserv Mailing List:**

List Name: **hunting**
Subscribe to: **listserv@tamu.edu**

## In-Line Skating

Skating can be really scary at first. It will help if you read about some techniques for in-line skating, such as how to deal with stairs and most importantly: how to stop. More advanced skaters can read about skating backward, racing and tricks.

**Web:**

**http://ourworld.compuserve.com/homepages/Martin_Rivers/**
**http://www.skatefaq.com/**

## Kayaking and Canoeing

There are lots of great resources on the Net about kayaking and canoeing. (And you thought surfing was popular.) Read some paddling FAQs, find information about specific trips and activities, read the hints and tips, and enjoy the photos.

**Web:**

**http://siolibrary.ucsd.edu/preston/kayak/**
**http://www.gorp.com/gorp/activity/paddle.htm**

## Human-Powered Vehicles

Why should you depend on gas or electricity when you can do it yourself?

E
F
UNLEADED FUEL ONLY
FUEL GAUGE

A human-powered vehicle is quiet, non-polluting and innovative.
Best of all, when you are finished with the engine, it is 100% biodegradable.

## Mountain Biking

Mountain biking is a blast and I do it every chance I get (that is, when I'm not surfing). Check out the mountain biking resources on the Net and learn about technique, racing, safety and more.

**Web:**

**http://catless.ncl.ac.uk/mtb/**
**http://www.mbronline.com/**

**Usenet:**

**rec.bicycles.off-road**

## Nude Beaches

If you have never spent an afternoon at a nude beach, you don't know what you are missing. But don't worry, I can show you what it is like right now. Wherever you are, take off your clothes and, for the next 30 minutes, lie down on the floor and think pleasant thoughts. (If you are reading this in a bookstore, you can tell the manager I said that after the 30 minutes are up he or she must give you a discount.) Now, wasn't that great? Doesn't that make you want to try out a real nude beach? Here is the list.

**Web:**

**http://www.cis.ohio-state.edu/hypertext/faq/usenet/nude-faq/beaches/top.html**

## Orienteering and Rogaining

Grab a map and a sack lunch and head to the woods for some exciting, competitive, cross-country navigation. If you think trying to read a map while driving through Los Angeles is bad, try doing it in the middle of a forest where all the trees look the same and there are no road signs or even flushable toilets. Learn about orienteering and rogaining—the rules, how to compete, and what other people are doing.

**Web:**

**http://www2.aos.princeton.edu/rdslater/orienteering/**

**Usenet:**

**rec.sport.orienteering**

**Listproc Mailing List:**

List Name: **o-train**
Subscribe to: **listproc@u.washington.edu**

Imagine this. You wake up one day to find yourself in a new world. A world in which direction and time have a will of their own and have become as alive as the wind. All your common landmarks are gone; you move from one spot to another, lost in a haze of misdirection. Nothing you have experienced has prepared you for this. Everything you know seems to be wrong, and you are caught in a land of disinformation and shifting visual cues, an ever-changing environment in which the slightest mistake will send you off into the wilderness. Are you in the Twilight Zone? You wish. No, you are **Orienteering**. (You know what? Maybe you had better check it out on the Net first.)

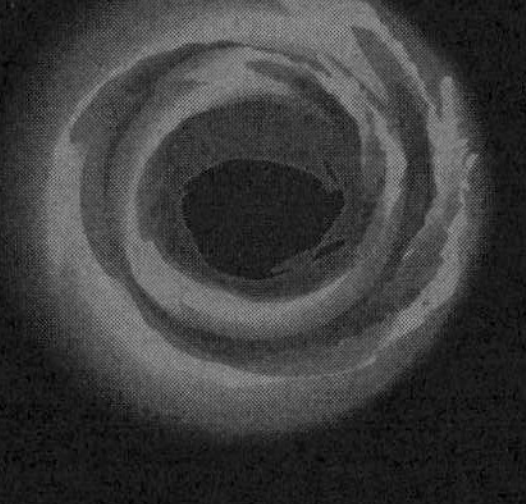

**Don't get fooled. Read "Consumer Information".**

**Quick, turn the page.**

## Paragliding

Paragliders are the most simple of all aircraft. They consist of a canopy (which acts like a wing), risers (cords) and a harness (suspended from the risers). Where I live there are a lot of paragliders and, when you watch them, they look like large colorful birds, slowly soaring back and forth across the sky. Paragliders are flown and landed with no artificial source of energy; just the wind, gravity and the pilot's muscles. Unlike a hang glider, a paraglider does not have a rigid frame—the shape of the canopy is maintained by air pressure. In addition, paragliders are easier to manage and handle than hang gliders. (A paraglider can be folded into a package the size of a large backpack.) If you are a paraglider, you will appreciate the information and resources at this web site. If you are interested in learning about paragliding, go to the web site and read the FAQ.

**Web:**

**http://www.web-partners.com/paragliding/**

## Radio-Controlled Model Aircraft

For people who like model aircraft, nothing can be more fun than spending a Saturday afternoon out in a large field, putting your favorite radio-controlled (R/C) airplane through its paces. To be good at flying a model plane, you have to understand a lot about flight and flying in general. One of the web pages contains the FAQ (frequently asked question list) for R/C aircraft. Read about buying, building, learning to fly, gliders, powering with gas or electricity, helicopters, aerodynamics, and supplies and materials. The other web page is a well-organized collection of R/C aircraft resources. For discussion, you can talk to the many radio-controlled aircraft buffs on Usenet.

**Web:**

**http://members.gnn.com/jimmartin/hobbie.htm**
**http://www.crl.com/~spm/RC-faq.html**

**Usenet:**

**rec.models.rc.air**

## Rowing

This is not the place to discuss row-row-rowing your boat, gently down the stream. This is muscle-rippling, back-bending, sweat-producing athletic labor that would make a Viking proud.

**Web:**

**http://www.comlab.ox.ac.uk/archive/other/rowing.html**

**Usenet:**

**rec.sport.rowing**

## Scuba Diving

The Net has lots of resources for the recreational and technical scuba diving community. On the web site you can find an archive of the **rec.scuba** Usenet group, mailing list archives, a database of diveable shipwrecks, reviews of dive gear and equipment, details of popular dive destinations, lists of training agencies, clubs, underwater pictures, a catalog of marine fish and invertebrates, classified ads, weather maps, and more. Join IRC or Usenet for some more interactive scuba action.

**Web:**

**http://www.aquanaut.com/**

**Usenet:**

**bit.listserv.scuba-l**
**rec.scuba**
**rec.scuba.equipment**
**rec.scuba.locations**

**Listserv Mailing List:**

List Name: **scuba-l**
Subscribe to: **listserv@brownvm.brown.edu**

**IRC:**

**#scuba**

**The Net loves poetry.**

Scuba Diving
Would you like to learn how to visit the vast underwater parts of our planet? The Net has lots of information to help you get started scuba diving. Personal note: When I learned to scuba dive, I took all the classes, training dives and examinations—and became certified—in four and a half days. (It was an immersion course.)

## Shooting

Shooting and guns are enjoyed by many people, either as a recreational activity or as part of an organized competition. The web sites I have listed here will lead you to a large number of shooting and gun resources on the Net. For an ongoing discussion, you can participate in the **rec.guns** Usenet group. If you are concerned about the politics of gun ownership—a highly contentious area of debate—you can join the discussion in **talk.politics.guns**.

**Web:**

**http://www.geocities.com/Colosseum/2325/shooting.html**
**http://www.prairienet.org/guns/categories/**

**Usenet:**

**rec.guns**
**talk.politics.guns**

## Skateboarding

Fun does not have to be complex. Take a plank, slap some wheels on it and suddenly you have a sport. Today's equipment is a lot better built, but the basic idea is the same. Skateboard enthusiasts can check out lots of good skateboarding stuff at this web site.

**Web:**

**http://web.cps.msu.edu/~dunhamda/dw/dansworld.html**

## Skating

Origins, equipment reviews, technique instructions, maintenance advice, FAQs, location lists, and much more for in-line (rollerblading), roller, figure, and speed skating.

**Web:**

**http://www.smartpages.com/faqs/rec-skate-faq/top.html**

## Skydiving

Do you like to risk your life? If so, there are quite a few things you could do to have a good time, such as participate in a Los Angeles riot, cross rush hour traffic blindfolded, or just jump out of an airplane. At least with skydiving there is a FAQ, so maybe you should start there. In fact, take a look at this web site, which has all sorts of information on diving organizations, base jumping and sit-flying, plus safety tips, movies and pictures. If you hang out on Usenet, you can trade war stories with other people who like to jump out of perfectly good airplanes.

**Web:**

**http://www.afn.org/skydive/**

**Usenet:**

**rec.skydiving**

## Snowboarding

Snowboarding is a difficult, but enjoyable sport that has fans everywhere you find hills and snow. Here is a variety of resources to help you enjoy the snowboarding scene on the Net. For discussion, you have the Usenet group. One of the web sites contains the FAQ (frequently asked question list) for this group. The other web site is a general site where you will find photos, links, products, contest results, lots of information, and a forum in which you can participate.

**Web:**

**http://www.nyx.net/~mwallace/sb_faq.html**
**http://www.snwbrdr.com/**

**Usenet:**

**rec.skiing.snowboard**

**When life hands you a lemon, put it on your web page.**

### *Look What I Found on the Net...*

```
Newsgroup: rec.sport.snowmobiles
Subject: When Can I Ride?

>> From what I understand, the official snowmobile season
>> doesn't begin until December 1.  The snowmobile trails are
>> closed until then, but that doesn't mean you can't ride
>> anywhere else.  You can ride on any field, or non-"official"
>> trail any time you want.  You only need to get the $10 trail
>> permit sticker if you plan on riding on an actual trail.

> Living in Alaska, it never ceases to amaze me how regulated
> riding is in the lower 48 states.  It may be fine, justified,
> necessary and all that -- it just amazes me.  The trade-off is
> that we have no "actual" trails to speak of in Alaska.  Just
> go out and ride.

Here in Michigan, the issue isn't regulation as much as common
sense.  The woods are chock-full of deer hunters with
high-powered rifles from Nov. 15-30, and most of the trails
cross public land.  I'll wait, thank you.

As for the relative advantages of the wide open spaces in Alaska
compared to the lower 48, I'll give you that one.  I kind of
like having a summer though.
```

## Snowmobile Talk and General Discussion

A snowmobile is one thing at which you won't have to yell, "Mush!" Feed it some gas, tell it you love it, then ride like a maniac across the frozen tundra (or whatever happens to be in front of you). Avid snowmobile fans tell how they keep their machines happy, safe and healthy.

**Usenet:**

**alt.snowmobiles**
**rec.sport.snowmobiles**

## Spelunking

If you like crawling around in something that is cool, dark and wet, you are digging in the right place. Here you will find connections to speleological societies and servers around the world. If you just want to talk about caving, check out **alt.caving**.

**Web:**

**http://www.goodearth.com/virtcave.html**
**http://www.gorp.com/gorp/activity/caving.htm**
**http://www.infohub.com/TRAVEL/ADVENTURE/RECREATION/caving.html**

**Usenet:**

**alt.caving**

## Surfing

When I was a graduate student in San Diego, I took a surfing class during my first year. Since then, I have spent a lot of time in the ocean, usually with my bodyboard or body surfing. This web site is a great place for surfers who want local and general information. There are lots of links, not only to surf pages, but to just about everything you can imagine relating to surfers and surfing: activism (such as "Surfers Against Sewage"), safety and lifesaving, technical forecasting information (weather and oceanography-type stuff), magazines, museums, pictures, ascii art, shops and surf-oriented travel. For discussion, you have the Usenet groups.

**Web:**

**http://www.sdsc.edu/surf/surfer_resources.html**

**Usenet:**

**alt.surfing**
**alt.surfing.bodyboard**

## Water Skiing

When I was a young sprout at summer camp, I was able to water ski from time to time. Water skiing was the most popular waterfront activity, and we always had to wait a long time for our turn. We were then able to ski about 2-3 minutes, at which time the ride ended so someone else could have a try. If you are a water skier, here is a web site you will enjoy: lots of links, including general information, competition (slalom, jumps, tricks), barefoot skiing, seated skiing, wake boarding (surfing behind a boat), and kneeboarding. For discussion, you can participate in the Usenet group. You know, for some reason, when I was at camp water skiing was considered the coolest activity at camp, and the water ski instructors were considered among the coolest guys in the entire camp. It was not uncommon to see them swanking around the ski area as if they owned the place, talking with pretty girls and working on their tan. From time to time, they would pause long enough to treat themselves to long rides during which they would show off to everyone else. Personally, I didn't care one whit, although I have no doubt that, today, all those guys are working in gas stations.

**Web:**

**http://waterski.net/**

**Usenet:**

**rec.sport.waterski**

## Windsurfing

Information on windsurfing at various areas in the United States. Get the scoop on windsurf shops, launch sites, and conditions. You can also participate in lively discussion topics and download cool windsurfing images.

**Web:**

**http://wwww.aquatica.com/Aquatica/A/Wind/Windsurfing.html**

**Usenet:**

**rec.windsurfing**

**Stay away from "X-Rated".**

## PEOPLE

### Babes on the Web

Why risk rejection, when you can look at women on the Internet and never have to think of clever and witty things to say? Yes, you can join this exercise in voyeurism by browsing through this collection of links to web pages made by women.

**Web:**
**http://www.toupsie.com/BABE.html**

### Bob's Tavern

When you are on IRC and you are looking for a friendly place to go, try Bob's Tavern, the friendliest channel on IRC. It's a busy place in which visitors and newcomers are greeted warmly. Check out the web page for more information and for pictures of channel regulars.

**Web:**
**http://www.prairienet.org/~craig/bobs.htm**

**IRC:**
**#bob's_tavern**

### Cafe Bob

Brew up a hot cup of coffee and take a break at Cafe Bob on Usenet. Posts are friendly, comfortable and written as if you were coming in to sit in the cafe. Help create the shared reality of a cafe environment with stories and tales and descriptions of who you are and what you are doing in the cafe.

**Usenet:**
**alt.pub.cafe-bob**

### Callahan's Bar

A home away from home: meet the regular patrons of Callahan's Bar, a virtual bar for real people. Friends, fellowship, good will, and bad puns.

**Usenet:**
**alt.callahans**

Life can be tough.
Take a break at
Callahan's
Bar

### Chatting in 3-D

Get a little closer to a 3-D Internet chatting experience with Worlds Chat. This free client software allows you to choose an avatar to represent yourself as you walk through the chat world and talk to people.

**Web:**
**http://www.worlds.net/products/wchat/**

### Court of Last Resort

The Court of Last Resort is a web site to which people submit their grievances against one another in the form of a court case. Then people from all over the Net read the complaints and vote on the verdict. It's a great way to help people decide their differences, and it actually works. And, I guess I don't have to tell you, it's a lot of fun to read about arguments between strangers.

**Web:**
**http://www.sandbox.net/court/**

### Elders

It's nice to have an older person to talk with or look up to. As an elder, it's fun to get together with other people and work on projects or discuss political and social issues and find new friends. If you are an elder and want to network with other people or if you want the opportunity to act as an electronic grandparent or mentor, this is the perfect place for you, carved out by St. John's University.

**Listserv Mailing List:**
List Name: **elders**
Subscribe to: **listserv@sjuvm.stjohns.edu**

### The Internet Court of Last Resort

Your neighbor had promised to feed your cat while you were away on your trip to Sandpoint, Idaho, to take a free tour of a furniture factory. However, when you got back, you find that your neighbor fed more than the cat: he had a big party at your place and cleaned out the fridge.

You send him a house cleaning bill for $75, but he says that you told him to "make yourself at home" and, besides, he didn't charge you anything for feeding the cat.

Who is right? Should he pay, or should you bite the financial bullet and start a good old American neighborly feud?

No problem. Just submit your case to the Internet Court of Last Resort and let people all over the Net discuss your case and render a verdict. And when you feel like being a good citizen (and poking your nose into someone else's business), visit the court and see what dumb things other people are arguing about.

## Entertainment and Party Ideas

Whose bright idea was it to give this party in the first place? You are a nervous wreck. What if nobody comes? What if everybody comes, but nobody has fun? How do you break the ice? The host and hostess are supposed to be cool and graceful under pressure, so before the party check the Net for great ideas on games, get-to-know-you exercises, songs, and other ways to have fun at parties. People will be talking about your party for weeks.

**Web:**

**http://www.nemonet.com/planet/greek/party/prtyidea.htm**
**http://www.pacifier.com/~shaffer/games/games.html**

**Need some party games? Check the Net for ideas.**

## FBI's Ten Most Wanted Fugitives

Perhaps the most famous thing about the FBI (the United States Federal Bureau of Investigation) is their Ten Most Wanted Fugitives program. Since 1949, the FBI has published a list of the ten men or women they would most like to apprehend. Since then, a total of more than 440 people (7 of which were women) have had the honor of making the list. Except for about 30 of these people, everyone on the list has been captured; about one third because a member of the public saw a familiar face on the list. Do you have some questionable friends? Check this web site now. If you manage to turn in an actual fugitive, you could get rewarded with some big bucks.

**Web:**

**http://www.fbi.gov/mostwant/tenlist.htm**

## Find-A-Grave

What do these people all have in common: Desi Arnaz, Albert Einstein, Greta Garbo, Jerry Garcia, Woody Guthrie, Alfred Hitchcock, Rock Hudson, Janis Joplin and John Lennon? The answer is, they were all cremated. This is just one of the fascinating facts I found at the Find-A-Grave web site. Look for your favorite dead person, and I bet you a cookie they are in the database. Isn't it comforting to know that, wherever you are in the world, you can find out where Marilyn Monroe is buried (at Westwood Memorial Park), display the exact street address, and look at a picture of her tombstone? This is an amazing site that you simply *must* visit at least once in your life.

**Web:**

**http://www.orci.com/personal/jim/**

**Don't leave home without this book.**

## Finding Email Addresses

You can run all over the Net, but it's getting harder and harder to hide. Here are several free services that you can use to track down that elusive someone. Although all of them will give you email addresses, various services also offer other information such as phone numbers, web page addresses, and so on. If you do not want your name listed in these directories, send *them* email and let them know. Hint: When all else fails, call the person on the phone and ask for the address.

**Web:**

**http://www.accumail.com/**
**http://www.bigfoot.com/**
**http://www.four11.com/**
**http://www.iaf.net/**
**http://www.intbc.com/sleuth/peop.html**
**http://www.whowhere.com/**

## Friends

Looking for some new friends? Try chatting on IRC. These channels are lively and always populated. It's the perfect place to start up a conversation and meet new people. These channels are not for the discussion of the television show Friends.

**IRC:**

**#Chatfriends**
**#friend**
**#friends**

## Kooks

On the Net, kooks are not only tolerated, they are venerated. Want to explore the mental cutting edge of humanity? Start with the web site, where you can visit Conspiracy Corner, the Hall of Hate, the Library of Questionable Scholarship, the Gallery of the Gods, and other bizarre exhibition halls. Then move to Usenet, where you can discuss the real-live kooks who infest the discussion groups and find out who is the new winner of the Kook of the Month Award.

**Web:**

**http://www.teleport.com/~dkossy/**

**Usenet:**

**alt.folklore.kooks**
**alt.usenet.kooks**

## Names

Names mean a lot. For example, suppose you are a guy in college, and a friend calls up and says, "Come and visit me next weekend, and I can get you a date with one of two girls. You can either have Bertha or Wendy. Who do you want?" Come on, you know who you're going to pick. Since names are so important, I have found some resources that will help you understand names and what they mean to us. First, you can try a free name analysis. Find out what your name says to others, or says about you. Second, if you are having a baby, I have included a web site to help you find the perfect name for your little one. And finally, you can look at web pages created by or about people with the same first name (for example, people named "Bob").

**Web:**

**http://www.chaco.com/useless/useless/names.html**
**http://www.k-net.net/~jamoss/**
**http://www.kabalarians.com/articles/your.htm**

## Obituaries

Don't settle for reading the obituaries in your local paper, go global. Get a list of people, well-known or obscure, who have died, as well as information on various death hoaxes. Lists are arranged alphabetically or by category. Also available: movie stars who were born or died today.

**Web:**

**http://catless.ncl.ac.uk/Obituary/**

**Usenet:**

**alt.obituaries**

**Don't forget to email your mother.**

Wondering who's dead?
Read the **Obituary Page**.

(As a matter of fact, why not look for your own name? No need to wait until the last moment.)

## Party Talk and General Discussion

On the Internet, it's party time all the time. At least in Usenet. Thousands of people around the world crash **alt.party** to see the latest business in the party scene. Talk about upcoming parties, ideas and plans for parties, or wild party experiences. And you don't have to worry about regretting anything in the morning.

**Usenet:**

**alt.party**

**PARTY TILL YOUR MODEM CONNECTION DROPS**

Hey, all you Internet party animals. Your friends on Usenet are ready to talk about partying until the sun comes up.
**alt.party**:
be there or be square.

## Personal Web Pages

Once you get caught up in the Web, it's hard to get away. Everywhere you look there are paths leading all over, and it's nearly impossible to get where you are going without getting sidetracked. One of my favorite ways to get sidetracked is to start with someone's personal home page and see where it leads. These web sites attempt the impossible: to keep track of all the home pages on the Net. Look here if you are searching for someone's page, or if you want to pick a place at random to explore.

**Web:**

**http://homepages.whowhere.com/**
**http://www.excite.com/Reviews/Personal_Home_Pages/**
**http://www.nitehawk.com/SherlockHomes/**

## Random Portrait Gallery

The Random Portrait Gallery contains self-portraits from the home pages of web users around the world. The gallery is divided into rooms, including the Variable Room, which displays different portraits each time you visit it.

**Web:**

**http://moonmilk.volcano.org/portraits/portraits.html**

## Reminder Service

I know how you feel. You *would* have sent a present for your Aunt Riva's birthday, if only it hadn't slipped your mind. Next year, don't get caught again. Fill out a form with the email notification service and you will be sent email automatically, just in time to help you remember birthdays, anniversaries and other special days. (Hint: My birthday is December 21st, and money is always in good taste.)

**Web:**

**http://www.candor.com/birthday/**

**Stay connected.**

## Shared Realities

Some days you just wake up and think to yourself, "Hey, I think I will be someone else today." It's easy when you participate in some of the shared realities of Usenet. In these groups, people assume a persona and write about their thoughts, feelings and actions as that character. Meet people, form bonds, make friends, entertain and be entertained. Even if you don't want to participate, these groups are fun to read because it's like seeing a story unfold before your eyes.

**Usenet:**

**alt.dragons-inn**
**alt.kalbo**
**alt.pub.cafe-bob**
**alt.pub.cloven-shield**
**alt.pub.coffeehouse.amethyst**
**alt.pub.dragons-inn**
**alt.pub.havens-rest**
**alt.pub.kacees**
**alt.shared-reality.sf-and-fantasy**
**alt.shared-reality.startrek.klingon**
**alt.shared-reality.x-files**
**alt.world.taeis**

## Tea and Conversation

Join the silly, comfy, cozy good times at this tea party on the Web. Chatters sit having tea and conversation, making up stories, talking about their lives and generally having a fun time. The atmosphere is relaxed, friendly and comfortable.

**Web:**

**http://www.xroads.com/~pct/tea.html**

## Telephone Directories

Looking for someone's phone number and address? Try these free services. If it's in a phone book somewhere, it's probably on the Net.

**Web:**

**http://www.contractjobs.com/tel/**
**http://www.four11.com/**
**http://www.infospace.com/**
**http://www.switchboard.com/**

## Virtual Campfire of Nerds

Never again will you have to hang your head in shame. Being a nerd is something to be proud of, especially when you have your own mailing list. What started as a local group has gained international popularity. This is a place for people to gather for chit-chat and share stories. It is described as a "virtual campfire". Check out the web page for background information and to see the web pages of some of the NerdNosh regulars.

**Web:**

**http://www.corcom.com/reloj/Nerdnosh.html**

**Listserv Mailing List:**

List Name: **nerdnosh**
Subscribe to: **listserv@clovis.nerdnosh.org**

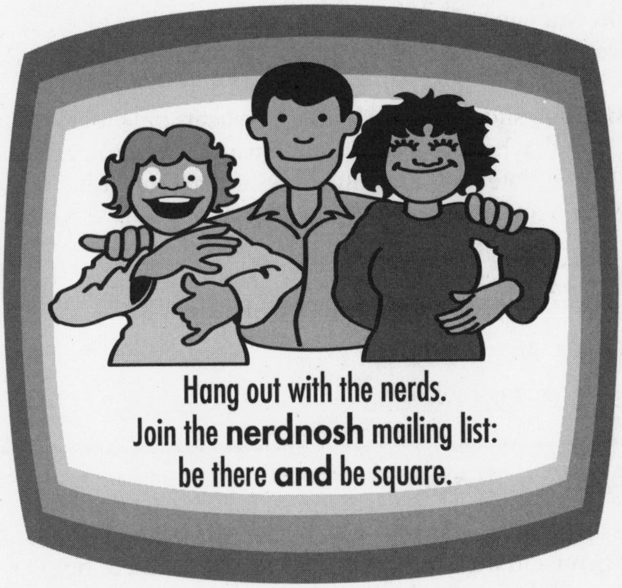
Hang out with the nerds.
Join the nerdnosh mailing list:
be there and be square.

## Wendy Pages

There are many, many people who create their own personal web pages. Here is a web site that collects links to pages created by people named Wendy. Check out the Wendy Pages, where you will find links to a lot of wonderful Wendy-made web sites. (Maybe you will be inspired to create your own web page.)

**Web:**

**http://www.wendy.com/wendyweb.html**

## World Birthday Web

Come here to find out if anybody you know on the Net is having a birthday. Send them greetings and well wishes. Or you can add your own birthday, so you can get birthday email from friends and total strangers.

**Web:**

**http://www.boutell.com/birthday.cgi/**

# PEOPLE: FAMOUS AND INTERESTING

## Adams, Scott

Do you enjoy the Dilbert comic strip? Do you like Dogbert, the cute little dog that looks like a balloon with glasses? If so, tell the artist himself: Scott Adams. The web site takes you right to the heart of Dilbert Central, where you can look at an archive of comic strips. (Note, this site only works if you look at it when you should be working.)

**Web:**

**http://www.unitedmedia.com/comics/dilbert**

**Mail:**

**scottadams@aol.com**

## Asimov, Isaac

Isaac Asimov was the consummate explainer. He was a genius in the sense that whatever he touched, he illuminated. In his lifetime, he wrote hundreds of books on a large variety of subjects, opening the doors of understanding to countless people around the world. And, oh yes, I think he wrote a science fiction story or two. (I will have to check.)

**Web:**

**http://www.clark.net/pub/edseiler/WWW/asimov_FAQ.html**
**http://www.clark.net/pub/edseiler/WWW/asimov_home_page.html**

**Usenet:**

**alt.books.isaac-asimov**

### Advice from Isaac Asimov

When I was a graduate student, I wrote a letter to Isaac Asimov. I told him I wanted to learn biochemistry, but I didn't want to have to take a whole lot of beginning organic chemistry and biology courses. He wrote back and gave me the following advice:
"If you have a good library at your disposal, you can teach yourself anything. I did."
I took his advice and taught myself biochemistry out of a textbook. (Ironically, I later went to medical school and ended up learning enough biochemistry to supply the entire Peruvian army. Still, the advice is well-taken and, to this day, I have kept Asimov's note, framed and hanging on the wall beside my desk.)

## Bell, Art

Art Bell is a nationally syndicated radio talkshow host who has two shows called "Dreamland" and "Coast to Coast AM with Art Bell". The web site has a huge amount of information on Art Bell, including many pictures of UFOs, aliens and paranormal subject matter, which is the majority of the content of the "Dreamland" show. You can also see pictures of Art and his family and learn more about his shows and when they are on the air. Find links to the home pages of guests he has had on the show. The IRC channel is busy during the times Art is on the air, so you can listen to the show and talk on IRC to other people who are listening at the same time.

**Web:**

**http://www.artbell.com/**

**Usenet:**

**alt.fan.art-bell**

**IRC:**

**#ArtBell**

**Mail:**

**artbell@aol.com**

## Brite, Poppy Z.

Have you been entertaining fantasies lately about being bitten on the neck? Biters, bitees and anyone else who has an interest in scary things that go bump in the night will love Poppy Z. Brite, the vampire authoress who wrote Lost Souls. Learn more about Poppy, her writing and her appearance than you could ever accurately imagine. The email address is attended to by Poppy's publicity assistant.

**Web:**

**http://www.hooked.net/users/mocat/pzb.htm**
**http://www.paranoia.com/~kevintx/pzb/**

**Mail:**

**rsage@well.com**

## Celebrity Addresses

Would you like to write to your favorite celebrity? Here are some web sites that contain lots and lots of celebrity address, for both regular mail and email. You can also find some good tips on getting autographs, as well as other interesting information. Hint: If you send email to a celebrity, do not expect anything but an automated reply. If you get a personal reply, consider yourself doubly blessed (once because you got the reply, and once because you are one of my readers).

**Web:**

**http://oscar.teclink.net/~chip1120/**
**http://www.islandnet.com/~luree/fanmail.html**

## Celebrity Burial Sites

I know this sounds macabre, but it really is a fascinating place to visit: a huge collection of information about where dead celebrities are buried. Not only will you find out where the bodies are, you can also obtain exact addresses of the cemeteries in case you want to make a personal visit to pay your respects. For some of the people, there are also photos showing the actual tombstones.

**Web:**

**http://www.cjnetworks.com/~roryb/oldobit/oldobits.html**

## Celebrity Meetings

Have you ever accidentally bumped into a celebrity? Or at least seen a celebrity? I have. Two times I was eating at Cantor's Deli in Los Angeles and I saw Nicholas Cage. And once I was on a commuter flight with Kenny Loggins, and we talked together the entire time. This web site is a huge repository of stories about ordinary people meeting famous people. If you like reading about celebrities, you will enjoy this site. And if you are lucky enough to run into a famous person yourself, you can send in your story for the archives.

**Web:**

**http://www.polaris.net/~merlin/fame.html**

## Celebrity Romantic Links

This is an interesting Net-based game interlaced with some good, homestyle gossip. The game—called "Romantically Linked"—uses a vast storehouse of information showing which celebrities have links to other celebrities. The idea is start with a particular person (say, Woody Allen), and find the shortest set of connections to another person (say, Nancy Reagan). To start, you display the information about Woody Allen. This shows you a list of celebrities to which Woody Allen has some type of link. Choose one of these people, say Mia Farrow. You will then see a list of people who are linked in some way to Mia Farrow. Choose from this list, and so on. The goal is to end up with Nancy Reagan. As an example, one of the contests was to find your way from Elvis Presley to Nicolas Cage. Someone did it in only four links: Elvis Presley to Tuesday Weld to Richard Gere to Uma Thurman to Nicolas Cage. Besides playing the game, you can access a list of hundreds of celebrities, for which you can display a brief biography, a picture, and the pictures of all the people with whom the celebrity has been romantically involved. (Interesting observation: When you see a particular celebrity's paramours side by side, you will often notice that they resemble one another. How true it is that most of us are attracted to a certain type of person.)

**Web:**

**http://www.mrshowbiz.com/features/games/linked/**

A B C D E F G H I J K L M N O P Q R S T U V W X Y Z

## Celebrity Talk and General Discussion

You've devoured every newspaper, magazine and tabloid in sight and you still want more news and information about celebrities. Here is a source that is available 24 hours a day, so you can always get a fix. Read stories, news and rumors of old and new famous people.

**Usenet:**

**alt.celebrities**

## Colmes, Alan

Here is the most computer-knowledgeable radio talk show host in America. Drop a note to Alan and let him know how much you like his show, his liberal point of view, and his wry sense of humor. Colmes is the inventor of "Radio Graffiti," where anyone can call in and say one sentence about anything they want.

**Web:**

**http://www.alan.com/**

**Mail:**

**alan@alan.com**

Want to talk to America's most Net-literate radio talk-show host?
Drop a line to Alan Colmes.
Better yet, listen to his daily program.

## Dangerfield, Rodney

This is the official page of Rodney Dangerfield, the American comedian who complains, "I get no respect". There is a lot of great stuff here: sound files of Rodney talking (some of which are suitable to put on your answering machine), information about Rodney's movies, a joke of the day, lots of pictures, and more. ("I don't get no respect. I told my psychiatrist I got suicidal tendencies. He said from now on I have to pay in advance.")

**Web:**

**http://www.rodney.com/**

## Einstein, Albert

If you ask the man on the street who the greatest scientist of all time was, you would probably get the answer Albert Einstein. Einstein (1879-1955) was born in Germany, although he went to university in Switzerland and, later, became an American. (Like many other great men, Einstein had the distinction of ending his life in New Jersey.) It would be difficult to exaggerate Einstein's contribution to twentieth century physics (but let me try anyway). His work on relativity completely changed the way mankind thought about space and time, while his work on quantum physics helped create our modern understanding of how energy and matter are constituted and laid the basis for the exploitation of atomic energy. Einstein won the 1921 Nobel Prize in Physics (for his explanation of the photoelectric effect, not for relativity theory). Like many other great scientists, Einstein did not seem to have as great an acumen about people and society as he did about science. His scientific insight—at least when he was young—was astonishing. His social insights were well-intentioned but somewhat naive. I guess the best way to put it is that, when it came to understanding the universe Einstein had no peer, but when it came to understanding people he was no Einstein.

**Web:**

**http://www.sas.upenn.edu/~smfriedm/einstein.html**

**Do a backup.**

## Famous People's Wills

Are you surprised? Not me, I knew it had to be somewhere on the Net: a large collection of the last wills and testaments of famous people. See what the likes of Jacqueline Kennedy Onassis, John Lennon, Walt Disney, Babe Ruth and Benjamin Franklin left to posterity. (They also have Elvis' will. I checked but, unfortunately, he didn't leave me anything.)

**Web:**

**http://www.ca-probate.com/wills.htm**

## Fuller, Buckminster

What do you do in your spare time? Most people read, play sports, or watch TV. Not many could say, "Well, I had a lot of time on my hands last weekend, so I invented the geodesic dome." Get to know Buckminster Fuller, his works and philosophy.

**Web:**

**http://www.lsi.usp.br/usp/rod/bucky/buckminster_fuller.html**

**Listserv Mailing List:**

List Name: **geodesic**
Subscribe to: **listserv@ubvm.cc.buffalo.edu**

## Gates, Bill

Isn't it great that we all get to live on this Earth at the same time as Bill Gates? Send Mr. Microsoft a note and tell him how much you appreciate his efforts to save mankind.

**Mail:**

**billg@microsoft.com**

## Gingrich, Newt

Few people in American politics can match Newt Gingrich. He spent years clawing his way to the top so effectively that most people forget he got there by clawing. Notwithstanding his personal and political habits, Mr. Newt, the Speaker of the U.S. House of Representatives, is a tropical storm in the American weather pattern and, as such, deserves to be noticed. So notice him. (His mother will thank you.)

**Web:**

**http://www.nerdworld.com/users/dstein/nw618.html**

### Buckminster Fuller

Richard Buckminster Fuller was a genius in that he could shed light on just about any area to which he turned his attention. During his lifetime, he received 39 honorary degrees and became the inspiration for a cult-like following based not so much on a belief system, but on a way of looking at the world and solving its problems. He described himself as an "engineer, inventor, mathematician, architect, cartographer, philosopher, poet, cosmologist, comprehensive designer and choreographer".

What I like best about Fuller is how he lived his life as an experiment, and his recognition that if one contributes to one's culture, the economy will lend support in an appropriate manner. Although this may seem far-fetched, it is this Fuller-inspired philosophy that has helped me to choose my lot in life and is indirectly responsible for the book you are now reading.

If you would like to learn more about Fuller, his teachings and his followers, subscribe to the **geodesic** mailing list. It is wonderful to contemplate the work of someone who has the capacity to rise above the petty concerns of day-to-day life and to see the universe with the eyes of enlightened curiosity.

## Hall of Annoying Buttons

Would you like to bother a famous person? This web site has a collection of buttons. Each button is associated with a famous person (for example, the President of the United States, David Letterman, Mick Jagger, Bill Gates, Roger Ebert and Wayne Newton). When you press a button, it automatically emails a short meaningless message—"Hello, how are you?"—to the person. Of course, these people don't really read most of their messages, but it's the thought that counts.

**Web:**

**http://www.portalinc.com/fractal/hall.htm**

A B C D E F G H I J K L M N O P Q R S T U V W X Y Z

## Horror Authors

Here is a collection of email addresses of horror authors, such as Clive Barker, Robert Devereaux, Nancy Etchemendy, and more. Unlike other celebrity lists, these addresses have all been confirmed, and the people have given their permission to be listed.

**Web:**

**http://www.cat.pdx.edu/~caseyh/horror/author/email.html**

## Internet Millionaires

Want to see the names of some of the people making big bucks from the Internet? This is a list of publicly traded Internet companies and the owners of large blocks of stock. To estimate a particular person's total wealth derived from stock ownership, all you need to do is multiply the number of shares by the current price. For example, at the time I checked, the Chairman of Netscape held 19,440,000 shares of stock in that company which, in theory, was worth $874,800,000. Of course, such amounts depend on the share price, which fluctuates constantly. So, as a public service, the numbers on this site are automatically updated every 15 minutes to reflect current prices.

**Web:**

**http://www.pulver.com/million/**

## Kennedy, Edward

Undoubtedly there is a thing or two you would like to say to Edward Kennedy—especially if you live in his political stomping ground. Now that the government has a passion for the Internet, you can find many politicians are becoming available electronically. Tell Ted what's on your mind.

**Web:**

**http://www.senate.gov/member/ma/kennedy/general/**

**Mail:**

**senator@kennedy.senate.gov**

## Limbaugh, Rush

Rush Limbaugh—the conservative radio and TV commentator with a huge audience of ditto-heads—is more an act of God than anything else. Send mail to the man who routinely performs with "half his brain tied behind his back." (If he were using his whole brain, he would be on the Internet, wouldn't he, not Compuserve.)

**Mail:**

**70277.2502@compuserve.com**

**Stop whatever you are doing –right now–and send Rush Limbaugh a message. Tell him to make sure that all his listeners buy a copy of *The Internet Complete Reference.***

## McCaffrey, Anne

American writer Anne McCaffrey (1926-) is the author of the Pern book series, the Crystal Singer series, and many other sci-fi/fantasy works. This is her official web site, where you will find biographical information, a FAQ (frequently asked question list), information about new books, and some sample chapters. Although the email address is reputed to be McCaffrey's, you will probably not get a response. She is, however, Net savvy and well aware of all the goings-on around the Net using her work as a basis (such as the Pern mud and fan fiction on Usenet). McCaffrey is happy with people participating in her make-believe worlds, and she has set up guidelines about what they should and shouldn't do.

**Web:**

**http://members.aol.com/dragonhld/**

**Mail:**

**72007.45@compuserve.com**

## Penn and Teller

Even if you can't do it, magic is fun to watch, and Penn and Teller are masters of the trade. Read interviews, see pictures, and get information on upcoming gigs of this mismatched but perfect-for-each-other duo.

**Web:**

**http://www.sincity.com/**

## Pope John Paul II

If you need a fast dose of some religious experience, check out the web page of the Pope. Read some of his writings and find out where the Pope is traveling in case you want to call ahead and make arrangements to have dinner with him.

**Web:**

**http://esoptron.umd.edu/pope/pope.html**

> There is no doubt about it: the **Pope** is one of the greatest human beings in the world. If you would like information about the Pope's books or biographical data, check out this unofficial home page.
> By the way, the Pope and I have a deal. I promised to mention him in my books, and he promised to mention me in his books. (I'm still waiting.)

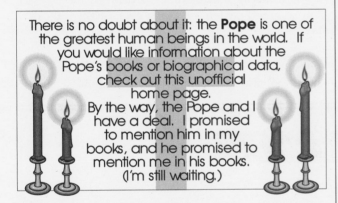

## Poundstone, William

William Poundstone is one of my favorite writers. Poundstone, an American, is the author of a number of books; among them the "Big Secrets" series, in which he reveals all kinds of stuff people do not want you to know. My advice is to visit the web site, admire Poundstone's picture, send him an email note, and then rush out and buy one of the Big Secrets books. Not only are the books filled with fascinating (secret) information, but Poundstone is an excellent writer whose witty and captivating style will inform, entertain and amuse you.

**Web:**

**http://members.aol.com/bigsecrets/**

**Mail:**

**bigsecrets@aol.com**

## Pratchett, Terry

Humorous fantasy-based science fiction novelist Terry Pratchett has been compared to Douglas Adams and P.G. Wodehouse. Author of Discworld, Pratchett resides in England.

**Mail:**

**terryp@unseen.demon.co.uk**

## President of the United States

Does anyone really believe that the President of the United States even sees any of his email? Just between us, the real truth is that nobody even reads it. Still, if you send in a letter you will get an automated response (which is more than you can say about writing to Bill Gates or the Pope). Actually, I don't really expect the President of the U.S. to drop everything just to respond to his email. After all, he has his hands full being Leader of the Free World, Commander-in-Chief of the U.S. Armed Forces, as well as Grand Poobah of the Illuminati. Still, if you drop him a note and tell him what is wrong with America, you will at least earn a few karma points. Couldn't hurt.

**Mail:**

**president@whitehouse.gov**

## Randi, James

James Randi (1928-)—The Amazing Randy—is a Canadian-born American magician and skeptic who debunks fraudulent paranormal events and claims. Randi offers a half million dollars to any person who can prove, under his scientific conditions, that he or she has psychic powers. This web site explains about Randi and what he does, including the James Randi Educational Foundation. To me, Randi is truly one of the heroes of our time, debunking foolishness and superstition, and shedding light into the dark recesses of ignorance and dishonesty.

**Web:**

**http://www.randi.org/**

**Mail:**

**76702.3507@compuserve.com**

## Santa Claus

It's nice to know that as busy as Santa is, he always has time to stay up with the latest technology. Send your wish list to Santa by email or you can see what he, the elves and reindeer are doing on the Web. Maybe if you are especially good this year, Santa will bring you a high-speed Internet connection for the holidays.

**Web:**

**http://north.pole.org/talk_to_santa.html**
**http://web.telepost.no/Santa/santamail.html**
**http://www.santaclaus.com/**

**Mail:**

**santa@north.pole.org**

**On the Net, there is always someone to talk to.**

## Thompson, Hunter S.

Hunter S. Thompson (1939-) is an American writer and ex-journalist, best known for his books (such as Fear and Loathing in Las Vegas) and his articles (many of which were published in Rolling Stone magazine). Thompson is the originator of gonzo journalism, an imaginative and opinionated style of writing in which the author becomes involved in the very story he is trying to cover. Despite his questionable lack of social skills, his drug and alcohol addiction, and his degeneration from a highly skilled writer to a literary non-entity, Thompson is worshipped by fans (of which I am one) for his legendary exploits, as well as a legacy of some of the finest writing produced in twentieth century America. This site has information about Thompson's life, his books and what he's doing now (mostly looking for beer and fretting over legal problems because he drinks and drives). Unfortunately, when the going gets tough, you can't stay cool forever.

**Web:**

**http://members.aol.com/hstsite/menu.html**

### *Look What I Found on the Net...*

```
Newsgroups: alt.internet.services
Subject: The Whitehouse Address

> Just clearing up a few points, the Whitehouse Internet
> address is:
>
>      whitehouse.gov
>
> The President's email address is:
>
>      president@whitehouse.gov
>
> and it works.  (You get a canned reply message, saying that
> they read all of the mail, etc.)
>
> My girlfriend was wondering:
> Is there an email address for Hillary Rodham Clinton?

I've heard that Hillary is:

     root@whitehouse.gov
```

## Vice President of the United States

No, there is no truth that the Vice President of the United States is really a Turing Machine. (Actually, he couldn't even pass the test.) Write him and tell him how nice he looks on TV.

**Mail:**

**vice-president@whitehouse.gov**

### Vice President of the United States

The Vice President of the United States is lonely. He can't run the country, but he has to hang around just in case something happens.

I bet he would really enjoy it if you dropped him a nice note, complementing him on his tie, and mentioning how much you appreciate the fine job he is doing.

## Yolen, Jane

Jane Yolen is a skilled science fiction and fantasy storyteller. She has written more than 150 books for all ages, as well as hundreds of stories and poems. Yolen is an active Net user, who regularly posts to the **rec.arts.books.childrens** Usenet group. (Please do me a favor. Do not send her mail saying you have always wanted to write children's books, and could she take a look at what you have written? Authors have to be careful how they look at unsolicited work, so as to avoid the appearance of having copied someone else's idea.)

**Web:**

**http://www.ipl.org/youth/AskAuthor/Yolen.html**

**Mail:**

**janeyolen@aol.com**

# PERSONALS AND DATING

## 41 Plus

When you don't want to hang out with all the youngsters on IRC, try the **#41plus** channel where people over the age of 41 hang out and chat.

**IRC:**

**#41plus**

## American Singles

Browse a huge list of men and women who have written a short paragraph about themselves, hoping that in a few lines you will be hooked. If anyone catches your interest, you can call, write or email them.

**Web:**

**http://www.apk.net/as/**

## Amoree

Make a personal web page to find your true love. Fill out a simple form that is provided and you can even send a picture of yourself that anyone on the Internet can see (even your mom). For those who are shy, you can just browse the pages that are already there.

**Web:**

**http://www.kaiwan.com/~bayers/mates.html**

## Articles for Singles

If you are on the prowl for some unsuspecting future love, get some tips on the best way to be cool, effective and safe. Articles include topics such as dating etiquette, the wilds of the American singles scene and even serious articles on intimacy.

**Web:**

**http://www.cupidnet.com/cupid/articles/**

## Bisexuals

Response will come easily for people posting to this personals group since they are not limited by gender classification. Bisexuals from around the world post ads for friendship, love, and encounters of an intimate nature.

**Usenet:**

**alt.personals.bi**

**Feel lucky?**

**Try alt.personals.bi, the bisexual discussion group. Right away it will double your chances of getting a date for Friday night.**

## Blind Date on the Net

Do you feel lucky? Here is a personals site where you can post information about who you are and what you want. There is a section for men, women and one for "alternative lifestyles". (My cat wanted to try that one.) There is a live chat area, as well as interesting information (such as "Fifty Ways to Get Rid of a Blind Date").

**Web:**

**http://carrcom.com/date/**

## Blind Dates

It's one of those really bad experiences: your friends made the blind date sound fabulous, yet you are stuck in the reality of actually interacting with a person whom you would rather be helping board a plane to the Bermuda Triangle. Don't get stuck in this kind of situation. Read this list of "Ways to Get Rid of Blind Dates". It may save your life.

**Web:**

**http://garnet.acns.fsu.edu/~bws5555/date.html**

## Chit-Chat

The nice thing about IRC is that you can join a channel to talk about something specific, or you can just sit around and talk, talk, talk. If you are in the mood to chat about nothing in particular, try one of these channels and ramble to your heart's content.

**IRC:**

**#hottub**
**#talk2me**

## Classified Personal Ads

A well-designed personal ad page sorted by sexual preference and phone area code. Browse until you find someone you like, then reply to the person right away through the provided electronic form.

**Web:**

**http://ep.com/h/ps.html**

## Cupid's Network

Cupid has traded his bow and arrow for a fast Internet connection. Check out the Network, which has several links to other personals sites, romantic links and helpful articles for single people. There are also links to regional areas for people who are in larger metropolitan areas.

**Web:**

**http://www.cupidnet.com/cupid/**

## Dating and Personals Collections

There is no need to flounder around the Net looking for places to find new friends and lovers. Here's a place that has a collection of dating and personals links. Never again will you have to spend a lonely Friday night at the computer.

**Web:**

**http://www.epix.net/~tlizotte/date1.html**

**Here is a plan for lifetime happiness.**

(1) Use the Dating and Personals Collections to find a date.

(2) Send your date a copy of *The Internet Complete Reference.*

(3) Live happily ever after.

Repeat as necessary.

## Dating Tests

Take these tests to see if you are worth dating. These lists of questions might be painful, so have the number of a good therapist close at hand. Give the dating form to someone you have met who you are considering dating. See how they score before you make any commitments.

**Web:**

**ftp://ftp.cco.caltech.edu/pub/humor/tests/dating.test**
**ftp://ftp.cco.caltech.edu/pub/humor/tests/dating2.form**

## EEN Personals

People of all lifestyles can post, browse or respond to ads in the Electronic Entertainment Network. Get creative when you post an ad. You can use HTML, sound and graphics with your personal ad. You have to be a member to browse through the personals, but membership is free.

**Web:**

**http://www.lyb.com/welcome/**

## Fat People

Don't bother with skinny, insubstantial waifs when you can go for the gusto. Place your ad expressing your desire to interact with fat people.

**Usenet:**

**alt.personals.fat**

## Friendly Folk

You can never have too many friends (unless they all want to stay over at your house on the same particular weekend). Make and keep friends all over the world by visiting **#friendly** on IRC. It's fun and fast-paced and best of all, it's cheaper than paying for a long-distance phone call.

**IRC:**

**#friendly**

## Intercultural Personals

Looking for something different, something special? Meet people of different racial and ethnic backgrounds and mixes. People from all over the world can be found in this Usenet group.

**Usenet:**

**alt.personals.intercultural**

## International Personals

Despite all appearances otherwise, this group is not for interplanetary dating. This Usenet group relates to dating immigrants to new countries or for people who are seeking to date people from foreign countries.

**Usenet:**

**alt.personals.aliens**

## Internet Personals

It's a total drag when you can't post to the personals because your mom hangs out on the Net and you are afraid she'll see your name. Worry no longer. This personals page uses an anonymous mail forwarding system to ensure your privacy.

**Web:**

**http://www.montagar.com/personals/**

**"Fun" is fun.**

## Internet Romances

Have you met on the Net? Are you planning a hot romance with a net.friend? Optimists, pessimists and fans of the electronic sociological experience should have a look at this collection of papers and articles about romance on the Internet. These writings offer some practical advice and a little dose of reality.

**Web:**

**http://web2.airmail.net/walraven/romance.htm**

## Jewish Personals

If you are looking for more than a good matzo ball recipe, take a look at this personal group specifically related to Jewish people. You can post ads whether you are Jewish or just looking for someone Jewish to date.

**Usenet:**

**alt.personals.jewish**

### *Look What I Found on the Net...*

```
Newsgroup: alt.personals.aliens

    [various postings I found in this Usenet group]

Subject: Indiana Sex?

I am a 36-year-old married male who is going through a mid-life
crisis or something like that.  I am a straight male looking for
single/married females interested in just sex, no relationships.
I would also be interested in meeting couples, and am open to
their suggestions.  I have never been in a multiple-sex
situation or with another man, but may explore bi-sex with a
couple.  I am into all kinds of sex: domination, voyeurism,
cross-dressing, bondage, light spanking, etc., and, of course,
just straight sex.  I am a non-drinker or drug user.  I will
trade personal picture of me upon request.
-- Central Indiana area

==============

Subject: Indiana Female Wanted for Wild Sex

Are you lonely?  If you are, I'm your man, 'cause I am too.
Live in Indiana, will try anything.

==============

Subject: Female Sex Toy for Orgies in Indiana

Ladies, explore your hidden fantasies by going to a wild,
private sex party, where all your fantasies can be fulfilled.
Email now and send a description of yourself and your desires.

==============

Subject: Nice Indiana Girls

Are there any nice teenage girls near Indiana who are interested
in a normal 17-year-old guy?
```

## Large People

Big and tall people or those who are seeking big and tall people will love this Usenet group. Post your requests and see what happens. You will probably find just the response you are looking for. Or at least some response.

**Usenet:**

**alt.personals.big-folks**

## Long Distance Relationships

Is it "absence makes the heart grow fonder" or "out of sight, out of mind"? If you are in a long distance relationship and you really want to make it work, check out the web site or this mailing list for the Rainbow Connection. The mailing list is for people who are involved in long distance relationships and want to share tips on making the relationship work, give each other support and discuss issues common to these types of relationships. The web site has information about the mailing list including the FAQ and links to listmembers' web pages.

**Web:**

**http://www.wam.umd.edu/~sek/rainbow.html**

**Majordomo Mailing List:**

List Name: **rainbow**
Subscribe to: **majordomo@exxilon.xx.rmit.edu.au**

## Match Maker

Don't despair over not having found the person of your dreams. Fill out a quick survey and let the computer suggest a match for you. This beats endless hours browsing the classifieds trying to narrow down your choices.

**Web:**

**http://nis-www.lanl.gov/~yoseif/match/intro.cgi**

**FAQs are cool.**

## Meeting People

Welcome to the smorgasbord of personal ads. There is something for everyone, and you can take as much as you like. Non-fattening, hypo-allergenic, 100 percent of your recommended daily allowance of fun and good times. Participate in one of these Usenet groups and maybe you'll meet the man, woman, or none-of-the-above of your dreams.

**Usenet:**

**alt.personals**
**alt.personals.ads**
**alt.personals.misc**

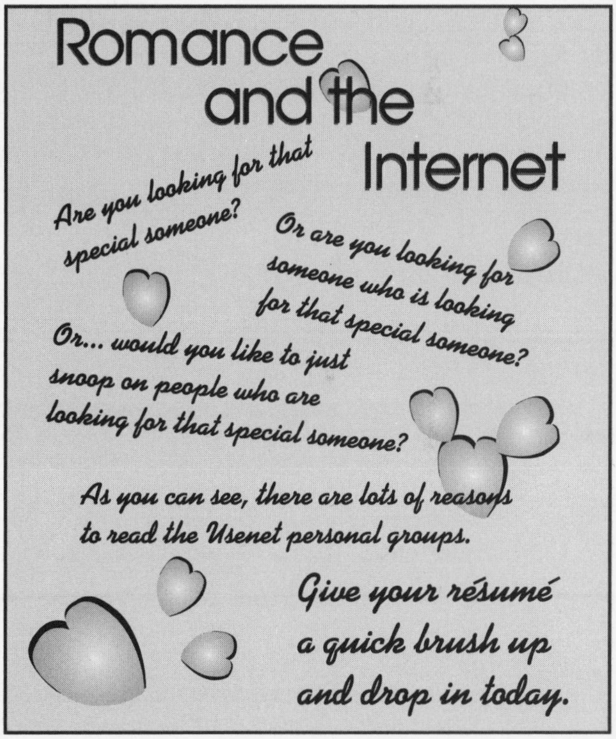
Romance and the Internet
Are you looking for that special someone?
Or are you looking for someone who is looking for that special someone?
Or... would you like to just snoop on people who are looking for that special someone?
As you can see, there are lots of reasons to read the Usenet personal groups.
Give your résumé a quick brush up and drop in today.

## Pen Pal Brides

A long article about pen pal brides, commonly referred to as mail order brides. Get tips on meeting women, getting them into the country, how to choose a good wife, and advice on avoiding international dating companies that charge hefty fees for their services.

**Web:**

**http://info-sys.home.vix.com/pub/men/romance/pen/intro.htm**

A B C D E F G H I J K L M N O P Q R S T U V W X Y Z

## Personal Ads Menu

It has been said that the best things in life are free. That's not always the case. If you don't find what you are looking for in the free personal ads that are on the Net, you can always submit to the indignity of paying by the minute to look for love in all the wrong places. Some of the links on this page are free, but most are not.

**Web:**

**http://www.aral.com/singles.htm**

## Personal Ads Talk and General Discussion

This is the Usenet group for talking about personal ads that you may have seen on Usenet or in a newspaper or magazine. Discuss style, what works and what doesn't, and your experiences. And, oh yes, while you're looking around, maybe you'll find something to pique your interest.

**Usenet:**

**alt.personals.d**

## Personals for Gays

Here's a place to hang out if you want to be with people who consider same-sex relationships the norm. Find heaps of personal ads written by people who are on a quest for other members of the gay community.

**Usenet:**

**alt.personals.motss**

## Psychedelic Personals

If you are on a quest for the most colorful personal ads on the Internet, try the personals for those people in the psychedelic community. You don't have to do drugs to participate in the Usenet group, but it might help.

**Usenet:**

**alt.personals.psychedelic**

### *Look What I Found on the Net...*

```
Newsgroup: alt.personals.d
Subject: Hasty Generalizations

> Before holding forth to the masses, we should all take time to
> be wary of making hasty generalizations about gender.
>
> Women and men are different, and there are differences within
> genders.  Not all men are of that opinion, by the way.
>
> I have personally found that it is better to talk to women
> about certain things and to men about others, each
> contributing in their own way.

Very nicely stated.

Women and men are different.  They talk and shop and walk and
see differently.  They love and want differently.

I have learned that my male friends aren't interested
in hearing the "he said, she said" tales my girlfriends and I
tell.
```

## Recontres

French for *encounters*, Recontres offers a place for you to place any type of ad that suits you. If you are seeking a way to post anonymous ads, this is not the place, unless you can get mail through an anonymous remailer. Responses go directly to the email address you supply.

**Web:**

**http://www.cyberiacafe.net/findlove/**

## Romance Rendezvous

Sometimes the hunt for a significant other is more fun than when you finally catch your prey. When you post an ad at this site, you get the chance to select a little cute animal icon that best represents your personality. You can also search listings according to your preferences, then send email to anyone who looks interesting to you.

**Web:**

**http://www.start.com/start/romance.html**

## Singles Web

It's nice to have all the help you can get when you are on the dating scene. Singles Web offers tips for dating: things to do with your date, dating skills for men and women, a list of gifts you can give to your date, massage skills and novel trivia such as the meaning of various flowers and how to say "I love you" in many different languages.

**Web:**

**http://www.jjplaza.com/singles/**

## Spanking

Everyone needs a good spanking now and then. If you like getting your bottom blistered or warming up someone else's backside, try placing an ad here to find a spanking partner.

**Usenet:**

**alt.personals.spanking**
**alt.personals.spanking.punishment**

Are you bored? Go get
spanked. NOW.

## Tall People Personals

Here is the place where tall people are sought after and desired. If you are tall, post an ad and strut your stuff. If you are short or average, feel free to post an ad as long as you are looking for a tall person.

**Usenet:**

**alt.personals.tall**

## Virtual MeetMarket

Need a hot date, a friend, or just someone to talk to? Place a personal ad on the Web. You can retain anonymity with your personal ad, as your identity is kept hidden and responses are forwarded to you from a server.

**Web:**

**http://vmm.ravenna.com/**

## Web Personals

Here's a great multi-purpose personals service. It's not your typical sex maniac stomping ground where anyone breathing will get pounced on. This semi-moderated personals service allows you to use a secret ID to respond to ads anonymously until you feel safe giving out your real email address. Not only will you find personal ads for dating or romance, but you can also find listings for pen pals, roommates and activity partners.

**Web:**

**http://w3.com/date/**

## WorldPort Personals

These listings give you direct email access to personal ads that light your fire. These ads are free, but before you can place your own personal ad, you are required to fill out a form of personal information so you can receive a membership ID.

**Web:**
**http://www.webmatch.com/**

## Writing Tips

Don't be boring or normal. It's the death-kiss in the personals business. Instead, before you bare your soul on the Net, read these tips on how to write eye-catching personal ads when you are trying to meet someone online.

**Web:**
**http://techweb.cmp.com/techweb/hpc/feb95/08onlin2.html**

# PHILOSOPHY

## American Philosophical Association

A web site offering information about philosophical societies, grants, fellowships, seminars, and institutes. Also a mail directory of the APA membership and bibliographical and journal information.

**Web:**
**http://www.oxy.edu/apa/apa.html**

## Ancient Philosophy

Do you ever get tired of the same old chit-chat at parties? Brush up on your ancient philosophy and you'll be able to discuss Hesiod over the clam dip and ponder Iamblichus while munching on meatballs.

**Listproc Mailing List:**
List Name: **sophia**
Subscribe to: **listproc@liverpool.ac.uk**

## Buddhist Studies

There is more to Buddhism than just sitting around thinking about what some short, fat guy said many centuries ago. It's a whole way of living. The Coombs Computing Center offers an entire library relating to Buddhist studies.

**Web:**
**http://coombs.anu.edu.au/WWWVL-Buddhism.html**

## Chinese Philosophy

Have a hankering for a little Chinese philosophy? Learn about the various schools of thought and read some texts by Confucius and Zhu Zi, many of which are in English. Also available are bibliographies and mailing lists about Chinese philosophy which are also in English.

**Web:**
**http://www.monash.edu.au/cc/staff/sas/sab/WWW/**

## Electronic Journal of Analytic Philosophy

This journal is peer-reviewed and has an interesting selection of articles and topics relating to analytic philosophy. Skim through the current hypertext issue or look at back issues. Also available are subscription and referee registration forms and submission guidelines.

**Web:**
**http://www.phil.indiana.edu/ejap/ejap.html**

## Enquiry Concerning Human Understanding

David Hume (1711-1776) was a Scottish philosopher and historian. His first philosophical work was called "Treatise on Human Nature" (1739-1740). The treatise stresses that there is no connection between reason and the empirical world. Hume's "Enquiry Concerning Human Understanding" is a simplified version of his Treatise.

**Web:**
**http://unix1.utm.edu/research/hume/wri/1enq/1enq.htm**

### David Hume

This well-known 18th century Scottish philosopher managed to bring to Western culture that certain something that was missing in the work of Locke and Berkeley. He suggested that the mind contained only a series of "impressions" (sensations) and, thus, discounted the possibility of certainty in knowledge. Although his underlying assumptions might be considered somewhat naive and primitive by modern standards, he was able to engender a posture of skepticism that was important, not only to his fundamental work, but to his commentaries on religion.

If you are interested in Hume and his thinking, you can download one of his most important works, "An Enquiry Concerning Human Understanding", from the Net.

## Extropians

It's not an alien life form, nor is it a variety of insectoid species. Extropians are people who are interested in anarchocapitalist politics, cryonics and other life extension techniques, the technological extension of human intelligence and perception, and nanotechnology. It's not just another little hobby. It's a way of life.

**Web:**

**http://www.c2.org/~arkuat/extr/**

**Listserv Mailing List:**

List Name: **xtropy-1**
Subscribe to: **listserv@ubvm.cc.buffalo.edu**

**Why die when you can become an**
*EXTROPIAN?*

## Krishnamurti

Krishnamurti (1895-1986) was a world-renowned teacher who conducted deep investigation on the nature of humanity and the Self, and gave talks and wrote books on love, religion, belief, relationships, death, thought, time, fear, envy, meditation and beauty. Gather around to talk about the teachings of J. Krishnamurti and join with others in some deep self-questioning.

**Listserv Mailing List:**

List Name: **listening-l**
Subscribe to: **listserv@zrz.tu-berlin.de**

## Memetics

There is a theory that ideas can propagate biologically. So, if you start getting funny thoughts in your head and you don't know where they came from, you can blame it on your parents and the theory of Memetics. Never again will you have to take responsibility for those strange ideas that keep coming to mind. Learn about memes and their effects on humanity.

**Web:**

**http://www.hok.no/marius/memetics/**

**Usenet:**

**alt.memetics**

## Metaphysics Talk and General Discussion

Do you ever get the impression that there is more going on in the universe than you realize? Sit around with the folks on Usenet who love to contemplate the philosophical aspects of our "beingness" as well as the workings of the cosmos.

**Usenet:**

**alt.paranet.metaphysics**
**sci.meta.philosophy**
**sci.philosophy.meta**

## New Ways of Thinking

Break away from the herd and think for yourself, like those who find inspiration in Timothy Leary, Robert Anton Wilson and John Lilly. Push Darwin aside and help speed up the evolution of humankind by developing new ways of thinking and expanding consciousness. This is the fast food of philosophy.

**Listserv Mailing List:**
List Name: **fnord-l**
Subscribe to: **listserv@ubvm.cc.buffalo.edu**

## Objectivism

Ayn Rand created the philosophy of Objectivism. She summarizes: "My philosophy, in essence, is the concept of man as a heroic being, with his own happiness as the moral purpose of his life, with productive achievements as his noblest activity, and reason as his only absolute." Here is a web page and Usenet group dedicated to things of interest to Ayn Rand fans.

**Web:**
**http://www.vix.com/objectivism/**

**Usenet:**
**alt.philosophy.objectivism**

## Personal Idealogies

Everyone has an opinion, and some people even have opinions by which they consistently stand. If you feel strongly about your beliefs and want to share them, or want to hear others, join in the discussion of **belief-l**. Note: This group will not tolerate religious proselytizing or flame wars.

**Listserv Mailing List:**
List Name: **belief-l**
Subscribe to: **listserv@listserv.aol.com**

## Philosophy Archive

Before you draw your next hot bath, go look at the English Server's philosophy archive. It contains text by such notable thinkers as Nietzsche, Descartes, Kant, Aristotle, Bacon and Burke. Read a few of these while the tub is filling, so it will give you something to think about as you have a nice soak.

**Web:**
**http://english-www.hss.cmu.edu/philosophy.html**

## Philosophy of the Middle Ages

Every period has its great thinkers and the Middle Ages is no exception. Scholars examine the philosophy and socio-political thought of the medieval era, ask questions and share insights, as well as post announcements of conferences and calls for papers.

**Listserv Mailing List:**
List Name: **mdvlphil**
Subscribe to: **listserv@lsuvm.sncc.lsu.edu**

## Philosophy Talk and General Discussion

When the going gets tough, the tough start talking about philosophy—and these are the places to do it. Whatever your philosophical preference, there's room for you on Usenet. Just remember to be polite, and show respect for other people's point of view (unless they disagree with you).

**Usenet:**
**alt.philosophy.debate**
**sci.philosophy**
**sci.philosophy.tech**
**talk.philosophy.humanism**
**talk.philosophy.misc**

## Plato

Plato (427-347 B.C.) was a Greek philosopher who founded a school in Athens where he taught philosophy and mathematics. (One of his notable students was Socrates.) A great thinker, Plato concerned himself with the art of living and knowing. Take a look at this nice archive of his life's work.

**Web:**
**http://www.hccs.cc.tx.us/Library/elibrary/Plato.htm**

## Principia Cybernetica Web

The Principia Cybernetica Project (PCP) is a collaborative, computer-supported attempt to develop a complete cybernetic and evolutionary philosophy. This page offers many articles and links to discussions of tools, structure, topics, philosophy, and the practical organization of the PCP.

**Web:**
**http://pespmc1.vub.ac.be/NUTSHELL.html**

## Russell, Bertrand

Bertrand Russell was a well-known British philosopher, activist and essayist who lived from 1872-1970. You can read some of his more memorable quotes, writings and correspondence at this site dedicated to his life and work.

**Web:**

**http://www.mcmaster.ca/russdocs/russell.htm**

## Utopia

Thomas More (1478-1535) was an English statesman who was a martyr for the Roman Catholic Church. More refused to subscribe to the Act of Supremacy, which would make Henry the VIII the head of the Church instead of the Pope. Because of this, and probably aggravated by the fact that More did not acknowledge Henry's divorce of Katherine of Aragon, King Henry imprisoned More in the Tower of London and eventually had him beheaded. More's "Utopia" is about an ideal state based entirely upon reason. I'm sure you can see where he got his inspiration.

**Web:**

**http://wiretap.spies.com/Gopher/Library/Classic/utopia.txt**

## Women in Philosophy

Tired of reading the same old philosophy by Kant, Descartes and Aristotle? For a little change of pace, take a look at this extensive bibliography of women philosophers, then go right away to the nearest library and check out one of their books. This is a searchable database so you can look for philosophers by name, year of publication, title or other methods.

**Web:**

**http://billyboy.ius.indiana.edu/WomeninPhilosophy/WomeninPhilo.html**

## Zen Philosophy Talk and General Discussion

Experience the serenity and logic of Zen philosophy. Learn the ways of action through non-action and how to get there from here without even trying.

**Usenet:**

**alt.philosophy.zen**
**alt.zen**

**The Net cares.**

### *Look What I Found on the Net...*

```
Newsgroup: alt.zen
Subject: Why Learn Zen?

> What can I do to learn Zen?

Look both ways, inside and out.

> And why?

There is heavy traffic out there,
Lighter traffic in here,
Please take care of yourself and others in crossing.

> Would I get something out of it?

No, sorry.  Nothing for sale.
```

# PHOTOGRAPHY

## Black and White Photography

I love black and white photography. It's so clean, basic and accessible. If you want to find good black and white photography on the Net, all you need to do is check this web site. You will find a monthly list of the top black and white photo web sites, as well as an archive of the past selections. They also have a great resource center for photographers, with some useful FAQs (frequently asked question lists).

**Web:**

**http://gramercy.ios.com/~mresnick/**

## Daguerreotypes

A daguerreotype is a photographic image made on a light-sensitive silver-coated metallic plate. The daguerreotype was invented in 1839 by Louis Jacques Mandé Daguerre (1789-1851), a French scene painter and physicist. (Daguerre was also the man who helped invent the diorama, a sort of three-dimensional pictorial scene.) This web site has galleries of 19th century imagery, exhibits of modern photographers using daguerreotypes and a history of the daguerrotype. There is also a description of all the steps involved in making a daguerreotype. Read this and you will appreciate how easy photography is today.

**Web:**

**http://java.austinc.edu/dag/**

## Darkroom Photography

Photographic creativity certainly doesn't stop with a click of the shutter. When you head to the darkroom you have to ask yourself all sorts of questions like "Should I print on warm or cold tone paper?" and "What kind of developer should I use?" Topics cover being creative in the darkroom as well as technical issues such as chemical usage, paper, tools, and equipment.

**Web:**

**http://www.sound.net/~lanoue/**

**Usenet:**

**rec.photo.darkroom**

## Digital Doctor's Photo Links

Here's a great one-stop shop for photography resources on the Net. The Digital Doctor offers a tour of design and graphic resources, photography mailing lists and Usenet groups, galleries and exhibitions, and online photo zines.

**Web:**

**http://aleph0.clarku.edu/~bmarcus/weblink.html**

## History of Photography

The development of photography involved the marriage of two different technologies: optical and chemical. Basic optical technology—in the form of the "camera obscura" (a dark box or room with a small hole in one end that could be used to project an inverted image on the wall opposite the hole)—was understood as far back as the time of Aristotle. And scientists have known about optical processes involving light and chemical reactions for hundreds of years. In the seventeenth century, the British physicist Robert Boyle discovered that silver chloride turned dark upon exposure. However, Boyle thought the discoloring was due to exposure to air, not to light. In the next century, Angelo Sala noticed that powdered silver nitrate became dark in the sun. In 1727, Johann Schulze realized that particular liquids turn color upon exposure to the sun. In the early nineteenth century, Thomas Wedgewood was able to capture images, but only temporarily. Finally in 1827, Joseph Niépce produced the first permanent photographic image, which he called a heliograph. Read about the history of photography, and you will find it encompasses politics, culture, science and intrigue. These web sites are good sources of information. If you are interested in the history of photography as a hobby, you can join the mailing list for an ongoing discussion.

**Web:**

**http://www.kbnet.co.uk/rleggat/photo/**
**http://www.webcom.com/cityg/resource/pa/photarch.html**

**Listserv Mailing List:**

List Name: **photohst**
Subscribe to: **listserv@asuvm.inre.asu.edu**

## Room in the Darkroom

Some of the most mysterious things in the world go on in a darkroom. If you are not a photographer, sorry, this part of human culture is closed to you and there's not much you can do about it except feel wistful in a polite sort of way. If, however, you are among the cognoscenti who can distinguish between lith processing and posterization, the discussion group rec.photo.darkroom is waiting for you. Join the club and see what develops.

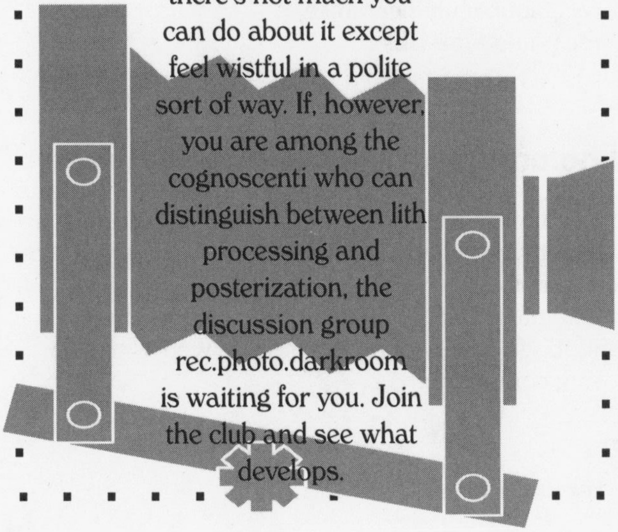

## Infrared Photography

Infrared photography uses film that is sensitive to visible light, as well as ultraviolet and infrared radiation. The results are fascinating, often even eerie. Although the images look familiar, the contrast and details are not what you are used to. If you are interested in photography, you have to try infrared photography at least once in your life. To help you get started, I have chosen one web site that contains an infrared photography FAQ (where you can find out about cameras, lenses, exposures, focusing, developing and printing), and another web site that offers a collection of infrared photos for you to enjoy.

**Web:**

**http://ruly70.medfac.leidenuniv.nl/~cor/ir_g_nfr.html**
**http://www.mat.uc.pt/~rps/photos/FAQ_IR.html**

## Nature and Wildlife Photography

The web site is maintained by a non-profit organization that promotes environmental photography. You can enjoy their gallery and read news about environmental photography. If you join the organization, you can get an email alias and a space to display your own environmental photography on the Web. The Usenet group is to discuss nature and wildlife photography tips.

**Web:**

**http://photogreen.org/**

**Usenet:**

**rec.photo.technique.nature**

## Panoramic Photography

Panoramic photography uses a wide angle lens in order to capture an unbroken view of the surrounding area. In general to qualify as panoramic, your picture must have an angle of view of at least 100 degrees (a little less than a third of a full circle). Panoramic photography is perfect for landscape shots in which you want to capture expansiveness of the area you are photographing (the Grand Canyon, a spectacular snow-covered mountain range, a sweeping city skyline, and so on). Here is how a typical panoramic camera works. The camera rotates on top of a tripod. As the camera turns, the shutter is held open. The film moves past the aperture (shutter opening) with the same speed and direction as the camera itself. The result? A panoramic picture with a view to remember. This web site has the scoop on panoramic photography, including information on equipment, tips for taking photos, and a gallery of panoramic images.

**Web:**

**http://ourworld.compuserve.com/homepages/radia/**

**Wow, free software.**

## Photograph Exposure

It's good to be well-exposed, but it's better to expose well. If you are a beginner, this web site has some great tips and tricks relating to light and film exposure. Take a crash course about photography. Then learn some low-tech tips to make your pictures more creative, and read a basic explanation of exposure theory. Check out the sim-cam—a great learning tool—that simulates exposure times and aperture settings. This allows you to see the changes that are produced on film by the adjustments you make to your camera.

**Web:**
**http://www.88.com/exposure/**

## Photographers Directory

This web site contains a large list of photographers from all around the world who use the Net. You can check the list either alphabetically or geographically. This is a good site to know about, if you are looking for a photographer, or if you are a photographer looking for clients.

**Web:**
**http://www.mindspring.com/~jdsmith/plist.html**

## Photography Archives

The Photo Forum offers a good selection of material for the novice or professional. At this site you can find FAQs, equipment reviews, lens information, useful addresses and phone numbers, archives having to do with photos and cameras, and a rotating display of the work of members of the Forum's list.

**Web:**
**http://www.rit.edu/~andpph/photoforum.html**

## Photography Basics

Do you want to learn how to go beyond basic pointing and shooting? This web site has information about cameras and how they work, the history of photography, natural and artificial lighting, and composing and balancing images. You can also learn about the different kinds of photography—portraiture, documentary, macro and micro, art photography—and explore links to some useful photo sites around the Net. If you are a beginner, I recommend this site to you.

**Web:**
**http://www.goldcanyon.com/photo/**

## Photography Equipment Talk and General Discussion

There are a lot of photographers on the Net and, no matter what your particular interest, there is someone to talk to. So why not choose a Usenet group and see what develops?

**Usenet:**
**rec.photo.equipment.35mm**
**rec.photo.equipment.large-format**
**rec.photo.equipment.medium-format**
**rec.photo.equipment.misc**
**rec.photo.film+labs**

## Photography Questions and Answers

No matter what the problem is, there is someone on Usenet who is bound to have an answer for you. Post questions or help someone solve a photography dilemma, and pick up some helpful hints about shooting and developing photos as well as tips on using equipment.

**Usenet:**
**rec.photo.misc**

## Photography Talk and General Discussion

Whether you are just a snapshot shooter or a pro with hundreds of pounds of equipment, there is a Usenet group that is perfect for you. Fans of photography hang out and talk about taking pictures from a creative as well as a technical point of view. Try the mailing list for photo talk that comes straight to your mailbox.

**Usenet:**
**rec.photo**
**rec.photo.advanced**
**rec.photo.misc**

**Listproc Mailing List:**
List Name: **photo-l**
Subscribe to: **listproc@csuohio.edu**

## Power Tips and Tricks for Photoshop

This web page features a hypertext version of Power Tips and Tricks for Adobe Photoshop. Jump right in at Tip 1 (Secrets of Chops) and work your way down to Tip 23 (Complexity-city! The Snowy Mask Technique).

**Web:**

**http://the-tech.mit.edu/KPT/KPT.html**

## Toy Cameras

I think toy cameras are cool. Toy cameras are, literally, toys: cheap little plastic cameras that use 120 film. They leak light; produce distortion, fog and vignetting on film; they have an unknown shutter speed and film that is wound loosely. (And those are just the obvious problems. There are all kinds of bizarre things that can happen when you use a toy camera.) So, why would anyone use them? Because they are fun and you never know what you are going to get. Moreover, toy cameras are great for experimenting. This web site has information about taking photos with toy cameras. Learn how to correct problems in the darkroom, read about the history of toy cameras, and admire the gallery of toy-camera pictures. It's a great break from high-tech photography, and it's fun.

**Web:**

**http://www.concom.com/~winters/toy_home.htm**

## Underwater Photography

I once took some underwater pictures. I went on a trip to the Caribbean and, before I left, I bought a waterproof disposable camera. During my snorkeling sessions, I happily snapped away at a variety of colorful fish and underwater scenery. When I returned home and had the pictures developed, I enjoyed them, but I realized they were nothing like the quality you would get with special equipment and techniques. Still, I had a great deal of fun, and I enjoy looking at my favorite picture of a turtle swimming around a reef. If you are interested in underwater photography, join this mailing list to discuss techniques, equipment, tips and locations with other photographers around the world.

**Majordomo Mailing List:**

List Name: **uw-photo**
Subscribe to: **majordomo@world.std.com**

# PHYSICS

## American Institute of Physics

The American Institute of Physics home page offers information about the AIP, links to AIP publications, newsletters and mailing lists, and links to other physics resources.

**Web:**

**http://www.aip.org/**

## Center for Particle Astrophysics

According to modern theories, there should be a lot more matter in the universe than we can currently detect. This missing stuff is referred to as "dark matter"—because it does not emit electromagnetic radiation—and a lot of scientists spend their time trying to discover where it is and what it is made of. The Center for Particle Astrophysics is primarily devoted to the "dark matter problem". As such, the Center brings together a large number of physicists in various fields such as cosmology (the study of the universe as a whole), astrophysics (the study of stars), and particle physics (the study of subatomic particles). Their web site offers a lot of interesting information about the Center and its research (black holes and so on), as well as links to other physics resources on the Net.

**Web:**

**http://physics7.berkeley.edu/home.html**

## Computational Fluid Dynamics

Fluid dynamics is the science that studies the movement of fluids (liquids and gases). Here is a web site that contains resources for people who are concerned with the computational aspects of fluid dynamics. These pages will help you find academic institutions, companies, web sites devoted to specific topics (such as turbulence and hypersonic flow), documents, and lots of other related information. For ongoing discussion, you can participate in the Usenet group.

**Web:**

**http://www.tfd.chalmers.se/CFD_Online/**

**Usenet:**

**sci.physics.computational.fluid-dynamics**

## Einstein in 3D

Experience Einstein's theory of relativity in a graphical, three-dimensional environment. Mathematical equations are turned into pictures for a much more visual physics experience.

**Web:**

**http://www.ncsa.uiuc.edu/Apps/GenRel/SC93/HOME_sc93.html#workb**

### Einstein Made Easy (sort of)

There are many different ways to understand Einstein's theories, the best being those that depend on mathematics. However, for those of you who are mathematically challenged, there is a web site at which you can find a visual introduction to relativity. If you can't understand the numbers, at least you can look at the pictures and wave your hands.

E=MC²
a²-b²=c²
π=3.14
6.022x10²³


## Electromagnetic Fields and Microwave Electronics

This web page is provided by the Swiss Federal Institute of Technology and offers information on the Institute's research into electromagnetic field theory and high-frequency electronics. The page also has links to other related resources.

**Web:**

**http://www.ifh.ee.ethz.ch/**

## Fusion

This web page offers links to fusion resources and pages at a number of institutions, including the University of Texas, MIT, U.C. Berkeley, the Office of Fusion Energy, an index of fusion research and related sites, and a link to the Usenet group **sci.physics.fusion**.

**Web:**

**http://fusioned.gat.com/webstuff/FusionInfo.html**

## High Energy Physics Information Center

The High Energy Physics Information Center (HEPIC) web page provides access to information about this organization, documentation and publications of HEPIC, information about HEPIC experiments, high energy physics software, and links to other high energy physics resources.

**Web:**

**http://www.hep.net/**

## Index of Physics Abstracts

This is the perfect place to find papers relating to high energy physics, astrophysics, condensed matter theory, general relativity, quantum cosmology, and nuclear theory. A keyword search will help you track down the information you need.

**Web:**

**http://xxx.lanl.gov/**

## OpticsNet

OpticsNet is the home page of the Optical Society of America (OSA). It covers all aspects of optical physics and engineering. The server provides information about quantum electronics, photonics, and vision.

**Web:**

**http://www.osa.org/**

## Particle Surface Research

Particle surface research involves the study of how an ion beam interacts with a particular surface. Here is a web site where you will find links to computational, experimental and theoretical resources all over the Net. (If you run out of places to visit and you get bored, try shooting some beta particles at this book and see what happens.)

**Web:**

**http://chaos.fullerton.edu/mhslinks.html**

## Particles

Here is an easy-to-understand list of elementary and fundamental particles, giving the mass, lifetime, and properties of each. (This is mandatory reading if you plan on creating your own reality.)

**Web:**

**http://sun1.hep.anl.gov/html/particle.tbl**

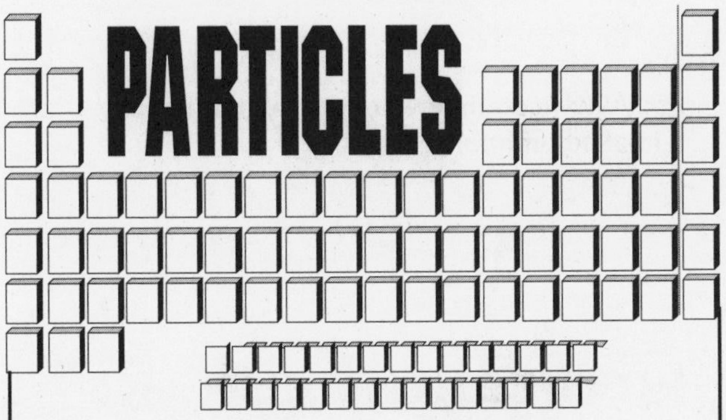
PARTICLES

A lot of people think that everything consists of protons, electrons and neutrons.

However, there is a lot more variation than that.

Check out the Particles list, and you can see the names of the 23 elementary particles (not to mention 6 types of quarks).

## Physics Conferences

In case you feel the overwhelming urge to attend a physics conference, you can visit this site to search by month or by field of physics. Personally, I was going to go to the Aerosol Symposium, but I blew it off. As well as conferences, there are listings for workshops and summer schools.

**Web:**

**http://www.tp.umu.se/TIPTOP/FORUM/CONF/**

## Physics on the Net

A condensation of postings to Usenet groups about some cutting edge issues in physics, including black holes and what happens inside of them, gravitational radiation, the paradox of Einstein's relativity, tachyons, and the theoretical possibilities of time travel.

**Web:**

**http://physics.hallym.ac.kr/education/faq/faq.html**

## Physics Preprint Archives

This server acts as a large archive for preprints of papers in many areas of physics, as well as some areas of mathematics and other sciences. Using this web site is a great way to get an electronic copy of any paper you want.

**Web:**

**http://xxx.lanl.gov/archive/gr-qc**
**http://xxx.lanl.gov/archive/hep-th**

## Physics Talk and General Discussion

Without physics, the world would be so much more dull and life would be much too easy to understand. Exercise your brain by getting in on some physics discussion.

**Usenet:**

**alt.sci.physics.acoustics**
**alt.sci.physics.new-theories**
**alt.sci.physics.plutonium**
**alt.sci.physics.spam**
**bionet.biophysics**
**bit.listserv.physhare**
**sci.astro.research**
**sci.med.physics**
**sci.physics**
**sci.physics.accelerators**
**sci.physics.computational.fluid-dynamics**
**sci.physics.fusion**
**sci.physics.particle**
**sci.physics.plasma**
**sci.physics.research**

## Plasma Physics

When you have to attend a potluck dinner and you just don't know what to bring, consider a nice quasineutral gas such as plasma. Admittedly, it doesn't sound entirely appetizing, but just think of all the great things you can do with it. You could make an advanced microwave device, use it in ceramic production or toxic waste treatment or, for a really fun time, you could design a power grid for a spacecraft. Find out the other reasons why plasma is cool by reading information about the science and possible applications of this branch of physics.

**Web:**

**http://plasma-gate.weizmann.ac.il/Plasmal.html**

## Polymer Physics

Polymers are large molecules constructed out of repeating units of small building blocks, joined to one another by covalent bonds. Here are some resources for people involved in the scientific study of the physics of polymers. For discussion, there is the group and the mailing list. For information, one web site has the FAQ (frequently asked question list) for the Usenet group, while the other has links to polymer-related sites around the Net.

**Web:**

**http://irc.leeds.ac.uk/spfaq/**
**http://www.dur.ac.uk/~dch0www2/polymer.html**
**http://www.polymers.com/poly-faq.html**

**Usenet:**

**sci.polymers**

**Listserv Mailing List:**

List Name: **polymerp**
Subscribe to: **listserv@hearn.nic.surfnet.nl**

## Radioactive Waste

What do you do when your in-laws are spending their vacation with you and you have all this radioactive waste that you suddenly have to get rid of? Quickly take a look at this web site which offers information on nuclear reactor systems, hybrid systems, the chemical aspects of transmutation, and the transmutation of radioactive waste.

**Web:**

**http://www.nea.fr/html/trw/index.html**

## Relativity

This page offers links to pages on mathematical relativity, gravitational physics and geometry, hyperspace, and the home pages of several organizations with interests in relativity.

**Web:**

**http://jean-luc.ncsa.uiuc.edu/World/**

## Sounds from Chaos

Papers, sounds, and references about Chua's Circuit, one of the most interesting chaotic systems. Chua's Oscillator Circuit generates many strange and varied sounds and is one of the few physical systems for which the presence of chaos has been observed experimentally, verified by computer simulations, and proven mathematically.

**Web:**

**http://www.ccsr.uiuc.edu/People/gmk/Papers/ChuaSndRef.html**

# PICTURES AND CLIP ART

## alt.binaries.pictures Image Server

This page helps you select and retrieve files distributed on the **alt.binaries.pictures** Usenet groups in the last few days. The nice thing about it is that you can view miniature pictures of the images through your browser and read the picture description before you actually decide if you want to download the whole file.

**Web:**

**http://web.cnam.fr/Images/Usenet/**

## Animations

More than one hundred short descriptions and links to servers on the Web which offer computer generated animations, visualizations, movies and interactive images. It includes an mpeg movie of the Big Bang, calculus visualizations, movies of NASA LaRC's F-16 project, 3-D visualization of a frog, cosmic movies, sports movies, scenery movies, *Star Trek* movies, and many more. The movies and animations are in varying formats.

**Web:**

**http://mambo.ucsc.edu/psl/thant/thant.html**

## Ascii Art

You don't have to be able to draw to make cool pictures. Check out the ascii art resources on the Web to see what you can do with your flying fingers. This site has lots of ascii pictures. Memorize a few and impress your friends the next time you have them over for alphabet soup.

**Web:**

**http://miso.wwa.com/~boba/scarecrow.html**

**DO YOU LIKE free pictures?**
Take a moment to visit the **ASCII ART BAZAAR**. Find out why ascii art is now an accepted topic among the New York intelligentsia, and why ascii animation may be added to the next Cannes Film Festival.

### *Look What I Found on the Net...*

```
        (From the polymer FAQ posted to sci.polymers)

Recycling

Most thermoplastic polymers can be recycled: that is, converted
from their initial use as a consumer, business, or industrial
product, back into a raw material from which some other product
can be manufactured.

There are three versions of the recycling logo.  The original
one was three arrows chasing each other in the shape of a
triangle, the second was just a triangle, and the current one is
a pair of angle brackets:

    < 1 >

The number inside the triangle or brackets indicates the
material used in the part.

There are six specific categories, and a generic seventh for
"other". In the case of "other" it is good form to put the
material name under the recycling logo.

< 1 > PET (polyethylene terphthalate)
      -- beverage containers, food pouches, meat packages

< 2 > HDPE (high density polyethylene)
      -- milk or detergent or oil bottles, toys, plastic bags

< 3 > PVC (polyvinyl chloride)
      -- food wrap, vegetable oil bottles, blister packaging

< 4 > LDPE (low density polyethylene)
      -- shrink-wrap, plastic bags, garment bags

< 5 > PP (polypropylene)
      -- margarine containers, grocery bags, food wrap

< 6 > PS (polystyrene)
      -- plastic utensils, clothes hangars, foam cups or plates

< 7 > Other (all other polymers and polymer blends) including
      polycarbonate, ABS, PPO/PPE
```

## Cartoon Pictures

There's no need to have a bare room or office cubicle. Go to Usenet right now and download some pictures of your favorite cartoon characters—Rescue Rangers, Snow White, Ren and Stimpy, Chip 'n' Dale, Bill and Hillary—here they are, waiting for you to download.

**Usenet:**

**alt.binaries.pictures.cartoons**
**alt.toon-pics**

## Clip Art

Need clip art for your books, publications, garage sale fliers, home pages, term papers or whatever? But just as soon not (shudder) pay for them? Okay, here's a huge archive of public domain clip art ripe for the plucking. In its copious archives, you'll find all the royalty-free drawings, etchings, and what not that you could possibly use. If, as 'tis said by those who know such things, a picture is worth a thousand words, then these resources will increase your vocabulary by several million.

**Web:**

**http://www.acy.digex.net/~infomart/clipart/**
**http://www.barrysclipart.com/**
**http://www.thehouse.com.au/artroom.html**

**Usenet:**

**alt.binaries.clip-art**

## Fantasy Art

When the view out your window becomes boring and tedious, take a break from real life by browsing these huge archives of images of knights, castles, dragons, unicorns, wizards and more.

**Web:**

**http://www.acm.uiuc.edu/rml/Gifs/Fantasy/**
**http://www.teleport.com/~debdz/photo.html**

**Get into "Mischief".**

## Fine Art

As Tennyson said when he first started using the Internet, "The fact that picture-oriented Usenet groups exist for more than just erotica proves that man can rise on the stepping stones of his lower self to better things." Participate and download fine art, suitable for framing. The **.d** group is for discussion. The other groups are for pictures only. The rules (if you care to follow them) are that **.digitized** is for original, digitized artwork; **.graphics** is for original pictures created with a computer; **.photos** is for original photographs.

**Usenet:**

**alt.binaries.pictures.fine-art.d**
**alt.binaries.pictures.fine-art.digitized**
**alt.binaries.pictures.fine-art.graphics**
**alt.binaries.pictures.fine-art.photos**

## Fractals

All you ever wanted to know about fractals, including reading and resource lists, FAQs about chaos, the Mandelbrot set, Julia set, quaternion arithmetic, plasma clouds, and other related subjects.

**Web:**

**http://online.anu.edu.au/ITA/ACAT/contours/contours.html**
**http://webpages.marshall.edu/~stepp/fractal-faq/faq.html**
**http://www.cnam.fr/fractals.html**

**Usenet:**

**alt.binaries.pictures.fractals**
**alt.fractals**
**alt.fractals.pictures**
**bit.listserv.frac-l**
**sci.fractals**

## Holography

This cool holographic pattern generator is something you have to see. Play around with the form to design a hologram to your specifications, make a million of them or fiddle with one to get it just perfect. You can save the images you make, too. At this site you will also be able to read news about the holography industry and a FAQ for those of you who are more technically inclined.

**Web:**

**http://www.holo.com/holo/gram.html**

## HOLOGRAPHY

HOLOGRAPHY IS THE SCIENCE OF CREATING A TYPE OF "PHOTOGRAPH"—CALLED A HOLOGRAPH OR HOLOGRAM—THAT RECORDS THE LIGHT WAVES REFLECTING OFF AN OBJECT IN A SPECIAL WAY. UNLIKE A REGULAR PHOTO, A HOLOGRAPH RECORDS THE LIGHT AS YOU WOULD HAVE SEEN IT IF YOU WERE THERE. THUS, A HOLOGRAPH WILL SHOW YOU MORE THAN A FLAT, TWO-DIMENSIONAL IMAGE.

THIS IS THE TECHNOLOGY THAT HAS GIVEN US SUCH WONDERFUL PRODUCTS AS BUSINESS DOCUMENTS THAT CANNOT BE PHOTOCOPIED, COUNTERFEIT-PROOF CREDIT CARDS, AND KEY CHAINS WITH A 3D IMAGE OF ELVIS PRESLEY THAT WINKS AT YOU AS YOU MOVE FROM SIDE TO SIDE.

THE INITIAL THEORY OF HOLOGRAPHY WAS DEVELOPED BY A HUNGARIAN PHYSICIST, IN 1947 NAMED DENNIS GABOR (NO RELATION TO ZSA ZSA). IF YOU WOULD LIKE MORE INFORMATION ABOUT THIS FASCINATING BRANCH OF SCIENCE—OR IF YOU JUST WANT TO SEE SOME COOL PICTURES—CHECK OUT THE HOLOGRAPHY WEB SITE.

## Hyperbolic Tiles

Hyperbolic tile images in jpeg format, and the Unix source code for the hyperbolic tiler that created them are available from this page. Immerse yourself in hyperbolic spheres and tiles of money, weird patterns, and even portraits.

**Web:**

**http://www.cs.cmu.edu/Web/People/jmount/moretilings.html**

## Hypergarden 3D Art

A virtual tour through an unusual house and garden is the sure cure for your housebound blues. These images are beautifully three-dimensional and offer a strong sense that what you see is real. Is it or isn't it? Take the tour and decide for yourself.

**Web:**

**http://www.unomaha.edu/~gday/hypergarden.html**

## Icon Collections

No home page is complete without a few cool icons, either as just plain old decoration, or hot links to something wild and crazy. Where, though, to get the icons in question? Well, this web site is a good place to start. It contains a vast collection of icons, some painstakingly created, that you can use for anything from simple clip art to clickable links.

**Web:**

**http://members.aol.com/minimouze/private/ICONS.html**
**http://www.jsc.nasa.gov/~mccoy/Icons/index.html**

## Images and Icons Archive

This is a charming site devoted to graphics and photography. In addition to a small but impressive collection of travel photos, the site maintains a host of nicely arranged links to servers full of NASA space images, stock photo archives, medical images, and even archives of national flags.

**Web:**

**http://www.nosc.mil/planet_earth/images.html**

## Kai's Power Tools Backgrounds Archive

Spiff up your graphics or your web page with these downloadable backgrounds for use with Photoshop. If you want to make your own backgrounds, read the tutorial on how it's done.

**Web:**

**http://the-tech.mit.edu/KPT/bgs.html**

## Mandelbrot Explorer

Be a Mandelbrot artist without having to strain your brain. All you have to do is enter some coordinates, and the computer will do the work for you. Print out the results and stick them on the wall, and when everyone asks about your cool wallpaper you can act casual and say, "Oh, this? I made it myself."

**Web:**

**http://www.ntua.gr/mandel/mandel.html**

Do you like those cool Mandelbrot patterns that everyone talks about but no one really understands? If so, try the **MANDELBROT EXPLORER.**

## Picture Miscellany

Free trade hits Usenet. Check out the great pictures that people around the world post to Usenet every day.

**Usenet:**

**alt.binaries.misc**
**alt.binaries.pictures**
**alt.binaries.pictures.misc**

## Picture Talk and General Discussion

On Usenet, groups that have the words **binaries.pictures** in their names are specifically devoted to posting pictures (for example, **alt.binaries.pictures.astro** is for people to share astronomy pictures). If you want to discuss the idea of sharing pictures, or you have any questions (such as how do I post a picture?), you should use these two groups. They are specifically for such discussions. The idea is to keep everything out of the other groups except actual pictures. In general, groups whose names end in **.d** are for discussion of topics raised in related groups. For example, **rec.humor** is for sharing jokes; **rec.humor.d** is for talking about jokes, asking questions or making requests.

**Usenet:**

**alt.binaries.pictures.d**
**alt.binaries.pictures.misc.d**

## Picture Viewing Software

With some Usenet newsreader programs, you will have to decode picture files before you can view them. Read this Usenet group to get info on what programs are available and how to use them.

**Web:**

**http://mrcnext.cso.uiuc.edu/~deej**

**Usenet:**

**alt.binaries.pictures.utilities**

## Realm of Graphics

Snazz up tired graphics with a smattering of backgrounds, buttons, lines, bullets and icons designed to impress. This is a great collection of doo-dads.

**Web:**

**http://www.contrib.andrew.cmu.edu/~ender/ed/rg/**

## Rob's Multimedia Lab

Rob's Multimedia Lab (RML) is a massive collection of images, sounds, and movies. It contains gif images, audio files, and mpeg movies. The images and sounds are categorized into sections, and there are links to many other sites containing picture, sound, or movie archives. If you are looking for a specific picture or sound, there is a good chance that you can find it here.

**Web:**

**http://www.acm.uiuc.edu/rml/**

*A Thousand Pictures Are Worth a Single Word*

There are so many fabulous pictures just waiting to be downloaded that I sometimes wonder why anyone would use a computer for anything else.

All you need is an Internet connection, a web browser (or a few utility programs), and a lot of time, and you too can turn your personal computer into a sophisticated photo album.

## Shuttle and Satellite Images

If you aren't an astronaut, you don't really get to see the cool outer space stuff up close. What I say is save your money or spend it on a nice vacation at the beach. On the Web, you can look at pictures of space and spacecraft and planets and stuff for free. And you don't have to wear one of those funny suits, either.

**Web:**

**http://ceps.nasm.edu:2020/RPIF/SSPR.html**
**http://edcwww.cr.usgs.gov/dclass/dclass.html**
**http://images.jsc.nasa.gov/html/home.htm**

## Stereograms and 3D Images

This web page collects an assortment of links to fun 3D images and stereograms. There are also links to other web pages that store archives and galleries of stereograms.

**Web:**

**http://www.ccc.nottingham.ac.uk/~etzpc/sirds.html**
**http://www.netaxs.com/~mhmyers/rds.html**

## Supermodels

The next best thing to living next door to a supermodel is being able to download one whenever you want. Just the thing to look at when you get tired of fractals.

**Usenet:**

**alt.binaries.pictures.supermodels**

## Tasteless Pictures

Here is a Usenet group for the posting of tasteless, bizarre, and grotesque pictures only. For the truly demented: get your fill of car wrecks, mangled bodies, freaks, and so on. What is tasteless? Well, all I can say is that this group is not for the faint of heart. You will see pictures of things that I can't even mention in a family book. Suffice it to say that if you are the type of person who likes to look at things that make other people cringe, this group is for you.

**Usenet:**

**alt.binaries.pictures.tasteless**

**Stereograms and 3D Images**

Do you want to be omniscient? Practice looking at stereograms until you can see the 3D images every time.

You will then know all and see all.

## Thesaurus for Graphic Material

It's so annoying when you are sitting around the house trying to think of another word for "daguerreotype". No longer do you have to fret over finding just the right word. Browse the thesaurus or search using keywords.

**Web:**

**http://palimpsest.stanford.edu/lex/lctgm/lctgm.html**

# POETRY

## Blake, William

William Blake (1757-1827) was an English writer and poet whose work evolved from bright and gentle poems to often fierce and terrifying "prophetic" pieces about his intense spirituality and messages from heaven. Here is your chance to read the poems of William Blake, including "The New Jerusalem" which was made into the song "Jerusalem" by Emerson, Lake and Palmer.

**Web:**

**http://wcarchive.cdrom.com/pub/obi/William.Blake/**

## British Poetry Archive

When you are in the mood for some poetry, light a fire and snuggle down with a screenful of works by British writers from 1780-1910. This page includes most of the biggies: Coleridge, Keats, Wordsworth and many others.

**Web:**

**http://etext.lib.virginia.edu/britpo.html**

A B C D E F G H I J K L M N O P Q R S T U V W X Y Z

## Browning, Elizabeth Barrett

Elizabeth Barrett Browning (1806-1861) was a British poet who married Robert Browning (another British poet). Her most noted works are "Sonnets from the Portuguese" (a series of love poems written to her husband), "Casa Guidi Windows" and "Aurora Leigh". Visit these web sites where you will find biographical material, collections of poems, scholarly writing, and links to related resources.

**Web:**

**http://www.inform.umd.edu:8080/EdRes/Topic/WomensStudies/ReadingRoom/Poetry/BarrettBrowning/**
**http://www.stg.brown.edu/projects/hypertext/landow/victorian/ebb/browningov.html**
**http://www.zia.com/arts/literature/englit/browning/**

## Chinese Poetry

Chinese poetry is beautiful in its imagery and simplicity. Read some Chinese poems at the web site. (You have the option of reading them in either in English or Chinese.) Or discuss Chinese poetry by joining the mailing list.

**Web:**

**http://www.chinapage.com/poetry.html**

**Listserv Mailing List:**

List Name: **chpoem-l**
Subscribe to: **listserv@ubvm.cc.buffalo.edu**

### Chinese Poetry

I love Chinese poetry and you will too once you give it half a chance. My favorite Chinese poem is that traditional work from the Chi'ing dynasty that starts, "There was a young girl from Beijing...". If you would like to be involved in one of the most beautiful art forms and its oriental incarnations, subscribe to the **chpoem-l** mailing list.

## Collective Poem

Participate in this exercise in silliness by helping write a collective poem. Use the form provided to submit a poetic line that will be added to the end of the poem in progress. For the less adventurous, you can take a look at the work without having to add anything yourself.

**Web:**

**http://sp1.berkeley.edu/caustic.html**

## Dickinson, Emily

Emily Elizabeth Dickinson (1830-1886) was a prolific American poet. Her verse is characterized by style, wit and imagery. Dickinson was a recluse who stayed in her house most of the time, writing poetry. Although she wrote a great many poems, Dickinson was virtually unpublished until after her death. (In her lifetime, she published only a handful of poems.) This web site has hundreds of Dickinson's poems along with links to biographical information and other Dickinson resources. The mailing list is for the discussion of the word play found in Dickinson's poetry.

**Web:**

**http://lal.cs.byu.edu/people/black/dickinson.html**

**Majordomo Mailing List:**

List Name: **emweb**
Subscribe to: **majordomo@lal.cs.byu.edu**

## Dogwood Blossoms

Lovers of haiku join together to discuss their favorite haiku or to show something they have written in haiku form. This digest is compiled approximately once a month and is receptive to new haiku and to suggestions and input from readers. It's a friendly poetic community.

**Web:**

**http://glwarner.samford.edu/data/haiku/haiku.htm**

## Internet Poetry Archive

This is a wonderful project from the University of North Carolina—famous poets can be experienced through pictures, sound files and text. Even if you don't have a graphical browser, you can still read the poetry from writers around the world, including Nobel Prize winners.

**Web:**

**http://sunsite.unc.edu/dykki/poetry/home.html**

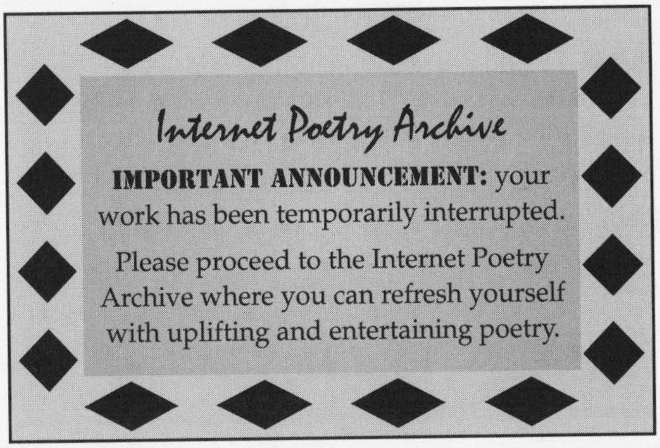
Internet Poetry Archive
IMPORTANT ANNOUNCEMENT: your work has been temporarily interrupted.
Please proceed to the Internet Poetry Archive where you can refresh yourself with uplifting and entertaining poetry.

## Irish Poetry

If you don't have time to run down to your local pub for a poetry reading, try just getting a brew from the fridge and downloading a poem or two written by an Irish poet. For a really good time, you can even find some poetry set to music.

**Web:**

**http://www.spinfo.uni-koeln.de/~dm/eire.html**

## Keats, John

John Keats (1795-1821) is one of the greatest English poets. Experience the mysterious, beautiful and joyful works of Keats firsthand by connecting to this nice archive of his poetry.

**Web:**

**http://wcarchive.cdrom.com/pub/obi/John.Keats/**

## Millay, Edna St. Vincent

Edna St. Vincent Millay (1892-1950) was a Pulitzer prize-winning American poet. Her most famous works are "The Harp Weaver" (a play) and "Renascence". These web sites offer a collection of Millay's poetry for you to enjoy, along with some biographical information. Millay was a bisexual and, even today, her work commands attention and respect in the lesbian community.

**Web:**

**http://physserv1.physics.wisc.edu/~shalizi/Poetry/Millay/**
**http://www.columbia.edu/acis/bartleby/millay/**
**http://www.sappho.com/poetry/e_millay.htm**

## Plath, Sylvia

Sylvia Plath (1932-1963) was an American poet whose work is characterized by intense imagery and highly personal quality. Her most famous work, The Bell Jar, is an autobiographical novel. Plath possessed a rare writing skill and sensitivity. She wrote her first poem at the age of eight, and throughout her schooling, achieved a great deal of critical recognition. However, she was also a deeply troubled woman and committed suicide at the age of 30, after the breakup of her marriage. Perhaps because of her notoriety and unfortunate demise, Plath became popular among young women in the early '70s, along with the growth of the feminist movement. Even today, Plath's work is required reading in most courses of women's literature. This web site has biographical information about Sylvia Plath, a bibliography of her work, as well as a collection of poems.

**Web:**

**http://www.informatik.uni-leipzig.de/privat2/beckmann/public_html/plath.html**

## Poems and Prose

Poetry archives with links to the poems of Rossetti, Wordsworth, Browning, Burns, Keats, Wyatt and other famous poets. You can also find links to web sites of the not yet rich and famous or make a link to your own.

**Web:**

**http://www.ece.ucdavis.edu/~darsie/library.html**
**http://www.hypersven.com/poets.corner/**

## Poetry Archives

There is a lot of poetry for you on the Net. Here are some collections that I think you will enjoy: lots and lost of well-known poems, as well as links to other poetry sites. These are good places to visit if you are looking for a particular poem or work from a particular author, or if you just feel like browsing for something to read.

**Web:**

**http://english-server.hss.cmu.edu/Poetry.html**
**http://www.ece.ucdavis.edu/~darsie/library.html**
**http://www.hypersven.com/poets.corner/**

***Why pay retail?*** *You can get all the poetry you want, for free, at the Poetry Archives.*

## Poetry Assortments

A thoughtful collection of poetry, representing major poets with a selection of their best known works. This is a good place to browse when you have a few moments and you need a breath of intellectual fresh air.

**Web:**

**http://english-www.hss.cmu.edu/poetry/**

## Poetry Garden Project

This is a nice collection of original poetry combined with images. A different poet is featured every month and each poet's work is archived so you can come back again and again.

**Web:**

**http://sashimi.wwa.com/~uschwarz/poetry.html**

## Poetry Talk and General Discussion

Spirits soar free on the wings of poetry. Show your verses to like-minded, creative people. If you ask, you can get advice, but there are more poems posted than critiques.

**Usenet:**

**rec.arts.poems**

## Shelley, Percy Bysshe

Percy Bysshe Shelley (1792-1822) was an English romantic poet who had a strong belief in reason and that humanity could evolve into perfection. Shelley eventually married Mary Wollstonecraft Shelley, who wrote the famed "Frankenstein". Read some of the beautiful lyric poems at this page devoted to the works of Percy Bysshe Shelley.

**Web:**

**http://wcarchive.cdrom.com/pub/obi/Percy.Bysshe.Shelley/**

## Shiki Internet Haiku Salon

An introduction to haiku, including its history, information about Shiki Masaoka, the founder of modern haiku, and links to many haiku poems and resources, including mailing lists and poetry servers.

**Web:**

**http://mikan.cc.matsuyama-u.ac.jp/~shiki/**

### *Shiki Internet Haiku Salon*

*Haiku is a form of poetry, developed in Japan, in which the writer seeks to capture a specific transient observation about the natural world. The world changes so quickly, and haiku is one way to capture a particular image or sensation.*

*A haiku poem (usually referred to as a "haiku") consists of three lines. The first line has 5 syllables, the second has 7, and the third has 5.*

*In addition, it is traditional for a haiku to indicate a particular season. Often, this is done by including a word that invokes a feeling of either winter, spring, summer or fall. In English, the tradition is slightly different: a poem should contain a reference to nature, but not necessarily to a particular season.*

*By its nature, haiku is concentrated. Although it uses only 17 syllables, a well-written haiku can invoke deep spiritual feeling. The best haiku is simple and clear, without metaphor, personification or other literary device.*

*If you would like to learn more about haiku, please visit the Shiki Internet Haiku Salon. In the meantime, here is a haiku for you to enjoy:*

fog blanket covers
tall green trees wait silently
quiet brings soothing peace

## Tennyson, Alfred

Alfred Tennyson (1809-1892) was an English poet who became poet laureate in 1850. He was a strong spokesman for Victorian values and is known for his excellent use of language and mastery of poetic technique. Two of his famous poems are "The Charge of the Light Brigade" and "In Memorium". The latter is a beautiful elegy written after the death of a close friend.

**Web:**

**http://wcarchive.cdrom.com/pub/obi/Tennyson/**

## Whittier, John Greenleaf

John Greenleaf Whittier (1807-1892) was an American poet and writer, a Quaker and a vigorous abolitionist. His poems are often sentimental pieces about the New England region of America. Whittier is the poet who said "For of all sad words of tongue or pen, the saddest are these: It might have been!"

**Web:**

**http://wcarchive.cdrom.com/pub/obi/John.Greenleaf.Whittier/**

## Wordsworth, William

William Wordsworth (1770-1850) was an English poet who became poet laureate in 1843. Wordsworth and his friend, Samuel Taylor Coleridge, wrote a book called "Lyrical Ballads" which introduced romanticism into England. Here's a nice selection of poems by Wordsworth.

**Web:**

**http://wcarchive.cdrom.com/pub/obi/William.Wordsworth/**

# POLITICS

## Arms and Disarmament

Although most people believe in arms control, no one wants to be first. Clearly, there is a lot to talk about. Here are some places to discuss politics, peace, war, the cold war, disarmament, and other related subjects.

**Usenet:**

**soc.politics.arms-d**

**Listserv Mailing List:**

List Name: **arms-l**
Subscribe to: **listserv@buacca.bu.edu**

## Conservative Political News

What is the latest news in the world of conservative politics? Find out about the most recent buzz in Washington and read about political agendas that relate to conservatives. This is not a discussion group, but rather a news list to stir discussion on other groups and to keep you informed on the latest political happenings.

**Majordomo Mailing List:**

List Name: **c-news**
Subscribe to: **majordomo@world.std.com**

## Democrats

The Democratic party was founded in 1792 by Thomas Jefferson. Originally, party members were called "Republicans" or "Democratic-Republicans" but in 1830, the name was shortened to "Democrats". This is the official web site of the Democratic party and, like the Republican site, there are no huge surprises. Visit the "Donkey Stomp" (a Republican bashing section) and the hilarious Quote-o-Rama page (which brings back memories of Dan Quayle). You can also read news and articles about the party and what you can do to help. The Usenet group is for the discussion of Democratic views and platforms.

**Web:**

**http://www.democrats.org/**

**Usenet:**

**alt.politics.democrats.d**

## Global Topics

A collection of pointers that looks at information resources with a global scope. It includes such topics as environment, government, military, peace, health, education, general reference and more.

**Web:**

**http://galaxy.einet.net/GJ/world.html**

**Don't click here.**

## Gun Control Talk and General Discussion

What could be more simple that deciding whether or not ordinary citizens should be allowed to own guns? Well, in the United States, the answer is, just about anything. This Usenet group is for the discussion of the political issues surrounding the regulation of the sale and use of handguns and rifles. I have only two remarks to make about the whole debate. (1) Gun ownership has a great deal to do with men and unconscious sexuality, and the sooner we realize that the better. (2) If ignorance is outlawed, only outlaws will be ignorant.

**Usenet:**

**talk.politics.guns**

## Hate Groups

Hate comes in many variations but only one basic form. Here is a collection of information to help you understand and work against those who would hate: racists, neo-nazis, people who deny the Holocaust, anti-gay bigots, and so on. Here you will find links to the web pages maintained by hate groups, as well as the names of Usenet groups and mailing lists in which such people hang out.

**Web:**

**http://www.law.harvard.edu/library/guides/hateweb/hate.html**
**http://www.vir.com/Shalom/hatred.html**

### *Look What I Found on the Net...*

```
Newsgroup: rec.guns
Subject: Pocket Holsters Are Now Illegal

>>>> Yesterday afternoon, my holster maker told me he couldn't
>>>> make pocket holsters anymore.  He received a certified
>>>> letter from local law enforcement that a recent BATF
>>>> (U.S. Bureau of Alcohol, Tobacco and Firearms) decision /
>>>> interpretation now makes it illegal to make, possess or own
>>>> a pocket holster that allows the gun to fire while still in
>>>> the holster unless they are registered.

>>> I think it is wonderful how government agencies can make any
>>> rule that they want without the help of Congress.

>> They don't and can't.  Congress GAVE them that authority!
>> That's what we should be screaming about, not that they
>> exercise every bit of power they can.  Take away their
>> ability to interpret the law, and they will be crippled.

> Is this for real?  Nothing with regard to BATF surprises me
> anymore, but this is just a little weird.
>
> I carry a NAA .22LR in my pants pocket at all times, without
> the assault pocket holster.  Ninety percent of the time I have
> a Makarov or G17 on my hip.  If they ban my belt, it's time to
> fight.
>
> -- Xxxxxx Xxxx, NRA Life Member

Here's the facts.  Not all pocket holsters are illegal.  And,
certainly, belts aren't going to be outlawed.

The holsters the BATF doesn't like are those which allow the gun
to be fired while it's still in the holster.  They claim that,
since it's a firearm that doesn't look like a firearm, then it
qualifies as an Any Other Weapon (AOW) -- the same as pen guns
and those neat briefcases that let you fire the MP5 or MAC-10
inside.

So that's it.  Do I like it?  No way!  Is there something you
can do about it?  Vote Republican.  Otherwise, get ready to
watch the constant erosion of our rights.

"Some men are alive simply because it is against the law to kill them"
```

## International Politics Talk and General Discussion

Usenet has a number of discussion groups specifically for the discussing of the politics of particular countries and regions: Britain, Europe, India, Italy, China, Middle East, Tibet and the former Soviet Union. As long as you stay more or less on topic, anything goes. However, please remember that if you are responding to an article written by someone in a foreign country, their first language may not be the same as yours. On the Net, irony and politics do not mix well. The world is a big place, and there is lots of room for two people to disagree and still both be right.

**Usenet:**

**alt.politics.british**
**alt.politics.ec**
**alt.politics.europe.misc**
**alt.politics.india.communist**
**alt.politics.india.progressive**
**alt.politics.italy**
**talk.politics.china**
**talk.politics.european-union**
**talk.politics.mideast**
**talk.politics.soviet**
**talk.politics.tibet**

## Internet Politics

This Usenet group is the place to go to discuss the politics of the Internet, and to complain about how the government is interfering with your right to do whatever you want on the Net. Remember, as one of my readers you are always right, so don't take any guff from anyone (unless you run into another one of my readers, in which case you must compromise graciously).

**Usenet:**

**alt.politics.datahighway**

## Irish Politics

This list is for the discussion of the kinder, gentler side of Irish politics as defined by the 26 counties of the Republic of Ireland since 1922. Discussions of Northern Ireland are welcome only if they directly relate to the politics of the Republic.

**Listserv Mailing List:**

List Name: **irl-pol**
Subscribe to: **listserv@irlearn.ucd.ie**

## Israeli Politics

The Israeli government is based on proportional representation. Here is how it works. The national house of representatives (the Knesset) has 120 members. In preparation for an election, each party creates a list of preferred candidates. However, when a person votes, he or she votes for a party, not for a particular person. After the votes are counted, the number of representatives elected to the Knesset is proportional to the percentage of votes that party received. For example, a party receiving 10% of the overall votes, would be send the top 12 candidates from its list to the Knesset. This sounds like a good idea, but it makes for a fractured system, in which no party can ever manage to get a majority on its own. Moreover, small, less popular parties can often wield disproportionate power as their votes are needed to form a coalition. Israel has fewer people than the city of Chicago in an area about the same size as New Jersey. However, in the 1996 election, there were 21 political parties (six of which were major organizations). Is it any wonder why Israeli politics is so... interesting. You know, when you think of it, Israel has a lot in common with Chicago and New Jersey.

**Web:**

**http://gauss.technion.ac.il/~nyh/israel/politics.html**

Israeli Politics

Israel is a small place. In fact, the pre-1967 borders afford it only 17 miles across at the narrowest point. If you wanted, you could comfortably fit the entire country into New Jersey (although why you want to do so is beyond me). Still, when you measure it in brouhaha per unit area, Israel has, pound for pound, the most robust set of mixed-up and eclectic political dynamics this side of a university sociology department.

As a Net person, there is no need for you to miss out on the fascinating and eccentric happenings in what is surely the most effervescent spot in the Middle East. If nothing else, it will make you appreciate the stability and peacefulness of your own country.

## Jefferson Project

The Jefferson Project is a guide to "online politics". It has loads of resources about political personalities, publications, political humor, the government, international politics, parties and activism. The resources are not geared to any particular political audience and so will appeal to (and aggravate) radicals, conservatives and liberals alike.

**Web:**

**http://www.voxpop.org/jefferson/**

## NATO

On April 4, 1949, the North Atlantic Treaty was signed in Washington, D.C., giving birth to NATO: the North Atlantic Treaty Organization. The original purpose of NATO was to support the defense of European and North American states against the threat of Soviet aggression. Today, the threat is gone (mostly), but NATO still plays a major role in Europe by talking softly while carrying a big stick.

**Web:**

**http://www.nato.int/**

**Listserv Mailing List:**

List Name: **natodata**
Subscribe to: **listserv@cc1.kuleuven.ac.be**

## Political Talk and General Discussion

If you like being contentious and opinionated, you'll love these Usenet groups. (Actually, as one of my readers, you are sensible and insightful. It's everyone else who is contentious and opinionated.) These are the Usenet groups specifically designated for political discussion. Anything goes, but in most areas of the Net, the power lies with the people who are the most intelligent, witty and well-spoken. If you would like more immediate interactive screaming matches, connect to IRC and join the **#politics** channel.

**Usenet:**

**alt.politics**
**bit.listserv.politics**
**talk.politics**
**talk.politics.misc**

**IRC:**

**#politics**

**Don't get fooled. Read "Consumer Information".**

### *Look What I Found on the Net...*

```
Newsgroup: alt.politics
Subject: Canada Has No Guarantees of Freedom

> ...People in Canada are so cute!  It's almost like they
> think they have their own COUNTRY up there.
>
> -- Xxxx Xxxxx,
>    Columbus, Ohio

From Ohio? Hmmm...

Tell me, if your parents moved to California and got a divorce,
would they still legally be brother and sister?

-- Xxxxxx Xxxx,
   Montreal, Quebec, Canada
```

A B C D E F G H I J K L M N O P Q R S T U V W X Y Z

**Want to send some fan mail? Read "People: Famous and Interesting".**

## Politics of Government Organizations

As all of us travel together through Modern Life, government organizations are forced to carry their own political baggage. These are the Usenet groups for the discussion of politics as it relates to various government organizations, mostly American: the Bureau of Alcohol, Tobacco and Firearms (ATF); the Central Intelligence Agency CIA); general covert operations organizations; the Federal Bureau of Investigation (FBI); the National Security Administration (NSA); and the United Nations. The **.misc** group is for the discussion of government organizations that do not have their own groups.

**Usenet:**

**alt.politics.org.batf**
**alt.politics.org.cia**
**alt.politics.org.covert**
**alt.politics.org.fbi**
**alt.politics.org.misc**
**alt.politics.org.nsa**
**alt.politics.org.un**

## Republican Discussion

It's not easy being a conservative these days. But now you have your own support groups in which to discuss the GOP and conservative movement, national conventions, conservative talk show hosts, and elections.

**Listserv Mailing List:**

List Name: **repub-l**
Subscribe to: **listserv@vm.marist.edu**

**Listserv Mailing List:**

List Name: **right-l**
Subscribe to: **listserv@cmsa.berkeley.edu**

## Republicans

The United States Republican Party was founded in 1854. The first Republican to be elected President was Abraham Lincoln (in 1860). This is the official Republican web site, and you pretty much get what you would expect. For instance, when I visited, I saw an opponent-bashing section in which I could view the "Outrage of the Day" (a hilarious animated picture of Bill Clinton as Pinocchio). There are also news releases, a chat room, some fun political stuff (games, crossword puzzles), email addresses of political people, information about GOP-TV, as well as background information on various governmental and political topics. Overall, there is lots and lots of pro-Republican, anti-Democrat stuff. For discussion of Republican views and platforms, you can participate in the Usenet group.

**Web:**

**http://www.rnc.org/**

**Usenet:**

**alt.politics.usa.republican**

## Richard Nixon Audio and Video Archive

People of the youngest generations will never know what it was like to hear Richard Nixon address the people of the United States. Thanks to modern technology and the Internet, anyone young or old, can hear the voice of Richard Nixon at any time of the day or night without having to pay $20 to hire the neighborhood psychic to perform a seance. Listen to his resignation speech, the Checkers speech, a portion of the Nixon debate and his explanation of Watergate.

**Web:**

**http://webcorp.com/sounds/nixon.htm**
**http://www.webcorp.com/video/nixon/**

**Read a zine today.**

A B C D E F G H I J K L M N O P Q R S T U V W X Y Z

## Treaties

If you are having trouble with your neighbor trimming the trees that are actually on *your* property and you want to take some firm action, I have an idea for you. Go to this web site for treaties and other international agreements. Download the treaty of your choice and open the document in your word processing program. Fill in your name and your neighbor's name in the appropriate slots then trot next door and make him sign it. Not only will he stop trimming your trees, but he might also be morally bound to notify you at the earliest possible moment that there has been a nuclear accident in his house.

**Web:**

**http://law.wuacc.edu/washlaw/doclaw/treat5m.html**

*Treaties are made to be broken, of course, but unless you know exactly what was in a treaty, you can't tell who is breaking what rule. Take a moment and snarf your own personal copy of the Geneva Convention. Just the thing for really understanding reruns of Hogan's Heroes.*

India INK

## United States Political Talk and General Discussion

I grew up in Canada, where there was a fair amount of politics. But that was nothing compared to the United States, where political wrangling and commentary is the national obsession (second only to watching highly paid athletes perform on TV). The great thing about American politics is that once you choose a point of view, you have all kinds of beliefs, opinions and avocations to adopt and defend without having to do any original thinking for yourself. Don't get me wrong, American politics is *interesting*, and there is nothing that I like better than a good old political argument. Actually, I'm not even that fussy. I just like to argue, so I'm always ready to take whichever side is opposed to whomever I am talking with. If you also like a good discussion, visit these Usenet groups and argue about the topic of your choice. The **.misc** group is for discussion of general politics that does not fit in one of the other, more specific groups.

**Usenet:**

**alt.politics.greens**
**alt.politics.libertarian**
**alt.politics.usa.congress**
**alt.politics.usa.constitution**
**alt.politics.usa.misc**
**talk.politics.libertarian**

## Weird Politics and Conspiracies

Some days do you get the feeling there is a lot of stuff going on around you that you don't know about? It's probably true. Find out what sort of weird things the government is doing while you aren't looking. This site has lots of documents and archives from some of the more unusual political movements. If you like conspiracy theories that relate to assassinations, check out the Usenet discussion group.

**Web:**

**http://www.physics.wisc.edu/~shalizi/hyper-weird/conspiracy.html**

**Usenet:**

**talk.politics.assassination**

**For some cool dreams, try sleeping with this book under your pillow.**

## PRIVACY

### Anonymous Remailers

It's embarrassing when your mom catches you posting to **alt.binaries.pictures.erotica.furry**. Avoid all the hassle of trying to explain by not getting caught in the first place. Try using an anonymous remailer. Here is information on what these services are and how they work.

**Web:**

**http://electron.rutgers.edu/~gambino/anon_servers/anon.html**
**http://www.cs.berkeley.edu/~raph/remailer-faq.html**

### Digital Money and Privacy

Digital money refers to a facility by which economic transactions are conducted entirely within electronic information systems. Many people think that, in the future, we will conduct a lot of our monetary transactions using digital money. Maybe yes and maybe no. But what is for sure, is that if we do start using digital money there will be a lot of important privacy considerations. For example, how would you feel if the government (or your loved ones) could find out the details every time you buy or sell something? This is a fascinating area of human development, and if you would like to see what people are saying (and planning), start with this web site devoted to digital money and privacy.

**Web:**

**http://www.eff.org/pub/Privacy/Digital_money/**

### Electronic Privacy Information Center

The Electronic Privacy Information Center (EPIC) is a public interest research center based in Washington, D.C. EPIC concerns itself with all types of privacy issues: Internet privacy, medical records, proposals for national ID cards, and so on. The EPIC web site houses a large collection of privacy-related information and resources on many different topics. If you care at all about these issues, take a few minutes to look around. I guarantee you will find something useful or interesting.

**Web:**

**http://www.epic.org/**

Are you worried that somebody may be trying to intercept the secret messages you send to your best friend? If so, visit the **Information Privacy** Web site and see what it takes to make sure you're always in the dark.

### Government Privacy Library

This is a repository of articles and case studies related to privacy, archived at the United States House of Representatives's Internet law library. You can read task force reports, information access laws, and a variety of other information.

**Web:**

**http://law.house.gov/107.htm**

### Information Privacy

This web site contains awareness alerts, pointers to privacy resources, information about Internet privacy and mailing lists. When you start to get serious about privacy, this is a good place to explore. (Just make sure no one is looking over your shoulder.)

**Web:**

**http://www.anu.edu.au/people/Roger.Clarke/DV/**

**Do you have a code in the head?**
**Try "Cryptography".**

A B C D E F G H I J K L M N O P Q R S T U V W X Y Z

A B C D E F G H I J K L M N O P Q R S T U V W X Y Z

## Privacy Forum Digest

If you are concerned about privacy in our new-fangled age of information, subscribe to **privacy**, a moderated mailing list. All manner of topics are discussed, including privacy issues relating to individuals and society as a whole. The information is useful, thoughtful and authoritative. The web page allows you to search previous issues of the digest—an extremely useful resource—all the way back to its beginning in May 1992. Take my word for it, there is a *lot* of interesting information here.

**Web:**

**http://www.vortex.com/privarch.htm**

**Listserv Mailing List:**

List Name: **privacy**
Subscribe to: **listserv@vortex.com**

## Privacy News Archive

Issues of privacy continually arise, with no end in sight. The faster we can process and transmit information, the more likely that individual rights will be invaded. To keep up on this most important part of our brave new world, you can check this web site and catch up on the news. You will find an annotated list of news stories and papers on privacy, telephony issues, wiretapping and other related issues.

**Web:**

**http://www.hotwired.com/Lib/Privacy/**

**I've never met a high-speed Internet connection I didn't like.**

## Privacy Online

What do you do when someone invades your privacy? Visit this web site and find out how to report privacy abuses. While you are there, read about how you risk losing privacy as a consumer. For example, direct marketing people get information about you when you use your credit card, subscribe to a magazine, make charitable donations, and so on.

**Web:**

**http://www.paranoia.com/~ebola/privacy.html**

## Privacy Resources

Privacy is everyone's business: you and you, and you there hiding behind your Macintosh thinking I won't notice you. Once the big boys (Netscape, Microsoft, AT&T, and so on) get into the "free software" act, it won't be long until you find that somewhere along the line, your personal interests were sold out for a handful of magic stock options and advertising revenues. I feel strongly that it is up to all of us to protect our privacy. The best way to start is by understanding the issues, and these sites are a good place to begin. Remember, once "they" control your browser, you will be able to run all over the Net, but you won't be able to hide.

**Web:**

**http://world.std.com/~franl/privacy/privacy.html**
**http://www.vortex.com/privacy.html**

## Privacy Rights Clearinghouse

This is a great web site. It contains a lot of useful information about privacy, your rights, and what you can do to protect them. I have personally found a lot of interesting and useful help here. One caveat: the information is designed for the United States, particularly California. However, don't let that discourage you. These people do a good job and much of the information is helpful to anyone.

**Web:**

**http://pwa.acusd.edu/~prc/**

## PRIVACY RESOURCES

**Privacy means a lot more than being safe and secure in your own home.**

Privacy means having control over who is allowed to keep and use information about you: your name, address, email address, phone number, government identification number (such as the U.S. Social Security Number and the Canadian Social Insurance Number), medical records, bank account information, credit rating, tax records, investment information, use of credit cards, frequent traveler information, magazine subscriptions, and on and on.

Want to learn more?
Explore the Privacy Resources.

### Privacy Talk and General Discussion

What better place to discuss privacy and security issues than out in the open on Usenet, where thousands of people you don't even know can read your every word. These discussion groups cover technical issues as well as cultural, political and social topics relating to privacy and security (such as the ill-conceived Clipper chip).

**Usenet:**

**alt.privacy**
**alt.privacy.anon-server**
**alt.privacy.clipper**
**comp.society.privacy**

### Privacy Tips

The more information can be processed by computers, the more your privacy becomes important. These web sites contain some good resources to help you get the privacy you want. Find a wealth of tips and information regarding email, voice mail, social security numbers, cordless phones, the Net, computers, and much more.

**Web:**

**http://www.northcoast.com/savetz/yic/YIC12FI.html**
**http://www.playboy.com/forum/archive/privacy2.html**

### Using the Web Anonymously

Did you ever ask yourself, how can the browser companies (Netscape, Microsoft, and so on) afford to develop browsers and give them away for free? Browser companies design software to please their customers, and *you* are not a customer. The customers are the companies that actually pay for software, such as web server programs. So it should come as no surprise when I tell you that all modern browsers are designed to pass information about you and your computer system to any web server that asks for it. Think about it, each time you connect to a web server, your browser may be passing private information to that server. (In other words, you only *think* you got your browser for free.) To circumvent this system, you can route all your browser requests through an "anonymizer", a service that will submit your web request to the appropriate server on your behalf. This will completely preserve your privacy (as long as you trust the people who provide the anonymizer service), however it does slow things down. At the very least, you should connect to the anonymizer web site, and let it show you exactly what information your web browser is happily giving out to any web server that asks.

**Web:**

**http://www.anonymizer.com/**

## PROGRAMMING

### Ada

This site contains compilers, tools, documentation, FAQs and other software for the Ada programming language, as used by the U.S. Department of Defense.

**Web:**

**http://lglwww.epfl.ch/Ada/**

### Basic

These Usenet discussion groups provide forums for questions and answers on topics relating to the Basic programming language. The web site is a large repository of things Basic. Lots of great stuff. Free for the entire family.

**Web:**

**http://www2.cybernex.net/~peterp/**

**Usenet:**

**alt.lang.basic**
**comp.lang.basic.misc**

## C

Here are some interesting resources for C programmers. One web site contains explanations of the most important aspects of C. The other web site contains links to the C frequently asked question lists. Both of these resources are excellent if you are just starting with C. For a lot of ongoing discussion, there are the Usenet groups.

**Web:**

**http://pitel_lnx.ibk.fnt.hvu.nl/~rbergen/cmain.html**
**http://www.cis.ohio-state.edu/hypertext/faq/bngusenet/comp/lang/c/top.html**

**Usenet:**

**comp.lang.c**
**comp.std.c**

## C++

If you are interested in learning how to program in C++ (an object-oriented language based on C), one of these web sites contains a great primer. A second site will help you find C++ resources around the Net. The third site contains a FAQ. For talk, try the IRC channel or Usenet.

**Web:**

**http://www.cerfnet.com/~mpcline/C++-FAQs-Lite/**
**http://www.cl.ais.net/morph/c++/**
**http://www.inquiry.com/techtips/cpp_pro/**

**Usenet:**

**comp.lang.c**
**comp.std.c**

**IRC:**

**#C++**

If you're thinking of making the most serious commitment that a computer programmer can make—jumping into C++—stop, take a deep breath, and read the frequently asked question list.

C++

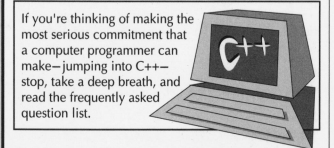

## DOS Programming Talk and General Discussion

DOS may be well along the way to a well-deserved final resting place, but it is still alive and well on Usenet. Here are the groups devoted to general discussion of DOS programming. If you are a DOS person, these are good places to look for tips, questions and answers. If you are not a DOS person, do not pass "Go" and, definitely, do not collect $200.

**Usenet:**

**alt.msdos.programmer**
**comp.os.msdos.programmer**

## Free Compilers and Interpreters

You can pay a lot of money for a language translator, or you can check this site and find many, many free compilers and interpreters. If you ever find yourself with some free time and nothing to do, why not download a free compiler and teach yourself a new language? (Actually, I tried to teach myself French that way, but I kept getting parsing mistakes.)

**Web:**

**http://www.idiom.com/free-compilers/**

## Free Programming Tools

To say that this resource is extensive is like saying that the Queen of England insists on getting her own way: it doesn't even begin to describe the reality of the situation. What we have here is page after page after page of serious tools for serious programmers doing serious things (seriously). If you have even the least bit of interest in being a programming nerd, this site is a must-have for your bookmark list.

**Web:**

**http://explorer.execnet.com/filelibs/l169p001.html**

**Wow, free software.**

## Hello World

It is said that when you learn a new computer language the first thing you do is write a program to display the words "Hello World". Well, I have been programming for years, in a variety of languages, and I have never, ever written a program that says "Hello World". But then, I have never seen a Rocky movie, watched an episode of Beverly Hills 90210, or had tiramisu for dessert. However, if you happen to be someone who is at home in popular culture, and you happen to be a programmer who likes exploring strange new languages, here is a site that will amuse and entertain you endlessly.

**Web:**

**http://www.latech.edu/~acm/HelloWorld.shtml**

## Interactive Fiction Game Programming

Interactive fiction is a type of game in which a story is told. The development of the story depends on choices made by the reader. This web site contains some useful and interesting interactive fiction resources. For a discussion of all aspects of interactive fiction, you can participate in the Usenet groups.

**Web:**

**http://www.khoros.unm.edu/staff/neilb/intfiction/index.html**

**Usenet:**

**rec.arts.int-fiction**
**rec.games.int-fiction**

### *Look What I Found on the Net...*

```
            (from the 1986 Obfuscated C Code Contest)

===========

Note from  Harley:

This program, written by Jack Applin, displays:

     Hello, world!

The program works in C, Fortran 77 and Bourne shell.  Programs
such as this are now common, but as far as I know, this was the
original one.

===========

cat =13 /*/ >/dev/null 2>&1; echo "Hello, world!"; exit
*
*  This program works under cc, f77, and /bin/sh.
*
*/; main() {
      write(
cat-~-cat
     /*,'(
*/
     ,"Hello, world!"
     ,
cat); putchar(~-~-~-cat); } /*
     ,)')
      end
*/
```

A B C D E F G H I J K L M N O P Q R S T U V W X Y Z

## Obfuscated C Code

Entries and winners for the International Obfuscated C Code Contest, in which programmers compete to create the most artistic, beautiful and obscure C program. The program must be small (less than a specified number of bytes), and it must work.

**Web:**

**http://reality.sgi.com/csp/ioccc/**

## Object-Oriented Programming

Object-oriented programming is just like regular programming except that you look at everything differently, write your programs differently, maintain them differently, and think with a different part of your temporal lobe. Join the discussion and talk about object-oriented tools, techniques, and problems. The **.misc** group is for general discussion of Macintosh object-oriented programming. The **.macapp3** group is devoted to Version 3 of the MacApp system. The **.tcl** group is for discussion of the Think Class Libraries.

**Usenet:**

**comp.sys.mac.oop.macapp3**
**comp.sys.mac.oop.misc**
**comp.sys.mac.oop.tcl**

## Operating Systems Research

Join this Usenet discussion group to keep up on the latest research and developments in operating systems technology. This is a good place to participate if you are doing operating systems research. If you are new to this area, check out the web site and read the FAQ (frequently asked question list).

**Web:**

**http://www.best.com/~bos/os-faq/**

**Usenet:**

**comp.os.research**

**The Net loves poetry.**

## Operating Systems Talk and General Discussion

An operating system is the master control program that runs a computer: for example, Windows 95, Windows NT, DOS, MacOS and Unix are all operating systems. If you are interested in issues relating to the design and implementation of operating systems, here is a Usenet group in which you can talk with people working in this area. This group is for general operating system discussion. For issues relating to specific systems, there are more specific Usenet groups.

**Usenet:**

**comp.os.misc**

## OS/2 Programming Talk and General Discussion

Questions, answers and discussion relating to programming under OS/2: general discussion, as well as groups devoted to tools, porting and object-oriented programming.

**Usenet:**

**comp.os.os2.programmer.misc**
**comp.os.os2.programmer.oop**
**comp.os.os2.programmer.porting**
**comp.os.os2.programmer.tools**

## Programmer of the Month

When I was a graduate student, I was on the U.C. San Diego computer programming team (along with Bart, Don and Madeline). In those days, programming competitions were uncommon, and we competed by writing a Fortran program which we created on punched cards. Today, computer systems are a lot more sophisticated, but we are still waiting for programming to become an Olympic event. In the meantime, anyone can compete to be Programmer of the Month. This contest—started in 1993 at AT&T—is open to anyone in the world. Check out the current contest, see the past winners, and marvel at the beautiful trophy awarded to the best programmers.

**Web:**

**http://www.cs.washington.edu/homes/corin/POTM.PAGES/**

## Programming Languages

Here is your central switching point for language-oriented web sites: a comprehensive list of resources categorized by language type. Even if you are a programmer supreme, I bet you can find something you have never heard of.

**Web:**

**http://src.doc.ic.ac.uk/bySubject/Computing/Languages.html**

**Need even more information on programming languages?**

**Try the Net**

## Programming the Mac

If you are a Mac programmer, there are lots of people you can talk to on Usenet. Here are some of the discussion groups devoted to Macintosh programming.

**Usenet:**

**comp.sys.mac.programmer.codewarrior**
**comp.sys.mac.programmer.games**
**comp.sys.mac.programmer.help**
**comp.sys.mac.programmer.info**
**comp.sys.mac.programmer.misc**
**comp.sys.mac.programmer.tools**

## Software Engineering

As you might imagine, programming is an important topic on the Net, and there are lots of software engineering resources. Here is a web site that has a wide variety of information including institutes, libraries, and various web pages relating to software engineering. For ongoing discussion, you can join the Usenet groups.

**Web:**

**http://rbse.jsc.nasa.gov/virt-lib/soft-eng.html**

**Usenet:**

**comp.software.eng**
**comp.software.testing**

## Visual Basic

Fans of Visual Basic will love this web site. This site offers links to Visual Basic archives, Usenet groups, and much more. When you get tired of exploring, check out the Usenet discussion group and see what everyone else is saying.

**Web:**

**http://apexepa.apexsc.com/vb/**

**Usenet:**

**comp.lang.basic.visual**

## Windows Programming Talk and General Discussion

Questions and answers relating to general programming in the Microsoft Windows environment as well as more specific topics such as controls, dialogs, graphics and printing, memory management, multimedia and network programming, and so on.

**Usenet:**

**comp.os.ms-windows.programmer.controls**
**comp.os.ms-windows.programmer.graphics**
**comp.os.ms-windows.programmer.menus**
**comp.os.ms-windows.programmer.misc**
**comp.os.ms-windows.programmer.multimedia**
**comp.os.ms-windows.programmer.networks**
**comp.os.ms-windows.programmer.ole**
**comp.os.ms-windows.programmer.vxd**
**comp.os.ms-windows.programmer.win32**
**comp.os.ms-windows.programmer.winhelp**

## X Window

Here is information about the X Consortium (the X Window people) as well as links to many X-related sites. Find out what you need to work with X today, and why you will need to work with X tomorrow as it turns into Broadway: a system for creating and accessing interactive applications over the Web.

**Web:**

**http://www.rahul.net/kenton/xsites.html**
**http://www.x.org/**

A B C D E F G H I J K L M N O P Q R S T U V W X Y Z

# PSYCHOLOGY

## Adler, Alfred

Alfred Adler (1870-1937) was an Austrian psychiatrist, who started with Freud, but eventually rejected Freud's emphasis on sexuality. Adler founded the school of individual psychology and maintained that neurosis was not a matter of repressed sexuality, but rather a reaction to feelings of inferiority. ("It is always easier to fight for one's principles than to live up to them.") Adler felt that the relation of the individual to his or her community was of prime importance, and that a feeling of connection to society was paramount to maintaining mental health. This web site is devoted to classical Adlerian psychology. You will find readings, biographies, interviews, links to related resources, and more. The Usenet group is for the discussion of Adlerian psychology.

**Web:**

**http://ourworld.compuserve.com/homepages/hstein/**

**Usenet:**

**alt.psychology.adlerian**

## American Psychological Association Journals

The abstracts and table of contents for a large number of journals sponsored by the American Psychological Association. The information at this site allows you to scan through the summaries of your favorite journals: an easy way to keep up on what is happening.

**Web:**

**http://www.apa.org/journals/journals.html**

## American Psychological Society

The web server of the American Psychological Society (APS) offers articles from publications of the APS, as well as information about membership, teaching psychology, doing research, job support services, publishers, and links to psychology software archives.

**Web:**

**http://psych.hanover.edu/APS/**

## Cognitive and Psychological Sciences Index

This web page is a huge index to academic programs, organizations and conferences, journals and magazines, Usenet groups, mailing lists, announcements, publishers, and many more resources relating to cognitive and psychological sciences.

**Web:**

**http://matia.stanford.edu/cogsci/**

## Consciousness

Consciousness is a good thing, especially when you are driving a car or operating heavy machinery. Here are a mailing list and some Usenet groups that have been created to offer people the chance to share ideas and discuss research in the area of consciousness and to talk about articles that appear in the journal *Psyche*.

**Usenet:**

**sci.psychology.consciousness**
**sci.psychology.journals.psyche**

**Listserv Mailing List:**

List Name: **psyche-l**
Subscribe to: **listserv@rfmh.org**

## Creativity and Creative Problem Solving

That problem has really been nagging at you. It sits in the back of your mind taunting you, demanding attention, begging to be dealt with. No ordinary problem solving is going to take care of it. What's the difference between plain old problem solving and creative problem solving? Discover the answer to that question by examining stimulating factors for creativity in product development, strategic issues, and organizational settings.

**Listserv Mailing List:**

List Name: **crea-cps**
Subscribe to: **listserv@nic.surfnet.nl**

## PSYCOLOQUY

**What do you do when you have a house guest you are just too busy to entertain? Sit him down at the computer, connect him to the American Psychological Association web site, and let him read back issues of psychology journals.**

**Just listen to this:**
**"According to Wallis (1992), philosophers of mind agree that a successful theory of representation must 'describe conditions for representation in nonintentional and nonsemantic terms.' If we restrict representation talk to what goes on in frogs, the visual systems of humans, etc., then perhaps Wallis is right. But once we count beliefs as representations, there is no such agreement. Indeed..."**

**Your friends will be coming back to visit you, again and again.**

## Family Science

Life should be just like the Family Circus—the comic strip in which the round-faced little children and happy mom and dad bring cheer to each other's lives. But for those of you not into fantasy, explore the field of family science, which focuses on marriage and family therapy, family sociology, and the behavioral science aspects of family medicine. This is a great opportunity to communicate with other family scientists and to learn about research programs in family science.

**Listserv Mailing List:**

List Name: **famlysci**
Subscribe to: **listserv@lsv.uky.edu**

## Family Violence

Home is supposed to be a haven, a place for nurturing and safety. But life doesn't always quite go the way you expect it to and sometimes home is the place you feel the least safe. A networking system has been established to study all aspects of family violence. It is not limited to topics of child abuse or violence within the family, but serves a wide range of areas covered by the term "intimate violence".

**Listserv Mailing List:**

List Name: **intvio-l**
Subscribe to: **listserv@uriacc.uri.edu**

## Freud, Sigmund

Sigmund Freud (1856-1939) was an Austrian psychiatrist and one of the great geniuses of the twentieth century. Freud opened vast areas of human thought—for example, the idea that there is an unconscious mind—and can rightly be considered the father of modern psychology. Freud's basic theory (which he developed and expanded over the years) is that unresolved infantile conflicts are responsible for much of adult neurosis and other aberrant behavior. Freud developed the techniques of psychoanalysis: the use of free association and dream interpretation to bring these conflicts to light, and to deal with them appropriately. As Freud developed his theories, it became more and more clear to him that the repressed feelings and memories were often of a sexual nature. He described, for example, the Oedipus Complex: a subconscious desire in a child for the parent of the opposite sex. If this complex does not resolve itself naturally, it will have a great effect on the person. As an adult, he or she may become neurotic and may be unable to form a normal, sexual relationship. Freud's strong belief in repressed sexual feelings as the root of much human pathology was extremely controversial at the time, and led to his breaking with some of his followers, in particular, Carl Jung and Alfred Adler. Throughout the years, Freud's theories have been studied, expanded (and even partially discredited) by several generations of psychoanalysts and physiologists. However, the bulk of Freud's insight and contributions have stood the test of time. Although there are those who criticize Freud's theories, I find that most such people know very little about what Freud really said and did. If you have never actually read anything Freud wrote, you may enjoy doing so. (I suggest starting with the book The Psychopathology of Everyday Life.) Freud was a real genius in the sense that whatever he turned his attention to, he illuminated.

**Web:**

**http://plaza.interport.net/nypsan/freudarc.html**

**Sigmund Freud**

If you want to find out what Freud really said, read what Freud really said.

A B C D E F G H I J K L M N O P Q R S T U V W X Y Z

## Jung, Carl

Carl Gustav Jung (1875-1961) was a Swiss psychiatrist. At one time, Jung was one of Freud's disciples. (In fact, Jung was the first president of the International Psychoanalytic Association.) However, in 1912 he published a book called Psychology and the Unconscious, which described two dimensions of the unconscious. In addition to the regular unconscious which Freud had discovered (containing repressed and forgotten memories and thoughts), Jung postulated a "collective unconscious" (mental patterns shared within a culture or by all human beings). This was enough of a revolutionary hypothesis to cause Jung to break with Freud. Jung founded the school of "analytical psychology" and achieved a career of great renown. (It was Jung, for instance, who developed the ideas of introversion and extroversion.) This web page has a nice selection of Jung's writings. You can see a bibliography of his collected works and hang out in the chat room and talk about Jung's theories. The Usenet group is for the discussion of Jungian psychology.

**Web:**

**http://www.enteract.com/~jwalz/Jung/**

**Usenet:**

**alt.psychology.jung**

## Mind Games

Psychology doesn't have to be all science and academics. There is so much you can do aside from hypnotizing people at parties. For instance, here are lots of mind games and brain teasers that are guaranteed to intrigue you as well as pass the time. A few of the games involve picking numbers, math and grammar, and patterns.

**Web:**

**http://weber.u.washington.edu/~jlks/mindgame.html**

**Stay away from "X-Rated".**

**Feel lucky? Try "Contests".**

## National Guild of Hypnotists

You could make a lot of money if you knew how to hypnotize people. For instance, you could stroll up and down your neighborhood about the time all the businessmen are getting ready to go to work. Then, when they are just about to leave and they forget where they have put their car keys, you could offer to help them remember, for a small fee. In fact, if you were a qualified hypnotist, you could even join the National Guild of Hypnotists and go to conventions and conferences. Find out more about the Guild and the hypnosis resources they offer.

**Web:**

**http://www.hollys.com/ngh/**

## Optical Illusions

Optical illusions are really cool, even without the benefit of caffeine or other artificial substances. This site has a nice collection of images that make you think twice (or more) about what you are seeing.

**Web:**

**http://lainet3.lainet.com/~ausbourn/**

Is life too much (right now)?
Try **alt.psychology.help**.

## Personality Testing

One way to analyze the human personality is by studying a person and classifying him or her as being a particular "psychological type". This idea was originally developed by Carl Jung, who believed that human behavior follows specific patterns that develop from the characteristics of the human mind. Jung believed the conscious human mind was continually perceiving (taking in information) and judging (organizing information to arrive at decisions). However, each person is born with a tendency to favor one type of mental activity over the other. According to Jung, a person could perceive either by "sensing" or by using "intuition". Similarly, one judges either by "thinking" or "feeling". (You can see how one could classify people according to this criteria.) Jung also identified two opposite human tendencies: extroversion (an outward focus) and introversion (an inward focus). Here are some resources that can help you understand personality testing, Jungian and otherwise. If you enjoy self-analysis, one of these web sites has a test you can take to estimate your Jungian-based personality characteristics. This will allow you to summarize your personality using a standard, four-letter acronym, for example, INTJ (introvert, intuition [N], thinking, judging) or XNFP (split extrovert/introvert [X], intuition [N], feeling, perceiving). For a discussion of personality testing, you can participate in the two Usenet groups.

**Web:**

**http://sunsite.unc.edu/personality/keirsey.html**
**http://www.2h.com/Tests/personality.phtml**
**http://www.brad.ac.uk/~mdavarle/personality.html**
**http://www.shrubbery.com/ingram/mbti/**

**Usenet:**

**alt.psychology.personality**
**sci.psychology.personality**

## Psychological Help

There are days when things seem overwhelming and unpleasant or you encounter a problem and you don't know exactly what to do with it. Check out the Usenet group that offers discussion about the problems people face. Maybe you will find an answer or just someone to talk to.

**Usenet:**

**alt.psychology.help**

## Psychology Database

This web site allows you to access a search engine maintained by the American Psychological Association. Specify one or more words, and the search engine will return a set of links to psychology web sites and articles that relate to your request. I searched for the word "Harley". The result was an article co-authored by a person with the last name of Harley. (In case you are wondering, the article is "Object Representation in the Bottlenose Dolphin: Integration of Visual and Echoic Information".)

**Web:**

**http://www.psychcrawler.com/**

## Psychology Resources

If you are interested in psychology, you will want to explore this web site, where you will find information about many psychology-related resources on the Net: web sites, discussion groups and mailing lists. The mailing list I have listed here is for sharing information about Net-based psychology resources.

**Web:**

**http://www.gasou.edu/psychweb/psychweb.htm**

**Majordomo Mailing List:**

List Name: **inetpsych**
Subscribe to: **majordomo@psyc.uow.edu.au**

## Psychology Talk and General Discussion

The good thing about psychology is that anyone can talk about it. The bad thing is that everyone does. Of course, as one of my readers, your insights are particularly valuable, so if you have any interest in psychology, I encourage you to join the discussion. Here are several Usenet groups devoted to different aspects of psychology. If you are not sure which one is for you, choose the **.misc** group.

**Usenet:**

**sci.psychology.misc**
**sci.psychology.research**
**sci.psychology.theory**

A B C D E F G H I J K L M N O P Q R S T U V W X Y Z

## Self-Help and Psychology Magazine

Self-Help and Psychology features articles by renowned psychologists and respected experts. There are also links to departmental areas where you can find more articles and information on subjects such as relationships, sexuality, addictions, family, sports psychology and health.

**Web:**

**http://www.cybertowers.com/selfhelp/**

**Read the FAQs of life.**

## Social Psychology

Social psychology is the branch of human psychology relating to group behavior and the influence of social factors on individuals. This site is a listing of social psychology resources on the Net: general resources, programs, researchers, schools and societies. The mailing list is for the discussion of applied social psychology.

**Web:**

**http://cac.psu.edu/~arm3/social.html**

**Listserv Mailing List:**

List Name: **aspsych**
Subscribe to: **listserv@gwuvm.gwu.edu**

### *Look What I Found on the Net...*

```
Newsgroup: sci.psychology.misc
Subject: How Would You React to This?

What would your reaction be if someone said to you:

  I think you are connected to a murder.

Now, if you were innocent, how would you react to this accusation?

If you were guilty, but didn't want to show it?
If you were guilty, but didn't care if anyone knew it?

I've been having a really hard time connecting to this...

=============

Newsgroup: sci.psychology.misc
Subject: Do You Know a Doctoral Program in Parapsychology?

I'm posting this for a friend who's about to complete her
Masters in physiological psychology and is looking for a
doctoral program in cognitive psychology.

The point is that her research interests are -- how to say it --
precognition, telepathy, clairvoyance, psychokinesis; in one
word: parapsychology.

I should stress that she's neither a magician nor looking for a
training program in secret spells...
```

## QUOTATIONS

### Allen, Woody

You probably think I have a good sense of humor but, actually, I've just memorized all of Woody Allen's famous quotes. No reason why you can't do the same.

**Web:**

**http://www.cp-tel.net/~miller/BilLee/quotes/Woody.html**

### Daily Quotations

There are a lot of people in the world and, every day, somebody says something interesting. This web site will show you a new quote every day, selected from a current event of some type. This site is a great place to visit every day, so you can have something to read while you take your daily vitamin. And when you have a little extra time, you can browse the collections of old quotations looking for some instant nostalgia.

**Web:**

**http://www.sfgate.com/quotes/archive/**

### Dangerfield, Rodney

I get no respect. I went to use my Internet account the other day, and found that somebody had changed my username to **shicklegruber**. But I've got nothing to complain about; take a look at what Rodney has to say.

**Web:**

**http://www.interlog.com/~meil/quotes2.html**
**http://www.rodney.com/rodney/joke.of.the.day/joke.html**

**FOR MEN ONLY**

Hey guys, need a quick way to impress a woman?

If she is under 20 years old, quote Beavis and Butthead.

If she is between 20 and 30, quote Jerry Seinfeld.

If she is between 30 and 40, quote Steven Wright.

If she is between 40 and 50, quote Woody Allen.

If she is over 50, quote Rodney Dangerfield.

## Quotation Archives

The Internet has a number of sites at which you can find all kinds of quotations. Just the thing for spicing up your conversation and enhancing your reputation. Here is a typical example showing how it works.

*[You are talking to your teacher or boss.]*

Teacher/Boss:

So what do you have to say for yourself?

*[At this point you repeat a quote that you downloaded the night before from one of the Internet quotation archives.]*

You:

Well, I think blah, blah blah, blah, blah...

Teacher/Boss:

Wow, you really are terrific. I'm going to give you an A (or a raise).

Very good looking woman/man who happens to be listening:

You are an unbelievably attractive person. Would you like to have dinner with me tonight?

### Famous Quotations

This web site has a large collection of quotations from famous people: Herodotus, Confucius, Adolf Hitler, Reggie Jackson, John Kennedy, Martin Luther King, Helen Keller, Mae West, Oscar Wilde and many more. When you have a few extra moments, take some time to read through the list. Soon you will be wise and pithy, fawned over by all your friends. As Winston Churchill once said, "It is a good thing for an uneducated man to read books of quotations." (Uneducated women, I suppose, are on their own.)

**Web:**

**http://www.labyrinth.net.au/~pirovich/quotes.html**

## Fields, W.C.

W. C. Fields (1879-1946) was an American movie actor whose wit is legendary even today. After all, anyone who hates kids, dogs and books for dummies can't be all bad.

**Web:**

**http://inet.uni-c.dk/~bruno/fields.htm**

## Goldwyn, Samuel

Samuel Goldwyn (1882-1974) was a Polish-born American film producer who merged his own company with that of Louis B. Mayer to form Metro-Goldwyn-Mayer. Goldwyn is best remembered for the original way in which he expressed his ideas. For example, he once said that "Pictures are for entertainment, messages should be delivered by Western Union." Are all the Samuel Goldwyn quotes real? I can tell you in two words: a pocryphal.

**Web:**

**http://www.eng.wayne.edu/Carlo/Sam.html**

## Humorous Quotations

A long list of topics from which to choose. Random quotation generators or files of one-liners, jokes and other humorous tidbits. Wide variety of subjects.

**Web:**

**http://meta.stanford.edu/quotes.html**

## Internet Quotes

Would you like to sound witty and knowledgeable about the Internet? Visit this web page, where you can look at a quote about the Net and related topics. The quotes come from various places: speeches, stuff found on the Net, books, news stories, and so on. Would you like to see another quote? Just reload the page.

**Web:**

**http://www.sbt.net/cgi-bin/sbt/quote.cgi**

## Marx, Groucho

Groucho Marx (1894-1977) was one of America's funniest funny men. Check out some of his quotes and maybe you can pass them off as your own.

**Web:**

**http://inet.uni-c.dk/~bruno/groucho.htm**

## Presidential Quotes

This archive has a collection of quotes from various American Presidents: Jefferson, Lincoln, Clinton, Reagan and others. This is the place to go when you need to remind yourself whether or not it was Ronald Reagan who said, "Ask not what your country can do for you; ask what you can do for your country." In addition, you will also find quotes from other notables, such as Linus Torvalds, the creator of the original version of the Linux operating system. ("Linux does endless loops in six seconds.")

**Web:**

**http://wormhole.res.cmu.edu/~adavenpo/quotes/**

## Quotation Talk and General Discussion

Here is the Usenet group devoted to a discussion of quotations. This is the place to ask if anyone knows who said "It isn't necessary to have relatives in Kansas City in order to be unhappy." Of course, questions like this only get answered if people participate, so if you like quotes, why don't you follow the discussion and see if you can help someone else.

**Usenet:**

**alt.quotations**

## Quotes from Skeptics

It's always fun to look back in life and take a moment to shake our heads at the foolishness of skeptical folly. Here are some quotes from skeptics of the past and their estimation of what things would be like in the future.

**Web:**

**http://www.athenet.net/~jlindsay/SkepticQuotes.html**

## Look What I Found on the Net...

(from the Samuel Goldwyn quotation archive)

---

Note: Samuel Goldwyn was an American immigrant who became one of the most powerful film producers in Hollywood. He controlled MGM (Metro-Goldwyn-Mayer) and was well known for his eminently quotable remarks, many of which are, no doubt, apocryphal.

---

"It rolled off my back like a duck."

[When told his son was getting married]
"Thank heaven. A bachelor's life is no life for a single man."

"I can give you a definite maybe."

"Gentleman, include me out."

"A verbal contract isn't worth the paper it's printed on."

Bookkeeper: Mr. Goldwyn, our files are bulging with paperwork we no longer need. May I have your permission to destroy all records before 1945?
Goldwyn: Certainly. Just be sure to keep a copy of everything.

"I can tell you in two words: im possible."

[On being told that a friend had named his son Sam, after him]
"Why did you do that ? Every Tom, Dick and Harry is named Sam!"

"I paid too much for it, but it's worth it."

"Don't worry about the war. It's all over but the shooting."

"Gentlemen, for your information, I have a question to ask you."

"I read part of it all the way through."

"If I could drop dead right now, I'd be the happiest man alive."

"I never put on a pair of shoes until I've worn them at least five years."

"I don't think anyone should write their autobiography until after they're dead."

"Anyone who goes to a psychiatrist ought to have his head examined."

"Gentlemen, listen to me slowly."

[in discussing Lillian Hellman's play, "The Children's Hour"]
Goldwyn: Maybe we ought to buy it?
Associate: Forget it, Mr. Goldwyn, its about lesbians.
Goldwyn: That's okay, we'll make them Americans.

## Random Quotes

Random quotes from Dave Barry, Jack Handey, Steven Wright, Star Trek, the Simpsons and others. Also available is the Fortune Cookie and the Shakespearean Insult Server.

**Web:**

**http://www.nova.edu/Inter-Links/quotes.html**

## Selectable Quote Server

Visit this site and order up a quote from one of your favorite people. Select the person you want and you will furnished with a quote. Choose from a variety of sources: writers, politicians, the Simpsons, insults, answering machines. Even your mother has quotes of her own in this archive.

**Web:**

**http://cruciform.cid.com/~werdna/fun.html**

## Signature Quotes

In case you don't get enough of them from Usenet and email, here are a collection of quotes taken from **.signature** files from around the world. Some quotes are written by people on the Net, some are from famous people.

**Web:**

**http://forum.swarthmore.edu/~heather/oldstuff/random.html**

## Star Trek Quotes

Dammit, Jim, I'm a writer, not a trivia buff. If you want quotes from the original Star Trek, the Next Generation, the Star Trek movies, or Deep Space Nine, you'll have to get them yourself.

**Web:**

**http://www.netshop.net/Startrek/web/Quotes.html**

### *Look What I Found on the Net...*

```
Newsgroup: alt.quotations
Subject: Geometry or Math Quote Wanted

> Would anyone kindly offer a special quotation pertaining to
> geometry or math, please?

[to which various people send in replies...]

There is no royal road to geometry.
  -- Euclid to Ptolemy I

Sex is the mathematics urge sublimated.
  -- M.C. Reed


Anyone who cannot cope with mathematics is not fully human.  At
best he is a tolerable subhuman who has learned to wear shoes,
bathe and not make messes in the house.
  -- Robert Heinlein (in "Time Enough for Love")

There are three kinds of people in this world: Those who can
count to three and those who can't.
  -- anonymous

Stand firm in your refusal to remain conscious during algebra.
In real life, I assure you, there is no such thing as algebra.
  -- Fran Leibowitz

As long as algebra is taught in school, there will be prayer in
school.
  -- Cokie Roberts
```

## Today's Fortune

If you are trying to cut down on sweets and you are bypassing the after-dinner fortune cookie, at least you don't have to feel deprived. Load up this page to get a nice fortune quote. And if you don't like it, you can reload to get another one.

**Web:**

**http://www.bsdi.com/fortune**

# Today's Fortune

**Every day, start your day by reading a witty, interesting saying.**

It's better for you than coffee and more inspiring than television.

**Just connect to Today's Fortune web site, and a randomly chosen quotation will be yours.**

**Special service:** I recognize that it may not be possible for you to check **Today's Fortune** every day. So, as a public service, I am giving you two dog-oriented quotes. You can use these when you need to be away from the Net (for example, if you have to leave town for the weekend).

(1) **Mark Twain:** If you pick up a starving dog and make him prosperous, he will not bite you. This is the principal difference between a dog and a man.

(2) Groucho Marx: Outside of a dog, a book is a man's best friend; inside of a dog, it's too dark to read.

**When it's your turn to fix dinner, read "Cooking and Recipes".**

## Twain, Mark

Mark Twain (1835-1910) was the father of modern American literature, and like most fathers, he said a lot of things worth remembering. Here is a nice collection of Mark Twain quotations which you can explore when you need something sardonic and wise, with just the right amount of irony (for example, to say to your own father).

**Web:**

**http://salwen.com/mtquotes.html**

## Wilde, Oscar

Oscar Wilde (1854-1900) was an Irish writer best known for his witty plays—especially "The Importance of Being Earnest"—and for his novel "The Picture of Dorian Gray". In addition, Wilde wrote short stories, fairy tales and essays. Aside from his wit, which was considerable, Wilde is remembered for his personal philosophy. He believed that beauty is valuable as an end unto itself (the aesthetic movement), and that this is not, perhaps, the best of all possible worlds (Wilde's own experience). The best example of this philosophy is the story of Dorian Gray, a young man of exceptional beauty who is corrupted by excessive sensual gratification coupled to an under-developed sense of morality. According to Oscar Wilde, the only way to get rid of a temptation is to yield to it. So don't wait. Rush out today and buy ten copies of my book *The Internet Complete Reference*.

**Web:**

**http://www.cascss.unt.edu/~wpalmer/wilde.htm**
**http://www.clients.anomtec.com/oscarwilde/wilde-wit.html**
**http://www.walrus.com/~jonnonyc/cgi-bin/quotes.cgi**

## Wright, Steven

Probably one of the things that makes you so popular is your ability to tell Steven Wright jokes at parties. But what do you do when you run out of material? Here's a large archive of Steven Wright quotations that will last you for years.

**Web:**

**http://cs-www.bu.edu/students/acm/alumni/rycshaw/steven-wright.quotes.html**

# RADIO

## Amateur Radio

Radio is a great hobby and one day when you are an expert, you can have your own nationally syndicated talk show and screaming fans will throw themselves at your feet when you go out in public. Until then, you can spend time reading Usenet groups especially for amateur radio enthusiasts. Topics cover construction, packet and digital radio modes, transmission, regulations, repair and other general topics.

**Web:**

**http://www.acs.ncsu.edu/HamRadio/**

**Usenet:**

**rec.radio.amateur.antenna**
**rec.radio.amateur.digital.misc**
**rec.radio.amateur.equipment**
**rec.radio.amateur.homebrew**
**rec.radio.amateur.misc**
**rec.radio.amateur.packet**
**rec.radio.amateur.policy**
**rec.radio.amateur.space**
**rec.radio.amateur.swap**

## Amateur Radio Talk and Discussion

This mailing list is devoted to all aspects of amateur radio, including low power radio, portable radio operation, equipment design and construction, solar and battery power, and so on.

**Listproc Mailing List:**

List Name: **qrp-l**
Subscribe to: **listproc@lehigh.edu**

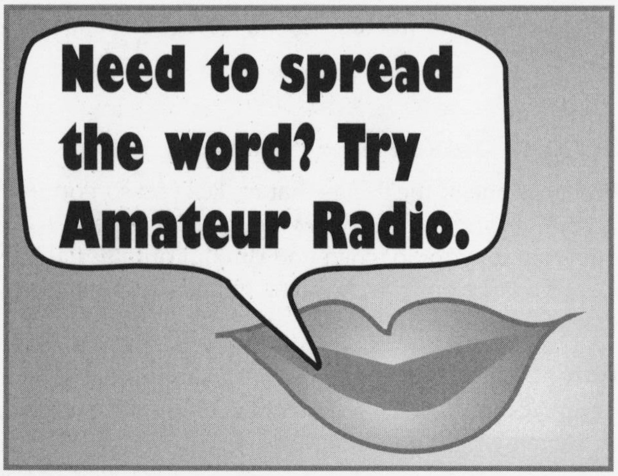
Need to spread the word? Try Amateur Radio.

## Campus Radio Disc Jockeys

What a cool job it is to sit in a climate-controlled booth jamming out to the latest tunes for hours on end. And in between the songs you get to offer some profound remarks that will reach the ears of every student on campus. What power! Hone your communication skills by hearing what other DJs and station managers discuss on this mailing list about college radio, federal and campus regulations, station policies, and equipment reviews.

**Listserv Mailing List:**

List Name: **dj-l**
Subscribe to: **listserv@vm1.nodak.edu**

**Campus Radio Disc Jockeys**

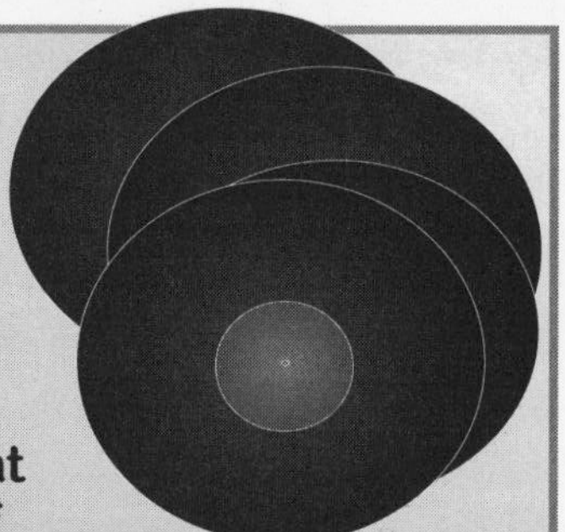

**When I was an undergraduate at the University of Waterloo, Canada, I was a CRDJ. Actually, I was a CCCRDJ (Cool Canadian Campus Radio Disc Jockey). If you too are a member of this elite corps, join the dj-l mailing list and see what your fellow CRDJs are up to.**

## Canadian Broadcasting Corporation

For years, the Canadian Broadcasting Corporation (CBC) has been providing the best television and radio broadcasting that government money can buy. If you live in Canada, spend some time at this web site where you can find all kinds of information including schedules, audio versions of various programs, discussion and much more (in French and in English). My favorite items are the transcripts of various shows. In particular, it's revealing to read the transcript of the daily national news broadcast ("...and on our magazine: Just 14 and sexually active. Why more kids are having sex at a younger age. What they want their parents to know...")

**Web:**

**http://www.radio.cbc.ca/**

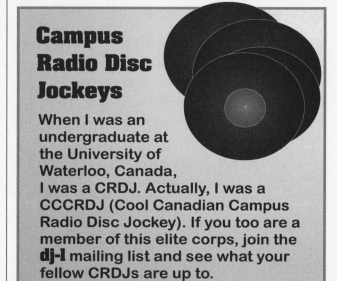

## Citizens Band Radio

Breaker breaker, anybody got your ears on? While the CB craze is not what it used to be, there are still a load of CB radio fans looking for people to talk to. Check out the citizen band action on Usenet.

**Usenet:**
**rec.radio.cb**

## Digital Audio Broadcasting

Imagine: your voice—static-free, flying silky smooth through the air at the speed of sound, straight into someone's ear. They turn and could swear that you were right there behind them. This is the wonder of digital audio broadcasting with its improved sound quality and technical superiority. Join with other DAB enthusiasts to talk not only about the technological merits of digital audio broadcasting, but also the social and economic issues.

**Usenet:**
**alt.radio.digital**

**Listserv Mailing List:**
List Name: **radio-l**
Subscribe to: **listserv@tc.umn.edu**

## Ham Radio

Do you want to be famous? Start practicing now by becoming a ham radio operator. After a while you will get a reputation around the neighborhood as that studly ham guy. Then you can start telling your opinions on the radio, build up your ego, put on a few pounds and eventually have your own conservative talk show on mainstream radio. Wouldn't that be fun? So get on the Net now and learn all about ham radio. The faster you learn, the faster you will be on your way to success.

**Web:**
**http://www.acs.ncsu.edu/HamRadio/CallServers.html**
**http://www.qrz.com/cgi-bin/webcall**
**http://www.raper.com/~hlr/hamradio/**

**IRC has many ways to make you talk.**

## NPR Online

NPR (National Public Radio) is an American non-commercial radio network. NPR offers a large variety of programs, many of which are oriented toward news and current events. Some of the more popular programs are All Things Considered, Car Talk, Morning Edition, Seasonings, Talk of the Nation and Weekend Edition. In the United States, NPR is considered by some people to be controversial due to a "liberal bias". However, their programs are well-produced and informative, and they have many listeners across the country. If you would like to listen to some NPR programs, you can do so by connecting to this web site (NPR Online). You will also find information about NPR itself such as where to listen to NPR, member stations, how to get transcripts of shows, and so on. For discussion about NPR, you can participate in the Usenet group.

**Web:**
**http://www.npr.org/**

**Usenet:**
**alt.radio.networks.npr**

## Old-Time Radio and Television

I love old radio shows like Jack Benny and Burns and Allen. This web site offers historical information about old radio shows and links to radio-related pages. Get a blast from the past.

**Web:**
**http://www.airwaves.com/history.html**

## Old-Time Radio Sounds

Have you ever heard any of the old-time radio shows? I have heard a great many, and I really enjoy them. These web pages have audio clips taken from many such shows. Listen to samples from shows such as Jack Benny, Charlie McCarthy, Amos and Andy, the Lone Ranger and so on. You can also listen to old radio news broadcasts and many other curiosities.

**Web:**
**http://www.otr.com/**
**http://www.pacificrim.net/~radio/sounds.html**

## Packet Radio

Packet radio is a system that sends information from one computer to another using radio broadcasting. The name "packet radio" refers to the fact that the information is broken into small groupings of data called "packets". (The Internet itself is a packet-based network.) With packet radio, you use a device called a TNC (terminal node controller) to connect your computer to a radio. The TNC acts like a bridge between your computer and the radio, which sends and receives data. (Conceptually, the TCM is like a modem only instead of using a phone line, data is transmitted using radio waves.) Most packet radio enthusiasts use VHF frequencies, which limit transmissions to a little better than unobstructed line of sight. However, once you have the appropriate equipment, packet radio is easy to use and requires no special license. And there exist networks of packet radio systems that make it possible to propagate data over long distances. The web site contains a variety of packet radio resources, and is a good place to start if you are a beginner. The Usenet group is for packet radio discussion.

**Web:**

**http://www.tapr.org/tapr/html/pkthome.html**

**Usenet:**

**rec.radio.amateur.digital.misc**
**rec.radio.amateur.packet**

## Pirate Radio

In most countries, radio broadcasting is strictly regulated by the government. In the United States, that job is performed by the FCC (Federal Communications Commission). In Canada, the organization is the CRTC (Canadian Radio-television and Telecommunications Commission). These government agencies do not allow private individuals to broadcast willy-nilly over the most commonly used frequencies, such as those set aside from AM and FM radio. Pirate radio refers to non-sanctioned broadcasting over such frequencies. The philosophical justification within the mostly underground pirate radio community ranges from freedom of speech to good plain fun. These web pages contain lots of pirate radio resources. If the idea of broadcasting illegally in front of the government's back appeals to you, start reading here. For ongoing discussion, you can participate in the Usenet group.

**Web:**

**http://www.access.digex.net/~cps/pirate.html**
**http://www.clandjop.com/~jcruzan/frn.html**

**Usenet:**

**alt.radio.pirate**

Enjoy the voices of yesterday, today.
Tune into Old Time Radio Sounds.

## Punch Rush Limbaugh

Not everyone likes Rush Limbaugh. There are those who feel like they have to listen to Rush every day just to see what he says and then go home and take their frustration out on the family cat. Fortunately, there is a way for you to express your hostility in a more healthy fashion. Just click on Rush's picture to leave your mark on Rush. Cats around the world will thank you.

**Web:**

**http://www.indirect.com/www/beetle87/rush/**

## Radio Broadcasting

Boy, radio has just got to be the best invention since television. Join the folks who love to listen. The **broadcasting** newsgroup is for discussing local broadcast radio. The **info** group is for informative postings about radio in general. Both of these groups are moderated. For those who hate advertising, **noncomm** is for talking about noncommercial radio. Finally, the **scanner** group is for utility broadcasting, above 30 MHz. (Just the place to learn how to eavesdrop on your neighbor's cordless phone.)

**Usenet:**

**alt.radio.scanner**
**alt.radio.scanner.uk**
**rec.radio.broadcasting**
**rec.radio.info**
**rec.radio.noncomm**
**rec.radio.scanner**

## Radio Broadcasts on the Internet

When you download a file—that is, copy a file from a remote computer to your machine—you must wait until the entire file has arrived at your computer before you can use the data. If you were to listen to audio in this way, it would be very slow. For example, you might have to wait 10 minutes just for a single song to completely download to your computer before you would hear anything. However, there is a technology called "streaming" that allows you to listen to sounds and broadcasts with only a short delay. The streaming technology starts playing the sound as soon as it arrives. While you are listening, the next bit of sound is arriving in the background. When it works well, it sounds okay. When it works poorly (say, if your Internet connection is too slow), the sound can be jumpy. Still, it's an amazing technology that is changing the way people think about broadcasting. (By the way, the same streaming idea can also be used to look at video over the Net, so you don't have to wait huge amounts of time before you can start watching.) Two of the most important streaming audio technologies used on the Net are developed by the Real Audio company and Xing Technology (Streamworks). The web sites I have listed here will show you what you need to do to listen to streaming audio. I have also included sites from which you can select a wide variety of sound and music to enjoy. Hint: Your web browser may already be set up for some type of streaming audio.

**Web:**

**http://www.crux.org/cyber/**
**http://www.realaudio.com/**
**http://www.timecast.com/**
**http://www.xingtech.com/**

## Radio History

The history of radio covers less than a century. However, it is one of the most fascinating stories in the world of technology. These web sites contain a lot of fascinating information about radio and its early days. Read about the development of radio technology and see a timeline of radio broadcasting. There are even pictures of radios as well as a listing of important radio events.

**Web:**

**http://www.antique-radio.org/timeline/time.html**
**http://www.itd.umd.edu/UMS/UMCP/NPBA/timeline.html**
**http://www.radiohistory.org/**

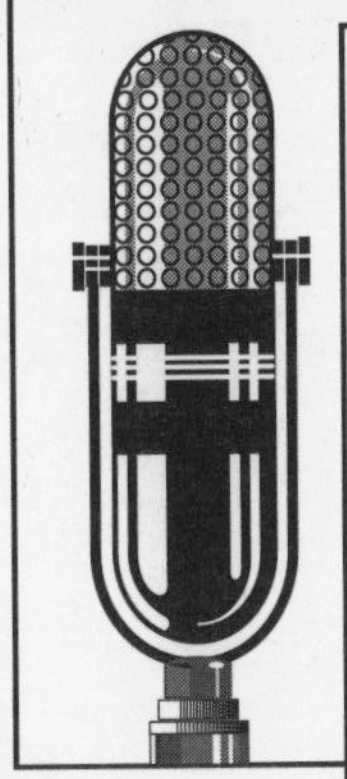

**RADIO HISTORY**

In 1901, the very first transatlantic message was broadcast by Guglielmo Marconi from Cornwall, England, to Saint John's, Newfoundland.

The transmission consisted of the Morse code signal for the letter "S".

(Immediately afterward, Marconi's wife took over the system in order to talk to her sister in Canada.)

## Radio Scanner Frequencies

A radio scanner is a device that lets you monitor radio frequencies not accessible with regular AM and FM receivers. These frequencies are used by a variety of organizations, especially law enforcement and public service groups. These web pages will help you find frequencies that you can monitor to eavesdrop on various types of conversations. You can also find the frequencies used by drive-through restaurants (MacDonalds, etc.), theme parks (Disneyland, etc.), TV stations, canned music (Muzak) and cordless phones. After all, if they didn't want you to listen, why would they be talking?

**Web:**

**http://exo.com/~rbarron/**
**http://www.agt.net/public/gpnet/gpnet.htm**

## Radio Stations

There are a huge number of radio stations with web sites. Here is a collection of links where you can find the web sites for radio stations across the United States and Canada. If you are looking for your favorite station, this is the place to find it.

**Web:**

**http://starcreations.com/abstract/freq/**

## Shortwave Radio

Shortwave radio enthusiasts talk tech-talk about what makes shortwave radio work. Learn tips about building, repairing and operating shortwave radios.

**Usenet:**

**rec.radio.shortwave**

## Vintage Radios and Broadcasting Equipment

Are you a collector? This web site is devoted to the collecting of vintage broadcast microphones. The pictures are interesting and well worth a look. The Usenet group is for the discussion of antique radios and phonographic equipment.

**Web:**

**http://www.k-bay106.com/mics.htm**

**Usenet:**

**rec.antiques.radio+phono**

# RELIGION

## Anglican Christianity

If you are an Anglican or just curious about Anglican Christianity, join the **anglican** mailing list to discuss any topic relating to the Episcopal Church and the worldwide Anglican Communion.

**Listserv Mailing List:**

List Name: **anglican**
Subscribe to: **listserv@auvm.american.edu**

### *Look What I Found on the Net...*

```
Newsgroup: alt.atheism
Subject: Question for Fellow Atheists

> Although I am an atheist, I have always been fascinated by the
> beliefs of religions around the world.  Is this unusual for an
> atheist?
>
> I do not believe in God, but I see in the world's religions
> some vital information and insight into the nature of man.
> When I explore various religions -- taking them as metaphors
> -- I learn a great deal about myself and my fellow human
> beings.  I have assumed that most atheists are more interested
> and educated in the world's religions, even after their
> acceptance of atheism, than most followers of individual
> faiths.  Is this true?

I don't know.  It's hard to speak authoritatively for "most
atheists".  Certainly among those who participate in discussions
of religion and atheism on the Net, this seems to be the case.

In my own case, early exposure to other religions was
instrumental in the development of my atheism.  I was always
interested by religious mythology, both as story and as it
related to the development of our culture.

Interestingly, I tended to give a fairly wide berth to
Christianity and the major modern religions until around the
time I started participating in alt.atheism.  Since then, it's
been a fairly major topic with me.

--
"A little rudeness and disrespect can elevate a meaningless
interaction to a battle of wills and add drama to an otherwise
dull day." -- Calvin
```

## Atheism

If you are one of those people who thinks "god" is just "dog" spelled backwards, this may be the group for you. Discuss how, why and where there is no God, and what this means for ordinary people who must pay their bills and remember their computer password. Atheists take their beliefs seriously and so should you.

**Web:**

**http://www.domino.org/~meta/atheism/**
**http://www.qtp.ufl.edu/~piotr/MY/faq.html**

**Usenet:**

**alt.atheism**
**alt.atheism.moderated**
**alt.christnet.atheism**

## Bible Study

When Paul said not to "forsake the gathering of ourselves together," the odds are this is not how he anticipated things would evolve. But if he were here today he would be telling you to stop mudding and join this forum of people interested in studying the Bible together electronically. The assumption is made that participants consider the Bible authoritative, so it's not a sparring ground for belief systems, nor is it for purely academic purposes.

**Usenet:**

**soc.religion.christian.bible-study**

## Bibles Online

You can use these online Bibles to search and read specific passages. There are a variety of languages available as well as links to related reference material. On the Net, inspiration is never more than a few mouse clicks away.

**Web:**

**http://ccel.wheaton.edu/wwsb/**
**http://www.gospelcom.net/bible**

## Biblical Timeline

Keep track of important Bible events such as the Flood, the building of the tower of Babel and the chronology of your favorite Bible characters. The biblical timeline also corresponds with a secular timeline so you can see the biblical events in juxtaposition with other historical events.

**Web:**

**http://www.cynet.com/Jesus/time.htm**

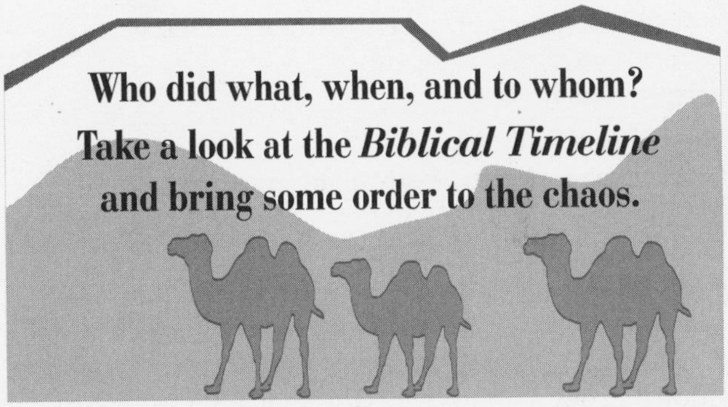
Who did what, when, and to whom?
Take a look at the *Biblical Timeline*
and bring some order to the chaos.

## Buddhism

Buddhism is a religion and philosophy founded in India by Siddhartha Gautama (the Buddha) in the 6th and 5th centuries B.C. Buddhism teaches the practice of meditation and the observance of moral tenets. Several sects have evolved from basic Buddhism, so there are variations on traditional Buddhism such as Taoism and Zen Buddhism. Read up on Buddhism or chat about it on Usenet or the mailing list.

**Web:**

**http://www.sfn.saskatoon.sk.ca/rel/buddhism.html**

**Usenet:**

**alt.religion.buddhism.nichiren**
**alt.religion.buddhism.tibetan**

**Listserv Mailing List:**

List Name: **buddha-l**
Subscribe to: **listserv@ulkyvm.louisville.edu**

**What if...?**

A B C D E F G H I J K L M N O P Q R S T U V W X Y Z

## Catholicism

The Roman Catholic Church has many millions of members around the world. The church is headed by the Pope, who is the bishop of Rome. You can learn more about the Catholic church, its rituals, sacraments and the Pope by viewing these web pages, or you can talk to members of the church on the mailing list.

**Web:**

**http://www.cs.cmu.edu/Web/People/spok/catholic.html**
**http://www.csn.net/advent/cathen/cathen.htm**

**Listserv Mailing List:**

List Name: **catholic**
Subscribe to: **listserv@auvm.american.edu**

## Christia

Free-spirited discussions about practical Christian life among strongly motivated Christians who agree to disagree. Immerse yourself in the everyday culture of people who practice their religion with the volume turned up.

**Usenet:**

**bit.listserv.christia**

## Christian Dating Advice

If you think it is bad trying to please some girl's father, wait until she asks God if you are The One. After all, God knows Santa and Santa knows if you've been naughty or nice. If you are needing some helpful hints, have a look at this web site, which has a paper containing dating guidelines for Christians, advice on who to select as a dating partner, tips on how to behave on dates and how to ask for God's guidance in dating situations.

**Web:**

**http://linus.cs.ohiou.edu/~bridge/v2n4/dating.html**

**Stay connected.**

## Christian Leadership Forum

Nobody said it was easy being a Christian leader, but at least you know you are not the only one who's struggling. Meet other Christian leaders and share with them your concerns, problems, ideas and insights. Christians from around the world participate, and you can hear their various struggles and pray for one another.

**Majordomo Mailing List:**

List Name: **leadership**
Subscribe to: **majordomo@iclnet93.iclnet.org**

## Christian Resources

Here are some collections of links to many Christian resources, including mailing lists, home pages of churches on the Web, music, ministries, online Bibles, executable outlines, a guide to Christian literature on the Net, and much more.

**Web:**

**http://iclnet93.iclnet.org/pub/resources/christian-resources.txt**
**http://www.christianity.net/search/**

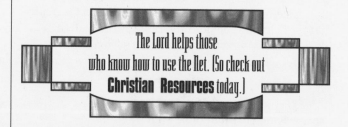

The Lord helps those who know how to use the Net. (So check out **Christian Resources** today.)

## Christianity and Literature

There is a close relationship between Christianity and literature—just look at the Bible. Holy books are about as heavy as literature gets. This forum is not intended for theological dispute, but if you want to discuss and explore the interrelations between Christianity and literature, this would be a good list to join.

**Listserv Mailing List:**

List Name: **christlit**
Subscribe to: **listserv@bethel.edu**

## Christianity Talk and General Discussion

Discover important topics on Christianity. Fundamentalism, evangelism, interfaith marriages, the Trinity, biblical history, tithing, holidays, and the effects of the New Age movement are just a taste of what you will find.

**Usenet:**

**alt.christnet**
**alt.christnet.christianlife**
**alt.christnet.christnews**
**alt.christnet.ethics**
**alt.christnet.evangelical**
**alt.christnet.hypocrisy**
**alt.christnet.philosophy**
**alt.christnet.prayer**
**alt.christnet.theology**
**alt.religion.christian**
**soc.religion.christian**
**soc.religion.christian.youth-work**

## Comparative Religion Reference

This is a table which organizes an enormous amount of useful and interesting information about many different religious faiths. I recommend this as a resource to anyone who needs to find out the basics of a particular religion or sect. What is especially insightful is you can see how various sects are related to their parent faiths. To help you use this site I have two suggestions. (1) Maximize your browser window, to make the table as large as possible. (2) Read the introduction before you start using the table.

**Web:**

**http://www.servtech.com/public/mcroghan/religion.htm**

## Different Christianities Dialog

There are many different varieties of Christianity and this discussion explores those varieties, opening up tolerant and respectful dialogs between them.

**Listserv Mailing List:**

List Name: **diftx-l**
Subscribe to: **listserv@yalevm.cis.yale.edu**

## Eastern Orthodox Christianity

Eastern Orthodox Christianity originated in Eastern Europe and Southwest Asia when it split with the Western church in the 5th century. You can find more about the modern day version of this Old World religion by checking out these web pages.

**Web:**

**http://www.nauticom.net/www/balouris/orthodox.html**
**http://www.theologic.com/links.html**

## Eastern Religions

If you are interested in Eastern enlightenment, read about Buddhism, Hinduism, and other Eastern religions. Often points are related through the tradition of parable, illustrating the beauty of the spiritual path. This group is moderated. (What is the sound of one hand holding open an Internet book?)

**Usenet:**

**soc.religion.eastern**

## First Century Judaism

Join in on this electronic seminar devoted to the exploration of first century Judaism. It's just the thing for those of you who can't get enough of the writings of Flavius Josephus or Philo of Alexandria.

**Listproc Mailing List:**

List Name: **ioudaios-l**
Subscribe to: **listproc@lehigh.edu**

### First Century Judaism

*In the first century A.D., religions were nothing like they are today. The cult that was to grow into Christianity was just beginning to establish itself from within the Jewish community, and the Jewish religion itself was far different from anything we would recognize.*

*For this reason, the practices and beliefs of the first century Jews are important to anyone who wishes to understand the foundation of modern-day Judaism and Christianity.*

*Join the First Century Judaism mailing list, and discuss this most important period in history with people around the world.*

## Global Christianity Discussion

There are many forms of Christianity around the world. This mailing list is devoted to the discussion and study of global Christianity.

**Listserv Mailing List:**

List Name: **globlx-l**
Subscribe to: **listserv@qucdn.queensu.ca**

## Hindu Dharma

The Hindu religious philosophy is accepted by millions of people around the world. Followers of this way of life discuss the idea of many religious paths, the universal family and how Hinduism applies to everyday life. Topics also include other issues that might affect Hindu living, such as war and politics.

**Listserv Mailing List:**

List Name: **hindu-d**
Subscribe to: **listserv@listserv.nodak.edu**

## Hinduism

Hinduism is one of the world's major religions, having nearly one billion followers. The majority of Hindus live in India, where the religion forms a spritual and cultural base for most of the country. However, there are also large numbers of Hindus in many other countries around the world. Hinduism is actually a family of faiths whose beliefs range from many gods (pluralistic theism) to a single all-pervasive deity (absolute monism). There are four principle denominations of hinduism—Saivism, Vaishnavism, Shaktism and Smartism—each of which is different enough and complete enough to be considered a self-contained religion in its own right. All Hindus share a number of important spiritual and philosophical traditions in common, among which are karma, dharma, reincarnation, temple worship, and recognition of the Vedas as their holy writings.

**Web:**

**http://www.hinduismtoday.kauai.hi.us/htoday.html**
**http://www.hindunet.org/**

**Usenet:**

**alt.hindu**
**soc.religion.hindu**

## Islam

Discuss a variety of issues that are important in the Islamic faith. While topics cover the Qurán, judgement day, Jesus, prophets and religious traditions, there is also spirited discussion regarding current events in the Middle East. The **soc** group is moderated.

**Usenet:**

**alt.islam.sufism**
**alt.religion.islam**
**soc.religion.islam**

**IRC:**

**#islam**

## Jainism

Jainism is an ascetic religion of India, founded in the sixth century B.C. The religion stresses non-violence, teaches the immortality and transmigration of the soul and denies the existence of a perfect or supreme being. This web site has pictures illustrating Jainism history and way of life.

**Web:**

**http://www.cs.colostate.edu/~malaiya/jainhlinks.html**

## Judaism

There's lots of information on the Net relating to Judaism. Connect to these web sites and read about Israel, the Holocaust, the Torah, Reconstructionism, Reform Judaism and more. For discussion, you can participate in the Usenet groups and the mailing lists.

**Web:**

**http://shamash.nysernet.org/**
**http://www.cs.cmu.edu/afs/cs.cmu.edu/user/clamen/misc/Judaica/README.html**

**Usenet:**

**alt.music.jewish**
**soc.culture.jewish**

**Listproc Mailing List:**

List Name: **halacha-yomi**
Subscribe to: **listproc@israel.nysernet.org**

**Listproc Mailing List:**

List Name: **mail-jewish**
Subscribe to: **listproc@shamash.org**

## Koran (or Qurán)

The Koran is the sacred book of Islam. According to the Islamic belief, the Koran was revealed by God to the Prophet Muhammad in various revelations. On the Net you can read the translated Koran or search it, if you are looking for something specific.

**Web:**

**http://www.hti.umich.edu/relig/koran/**
**http://www.mv.com/ipusers/submission/English.html**
**http://www.utexas.edu/students/amso/quran_html**

### The Qurán

Strictly speaking, the Qurán (Islamic Holy text) should be read in the original Arabic and is not considered to be correct when translated into another language. Still, if your Arabic skills are a bit rusty, you might get more out of reading the Qurán in English. Download it and give it a try.
(Allaah yusallimukum.)

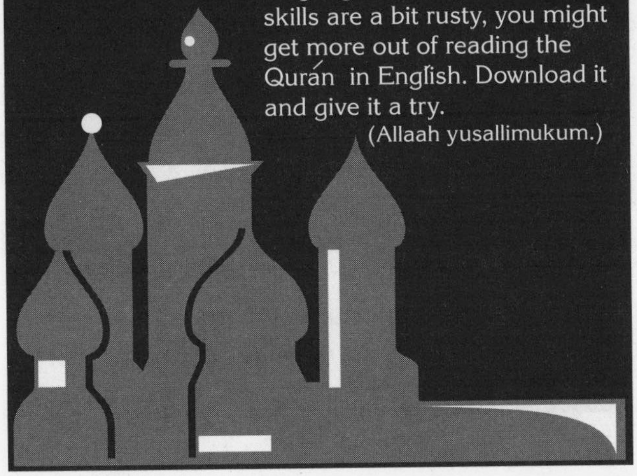

## Orthodox Christianity

Orthodox Christianity is not just any old Christianity. It's vitamin-fortified, steel-belted Christianity. This moderated list is dedicated to the discussion of this religion on a worldwide basis, in particular its recent rise in popularity within Russia and its neighboring countries.

**Listserv Mailing List:**

List Name: **orthodox**
Subscribe to: **listserv@iubvm.ucs.indiana.edu**

## Practical Christian Life

Christians are Christians 24 hours a day. Here's a mailing list for the discussion of practical Christian life, living the Christian way of life on a daily basis.

**Listserv Mailing List:**

List Name: **christia**
Subscribe to: **listserv@asuvm.inre.asu.edu**

## Religion Talk and General Discussion

Sit in on discussions that are religious, ethical, and moral in nature. Talk includes reference to scriptures and parables, but much of it concerns heavily debatable topics—for example, does the Pope use the Internet?—all of which makes for lively banter.

**Usenet:**

**talk.religion.misc**

## Religious Tolerance

Here's a refreshing change of pace from the hurry-scurry of everyone evangelizing on the Net or the eruptions of arguments between believers and non-believers. This web page promotes religious tolerance and makes an attempt to education everyone about the various religions around the world. You can also read the United Nations Declarations on Religious Intolerance, articles on religious freedom, a glossary of terms, information on ritual abuse and cults, and find links to religious home pages.

**Web:**

**http://www.kosone.com/people/ocrt/ocrt_hp.htm**

## Sexuality and Religion

Everyone knows you are not supposed to talk about sex and religion at the same time, so you should only read this paragraph if nobody is looking. These Usenet groups actually do talk about sex in relation to Christianity. Understand the Christian's viewpoint of sex and get in on the "to do or not to do" debate.

**Usenet:**

**alt.christnet.sex**
**alt.religion.sexuality**

## Sikhism

Founded by Guru Nanak, who was born in 1469, Sikhism has gained a loyal following over the centuries. Guru Nanak criticized the rituals of the Hindus and Muslims and preached that the most important things in life were love, understanding and directing worship toward the one true God. The word "Sikh" means "disciple" in the Punjabi. You can read more about the history and practices of this religion at this web site which is loaded with details.

**Web:**

**http://www.io.org/~sandeep/sikhism.htm**

## Society of Friends (Quakers)

The Society of Friends (commonly referred to as Quakers) began in 1647 under George Fox. One strong tenet of the Friends is that believers do not need a spiritual intermediary, they can receive guidance from within by the Holy Spirit. Here are a couple of places where you can discuss the philosophies of the Society of Friends.

**Usenet:**

**soc.religion.quaker**

**Listserv Mailing List:**

List Name: **quaker-l**
Subscribe to: **listserv@postoffice.cso.uiuc.edu**

### *Look What I Found on the Net...*

```
Subject: Could Life Have Evolved by Chance?
Newsgroups: talk.religion.misc, alt.atheism, rec.org.mensa

>>> Could life have evolved by chance?  The probability of
>>> forming one protein molecule by chance is one in 10 to the
>>> 243rd power, which is a figure of 1 followed by 243 zeros.
>>>
>>> This fraction is so small, one may say that the probability
>>> is zero.

>> One chance out of:
>>
>>   1,000,000,000,000,000,000,000,000,000,000,000,000,
>>     000,000,000,000,000,000,000,000,000,000,000,000,
>>     000,000,000,000,000,000,000,000,000,000,000,000,
>>     000,000,000,000,000,000,000,000,000,000,000,000,
>>     000,000,000,000,000,000,000,000,000,000,000,000,
>>     000,000,000,000,000,000,000,000,000,000,000,000,
>>     000,000,000,000,000,000,000,000,000?
>>
>> You might be off by plus or minus a few zeros, but so what?
>> They only illustrate, or prove, NOTHING.
>>
>> My question is, with your probabilistic argument, if that is
>> the probability of forming just one lowly protein molecule,
>> what is the  probability of forming an omniscient, omnipotent
>> God?

> It matters not.  God was not created per se.  He always has
> been and always will be.  No, I can't understand that, but no
> one else on the planet can either.  Our brains just don't
> have the capacity to comprehend infinity.  It's kind of like
> trying to teach algebra to an earthworm.

I don't know much about earthworms, but MY brain is perfectly
capable of perceiving and comprehending infinity.
```

## Vedic Civilization

Examples of Vedic ideas concerning time and human longevity, as detailed by the Vedic literature of India.

**Web:**

**http://www.spiritweb.org/Spirit/Veda/Overview.html**

## Youth Ministry

Young people interested in working in the Youth Ministry can get information about job openings, a list of conventions and seminars. There is also a quote of the week and a way to participate in youth ministry discussion.

**Web:**

**http://www.gospelcom.net/ys/**

## Zen Buddhist Texts

Zen Buddhism is a Buddhist sect of Japan and China that bases religion on the practice of meditation rather than doctrine. It was founded by a Chinese man named Bodhidharma in the 5th century A.D. Zen Buddhism concentrates strongly on enlightenment, consciousness and meditation. This site has a collection of Zen Buddhist writing from various sources as well as a page where you can get a random Zen thought for the day. Just the thing to escape from the hustle and bustle of everyday life.

**Web:**

**http://www.uth.tmc.edu/~snewton/zen/**

## Zoroastrianism

Originating in ancient Iran, Zoroastrianism today has a small following in isolated areas of Iran and India. Join discussion on this religion founded in 6th century B.C. and hear the stories of Ahura Mazda as he battles his evil twin, Ahriman. This is the stuff good movies are made of.

**Usenet:**

**alt.religion.zoroastrianism**

# RELIGION: SECTS AND CULTS

## Ahmadiyya

Learn about Ahmadiyya, a messianic movement based on the principles of the Qurán and founded in the late nineteenth century by Mirza Ghulam Ahmad. (Can you say that name fast ten times?) Unlike traditional Muslims, adherents of Ahmadiyya believe Qadiyani to be a prophet after Muhammad.

**Web:**

**http://www.umn.edu/nlhome/g626/ahma0011/**
**http://www.utexas.edu/students/amso/**

**Usenet:**

**alt.sect.ahmadiyya**

### *Look What I Found on the Net...*

```
(from the Zen Buddhist Texts)

Ordinary-beings are innumerable, I vow to liberate them all
Defilements are endless, I vow to eliminate them all
Buddha's teachings are unlimited, I vow to learn them all
The ways of enlightenment are supreme, I vow to achieve them all

I vow to liberate all ordinary-beings from my mind
I vow to eliminate all defilements from my mind
I vow to embrace every teaching of my self-nature
I vow to achieve the way of enlightenment from my self-nature
```

## Baha'i Faith

Who was Baha'u'llah (a.k.a. Mirza Husayn Ali)? What did he do in Iran in the mid-19th century that was so important? Was he really the Bab (with a direct line to the twelfth Imam)? Learn about the message of the Baha'u'llah and the Baha'i view of life. Read quotes from Baha'i scriptures and discuss such topics as gender equality and spiritual revelations.

**Web:**

**http://towers.usask.ca/bahai.html**

**Usenet:**

**soc.religion.bahai**

## Baptist Discussion

A list for the discussion of any and all topics relating to the Baptist experience. It includes all nationalities and denominations of Baptists and is a forum for sharing information, ideas and opinions.

**Listserv Mailing List:**

List Name: **baptist**
Subscribe to: **listserv@lsv.uky.edu**

## Brother Jed

Follow the comings and goings of Brother Jed (George E. Smock) as his itinerant travels take him from campus to campus throughout America, spreading the word that Christianity is incompatible with homosexuality, long hair, drugs, and rock music. (Yes, it's true. Would we make up something like this?)

**Usenet:**

**alt.brother-jed**

## Chabad Lubavitch Judaism

Official home of the world Chabad-Lubavitch movement, there are many Jewish resources here including articles, inspirational passages, a glossary of Jewish words and terms, and links to many other Jewish and Judaism resources.

**Web:**

**http://www.chabad.org/**

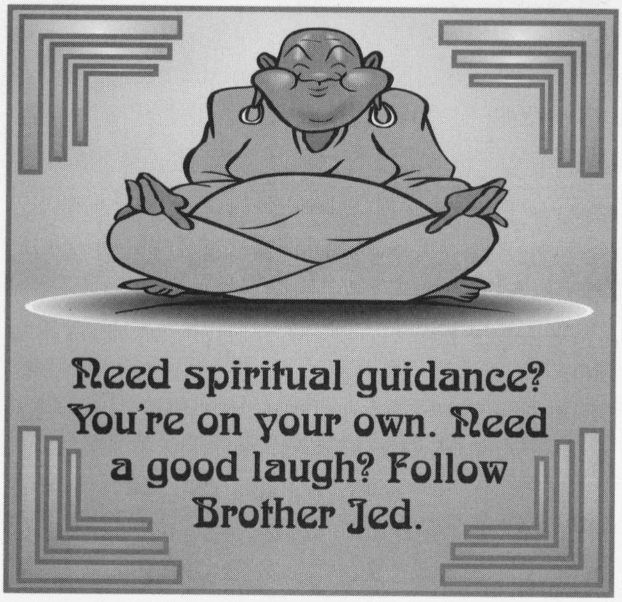
Need spiritual guidance? You're on your own. Need a good laugh? Follow Brother Jed.

## Coptic

The Coptic Church is based on the teachings of Saint Mark, who brought Christianity to Egypt in the first century. The Copts observe seven sacraments, baptize newborns, and participate in fasting. Learn more about this religion by going to this Coptic page. They give a nice history of the Church and other detailed information, including their Coptic liturgy.

**Web:**

**http://pharos.bu.edu/Coptic/Menu.html**

## Cyberculture Religions

The Internet is the new medium for enlightenment, according to some people. Join in the cyberevangelistic movement, by checking out some of these religions that have been spawned by the online culture.

**Web:**

**http://ourworld.compuserve.com/homepages/shadowcat/**
**http://www.technosophy.com/**
**http://www.tiac.net/users/ighf/**

**Do a backup.**

## Eckankar

The basis of Eckankar spirituality is coming closer to God through dreams and the expansion of consciousness. This site explains more about the philosophy of Eckankar, gives spiritual exercises that are designed to bring you closer to enlightenment, and has various other tidbits of interest to those in search of Sugmad. On the Usenet group you can join Eckists as they explore visualization, reality, and waking dreams.

**Web:**
**http://www.eckankar.org/**

**Usenet:**
**alt.religion.eckankar**

## Episcopal Church

When you have turned the house upside down looking for the Book of Common Prayer and you still can't find it, try the web site of the Episcopal Church. They have this and other liturgical texts, information about different religious orders and brotherhoods within the church, articles from officials, news reports and links to church home pages.

**Web:**
**http://www.ai.mit.edu/people/mib/anglican/anglican.html**

## Gnosticism

Take a few Christian terms, add in a liberal dose of Greek philosophy, a dash of mythology and a handful of magickal rituals. Let sit for several centuries and voila! You end up with a religion that can serve millions and is very low in calories. Learn more about Gnosticism, its origins and tenets. The **soc.religion.gnosis** group is moderated.

**Web:**
**http://www.webcom.com/~gnosis/**

**Usenet:**
**alt.religion.gnostic**
**soc.religion.gnosis**

## Goddess Names

This "Encyclopedia of the Goddess" offers a gigantic list of all the names of the "Goddess". (This seems to be a catch-all term for any sort of goddess that appears in any type of document or literature.) Along with each name is an explanation of the particular goddess or deity. The listing is a bit liberal—for example, you will find Echo, who is actually just a Greek nymph, not a goddess—but it is interesting nonetheless.

**Web:**
**http://members.gnn.com/shickman/names.htm**

Goddess Names

So you have a new baby girl. Don't settle for giving her an ordinary name like Jessica, Michelle, Kimberly or Brandy.

(And for goodness sake, don't name her Jennifer. Every Tom, Dick and Harry is named Jennifer.)

Instead, connect to the Goddess Names web site where you find something *really* special, like Angerona, Blodeuwedd, Caillech, Dakini, Erigone, Freya, Galatea, Halja, Inanna or Juno.

## Goddess Spirituality and Feminism

Hera really did give goddesses a bad name, but they are finally starting to become popular, and not just with women, either. Men and women alike are interested in goddess spirituality, feminism, and the incorporation of the feminine/feminist idea in the study and worship of the divine. Listen in on their discussions of spirituality in relation to the goddess.

**Listserv Mailing List:**
List Name: **wmsprt-l**
Subscribe to: **listserv@ubvm.cc.buffalo.edu**

**FAQs are cool.**

A B C D E F G H I J K L M N O P Q R S T U V W X Y Z

## Jehovah's Witnesses

Jehovah's Witnesses is an international Christian organization, founded in 1870 as a Bible study group by Charles Taze Russell. In 1931, they adopted the name "Jehovah's Witnesses" (from Isaiah 43;12). One of the main things people notice about Witnesses is they are active proselytizers, going from door to door to talk to people about Jehovah (God). Witnesses do not believe in eternal torment or that all good people go to heaven. Rather, they believe that, upon the destruction of wickedness and human governments, a "new system" will be established, and most of God's people will live in human perfection on Earth. Although Witnesses have a Christian love for people, they make an effort to stay "separate from the world" and do not involve themselves in excessive pursuit of material things or political and social movements. Witnesses do not salute the flag, vote, bear arms, or participate in government; nor (for biblical reasons) will they take blood transfusions. This web site is designed for Jehovah's Witnesses. You will find a number of useful resources such as a daily text from the Bible, a listing of events, links to pages of other Jehovah's Witnesses, news stories, a listing of new releases from the Watchtower (the Witness magazine), and more. If you are interested in learning more about the Witnesses, you will find an overview of what they believe.

**Web:**

**http://www.wpg.ramp.net/~mptech/**

## Joke Religions

Religion doesn't have to be all stuffy and business-like. If you are looking to convert, consider one of these religions that is definitely not mainstream. Or if religion is not really what you want, you can always try a cabal or a secret society. Check out this list of bizarre groups and find out more about their dogma and beliefs.

**Web:**

**http://thunderdome.goucher.edu/Hairboys/religion.html**

**The Net cares.**

**Wow, free software.**

## Mennonites

The Mennonites are a sect that departed from the Swiss Anabaptists around 1524. Mennonites believe in nonresistance and they refuse to take oaths. (A more conservative branch of the Mennonites are the Amish who broke away from the Mennonites in the late 17th century.) The Mennonites have a nice collection of information on the Web.

**Web:**

**http://www-personal.umich.edu/~bpl/ml-faq.html**
**http://www.prairienet.org/mennonite/**

## Mormons

The Church of Jesus Christ of Latter-day Saints (sometimes referred to as LDS or the Mormon Church) was founded by Joseph Smith in 1830. Mormon history says that Joseph Smith was visited by a prophet who told him some sacred history of the Americas. Smith translated this information and published it as the Book of Mormon in 1830. This book and the Bible are the main texts of the Mormon doctrines. You can read the text of the Book of Mormon online or do a search of the text if there is something specific you want to look up. On the Net there are lots of LDS resources, including interactive chatting on IRC.

**Web:**

**http://sci.dixie.edu/mormon/contents.html**
**http://www.athenet.net/~jlindsay/LDS_Intro.shtml**
**http://www.hti.umich.edu/relig/mormon/**
**http://www.mormon.net/**
**http://www.primenet.com/~kitsonk/mormon.html**

**Usenet:**

**alt.religion.mormon**

**Majordomo Mailing List:**

List Name: **mormon-l**
Subscribe to: **majordomo@sims.net**

**IRC:**

**#mormon**

## Mysticism Chat

When you want to get into some mystical or spiritual discussion, here are some places to do it. Chat or argue on many areas of mysticism from Christianity to Satanism, and everything in between.

**IRC:**

**#asatru**
**#atheism**
**#buddhist**
**#christ**
**#christian**
**#islam**

> **Mysticism Chat**
> If you like talking about any type of mysticism, someone is waiting to talk to you.
> Connect to one of the IRC channels and see what appears magically.

## Nazarenes

Do you know what the Nazarenes believe? Go right now to the web page, which is loaded with information on their beliefs and links to church home pages and some Christian resources. You never know when you might be suddenly called as a contestant on Jeopardy.

**Web:**

**http://www.nazarene.org/**

## New Religious Movements

From what we have seen, there is big money and fame in the business of religion. In addition to that, you can get all the women you want. This academic group discusses new religious movements. If you are interested in becoming a deity in this lifetime, you might check in and see if you can get any helpful hints.

**Listserv Mailing List:**

List Name: **nurel-l**
Subscribe to: **listserv@listserv.ucalgary.ca**

## Paganism

The nice thing about paganism is that you can pretty much do whatever you want. This is a nature-based religion with no central dogma. Pagans celebrate various gods and goddesses (one or many), nature and the cycles of the sun and moon. The best thing is that they don't have to wear uncomfortable clothes and sit in church. If any of this appeals to you, check out some of the pagan resources on the Net or talk to a friendly pagan at a Usenet group near you.

**Web:**

**http://www.cascade.net/arachne.html**

**Usenet:**

**alt.pagan**

## Santeria

Santeria (often called La Regla Lucumi) has its origins in West Africa and is the traditional religion of the Yoruba people. Santeria was spread to many countries of South America by slave trade. Members of Santeria worship a god named Olorun and interact with him through emmisaries called orishas. The religion is wrapped up in magic and forces of nature. If you want to learn more about their specific religious language and rituals, take a look at this web site devoted to Santeria.

**Web:**

**http://www.seanet.com/Users/efunmoyiwa/welcome.html**

## Satanism

Discover what Satanists feel are the misconceptions about their beliefs. See what Satanism means and discuss how Satanists feel it relates to Christianity. Other topics include music, books, and news items.

**Usenet:**

**alt.satanism**

> **Get into "Mischief".**

## Scientology-Related Talk and General Discussion

This is not official Scientology. Mostly you will find people talking about issues that, to them, are related to Scientology. So if you want to find out what is new and exciting in this oft-misunderstood marriage of science, religion, applied psychology, and science fiction, check out the discussion.

**Usenet:**

**alt.clearing.technology**
**alt.religion.scientology**

## Secular Web

A server of secular concerns with sections for atheists and agnosticists, magazines such as Free Inquiry and Skeptical Inquirer, religious parodies, satire, and links to many other organizations and resources of secular interest.

**Web:**

**http://freethought.tamu.edu/**

## Shakers

Everyone would like a little utopia in their life. There are actually people who have figured out a way to get it—or at least get closer to it than the rest of us. The United Society of Believers (Shakers) hold to the fact that a pure life is one that is lived simply. On this mailing list, discussion covers anything related to the Shakers including their history, religious beliefs, culture, and furniture.

**Listserv Mailing List:**

List Name: **shaker**
Subscribe to: **listserv@lsv.uky.edu**

## Shamanism

Delve into the natural spiritual practices of the shaman. Discover the full range of the shamanic experience, which includes such things as drumming, vision quests, and visiting sacred sites.

**Web:**

**http://www.cis.ohio-state.edu/hypertext/faq/bngusenet/soc/religion/shamanism/top.html**

**Usenet:**

**alt.religion.shamanism**
**soc.religion.shamanism**

### *The Secular Web*

Sometimes, "alternative religion" means a type of thought or belief that is so far into the ether as to be seriously wacko. However, another way to think about it is that "alternative" also means a thoughtful, skeptical, and perhaps lighthearted (or even satirical) approach to answering those deep questions that keep you up late at night (or perhaps satirizing other people's answers). If this is your bent, take a look at the Secular Web, wherein you will encounter the work of other similarly minded atheists and agnostics.

## Theosophy

Take a little religion, some Hindu philosophy, add a dash of mysticism, pantheism, or magic and you get Theosophy. If you like going on your own and not having to confess, tithe, or be organized in general, you might want to try this. Get an overview of what Theosophy is all about by reading selected papers and posts from related newsgroups.

**Web:**

**http://www.spiritweb.org/Spirit/Theosophy/Overview.html**

## Unitarianism

Share thoughts and opinions with the people who address their prayers "to whom it may concern". Discuss issues of interest to members of the Unitarian-Universalist church: the most free-thinking, tolerant, diverse, and intellectual group of people since the Nixon White House. The **uuyan-l** list is for the Unitarian Universalist Young Adult Network.

**Usenet:**

**bit.listserv.uus-l**

**Listserv Mailing List:**

List Name: **uus-l**
Subscribe to: **listserv@ubvm.cc.buffalo.edu**

**Listserv Mailing List:**

List Name: **uuyan-l**
Subscribe to: **listserv@info.terraluna.org**

A B C D E F G H I J K L M N O P Q R S T U V W X Y Z

## Wicca

Wicca is a neo-pagan religion that is more focused and ritualistic than traditional paganism. The Wiccan tradition is to worship a god and goddess (not necessarily in that order) or perhaps multiple deities. Wiccans are tuned into nature, cycles and life events, and perform magick rituals to mark the passing of holidays or special events. If you'd like to learn more about the Wicca way of life, check out these web sites or talk to some Wiccans who spend time on IRC or posting to Usenet.

**Web:**

**http://faraday.clas.virginia.edu/~crf8a/wicca.html**
**http://www.hway.net/ron/wern.htm**
**http://www.netspace.org/~athomps/pagan/alt_religion_wicca.html/**

**Usenet:**

**alt.religion.wicca**

**IRC:**

**#wicca**

# ROLE PLAYING

## Advanced Dungeons and Dragons

There is lots of Advanced Dungeons and Dragons material on the Net: spell and priest books, campaigns, modules, new monsters, new spells, rules, interactive games, comments; just about anything you can think of having to do with AD&D.

**Web:**

**http://gs216.sp.cs.cmu.edu/net_gen.html**
**http://www.miniworld.com/adnd/**
**http://www.ms.mff.cuni.cz/acad/webik/~pmit2218/adnd.html**

**Listserv Mailing List:**

List Name: **adnd-l**
Subscribe to: **listserv@utarlvm1.uta.edu**

**Don't click here.**

### *Look What I Found on the Net...*

```
(from the Wicca frequently asked question list)

What is basic Wiccan thealogy?

Some myths and associations are common to many Wiccan traditions,
such as the Goddess' giving birth to the Horned God,
the theme of their courtship and His death, the descent of the
Goddess into the realm of death and others.

Another thealogical point held in common by many Wiccans is the
immanence of deity/divinity within the natural world, self and
cycle of the seasons.  This places value on the Earth and this
world, as distinguished from views of transcendent divinity and
an unenchanted creation.

Wiccans as a whole are very much "into" cycles: of life, of the
moon and seasons.  Cyclical change as an erotic dance of life,
death and rebirth is a popular theme in Wiccan imagery, ritual
and liturgy.

(Thea is Greek for "goddess" by the way, so "thealogy" is not a
typo here, but a way of emphasizing the Goddess.)
```

A B C D E F G H I J K L M N O P Q R S T U V W X Y Z

## Advanced Dungeons and Dragons Discussion

There are times when you just can't stand talking to a regular person, and you have to make contact with another Dungeons and Dragons fanatic (especially if you are a Dungeon Master, and normal people just don't cut it). For example, suppose you need to talk to someone about the fine points of creating a crew for a spelljamming ship? What are you going to do—call your mother? She'll just want to know when you are coming to visit and why you don't call more often. Instead, you can always turn to the Net for some serious AD&D discussion.

**Usenet:**

**rec.games.frp.dnd**

**IRC:**

**#ad&d**

**Read a zine today.**

## American Gamers Association

This is the web site of the American Gamers Association, where you can find information on game clubs, conventions, retailers, magazines, files and databases (such as a spells, monsters, magic items databases), and links to many related resources. If you are into gaming, especially role-playing games, this is a place you should know about.

**Web:**

**http://www.aga-home.org/**

Reality is for people who aren't smart enough for role-playing games.

## *Look What I Found on the Net...*

Newsgroup: alt.pub.dragons-inn
Subject: Guess What's Coming to Dinner

Synopsis:
The party members have been ambushed at a dinner given by their host, the vampire Pericles. A great battle has just begun...

Unable to enjoy her food and not really interested in dessert, Matte had just begun to try to excuse herself from the table when the servants attacked. Halfway out of her seat already, she quickly leapt upon her chair and picked up a piece of cutlery from the table. She attempted to hit one of the creatures attacking Moria on the opposite side of the room, but was picked up from behind as she drew her arm back, the knife falling harmlessly to the floor.

Matte felt the grip of the armored servant tighten as she was lifted from her feet. The creature's grasp was very firm, and she was unable to free herself to conjure assistance or use her weapon. She grunted and kicked at her captor but to no avail.

Suddenly, she felt the iron grip give way as she landed on her feet and heard the clatter of armor fall to the floor above the din of battle in the room.

She turned to see Tomonobu behind her, his sword flashing at more armored servants further away. "Rescuing you is getting to be a habit, Little One," he said as he moved away to deal with problems of his own...

## Buying and Selling Role Playing Games

After a while, you can reach the burn-out stage on any particular role-playing game. And it's hard to let all that material just lay around. Don't let all that time, money and attention go to waste. On Usenet you can probably find someone who is interested in whatever you want to get rid of. Buy, sell or trade your fantasy role-playing material. It's all happening here.

**Usenet:**

**rec.games.frp.marketplace**

## Fantasy Role Playing Games

If you are into gaming, you have got to check out this great site. It has a huge list of role-playing game systems and a list of links for each system. When you start to get bored playing the same old rpg, check out this site and get some ideas for a new gaming direction.

**Web:**

**http://dax.cs.wisc.edu/~woodelf/RPG/RPG.html**

## Fantasy Role Playing Talk and General Discussion

Join up with the folks in Usenet and discuss your favorite or your most hated role-playing game and all the issues that come with it. Magic, mystery, and adventure await you once you step across the line that separates fantasy from reality.

**Usenet:**

**alt.dragons-inn**
**alt.games.frp.2300ad**
**rec.games.frp**
**rec.games.frp.advocacy**
**rec.games.frp.archives**
**rec.games.frp.cyber**
**rec.games.frp.dnd**
**rec.games.frp.gurps**
**rec.games.frp.storyteller**
**rec.games.frp.super-heroes**

## Live-Action Role Playing

What a great way to spend the evening—dress up as someone else and take on a whole new life. Say goodbye to reality by doing some live-action role playing where you talk to other characters and solve a mystery or a problem the way your character would. You'll never be able to go back to ordinary board games again.

**Web:**

**http://www.coil.com/~zargonis/shade.html**
**http://www.cs.wisc.edu/~desmet/live-action.html**

**Usenet:**

**rec.games.frp.live-action**

## Magic: The Gathering

Magic: The Gathering (MtG) is a popular D&D-type card-trading role-playing game. Magic has grown to encompass a complex world of its own. These web sites have a lot of interesting information about playing the game. There is a "customizable card list generator", an overview of Magic: The Gathering, a glossary, official rules information (FAQs, clarifications, a place to ask questions), card information (lists and databases), variations on the rules (such as how to play solitaire with Magic cards), a section for fiction, strategy and history, and a huge, huge list of related web sites all over the Net. The Usenet groups are for the discussion of MtG. The **.misc** group is for general talk; the other groups are for rules and strategy. The IRC channel is for MtG fans to hang out and talk in real-time.

**Web:**

**http://marvin.macc.wisc.edu/deckmaster/magic/**
**http://www.echo-on.net/~jelkouby/zone.html**

**Usenet:**

**rec.games.trading-cards.magic.misc**
**rec.games.trading-cards.magic.rules**
**rec.games.trading-cards.magic.strategy**

**IRC:**

**#MTG**

A B C D E F G H I J K L M N O P Q R S T U V W X Y Z

A B C D E F G H I J K L M N O P Q R S T U V W X Y Z

## Miniatures

If you like to take the time to buy miniatures, paint them or role-play with miniatures, this is a great resource for you. This archive offers information and rules to games in a variety of categories such as ancient, medieval, Napoleonic, world wars, modern, science fiction and many other types of settings.

**Web:**

**http://www.cabm.rutgers.edu/~hooper/miniatures/bill/Miniatures_Rules.html**

## Netrunner

Netrunner is a popular game that combines card trading along with role playing. The web sites will lead you to the FAQ and a collection of Netrunner resources. The Usenet group is where Netrunner fans gather to talk.

**Web:**

**http://www.egr.msu.edu/~jhl/netrunner.html**
**http://www.wizards.com/Netrunner/NR_FAQ_1_0.html**

**Usenet:**

**rec.games.trading-cards.misc**

## Role Playing Archives

I love free stuff and whenever I am looking for free role-playing materials, I check on the Net. Here you will find large archives of role-playing materials—pictures, programs, game sheets, stories, specific systems, and texts on all aspects of role playing.

**Web:**

**http://cip2.e-technik.uni-erlangen.de:8080/hyplan/langer/rpg.html**
**http://www.tiac.net/users/frj/getfiles.htm#RPG**

## Role Playing Crafts

One of the best aspects of role playing is that you can make your own props and costumes to enhance the game. This web site has information and hints on how to make your own role-playing accessories: chain mail, costumes, weapons and more.

**Web:**

**http://bull.got.kth.se/~annat/**

## Role Playing Famous Last Words

When your role-playing character commits the most amazing blunder of all time, you become a legend. It's a tradition to be ridiculed for the rest of your days about it. At least you are not alone. See page after page of other players' famous last words and take comfort that nobody is laughing at you—they are laughing near you.

**Web:**

**http://data.club.cc.cmu.edu/~pooh/lore/lastwords**

## Role Playing Games Magazine

Here is an online magazine devoted to role playing and related activities. Look at the convention calendar, as well as industry news, feature stories, role-playing game artist of the month, fiction, game reviews, maps, creatures and scenarios.

**Web:**

**http://www.roleplayers.com/**

## Role Playing Resources

A large collection of information connected to role playing, including convention reports, lists of links, list of games and companies, and game-system specifics.

**Web:**

**http://www.lextech.com/rpg/**

Role-Playing Games
Sometimes I wonder why people even bother with real life. Not only is it always in your face, but so much of the time it is noisy and ugly.
Take my advice:
find out about role-playing games and leave reality to the grown-ups.

## Star Trek Role Playing

Don't settle for just watching or reading Star Trek. You can actually be a Star Trek character. Trekkies discuss the game and its enhancements as well as putting together a group to play the game. It's not just fun, it's a way of life. Check out the web page for other Star Trek RPG information on the Net.

**Web:**

**http://www.virtual-northwest.com/asr/**

**Usenet:**

**alt.starfleet.rpg**

## Vampire: The Masquerade

Vampire: The Masquerade is a series of live-action role-playing games (LARP) based on commercial rulesets derived from the White Wolf's World of Darkness. (In LARP, you not only wear costumes and participate, you act out the parts.) These web sites contain a lot of information for Vampire enthusiasts around the world: information about conventions, role-playing groups, game rules and modifications, characters, game-related fiction, graphics, and much more. The Usenet group is for players and fans to gather and talk about gaming, rules and personal experiences.

**Web:**

**http://www.eleves.ens.fr:8080/home/granboul/Vampire/**
**http://www.rpi.edu/~chalod/vampire/**

**Usenet:**

**alt.games.vampire.the.masquerade**

## Warhammer

Warhammer is a medieval role-playing game. The web site has a large archive of files. You will find play aids, a bestiary, sample scenarios, and information on religion, rules, magick and careers. The mailing list is for discussing all aspects of Warhammer fantasy role play.

**Web:**

**http://home.sn.no/~tomasf/WFRP/WArch.html**

**Listproc Mailing List:**

List Name: **wfrp**
Subscribe to: **listproc@buddha.intecom.com**

## World of Darkness

World of Darkness is a general umbrella term for games such as Werewolf, Mage, Wraith, Changeling and the Vampire: The Masquerade series, all produced by White Wolf Game Studios. This web page has a hefty list of links to the various games, archives, and related Usenet groups. There is one Usenet group for the Storyteller system, and another group for White Wolf games.

**Web:**

**http://ezinfo.ucs.indiana.edu/~adashiel/wod/otherwww/otherwww.html**

**Usenet:**

**alt.games.whitewolf**
**rec.games.frp.storyteller**

## X-Files Simulations

This is an X-Files simulation game. The X-Files is a television show about two FBI agents who investigate unsolved cases that may (or may not) involve paranormal and supernatural activity. The X-Files game is a simulation derived from the ideas on the program. A group of people meet on IRC every week to do various role-playing things. The web page tells how to get started. You can see samples of dialogue, read an overview of how the games work and how to play, read about etiquette, see some sample characters, and find out how you can join in the action. (I didn't put the IRC channel in here, because you have to read documents and learn about the game before you can play.)

**Web:**

**http://members.gnn.com/abbebeck/basement.htm**

**Do you have a code in the head? Try "Cryptography".**

A B C D E F G H I J K L M N O P Q R S T U V W X Y Z

## *Look What I Found on the Net...*

Newsgroup: alt.starfleet.rpg
Subject: alt.starfleet.rpg (ASR) Introduction

From: Admiral Jefferson Lee, Commander-in-Chief, Starfleet

Stardate: 80808.0700

Welcome to ASR, the Usenet newsgroup alt.starfleet.rpg. Here, hundreds of people from all over the world read and write stories in the universe of Star Trek.

What brings us together is a common enjoyment of interactive drama: the opportunity to combine the passive enjoyment of reading a book or watching a movie with the creative thrill of making the story move in a direction WE choose.

The synthesis of several writers' contributions often ends up being a story more entertaining, and "better Trek", than any one writer would have written...

=============

Newsgroup: alt.starfleet.rpg
Subject: USS Philadelphia/Suffolk

Scene: Station Sickbay

The two had finished the quick meal and headed back towards sickbay. Upon entering the room, the both expected something to have changed, but the room was still the same way they had left it.

Caroline went back to the bio bed to continue taking readings on the Ferengi body while Nick went back to searching out the room. Entering the Chief Medical's office, Nick glanced over the monitor sitting on the desk. Sitting down at the desk, Nick started to access the log entry from the terminal. He stopped looking when he saw an entry marked:

STARFLEET COMMAND FILE ACCESS..............
MEDICAL RESEARCH.........
INVENTIONS........
COMA/HOLO VIEWER........

Before he could read further, a loud crash was heard from the other room...

# ROMANCE

## Chatting in the Big City

If you just moved to a new town or you are thinking of moving, you can find people on IRC who live in the city of your destination. Make new friends before you go or ask about great vacation spots in the city of your choice.

**IRC:**

**#atlanta**
**#austin**
**#boston**
**#chicago**
**#cleveland**
**#dallas**
**#denver**
**#detroit**
**#houston**
**#london**
**#montreal**
**#nyc**
**#paris**
**#perth**
**#sandiego**
**#seattle**
**#singapore**
**#sydney**

## Couples

It's the best of times, it's the worst of times. Relationships have their ups and downs, but like a roller coaster, it's fun and thrilling, makes you afraid, and makes you laugh. See what is going on in the lives of other couples. Get ideas for romantic outings, anniversaries, how to patch up a fuss, or what to do with in-laws.

**Usenet:**

**soc.couples**
**soc.couples.intercultural**

**Listserv Mailing List:**

List Name: **couples-l**
Subscribe to: **listserv@cornell.edu**

Couples: Need to work on the relationship? Why not do it in front of the rest of the world? Participate in the **soc.couples** discussion group and the **couples-l** mailing list.

## Email PenPals

Looking for someone to exchange email with? Check out this list of people who are looking for email penpals. Along with the names of the people, there is also information about the languages they speak and their hobbies.

**Web:**

**http://www.ping.be/vademecum/emaits/**
**http://www.thebook.com/penpal/welcome.htm**

## Flowers by Email

Send a bouquet or arrangement of electronic flowers to anyone you want, anywhere on the Net. First, you pick out the type of flowers you wish to send, then you specify a message (which can even include HTML tags). A email note will be sent to the recipient you specify, along with instructions showing him or her how to view the flowers and your message.

**Web:**

**http://www.azstarnet.com/flowers/**

## Incurable Romantix

From singlehood to married with children, this site will take you from stage to stage instead of leaving you at the altar. Not only are there dating services and advice for singles, but there are special features for married people who want to keep their love alive. If you are a romantic or you just want to be, check out this site for interesting hints and tips for love.

**Web:**

**http://www.autonomy.com/luv.htm**

## Kissing

If you haven't been able to get any kissing action lately, you can at least hear how kisses sound. Download a few different kisses in a variety of nationalities: French, English-French, Italian and more. This is good, clean, germ-free fun.

**Web:**

**http://www.purple.co.uk/purplet/love/smooch/smooch.html**

### *Language of Love*

*Every time you kiss me,*
*I'm still not certain that you love me.*

*However, if you use the Language of Love web site, you could tell me you love me in more than 100 languages, including Bulgarian (Obicham te), Esperanto (Mi amas vin), Klingon (qaparHa') and Vulcan (Wani ra yana ro aisha).*

## Language of Love

World travelers: it's always handy to know how to say "I love you" in any language. You never know when it could be important. For instance, say you are on a brief layover at an airport in Rome and the woman of your dreams comes racing by dragging behind her four suitcases on wheels. She runs over your foot and you realize that, yes, this is The One For You. How are you going to get her attention? Check out this site, so you'll be lucky in love no matter what your native language.

**Web:**

**http://aurora.etsiig.uniovi.es:3080/WWW/w.dir/pippin.dir/pgg/2r95.html**

## Love Advice

Here's advice for the lovelorn. Ms. Loquita's weekly advice column will touch on topics such as friendship, first dates, what to do if your best friend is a guy and your boyfriend gets jealous and even some hygiene advice. Send Ms. Loquita mail if you need advice or just read the archive of past columns. Before long, you will realize that being normal is not necessarily a bad thing.

**Web:**

**http://www.hyperweb.com/loquita/loquita.html**

## Love Chat

Whether you are looking for love or looking to talk about love, IRC is a good place to start. Not only can you talk romantic, but you can eat pizza at the same time and nobody will know the difference. You can't get much better than that. Check out these channels for some romantic talk or possibly some romantic action.

**IRC:**

**#love**
**#love_nest**
**#loveboat**
**#lovecafe**
**#truelove**

## Love Letters

Every time you sit down to write a nice love letter to the person of your dreams, it never seems to come out sounding as wonderful as it does in your head. Don't let that stop you. Instead, get help from Cyrano de Bergerac, the notable romantic. Fill out a form with a few details and Cyrano will write the letter for you. Love was never so easy.

**Web:**

**http://www.nando.net/toys/cyrano.html**

## Love Recipes

When you have company coming over and you want to plan a nice romantic refreshment, use one of these nice recipes from the Web to impress the object of your desire. Learn how to make exciting refreshments like Cupid's Exotic Love Tea or Cyberspace Cupid Cupcakes. If it turns out to not be tasty, call the pizza delivery place immediately and if you set the kitchen on fire, call 9-1-1. Beyond that, you are on your own. I can't do everything for you.

**Web:**

**http://www.neosoft.com/citylink/cupid/yummy.html**

## Love Test

Here are two different tests that you can take: one about your concept of love, the other about your experiences with love. If you are currently in a relationship, you can take the "combination test", to see how your current experience of love matches your concept of love. After you take the tests, you can compare your results to various statistics that have been compiled from experience with these tests.

**Web:**

**http://okcforum.osrhe.edu/~psyche/lovetest/**

### *Love and Romance*

Where would we be without love and romance? Probably at home in front of the TV set. At least with romance we can be in front of the TV with someone to keep us company. As a Net person, you never need to worry about getting your share. There are lots of resources for the romantically inclined (and even for the romantically challenged).

But remember, even in a Harley Hahn book, "Romance" comes before "Sex".

## Men and Women

We all got along fine when we were algae. But somewhere between floating gently on the lake and the invention of the bikini, men and women started to have their differences. Get up close and personal. See what the factions are saying about each other. It's not too much of a secret since there is a lot of crossposting.

**Usenet:**

**soc.men**
**soc.women**

## Online Romance Talk and General Discussion

Voyeurs and participants alike can experience fun and romance in Usenet. In this Usenet group you can meet people, talk about the concepts of romance, being romantic, ideas that are romantic or talk about places on the Net where you can find romance.

**Usenet:**

**alt.romance.online**

## Poetry

Send a wonderful poem to that special someone in your life. You can choose from any number of famous poems and personalize it by adding your own message as well.

**Web:**

**http://www.purple.co.uk/purplet/love/poems/poems.html**

## Random Love Poems

Close your eyes, count to three and click. Suddenly you will be transported to a randomly selected romantic poem by people who have been dead for many, many years. This, of course, doesn't detract from the romantic value of the poem, so by all means, read on. Don't think about how, as you imagine being in love and laughing with your wonderful partner, these poets have long since been eaten by worms. But don't let that stop you. Carry on. Be happy.

**Web:**

**http://www.public.com/romance/poem.cgi**

## Romance Readers Anonymous

You've been sucked in. It's impossible to walk past a rack of romance novels without picking up at least one. The bronzed man holding the lithe woman with the heaving bosom makes your heart beat quickly, loud enough for everyone else in the store to hear. The television has cobwebs and you haven't been out of the house in months since you got a subscription to Romance of the Week. Get help now. You are not alone.

**Usenet:**

**bit.listserv.rra-l**

**Listserv Mailing List:**

List Name: **rra-l**
Subscribe to: **listserv@kentvm.kent.edu**

A B C D E F G H I J K L M N O P Q R S T U V W X Y Z

## *Look What I Found on the Net...*

Newsgroups: soc.men
Subject: Marriage Makes Men Fearless

Al Bundy's T-shirt said it best: "Kill Me, I'm Married".

There seems to be nothing more courage hardening than being trapped in a marriage. Men will willingly work a hundred hours a week to avoid going home, even if the work has an early death warranty.

Men go to war, to sea, to space, and anywhere they can avoid facing their wives with no fear of the risks they are taking; because they have nothing to lose. Marriage must be one of the most powerful tools a culture has for its own protection. Without the terror of "going home" how would any country get hundreds of thousands of men to head off to war? Couldn't happen. We aren't "protecting our country," we are protecting ourselves...

============

Newsgroup: soc.women
Subject: Women Aren't Automobiles

```
>>> What I disagree with, however, is the notion that the man is
>>> in any way responsible for the woman's EXTRAVAGANT ways of
>>> dealing with such reproductive "accidents".  That's like
>>> saying if I put a dent in the bumper of someone's Yugo in a
>>> parking lot, and they decide to replace the entire car with
>>> a Rolls Royce, that I'm liable for the entire cost of the
>>> "replacement".

>> Uhhh... women aren't automobiles.  Perhaps your seeming to
>> consider them such is partially the cause of your being a
>> "voluntary chaste virgin".

> All right.  Then how do you explain the classic show
> "My Mother the Car"?
```

Well, of course *some* women *are* automobiles. I don't think that anyone was denying this. But I still don't think that you can make the sweeping generalization that *all* women are automobiles.

I did date a Ford Pinto once, but the relationship ended tragically...

## Romance Talk and General Discussion

Have you noticed life isn't quite like the covers of paperback romance novels (or the inside of the romance novels, for that matter)? Do something about that by generating a romantic fire with others who mourn the death of romance. Remember Cyrano de Bergerac and his words that could melt the hair off a moose? Where do you think he got his start?

**Usenet:**

**alt.romance**
**alt.romance.chat**
**alt.romance.mature-adult**

## Romantic Ascii Graphics

Stop with the boring email. Send your loved one a nice romantic greeting spiced up with some ascii graphics. For those of you who don't know how to make your own, just cut and paste some of these into your letter and nobody will know the difference. It will be our little secret.

**Web:**

**http://www.dina.kvl.dk/~fischer/alt.romance/ascii.html**

## Romantic Cards

There's no need to race out to the store just because you forgot to get a nice card for your anniversary. Just fire up the web browser and make one yourself. The card will be all the more special because you made it yourself. These are spiffy ways to design a card with text and pictures.

**Web:**

**http://buildacard.com/**
**http://www.fwy.com:2000/**

## Romantic Gestures

Don't flounder around in your romantic life when you could be someone's future knight in shining armor. Here's a list of romantic ideas if you don't know exactly what to do or how to get started in the romance game.

**Web:**

**http://mondrian.math.swt.edu/~bg01699/**

## Romantic Whisperings

A place to whisper sweet nothings and tell tales of candlelight dinners, moonlight strolls, and hearts shared with other romantics from around the globe.

**IRC:**

**#romance**

## Singles

Your mother probably said that anyone you can pick up in a bar is not someone with whom you want to develop a serious relationship. (What you probably didn't want to tell her was that you weren't looking for a serious relationship.) In the event that you change your mind, stop in at the nicest singles hangout in Usenet and the IRC and find that special someone just right for you. The web site has the **soc.singles** FAQ (frequently asked question list).

**Web:**

**http://csclub.uwaterloo.ca/~rridge/ss/big/faq.html**

**Usenet:**

**soc.singles**

**IRC:**

**#singles**

## Soulmates

There is a moment when you look into someone's eyes and you feel, in an instant, that you have known this person your entire life and that you can never bear to be separated from him or her again. This is the feeling of finding a soulmate, someone who feels like the other half of you. Read anecdotes about people who have found their soulmates, people who are looking for soulmates and discuss the writings of authors who write on the concept of soulmates.

**Usenet:**

**alt.soulmates**

## Togetherness Tips

Getting married? Here are some questions you should ask yourself before you officially take the plunge. There are also tips on planning a wedding, staying together and how to make things work over the years.

**Web:**

**http://www.commerce.digital.com/palo-alto/WeddingPhoto/ArticleTips.html**

## Unhappy Romances

The only thing worse than no romance is unhappy romance. Unrequited love, romance gone bad or people who are inept in the romance department—these are all topics that are fair game in this Usenet group.

**Usenet:**

**alt.romance.unhappy**

## Valentine Game

Would you like to play Valentine-related trivia games? Choose a game and you are presented with some tiles to press. Each tile you press gives you a multiple choice question. If you answer correctly, the tile is replaced with a fragment of a picture. If you answer wrong, you get a "broken heart". If you answer all the questions correctly, you will eventually see all the pieces of a picture, as well as a love poem you can send to someone special.

**Web:**

**http://equity.stern.nyu.edu/Valentine/**

**The Net is immortal.**

*Look What I Found on the Net...*

```
                 (from Romantic Ascii Graphics)

              ____                ____
             /,,,,\______________/,,,,\
            |,(  )/,,,,,,,,,,,,,,\(  ),|
             \__,,,,___,,,,,___,,,,__/
               /,,,/(')\,,,/(')\,,,\
              |,,,,___ _____ ___,,,,|
              |,,,/    \\o_o//    \,,,|
              |,,|        |        |,,|
              |,,|    \__/|\__/    |,,|
               \,,\       \_/      /,,/
                \__\______________/__/
  ________________/,,,,,,,,,,,,,,\________________
 / \,,,,,,,,,,,,,,,,______________,,,,,,,,,,,,,,,,/ \
(   ),,,,,,,,,,,,,,,/              \,,,,,,,,,,,,,,,(   )
 \_/______________,,/              \,,______________\_/
                 /,/                \,\
                |,|                  |,|
                |,|   I LOVE YOU     |,|
                |,|                  |,|
                |,|                  |,|
                 \,\       o        /,/
                 /,,\______________/,,\
                /,,,,,,,,,,,,,,,,,,,,,,\
               /,,,,,,,,,________,,,,,,,,\
              /,,,,,,,,/          \,,,,,,,,\
             /,,,,,,, /            \,,,,,,,,\
            /_____,,,/              \,,,_____\
           //     \,/                \,/     \\
           \\_____//                  \\_____//
```

A B C D E F G H I J K L M N O P Q R S T U V W X Y Z

## Virtual Wedding Chapel

Well, it had to happen:: a virtual, real-time wedding chapel. To start, you can fill out a form and specify the email address of someone you know. A program will then email that person a "proposal". If they accept—and, since you are one of my readers, of course they will accept—you can arrange to have your wedding in a virtual chat session. Afterward, you will get a nice electronic marriage certificate.

**Web:**

**http://www.hollywoodandvine.com/Itheeweb/**

## Wedding Announcements

You don't have to listen to rumors about so-and-so getting married. Find out if it's true by browsing this web site where people post their wedding announcements. You can also announce your own wedding and display a photograph of you and your mate-to-be.

**Web:**

**http://www.cipsinc.com/wedding/announce/info1.htm**

## Weddings

Don't let your wedding be a remake of Father of the Bride (or the Bay of Pigs). Learn what is proper and what is not. Find out shortcuts from folks who have done this before (or again and again). Topics cover a wide range, such as invitations, RSVPs, dresses, parties, garters, underclothes, and much more.

**Web:**

**http://www.wam.umd.edu/~sek/wedding.html**

**Usenet:**

**alt.wedding**
**soc.couples.wedding**

**There's no such thing as too much bandwidth.**

### *Look What I Found on the Net...*

```
Newsgroup: alt.romance.unhappy
Subject: Help: Problem With a Girlfriend to Be

> I am in a situation where I am in love with this fabulous girl
> that I work with, and we are great friends.
> (She's 27 and I'm 26.)
>
> Unfortunately, because she is married, I have not told her
> how I feel.

Although she may know that you have feelings for her, she is
already married.  Y'know -- vows and commitment and all?

If you tell her, then what?

Redirect your energy, my man.  You're only gonna hurt yourself
and your friendship with her.
```

# SCIENCE

## Annals of Improbable Research

The Annals of Improbable Research (AIR) is a science humor magazine. It's hard to describe what you find here; suffice to say that, if you like science and you have a good sense of humor, you'll enjoy what you see. (Think of AIR as the National Lampoon for smart people.) Footnotes: (1) If you liked the old Journal of Irreproducible Results, you'll enjoy the AIR. (2) These same people also give out the annual Ig Nobel Awards to honor people whose achievements "cannot or should not be reproduced".

**Web:**

**http://www.improb.com/**
**http://www.improb.com/airchives/mini-AIR/**

## Anthropology

Anthropology is the study of the origin and development of human beings. There are two main divisions: physical anthropology, which concentrates on human evolution and variation, and cultural anthropology, which includes the study of archeology (material remains of various civilizations), ethnology (races of mankind), social anthropology (social organizations), and linguistics (nature of languages). If you are interested in anthropology, there is a lot for you on the Net: research, resources and discussion.

**Web:**

**http://www.sscf.ucsb.edu/anth/**
**http://www.usc.edu/dept/v-lib/anthropology.html**

**Usenet:**

**sci.anthropology**
**sci.anthropology.paleo**

**Listserv Mailing List:**

List Name: **anthro-l**
Subscribe to: **listserv@ubvm.cc.buffalo.edu**

:-)

### Annals of Improbable Research

If you are like me, you enjoy nothing better than spending Saturday night curled up at home with a good mathematics or physics journal. However, even the best times end, and what do you do when you have read all your scholarly publications and it's only 9:00 PM? Time to fire up the old web browser and connect to the **Annals of Improbable Research** archives. For scientist and non-scientist alike, this lighthearted approach to research and its detritus will entertain for hours.

## Color Perception

This mailing list explores color concepts by drawing from color studies in anthropology, linguistics, philosophy, psychology and cognitive science.

**Listserv Mailing List:**

List Name: **colorcat**
Subscribe to: **listserv@brownvm.brown.edu**

## Dinosaurs

These web sites will show you fossils and sculptures during a narrated dinosaur tour complete with sound and images. There are also links to other interesting dinosaur resources. For more interactive dinosaur discussion, check out the mailing list.

**Web:**

**http://ucmp1.berkeley.edu/exhibittext/cladecham.html**
**http://www.hcc.hawaii.edu/dinos/dinos.1.html**

**Listproc Mailing List:**

List Name: **dinosaur**
Subscribe to: **listproc@lepomis.psych.upenn.edu**

## Earth and Sky

"Earth and Sky" is a popular radio presentation that is aired daily on hundreds of stations in the U.S., Canada and the South Pacific, as well as on various international networks. Each day the show provides a short discussion of one scientific topic. The web site offers the dialogs from the actual shows. You read about the most current show, or search for one that interests you.

**Web:**

**http://www.earthsky.com/**

## Earth Science Site of the Week

Earth science refers to the family of geological sciences that study the Earth: its origin, its structure and the physical phenomena found within it. The principal Earth sciences study various characteristics of the Earth: geography (physical characteristics of the surface), geology (nature of its composition), orography (mountains), oceanography (oceans), geomorphology (landforms), speleology (caves), geodesy (size and shape) and hydrography (surface waters). Each week, a new Earth science resource is chosen, and a link to the resource along with a brief summary is displayed at this web site. The past sites of the week are archived if you want to browse some of the selections. I like to visit once in a while to see what's new. Try it, and I bet you will learn something interesting.

**Web:**
**http://agcwww.bio.ns.ca/misc/geores/sotw/sotw.html**

## Electromagnetics in Medicine, Science and Communication

What good is electromagnetics? Is it likely that it will improve how pizza tastes or help the Dodgers win their next game? According to the Electromagnetic Society, there is more to life than good pizza. Read literature concerning the interaction between electromagnetic fields and biological systems. Yes, there is even data on 60 Hz and microwave radiation.

**Listserv Mailing List:**
List Name: **emflds-l**
Subscribe to: **listserv@ubvm.cc.buffalo.edu**

## Folklore of Science

Science is rich in folklore, legends and mysteries. This Usenet group is for the discussion of various folklore topics as they relate to science. The web page contains a listing of science-related urban legends. Will a penny falling from a great height kill someone? Will hot water freeze faster than cold water? Why does the moon look smaller when it is overhead than when it is near the horizon? Visit the web site and find out the answers to these questions and more. (By the way, the quick answers are no, yes and it's an illusion.)

**Web:**
**http://www.urbanlegends.com/science/**

**Usenet:**
**alt.folklore.science**

**DINOSAURS**

The fact is, just about everybody likes dinosaurs (unless they are named "Barney"). If you've got kids, show them how to use your web browser and point it to a Dinosaur Exhibit. We owe it to ourselves to spend some time learning about these great beasts from the past and how they influence our modern culture. (After all, dinosaurs are people too.)

For example, few people realize it but, before David Letterman, the top-rated American nighttime TV talkshow host was a dinosaur. And fully 75% of modern American publishing companies are run by dinosaurs. Let's teach our kids to understand and appreciate our friends in the dinosaur kingdom, and soon we will all be living in peace and harmony.

## Global Positioning System

The Global Positioning System (GPS) is an amazing system that will tell you your (almost) exact position and time anywhere on the Earth. There are three parts to the system: (1) In space, there are 24 satellites (three of which are spares) that circle the Earth in 12-hour orbits. From any point on the Earth, there are five to eight satellites above you somewhere. (2) Around the world, there is a whole system of tracking stations. The master station is at Falcon Air Force Base in Colorado. (3) To receive data, you use a GPS receiver. This receiver uses the signals from at least four of the satellites to give you navigation, positioning and time information. If you are a special authorized user (U.S. Department of Defense, etc.) your receiver can tell you your exact position within an 18 by 28 meter area, and the time will be accurate within 100 nanoseconds (billionths of a second). Everyone else gets a position within a 100 by 156 meter area, with a time accurate within 167 nanoseconds. Are you intrigued? Check the Net for a lot more information.

**Web:**
**http://www.utexas.edu/depts/grg/gcraft/notes/gps/gps.html**

## History of Science

The history of science is the story of our systematic and endless quest to understand the nature of ourselves, our world and the universe in which we live. This Usenet group is devoted to a discussion of the history of science and scientific discoveries, as well as the ways in which mankind's development affects our modern existence.

**Usenet:**
**soc.history.science**

## Human Evolution

Human evolution is the theory of the origin of human beings. In particular, evolution explains how man and the apes descended from common ancestors and how, about five million years ago, our most immediate ancestors (hominids) began the development that would result in our own species (Homo sapiens). There is a great deal of foolish and ignorant thought (and talk) among people who believe that mankind was created supernaturally. As far as I am concerned, the more people learn about the science, the better off we all are, and here are some places to start. In particular, one of the web sites has a collection of FAQs (frequently asked question lists) about evolution.

**Web:**
**http://earth.ics.uci.edu:8080/origins/faqs-evolution.html**
**http://www.dealsonline.com/origins/**

**Usenet:**
**talk.origins**

## Mind Science

Explore the mysteries of the mind by taking part in serious discussion of the mind and how it learns, processes information and creates the body's reactions. Experiment with a little transcutaneous electrical neural stimulation, or perhaps those of you who need a little break from everything can spend the day in a sensory deprivation tank. Just remember—wherever you go, there you are.

**Listproc Mailing List:**
List Name: **mind-l**
Subscribe to: **listproc@gate.net**

**Listserv Mailing List:**
List Name: **scimind-l**
Subscribe to: **listserv@nosferatu.cas.usf.edu**

## National Science Foundation

The National Science Foundation (NSF) is an independent agency of the United States government. Its purpose is to promote the progress of science within the United States. Toward this end, the NSF funds a great deal of research within the science and engineering disciplines, as well as awarding many graduate scholarships. The NSF also promotes the use of computers in science research and education. If you are a technical researcher or grad student, you can't go far without bumping into the NSF. Their web site features information about the organization itself, its publications, grants and scholarships and research.

**Web:**
**http://www.nsf.gov/nsf/**

## Oceanography

The Earth has one large interconnected sea of water, covering 71 percent of the planet's surface. Traditionally, we divide all this water into four main oceans: the Pacific Ocean, the Indian Ocean, the Atlantic Ocean and the Arctic Ocean. Taken together, these oceans cover about 139,400,000 sq mi (361,000,000 sq km) and contain about 322,280,000 cu mi (1,347,000,000 cu km) of water. The average depth is about 12,230 ft (3,730 m). Oceanography is the study of the ocean and the life it supports. As such, oceanography integrates biology, chemistry, geography, geology, physics and meteorology into one marine-oriented field of study. There are a great many oceanography resources on the Net. Here are some web sites that contain particularly good collections. I have also included the web sites of two of the main oceanographical research organizations in the United States: Scripps Institution of Oceanography (California) and the Woods Hole Oceanographic Institution (Massachusetts).

**Web:**
**http://scilib.ucsd.edu/sio/inst/**
**http://sio.ucsd.edu/**
**http://www.cms.udel.edu/**
**http://www.mth.uea.ac.uk/ocean/oceanography.html**
**http://www.whoi.edu/**

## Origin of the Universe

Stephen Hawking is one of the most brilliant theoretical physicists of our time. Here is a short essay where Hawking discusses the origin of the universe. The essay starts with a brief synopsis of how people have thought of the universe throughout history, and then goes on to discuss modern ideas in (relatively) simple terms. If you need to create your own universe—or even if you are only thinking about it—this is an invaluable guide.

**Web:**
**http://www.astro.nwu.edu/lentz/astro/hawking-1.html**

Do you like the universe? (It's always been one of *our* favorite places.)
If so, read what Steven Hawking has to say about it.

## Radiocarbon

Radiocarbon is the main international journal of record for research articles and datelists related to C-14 and other radioisotopes and techniques used in archeological, geophysical, oceanographic and related dating. This site offers related news and announcements, abstracts, datasets, and information about radiocarbon publications and links to other relevant resources.

**Web:**
**http://packrat.aml.arizona.edu/**

## Radiocarbon and Radioisotopes Mailing List

This is a mailing list for researchers and others involved in radiocarbon dating. Talk about the use of radioisotopes in dating, and scientific dating issues in general.

**Listserv Mailing List:**
List Name: **c14-l**
Subscribe to: **listserv@listserv.arizona.edu**

## Research Methods in Science

You need a certain kind of mind to be an organized and efficient researcher. Here is a list that helps researchers in classification, clustering, phylogeny estimation and related methods of data analysis to contact other researchers in the same fields. All professions are welcome to the list.

**Listserv Mailing List:**
List Name: **class-l**
Subscribe to: **listserv@ccvm.sunysb.edu**

## Science Fraud

This mailing list is dedicated to the discussion of fraud in science, including current and recent events, and historic accounts of fraudulent science. Also available is a database on fraud in science with thousands of references.

**Listserv Mailing List:**
List Name: **scifraud**
Subscribe to: **listserv@uacsc2.albany.edu**

## Science Magazines

Here are links to a massive number of science-related magazines. This is a great way to check out a mag if you think you may want to subscribe, or to browse unfamiliar publications just to see what they are.

**Web:**
**http://www.enews.com/monster/science.html**

## Science Resource Guide

This is a large, comprehensive list of pre-screened science resource sites on the Net. There are sites for just about every type of science and science-related category you can think of. If you are looking for something in a particular area, here is one of the places to check first.

**Web:**
**http://www.clearinghouse.net/tree/sci.html**

## Science Talk and General Discussion

Science is the organized, rational study of the nature of our universe. As a whole, science is broad, almost beyond description. I think of science in two ways: as a method of thinking, and as a human activity. The activity of science depends upon three basic traditions: employing trustworthy methods for experimentation and observation, systematically classifying observed facts, and connecting a body of demonstrated truths in order to reach conclusions. Mankind already knows a great deal about our universe (including the planet on which we live and the nature of the biology it supports). A great deal of mankind's suffering is caused by widespread ignorance of basic scientific knowledge and the inability to apply such knowledge wisely. For this reason, I encourage you to use the resources I have prepared for this book to teach yourself more about science. I hope that, within the many scientific resources, you will find much to interest you. If you would like to talk about science in general, here is the Usenet group devoted to such discussions. Remember what I say: as much as anything else, science is a way of thinking. There is no better way to fulfill your birthright as a sentient human being than by studying the world around you and all its wonders. (Perhaps I can put it another way. My cat can't learn about science, so I have to do it for both of us.)

**Usenet:**

**sci.misc**

## Scientific Skepticism

This is an archive of postings from **sci.skeptic**, the Usenet group devoted to turning the cold light of scientific study onto all kinds of paranormal subjects, such as ESP, UFOs, and other pseudo-scientific beliefs.

**Web:**

**http://www.cis.ohio-state.edu/hypertext/faq/usenet/skeptic-faq/faq.html**

**What if...?**

## Vision Science

It's embarrassing to leave the house in the morning, go to work, and discover that your clothes don't match. Well, the Net is always there to help. Here is a comprehensive collection of resources relating to vision science (vision research in humans and other animals). Even if you can't see the light, you can always see what everyone else is doing.

**Web:**

**http://vision.arc.nasa.gov/VisionScience/VisionScience.html**

## Why Files

"The Why Files: The Science Behind the News" is a project funded by the United States National Science Foundation (NSF) and managed by the National Institute for Science Education (NISE). Based on the premise that science should be for everyone, the project examines the science behind various current news stories. The idea is to use news stories as a way to interest people in learning about science. For example, the legal battles involving the cigarette industry provide an opportunity to examine nicotine addiction and how it affects the brain. The stories, which are well-researched and intriguing, are changed at intervals. The old stories are archived.

**Web:**

**http://whyfiles.news.wisc.edu/**

# SCIENCE FICTION, FANTASY AND HORROR

## Ansible Newsletter

Get the latest buzz on the sci-fi scene. *Ansible*, a Hugo-award winning newsletter, will give you news and gossip about your favorite authors, dates for conferences and conventions, book reviews and releases, as well as the occasional obituary. *Ansible* is archived at the web sites, but is also available by electronic subscription.

**Web:**

**http://www.dcs.gla.ac.uk/SF-Archives/Ansible**
**http://www.lysator.liu.se/sf_archive/sf-texts/Ansible/**

**Majordomo Mailing List:**

List Name: **ansible**
Subscribe to: **majordomo@imi.gla.ac.uk**

## Bibliographies of Science Fiction

You no longer have to wonder if you have read everything written by your favorite science fiction or fantasy author. This list of bibliographies arranged alphabetically by author will give you a brief biography of the writer, a list of pseudonyms, listings of books and stories, and other related information, such as movie adaptations or collaborations.

**Web:**

**http://www.lysator.liu.se/sf_archive/sub/jwenn.html**

**Stay connected.**

### Who Wrote What?

It's late at night. You get a mysterious phone call. A stranger with an Armenian accent makes you an astounding offer: If you can tell him, within five minutes, who wrote The Package in Hyperspace, he will send you a million dollars plus an autographed copy of The Internet Complete Reference. No problem. Simply point your browser at the **Bibliographies of Science Fiction** web site and within a few minutes you will have your answer, a million dollars, and a copy of the best Internet book ever written. (By the way, the answer is "Janet Asimov.")

### *Look What I Found on the Net...*

```
Newsgroup: sci.misc
Subject: Help With a Kid's Question

> My 11-year-old son stumped me with the following syllogism:

> -- Diamonds are supposed to be the hardest matter.
> -- Liquids are distinguished from solids by the fact that
>    solid matter is "crushable", in other words liquids cannot
>    be "crushed".
> -- Ergo, water is actually "harder" than diamond.
> -- Perhaps we should use water in lieu of diamonds in cutting
>    processes.

>Is he wrong? Where are the flaws in this argument?

Hardness is essentially a measure of how difficult it is to get
a material to plastically deform under a point load; how
difficult it is to get a material to flow.

It is very easy to get water to flow.  It is very difficult to
get diamonds to flow.  Water is soft, diamonds are hard.

For what it's worth, water can actually cut things, if it under
enough pressure.  Some of the "power washers" which are
available at most hardware stores create a stream of water
powerful enough to blast through the aluminum siding on houses.
```

## Classic Science Fiction and Fantasy Reviews

Old news is good news. At least in this case. Here is a large collection of reviews of science fiction and fantasy books that have been in circulation for quite a while. Read about Lovecraft, Burroughs, Wyndham, Zelazny, LeGuin and many more.

**Web:**

**http://www.lysator.liu.se/sf_archive/sub/belated.html**

## Darkecho's Horror Web

When you are not reading horror stories, you should at least be immersing yourself in the culture. This web site has a nice collection of horror links. You can also read interviews with artists and writers, find out about conventions and check out the book reviews.

**Web:**

**http://w3.gwis.com/~prlg/**

## Fans of Science Fiction Writers

Lose yourself in the fantasy worlds that come pouring out of the minds of great science fiction writers. Anne McCaffrey, Piers Anthony and Terry Pratchett are creators who have a strong following.

**Usenet:**

**alt.books.arthur-clarke**
**alt.books.briam-lumley**
**alt.books.kurt-vonnegut**
**alt.books.larry-niven**
**alt.fan.harlan-ellison**
**alt.fan.heinlein**
**alt.fan.pern**
**alt.fan.piers-anthony**
**alt.fan.pratchett**

**If you are a science buff and you also enjoy science fiction, join the Highly Imaginative Technologies mailing list and see what strangeness the future may (or may not) hold.**

## Furry Stuff

Being a human is really overrated. You don't have much license to romp and play, and most people frown upon licking yourself at the table after a satisfying meal. At least there is a way to redirect your energy. Furry fans will rejoice to see this web site containing information about artists, publishers, and publications that cover anthropomorphic or "furry" art.

**Web:**

**http://rat.org/furry/**

## Highly Imaginative Technologies

There's nothing wrong with suspending reality. It's certainly a great way of brainstorming. Science fiction writers and movie makers get paid to sit around all day and invent cool things, and they don't even have to worry about the laws of physics or people being blown up. Get together with other techies and talk about technology that can or can't be implemented in the future. Any advanced technology, such as interactive video, artificial reality and speech-commanded devices, is a fair topic for discussion.

**Majordomo Mailing List:**

List Name: **hit**
Subscribe to: **majordomo@acd.ufrj.br**

## Horror Fiction Online

Wow. You can scare yourself silly without moving from your computer. These web addresses point to different pages at the same site. One page is a list of horror books and short stories, including The Legend of Sleepy Hollow, The Strange Case of Dr. Jekyll and Mr. Hyde, The Turn of the Screw, Dracula, and The Picture of Dorian Gray (one of my favorites). The second page contains the archives of an ongoing project entitled "Tales From the Internet", in which horror stories are contributed by people around the Net.

**Web:**

**http://www.cat.pdx.edu/~caseyh/horror/online.html**
**http://www.cat.pdx.edu/~caseyh/horror/stories/**

## Horror Literature

This web site has a lot of original content created by a deluxe horror fanatic. Enjoy the reviews of horror fiction, personal thoughts about reading and writing, a scary picture or two, lists of the best horror books, and much more. What I like best about this site is there is so much original content: lots of stuff to read and appreciate. It's refreshing to find web sites created by people who do more than simply link to other sites.

**Web:**

**http://www.oceanstar.com/horror/**

## Horror Magazines Online

Tie down your socks. Here are some online horror magazines to delight, entertain and scare you to bits. Read—if you dare—stories, poems and folklore. Then follow the links to other sites and exhibits too horrible to mention.

**Web:**

**http://www.best.com/~gazissax/alsirat.html**
**http://www.iquest.net/~jhall/evileye.htm**
**http://www.rictus.com/**

## Horror Talk and General Discussion

Lots of people, all over the world, love talking about horror. Moreover, if you like to write, it is encouraging to have a place to show your work to others. Usenet has groups for both purposes. To talk, join **alt.horror**. You may also want to participate in the mailing list. To share your writing (or to read other people's work), try the alt.horror.creative group, where you can discuss anything related to the creation of things horrible. If you are new to horror on the Net, start with the web site where you will find an informative FAQ (frequently asked question list). Read this before you start posting.

**Web:**

**http://ezinfo.ucs.indiana.edu/~mlperkin/faq.html**

**Usenet:**

**alt.horror**
**alt.horror.creative**

**Listserv Mailing List:**

List Name: **horror**
Subscribe to: **listserv@iubvm.ucs.indiana.edu**

## Mystery Science Theatre 3000

There are worse things than being consigned to review bad sci-fi for your entire life. Experience the hilarity of Mystery Science Theater 3000 with other fans of this TV program, where you can watch strange sci-fi movies while listening to the comments of even stranger observers.

**Usenet:**

**alt.fan.mst3k**
**alt.tv.mst3k**
**rec.arts.tv.mst3k**
**rec.arts.tv.mst3k.announce**
**rec.arts.tv.mst3k.misc**

## Red Dwarf

Red Dwarf is a British science fiction comedy series. The premise is described by an opening used on the first show: "This is an S.O.S. distress call from the mining ship Red Dwarf. The crew are dead, killed by a radiation leak. The only survivors are Dave Lister, who was in suspended animation during the disaster, and his pregnant cat, who was safely sealed in the hold. Revived three million years later, Lister's only companions are a life form who evolved from his cat, and Arnold Rimmer, a hologram simulation of one of the dead crew."

**Web:**

**http://www.queeg.crater.com/**

**Usenet:**

**alt.tv.red-dwarf**

**Listserv Mailing List:**

List Name: **reddwarf**
Subscribe to: **listserv@uel.ac.uk**

## Science and Science Fiction

Stretch your mind by pushing your imagination to the limit. How real is the science in science fiction? A wide variety of topics are covered, such as the possibility of force fields, transcendental engineering, and Hawking radiation. Invent your own theories or pick apart someone else's.

**Usenet:**

**rec.arts.sf.science**

A B C D E F G H I J K L M N O P Q R S T U V W X Y Z

## SCIENCE FICTION

The best part about science fiction is that you can enjoy it without having to know anything about science or about fiction. What could be more appealing than a world in which all the basic rules of life are up for grabs? Still, it is interesting to discuss the ideas of science fiction from a scientific point of view. If this sounds good to you, spend some time with the speculative science buffs on rec.arts.sf.science.

## Science Fiction and Fantasy Archive

Science fiction and fantasy are the perfect things to read when you don't want to study for a test or work on something around the house. Cozy up to the computer and read these science fiction and fantasy archives, which will not only give you some great stories, but will also show you reviews of books, movies. There are also links to newsletters and zines that relate to the genre.

**Web:**

**http://www.lysator.liu.se:7500/sf_archive/sf_main.html**

## Science Fiction and Fantasy Online

The Net loves people who love science fiction and fantasy. Start at this web site, and choose your favorite author. You will find work by such writers as Francis Bacon ("The New Atlantis"), L. Frank Baum (the Oz books), Terry Bisson ("Dead Man's Curve"), Edgar Rice Burroughs (the Tarzan books, "The Land That Time Forgot"), Wilkie Collins ("The Haunted Hotel", "The Woman in White"), and Gaston Leroux ("The Phantom of the Opera"). You can also find short stories and sample chapters from various publishers. If you have a day on which you are feeling particularly adventurous, connect to this site and try something that is brand new to you. This is a wonderful site. Visit often and enjoy.

**Web:**

**http://www.users.interport.net/~jfreund/sfbooks/sfbooks.html#complete**

## Science Fiction Announcements

Attention science fiction buffs! Find out what's up and coming in sci-fi land. This moderated group will provide you with all the information you need on new movies, books, television shows and anything that is new in science fiction.

**Usenet:**

**rec.arts.sf.announce**

*Science fiction fanatics: keep up on what's happening by reading* **rec.arts.sf.announce.**

## Science Fiction Convention Calendar

When you need a little break from the real world, pack up your bags and head to a science fiction convention. Here's a list of cons all over the world, including information about the guests of honor and contact information so you can pre-register.

**Web:**

**http://www.mrnet.com/~peed/SFCons/top.html**

## Science Fiction Fandom Talk and General Discussion

Fans from all over the world live, eat and breathe science fiction. They travel in packs, eager to suck the nectar from the sci-fi flower. If you have a taste for something out of the ordinary, join the crowd, go to cons and be a groupie.

**Usenet:**

**alt.fandom.cons**
**rec.arts.sf.fandom**

## Science Fiction Marketplace

Are you looking to trade your extra copy of the "Pegasus" episode of Battlestar Galactica for a signed copy of a Friday print by Whelan? Shop at the science fiction flea market—rare commodities for rare people. Buy, sell or trade. Display your merchandise in this shoplifter-free environment.

**Usenet:**

**rec.arts.sf.marketplace**

## Science Fiction Movies

You just saw the best movie ever and you have to tell someone or you'll explode. You can either run screaming through the parking lot of the movie theater and risk being arrested for disturbing the peace, or you can tell the sci-fi movie fans on the Internet.

**Usenet:**
**rec.arts.sf.movies**

## Science Fiction Resource Guide

This guide has everything under the sun about science fiction, including details on authors, awards, bibliographies, bookstores, fan clubs, movies, publishers, role-playing games, television, Usenet groups, and zines, as well as archives, reviews and criticism, fiction writing and more.

**Web:**
**http://sflovers.rutgers.edu/Web/sf-resource.guide.html**

## Science Fiction Reviews

Zip up your spacesuit, fire all thrusters, and launch into a review of the best and worst of science fiction. Don't hesitate to tell how you feel, because no one else does. Sometimes sublime, but more often not, reviews are always revealing and informative.

**Usenet:**
**rec.arts.sf.reviews**

## Science Fiction Talk and General Discussion

Science fiction isn't a hobby: it's a lifestyle. Are you one of those people whose walls and cabinets (and floors) are covered with sci-fi books, magazines, tapes and memorabilia? Scoot all of it out of the way so you can get to the computer and find your sci-fi soulmates. Anything science fiction goes.

**Usenet:**
**rec.arts.sf.misc**

## Science Fiction Television

It's natural to feel like you can never get enough science fiction. Your mouth goes dry, your hands press continually on the remote control even though you know it will not make science fiction magically appear before you. You need a source or you are going to lose your mind. When you can't find it on the tube, seek your sci-fi television support group and get a quick fix.

**Usenet:**
**rec.arts.sf.tv**

## Science Fiction TV Series Guides

This server, run by Duncan White and Bevis King, contains a number of guides to sci-fi shows such as Star Trek, Dr. Who and Blakes' 7. There are extensive guides which include up-to-date episode summaries, cast lists and trivia, and there are short form guides which give information on little-known science fiction shows no longer in production.

**Web:**
**http://www.ee.surrey.ac.uk/Contrib/SciFi/**

## Science Fiction Writing

Allow yourself to linger on the words, your eyes playing gently back and forth across the pages of your latest sci-fi novel. There is something tangible about a book that you just can't get from television or movies. Discuss your favorite book, hear about someone else's. Find out what's new and what is hopelessly out of print.

**Usenet:**
**rec.arts.sf.written**

## SciFaiku

What do you get when you mix science fiction and haiku poetry? You get SciFaiku, a form of haiku poetry about science fiction topics. Read the rules describing this form of poetry and an archive of a nice selection of SciFaiku.

**Web:**
**http://www.crew.umich.edu/~brinck/poetry/manifesto.html**

## Sci-Fi Lovers

Get your fill of science fiction information at this site. These archives contain science fiction or fantasy-related subjects, such as stories, reviews, convention information, FAQs and reference material.

**Web:**

**http://sflovers.rutgers.edu/**

## Speculative Fiction Clearing House

When you get tired of reality, or just want to explore a new one, check out this huge archive of science fiction and fantasy. Find links to other sci-fi archives, databases of information about authors and bibliographies, and a list of science fiction awards as well as the winners of the awards. There are also links to contests, conferences, publishers, writing resources and zines.

**Web:**

**http://thule.mt.cs.cmu.edu:8001/sf-clearing-house/**

## Star Wars

What would happen if... ? Speculation abounds regarding the Star Wars universe. Star Wars fans reinvent the movies daily, wondering what would happen if certain characters had done things differently. Discover inconsistencies you may have missed in the movies and learn what has happened to everyone involved, from the big screen to the cutting room floor.

**Usenet:**

**rec.arts.sf.starwars**

# SECRET STUFF

## 2600

A channel dedicated to the 2600 magazine, the Hacker Quarterly. There are monthly meetings, usually on the 26th of the month, and subjects include freaking, hacking, cellular phones, scanners, hardware, credit cards, and much more secret stuff.

**IRC:**

**#2600**
**#2600talk**

### *Look What I Found on the Net...*

```
Newsgroup: rec.arts.sf.written
Subject: Secret Messages in DNA

> There is quite a bit of "junk" DNA lying around a genome.
> Theoretically, there shouldn't be any reason for this DNA not
> to hide a message (mind you, you'd have to be pretty clever in
> finding the key to decode those base pair sequences).  And a
> lot of this is supercoiled and packaged by histone and
> non-histone proteins that prevent DNA degradation, so if the
> message lay in introns in that "protected" section, it could
> remain largely unevolved/altered.

Well, the issue is not really how the DNA is packaged.  The
problem is that there would be a steady accumulation of errors
occurring during the replication or repair of DNA.  Not to
mention more dramatic errors caused by chromosomal
rearrangements, unequal crossing over, etc. etc.  So if the
message was going to last a long time, you would need to
incorporate some pretty complex error correction.
```

**Hacker? 2600? Good. Meet you on IRC. 'Nuff said.**

## ATM Secret Codes

Have you ever wondered what is on the little magnetic strip on your ATM card? Now you can find out, along with other secret stuff the banks don't want you to know.

**Web:**

**http://cluon.com/~moore/sub/atm.txt**
**http://www.cyberus.ca/~sgi/atm.txt**

## Backward Masking

Backward masking refers to hiding messages on recorded music by inserting sounds that are meaningful when played backward. Some people feel that cunning malevolent fiends insert such messages into music in order to subliminally influence unsuspecting listeners. This idea first surfaced some years ago when fanatical Bible-thumpers were convinced that various popular rock groups were putting reversed Satanic messages in selected recordings. Since then, a number of musicians and bands have embedded such messages on purpose (for the novelty I suppose). Here are some web pages that offer audio snippets of actual recordings played backward. (Between us, the possibility that anyone could be affected by listening to backward sounds is about as likely as your being affected by the brain emanations of aliens from a nearby star system.)

**Web:**

**http://parallel.park.uga.edu/~nholt/backmask.html**
**http://rampages.onramp.net/~myersrj/secrets.htm**
**http://www.iqsoft.hu/~frank/backward_english.html**

**Do a backup.**

**"Fun" is fun.**

## Cellular Phone Hacking

If you want to be able to hack cellular phones (or even just talk about it to impress people at parties), you need to know the basics and then some. Here is a web site with a collection of information that will set you on the road to getting inside those funny little boxes that cost so much. And if you want to talk, there is always IRC.

**Web:**

**http://www.netwalk.com/~silicon/hack-fon.html**

**IRC:**

**#cellular**

## Disney Secrets

Disney theme parks are very controlled. Try causing even a slight amount of trouble and see how fast the security people (materializing out of nowhere) will give you the bum's rush. When you visit a Disney park, everything you see and everything the employees do is planned carefully. For instance, you are never more than 25 paces away from a garbage can. Disney management goes to a great deal of trouble to sustain the illusion of "the happiest place on Earth". That is why people who work at Disney theme parks are called "cast members". (Repeat this often enough and even the employees think it's normal.) That is why I love to read about Disney secrets. None of these secrets are all that important. Nevertheless, they are intriguing because you just know that the pleasant folks who control the world of Disney would very much prefer that you didn't know anything about their behind-the-scenes management.

**Web:**

**http://musky.oitc.com/Disney/Secrets.html**

**Usenet:**

**alt.disney.secrets**

## Look What I Found on the Net...

(from the Disney Secrets web site)

The next time you see a Disney theme park cast member [employee] looking bored, frustrated, mad, etc., try this.

Make eye contact, put your index finger and thumb together, pull the top of your head up from an imaginary string, and smile sheepishly.

Chances are their attitude will change, at least until you're out of sight.

This action is a little signal cast members and undercover orientees are supposed to give each other when someone is not being what I like to call "Too Cute to Live!"

## Easter Eggs

An Easter egg is a secret something or other hidden in a program. Many programs have Easter eggs—hidden there by the programmers—that you can invoke if you know the secret key combinations. (For example, if you use Netscape, try pressing Ctrl-Alt-F and see what happens. Then try Ctrl-Alt-T.) For more fun, here is a list of the Easter eggs hidden in many different programs (both PC and Mac).

**Web:**

**http://weber.u.washington.edu/~davidnf/eggnorm.html**

## Macintosh Secret Tricks List

There are lots of secret key+mouse combinations hidden in your Mac. Check out the list and I bet you will find something useful. Why doesn't Apple tell you this stuff? Maybe it's in the documentation. (Documentation? I use a Mac. I don't need no stinkin' documentation.)

**Web:**

**http://www.cs.cuhk.hk/~chngai/easter-eggs/**

**FAQs are cool.**

## Look What I Found on the Net...

```
                (from the Easter Eggs site)
     --------------------------------------------------
                        Windows 3.1
     --------------------------------------------------
          Hold down Ctrl and Shift simultaneously.
  (Keep holding them down for all of the following steps).

          1. Select Program Manager's Help menu option.
          2. Select "About Program Manager".
          3. When the box pops up, double click inside
             one of the four panes in the Windows 3.1 logo.
          4. Click OK.

      Repeat all these steps to see a flag waving.
      Repeat again to see the credits.
```

**Are you a Mac person? Take a look at the Macintosh Secret Tricks List and amaze all your friends.**

## Easter Eggs

One of the most important legends of Western culture is the story of how Jesus was put to death by the Romans and how, a short time later, was resurrected, symbolizing God's devotion to mankind and showing us that the devout and the faithful will themselves be resurrected at the appropriate time.

Today, these occurrences are remembered during the various Easter observances around the world, one of the most notable being the insertion of secret actions within important computer programs. These so-called "Easter eggs" are found in a number of PC and Macintosh programs and are documented in the **Easter Egg** web site. So, if you are feeling especially devotional one day, take a moment to find out about these Easter eggs and demonstrate them for yourself. After all, it is too easy to concentrate exclusively on work and other secular matters, and a few moments spent in a spiritual activity would be good for just about anybody.

## Magic Secrets Talk and General Discussion

Want to find out how magic tricks really work? This is the Usenet group where people discuss how magicians make sure that the hand is always quicker than the eye. For example, how does David Copperfield take rings from three people in the audience (seemingly at random), link the rings together, show everyone that the rings are really linked, and then separate them so as to give the rings back to the people? (Answer: One of the rings is a fake. It has a piece cut out of it, allowing it to be linked to two other completely whole rings. Copperfield makes sure that the audience never sees the cut-out part. When he borrows the three rings, he palms one and substitutes the special one he has prepared ahead of time.)

**Usenet:**
**alt.magic.secrets**

## Pay TV Decoders

What would you do if someone gave you instructions for building a Pay TV decoder from simple parts you could buy at any electronic supply store? Don't tell me, I don't want to know. I think television is bad for you.

**Web:**
**http://bacon.gmu.edu/mon/Outlaws/PayTVDecoderPlans**

## Phreaking

What to talk about phone phreaking: telephones, exchanges, toll fraud, kodez, signaling, and so on? Walk gently into that good night and talk to the people who love to phreak. To help you fit in, look at the web sites for help with phreaking terms and abbreviations. Or, if you would actually like to build a "box", you can get the plans. (However, now that phone companies use modern switching systems, most of these boxes don't work. Still, maybe you can find a red box somewhere.)

**Web:**
**http://arirang.miso.co.kr/~xter/phreak/**
**http://ipswitch.loyalistc.on.ca/student/elecmech/mattrick/matp.htm**

**IRC:**
**#phreak**

## Police Codes

The police use a lot of different codes when they talk to one another over the radio. If you have the right type of receiver, you can listen too. But how do you know what the codes mean? Here is the info you need to keep up on what the serve-and-protect guys are doing.

**Web:**

**http://rembrandt.erols.com/mon/Outlaws/PoliceScannerCodes**
**http://www.jaxnet.com/~habedd/10codes.html**

## Questionables

I bet you would enjoy information and material of a questionable nature. How about articles on ATM secret codes, garage-door opener plans, pyrotechnics, police scanner codes and pay-TV decoder plans.

**Web:**

**http://iti2.net/k0p/ob_tphile.html**

Do not look in the *Questionables* archive. And once you get there, do not read anything. And once you read something, do not do what it says. And, most important, do not tell people that you learned about it here.

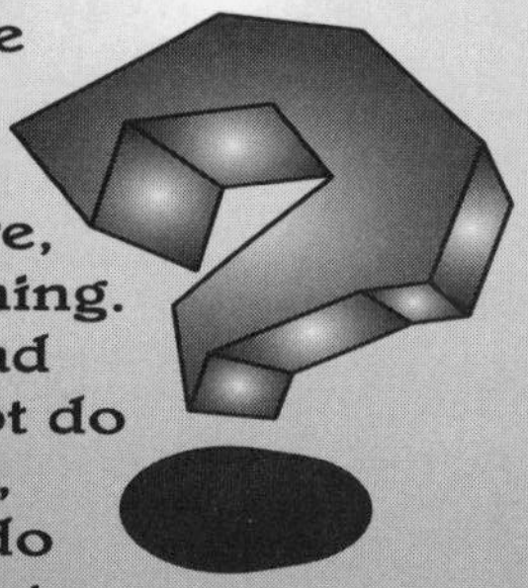

## Secret Societies

It's hard to find good material on secret societies (are you surprised?), so when you read articles that talk about organizations that conspire in secret, you have to judge for yourself how much you think is true. However, if you like finding out things that you are not supposed to know, it's always fun to read something about a group of people who go to a great deal of trouble to hide their traditions and aims. Visit this web site to read about the Illuminati, the Knights Templar, the Skull and Bones, the Thule Society, the Rosicrucian Order, the Bilderberg Conference and more.

**Web:**

**http://www.eye.net/Howling/Conspiracy/Hive/Arc-Hive/hiv_sec.htm**

## Software Cracks

This Usenet group is for the discussion and trading of information on how to crack software or otherwise break the copy protection. You can also discuss cracks and the uploading of cracked files (to various unspecified locations). I didn't include any web sites, because they get moved so frequently. (By the way, the name **2600** is taken from a well-known hacker's zine. The zine itself was named after the sound with a frequency of 2600 hertz. Telephone switching equipment used to use this sound as a special signal. By building a device—called a blue box—that could produce this and other sounds, a hacker could make free long-distance calls.)

**Usenet:**

**alt.2600.crackz**

## Software Serial Numbers

This is a list of software serial numbers that can be used for... well, I can't tell you, but if you have to ask you won't understand the answer. As you might imagine, sites like this tend to disappear. However, I am putting it in to inspire you. There are lots of places with similar information if you know where to look.

**Web:**

**http://www.x-net.net/dracul/serial.html**

## Solve a Mystery

Do you like mysteries? Every week, there is a new mystery to solve. You can read the mystery at the web site, or register and receive the information by email. There is also a contest where you can look at an intriguing photo and write a small mystery story. (If you like mysteries, perhaps you can help me. I am trying to find the sneaky person who ate the last non-fat chocolate muffin.)

**Web:**

**http://www.thecase.com/thecase/**

## Super Secret Web Site

I have found a web site that is so totally cool, so awesome, that I know you will be completely blown away. However, the site is a big secret and I can't print the address in this book, so you will have to discover the web site for yourself. (I have left a space for you to write in the address once you find it.)

**Web:**

**http://**

## Warez

Discussion of where and how to obtain the latest cracked and pirated software, much of it available through hidden sites on the Internet. Some of the channels are often by invitation only, so you will require contacts to get inside. There are lots of these channels. Start at the highest number you can find at any time and work your way down, seeing if they will let you in. (Unless you are a personal friend of God, you will never get in anything lower than **#warez5**.)

**IRC:**

**#warez**
**#warez1**
**#warez2**
**#warez3**
**#warez4**
**#warez5**
**#warez6**
**#warez7**

# SEX

## Adult Movies

Step aside, Siskel and Ebert. Meet the pros: people who really know their films intimately. Learn what movies are hot and what movies are not worth warming the television up for. Who are the superstars of sexy films and which movies actually have plots? Bone up on your erotic movie trivia.

**Web:**

**http://homepage.eznet.net/~rwilhelm/asm/dbsearch.html**
**http://www.gti.net/director/home/**

**Usenet:**

**alt.sex.movies**
**rec.arts.movies.erotica**

**"Romance" is waiting for you.**

## Auto-Eroticism

In life, if you are going to do something, you should do it well. On the Net you can read up on auto-erotic facts, hints and techniques, and follow various related discussions on Usenet.

**Web:**

**http://bianca.com/shack/goodvibe/masturbate**
**http://www.neosoft.com/~mick/mast.html**

**Usenet:**

**alt.sex.masturbation**

### Adult Movies

Lights, camera, and lots and lots of action. If you are at all visually inclined, you may want to look in on the **alt.sex.movies** Usenet group and find out what the cognoscenti think about the latest adult films. Our favorite is *Beyond the Internet Yellow Pages, Part III.*

## Bondage

All tied up with no place to go? You're in the right place. If having the most toys means having the most fun, then this is the zenith of extracurricular sexual activity. Read stories, share experiences, and discuss techniques and safety tips. If you love something, set it free; if it comes back to you, tie it up again.

**Web:**

**http://www.unreal.com/adult/asb/faq.htm**

**Usenet:**

**alt.personals.bondage**
**alt.sex.bondage**

**IRC:**

**#bdsm**
**#bondage**

## Complete Internet Sex Resource Guide

If you are looking for the latest sex resources on the Net, it's likely that you will find them here. Check out this index of mailing lists and Usenet groups.

**Web:**

**http://sleepingbeauty.com/world/netsex.html**

## Cross-Dressing Chat

Why is it normal for a woman to dress like a man, but bizarre for a man to don lace and satin? Maybe someone on the **#crossdres** IRC channel will have the answer (or at least a reaction).

**IRC:**

**#crossdres**

## Diaper Fetish

Some people don't have a preference between cloth or plastic, Velcro or safety pins. Find out more in the diaper fetish discussion group or on the web page.

**Web:**

**http://www.cris.com/~Mckebp/diaper/**

**Usenet:**

**alt.sex.fetish.diapers**

## Exhibitionism

If you've got it, flaunt it. Or even if you don't have it, flaunt it. Exhibitionism is not for the faint of heart. Be gutsy, be bold. Hear stories of the exploits of the daring. Bring your own raincoat.

**Usenet:**

**alt.sex.exhibitionism**

Take it off.
Then put it on.
Then take it off again.
If you like to share
(or even watch),
alt.sex.exhibitionism
is for you.

## Fat Fetish

Do you find the '90s body image preposterous? Don't continue to mourn the lost days when Rubenesque women were the norm. Revel in the rich, full quality of people who are fat and proud of it.

**Usenet:**

**alt.sex.fat**
**alt.sex.fetish.fa**

## Female Domination FAQ

This is a great source of information for dominant women and the men (and women) who love them. There is a FAQ that defines domination in a broader sense than the usual description of bondage and discipline.

**Web:**

**http://www.nether.net/~jlawson/femdom.html**

## Foot Fetish

You don't have to be a shoe salesman to enjoy yourself here. Experience the sensuous excitement of a well-shined pump wrapped around a delicately stockinged foot with deliciously painted toenails.

**Web:**

**http://www.shadow.net/power/asff/main.htm**

**Usenet:**

**alt.sex.fetish.feet**

## Hair Fetish

Montel Williams and Patrick Stewart hold no appeal for you. If it's not hairy, it's not happening. Don't think you're alone in your fantasies about Cousin It.

**Usenet:**

**alt.sex.fetish.hair**

## How to Use a Condom

Practice makes perfect and someone is perfect enough to film these instructional video clips. Take advantage of the expertise offered in these short demonstrations you can download to your own computer. No sense getting your information on the street when you can get it from the Net.

**Web:**

**http://www.safersex.org/condoms/howto.dunn.html**

## Oriental Fetish

Worship the exotic. Experience the mystery of the Far East by plunging yourself headfirst into its people and culture. Learn the secrets of Oriental sexuality.

**Usenet:**

**alt.sex.fetish.orientals**

**The Net cares.**

## *Look What I Found on the Net...*

(from a story posted to alt.pantyhose)

I was still reeling from the shock...I thought I'd seen everything that might ruin our marriage, but we've stuck together through thick and thin. Through sickness and health. Except for now.

"Stephanie...," I stammered. "You know that lesbianism doesn't bother me, but why did you wait after all this time to admit this to me? I'm your HUSBAND!..."

My head was a soup of confused feelings...the one person who meant more to me than anything may very well have made our marriage a lie. A good part of my life will have to be ripped away from me, unless I made some sacrifices to keep her in my life...

"Stephanie," I asked, mentally preparing myself for what I was about to do, "Would it be easier for you if I were a woman?"

Her eyes lit up like Christmas trees lights, and I could see that she was fascinated with this idea, a chance to save our marriage. "You would do that for me? That's, that's wonderful..."

Anyway, that's how all this started. I am going over that episode in my mind again as I now stand in the bedroom, showered, fully shaved, and powdered, trying to tell myself that this is for our marriage, and to at least give this scheme a chance....

"Okay, first you take one of the stocking legs and gather it up to the toe, like this," Stephanie explained, demonstrating with her pair, gathering the leg up with her thumbs which I emulated. "Then, you put your toes in, straightening out the toe seam across the toes. Personally, I like to put the seam just under the toes, so if you take off your shoes the seam will be invisible." I tried to follow her example as she put them on her smooth legs...

## Pantyhose and Stockings

Soft, sleek, sensual... and more. Talk to the people who really appreciate what the well-dressed leg is wearing this season. Share your opinions and read provocative stories.

**Usenet:**

alt.pantyhose

## Pick-Up Lines

Are you running out of lines and still haven't found Ms. Right? Here's a batch that may help (but I doubt it). Even if you don't win her heart, at least she will know you have a sense of humor.

**Web:**

http://supernova.uwindsor.ca/people/ha3/pickup.htm

### *Look What I Found on the Net...*

```
              (from the Pick-Up Lines web site)

I heard this one at a yuppie night club:

   "So... are you the one who is going to carve my heart out at
    midnight?"

It was appropriate because the female to whom this comment was
directed considers herself a ritualistic priestess.

--------

   "What do you like for breakfast?"

--------

   "Say, didn't we go to different schools together?"

-------

The best pickup line I've heard recently was something a friend
of mine heard at the bar where he works.  He told a girl that he
would like to get her phone number.  Came her casual reply:

   "Oh, you can just read it off of my phone in the morning."

-------

The best pickup line I witnessed was a friend of mine who walked
up to a young lady in a club and asked, "Are you ready to go home
now?"

They left together.

-------

   "Hi, the voices in my head told me to come over and talk
    to you."

-------

   "Can I buy you a drink, or do you just want the money?"
```

## Safe Sex

We've all heard the stories, the advice, the lectures and the arguments, excuses and rumors. "Safe sex" is the buzz phrase for the rest of the century, so acquire good habits—like brushing your teeth before bed or combing your hair before you go to work. Learn the do's and dont's, the ins and outs and all the in-betweens of sexual safety. And if you still want to take risks, you can always jump out of an airplane.

**Web:**

**http://gilligan.mc.duke.edu/h-devil/stds/protect.htm**
**http://www.safersex.org/**

## Sensual Massage

Massage is a romantic and sensual way to relax. This article will help you inderstand how to select sensual oils, create just the right atmosphere, and know what to do (and how to do it) with your partner.

**Web:**

**http://homearts.com/depts/relat/aromatb1.htm**

## Sex Sounds

Check out this Usenet group for some interesting sound-bytes. Post your own, too! Sounds come through here in formats for most popular machines and software. This is just the thing to liven up your computing environment.

**Usenet:**

**alt.sex.sounds**

## Sex Stories

There's nothing like curling up with a provocative story and a hot cup of tea or a little classical music. You won't find tea or music here, but you will never want for a good, sexy story (or a bad one, for that matter). Stories range from mildly erotic mainstream to bold, raunchy kink. There's something for everyone. And if you'd like to hang around afterwards over coffee or a smoke and discuss the literary merit of the writing, check out **alt.sex.stories.d** for discussion.

**Usenet:**

**alt.sex.stories**
**alt.sex.stories.d**
**alt.sex.stories.gay**
**alt.sex.stories.hetero**
**alt.sex.stories.moderated**
**alt.sex.stories.tg**

## Sex Talk and General Discussion

What's the weirdest place you have ever had sex? Care to share? Even if you don't, there are hoards of people who do. Not only will they tell you about the weirdest place, but also about the weirdest accident they've ever had during sex, how many times they've had sex, and what was going on around them before, during and after. Be informed as you are entertained. Read about birth control, STDs (sexually transmitted diseases), virginity (or lack of), and other topics of a sexual nature. The web site contains the FAQ (frequently asked question list) for this Usenet group.

**Web:**

**http://www.halcyon.com/elf/altsex/**

**Usenet:**

**alt.sex**

## Sex Wanted

Forget love, forget romance. If you're looking to cut to the chase, then cut in here. Don't bother being coy or shy, state what you want and let the good times roll. (However, government regulations require me to warn you that—as with bank accounts—there can be substantial loss of interest with early withdrawal.)

**Usenet:**

**alt.sex.wanted**

## Spanking

Have you ever been sitting around the house and suddenly you think, "Hmm, I feel like a good spanking"? Don't feel alone, we've all had that experience (not really, but you can believe that). Gather with others who like to take physical intimacy to another dimension. You'll recognize them: they're the ones who can't sit down.

**Web:**

**http://www.cris.com/~Redman/spkg/ass_faq.shtml**

**Usenet:**

**alt.sex.spanking**

## Strip Club List

There's no need to miss your favorite strip club if you have to travel out of town. Check out this list of reviews of strip clubs around the United States. The listings have legends that indicate whether the strip club is bikini, topless or full nude, as well as lengthy written reviews written by patrons of the club.

**Web:**

**http://www.tuscl.com/**

## Urban Sex Legends

You know that Batman story you love to tell your friends? Well, it's not true. Really, it's not. In fact, there are a lot of weird sex legends that are not true. You can read all about them at this urban sex legends site. It's full of amusing stories and urban legends with a sexual twist.

**Web:**

**http://www.urbanlegends.com/sex/**

### *Look What I Found on the Net...*

```
Newsgroup: alt.sex
Subject: Is this sexy or what?

> ...it is a decoy.  I also found something in my smoke detector
> even more sinister, a cylindrical metallic case which cannot be
> opened and is covered with warnings and threats with vague
> references to radio activity...

Yes, if you open the secret metallic cylinder, you will find a
fascinating substance.  It may take some work to open the box
up, but you should be able to pry it with a screwdriver.  The
substance in the smoke detector -- Hydropolyruthenium -- has
some amazing properties.

This substance was shown to the U.S. government by those
almond-eyed aliens without any hair, but superdeveloped brains
and telepathic ability.  By eating enough of this substance, a
transformation takes place in humans.  They begin to lose their
hair and exhibit telepathic abilities.

It is this radio frequency wave which may be used to listen in
on folks.  By eating the substance and gaining those abilities,
one can not only listen in to other's thoughts at will, but
shield oneself from others listening in (like the government).

Our government has a secret division of people who have
developed this ability and patrol the streets listening in on
people where there aren't "smoke detectors".  These folks are
almost always completely bald and usually wear baseball caps.
Their eyes are larger than normal.

I'm posting this anonymously for obvious reasons.
```

Is it really true?
Read the
*Urban Sex Legends*
and
judge
for
yourself.

## Voyeurism

There's something exciting about forbidden observation, peeking through the slats of the venetian blinds, pressing your ear against the cool, smooth wall, opening the door just a crack and watching. If you are more of a watcher than a doer, or you like doing while watching, post your thoughts, ideas and stories here.

**Usenet:**

**alt.sex.voyeurism**

Do you like to watch? Take a peek at alt.sex.voyeurism.

## Watersports

If you are looking for a good place to brag about your skill as a water-skier, go someplace else. For watersports of a more personal nature, like enemas and related fetishes, this is your place.

**Usenet:**

**alt.sex.enemas**
**alt.sex.fetish.watersports**
**alt.sex.watersports**

# SEXUALITY

## Alternative Sexuality

Alternative to what? Alternative to normal say some people; alternative to boring say others. Judge for yourself. This site is a collection of information about BDSM (bondage, domination, sadism, masochism), homosexuality, bisexuality, polyamory, health topics, transgender issues, advice columns and more. Be careful when you visit this site. As they point out, "The most important sexual organ is the brain."

**Web:**

**http://www.altsex.org/**

## Androgyny Information

It's uncommon to find information about androgyny, but on the Net, all things are answered. Read this document, which answers questions about androgyny and has an androgyny glossary.

**Web:**

**http://www.wavefront.com/~raphael/raq/raq.html**

## Dr. Ruth

This is the official site of Dr. Ruth Westheimer, a well-known American sex therapist. If you like Dr. Ruth, you will like this site. It has an extensive history of Dr. Ruth (with pictures), a daily sex tip (along with an archive of previous tips), an "Ask Doctor Ruth" section, and much more. You can also download funny icons—such as the wiggling sperm cursor—from the Dr. Ruth CD-ROM. Want more? You can find out about Dr. Ruth's books, her itinerary, and visit Ruth's Picks (favorite books, web sites, etc). You have to register to get some of the goodies, but it's free. (Is it my imagination, or has someone created a large commercial enterprise around the image of a nice old lady who gives advice?)

**Web:**

**http://www.drruth.com/**

A B C D E F G H I J K L M N O P Q R S T U V W X Y Z

## Gender Collection

This web site offers a gigantic collection containing a wide variety of documents about women and men, gays and straights. There is history, politics and even some plain old fun. This is an excellent source of gender information.

**Web:**

**http://english-www.hss.cmu.edu/gender/**

## Intergenerational Relationships

Relationships are tricky enough when you have more than one person involved. There are special considerations when a significant age difference exists between partners and this group was created as a space to talk about problems, stories and theories relating to intergenerational relationships.

**Usenet:**

**alt.sex.intergen**

**Intergenerational Relationships**

*Is your significant other significantly older? Talk to the people in the* ***alt.sex.intergen*** *Usenet group and find company, advice and personal stories.*

## Politics and Sex

For some reason, politics and sex are inseparable (and it's not just the Kennedys and Clintons). What do Gennifer Flowers, Donna Rice and Jessica Hahn know that Dr. Ruth has never figured out? Join the discussion and see what strange bedfellows politics and sex really make.

**Usenet:**

**alt.politics.sex**

## Polyamory

The Law of Romantic Physics states that when there is too much love to go around, the excess has to go somewhere. I've found where it goes, and if you want to get some of it to take home with you, feel welcome. These resources describe the lifestyle of polyamory, in which multiple intimate relationships are pursued simultaneously. Polyamorous people share themselves with you (and you and you and you).

**Web:**

**http://www.hal.com/~landman/Poly/**

**Usenet:**

**alt.personals.poly**
**alt.polyamory**

**Majordomo Mailing List:**

List Name: **poly**
Subscribe to: **majordomo@hal.com**

## Purity Tests

Purity tests have long been a staple of Usenet humor groups. These tests consist of many sexually oriented questions designed to help you find out just how "pure" you are.

**Web:**

**http://www.bath.ac.uk/~ee3ken/purity.html**
**http://www.nmt.edu/~kscott/purity/**
**http://xenon.stanford.edu/~sommda/newsbrief.html**

## Sex Addiction Recovery

There are worse things than sex to which a person could be addicted; maybe that makes it even harder to recover from this addiction. This support group offers a way for recovering sex addicts to share feelings and get ideas on the recovery process.

**Usenet:**

**alt.recovery.addiction.sexual**

## Sex, Censorship, and the Internet

Normal is boring. Don't follow the rules, make your own. Take advantage of the Internet as a marvelous place to be free in your speech. Read about censorship and the Internet and how some people want to put a stranglehold on your electronic freedom.

**Web:**

**http://www.eff.org/CAF/cafuiuc.html**

## Sex Experts Talk and General Discussion

You're in the heat of the moment and a problem arises. What do you do? There's no time to write a letter to Dear Abby. Admittedly, this is not going to happen often, but if you want answers or information from sex experts, they are available with a few keystrokes. Don't you wish everything was this easy?

**Usenet:**

**alt.sex.wizards**

**Wow, free software.**

## Sex Questions and Answers

Do you have a question about sex? It's probably already been answered in one of the FAQs. This web page has a listing of many of the **alt.sex** FAQs that are periodically posted to Usenet.

**Web:**

**http://www.cis.ohio-state.edu/hypertext/faq/usenet/alt-sex/top.html**

## Sexual Assault and Sex Abuse Recovery

These documents and discussions will help you deal with traumatic experiences, recover from sexual assault, and prevent acquaintance and date rape.

**Web:**

**http://gladstone.uoregon.edu/~service/**
**http://www.cs.utk.edu/~bartley/saInfoPage.html**

**Usenet:**

**alt.recovery.sexual-abuse**
**alt.sexual.abuse.recovery**
**alt.sexual.abuse.recovery.d**
**soc.support.abuse.sexual**

### *Look What I Found on the Net...*

```
Newsgroup: alt.sex.wizards
Subject: Stretch Marks

> I had heard that stretch marks on women are generated as a
> result of having a baby.  My girlfriend has stretch marks all
> over her hips and in surrounding areas, though she says she
> has never been pregnant.  Is it true that one could get
> stretch marks even without being pregnant?

Yes, this is very possible.

Almost every girl I know has some stretch marks.  They are
sometimes caused by fat, but they can also be a simple
part of the growing process.  I have also gotten them from
working.
```

## Sexual Identity and Gender Glossary

As times change, the language changes, and what was an acceptable label a few years ago is a serious faux pas today. Learn the difference between transgendered, transsexual and transvestite, and why you shouldn't call a bisexual "confused".

**Web:**

**http://socrates.ambler.temple.edu/~amanda/glossary**

## Sexuality Bytes

Here is a resource whose goal is to provide "an online encyclopedia of sex and sexual health". There is one version for adults and another for teenagers. This is a place to which adults and teens can turn for answers about reproduction, contraception, having sex, foreplay, sexual problems, sexuality, and so on. The details vary appropriately, depending on whether you are in the adult or teen section.

**Web:**

**http://www.sexualitybytes.com.au/**

## Society for Human Sexuality

If you are interested in human sexuality, you will find links to just about anything you can think of. In particular, you will find topics that other web sites do not like to include. (I won't mention them here where your parents might see them. You will have to check for yourself.) Should the need arise in your life, there is also a guide to safe sex.

**Web:**

**http://weber.u.washington.edu/~sfpse/**

## STD Information

This page gives information about STDs (sexually transmitted diseases), along with pictures. Pick a disease, any disease. (I picked trichomoniasis, which is caused by a protozoan.) Read about various STDs: how you get them, who gets them, how they are treated, and so on. To make sure you're safe, you can study a list of activities, ranked from high-risk to no-risk. This is a good, informative page, but not the least bit appetizing.

**Web:**

**http://med-www.bu.edu/people/sycamore/std/std.htm**

## Transgender

Changing your gender is not an easy thing to do. (Now that's an understatement.) Talk with people who think it's okay for you to be who you really are. Here is an informative forum with technical and emotional support for anyone in the transgender process.

**Usenet:**

**alt.sex.trans**
**alt.transgendered**
**soc.support.transgendered**

**Listserv Mailing List:**

List Name: **transgen**
Subscribe to: **listserv@brownvm.brown.edu**

## Transvestite, Transsexual, Transgenders

Anyone interested in transvestites, transsexuals or transgenders can find lots of information at this site. Topics include hormone FAQs, cross-dressing, the International Bill of Gender Rights, myths about transvestites, and songs and poetry.

**Web:**

**http://ezinfo.ucs.indiana.edu/~mberz/ttt.html**

# SOFTWARE

## Academic Software Development

If you're into academic software, you should check out the **acsoft-l** mailing list. On this list, you can join in discussion of all aspects of academic and educational software. Topics can include courseware development tools, research tool development, development practices, design techniques and others.

**Listserv Mailing List:**

List Name: **acsoft-l**
Subscribe to: **listserv@wuvmd.wustl.edu**

## *Look What I Found on the Net...*

```
Newsgroup: alt.transgendered
Subject: Mirrors
```

Who was he? The strange man in the mirror. I never knew. I laughed with him sometimes, cried with him more, yet I never knew who he was. We often stared at each other but he never spoke to me nor betrayed his secrets to me.

I've heard that some people believe the mirror holds their soul and provides them a short visitation of it. Yet each time I came to the mirror, I was met by this cold stranger. I was forced by him to search within me to find my soul.

After long searching I finally came to her, sealed behind many walls and buried beneath tears and lies. I looked to her and cried, embracing her after so long. I began tending her wounds and helped her from that place, giving her freedom. She smiled and rose, filling me and embracing me. Now when I meet the mirror, I see her and she smiles tenderly to me. We share our thoughts and secrets. I speak fondly to her and feel her reply.

But I wonder what happened to the man in the mirror and who he was. I wish I could have known him and spoken to him. He is gone forever now. Perhaps he never existed, except as the guardian protecting my soul until she was strong enough to stand alone.

## Cool Tool of the Day

This site picks a new "cool tool" every day. It's mostly technical stuff—Java programs, virtual reality, HTML editors, file management software, mail software, plug-ins, and so on—so if you are an Internet nerd, this is a nice place to check from time to time.

**Web:**
**http://www.cooltool.com/**

## Jewish Software

Here is a nice collection of Jewish and Hebrew software: programs for using Hebrew on your computer, studying the Torah, Jewish calendars, Hebrew Internet software, and more (including a collection of pictures of the great rabbis). Now, if I can only find a program that can bake me a nice challah while I am waiting for a long download.

**Web:**
**http://www.jer1.co.il/gate/ftp/softmain.html**

## Macintosh Applications

Visit these Usenet groups for discussions of all types of Macintosh applications. The **.apps** group is for talk about any type of application; **.word** is for word processing; **.comm** is for communications; and **.databases** is for database systems.

**Usenet:**
**bit.mailserv.word-mac**
**comp.sys.mac.apps**
**comp.sys.mac.comm**
**comp.sys.mac.databases**

**Get into "Mischief".**

A B C D E F G H I J K L M N O P Q R S T U V W X Y Z

## Macintosh Games

What's the point of having a computer without games? Join these Usenet groups to talk about all aspects of Macintosh games: which ones are best, which ones to avoid, copy protection issues, as well as hints and tricks.

**Usenet:**

**comp.sys.mac.games**
**comp.sys.mac.games.action**
**comp.sys.mac.games.adventure**
**comp.sys.mac.games.announce**
**comp.sys.mac.games.flight-sim**
**comp.sys.mac.games.marketplace**
**comp.sys.mac.games.misc**
**comp.sys.mac.games.strategic**

**Macintosh Games**

Macintoshes are good for a lot more than graphics, desktop publishing, and impressing your friends with your good taste in computers. Macs are great for playing games, and the sooner you start the faster you can fulfill your destiny as a human being.

## Macintosh Software Archives

There is more free Macintosh software on the Net than you can shake a mouse at. Here are some good places to start foraging for goodies. Surely, your Mac-cup will runneth over (and goodness and mercy shall follow you all the days of your life).

**Web:**

**http://mirror.apple.com/**
**http://pubweb.nexor.co.uk/public/mac/archive/welcome.html**
**http://www.softwarez.com/macintosh/**

## Macintosh System Software

This is the place for discussion about all aspects of the Macintosh system software (such as Finder and Multifinder), as well as working with disks, dealing with viruses, and so on.

**Usenet:**

**comp.sys.mac.system**

## Non-English Software

Not everyone in the world speaks English, so it's great to have a resource where you can get information on non-English software. Post your queries or your finds on this Usenet group. Visit the web site for online resources.

**Web:**

**http://www.iijnet.or.jp/horse/kotoba/**

**Usenet:**

**comp.software.international**

## OS/2 Games

This is a collection of games specifically for OS/2. The list is fairly large (considering it is OS/2). In general, there is a pathetic lack of OS/2 game collections on the Net. If IBM were smart, they would spend some time and money getting obsessive gamers caught up in an OS/2. My idea is for them to provide summer internships for students to create shareware gaming software for OS/2. IBM could pay the students a stipend to develop games, with the understanding that the finished products would be released as shareware on the Net. The students would then get to keep any money brought in by shareware registrations. It would be a win-win-win situation (IBM-programmers-you), that would help increase the installed base for OS/2. In the meantime, OS/2 people, you can enjoy the games at these sites.

**Web:**

**http://havoc.gtf.gatech.edu/buie/os2games.html**
**http://www.msoasis.com/pcb/161.htm**

## OS/2 Utilities

I love utilities. I could spend hours and hours downloading and experimenting with new programs. To tell you the truth, I usually end up not using most of the utilities I download, but I love trying them out. This is a huge, comprehensive, well-organized archive of everything under the OS/2 sun. If you are looking for a specific type of program (such as a utility or Internet client), this is a good place to work.

**Web:**

**http://www.intergate.net/OS2/**

## OS/2 Networking Environment

If you love the OS/2 operating system and want to get it networked, check out these discussion groups relating to the OS/2 environment. You will find general discussion and information on TCP/IP, as well as troubleshooting opportunities. Don't leave your home directory without it.

**Usenet:**

**comp.os.os2.networking**
**comp.os.os2.networking.misc**
**comp.os.os2.networking.tcp-ip**

## OS/2 Software Archives

There is lots of OS/2 software available, if you know where to look for it. I know where to look for it. And now, so do you.

**Web:**

**http://hobbes.nmsu.edu/**
**http://www.cdrom.com/pub/os2/**
**http://www.cyberblue.com/software.html**
**http://www.teamos2.org/resource/index.html#SOFTWARE**

## Software Archives

If you like computers and you like trying out software for free, you will love these places: huge archives where you can find programs for every popular operating system. When I die, I am going to have someone sprinkle my ashes on these web sites. You could spend an eternity here, just downloading and playing with software.

**Web:**

**http://www.jumbo.com/**
**http://www.shareware.com/**

**You need some more software.**
Don't ask me how I know, I just know.
**Visit the Software Archives right away.**

## Software Archives List

There is more free software on the Internet than any one person can even imagine. But how do you find it? Here is an absolutely huge list of free software repositories around the world. If you like free software, write this site on your bookmark list in indelible ink.

**Web:**

**http://dns.uncor.edu/links/siterepo.htm**

## Software Licensing

If you are thinking about starting to license software that you have written, read up on licensing issues. This is an archive of articles about licensing software, legislation and software license agreements.

**Web:**

**http://www.viman.com/license.html**

## Software Testing Talk and General Discussion

Testing software is not easy. You need lots of time, effort and a good design. Then, you need to know someone to pray to. The problem is that too much software is rushed without proper planning and quality control. This Usenet group is for talking about the testing of software and computer systems. If you are interested in this area of programming, you will find useful discussion and sympathetic colleagues.

**Usenet:**

**comp.software.testing**

## TCP/IP

TCP/IP is the glue that holds the Internet together. If you want to have your computer on the Internet, it will have to run some type of TCP/IP software. These Usenet groups are for discussion of the zillions and zillions of technical considerations that are unavoidably relevant. A good way to start is by reading the FAQ, which is posted regularly to the groups. Don't get discouraged: all things come to those who think.

**Usenet:**

**comp.protocols.tcp-ip**
**comp.protocols.tcp-ip.domains**
**comp.protocols.tcp-ip.ibmpc**

A B C D E F G H I J K L M N O P Q R S T U V W X Y Z

## Windows Game Software

If you want games for Windows, here are the places to look, especially if you want something to keep the kids busy at the computer while you are off somewhere doing adult stuff. There is a huge selection of games, enough to keep you occupied from now through St. Swithin's Day.

**Web:**

**http://www.happypuppy.com/games/link/**
**http://www.happypuppy.com/games/lordsoth/**

## Windows Networking Environment

Getting a network running is often troublesome. Have some back-up help ready in the form of Usenet groups. These groups offer a good source of information on general networking, TCP/IP, and network programming with the Microsoft Windows operating system.

**Usenet:**

**comp.os.ms-windows.networking.misc**
**comp.os.ms-windows.networking.tcp-ip**
**comp.os.ms-windows.networking.windows**
**comp.os.ms-windows.programmer.networks**

## Windows Software Archives

These are my picks as the best Windows software sites on the Net. They contain grotesque amounts of shareware and freeware for you to download and enjoy. Everything you could possibly want is here somewhere. When it comes to free Windows software, if you can't find it at one of these sites, it's not worth finding.

**Web:**

**http://www.cwsapps.com/**
**http://www.hotfiles.com/**
**http://www.tucows.com/**
**http://www.windows95.com/**
**http://www.winsite.com/**

**Don't click here.**

**Don't get fooled. Read "Consumer Information".**

# SOUNDS

## Animal Sounds

These sounds are a lot of fun, especially if you have children. Listen to birds, whales, dolphins, seals, ducks, cows, zebras, polar bears, tigers, turkeys, pigs, dogs, donkeys, elephants, frogs, goats, cats and more. I have also included a site that has a list of animal noises as they are pronounced in other languages. For example, a cat noise in English is "meow", but in other languages it is "miao" (Chinese), "meu" (Catalan), "myau" (Ukrainian) and "niaou" (Greek). (I wonder what cats say in Klingon?)

**Web:**

**http://betty-boop.unk.edu/unk_home/jason/psy_project/one.html**
**http://netvet.wustl.edu/sounds.htm**
**http://www.bev.net/education/SeaWorld/sounds/quiz.html**
**http://www.georgetown.edu/cball/animals/animals.html**

## Audio Formats and Software

Understanding audio formats is not easy. Here is information that explains all the important audio formats and tells you something about how they work. There are also links to the software you need to work with various types of audio files, as well as answers to some frequently asked questions.

**Web:**

**http://www.mps.org/~ebennett/xplat/xplat.aud.html**

## Bird Sounds

Here is a cool collection of bird sounds that are pleasant and engaging. One of my favorites is the kookaburra (a large Australian kingfisher bird that sounds like a fat lady laughing at a Marx Brothers movie). You can also listen to blue jays, chickadees, crows, cockatoos, magpies, peewees, ravens and more. (Quick bird-sound story: When I was in medical school, I once had a couple of friends over to my apartment. As a trick, one of the friends [Paul Walton] and I put on an album of tropical bird sounds and turned the volume down very low. The other friend, whose name I won't mention [Tim Rutledge], had no idea what we had done. Now this was in a small apartment in downtown Toronto, and every few minutes Tim would sit up and say, "Do you guys hear anything?". "No Tim," we would reply, "you must be hearing things." He never figured it out. Today, Tim is a respected emergency room physician, a wonderful husband and the father of three sons. So, if you ever meet him, don't mention anything.)

**Web:**

**http://www.ocean.ic.net/rafiles/nature/**

## Christmas Sounds

On the Net, Christmas lasts all year. Not only is the entire Internet suffused with the spirit of charity, love, forgiveness and sanctity, but you can listen to Christmas sounds whenever you want: enjoy dogs barking the tune "Jingle Bells", listen to sound clips from "The Grinch That Stole Christmas", laugh at parodies of traditional Christmas songs. Truly, the spirit of holiness and reverence is never out of season.

**Web:**

**http://www.acm.uiuc.edu/rml/Sounds/Xmas-snds/**

**Over 95% of people check the "Trivia" section.**

## Goldwave

Goldwave is a digital audio editor that can open, play, modify and convert just about any sound format you have heard of. You can make use of special effects such as Doppler, distortion, echo, flange and transposition. Goldwave is especially useful if you do audio work with Java applications. This is great software. Once you try it, I know you will like it (and I bet you will want to pay the registration fee). There are enough auditory bells and whistles here to equip the entire Peruvian army.

**Web:**

**http://web.cs.mun.ca/~chris3/goldwave/**

## Human Noises

I warn you. This stuff is disgusting: web pages full of cacophonous collections of human sounds: burps, laughs, coughs, and others too gross to mention in mixed company. Check it out for yourself, and see if I'm not right. (Hint: Here is a good trick to play on someone. If a friend uses a mail program that makes a sound when mail arrives—such as Eudora—download a rude sound and, when he is not looking, tell the program to play that sound whenever a message appears. However, don't mention to anyone that I gave you the idea. This is just between you and me.)

**Web:**

**http://www.cyberspy.com/~visual/sound.html#BODY**
**http://www.earthtrek.com/fart.html**
**http://www.wbm.ca/users/kgreggai/html/bodymus.html**

## MIDI Archives

Put away that CD player and download some MIDI sound files. If you don't have the software, don't worry. The MIDI Archives has gone on safari in the wilds of the Internet to find all the software you need to process MIDI sound files.

**Web:**

**http://www.cs.ruu.nl/pub/MIDI/**

A B C D E F G H I J K L M N O P Q R S T U V W X Y Z

## Miscellaneous Sounds

Aren't sounds great? Without them there would be nothing to listen to. Join the Usenet group devoted to sharing those sounds that don't fit in any of the other specific sound groups.

**Usenet:**

**alt.binaries.sounds.misc**

Tired of the silence?
Download some sounds!!

## Movie Sounds Repository

Never again will you have to be nervous about thinking of witty repartee when you are at your next party. Just download lots of these movie sounds, memorize them and when people come up to talk to you, do your best to imitate what you've heard on the Web. Choose from lots of popular movies such as The Princess Bride, Apocalypse Now, Pulp Fiction, Psycho, The Shining, Full Metal Jacket, Ghostbusters, Cool Hand Luke and many more.

**Web:**

**http://www.moviesounds.com/**

## Movies and Television Sounds

Bring movies and television to life on your computer with sound files you can download from Usenet. You can get sounds from movies like The Princess Bride, Star Wars, Forrest Gump and Aliens. Television is equally as popular with sounds from Hawaii 5-O, The Simpsons, Beavis and Butthead, Mission Impossible and Star Trek.

**Usenet:**

**alt.binaries.sounds.movies**
**alt.binaries.sounds.tv**

## Musical Sounds

Here are all types of music, especially classical music. Endow your computer with the charms it needs to tame the savage beast within you.

**Usenet:**

**alt.binaries.sounds.music**

## Number Synthesizer

Type in a number and this program will read it out loud. For lots of fun, and some philosophical insight, you can use this program to count down the number of days in your expected life span.

**Web:**

**http://www.cs.yale.edu/cgi-bin/saynumber.au**

## Sound Archives

Special occasions call for special sounds. Some days you will need a little Beavis and Butthead. Some days you will need some classic Monty Python or maybe a friendly cartoon sound file. Never again will you have to listen to the sounds of silence at your computer. Check out the many sound archives available on the Net.

**Web:**

**http://fairview.galileo.net/~kharr/**
**http://www.acm.uiuc.edu/rml/Sounds/**
**http://www.wintermute.net/pic.html**

Sound Archives
When you need that special sound that makes all the difference, the Net can help. Check with the Sound Archives, and you will never have to remain silent.

## Sound Talk and General Discussion

This is the Usenet group for the discussion of computerized sounds, as well as the hardware and software used for making sounds. Find information about how to post sounds to Usenet, as well as how to download and decode them. You can also talk about sounds posted to Usenet or sound resources on the Net.

**Usenet:**

**alt.binaries.sounds.d**

## Sound Tools

This is a collection of tools for dealing with sound files under various operating systems. Don't sweat the small stuff. Let the computer do the work.

**Web:**

**http://www.radio.cbc.ca/radio/tools/tools.html**

## Sound Utility Programs

There are sounds available all over the Internet, but that doesn't help you unless you know how to use them on your particular system. Find the information you need to play, convert or create sounds, and soon you will have your computer making enough noise to cause the neighbors to start complaining.

**Usenet:**

**alt.binaries.sounds.utilities**

## Sounds and Sound Effects

Here are some great collections of sound files good for various occasions (such as scaring your mother-in-law, or convincing your boss you are sick).

**Web:**

**http://www.cyberspy.com/~visual/sound.html**
**http://www.it.kth.se/sounds**

# SPACE

## Aeronautics and Space Acronyms

If your space capsule has just landed in the ocean and mission control asks if you want an ACRV, you certainly don't want to answer incorrectly. Take a moment and look it up in this long list of space-related acronyms: a good reference to keep on hand if you are reading anything about space exploration.

**Web:**

**http://www.ofps.ucar.edu/~mark/list.html**

## Center for Earth and Planetary Studies

Experience the excitement of outer space. The Center is the home of the Regional Planetary Image Facility, which houses over 300,000 photographs and images of the planets and their satellites. Also available at this server are images and information on the space shuttle.

**Web:**

**http://ceps.nasm.edu:2020/**

## Challenger

In the history of manned space flight, there have been some terrible disasters. The most well-known was the explosion of the Challenger space shuttle 73 seconds after takeoff on January 28, 1987. For information about that ill-fated mission, you can look at NASA's web site. There you can look at the official technical information regarding that particular mission, including a movie of the takeoff and explosion.

**Web:**

**http://www.ksc.nasa.gov/shuttle/missions/51-l/**
**http://www.ksc.nasa.gov/shuttle/missions/51-l/mission-51-l.html**

**Read a zine today.**

## Electronic Universe Project

Space is cool because there is so much of it and it's just waiting to be filled with stuff. Get a closer look at our very own galaxy with all its stars and nebulae and planets. See movies of interacting galaxies and images and light curves of a recent supernova. If you want to impress your special loved one with your knowledge of the stars, but the sky happens to be cloudy, this site can be your backup plan.

**Web:**
**http://zebu.uoregon.edu/galaxy.html**

> There's no place on Earth like the world. But when you get tired of all this Earth stuff, connect to the **Electronic Universe Project** and get the rest of the story.

## European Space Agency

The European Space Agency (ESA) was formed in 1975 through the cooperation of a number of European countries. Each of the countries makes a financial contribution based on which activities that country wishes to support. ESA's major programs include the Ariane rocket, the Spacelab scientific workshop (which is carried into orbit by the space shuttle), and Arianespace, a division of ESA which produces over half of all commercial satellite launches in the world.

**Web:**
**http://www.esrin.esa.it/**

**Listserv Mailing List:**
List Name: **esapress**
Subscribe to: **listserv@vmprofs.esoc.esa.de**

## European Space Information System

The European Space Information System (ESIS) is part of the European Space Agency (ESA). ESIS provides access to scientific data, including catalogs, images, spectra, and time series from ESA/non-ESA space missions. A bibliographic service allows you to read abstracts from a wide range of scientific journals.

**Web:**
**http://www.esrin.esa.it/htdocs/esis/**

## Goddard Space Flight Center

The Goddard Space Flight Center manages many of NASA's programs having to do with finding out information about Earth itself. As such, the Center is a major U.S. laboratory devoted to developing unmanned space probes. Their web site contains information about their programs and research.

**Web:**
**http://www.gsfc.nasa.gov/**

## Grand Challenge Cosmology Consortium

The questions are a little more complex than "How does the ship get in that glass bottle?" The scale is much more massive, like, "How are galaxies formed?" The Consortium is attempting to answer the latter question by teaming up with astrophysicists, computer experts and computational scientists to discover the origins of the universe. See current research and publications.

**Web:**
**http://zeus.ncsa.uiuc.edu:8080/GC3_Home_Page.html**

## History of Space Exploration

If you ever want to go to a new town and try to pass yourself off as an astronaut, it's best if you know some of the history of space exploration. You can never tell when a resident astrophysicist or know-it-all little kid will come in and start asking questions that will blow your cover. This site will fill you in on all the basics: a chronology, information about U.S. missions such as Apollo, Mariner, Viking and Voyager, as well details about some of the missions of the former Soviet Union.

**Web:**
**http://bang.lanl.gov/solarsys/history.htm**

## Hubble Space Telescope

The Space Telescope Electronic Information System (STEIS) contains information for Hubble Space Telescope proposers and observers. It offers documents, status reports, plans and weekly summaries. Get the daily update on the scheduled events and the outcome of experiments with the beleaguered Hubble Space Telescope.

**Web:**
**http://www.stsci.edu/**

A B C D E F G H I J K L M N O P Q R S T U V W X Y Z

## Lunar Photographs

If you want to see the moon, but it's a cloudy night and you can't see any celestial bodies, you take comfort in knowing that you can see the moon on the Internet. Brew up a hot drink, wrap yourself in a cozy blanket and curl up in front of the computer. These are gorgeous pictures and make cloudy nights a pleasure.

**Web:**
**http://www.netaxs.com/~mhmyers/moon.tn.html**

## The Real Challenge

To you and me, NASA (the National Aeronautics and Space Administration) may be the embodiment of our science fiction dreams of space travel. But in reality, NASA is a department of the U.S. government and, like all such departments, NASA must periodically justify its existence and its budget.

One way in which NASA does this is to make valuable information about their programs available to anyone on the Net. If you are interested in what NASA has done, take a few minutes to check out their site. Much of it is boring (remember, the "A" *does* stand for "Administration"), and a lot of the details are hidden behind cryptic acronyms. However, if you dig deeply enough, you will find some aeronautical jewels.

For example, the mission number of the ill-fated Challenger space shuttle was 51-l. (That's 51-hyphen-lowercase "L.") The technical descriptions of this mission are rather pedestrian, dismissing the final outcome in a few nondescript sentences. But if you know where to look, you can find a video clip of the actual explosion. Here it is:

```
http://www.ksc.nasa.gov/shuttle/
  missions/51-l/movies/51-l-launch2.mpg
```

Hints: (1) Remember, the character after "51-" is a lowercase "L." (2) You will need an mpeg viewer to watch this video clip.

## Mars Images

I've never been to Mars, but I hear it's quite the place to be in the springtime. See what you are missing out on by looking at these pictures of Mars taken by the Viking landers.

**Web:**
**http://esther.la.asu.edu/asu_tes/TES_Editor/SOLAR_SYST_TOUR/Mars.html**

## NASA News

NASA (the National Aeronautics and Space Administration) is always up to something. Now you can be in the loop. Just connect to the magic web site and get the straight poop from the official American space people. Be aware, though, that this is *official* NASA info, so you may not find out much about the government's cover-up of secret alien contacts.

## NASA Historical Archive

It's good to know your NASA space history. For instance, what if you are at the supermarket and the checkout girl says that if you can list the dates of all the Apollo missions you will be the lucky winner of a month's worth of Cheese Doodles. Imagine how sorry you'd feel if you couldn't do it. There's absolutely no need for this to happen as long as you make sure to read all the documents at the NASA Historical Archive. They offer the text of the NASA Space Act, information about rocket history, early astronauts, astronautics history, chronology, manned missions and details about the space shuttles. (Please, no spies allowed.)

**Web:**
**http://www.ksc.nasa.gov/history/history.html**

A B C D E F G H I J K L M N O P Q R S T U V W X Y Z

## NASA News

Up-to-date information on the status of spacecraft currently in space and other NASA happenings. Find out about the new discoveries made with the space-based Hubble telescope and unmanned probes launched towards distant planets and galaxies.

**Web:**

**http://spacelink.msfc.nasa.gov/html/NASA.News.html**

## NASA Research Labs

It's your turn to plan an exciting date for you and the one you love. How about a tour of some of the most famous NASA research labs? After a romantic candle-lit dinner you can go back to your place, fire up the old web browser and roam through the Goddard, Dryden, Ames, Langley and Kennedy space centers, to name just a few. In no time, word will be out that you really know how to entertain in style.

**Web:**

**http://www.gsfc.nasa.gov/hqpao/nasa_centers.html**

## NASDA

The National Space Development Agency (NASDA) is Japan's national agency for space development. NASDA's web site has information about their activities, publications and technical developments. Here you can find descriptions of NASDA's work on the international space station. There are also technical details regarding the H-II rocket (the central launch vehicle in the Japanese space program), just in case you want to build one for yourself.

**Web:**

**http://www.eoc.nasda.go.jp/**

## Planetary Data System

Take a tour of the planets and other stellar bodies. See information on geoscience, plasma interactions, and a variety of interesting topics that really are out of this world.

**Web:**

**http://pds.jpl.nasa.gov/**

## Planetary Image Finders

This web site has detailed maps and high-resolution raw images of some of the planets, including a Mars Atlas and Viking Orbiter image finder, and an image finder for the Voyager flyby.

**Web:**

**http://fi-www.arc.nasa.gov/fia/projects/bayes-group/Atlas/**

## Planetary Nebulae Gallery

When the weather outside is lousy, but you want to get in a little romantic star-gazing action with the person of your dreams, check out this gallery of beautiful, colorful images of nebulae. This might even be better than the real thing.

**Web:**

**http://www.ozemail.com.au/~mhorn/pneb.html**

## Politics of Space

Do people belong in space? Is all the money worth it? What should we be doing and who should we be doing it with? Discuss non-technical issues pertaining to space exploration.

**Usenet:**

**sci.space.policy**
**talk.politics.space**

## SETI

Do you get tired of the same old smart people here on earth? Get a new cultural and intellectual perspective on the Universe by looking in at the SETI Institute. These people spend their time searching for extraterrestrial intelligence and want to share what they have found with you. Their web site has links to science and technology relating to astronomy and planetary sciences as well as biological and cultural revolution. This is the perfect place to start if you are looking for new friends from other planets. Unless, of course, you already have your own spaceship.

**Web:**

**http://www.seti-inst.edu**

## *Look What I Found on the Net...*

Newsgroup: talk.politics.space
Subject: NASA knows about Nazi Moon Base. Important.

======================
GERMAN MOON BASE, 1942
======================

The Germans landed on the Moon in 1942 using larger exo-atmospheric rocket saucers.

The rocket craft was built in diameters of 15 and 50 meters, and the turbine powered craft was designed as an inter-planetary exploration vehicle. The craft had a diameter of 60 meters, had 10 stories of crew compartments, and stood 45 meters high.

Everything NASA has told the world about the Moon is a lie and it was done to keep the exclusivity of the club from joinings by the third world countries.

In my extensive research of dissident American theories about the physical conditions on the Moon, I have proven beyond the shadow of a doubt that there is atmosphere, water and vegetation, and that man does not need a space suit to walk on the Moon. A pair of jeans, a pullover and sneakers are just about enough. All these physical conditions make it a lot easier to build a Moon base.

Ever since their first day of landing on the Moon, the Germans started boring and tunneling under the surface, and by the end of the war there was a small Nazi research base on the Moon. A free energy tachyon drive craft was used after 1944 to haul people, material, and the first robots to the construction site on the Moon.

After the end of the war in May 1945, the Germans continued their space effort from their south polar colony of Neu Schwabenland. When Russians and Americans secretly landed jointly on the Moon in the early fifties with their own saucers, they spent their first night there as guests of the Nazi underground base.

In the sixties a massive Russian/American base had been built on the Moon, and it now has a population of 40,000 people. I have discovered a photograph of their underground space control center there, and I am working to make it available in gif format.

This is very sensitive information and I am sharing it with you at great risk. If you intend to save this information or share it with others, please delete my name and site location from the headers.

## Shuttle Snapshots

Snapshots of an astronaut's excursion are going to be much more exciting than Aunt Ethel's pictures of her trip to Haqualoochie, Oklahoma, to visit the grandkids. See images of places like Bangkok, Mount St. Helens, Finger Lakes, Alaska, and the Grand Canyon taken from various space shuttle missions.

**Web:**

**http://zebu.uoregon.edu/earth.html**

## Solar System Exploration

There has been a lot of exploration of our solar system, but except for some transient news coverage, few people really understand the significance of what has been done and what it means to us. Here is a web page with information about some of mankind's most impressive and most important achievements.

**Web:**

**http://www.hq.nasa.gov/office/solar_system/**

## Space Articles

A lot more has happened in the space industry than anyone can remember. Here is an archive of years of newspaper stories (from one particular newspaper) relating to NASA and their activities.

**Web:**

**http://www.chron.com/content/interactive/space/archives/archives.html**

## Space Calendar

If you think it's disastrous when you lose your datebook, how do you think NASA feels? When you are shooting live human beings into space at high speeds, it's important to keep your scheduling straight. Check here if you want to keep up on what's happening in the cosmos.

**Web:**

**http://newproducts.jpl.nasa.gov/calendar/**

## Space Environment Effects Branch

It can be really uncomfortable when you have anomalies in your GEO spacecraft. Especially when you find out that there is a link between the anomalies and electrical discharge phenomena between the spacecraft and the GEO plasma. Check out the web page of the Space Environment Effects Branch and see if they have come up with something in their research of GEO spacecraft design that will help you with your spacecraft.

**Web:**

**http://satori2.lerc.nasa.gov/**

## Space Frequently Asked Questions

Get answers to the most frequently asked questions (FAQs) regarding NASA, spaceflight and astrophysics. (For example, is it true that the blueprints for the Saturn V were lost?) If you are interested in space and spaceflight, this is a great source of fascinating information.

**Web:**

**http://www.cis.ohio-state.edu/hypertext/faq/usenet/space/top.html**

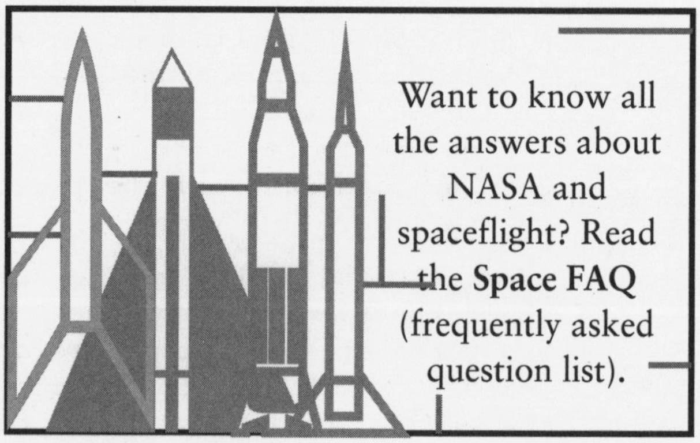
Want to know all the answers about NASA and spaceflight? Read the **Space FAQ** (frequently asked question list).

## Space Missions

Planning to go where no one has gone before? Check out the information on past or present space missions to make sure that nobody has been to your destination before you. You will find links to Apollo missions, the Cassini Mission, Clementine, Magellan and more.

**Web:**

**http://www.ksc.nasa.gov/history/history.html**

## Space Movie Archive

Would you like to see space scenes without having to leave the house? This site has a large number of space animations that you can view in the privacy of your own web browser.

**Web:**
**http://www.univ-rennes1.fr/ASTRO/anim-e.html**

## Space News Talk and General Discussion

Keep current on the final frontier. Read all the latest news about space, astronomy and spaceflight. Now that you have a connection to the Net, there is no excuse for being the last one on your block to know whether or not there really once was life on Mars.

**Usenet:**
**sci.space.news**

## Space Shuttle

The space shuttle is a reusable American space vehicle. The first shuttle test flight took place on April 12, 1981. The first operational flight was on November 11, 1982. For information about the shuttle program, including a lot of technical details, you can check NASA's web sites. For discussion, try the Usenet group.

**Web:**
**http://www.ksc.nasa.gov/shuttle/missions/missions.html**
**http://www.ksc.nasa.gov/shuttle/technology/sts-newsref/stsref-toc.html**

**Usenet:**
**sci.space.shuttle**

What in heaven's name is going on in the space shuttle?

Read **sci.space.shuttle** and keep up with the only government employees who are paid to get high.

## Space Talk and General Discussion

Talk, talk, talk about everything under the sun (and the sun as well). Discuss all manner of space-oriented topics with aficionados around the world.

**Usenet:**
**sci.space**
**sci.space.policy**
**sci.space.science**
**sci.space.tech**

## Students for the Exploration and Development of Space

SEDS is a student club devoted to the discussion and study of space. Meet people from SEDS chapters around the world. Find out all the latest space news and what SEDS members are up to.

**Web:**
**http://seds.lpl.arizona.edu/**

## United Nations Office for Outer Space Affairs

Everyone is anxiously awaiting the news about extraterrestrials joining the United Nations. The U.N. even has an office for Outer Space Affairs which focuses on international cooperation regarding the use of space technology to monitor space activities as well as our terrestrial environment. See the U.N.'s latest activities at their web site.

**Web:**
**ftp://ecf.hq.eso.org/pub/un/un-homepage.html**

## Viking Image Archive

The nice thing about unmanned orbiting vessels is that nobody has to spend all that time out in space without the benefit of pizza delivery. Take a look at some of the thousands of images sent back by Viking orbiters from 1976 to 1980. You can choose the resolution or coordinates you want to examine more closely. This is just like being in the driver's seat, except you don't have to wear a seat belt.

**Web:**
**http://barsoom.msss.com/http/vikingdb.html**

# SPORTS AND ATHLETICS

## Aikido

Aikido is a non-violent martial art that uses throws and joint locks to neutralize opponents instead of using kicks and punches. Aikido was developed by Morihei Ueshiba and was partially adapted from Daito-Ryu Jujitsu. This web site has a nice collection of general information about the art of Aikido.

**Web:**

**http://www.hal.com/~landman/Aikido/**

## Archery

Start practicing your archery now, because you never know when one day you will be called upon to play Robin Hood in your local community theater group. Imagine being up on stage and having to play out a rescue scene without being properly prepared. One wild shot and you could put out somebody's eye. Don't let this happen to you. Read the important archery documents that are available on the Net.

**Web:**

**http://www.epix.net/~gcarlson/archery.html**

**Usenet:**

**alt.archery**

## Badminton

When rollerblading is too rough and needlework is too tame, try a little badminton for a change of pace. Here are some tips for coaching and training, stretching and flexibility and backhand technique, as well as rules and a glossary of humorous terms.

**Web:**

**http://mid1.external.hp.com/stanb/badminton.html**

**The Net is immortal.**

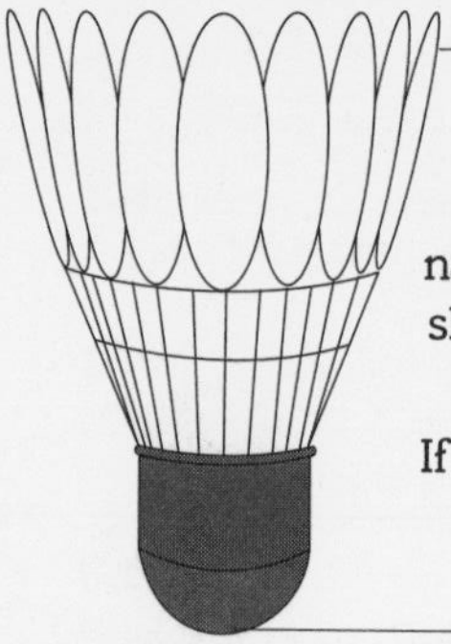

**Badminton**

Do you enjoy using a long, narrow-handled racket to volley a shuttlecock back and forth over a high, narrow net?

If so, the badminton resources on the Net will enhance your experience.

## Baseball

These sites are for baseball fans worldwide. Browse discussion groups, baseball collectible info, stats, rosters, team reports and fantasy leagues, and utilize the baseball search engine.

**Web:**

**http://www.atm.ch.cam.ac.uk/sports/baseball.html**
**http://www2.nando.net/SportServer/baseball/**

## Baseball: Major League Schedules

When you are at work and you don't have the latest TV guide with you, don't worry. You can still get Major League schedules from the Net. Go to this web site, find out when your favorite team is playing, and you will know whether to rush straight home from work or stop and have a beer first.

**Web:**

**http://www.tns.lcs.mit.edu/cgi-bin/sports-schedule?sport=mlb**

## Baseball: Minor League

Just because they are called "minor" leagues doesn't mean they are not as much fun as major league baseball. Enthusiasts of minor league baseball talk about issues affecting leagues, new stadium standards, franchise status and changes, road trips, schedules, team and league status, players and teams, collectibles and anything related to baseball that might make them whoop and holler.

**Listproc Mailing List:**

List Name: **minors**
Subscribe to: **listproc@plaidworks.com**

## Baseball Teams

On those days when it's not enough to watch your favorite team at the stadium or on television, do some reading on their stats, standings and other team information on Usenet.

**Web:**

**http://www.gnatnet.net/~hotrod/baseball.htm**

**Usenet:**

**alt.sports.baseball.atlanta-braves**
**alt.sports.baseball.az-diamondbacks**
**alt.sports.baseball.balt-orioles**
**alt.sports.baseball.bos-redsox**
**alt.sports.baseball.calif-angels**
**alt.sports.baseball.chi-whitesox**
**alt.sports.baseball.chicago-cubs**
**alt.sports.baseball.cinci-reds**
**alt.sports.baseball.cleve-indians**
**alt.sports.baseball.col-rockies**
**alt.sports.baseball.detroit-tigers**
**alt.sports.baseball.fla-marlins**
**alt.sports.baseball.houston-astros**
**alt.sports.baseball.kc-royals**
**alt.sports.baseball.la-dodgers**
**alt.sports.baseball.minor-leagues**
**alt.sports.baseball.mke-brewers**
**alt.sports.baseball.mn-twins**
**alt.sports.baseball.montreal-expos**
**alt.sports.baseball.ny-mets**
**alt.sports.baseball.ny-yankees**
**alt.sports.baseball.oakland-as**
**alt.sports.baseball.phila-phillies**
**alt.sports.baseball.pitt-pirates**
**alt.sports.baseball.sd-padres**
**alt.sports.baseball.sea-mariners**
**alt.sports.baseball.sf-giants**
**alt.sports.baseball.stl-cardinals**
**alt.sports.baseball.texas-rangers**
**alt.sports.baseball.tor-bluejays**

**Basketball**

In 1891, James Naismith invented the game of basketball at the Springfield, Massachusetts YMCA.

A little over one hundred years later, the Web was created.

Now you can combine the best of both worlds: visit the basketball web site of your choice today.

## Basketball

Having basketball fever doesn't mean that you just sit in front of the television making loud whooping noises. It's much more sophisticated than that. It's a fine balance of gathering statistics, analyzing trends, and making studied observations. On the Net you can find all you need to become a seasoned basketball fan.

**Web:**

**http://www.canoe.ca/Basketball/home.html**
**http://www.sportsline.com/u/basketball/nba/stats.htm**

## Basketball Team Talk and General Discussion

You don't have to get together with the guys to be able to talk about your favorite basketball team. On Usenet there are lots and lots of fan groups for basketball. Your team is bound to have one. (If it doesn't, you can make one.) Join up with other raging basketball fans and talk all night. (By the way, did you know that basketball is the only major sport that is entirely American in origin?)

**Usenet:**

**alt.sports.basketball.nba.atlanta-hawks**
**alt.sports.basketball.nba.boston-celtics**
**alt.sports.basketball.nba.char-hornets**
**alt.sports.basketball.nba.chicago-bulls**
**alt.sports.basketball.nba.clev-cavaliers**
**alt.sports.basketball.nba.dallas-mavs**
**alt.sports.basketball.nba.denver-nuggets**
**alt.sports.basketball.nba.det-pistons**
**alt.sports.basketball.nba.gs-warriors**
**alt.sports.basketball.nba.hou-rockets**
**alt.sports.basketball.nba.ind-pacers**
**alt.sports.basketball.nba.la-clippers**
**alt.sports.basketball.nba.la-lakers**
**alt.sports.basketball.nba.miami-heat**
**alt.sports.basketball.nba.mil-bucks**
**alt.sports.basketball.nba.mn-wolves**
**alt.sports.basketball.nba.nj-nets**
**alt.sports.basketball.nba.orlando-magic**
**alt.sports.basketball.nba.phila-76ers**
**alt.sports.basketball.nba.phx-suns**
**alt.sports.basketball.nba.port-blazers**
**alt.sports.basketball.nba.sa-spurs**
**alt.sports.basketball.nba.sac-kings**
**alt.sports.basketball.nba.seattle-sonics**
**alt.sports.basketball.nba.tor-raptors**
**alt.sports.basketball.nba.utah-jazz**
**alt.sports.basketball.nba.vanc-grizzlies**
**alt.sports.basketball.nba.wash-bullets**

A B C D E F G H I J K L M N O P Q R S T U V W X Y Z

## Basketball: Women

This is one sport where there are more women on the court than on the sidelines shaking their pompoms. Sports enthusiasts check in for daily scores and reports on games as well as to talk about women's basketball around the U.S.

**Usenet:**

**rec.sport.basketball.women**

**Listserv Mailing List:**

List Name: **wbball-l**
Subscribe to: **listserv@psuvm.psu.edu**

## Bicycle Commuting

Get your legs pumping and your heart racing, and save the environment and your bank book at the same time. Forget the hubbub of all those speeding cars trying to jockey for a position on the freeway—travel by bike. This list is mostly for Silicon Valley residents, but discussion centers around bicycle transportation and improving bicycling conditions in city and suburban areas. The web pages give you access to FAQ lists, help you choose routes, coexist with cars, and give you ideas for spiffing up your bike.

**Web:**

**http://cycling.org/veloweb/commuting/**

**Majordomo Mailing List:**

List Name: **commute-logistics**
Subscribe to: **majordomo@cycling.org**

**Majordomo Mailing List:**

List Name: **facilities-n-planning**
Subscribe to: **majordomo@cycling.org**

## Bicycling

It's not only great exercise, but riding a bicycle is a nice way to save the environment at the same time. Find out all the cycling resources on the Internet by checking out these web pages and the mailing list.

**Web:**

**http://cycling.org/mailing.lists/**
**http://eksl-www.cs.umass.edu/~westy/cycling/cycling-on-internet.html**
**http://www.cis.ohio-state.edu/hypertext/faq/usenet/bicycles-faq/top.html**

**Majordomo Mailing List:**

List Name: **bikepeople**
Subscribe to: **majordomo@cycling.org**

## Boxing

I am not sure, exactly, what the appeal is of watching men hit each other until they are unconscious or exhausted. Imagine the brain cells that could be in full use, but are instead being bashed about like a string of rugs during spring cleaning. But this thought doesn't bother the fans of boxing and they will be found in Usenet talking about the history of boxing as well as the latest knock-down-drag-out.

**Usenet:**

**rec.sport.boxing**

### Why Boxing Is Important

Some people think that boxing is an ugly, vicious, atavistic pastime whose usefulness in a polite, civilized society has long since expired. Other people think boxing is important, as it allows people to express their aggressive urges in a confined, limited fashion, with well-defined rules and procedures.

Actually, neither of those is correct.

The real reason boxing is important is it allows middle-aged men to get together and smoke cigars in a socially acceptable environment.

For more information about the sport of kings, you can follow the discussion in **rec.sport.boxing**.

## Cricket

Cricket is a game played primarily in Great Britain and the Commonwealth countries. This is how the game works: there are two wickets (a wicket is made of two crosspieces, or bails, resting on three stumps) placed in the middle of a field. Bowlers try to knock down the bails of the wicket while the batsmen try to defend the wickets. Each team consists of 11 men and because of structure of the scoring, games can sometimes take several days to complete. Cricket was developed in medieval England some time before 1400. In 1477, cricket was banned by Edward IV because it was interfering with the mandatory practice of archery. If a man was caught playing cricket, he was fined and sentenced to two years in prison. If the British had the Internet back then, I guess Ed would have been up a creek, wouldn't he? So, check out what your medieval brethren didn't have the chance to see in 1477. There are lots of cricket resources on the Net.

**Web:**

**http://www.cricket.org:8001/**

**Usenet:**

**rec.sport.cricket**
**rec.sport.cricket.info**
**rec.sport.cricket.scores**

**IRC:**

**#cricket**

## Exercise and Sports Psychology

"Mind over matter." "No pain, no gain." You've heard all the motivational clichés designed to inspire you to push that out-of-shape body of yours up the hill, down the hill, and over the finish line. Examine the brain behind the body by participating in the discussion of exercise and sports psychology.

**Listserv Mailing List:**

List Name: **sportpsy**
Subscribe to: **listserv@vm.temple.edu**

**Join the fun—now.**

## Fencing

Fencing is more than just making money off stolen goods. It's also a sport that takes speed, grace and finesse. (This is not to say the two are mutually exclusive, though.) This site offers you a glance at the rules, recommended books and other fencing information.

**Web:**

**http://mopus-box.rutgers.edu/~fenfool/page2/**

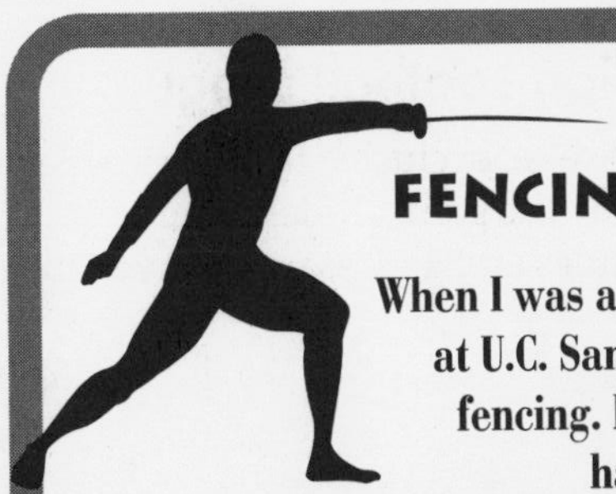

### FENCING AND ME

**When I was a graduate student at U.C. San Diego, I studied fencing. Here is how it happened.**

**At the time, registration for physical education (PE) classes was done manually. At the beginning of the term, on a particular day, each coach set up a table in the gymnasium. People lined up for hours in advance to register for their favorite classes. I woke up very early that day and stood in line a long time to register for surfing class.**

**I wanted to take more than one PE class, but by the time I worked my way to the front of the surfing line, there wasn't time to wait at another table. So I asked the surfing coach if he taught anything besides surfing. Yes, he replied, he also taught fencing.**

**Since I could sign up for both classes at the same table, I did. And that's how I came to take fencing (as well as surfing). Later, I went on to study theatrical fencing, and I even wrote a short play with fencing in it.**

**So, if you are a fencing buff, whether by design or fortune, check out the FENCING web page. And remember, as we wait patiently at the Table of Life, it's not how long we wait that matters, but how we use our opportunities when we get to the front of the line.**

A B C D E F G H I J K L M N O P Q R S T U V W X Y Z

## Football: American

Good old summertime. The sun is shining, the birds are singing, the flowers are blooming, and you can work on your tan. The problem is that there is no football. This is something that had to be tolerated until recently. Now you can get your fix during any season: scores, history and news articles on both college and professional football.

**Web:**

**http://www.atm.ch.cam.ac.uk/sports/gridiron.html**

## Football: Canadian Football League

Football is not just a disease exclusive to America. See how the Canadians play the game. Rules, referee signals, history, schedules and a glossary are available.

**Web:**

**http://www.cfl.ca/**

## Football: Professional

It's a good thing football is a seasonal sport. Otherwise, people might never have time to go to the Net and read about football. Check out these web sites for the latest news and information about professional football. On IRC you can chat with other fans of the National Football League (NFL). This is an especially fun channel to participate in at the same time you are watching the game.

**Web:**

**http://www.iis-sports.com/draft/**
**http://www.nfl.com/**

**IRC:**

**#nfl**

## Frisbee

Disc sports are fun and certainly not limited to throwing a frisbee at the beach. Fans of disc sports can check out these web sites full of information or talk about Ultimate, disc golf and other disc sports on Usenet.

**Web:**

**http://wol.ra.phy.cam.ac.uk/buf/**
**http://www.cs.rochester.edu/u/ferguson/ultimate/**
**http://www.hacks.arizona.edu/~upa/**

**Usenet:**

**rec.sport.disc**

## Golf

You don't have to wear funny pants to play golf, but it helps. What helps even more are secret tips on how to improve your game. I'll tell you a secret. The reason Arnold Palmer and Jack Nicklaus did so well is because when they were kids, they spent as much time on the Net as they did on the green.

**Web:**

**http://www.alta-oh.com/~thor/pages/golf.html**
**http://www.gdol.com/**

**Listserv Mailing List:**

List Name: **golf-l**
Subscribe to: **listserv@ubvm.buffalo.edu**

## Hockey

Hockey has certainly gotten less fun since they made a rule that everyone has to wear masks when they play. But if that doesn't put you off the game, check out these great sites available on the Internet. When you're not on the ice or in the stands, check into Usenet to blab with other hockey fans.

**Web:**

**http://maxwell.uhh.hawaii.edu/hockey/hockey.html**
**http://www.canoe.ca/Hockey/**
**http://www.hockeyguide.com/**

**Usenet:**

**alt.sport.street-hockey**
**alt.sports.hockey.ahl**
**alt.sports.hockey.cohl**
**alt.sports.hockey.echl**
**alt.sports.hockey.fantasy**
**alt.sports.hockey.ihl**
**alt.sports.hockey.rhi**
**alt.sports.hockey.whl**
**rec.collecting.sport.hockey**
**rec.sport.hockey**
**rec.sport.hockey.field**

**IRC:**

**#hockey**

**Quick, turn the page.**

# HOCKEY

I am the oldest child in my family and, as such, I had some special privileges when I was growing up.

One of them was that I often got to sleep over at my grandparents' house on Saturday night.

Every Saturday night, after I watched Leave It to Beaver on TV, my grandmother would make me a bowl of cereal. I would eat the cereal and sit on the couch with my grandfather as we watched the hockey game together.

That was a long time ago.

My grandparents have since passed away. I don't eat cereal nearly as often as I used to. Leave It to Beaver has been in reruns for many years. And I now spend my Saturday nights listening to the radio and writing.

But all across the country, I am sure that there are still little boys, sitting with their grandfathers, spending the evening watching the hockey game.

Thank goodness, some things never change.

## Hockey: College

It's exciting to watch a bunch of padded maniacs zip up and down a slab of ice and hit each other with sticks. You can get more involved in collegiate ice hockey by posting or reading scores, team information, and schedules for your favorite teams.

**Listserv Mailing List:**

List Name: **hockey-d**
Subscribe to: **listserv@maine.maine.edu**

**Listserv Mailing List:**

List Name: **hockey-l**
Subscribe to: **listserv@maine.maine.edu**

**Listserv Mailing List:**

List Name: **hockey3**
Subscribe to: **listserv@maine.maine.edu**

**Listserv Mailing List:**

List Name: **info-hockey-1**
Subscribe to: **listserv@maine.maine.edu**

## Hockey Team Talk and General Discussion

If hockey is too rough for you to participate, try getting on Usenet and talking about it. There's nothing like a vicarious thrill (except a real thrill). Fans of various hockey teams hang out and discuss the game and the players.

**Usenet:**

**alt.sports.hockey.nhl.ana-mighty-ducks**
**alt.sports.hockey.nhl.boston-bruins**
**alt.sports.hockey.nhl.buffalo-sabres**
**alt.sports.hockey.nhl.chi-blackhawks**
**alt.sports.hockey.nhl.clgry-flames**
**alt.sports.hockey.nhl.col-avalanche**
**alt.sports.hockey.nhl.dallas-stars**
**alt.sports.hockey.nhl.det-redwings**
**alt.sports.hockey.nhl.edm-oilers**
**alt.sports.hockey.nhl.fla-panthers**
**alt.sports.hockey.nhl.hford-whalers**
**alt.sports.hockey.nhl.mtl-canadiens**
**alt.sports.hockey.nhl.nj-devils**
**alt.sports.hockey.nhl.ny-islanders**
**alt.sports.hockey.nhl.ny-rangers**
**alt.sports.hockey.nhl.ott-senators**
**alt.sports.hockey.nhl.phila-flyers**
**alt.sports.hockey.nhl.pitt-penguins**
**alt.sports.hockey.nhl.Que-Nordiques**
**alt.sports.hockey.nhl.sj-sharks**
**alt.sports.hockey.nhl.stl-blues**
**alt.sports.hockey.nhl.tb-lightning**
**alt.sports.hockey.nhl.tor-mapleleafs**
**alt.sports.hockey.nhl.vanc-canucks**
**alt.sports.hockey.nhl.wash-capitals**
**alt.sports.hockey.nhl.winnipeg-jets**

## Horse Racing

When you are out of money, you can get your racing fix by keeping up with the sport on this web page. Find information on competitions like the Breeders' Cup and the Kentucky Derby.

**Web:**

**http://www.inslab.uky.edu/~stevem/racing.html**

**The Net loves poetry.**

## Karate

It's a nice feeling to know that if you are walking down the street and someone hassles you, you can simply give them a chop in the neck. Or you can give them a double-whammy, flying-though-the-air snap kick with a little spin on the end. Of course, for most people, karate is a sport or hobby, but that doesn't mean it's not handy to know. Get to know other people who train in one or more of the traditional Japanese/Okinawan karate styles. Share information and discuss issues that relate to teachers and students of karate.

**Listserv Mailing List:**

List Name: **karate**
Subscribe to: **listserv@ukanaix.cc.ukans.edu**

## Martial Arts

Here are some nice collections of martial arts resources around the Net. If you like karate, try the IRC channel to find other practitioners of this Oriental art.

**Web:**

**http://websites.radio-online.com/electromedia/quest/**
**http://www.stanford.edu/group/jujitsu/jujitsu.html**

**IRC:**

**#karate**

**The Internet has lots of information about martial arts: from Judo and Karate to the less mainstream schools, such as Kuk Sool Won (Korean) or Balintawak Eskrima (Filipino). So the next time you need a break from your physical training, try working out on the Net.**

## Polo

Polo is more than designer clothes and fancy cologne. Yes, it's a real sport. Get into the game by looking at this web site full of information on training and coaching, associations and alliances, an art gallery of polo images and documents on the game itself.

**Web:**

**http://www.cts.com/browse/polonet/**

## Rugby

Explore a basic overview of rugby, rules, trivia and FAQs, country-specific information, game schedules, match results, rugby jokes and songs, and video clips and pictures. Find out if the stories about rugby players are true.

**Web:**

**http://www.libertynet.org/~djrugby/web/rugbyweb.html**

## Rugby League

It has been said that in the event of nuclear annihilation, only the cockroaches and rugby players would survive. I don't know if that's true, but I do know that there is a variation on Rugby Union that is more intense, faster-paced, and guaranteed to give you new respect for the human body's ability to withstand punishment. Learn more about this game by reading the rules and the glossary, and by seeing some pictures relating to Rugby League.

**Web:**

**http://www.brad.ac.uk/~cgrussel/**

## Running

Besides being good exercise, running is great practice in case you ever encounter a pack of wild dogs or even a pack of wild children. But it's common to encounter other physical problems when running, such as sprains or impact-related pains. Get informed about running in general as well as event schedules for selected local areas.

**Web:**

**http://sunsite.unc.edu/drears/running/running.html**

## Skating: Figure Skating

A large competitive figure skating FAQ, pictures of skaters, inline skating information, and links to other skating resources and related material on the Net.

**Web:**

**http://www.cs.yale.edu/homes/sjl/skate.html**

## Skiing: Snow Skiing

If you are planning a ski vacation, these web pages provide you with everything you may or may not need to know, including upcoming ski events, ski conditions, interviews, photos and resort information.

**Web:**

**http://www.gorp.com/gorp/activity/skiing.htm**
**http://wwwmbb.cs.colorado.edu/~mcbryan/bb/ski/ski.html**

**Usenet:**

**rec.skiing**
**rec.skiing.alpine**
**rec.skiing.announce**
**rec.skiing.backcountry**
**rec.skiing.marketplace**
**rec.skiing.nordic**
**rec.skiing.resorts.europe**
**rec.skiing.resorts.misc**
**rec.skiing.resorts.north-america**
**rec.skiing.snowboard**

## Soccer

These web pages are your passport to a number of great soccer resources, including the Usenet group **rec.sports.soccer** and the World Cup '94 home page. Access Usenet groups, World Cup information, Fantasy Goal Scorers, mailing lists, hints, frequently asked question lists, terminology, and even soccer games for the computer.

**Web:**

**http://dmiwww.cs.tut.fi/riku/soccer.html**
**http://soccernet.com**
**http://www.vol.it/RETE_/32/00001.html**

**Usenet:**

**rec.sport.soccer**

## Sports

There is more to sports than just the brawl of physical contact. Sportsters also come in the form of writers and newsmakers. Read articles and news stories about sports of all kinds.

**Web:**

**http://www.awa.com/arena**
**http://www.sfgate.com/sports/**
**http://www.tns.lcs.mit.edu/cgi-bin/sports**

**If you can't play a sport, try to be one.**
**And if you can't be a sport, at least you can read about one on the Net.**

## Sports News

It's one thing to play a sport. It's another to watch sports on television. But clearly that's not enough. What do you do to fill in the time when you can't get outside and there is nothing on TV? You use the Net to keep up on sporting news, of course. Here are two web sites that will give you all the sports information you need (with enough left over in case you have to entertain unexpected company). Remember, whether you are after the latest scores, schedules or just plain gossip, the Net is there for you.

**Web:**

**http://www.cnn.com/SPORTS/**
**http://www.sportsline.com/**

## Sports Schedules

If the only reason you have been buying TV Guide is to look up when your favorite sporting event is on, now you can save all that money and avoid recycling at the same time. This web site will let you check schedules for various sporting events or create your own schedules for professional football, hockey, basketball and baseball events and more.

**Web:**

**http://www.cs.rochester.edu/u/ferguson/schedules/**

## Sports: Women

Forget that chili cook-off. Get out of the kitchen and on to the playing field. Here are links to all sorts of women's sports, teams and sports clubs: baseball, skating, volleyball, gymnastics, basketball, golf, bicycling and many others.

**Web:**

**http://fiat.gslis.utexas.edu/~lewisa/womsprt.html**

## Swimming

Whether you glide through the water like a torpedo or get water up your nose while dog-paddling, this list is for you. When they are not actually splashing about, swimmers of all skill levels talk about swimming. The only bad thing about this list is that you can't post to it while you are in the water.

**Listserv Mailing List:**

List Name: **swim-l**
Subscribe to: **listserv@uafsysb.uark.edu**

## Tennis

Player and equipment tips from the professionals, the rules and codes of tennis, an online tennis shop, competition guides, a FAQ, injury information, and links to several other tennis resources.

**Web:**

**http://www.tenisserver.com/**

## Volleyball

There is something so fascinating about volleyball. Especially volleyball on the beach where young, nubile people clad in swimsuits jump around energetically to hit a ball that bounces back and forth and back and forth. If you like to watch or even participate, check out this site dedicated to the sport of volleyball. Get information on collegiate or beach volleyball, the history of the sport, links to books, magazines, pictures, a schedule of TV coverage and more.

**Web:**

**http://www.volleyball.org/**

## Wrestling: Professional

There's nothing like spending a sunny Saturday morning in front of the tube with a box of Wheat Thins, a can of spray cheese and the remote control pointing at your favorite professional wrestling show. If you can't wait until the big day, get a wrestling fix from the Net. This site has lots of great information about professional wrestling, including links to cool video clips, that you can use to practice your moves at home or at the office.

**Web:**

**http://infoweb.magi.com/~ollie/wrestling.html**

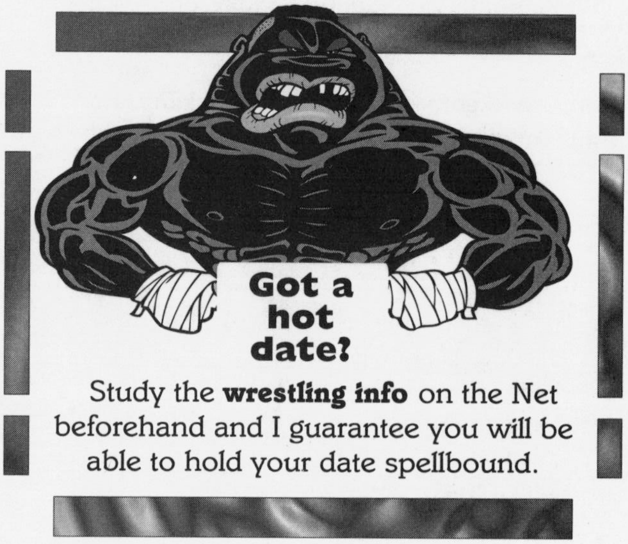
Got a hot date?
Study the wrestling info on the Net beforehand and I guarantee you will be able to hold your date spellbound.

## Wrestling: Sumo

Sumo wrestling is the national sport of Japan. Sumo uses a playing ring that is a few meters across and two men (who are also a few meters across). The object of the event is to force your opponent out of the ring or make any part of his body, except for the soles of his feet, touch the floor (sort of like a corporate takeover without the money). For more information about this fascinating sport, take a look at these sumo web sites. (For more information about corporate takeovers, call AT&T and ask for the chairman's office.)

**Web:**

**http://www-bcf.usc.edu/~tmccarth/sumo.htm**
**http://www.hal.com/~nathan/Sumo/**

## STAR TREK

### Animations and Images

I love Star Trek, so when I want to take a break from writing about Star Trek resources, I like to go look at Star Trek pictures and animations. This web site has a nice collection of images and movies, digitized from various Star Trek movies and TV shows.

**Web:**

**http://sherlock.berkeley.edu/docs/info/star_trek/trek.html**

### Beer Trek

Here is a fun game to play with your friends as you are sitting around watching Star Trek television shows or movies. Connect to this web site and look at the "rules". This is a long list of things that frequently occur in Star Trek. As you watch the show (or movie), whenever someone notices one of these occurrences, everyone has to take a drink. For example, on any show when someone is sexually harassed by a holodeck character, everyone must take a drink. On Deep Space Nine, when Worf butts heads with Odo or when a clipboard is passed from one person to another, everyone must take a drink. On Star Trek: The Next Generation, whenever there is an authorization to exceed warp speed limitations, whenever Data's head is open, or whenever Picard crosses his legs like a girl, everyone must take a drink. On the original Star Trek series, whenever Checkov substitutes a "W" for a "V", whenever Kirk grabs a woman by the shoulders, or anytime anyone sees someone besides Uhura with a "thingy" in his or her ear, everyone has to take a drink. (You get the idea.) There are lots and lots of rules, and some include additional actions besides drinking. For example, you may have to yell something or make a particular gesture. Note: On behalf of myself, my publisher, our lawyers and your parents, I must warn you that drinking to excess is bad for your health. (Right.)

**Web:**

**http://www.spacelab.net/~bongo/beertrek.html**

I was going to study to be a Sumo wrestler, but I didn't have time because I had to stay home and work on this book. But maybe it's not too late for you. Check out a Sumo resource or two on the Net.

### Captain Kirk Sing-a-Long Page

Undoubtedly some hardcore Star Trek fans have fantasized about hearing William Shatner, Nichelle Nichols (or others) singing in the shower. Here's what you should do: get an Internet connection running in the bathroom and load up this web site. After you get in the shower, you can download any of the sounds here. While you are in the shower, you will hear clips from albums put out by various Star Trek notables. It will be a fantasy come true.

**Web:**

**http://www.loskene.com/singalong/kirk.html**

### Conventions and Memorabilia

Dress up funny and romp around with other people dressed up like Star Trek characters. Conventions are a great place to really experience Trekker fandom. Discover where to get a replica of that communicator you love or collect the one action figure you are missing from your set.

**Usenet:**

**rec.arts.startrek.fandom**

**Stay away from "X-Rated".**

Okay, we know that you have a life—it's just that your life is built around Star Trek. Why waste your time with non-Trekkers? The only reasonable place to hang out is rec.arts.startrek.fandom.

## Final Frontiers

Take some time out for a little bit of role-playing, Star Trek style. This is an interactive online role-playing game where you pick a race, join a group and explore the galaxy or compete with other groups.

**Web:**

**http://www.planetx.com/~aradmin/trek/**

**Telnet:**

Address: **trek.microserve.com**
Port: **2499**
Login: **guest [it]your name[it] [it]your email address[it]**

## Future Technology Talk and General Discussion

You look back and laugh at old sci-fi from the '50s. How close are we getting to Star Trek technology? Speculate on how our technological progress compares with the technology dreamed up in the creative minds of Star Trek writers.

**Usenet:**

**rec.arts.startrek.tech**

## Klingon Phrasebook

Would you like to learn Klingon? Here is one way to start: with a small phrasebook of quotes translated into Klingon. There are quotes from famous television shows such as The X-Files, The Simpsons, Mad About You and Seinfeld. There are also other handy phrases such as insults and things to say when you are stoned (example: "QoQ vIleghlaH!" is Klingon for "I can see the music!").

**Web:**

**http://ariel.ucs.unimelb.edu.au/~cthulhu/say-it.html**

## *Look What I Found on the Net...*

```
        (from a message that was sent to me by Mike Lyons)

...I am going to call you on something printed in the first
edition of your book, within the Star Trek section, in an ad
entitled "Klingon is a Real Language".

You said: "What I want to know is, what is Klingon for
'Get a life'?"

I was given a copy of the Klingon dictionary, and I looked
it up.

      yIn'e' yISuq

   yIn  =  life (n)
  -'e'  =  noun prefix indicating topic
   yI-  =  verb prefix (you - [him her it], imperative)
   Suq  =  get (v)

Incidentally, it was a linguist named Marc Okrand who created
the Klingon language, based on the few words from the opening
scenes in the first movie, which were made up by James "Scotty"
Doohan.

Just a little trivia for you.
```

A B C D E F G H I J K L M N O P Q R S T U V W X Y Z

## Klingon Shared Reality

Wouldn't it be fun for a little while to pretend you are a Klingon and walk around making lots of gutteral noises and threatening people? Brush up on your Klingon language, don a persona and elbow your way into the crowd for a little Usenet role-playing.

**Usenet:**

**alt.shared-reality.startrek.klingon**

## Klingon Talk and General Discussion

Ignore the subtitles in the movies: learn to speak Klingon. Explore the culture that devoted fans have worked so hard to develop. Find a variety of interesting topics such as Klingon love poetry, haiku, and thoughts on Kronos as the homeworld.

**Usenet:**

**alt.startrek.klingon**

### Klingon is a Real Language

**Yes, it's true. There really is a language named Klingon. It was developed by fanatical Star Trek fans who have actually created a whole new language with its own grammar, rules of usage and a dictionary. There are also Klingon magazines and audio tapes (to help with your pronunciation) as well as clubs of people who want to live like real Klingons.**
**HIja. tlhIngan Hol vIjatlhlaH.**
**(Yes. I can speak Klingon.)**

**(What I want to know is, what is the Klingon for "Get a life"?)**

## Next Generation

If ST:TNG is your favorite, you will enjoy this web site. It has an introduction, cast list, information about the setting, explanations of the major alien species (along with the episodes in which they appeared), episode summaries, information about ST:TNG movies and video releases, trivia and more. What else could you possible want out of life (aside from a Ferengi joke book)?

**Web:**

**http://www.ee.surrey.ac.uk/Contrib/SciFi/StarTrek/STTNG/**

## Star Trek Archives

Life without Star Trek is simply not worth living. You don't have to take our word for it. See the archives that fans have compiled on the old and new Star Trek as well as Deep Space Nine.

**Web:**

**http://www.vol.it/luca/startrek/**

## Star Trek Fetishes

Sex and Star Trek. There's not much more to life than having both of those. Now the ultimate state has been achieved by combining the two. Read stories and commentary about sex, Star Trek and other naughty bits.

**Usenet:**

**alt.sex.fetish.startrek**

## Star Trek Games

Don't just watch Star Trek, live it! Command your own ship with Xtrek and match wits with the computer or go head to head (or torpedo to torpedo) with others like you on Netrek, the networking version of the game. The Usenet groups cover such topics as tactics, experiences and troubleshooting software.

**Usenet:**

**alt.games.xtrek**
**rec.games.netrek**

A B C D E F G H I J K L M N O P Q R S T U V W X Y Z

## Star Trek Lines

This is a collection of all-time great lines from Star Trek shows and movies. Submissions are posted and people can vote on what they think are the best lines. The collection of quotes is divided by series (Voyager, Deep Space Nine, the original series, and so on). "Damn it, Jim, I'm an Internet writer, not a doctor."

**Web:**

**http://www.localnet.com/~rseiden/startrek/lines.html**

## Star Trek News

Learn what's going on in the world of Star Trek. Fans report rumors and facts about new shows, books and movies. Get the latest word and keep up with the Bones's.

**Usenet:**

**rec.arts.startrek.current**

## Star Trek Resources

Here are some web sites that will point you to a large number of Star Trek-related resources all over the Net: web sites, Usenet groups, pictures, sounds, episode guides, book details, quotes, stories, parodies and even the Klingon language. It's all here somewhere. Just beam yourself into the Net.

**Web:**

**http://www.cosy.sbg.ac.at/rec/startrek/index.html**
**http://www.netshop.net/Startrek/web/**
**http://www.syix.com/spock/startrek.htm**

### Star Trek Resources

Have you ever noticed that in all depictions of the future (including Star Trek), there are never references to the Net?

This is because the Net snuck up on us, completely unanticipated.

Nevertheless, even though there isn't a Net on Star Trek, there is plenty of Star Trek on the Net.

## Star Trek Reviews

Nobody can review Star Trek like a Trekkie. Read what fans think about the latest books, movies and shows (but watch out for spoilers!).

**Usenet:**

**rec.arts.startrek.reviews**

## Star Trek Sounds

Imagine having the voices and sounds of your favorite Star Trek episodes coming out of your very own computer. You can almost pretend you are right there in the sound stage, or better yet, you are flying through space at high speeds seeking out new life and new civilizations—boldly going where no net.geek has gone before. Use these sounds to create some ambience in your computing environment.

**Web:**

**http://copper.ucs.indiana.edu/~mchaifet/tng.html**
**http://tos-www.tos.net/services/sounds/sound.html**

## Star Trek Stories and Parodies

If you can't get enough of Star Trek on television or in movies and books, check out this corner of the Internet universe. Creative and witty individuals post stories and parodies related to Star Trek in Usenet groups and on web sites. Often FAQs on submissions are posted containing tips for writing for Deep Space Nine and the Star Trek: Voyager series, where to send submissions, what to do, and what not to do when writing.

**Web:**

**http://www.netshop.net/Startrek/web/Parodies.html**
**http://www.netshop.net/Startrek/web/Stories.html**

**Usenet:**

**alt.startrek.creative**

## Star Trek Talk and General Discussion

Light and lively debate volleys, occasionally turning warm, then hot as you defend your favorite episode or character. Talk turns to old shows, bloopers, insider information on actors' lives, and burning questions like, "Why is Lt. Worf still only a lieutenant?"

**Usenet:**

**rec.arts.startrek.misc**

## Star Trek Trivia

If you want to test your skill in Star Trek trivia, check out this site that offers a set of questions for you to try. Selected questions cover each of the Star Trek series for a multi-level challenge.

**Web:**

**http://www.net-link.net/~jmeadows/trivia.html**

## Star Trek Universe

This moderated group offers in-depth and accurate information on the universe as it relates to Star Trek. Read press releases, episode credits, synopses and factual articles. Since all posts are filtered through a moderator, you can be assured of the reliability of what you read. Queries are best moved to one of the other Star Trek groups.

**Usenet:**

**rec.arts.startrek.info**

## Star Trek Video Clips

Enjoy this selection of Star Trek sequences, including some from the Star Trek VI motion picture, Deep Space Nine, Star Trek—The Next Generation, and Star Trek cast members' appearances on talk shows.

**Web:**

**http://tns-www.lcs.mit.edu/cgi-bin/vs/vsbrowser**

## Star Trek Writing

Beam aboard for Mr. Spock's wild ride. You will find yourself engaged in raucous laughter at Star Trek parodies, so don't read this group while in the library lest you be subjected to some severe ear-twisting by a librarian with a tight bun on her head. Stick to the safer, more suspenseful stories that will keep you at the edge of your seat, while the Star Trek crew race through the Universe, boldly taking you where no one has gone before.

**Usenet:**

**alt.startrek.creative**

**Star Trek fans**: When the television shows, videos, movies, books and conventions just aren't enough, turn to Usenet and read original stories based on the Star Trek universe.

## Trekkie Chat

Meet with other Star Trek enthusiasts for some real-time chat on IRC. If you like Star Trek, this is a good way to meet people from all over the world and make new friends. If you are shy and don't know what to say, ask if anyone has seen the Star Trek section in Harley Hahn's new book.

**IRC:**

**#ds9**
**#startrek**

What do you do when there are no Star Trek programs to watch?
Join the **Trekkie Chat** on IRC.

# SUPPORT GROUPS

## 30 Plus

I remember when people used to say, "Don't trust anyone over 30." Well, those people are all over 40 now, and the new slogan is "Don't pay attention to anyone under 30." If you're over 30, there are special support groups on the Net just for you. Anyone is welcome, regardless of age, but if you're not mature, do your best to pretend. (It's always worked for me.)

**IRC:**

**#30libris**
**#30plus**

## Adoption

There are quite a few resources on the Net for people who are involved in an adoption, no matter what end of the process you are on. These Internet resources have something for prospective adopters, adoptees looking for birth parents, or parents who already have adopted children.

**Web:**

**http://www.webreflection.com/aiml**

**Usenet:**

**alt.adoption**

**Listserv Mailing List:**

List Name: **adoptees**
Subscribe to: **listserv@sjuvm.stjohns.edu**

**Listserv Mailing List:**

List Name: **open-adoption**
Subscribe to: **listserv@home.dc.lsoft.com**

## AIDS Caregivers

AIDS (acquired immunodeficiency syndrome) is a disease caused by HIV (human immunodeficiency virus). Many AIDS patients require extensive care, and the people who give such care have their own special needs. This is especially so when the caregiver is a friend or family member. This mailing list is a support group for caregivers of AIDS patients. If you are talking care of an AIDS patient, you will find it helpful and energizing to talk with people who are in a similar situation.

**Majordomo Mailing List:**

List Name: **caregivers**
Subscribe to: **majordomo@queernet.org**

## Al-Anon and Alateen

Al-Anon and Alateen resources are available for those people whose lives are affected by friends or family members who are alcoholics. Here you can find information about self-help recovery programs, 12 step programs, and a list of phone numbers for Al-Anon or Alateen groups.

**Web:**

**http://solar.rtd.utk.edu/~al-anon/**

**Listproc Mailing List:**

List Name: **al-anon**
Subscribe to: **listproc@solar.rtd.utk.edu**

## Anxiety

This web site is for people who experience panic and anxiety. You will find information about anxiety disorders, various type of support, hints about relaxation techniques, personal stories, a reading list, and a collection of related resources including places you can talk to other people on the Net. The Usenet group is for people who suffer from panic attacks.

**Web:**

**http://www.algy.com/anxiety/anxiety.html**

**Usenet:**

**alt.support.anxiety-panic**

## Depression

Depression is a terrible condition. You can't see it, but it can incapacitate you just the same. If you suffer from depression (or if you are close to someone who is depressed), there are lots of discussion groups in which people are willing to talk, share and help one another. Choose the Usenet group that is the most appropriate for you. If you are not sure which one to choose, you can always join the people in the **.misc** group. The mailing list is called "Walkers in Darkness". It is for people who are depressed or who have a bipolar disorder. The web site is a supplement to the mailing list. You will find pictures of some of the people on the mailing list, links to related sites, FAQs, drug information and a list of related Usenet groups.

**Web:**

**http://www.primenet.com/~jtp/walkers.html**

**Usenet:**

**alt.support.depression**
**soc.support.depression.crisis**
**soc.support.depression.family**
**soc.support.depression.manic**
**soc.support.depression.misc**
**soc.support.depression.seasonal**
**soc.support.depression.treatment**

**Majordomo Mailing List:**

List Name: **walkers**
Subscribe to: **majordomo@world.std.com**

## Divorce

Those who are going through a divorce can access a huge amount of resources that can help you through your trying times. Available resources include law and legal resources, information on recovery, support and child custody, resources for men and women and support group lists. You will also find resources on parenting as well as things to help you cope, such as links relating to religion and spirituality and some fun stuff to cheer you up.

**Web:**

**http://hughson.com/**

**Usenet:**

**alt.support.divorce**

## Domestic Violence

There are a lot of domestic violence resources on the Net. I have selected two web sites that are particularly interesting and useful: one site is created by men, the other by women. Together, these sites offer a great deal of information and will help you find the resources you need. The Usenet group is for people who have suffered from—or are currently suffering from—this type of abuse.

**Web:**

**http://www.cybergrrl.com/dv.html**
**http://www.silcom.com/~paladin/madv/**

**Usenet:**

**alt.support.abuse-partners**

### *Look What I Found on the Net...*

```
                  (from an Anxiety web site)

Go through each category and keep track of how many symptoms
apply to you.

======================  ==================  ==================
Physiological Response  Cognitive Response  Emotional Response
======================  ==================  ==================

Feelings of warmth      I can't do it       Fear
Heart palpitations      Feel foolish        Keyed up, on edge
Rapid, pounding heart   People are looking  Panic
Tightness of chest      I could faint       Excessive worry
Butterflies in stomach  It's a heart attack Uneasy
Hyperventilation        Get me out of here  Feelings of gloom
Weakness all over       No one will help    Trapped: no way out
Tremors                 I can't go alone    Isolated, lonely
Dizziness               I can't breathe     Loss of control
Dry mouth               I'm going to die    Embarrassed
Sweaty all over         I'm going crazy     Criticized
Confusion               I'm trapped         Rejected
Speeded up thoughts     I'm not going out   Angry
Muscle tension/aches    Someone's hurt, sick Depressed
Fatigue

If you checked 3 or more from each response list, ask yourself:

-- Is fear of an anxiety attack limiting my involvement in life?
-- Am I avoiding every day situations?
-- Do I worry and feel tense most of the time?
```

## Eating Disorders

If you suspect you have an eating disorder, you should check out this web page. There you can read about the types of eating disorders and their signs and symptoms. If you know that you or someone close to you has a problem, you will also find useful information here, such as how to confront a loved one, how to get help, how to find a therapist, and much, much more. The Usenet group and mailing list are for people with eating disorders as well as supportive family members and friends.

**Web:**

**http://icewall.vianet.on.ca/pages/colleen/eatdis.htm**

**Usenet:**

**alt.recovery.compulsive-eat**

**Listserv Mailing List:**

List Name: **eating-disorders**
Subscribe to: **listserv@sjuvm.stjohns.edu**

## Grief

There are many reasons for grief, and sometimes it helps to be able to talk with someone who has gone through a similar experience. One of these web sites will help you find the people you need. There are a number of mailing lists, each with a specific topic. For example, have you lost a family member (child, parent, sibling, spouse)? Are you interested in becoming a grief counselor? There are lists for parents who have lost a child in an accident, parents who have lost an adult child, parents who have lost babies, parents who have lost their only child, parents whose child has committed suicide, and so on. You will also find helpful articles and suggestions of books to read, as well as other related resources. The Usenet group **alt.support.grief** is for people who are grieving, and the second web page contains the FAQ (frequently asked question list) for this group. Two hints: (1) The Usenet group is *not* for people who are grieving because of a broken romance. (2) The participants do not want to talk to people who are doing research for journals or academic papers.

**Web:**

**http://rivendell.org/**
**http://www.ids.net/~rebecca/grief-faq.html**

**Usenet:**

**alt.support.grief**

## Narcotics Anonymous

Narcotics Anonymous (NA) is an international community of organizations dedicated to helping drug addicts recover from their addiction. NA is based on the 12-step program used in other similar organizations. I have included two web pages: one is the official NA site, the other is a NA-oriented site created by private individuals. These web sites explain about NA and how it works, and offer a wealth of useful information. For discussion, you can join the Usenet group or the IRC channel.

**Web:**

**http://www.netwizards.net/recovery/na/**
**http://www.wsoinc.com/**

**Usenet:**

**alt.recovery.na**

**IRC:**

**#na**

## Pregnancy Loss

The Usenet group is for the support of men and women involved in the loss of an unborn child. The web site is the FAQ for the Usenet group. It has tips for coping, information about grieving and medical information about pregnancy loss. If you have recently experienced such a loss, I can tell you that it is a lot more common that most people realize. And please remember, on the Net, you are never alone.

**Web:**

**http://web.co.nz/~katef/sspl/faq.html**

**Usenet:**

**soc.support.pregnancy.loss**

**Feel lucky? Try "Contests".**

## Recovery for Christians

This web site is maintained by Christians in Recovery (CIR). The resources are for people recovering from all types of problems: drugs abuse, dysfunctional families, depression, anxiety, eating disorders, sexual addiction, and so on. There is information about the 12-step program, a checklist of symptoms that lead to relapse, computer programs that may help you recover (such as the Recovery Bible, quote-a-day programs, etc.), and links to Christian and non-Christian recovery sites. There is also information that will help you find other people to talk to on the Net using IRC, Usenet and mailing lists.

**Web:**

**http://www.goshen.net/cir/**

**"Fun" is fun.**

**Stay connected.**

## Recovery for Jews

This site is for Jews who are recovering from alcohol or drug abuse. The site stresses anonymity, so if the shoe fits, there is no reason not to wear it. At this web site you can read recovery stories, cartoons about Jewish denial, a zine about recovery and spirituality, words from rabbis and scholars, and information about online meetings. This site is sponsored by JACS (Jewish Alcoholics, Chemically Dependent People, and Significant Others).

**Web:**

**http://www.shamash.org/health/jacs/**

### *Look What I Found on the Net...*

```
Newsgroup: alt.recovery.na
Subject: Note of Thanks

I've been reading this newsgroup for about three weeks now.
I feel as though my 'problem' is trivial compared to others I
have read in the past weeks, but I figured I'd at least make an
effort.

I have been a daily user of marijuana for the past 4 years.
I've pawned nearly all of my possessions.  My life revolved
around how I was going to get my next bag of dope.  It got so
bad that I would offer to clean my friends smoking accessories
so that I could scrape the resin and get high.

Well, three weeks ago, with the help of my counselor
(psychiatric, for depression), I stopped using pot.  I've now
been clean for three weeks, and I feel, well, like I haven't
felt in years.  I've actually been going outside and becoming a
part of society again.  I realize that this feeling has a
lot to do with the fact that pot canceled out the effects of my
anti-depressant, but I no longer feel like I have a chain around
my neck, that I don't have to get high to have fun, laugh, etc.

Reading the posts in this newsgroup has been a great help to me.
Thanks to all those who unknowingly helped me through the past
three weeks by opening up and sharing their experiences through
their posts to this newsgroup.
```

A B C D E F G H I J K L M N O P Q R S T U V W X Y Z

## Support Talk and General Discussion

On the Net, you are never alone. Out of the millions of people, there are some that are a lot like you and that want to talk. The Net has a large number of resources to provide support to people. There are Usenet groups, mailing lists, IRC channels, and many, many web sites. This Usenet group is the general support forum, to which you can go with a question, a problem, a story or simply to satisfy your curiosity. If you are looking for support of a particular kind and you are having difficulty, this group would be a good place to ask people for suggestions. (Personally, I am looking for a group that supports writers who stay up all night to finish Internet books.)

**Usenet:**

**alt.support**

## Transgendered Support

Transgendered people are those whose sexual identities have significant ambiguity. This group includes transsexuals (people whose minds are trapped in a body of the opposite sex), cross-dressers or transvestites (people, almost always men, who enjoy dressing like the opposite sex), and intersexed (people born with ambiguous genitalia). The Usenet group is for an ongoing discussion of the many problems and topics of interest to transgendered people including, but not limited to, sex change procedures. For real-time talk, you can join one of the IRC channels. If you are new to discussing such issues on the Net, I have included a web site that contains a FAQ (frequently asked question list) that you will find helpful.

**Web:**

**http://www2.wintermute.co.uk/users/snuffles/The_Plaid/FAQs/s.s.tg-FAQ.html**

**Usenet:**

**soc.support.transgendered**

**IRC:**

**#crossdress**
**#transgen**

Troubled? Confused?
The Net is there for you

## Usenet Support Groups

It's great to know that when you have a problem, there are people who will be supportive of you. All over the world there are people who are willing to take the time to listen to the problems and try to meet the emotional needs of others. Get good information on nearly any subject like medical, emotional or psychological problems.

**Usenet:**

**alt.abuse-recovery**
**alt.abuse.offender.recovery**
**alt.abuse.recovery**
**alt.abuse.transcendence**
**alt.recovery**
**alt.recovery.aa**
**alt.recovery.adult-children**
**alt.recovery.cals-tables**
**alt.recovery.catholicism**
**alt.recovery.childhood.forced-therapy**
**alt.recovery.codependency**
**alt.recovery.compulsive-eat**
**alt.recovery.mormonism**
**alt.recovery.na**
**alt.recovery.religion**
**alt.support.abuse-partners**
**alt.support.aids.partners**
**alt.support.asthma**
**alt.support.ataxia**
**alt.support.big-folks**
**alt.support.breast-implant**
**alt.support.cancer**
**alt.support.cancer.prostate**
**alt.support.cerebral-palsy**
**alt.support.childfree**
**alt.support.chronic-pain**
**alt.support.dev-delays**
**alt.support.diabetes.kids**

**alt.support.disabled.artists**
**alt.support.disabled.sexuality**
**alt.support.dissociation**
**alt.support.dwarfism**
**alt.support.dystonia**
**alt.support.endometriosis**
**alt.support.epilepsy**
**alt.support.ex-cult**
**alt.support.food-allergies**
**alt.support.food-allergies**
**alt.support.glaucoma**
**alt.support.headaches.migraine**
**alt.support.hearing-loss**
**alt.support.hemophilia**
**alt.support.herpes**
**alt.support.inter-cystitis**
**alt.support.jaw-disorders**
**alt.support.kidney-failure**
**alt.support.learning-disab**
**alt.support.loneliness**
**alt.support.marfan**
**alt.support.menopause**
**alt.support.mult-sclerosis**
**alt.support.musc-dystrophy**
**alt.support.myasthe-gravis**
**alt.support.obesity**
**alt.support.ocd**
**alt.support.osteogenesis.imperfecta**
**alt.support.ostomy**
**alt.support.personality**
**alt.support.post-polio**
**alt.support.prostate.prostatitis**
**alt.support.schizophrenia**
**alt.support.shyness**
**alt.support.sinusitis**
**alt.support.skin-diseases**
**alt.support.social-phobia**
**alt.support.spina-bifida**
**alt.support.stuttering**
**alt.support.survivors.prozac**
**alt.support.thyroid**
**alt.support.tinnitus**
**alt.support.tourette**
**alt.support.trauma-ptsd**
**alt.support.turner-syndrom**
**soc.support.abuse.rape**
**soc.support.fat-acceptance**
**soc.support.loneliness**
**soc.support.youth.gay-lesbian-bi**

## Widows and Widowers

Widows and widowers have a place to find support and friendship. This mailing list and web site are for widows and widowers to learn and talk about issues that affect their daily lives.

**Web:**

**http://www.fortnet.org/~goshorn/**

**Majordomo Mailing List:**

List Name: **widow**
Subscribe to: **majordomo@fortnet.org**

## *Look What I Found on the Net...*

```
(from the Social Phobia Frequently Asked Question List, posted to alt.support.social-pho-
bia)

What is Social Phobia?

Social phobia can be defined as a feeling of anxiety.  Social phobics experience anxiety
which is intense and overwhelming in social situations.  They typically fear that their
behavior will humiliate or embarrass them in front of others.  They will often rather
withdraw entirely than face the anxiety they experience.

Anxiety can trigger a variety of physiological responses including a tightness in the
chest, an accelerated heart rate, a tingling sensation in the arms and legs, a knot in
the stomach or a cold, clammy feeling in the extremities.

Newsgroup: alt.support.shyness
Subject: Being Blocked

I found that when "blocked" at the urinal, it helps me if I think of a math problem, say
dividing 265 by 12 or finding the approximate square root of 234.

However, now I find that I get the urge to urinate whenever I do math.
```

A B C D E F G H I J K L M N O P Q R S T U V W X Y Z

# TALKING ON THE NET

## Chat Room Lists

So, you want to talk? Here are some web sites that list chat rooms all over the Net. Look for a chat room by language or by topic. There are even reviews of different chat rooms, so you can find one that appeals to your taste.

**Web:**

**http://sunsite.unc.edu/dbarberi/chats.html**
**http://www.lookup.com/Homepages/75669/chat2.html**
**http://www.solscape.com/chat/**
**http://www.webcom.com/fi/empo.html**

## Chatters Directory

This is a directory of people who talk over the Net. You will find names, pictures, email addresses and other information about people who use various popular web-based talking programs such as Powwow, Worlds Chat, Alpha World, Virtual Places and BlackSun. Using this directory is a good way to find people with similar interests.

**Web:**

**http://207.86.131.209/gallery/frames.html**

**Chatting Software**

Are you ready to talk? There are people all over the Net who are ready to talk to you. But you do need the appropriate software.

No problem. Visit the Chatting Software web sites where you will find everything you need.

## Chatting Software

Some chat rooms require nothing more than a standard web browser. The messages people send are displayed for you as a regular web page. To see new messages, you reload the page. Such a system is simple, but it doesn't have a lot of functionality. Moreover, it is a bother to have to reload a web page every time you want to see if someone has typed a new message. The basic problem is that the Web was never designed to support interactive conversation. For this reason, many chat rooms use special software designed specifically for talking. Thus, when you visit a chat room for the first time, you need to see what software they use. If you do not already have that program, you will have to download and install it. (However, it should be free.) Here are web sites at which you can find various types of web chat software. These programs are only alike in that they are all used to talk over the Web. Other than that, they are completely different programs with different features. For example, some programs allow you to send voice messages as well as text (if your computer has a microphone and speakers). One last point: Some chat rooms use IRC for their communications. IRC (Internet Relay Chat) is a system in which you use a client program to connect to a server. Once you are connected, you can talk to people on a large variety of different "channels". Most IRC clients run have nothing to do with the Web. They are separate programs you use only for IRC. The IRC clients included here are specially designed to work with your browser (as "plug-ins"). This allows you to access an IRC-based chat room without having to leave your browser and start a separate program. For serious IRC talking, however, you may want to get a standalone client program.

**Web:**

**http://www.globalchat.com/**
**http://www.ichat.com/**
**http://www.onlive.com/**

**Express yourself.**
**Make a web page.**

## Comic Chat

Comic Chat is sooooo cool. I just love it. It's a Microsoft IRC-like graphical chat client program. Whenever you or anyone else talks, it shows up as a comic strip on your screen. You actually see drawings of characters with speech balloons. You can choose what you want your character to look like and, if you want, the various poses and expressions the character uses. (If you don't specify, the character just goes through the variations automatically.) This is a fun program to use that you should try at least once. At this web site, you can download the chat program and find out which chat rooms you can visit that use this client.

**Web:**

**http://www.microsoft.com/ie/comichat/**

## CoolTalk (Netscape)

CoolTalk is an Internet communications program offered by Netscape. CoolTalk is designed to work well with the Netscape web browser, and is available for Windows 95, Windows 3.1, Macintosh, and various popular versions of Unix. With CoolTalk, you can talk to people all over the Net, by voice and by typing text messages. You can also collaborate with someone using a whiteboard (shared drawing area). If you leave CoolTalk running, it will act like an answering machine while you are away from the computer, taking messages if anyone on the Net tries to contact you. One of these web sites contains general information about CoolTalk. This is the place from which you can download the actual program (which is free). The other site is a directory of CoolTalk users. According to Netscape, CoolTalk is *the* way to communicate over the Net.

**Web:**

**http://home.netscape.com/comprod/products/navigator/version_3.0/communication/cooltalk/**
**http://live.netscape.com/**

**Join the fun—now.**

## Internet Phone Services

These web sites have products you can use to talk to people over the Net: real voice talking, like with a telephone. (Of course, you need a computer with a microphone and speakers.) There are three reasons why you might enjoy doing this. First, it's fun to talk to people using your computer; second, you can talk to people all over the world, people whom you otherwise would never have met; and third, you don't have to pay long distance charges. Some of these products cost money, but they all let you evaluate them for free. Compared to talking with a real telephone, talking on the Net does not sound as good, but it's fun and it's free.

**Web:**

**http://www.eurocall.com/e/**
**http://www.intel.com/iaweb/cpc/iphone/**
**http://www.net2phone.com/**

## IRC (Internet Relay Chat)

IRC is an old, well-established system for talking over the Net. To use IRC, you need an IRC client program. Your client connects to an IRC server. You can now talk to people all over the world. IRC is organized into "channels" (some of which you will see in this book). To participate, you "join" one or more channels. It is important to realize that, unlike Usenet groups, IRC channels are created and removed dynamically. Anyone can create a new IRC channel; and when the last person leaves a particular channel, it is removed automatically. (The channels in this book are so popular, there is almost always someone around to keep them open.) IRC is fabulous, but before you start I do want you to know what you are doing. Begin by visiting this web site where you will find a wealth of information: FAQs (frequently asked question lists), primers, RFCs (technical documents, aka "request for comments"), help files, information for channel ops (operators), and lists of IRC servers to which you can connect. For a comprehensive easy-to-understand introduction to IRC, see my book *The Internet Complete Reference*, published by Osborne McGraw-Hill.

**Web:**

**http://www.irchelp.org/**

A B C D E F G H I J K L M N O P Q R S T U V W X Y Z

## IRC Talk and General Discussion

Using IRC (Internet Relay Chat) is like going into a crowded bar only there is not as much smoke and no cover charge. Mingle with the crowds of people, make new friends, have philosophical discussions—use your imagination. Just about anything can happen when you're on IRC. Check out these Usenet groups which cover topics like announcements, specific IRC channels, questions and servers relating to IRC.

**Usenet:**

**alt.irc.announce**
**alt.irc.hottub**
**alt.irc.jeopardy**
**alt.irc.questions**
**alt.irc.undernet**

## Java Chat Applets

Java is a system that allows your browser to download programs which are then automatically run on your computer. Such programs are called "applets" (small applications). Here is a list of links to Java-based chat rooms that use various applets. You will also find special purpose chat applets, for IRC, muds and games. These applets are really fun—and convenient to use. I had one running in a little window in the corner of my screen, and I could still use my browser. If you like doing a lot of things at the same time, you can max out on Java.

**Web:**

**http://www.gamelan.com/pages/Gamelan.net.chat.html**

## Mirc Client

Mirc is a popular IRC client program that is used around the world. (I use it and like it a great deal.) Mirc is available for Windows 95, Windows 3.X, Macintosh and Unix. These web sites have a great deal of information about Mirc and IRC to help you get started: FAQs, command lists, help files (which are important), scripts, utilities, bots (programs that participate in IRC and provide particular services) and, of course, the Mirc program itself for you to download.

**Web:**

**http://www.geocities.com/SiliconValley/Park/6000/**
**http://www.phoenix.net/~lsimon/mirc.html**
**http://www.tera-byte.com/mirc/**

## NetMeeting (Internet Explorer)

NetMeeting is a full-featured Internet communication program developed by Microsoft. NetMeeting, which requires Windows 95, is designed to integrate with Microsoft's web browser, the Internet Explorer. With NetMeeting you can talk to other people (with voice, like a telephone); type text messages back and forth, share programs, files and the contents of your Windows clipboard; and work together using a shared whiteboard (drawing area). One of these web sites has all the information you need to get started, including the program itself (which is free). The other web site is a place you can visit when you are looking for someone to talk to. It will show you who is currently connected to a public chat area. According to Microsoft, NetMeeting is *the* way to communicate over the Net.

**Web:**

**http://www.microsoft.com/netmeeting/**
**http://www.microsoft.com/netmeeting/call/**

### *Look What I Found on the Net...*

```
Newsgroups: alt.irc, alt.irc.annnounce, alt.irc.hottub
Subject: New IRC Server

> ***NEW FREE SWINGERS IRC SERVER NOW ONLINE!!!***
> Server: 196.33.249.10
>
> Help build it up.

Will there be discussions about those carnival swing rides?

You know, the plastic seats on chains which swing around and
around until the chains break, sending you into the adjoining
vacant lot?
```

## Powwow

Powwow is a great program for Windows that allows multiple people to chat, trade files and explore the Web as a group. Go to this web page to download Powwow. You will also find extra sound files (you can send sounds to other people), add-on software (such as address book and a sound file sorter), address books of other Powwow users, conference listings, help files and more. Powwow is a lot of fun.

**Web:**

**http://www.tribal.com/powwow/**

## Talkers

A talker is an easy-to-use multiuser talk facility. You connect to a talker using telnet. (Telnet is a program that acts like a terminal and allows you to connect to a remote computer. Telnet is usually included with general Internet software, so there is a good chance that you already have a telnet program on your computer. This is the case if you use Windows 95 or OS/2.) Once you connect to a talker, you can talk to anyone else who happens to be there. If you are a mud person, you can think of a talker as being a simple mud or mush devoted entirely to conversation. These web sites contain lists of talkers and where you can find them. One of the sites has additional information, such as the history of talkers, and the rules and culture.

**Web:**

**http://donald.phast.umass.edu/~friedman/talkers.html**
**http://ulibnet.mtsu.edu/~msimms/lists/talkers/ew/**

## Web Chat Rooms

A web chat room is a facility that lets you talk to people over the web. Some chat rooms require you to have special software in order to participate. With others, your web browser will do everything you need. When you connect to a chat room web site, you will commonly find a number of rooms, each of which is devoted to discussing a specific topic. Other web sites are devoted to a specific organization or theme. For example, a radio talk show may set up a chat room for its listeners to talk to one another while they are listening to the show. Or a company may set up a chat room for customers to talk about its products. Many web sites allow you to specify a small image to identify yourself to other people. Each time you send a message, this image is displayed next to the message. Sometimes you can furnish your own image. You could use, for example, a small picture of yourself. Other chat rooms require you to choose an image from their library. The web sites I have listed all have chat rooms open to the public. However, some of the services may ask you to register. When you visit, you will find people from all over the Net talking on many different topics.

**Web:**

**http://chat.novia.net:8080/chat/**
**http://wbs.net/**
**http://www.chathouse.com/**
**http://www.mojoski.com/chat/**
**http://www.webamerica.com/directory/**

# TECHNOLOGY

## Artificial Intelligence

Not everything that is artificial is bad. In fact, in a world where watching television is the favorite pastime of the masses, a little artificial intelligence is certainly not going to hurt anyone. These sites have technical papers, journals, and surveys about artificial intelligence, robotics, and neural networks. Pick up some artificial intelligence today.

**Web:**

**http://lenti.med.umn.edu/~mwd/robot.html**
**http://www.ai.sri.com/**

A B C D E F G H I J K L M N O P Q R S T U V W X Y Z

## Compact Disc Formats

Can't tell your CD-DA from your CD-ROM, your CD-I and your Photo CD? Before you have that big party and you put the wrong compact disc in the stereo, consider giving this web site a read. This site gives a description and history of the various CD formats available. This will save you from accidentally showing your guests pictures of your summer vacation when you are really trying to give them some good '70s disco music.

**Web:**

**http://cuiwww.unige.ch/OSG/MultimediaInfo/Info/cd.html**

## Computer-Based Simulations

Computer-based simulations are good because you can do lots of terrible things on the computer and see what happens and chances are good that you won't kill or maim anyone. Here's a web site with various simulations such as defense modeling, fluid dynamics, oceanographic modeling and others. Go have fun.

**Web:**

**http://www.dataspace.com/WWW/vlib/comp-simulation.html**

## Distribute Interactive Virtual Environment

The Distribute Interactive Virtual Environment (DIVE) is a fully distributed, heterogeneous VR system where users navigate in 3D space and may see, meet, and interact with other users and applications in the environment. The DIVE system is available free of charge, and information about the project, software and hardware requirements, instructions on how to obtain DIVE software, DIVE mpeg movies, and online reports are available here.

**Web:**

**http://www.sics.se/dce/dive/dive.html**

## High Definition Television

High definition television is a system that is designed to replace regular TV. The basic changes are a wider aspect ratio and many more scan lines. High definition TV uses an aspect ratio of 16 x 9 (16 units across by 9 units up), similar to movies. The old TV standard uses a more square screen that is 4 x 3. In addition, high definition TV uses 1,125 lines of resolution, compared to only 525 on the old system. The result is a TV image that is wider and sharper. These web sites provide information for professionals and the general public. Read about the high definition technology and how it is used to create a whole new television system.

**Web:**

**http://teletron.com/hdtv/hdtvnews.html**
**http://www.spe.sony.com/Pictures/Hidef/sphweb.htm**

## Interactive Systems Laboratories

This page is divided into sections covering the history of synthesizers, current synthesizers, and current research projects. There are demonstrations, articles, papers, and links to related resources.

**Web:**

**http://www.is.cs.cmu.edu/**

## Journal of Artificial Intelligence Research

In a world of artificial coloring, artificial flavoring, and artificial body parts, why not have artificial intelligence? It seems almost natural. Explore the latest breakthroughs in the field of AI research.

**Web:**

**http://www.cs.washington.edu/research/jair/home.html**

## Mobile Computing

Here is a large collection of articles, list of universities, conferences, projects, products, and calls for papers related to the world of mobile computing. Never again will you have to leave home without it.

**Web:**

**http://snapple.cs.washington.edu:600/mobile/mobile_www.html**

MOBILE COMPUTING

If you are a man or woman on the move, you can stay with the flow by using the resources at the Mobile Computing Web site.

## Multicast Backbone FAQ

Here is the frequently asked questions list (FAQ) about the Multicast Backbone (MBONE). The MBONE is an outgrowth of two "audiocast" experiments in which live audio and video were multicast over the Internet. The idea is to construct a semi-permanent IP multicast testbed to carry transmissions and support continued experimentation. Details of the MBONE topology, multicast tunnels, maps, hardware and software requirements, teleconference events, and much more can be found here.

**Web:**
**http://www.research.att.com/mbone-faq.html**

## Nanotechnology

Nanotechnology is an area of technology that strives to work with extremely small devices: devices on the scale of molecules or even atoms. Such devices can be created by using a scanning tunneling microscope. Experiments have been devised in which a single atom is used as an electric switch, or a single molecule is used to convert AC to DC. The holy grail of nanotechnology is to develop the methods necessary to create vast numbers of tiny little machines. Although progress is slow, the implications are fascinating. Here is a web site that will introduce you to nanotechnology. There is a lot of general interest information (including a FAQ), as well as more technical material. The name "nanotechnology" is derived from "nano", the Greek word for "dwarf". In the metric system, "nano" is used as a prefix indicating "one billionth" (American terminology). For example, a nanosecond is one billionth of a second. (In the English terminology, this would be one thousand millionth of a second.)

**Web:**
**http://www.nanothinc.com/**

## Neural Network Home Page

This web page offers a brief introduction to artificial neural networks, articles and bibliographic references to specific areas of neural network research and interest, electronic journals, conference information, bibliographic search tools, mailing lists, Usenet groups, project details, reports, papers, and much more to do with neural networks and neuroscience.

**Web:**
**http://www.emsl.pnl.gov:2080/docs/cie/neural/**

## Robotics Video Gallery

If you are not lucky enough to have your own robot, at least you don't have to miss out on any visual robotic action. Here is a gallery of mpeg movies showing robotics at work. The demonstrations include a hand rolling a can, a hand performing an ordinary household chore, a hand-arm system performing an obstacle-avoiding reach, a clip showing grasping and path planning working together, and a peg-in-hole insertion.

**Web:**
**http://piglet.cs.umass.edu:4321/robotics-mpegs.html**

## Sony Research Laboratory

The SRL has a research goal to develop technology enabling the creation of a safe, evolutionarily stable, cohabitating information society. This server contains many documents and project-related papers on the progress of this goal.

**Web:**
**http://www.csl.sony.co.jp**

## Technology Marketing Failures

Marketing people are so clever that there is very little they can't get people excited about. Undoubtedly there are inventions that defy all the skills of marketing agents, like a device that washes your car and toasts bread at the same time. Read about technology marketing failures and be sure you don't duplicate someone else's mistakes.

**Usenet:**
**alt.technology.mkt-failure**

## Technology Talk and General Discussion

As technology gets more advanced, we get more new toys to try. Explore the ideas and philosophy of technology as well as the more technical side of applying technology to real life. This Usenet group is good to read while waiting for someone to invent robots who will do all your cooking and cleaning for you.

**Usenet:**

**alt.technology.misc**

## Virtual Reality Resources

Here's a great collection of virtual reality resources available on the Net, including web sites, ftp archives, bibliographies, mailing lists, research and academic institutions, Usenet groups, FAQs, software, papers, and other material related to virtual worlds and virtual reality.

**Web:**

**http://www.stars.com/WebStars/VR.html**

**Usenet:**

**sci.virtual-worlds**

**Listserv Mailing List:**

List Name: **virtu-l**
Subscribe to: **listserv@postoffice.cso.uiuc.edu**

# TELEPHONE AND TELECOM

## Business and Toll-Free Directory Listings

Looking for a particular business? If the company or organization you want has a telephone, they are probably in here somewhere. These web sites allow you to search for the phone number of a business. Some of the sites are directories of toll-free numbers, the others help you find regular numbers.

**Web:**

**http://inter800.com/search.htm**
**http://www.bigbook.com/**
**http://www.tollfree.att.net/**
**http://www.zip2.com./**

The trouble with reality is that, all too often, it is expensive and in your face. Take a break from the world of original existence and learn about virtual reality.

## Cell-Relay Communications

A "cell" refers to a small device that can be used for transporting and multiplexing information over a network. This discussion group is devoted to the technologies—such as ATM (Asynchronous Transfer Mode)—that make use of cells as transport mechanisms within local, metropolitan and wide-area networks.

**Usenet:**

**comp.dcom.cell-relay**

## Communications and Telecommunications

This site has lots of links to resources about data communications, telecommunications and related topics. If you are one of the lucky people who are telecom-enabled, this site is for you.

**Web:**

**http://www.analysys.co.uk/commslib.htm**

## Computers and Communications

This web page provides links to telecommunications companies, organizations, programs and projects, standards, and other computer communication-related resources. The page is intended to provide organization for the vast quantity of information available on the emerging global information economy.

**Web:**

**http://www.cmpcmm.com/**

## Data Communications Servers

On Usenet, you can find people who are ready, willing and able to discuss datacommunications 24 hours a day. This particular Usenet group is for discussion relating to selecting and operating data communications servers: special purpose computers that do the dirty work in moving information from one place to another: terminal servers, routers, hubs, and so on.

**Usenet:**
**comp.dcom.servers**

## Fax Technology

There is more to fax machines than just using them to transmit the latest Dilbert comic strip to someone who is not lucky enough to have Net access. This Usenet group is for the discussion of faxes: standalone machines, computer adaptors and software, technical specifications, faxing on the Net, and so on.

**Usenet:**
**comp.dcom.fax**

## Frame Relay Connections

If you live through getting frame relay up and running, then you can sit back and enjoy this great way of connecting up to the Net. Before you start, or during one of the many times you are put on hold by various engineers, receptionists and technical support people, do a little reading about frame relay. Here is a hotlist of related material: FAQs, RFCs, user groups, service provider lists, articles and documentation, class course lists, recommended reading lists, and an ever-helpful glossary.

**Web:**
**http://www.mot.com/MIMS/ISG/tech/frame-relay/resources.html**

## History of Telephony

Get a jump on all the people in your history class, by taking some spare time to read up on this history of telephones. You can learn some really cool things like Bell's first words over the phone, how telephone has developed over the years and how similar telephone discoveries hastened the development of television.

**Web:**
**http://spot.colorado.edu/~rossk/history/phone.html**

## International Dialing Codes

When you have to call a foreign country, but you are not sure where to start, check here. This site has a list of international dialing codes along with the time zones for each country.

**Web:**
**http://www.construction-site.com/int_dial.html**

## Internet Protocol

Kick off your shoes, loosen your tie and unbutton your collar. It's time to get down to the nitty gritty of discussing the technical aspects of the Internet Protocol—the IP in TCP/IP and the underlying mechanism for moving data around the Internet.

**Usenet:**
**alt.dcom.telecom.ip**

## ISDN

On the Internet, there is no such thing as too much speed. If you are interested in learning more about the ISDN way of life, read up on what you will find at these sites: ISDN news, magazines and periodicals information, dial tone provider lists, ISDN user groups, database searches, discussion archives, software and hardware information, and even some ISDN humor.

**Web:**
**http://www.alumni.caltech.edu/~dank/isdn/**
**http://www.interforce.com/technology/isdnprimer.html**

**Usenet:**
**comp.dcom.isdn**

## National Telecommunications and Information Administration

Whenever I want to know what the National Telecommunications and Information Administration is up to, I check out their official web site. They use the Web to make accessible their press releases, public notices and information on international telecommunications activities. When you just can't wait for the news to hit the streets, go straight to the source.

**Web:**
**http://www.ntia.doc.gov/**

A B C D E F G H I J K L M N O P Q R S T U V W X Y Z

## *Look What I Found on the Net...*

This is information I selected from the International Dialing Codes web site.

For each country you can see the international dialing code, followed by the time difference between local time and GMT/Universal Time (in hours). To find the time difference between two countries, simply subtract one number from the other.

| | | |
|---|---|---|
| Australia | 61 | (+8 to +10) |
| Austria | 43 | (+1) |
| Belgium | 32 | (+1) |
| Brazil | 55 | (-3) |
| Canada | 1 | (-3.5 to - 8) |
| China | 86 | (+8) |
| Czech Republic | 42 | (+1) |
| Denmark | 45 | (+1) |
| Egypt | 20 | (+2) |
| Finland | 358 | (+2) |
| France | 33 | (+1) |
| Germany | 49 | (+1) |
| Greece | 30 | (+2) |
| Hong Kong | 852 | (+8) |
| India | 91 | (+5.5) |
| Ireland | 353 | (0) |
| Israel | 972 | (+2) |
| Italy | 39 | (+1) |
| Japan | 81 | (+9) |
| Mexico | 52 | (-6 to - 8) |
| Netherlands | 31 | (+1) |
| Norway | 47 | (+1) |
| Poland | 48 | (+1) |
| Portugal | 361 | (+1) |
| Russia | 7 | (+2.5 to +10) |
| Singapore | 65 | (+8) |
| South Africa | 27 | (+2) |
| Spain | 34 | (+1) |
| Sweden | 46 | (+1) |
| Switzerland | 41 | (+1) |
| Syria | 963 | (+2) |
| Taiwan | 886 | (+8) |
| United Kingdom | 44 | (0) |
| United States | 1 | (-5 to -11) |

## Networking Page

Specific networking information can be hard to find. For example, what would you do, right now, if you needed some info on ATM, or ISDN, or SMNP, or NT Server? Would you know where to find the web sites for important networking magazines and journals? Here is everything you need—at least to get started—all in one place, well-organized and comprehensive. If you have anything to do with any aspect of computer networks, this site should be on your bookmark list.

**Web:**

**http://www.uleth.ca/~novotny/original/original.htmlx**

## Personal Telephone Listings

Find anyone, anywhere (as long as he or she has a listed phone number). This web site has an interface through which you can search numerous white pages around the Net. It has multiple search fields, so if one white pages listing doesn't have what you want, you can move to the next one. There are also links to maps and cross-references. Important: You can also do reverse searching; that is, you can put in a phone number and find the name of the person. (Now, if you see a note in a public restroom that says, "For a good time, call Hillary at (202) 456-1414," you can at least try to find out who she is before you call.)

**Web:**

**http://www.angelfire.com/pages0/ultimates/**

## Phone Number Translator

A web front end that will allow you to input your telephone number, then checks for all the possible word combinations that correlate. If you don't want to sift through the results to weed out the letter combinations that are garbage, you can have the computer compare the results to dictionary words and only give you the ones that make sense (sort of).

**Web:**

**http://www.soc.qc.edu/phonetic/**

### Your Telephone Number Secrets *Unmasked*

You know that it is possible to convert your phone number from numbers to letters: 2 = A, B or C; 3 = D, E or F; and so on. But have you ever taken your personal number and tried all possible combinations to see if they spell anything cool? If so, you will find that there are a lot of combinations. But why should you sweat when you have the Net?

Connect to the Phone Number Translator web site, and let a computer do the work. Plug your number into this handy-dandy form and, before you can say 1-800-HOWCOOL, you will be shown all the interesting alphabetic combinations that match your particular number.

Maybe you'll get lucky. One person I know found out her number spelled out "SEX-YOGA". (You can imagine what this did for her social life.)

Hint: Converting numbers to letters is useful for helping to remember anything you must enter on a telephone-like keypad, such as your ATM secret code.

## Telecom Atlas

What's going on in the world of telecommunications and where is it happening? Take a look at this telecom atlas which shows a map of various countries and marks what is going on in the region. You can find a map for freenets, research testbeds, telecom research centers, international carrier and other maps. This is great if you are a telecommunications person and you want to visit some of these landmarks on your next vacation.

**Web:**

**http://www.wiltel.com/atlas/atlas.html**

**Stay connected.**

A B C D E F G H I J K L M N O P Q R S T U V W X Y Z

## Telecom Discussions and Digest

The Telecom Digest is an online digest posted regularly to Usenet. If you are interested in telecommunications, this is a source of information worth reading regularly. The **telecom** discussion groups are for all manner of telecommunications including—but not limited to—the telephone system. For more immediate gratification, check out the web site.

**Web:**

**http://hyperarchive.lcs.mit.edu/telecom-archives/**

**Usenet:**

**alt.dcom.telecom**
**comp.dcom.telecom**

## Telecommunication Archives

There is more to telecommunications than picking up the phone and dialing a number. Get information on new developments in the phone business as well as other methods of data communications such as electronic mail and the Internet.

**Web:**

**http://far.mit.edu/diig/NII_info/telecom.html**

## Telecommunications Organizations

Here's a web page providing links to many, many telecommunications organizations on the Internet, located around the world. If you are into telecommunications, pop some popcorn and click down the row of links. You are bound to find something you like. (You can put off cleaning the gutters for one more weekend.)

**Web:**

**http://www.cmpcmm.com/cc/orgs.html**

**Do a backup.**

**"Fun" is fun.**

## Telecommunications Resources

There are a *huge* amount of telecommunications resources on the Net. (After all, the Net is a telecommunications-based organism.) Keep this resource in your bookmark list, and use it whenever you need to find a particular type of telecom resource: technical information, standards, organizations, research, government, publications, education, and much more.

**Web:**

**http://www.spp.umich.edu/telecom/telecom-info.html**

## Telephone Tech Talk and General Discussion

Next to the Internet, the phone is one of the greatest inventions of humankind. Without the phone, you could never dial the pizza place and have them make you a steaming hot pizza with everything (except black olives) and have it delivered to your door. That's all most of us need to know about the phone, but if you are interested in more than that—like learning what the guts of the telephone look like and how the wires connect, then join up with some telephone tech talk on Usenet.

**Usenet:**

**comp.dcom.telecom.tech**

## U.S. Area Codes

When you need to look up an area code or find the geographical location for an area code you already have, use these handy tools to look up the information you need.

**Web:**

**http://www.commerce.net:8000/directories/news/areacode.html**
**http://www.xmission.com/~americom/aclookup.html**

## TELEVISION

### Andy Griffith

It would be wonderful if every town sheriff was like Andy Griffith. But then, not every town is like Mayberry. We can't imagine Andy Griffith being sheriff of Los Angeles or New York City. Settle in for discussion of the nostalgia of The Andy Griffith Show and Mayberry RFD. It's a nice break from the real world.

**Web:**

**http://members.aol.com/anewsome/private/tagsrwc.htm**
**http://www.fxunlimited.com/andy_g.html**
**http://www.visi.com/~muff/andy-griffith.html**

**Majordomo Mailing List:**

List Name: **mayberry**
Subscribe to: **majordomo@bolis.sf-bay.org**

### Babylon 5 Reviews

Tune in to this electronic forum to read reviews pertaining to the Babylon 5 television series as well as novels, comic books, games, and parodies. This is not a discussion group for fan chatter—the founders of the list are looking for critical opinion features, so you have to at least pretend that you know what you're talking about.

**Listserv Mailing List:**

List Name: **b5-review-l**
Subscribe to: **listserv@cornell.edu**

**FAQs are cool.**

## *Look What I Found on the Net...*

```
Newsgroup: comp.dcom.telecom.tech
Subject: Return the Phone Call Scam

> One of my fellow users has received two identical copies of
> the following email.  He has no connection to Global,
> and given the 809 code,  it is assumed to be a scam.
> Watch out for a similar note coming your way.
>
> (Note the lack of a "To:" line.)
>
> ---------- Forwarded message ----------
> Return-Path: <accounts@global>
> Date: Tue, 1 Oct 1996 14:12:49 -0700
> From: "Global Communications"@demon.net
> Subject: Unpaid account
> Message-ID: <844184592.19166.164@[194.222.75.163]>
>
> I am writing to give you a final 24 hours to settle your
> outstanding account. If I have not received the settlement in
> full, I will commence legal proceedings without further delay.
> If you would like to discuss this matter to avoid court
> action, call Mike Murray at Global Communications on
> +1 809 xxx-xxxx.

A similar scam exists for pagers.  They page you with an
809 xxx-xxxx number expecting you to return the call.

When you do, you are routed to an expensive international call.

By dialing this number, you end up paying for an expensive
long distance call.
```

## The Andy Griffith Show

Perhaps somewhere, there are people who have not watched each of the 249 episodes of The Andy Griffith Show and have not immersed themselves in the stories of Andy, Barney, Aunt Bee, Opie, Floyd, Gomer, Goober, Helen, Thelma Lou, Otis and the rest of the inhabitants of Mayberry, North Carolina.

I feel sorry for such people because they are missing out on what is most noble and fine in life: a society in which people most always get along, in which life's problems are well within the capabilities of a small-town sheriff and the homespun wisdom God has seen fit to bestow upon him. Within the show, Andy was sometimes referred to as the "sheriff without a gun", but he might just as well have been called the "sheriff who doesn't need a gun".

For at least a few minutes each week (and now, every day in reruns), we could transport ourselves to a small town in which everyday problems were manageable and human dignity was preserved simply as a matter of course.

To ask whether there is justice in the world is an elegant but troubling question. To ask whether there is justice in Mayberry is both unnecessary and misleading. One does not watch The Andy Griffith Show for anything remotely involving one's higher cortical functionality. Rather, we worship at the shrine of blessed banality simply because, in a world of discomforting unpredictability and baffling complexity, Mayberry and its inhabitants occupy one of the few safe rest stops available to the human spirit in all of us, as it navigates the confusing and oft-times rocky road of life.

## BBC TV and Radio

The British Broadcasting Corporation (BBC) in the U.K. runs five radio networks, two television networks, as well as the World Service. Their web site contains information about schedules, services, announcements, transcripts and factsheets. What more could you want (aside from a copy of their secret videotape showing Prince Charles at a private Hunga-rom party with the cast of Monty Python)?

**Web:**

**http://www.bbcnc.org.uk**

**The Net cares.**

## Beverly Hills 90210

Only a city in California would be able to get a television show based on its zip code. Read mailing lists, archives, and see pictures relating to Beverly Hills 90210—the show where the only thing that rivals the price of the clothing is the price of the silicone enhancements.

**Web:**

**http://www.cu-online.com/~adept/90210/homepag1.htm**

**Majordomo Mailing List:**

List Name: **90210**
Subscribe to: **majordomo@tcp.com**

## Cartoons

I like cartoons. They're soothing, like a good book on a rainy day (except you can't turn up the volume on a good book and disturb the neighbors). If you like cartoons, check out some of the great toon resources on the Net. You can get pictures, sounds, movies and other cool cartoon stuff.

**Web:**

**http://hertz.njit.edu/~dzt8474/movies/cartoons.html**
**http://hops.cs.jhu.edu/~tavon/cartoons.html**

I like cartoons, and I bet that you do too. If so, check out the
cartoon site on the Net.
FRAGILE

## Comedy Central

Check out what's going on at Comedy Central, the laugh-a-minute cable comedy station. At their web site you can find funny stuff like sound clips or read the current day's schedule. You can even see what's happening on Comedy Central right this minute if you load up their live-eye view page.

**Web:**

**http://www.comcentral.com/com-menu.htm**

## Commercials

Some people are really annoyed by commercials, but if you think about it you will realize what a marvelous invention they are. If there were no commercials, you would never have the opportunity to dash to the kitchen for snacks or run to the bathroom for a quick bit of relief. So, pay your homage to the great commercial Mecca on Usenet and show how much you appreciate the service that companies are doing for television watchers around the world.

**Usenet:**
**alt.tv.commercials**

## C-SPAN

The C-SPAN cable network web site contains a schedule of the evening's programs, a picture of what is currently playing, links to various interesting political resources and more.

**Web:**
**http://www.c-span.org/**

## Dick Van Dyke Show

The Dick Van Dyke Show is my all-time favorite television show. In fact, I challenge any of my friends to ask me a Dick Van Dyke question I can't answer. If you enjoy watching the adventures of Rob, Laura, Buddy, Sally, Mel, Jerry, Millie, Alan Brady, and that obnoxious little kid Ritchie Rosebud, pay a visit to this web site, where you can re-live your hours of Dick Van Dyke watching (until it's time for the next rerun).

**Web:**
**http://hampshire.edu/~tdzF94/DVD.html**

## Doctor Who

He's wild-haired, strangely dressed, and often chased by hostile robots or aliens. Doctor Who doesn't have to take up jogging because he is almost always running for cover anyway. Join the people who love the excitement and adventure of this futuristic television series.

**Web:**
**http://nitro9.earth.uni.edu/doctor/**

## Dramas

Don't complicate your life with real drama. Keep the adrenaline safely confined within the space of your television or computer. Check out the television drama archives for some of your favorite shows.

**Web:**
**http://www.ahandyguide.com/cat1/t/t279.htm**

## Game Shows

Game show junkies now have something to do when they are not actually watching the game shows or reading trivia books to improve their game show skills. Read FAQs about popular Canadian and U.S. game shows.

**Web:**
**http://www.cis.ohio-state.edu/hypertext/faq/usenet/tv/game-shows/top.html**

## I Love Lucy

Is there anyone on our entire planet who does *not* love Lucy? The I Love Lucy show is the most popular situation comedy of all time, being in continual reruns with no signs of stopping. I have watched every I Love Lucy episode from "Lucy Thinks Ricky Is Trying to Murder Her" (#1) to "The Ricardos Dedicate a Statue" (#179). (And I don't even like TV.) But I am not alone in my love for Lucy. There are diehard fans all over the world and all over the Net.

**Web:**
**http://access.mountain.net/~paula/**

**Usenet:**
**alt.tv.ilovelucy**

**Majordomo Mailing List:**
List Name: **ilovelucy**
Subscribe to: **majordomo@bolis.com**

**IRC:**
**#lucy**

## Letterman, David

How to send mail to Dave, get tickets to the show, and get the Top Ten lists, including information about skits, stunts, guests, music, and, of course, Dave himself.

**Web:**

http://www.cbs.com/lateshow/
http://www.ibsys.com/~knagl/letterma.htm

**Usenet:**

alt.fan.letterman

## Muppets

Who couldn't like a Muppet? There are lots of Muppet fans on the Net and they have created wonderful pages in honor of Jim Henson's creations. Spend some time experiencing the Muppets through pictures, sounds, song lyrics and more. Or go to the Usenet group and talk with other fans of the various Muppet shows and movies.

**Web:**

http://www-leland.stanford.edu/~dsedy/muppets.html

**Usenet:**

alt.tv.muppets

### *Look What I Found on the Net...*

```
(from the list of U.S. game shows)

      About Faces
      All About the Opposite Sex
      All New Beat the Clock, The
      All New Dating Game, The
      All New Let's Make a Deal, The
      All Star Secrets
      All-Star Anything Goes
      All-Star Baffle
      All-Star Blitz
      Almost Anything Goes
      Amateur's Guide to Love
      American Gladiators
      Animal Crack-ups
      Anniversary Game, The
      Anything for Money
      Anything You Can Do
            .
            .
            .
            .
      Yahtzee
      You Bet Your Life
      You Don't Say
      You're in the Picture
      You're Putting Me On
      Your First Impression
      Your Lucky Clue
      Your Number's Up
      Your Surprise Package
      Yours for a Song
```

## Public Broadcasting Service (PBS)

The Public Broadcasting Service (PBS) is a private, nonprofit organization that serves well over 300 member television stations in the United States. PBS was founded in 1968 with a mandate to provide high-quality TV programming. Quality, of course, is in the eye and ear of the beholder and, in a highly politicized country in which the average television image lasts less than 10 seconds, you can bet there will be disagreement. Still, PBS offers a lot of programming that is just not available on commercial television. Check their web site to see what they are up to, and if you should be tuning in, or turning on and dropping out.

**Web:**

**http://www.pbs.org/**

## Satellite TV Images

Imagine holding a remote control in your hand that will show you channels from television stations from around the world. With each click you will get a random picture from satellite television. It's here and it's free. Point your browser to this web site and see random digitized images.

**Web:**

**http://itre.uncecs.edu/misc/images/images.html**

## Satellite TV Page

This web page is dedicated to the hobby of satellite television and radio. It offers FAQs, articles, program schedules, the archives of the Satellite Journal, a collection of satellite TV images, and satellite-related lists and charts.

**Web:**

**http://itre.uncecs.edu/misc/sat.html**

## Science Fiction TV Shows

Television is a great way to give your brain a break. Fans of science fiction television can access information on all their favorite shows like Babylon 5, Doctor Who, Star Trek, The X-Files, The Twilight Zone and Superman.

**Web:**

**http://www.scifi.com/orbit/scifitv.html**

## Series and Sitcoms

The great thing about watching network television is that during the commercials you can jump on the Net to see what is happening at these web sites containing loads of information about your favorite series and sitcoms. The next time someone interrupts your favorite weekly program, you can show them: Turn down the volume on the tube and tune in to the places on the Net where you can get episode guides, lists, FAQs, scripts, and other fun stuff relating to films and television series, including Star Trek, Cheers, Blade Runner, Twin Peaks, Monty Python and many more.

**Web:**

**http://pmwww.cs.vu.nl/service/sitcoms/**
**http://www.cc.ukans.edu/~kuinfo/tvseries.html**

## Soap Operas

Soap opera fans, the Net is *your* home away from the TV. There are so many soap opera-related resources, you can spend every waking moment—when you are not watching a show—following the adventures of your favorite characters, and talking with other soap fans. I picked out this web site to act as your gateway to a huge amount of interesting information. And when you feel like talking, there are several Usenet groups in which you can participate.

**Web:**

**http://members.aol.com/soaplinks/**

**Usenet:**

**rec.arts.tv.soaps.abc**
**rec.arts.tv.soaps.cbs**
**rec.arts.tv.soaps.misc**

## Television Guide

This web page offers the ultimate TV list containing links for more than 30 television shows, a list of major TV-related sites, a place to post your favorite links and remove everybody else's boring links, and a TV poll where you can broadcast your opinions to a few hundred people.

**Web:**

**http://www.tvnet.com/UTVL/utvl.html**

A B C D E F G H I J K L M N O P Q R S T U V W X Y Z

## Television Talk and General Discussion

Don't waste your life in sitting in front of the computer. Instead, you can waste it in front of another electronic box which gives you a continuous feed of images that will lull you into a hypnotic daze and make you susceptible to the lure of home shopping channels. If you are so hooked that you like to talk about television when you are not actually watching it, check out these Usenet groups. The **alt.fan** group is for discussion of characters and actors on television. The **alt.tv** and **rec.arts.tv** are for discussion of specific television shows. The **rec.arts.sf.tv** is for discussion of particular science fiction shows.

**Usenet:**

**alt.fan.***
**alt.tv.***
**rec.arts.sf.tv.***
**rec.arts.tv.***

**Wow, free software.**

## TV Episode Guides

This web site is a godsend to fanatics who need to know exactly when each episode of their favorite series aired. There are episode guides to many popular TV shows, including information about the individual episodes. After all, how many places can you turn to at three in the morning when you just have to know when Jerry put the Tweety Bird Pez dispenser on Elaine's knee? (It was episode #314 of Seinfeld, January 15, 1992, during a classical piano recital.)

**Web:**

**http://www.tardis.ed.ac.uk/~dave/guides/**

**Don't get fooled. Read "Consumer Information".**

### *Look What I Found on the Net...*

```
                    (from the television archives)

                    ==============================
The Star Trek Prime Directive
                    ==============================

"As the right of each sentient species to live in accordance
with its normal cultural evolution is considered sacred,
no Star Fleet personnel may interfere with the healthy
development of alien life and culture.

"Such interference includes the introduction of superior
knowledge, strength, or technology to a world whose society is
incapable of handling such advantages wisely.

"Star Fleet personnel may not violate this Prime Directive,
even to save their lives and/or their ship, unless they are
acting to right an earlier violation or an accidental
contamination of said culture.

"This directive takes precedence over any and all other
considerations, and carries with it the highest moral
obligation."
```

## TV Guide Postcards

Send some nostalgia to your friends and family. This site offers a wonderful collection of classic covers from TV Guide magazine to use as virtual postcards. You can send a general card or pick one that has a special theme such as Star Trek, Father's Day, Mother's Day, classic couples and others. Send a surprise TV-inspired card to someone you like, right now. Go ahead, make their day.

**Web:**
**http://www.iguide.com/tv/wayback/postcard/**

## TV Net

This is a fun place for television watchers to browse. Participate in polls and surveys, read reviews, chat with other people about your favorite shows, answer television trivia, write email to the networks or even find a job in the broadcasting industry.

**Web:**
**http://tvnet.com/TVnet.html**

## TV News Archive

Since 1968, Vanderbilt has been archiving major news broadcasts to make sure they are recorded, preserved and made accessible to researchers. They also keep special news events, like broadcasts of the Gulf War and the USSR coup attempt.

**Web:**
**http://tvnews.vanderbilt.edu/tvnews.html**

## TV Schedules

Schedules for the Sci-Fi Channel and information on the commercial custom viewer that permits subscribers to receive detailed, personalized TV listing guides via email. The web page has links to BBC-TV and Radio Program schedules, C-SPAN schedules, late night talk show schedules, The Discovery Channel and The Learning Channel monthly listings, and upcoming guests on The Tonight Show.

**Web:**
**http://www.tvshow.com/guide/**
**http://www.TV1.com/**

# TRAVEL

## Air Travel Handbook

Do research in advance of traveling. This web site makes it easy. You can find links to more travel resources than you could fit in your carry-on luggage. Browse links to airline home pages, travel agents and various non-affiliated travel resources, make reservations online or just read some travelogues.

**Web:**
**http://www.cs.cmu.edu/afs/cs.cmu.edu/user/mkant/Public/Travel/airfare.html**

## Amtrak Trains

If you are planning a romantic journey or you just don't feel like getting on a plane, consider taking a train. The Amtrak company has lots of information about train travel including various routes and the interesting things you will see along the way. Remember, in life it is the journey that is important, not the destination.

**Web:**
**http://www.amtrak.com/route.htm**

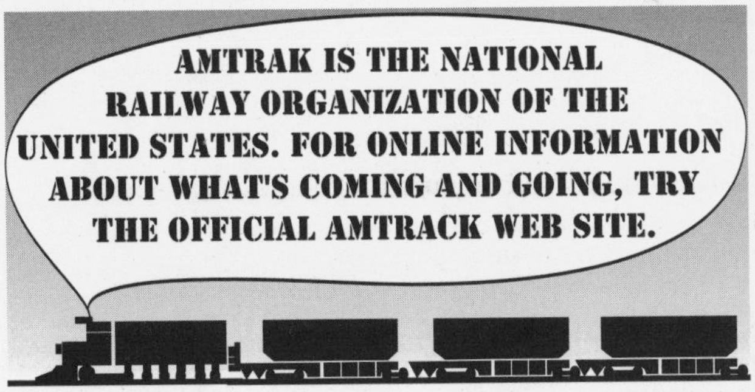
AMTRAK IS THE NATIONAL RAILWAY ORGANIZATION OF THE UNITED STATES. FOR ONLINE INFORMATION ABOUT WHAT'S COMING AND GOING, TRY THE OFFICIAL AMTRACK WEB SITE.

## Antarctica

Pick a unique place to go for a vacation adventure. Not many people can say they have been to Antarctica. Here's a web site that will lure you into going. It has a wealth of information about Antarctica, including tourism and travel, environment, news, science, treaty, and logistical information. When you go, don't forget to send me a postcard.

**Web:**
**http://icair.iac.org.nz/**

A B C D E F G H I J K L M N O P Q R S T U V W X Y Z

A B C D E F G H I J K L M N O P Q R S T U V W X Y Z

## Arctic

The Arctic is probably not at the top of many people's lists of summer vacation hot-spots, but it does have its magic. Read "Arctic Bites"—stories and thoughts on the spirit and experience of the Arctic. Track wildlife as it treks across the frozen land. You can pinpoint it on a clickable map that offers you more wildlife and migration information on request.

**Web:**

**http://ics.soe.umich.edu/ed712/IAPIntro.html**

## Australia

The other day my cat said to me, "Harley, let's go to Australia. I hear they have really good fish there." I put him in front of the web browser and pointed him at this web site which shows Australia really has a lot more than fish. We saw how the site had tons and tons of information about Australia, but all he wanted to do was play with the mouse. Don't you make the same mistake. Check out this great collection of Australian resources covering geography, environment, communications, travel, culture, weather, government, history and more. (But do it when your cat is busy preparing a bowl of tuna for dinner.)

**Web:**

**http://www.csu.edu.au/education/australia.html**

## Caribbean Corner

After many months of working on a book, there's nothing like going to the Caribbean with a beautiful woman and spending your days snorkeling or lying around on the beach. If that's what you like to do on your vacation, check out some of the Caribbean resources on the Net. You will find travel and tourist guides, links to other Internet sites, pictures, reading material, news, current weather conditions, and much more about the Caribbean.

**Web:**

**http://www.caribweb.com/caribweb/**
**http://www.freenet.hamilton.on.ca/~aa462/carib.html**

## Castles

Indulge in your fantasies of knights, dragons and castles galore, by taking this tour of castles around the world. Castle Web has a huge listing of castles including those in Edinburgh, Prague, Durham, Wales, Antrim, all over Europe and other countries.

**Web:**

**http://fox.nstn.ca/~tmonk/castle/casttour.html**

## Hawaii

Spend your lunch hour taking a grand tour of the Hawaiian Islands. Spread a little sand around the office floor, turn the fans on, crank up your CD of ocean sounds, and fire up the web browser—it will almost seem like you are there. There are many pictures and videos at these sites.

**Web:**

**http://bookweb.cwis.uci.edu:8042/Books/Moon/hawaii.html**
**http://www.hcc.hawaii.edu/dinos/hawaii.mpg**
**http://www.mhpcc.edu/tour/Tour.html**

## Hostels

Hostels are inexpensive places to stay, offering basic accommodation for informal travelers around the world. Many hostels are only for people below a certain age (youth hostels), but some are open to anyone. When I was younger, I stayed at a lot of youth hostels, and most of the time it was just fine. Hostels are usually centrally located and are great places to meet other people. This web site is the "Internet Guide to Hostelling". It has everything you need to know about hostels and budget travel including a worldwide hostel guide, a forum where you can read or post messages about backpacking, a FAQ about hostelling, information about events and special promotions relating to hostels, and more.

**Web:**

**http://www.hostels.com/**

HOSTELS

Are you young?
Is your travel budget small?
Are you a friendly person who likes to meet other people?

Stay at a hostel: you will fit right in.

## Japan

When you are planning a big trip to Japan, don't forget to check with the Net. Here is a travel guide that covers planning, airport arrival, the transportation network, accommodations, dining, touring, shopping and other useful information.

**Web:**
**http://www.jnto.go.jp/**

## Jerusalem

"Ten measures of beauty were bestowed upon the world; nine were taken by Jerusalem, and one by the rest of the world." Jerusalem is truly a world city. A spiritual center for Judaism, Christianity and Islam, Jerusalem is a city with connections to people all over the world. Visit this web site and explore Jerusalem: images, exhibits, paintings, maps, views of the Old City of Jerusalem, tours of the New City of Jerusalem, audio sounds and songs, and much more about this 4,000 year old city.

**Web:**
**http://www1.huji.ac.il/jeru/jerusalem.html**

## London

Here's a guide book that is so much fun to read you don't even have to go to London to have a good time. This London guide gives you hints and tricks about how not to get ripped off in the city, good places to go, a list of events to see, where to go ghost hunting and more. It's written in a fun and friendly fashion and is good for armchair travelers or veteran voyagers alike.

**Web:**
**http://www.a-london-guide.co.uk/**

## Mardi Gras

In the Christian Church, the holiday of Easter is preceded by Lent, a 40-day period from Ash Wednesday to Easter Sunday, which is observed as a season for fasting and penitence. The day before the beginning of Lent is called Shrove Tuesday. Many people traditionally use this day to feast, in preparation for Lent. Thus, Shrove Tuesday is also called Mardi Gras, which means "Fat Tuesday" in French. In many places around the world, the days leading up to Mardi Gras are celebrated as a large carnival, lasting a week or more. Among the most celebrated carnivals are those of New Orleans and Rio de Janeiro. Such carnivals involve non-stop music and dancing, and lots and lots of fun. If you think you can stand this much applied hedonism, use the Net to check out the Mardi Gras carnival closest to you.

**Web:**
**http://ipanema.com/carnival/**
**http://www.neworleans.net/carnpages/carngloss.html**
**http://www.usacitylink.com/mardigr/**

## Megaliths

A megalith is a structure made out of huge stone slabs. There are a number of ancient megalithic monuments in western Europe and the British Isles dating back to 2000-1500 B.C. Typically, the slabs are arranged singly, in rows or in a circle. Although no one knows for sure why these monuments were erected, it is thought that they were used for religious purposes or as part of a funeral ceremony. The most well-known such megalith monument is Stonehenge, located on Salisbury Plain in the south of England. This web site allows you to take a tour of megaliths in Europe. You can visit stone circles (like Stonehenge), cairns, stone settlements, stone rows, dolmens (chamber tombs) and manmade mounds.

**Web:**
**http://joshua.micronet.it/utenti/dmeozzi/homeng.html**

**Get into "Mischief".**

A B C D E F G H I J K L M N O P Q R S T U V W X Y Z

## Money Abroad FAQ

This FAQ (frequently asked question list) offers information about dealing with money in just about every country you are likely to ever visit. Learn about banknotes and coins, traveler's checks, credit cards, and how and where to get cash when you need it. There is a guide to which form of payment is best for each country, with the black markets covered appropriately.

**Web:**

**http://www.inria.fr/robotvis/personnel/laveau/money-faq/money-abroad.html**

**Money Abroad FAQ**

Before you leave on your next trip to a foreign country, check with the Money Abroad FAQ.

You will save yourself time and, very possibly, money by cashing in on your Net connection.

## Net Travel

Travel, any kind of travel, should be well planned, and a good traveler is a prepared traveler. This guide details how to use the Internet to prepare for a trip to distant lands. It discusses relative Usenet groups, IRC, GNN Travel Resource Center, and more.

**Web:**

**http://www.gnn.com/meta/travel/res/nettravel.html**

## New York City

I love New York in June, how about you? If you are visiting New York City in June or another month of the year, check out these great guides. Don't bite into the Big Apple without them.

**Web:**

**http://eMall.com/ExploreNY/NY1.html**
**http://www.theinsider.com/nyc/**

## Paris

Ah, romance. There is nothing more romantic than being with your very special person, relaxing after a romantic candlelight dinner in front of a warm fireplace, snuggled quietly together taking a multimedia tour of Paris on your laptop computer. There is lots of information about Paris on the Net and even an IRC channel for talking. And if you want to actually travel there in person, use the Net to get the info you need to be a happy camper in the City of Love.

**Web:**

**http://sunsite.unc.edu/wm/paris/**
**http://www.cnam.fr/wm/paris/**
**http://www.emf.net/wm/paris/**

**IRC:**

**#paris**

## Railroad Connections

Got a train to catch? Check out these timetables for many trains, subways, and metros around the world.

**Web:**

**http://rail.rz.uni-karlsruhe.de/rail/english.html**
**http://www-cse.ucsd.edu/users/bowdidge/railroad/rail-gopher.html**

## Recreational Vehicles

We must envy the turtle who carries his home on his back. While he can't run quick like a bunny or leap tall buildings in a single bound, at least he will never be without a nice place to stay as he travels. You can experience this feeling of mobile home comfort by driving around in a recreational vehicle. Talk to adventurous people who motor around the countryside in their home away from home.

**Usenet:**

**alt.rv**

**Don't click here.**

## Route 66

Details of a drive from Chicago to Santa Monica (Los Angeles) following as much as possible the remains of the historic route 66, that 2,448-mile long trek built in 1926 and crossing eight states. These web pages offer a list of Route 66 associations, book references, maps, stories, and some plain advice on traveling Route 66.

**Web:**

**http://route66.netvision.be/**
**http://www.basenet.net/~ebernabe/road.html**

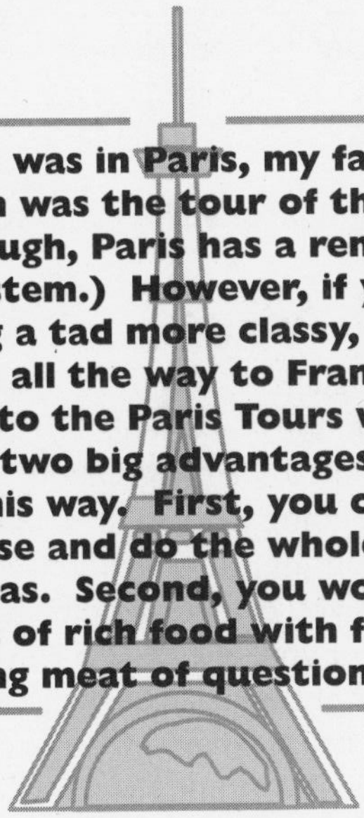

**When I was in Paris, my favorite attraction was the tour of the sewers. (Don't laugh, Paris has a remarkable sewer system.) However, if you want something a tad more classy, you don't have to go all the way to France: simply connect to the Paris Tours web site. There are two big advantages to seeing Paris in this way. First, you can stay in your house and do the whole thing in your pajamas. Second, you won't have to eat a lot of rich food with fattening sauces hiding meat of questionable origin.**

## Russian

Travel to Russia without leaving home. This two-week tour comes complete with photographs and illustrations as well as daily writings that will give you the flavor of Russian culture and environment.

**Web:**

**http://www.hyperion.com/~koreth/russia/**

**Read a zine today.**

**The Net is immortal.**

## Speedtraps

A speedtrap is a police setup designed to catch drivers who exceed the speed limit. Since citations for such an infraction generate income for a town, state or province, it is not unheard of for police to place speedtraps in places where they know out-of-town drivers are likely to be tempted to drive too fast. At the very least, if you are a stranger to an area, it helps to know the places where the local police are looking for speeders. This web site serves as a speedtrap registry for people driving in the United States, Canada, Australia and some European countries. Before you drive in a strange area, check here to make sure that you know where the speedtraps are. Even better, check for speedtraps in the town where you live. You may be surprised.

**Web:**

**http://www.speedtrap.com/speedtrap/**

## Staying Healthy in Asia, Africa and Latin America

Everyone knows not to drink the water, but do you know all the other stuff about not eating peeled fruit and why you shouldn't walk around barefoot? Learn what to do before, during, and after traveling in Asia, Africa and Latin America.

**Web:**

**http://www.moon.com/staying.healthy/travel.health.html**

## Subway Navigator

You will never have to get lost on the subway system again. No matter where you are, you can find your way home as long as you have your Internet connection with you. This site will compute subway routes in many major cities around the world. I computed a lengthy subway route in Helsinki and I don't even speak Finnish.

**Web:**

**http://metro.jussieu.fr:10001/bin/cities/english**

A B C D E F G H I J K L M N O P Q R S T U V W X Y Z

## SUBWAY NAVIGATOR

It's one thing to get lost. It's another thing to get lost underground.

If you are in any doubt as to the best subway route to take in a particular city, check with the Net. The Subway Navigator stands ready to help you find your way from A to B (or, if necessary, from C to D).

## Thailand

Experience Thailand through images and travelers' tales of journeys there, including an elephant safari and a trip over the river Kwai. Read articles on travel, Thai history, geography, and climate, as well as interviews and essays on Thailand.

**Web:**

**http://nearnet.gnn.com/gnn/meta/travel/mkt/focus/index.html**

## Tips for Travelers

Don't let your excitement about your big trip get in the way of being organized and careful about planning the details. You may end up stranded in a tiny country known for political unrest and lack of Internet access. Get tips on packing, passports, air travel—and don't forget to send your favorite Internet author cool postcards from exotic lands.

**Web:**

**http://www.webfoot.com/travel/tips/tips.top.html**

**Join the fun—now.**

## Tourism Offices

If you are planning your vacation to some exotic country (or some country that you wish was exotic), don't go jet-setting off without being fully prepared. At this web site you can enter in the name of the country you are going to visit and find out a list of all the tourism offices that are in the area.

**Web:**

**http://www.mbnet.mb.ca/lucas/travel/**

## Travel and Tourism Web Pages

There is no sense in keeping yourself closed off from the entire world. Check out all the places that you can travel and start planning your exciting world adventures. Even if you never go, it's certainly fun to dream.

**Web:**

**http://www.infohub.com/TRAVEL/traveller.html**

## Travel Health Advice

If you are planning a trip, you must take a look at some of the resources on the Net devoted to travel health advice. You can find information about particular countries you are going to visit, the hazards specific to that country, listings of immunizations you need and potential diseases you can bring home as unique souvenirs for you or your friends. While you are planning ahead, take a look at the tips on how to stay healthy while flying. You can learn about air quality on planes, what food to avoid during flights, how to prevent dehydration and much, much more. These sites will give you what you need to plan for a healthy vacation.

**Web:**

**http://www.maui.net/diana/index2.html**
**http://www.tekamah.com/travelmed/**

## Travel Information

Get travel information and personal accounts about a number of destinations. Travelers post detailed accounts of their vacations, including places to go, places to avoid, where and what to eat, reviews of hotels, and much more.

**Web:**

**http://gwis2.circ.gwu.edu/~mdathe/travel.html**
**http://www.nectec.or.th/rec-travel/**

**Usenet:**

**rec.travel.***

**Ah, travel. There's nothing like the feeling of exploring somewhere new, romantic and exciting where the hand of Man has never set foot. Ah, travel. A seductive mistress whose inner depths are shrouded in mystery, a temptress who could be leading you into unexpected adventure around the very next corner.**

**But before you set out on your next journey, use the Net to gather the information and hints you need to make your trip safe and interesting. The rec.travel discussion groups are populated with people who love to keep moving, and the rec.travel archives have a variety of useful information.**

**Travel can be uncomfortable, but if you are willing to take your chances, the opportunity of a lifetime may be waiting on the other side of the gate.**

## Travel Marketplace

Upgrades, frequent flyer plans, hotel discounts, travel guides—the longest journey begins with but a single step into Usenet's one-stop travel marketplace. Buy, sell, beg, borrow, steal—then go!

**Usenet:**

**rec.travel.marketplace**

## Travel Matters Newsletter

Whether you are traveling for business or for pleasure, this newsletter will have something to interest you. Read articles on becoming an air courier, contrasting cultures, how to stay healthy during travel, tips on renting a car, travel book reviews and news briefs.

**Web:**

**http://www.moon.com/tm/tmfront.html**

## Travel Talk and General Discussion

Travel is a lot of fun and—as they say—broadening. And, while you are traveling there is no substitute for inside information. These Usenet groups are for discussion of specific aspects of travel or particular locations. If you are going to visit a new place, I suggest reading the appropriate group before you leave. If you have any questions, post them in advance of your trip and you may get some useful answers. For general travel discussion, use the **rec.travel.misc** group.

**Usenet:**

**alt.travel.canada**
**alt.travel.canada.ontario**
**alt.travel.canada.ontario.toronto**
**alt.travel.new-orleans**
**alt.travel.road-trip**
**rec.outdoors.rv-travel**
**rec.scuba.locations**
**rec.travel.africa**
**rec.travel.air**
**rec.travel.asia**
**rec.travel.australia+nz**
**rec.travel.caribbean**
**rec.travel.cruises**
**rec.travel.europe**
**rec.travel.latin-america**
**rec.travel.marketplace**
**rec.travel.misc**
**rec.travel.usa-canada**

## Travelers' Tales Web Tour

Travelers' Tales is a wonderful series of books published by O'Reilly and Associates. Each book contains stories and anecdotes about a particular part of the world or a travel-related theme. For example, there are books on Thailand, Mexico, India and San Francisco, as well as two books on Women's Travel and Food. This web site is designed to complement the books. For each title in the series, there is a collection of links to related Internet resources. If you like travel, visit this site and see what's available. You don't have to read the books to enjoy the Net resources. By the way, I have all the books in the series. Next time you are in a bookstore, look for these books, and I bet you will end up buying one.

**Web:**

**http://www.ora.com/publishing/ttales/webtour/**

A B C D E F G H I J K L M N O P Q R S T U V W X Y Z

A B C D E F G H I J K L M N O P Q R S T U V W X Y Z

## U.S. National Parks

Occasionally, it's nice to get out of the big city and get back to nature where there are wild bears and chemical toilets. If you want to take a vacation in an American national park, check out this site which will give you information on parks all over the United States. Start planning now for your little getaway.

**Web:**

**http://www.gorp.com/gorp/resource/US_National_Park/main.htm**

## U.S. State Department of Travel Information

The U.S. State Department has extensive information on current and past travel advisories for those interested in traveling abroad. Each factsheet contains the addresses and phone numbers of American consulates, as well as passport, visa, and government information, and crime data.

**Web:**

**http://travel.state.gov/**

## Virtual Tourist

Whether you are planning a trip or just doing a little wishful thinking, this site will give you a world of information. Get connections to tourist guides for many exciting locations, including Europe, the United States, New Zealand, Australia, and Japan. The links are presented on a map of the world, from which you can choose the destination of your dreams.

**Web:**

**http://www.vtourist.com/vt/**

## World Guide to Vegetarianism

Vegetarians, you no longer have to worry about traveling around the world and not being able to find good food that will fit in with your dietary lifestyle. This site has a listing of vegetarian restaurants, natural food stores and vegetarian organizations around the world.

**Web:**

**http://www.veg.org/veg/Guide/**

### U.S. State Department of Travel Information

Whether or not you are American, you will find the information on this web site useful. Before you even put one toe outside your native country, look up what the U.S. State Department has to say about where you are going. Along with a great deal of useful information (mostly of interest to Americans) you can find out the basic travel facts about any country (of interest to anyone).

For each country, you can read a general description, as well as information about entry requirements, medical facilities, crime information, drug penalties, road and traffic information, and more.

For example, under Canada, I found the following: "Crime Information: There is a higher incidence of criminal activity in urban areas. However, violent crimes such as murder, armed robbery, and rape are infrequent..."

(Personal hint for travelers to Canada: If a Canadian thief tries to hold you up, federal law allows you to refuse to give up your possessions if the thief does not ask for them in both French and English.)

# TRIVIA

## Coin Toss

Need to toss a coin but don't have one? No problem; on the web you can simulate a toss. Never again will you have to worry about your buddy trying to do the old sleight-of-hand routine on you.

**Web:**

**http://meru.uwyo.edu/~haines/fun/coin-toss.html**

**Quick, turn the page.**

**The Net loves poetry.**

## Internet Index

What better way to break the ice at a party than to start up a little game of trivia? Get this list of factoids and you can ask fun questions like "What percentage of PCs were using TCP/IP in 1993?" and "What is the average number of megabytes of Usenet news per day?" Find out the answers to these questions and more from the Internet Index—a report of interesting statistics relating to net usage.

**Web:**

**http://www.openmarket.com/intindex/**

## Movie Trivia

If you like movies, you may be interested in trivia. For example, did you know that the working title for Annie Hall was "Anhedonia"? (It's a medical term referring to the inability to feel pleasure.) How about this? When Woody Allen was making The Purple Rose of Cairo, he originally case Michael Keaton in the male lead role. However, Allen wasn't satisfied with the first footage and replaced Keaton with Jeff Daniels. If you find factoids like this interesting, you may be a movie trivia person. Connect to these web sites and find out for sure. If you like to compete, you will find a great many movie trivia contests you can enter.

**Web:**

**http://www.cis.ohio-state.edu/hypertext/faq/usenet/movies/trivia-faq/faq.html**
**http://www.primate.wisc.edu/people/hamel/movtriv.html**

## Names of Famous People

This web site has a listing of the real names of famous people. For example, did you know that Cher's real name was Cherilyn Sarkisian La Pierre? And how about Meatloaf? His real name was Marvin Lee Aday. (Isn't that cute.) Judy Garland was Frances Ethel Gumm. And so on, and so on.

**Web:**

**http://www.infocom.com/~franklin/inaname/**

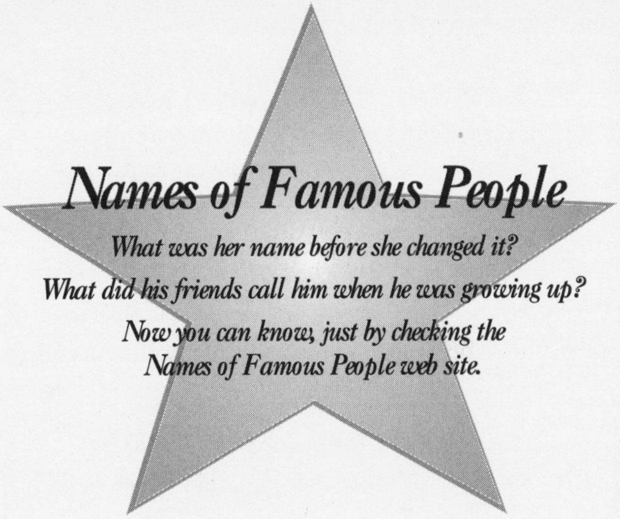
Names of Famous People
What was her name before she changed it?
What did his friends call him when he was growing up?
Now you can know, just by checking the
Names of Famous People web site.

## Oldies Music Trivia

If you were listening to popular music in the '60s and '70s, it's high time you started taking your nostalgic legacy seriously. Spend some time at these web sites and relive the golden days of something or other.

**Web:**

**http://homepage.interaccess.com/~ronsmith/cal.htm**
**http://www.oneglobe.com/trivia/**

## Today's Date

All sorts of things you didn't know about today's date, based on the book Numbers: Facts, Figures and Fiction.

**Web:**

**http://acorn.educ.nottingham.ac.uk/cgi-bin/daynum**

**I've never met a high-speed Internet connection I didn't like.**

## Today's Events in History

Do you ever feel like today is just like every other day? Well, I can tell you it's not. In fact, go right now and look up what happened on this day in history and I bet you will learn something wonderful. Just think, on this very day, something astounding happened. Watch what you do today. You might end up on this list.

**Web:**

http://astro.uchicago.edu/home/web/copi/events.html

**(FROM THE REC.GAMES.TRIVIA FREQUENTLY ASKED QUESTION LIST)**

What are the Seven Wonders of the Ancient World?

**The Pyramids of Egypt**

**The Hanging Gardens of Babylon**

**The Statue of Zeus at Olympia**

**The Temple of Artemis at Ephesus**

**The Mausoleum at Halicarnassus**

**The Colossus of Rhodes**

**The Lighthouse at Alexandria**

The pyramids are the oldest of the Seven Wonders and the only one of them still in existence.

===============

What were the names of the castaways on the Gilligan's Island television show?

**"The ship's aground on the shore of this**

**Uncharted desert isle,**

**With Gilligan,**

**The Skipper too, (Jonas Grumby)**

**The millionaire and his wife,**

**(Thurston Howell III, Lovey Howell)**

**The movie star (Ginger Grant)**

**And the rest ('Professor' Roy Hinkley, Mary Ann Summers) Are here on Gilligan's Isle."**

Gilligan didn't have a first name on the show, but Bob Denver has stated in interviews that he had talked the matter over with show creator Sherwood Schwartz. Had Gilligan ever needed a first name, it would have been Willie.

## Trivia Page

When your favorite game show is over and already you are starting to have withdrawals, check out this site which has lots of links to various trivia sites all over the Net. There is enough trivia here to choke Alex Trebek.

**Web:**

http://www.primate.wisc.edu/people/hamel/trivia.html

## Trivial Talk and General Discussion

Okay, we all know that Richie Petrie's middle name is Rosebud and that it stands for "Robert Oscar Sam Edward Benjamin Ulysses David." But what was Rob and Laura's address? How about the Ricardos' phone number? Join the pros and test your trivia skill. TV, radio, music, film, Internet books—all the great cultural achievements of mankind are grist for those who pursue the trivial.

**Usenet:**

rec.games.trivia

## Trivial Waste of Time

Trivia fans can use this bunch of trivia questions as a game on its own or as a supplement to trivia board games that you are playing in real time. There are listings of questions in a variety of categories, so there's no risk of running out of questions any time soon.

**Web:**

http://www.lexmark.com/data/trivia/trivia.html

## Useless Facts

What could be more useful than a collection of useless facts? Did you know that if you stretch a slinky out flat it measures 87 feet long? Did you know that the only word in the English language with all five vowels in reverse order is "subcontinental"? Did you know that the pupil of an octopus' eye is rectangular? And did you know what there is more of the same waiting for you at this web site?

**Web:**

http://www-leland.stanford.edu/~jenkg/useless.html

## UFOS AND ALIENS

### Abductees Anonymous

Abductees Anonymous contains articles, personal experiences, and incident reports covering various topics: spontaneous invisibility, walk-ins (when a spirit takes over a dead body), alien contact and kidnappings, a Bigfoot story or two, and so on. There are also hints on how to know if you have been abducted.

**Web:**
**http://www.cybergate.com/~ufonline/**

### Alien Autopsies

An autopsy is a medical procedure—often referred to as a postmortem examination—in which a dead body (cadaver) is examined in order to figure out why a person died. One of the basic facts about this procedure is that you cannot have an autopsy unless you have a body. So when you hear about an autopsy being conducted on an alien, the significance is not that we might find out how an alien died, but that there actually was an alien in the first place. There are many stories about alien autopsies, and if you are curious, here is a web site in which a lot of useful information is collected into one place.

**Web:**
**http://www.trudang.com/autopsy.html**

### Alien Encyclopedia

You can't talk about the players without a program. Here is a glossary of extraterrestrial words (along with some terms related to the mystical and paranormal). If you are interested in aliens, it behooves you to spend some time learning the vocabulary. After all, think how embarrassed you would be if some aliens were visiting you, and introduced them to your mother as grey aliens when they were really Lyrans.

**Web:**
**http://linex3.linex.com/ufo/aliengls.html**

### Alien Pyramids

It's easy to say that aliens built the pyramids. What's not so easy is to convince people that what you say is true. Well, don't get left behind the next time your social circle is debating the origin of the pyramids. Visit these web sites and get the real story.

**Web:**
**http://www.europa.com/~edge/pyramid.html**
**http://www.nltl.columbia.edu/students/iluwan/Aliensnf.html**

*Look What I Found on the Net...*

(from the Alien Encyclopedia)

MOON-EYED ALIENS:

A race of peaceable humans some 7-8 feet tall, with pale-blue skin and large wrap-around eyes which are extremely sensitive to light. They MAY be the same as the large humans allegedly encountered on the moon by our "astronauts", who in turn were silenced and not allowed to tell what they saw.

These people may be allied to the Nordics or Blondes. They claim to be descendants of Noah, who traveled to the western hemisphere a few centuries after the deluge and discovered ancient antediluvian cavern systems and technologies which had been abandoned in the subterranean recesses.

They have been encountered mostly in deep cavern-systems beneath the general region of the Ozarks-Arkansas and surrounding regions.

## Alien Research

Thoughts and discussions on where aliens might come from and if they have been to Earth before. Discussions include what aliens might look like, myths surrounding aliens, possible encounters and unexplained sightings. You can even read some alien autopsy reports, but it's probably best to save these for after breakfast.

**Usenet:**

**alt.alien.research**

## Area 51 Discussions

This Usenet group and web site are devoted to Area 51, the super-secret government base near Las Vegas. Read current speculations on alien aircraft, discuss the government's security measures at the base and ponder new ideas on how to spy on the base to see the aliens.

**Web:**

**http://www.ufomind.com/area51/**

**Usenet:**

**alt.conspiracy.area51**

## Contact Lab

This is a web site for serious UFO researchers as well as "experiencers". You will find information about space brothers, starseeds, visitations, alien breeding programs, implants, abduction and grey men. Explore the archives and read about flying saucers, the Puerto Rican Goat Sucker, temporal lobe epilepsy, cattle mutilations, the Bass Strait incident and the radiologist conspiracy. Unlike most UFO web sites, this one has a lot more than links, there is a lot of original content (with the accent on "original"). Oh yes, if you see a UFO, you can report the contact by filling out the UFO Report Form.

**Web:**

**http://www.ipacific.net.au/~pavig/**

## Crop Circles

Crop circles are large, sometimes intricate designs created on farmland when parts of a field of growing plants are flattened to form a large pattern. Many people believe that crop circles are of extra-terrestrial origin. If you would like to find out more about crop circles and what people have said about them, here is an extensive list of books, periodicals, documentaries and videos about the phenomenon. You can do research or, for those who are more artistically inclined, you can go make your own crop circle.

**Web:**

**http://www.tpoint.net/~mchorost/circles_biblio.html**

### Crop Circles:
### *Whence Comest Thou?*

Where did all the crop circles come from? They are mysterious patterns and designs that appeared in farmers' grain fields, starting in the middle 1970s and peaking between 1989 and 1992. Lots of explanations have been proposed: the crop circles were made by aliens, by supernatural beings, by natural phenomena that are not well understood, and so on.

Here is the real explanation:

The first crop circles appeared in English grain fields. The size and complexity and circumstances were such that many people said it was impossible for the whole thing to be a hoax. However, it was.

The original crop circles—and many of the later ones—were created by two Englishmen from Southampton, Doug Bower and Dave Chorley. One night while drinking beer in their pub, they started talking about all the UFO reports and thought it might be fun to fool all the gullible people who believed in UFOs.

They began by making simple designs in fields using only a steel bar. Eventually the graduated to making elaborate designs using boards and ropes.

Once the hoax caught on, other people started copying them, in England as well as in other countries. Bower and Chorley continued this for 15 years, fooling a lot of "experts". Finally, in 1991, they confessed and demonstrated to reporters how easy it was for them to create the complex patterns that—according to so many believers—could not be made by human beings.

For more information, see the book "Round in Circles" by Jim Schnabel (Penguin 1994).

(Actually, I have my own theory: I think the crop circles were created by Martian bacteria.)

## Galactic Central

When it's too cloudy to go watching for mysterious shapes in the sky, spend the time on the computer reading all the information archived at Galactic Central. This is a great source of information about alien abduction, skeptics, alien visitors, inter-dimensional travel, UFO sightings by astronauts and pointers to UFO and conspiracy Usenet groups.

**Web:**

**http://www.efn.org/~lcapt/**

## Internet UFO Group

The Internet UFO Group is a collaboration organizing UFO information to keep online. Texts include how the media reacts to UFOs, sightings and how to report them, zines, articles, papers and archives of UFO-related information.

**Web:**

**http://www.iufog.org/**

## Life on Mars

Is there life on Mars? Well, if not, how do you explain the Martian pyramids and lost civilizations? They may have been built by aliens. Of course, if there isn't alien life, there may be native life. One of these web sites explores the possible connection between aliens and Martian pyramids. The other site has information about the Cydonia region of Mars (the location of the "face" and the "pyramids"). This region was explored by the Viking I probe in 1976. You can look at Viking pictures, and read articles discussing the possibility of life on Mars. Is there life on Mars? Someone thinks so.

**Web:**

**http://home.navisoft.com/cydonia/cydonia.htm**
**http://www.newageinfo.com/res/mars/**

**What if...?**

## Roswell Incident

Anyone who is interested in UFOs and aliens has heard of Roswell, New Mexico. Read the facts and folklore about Roswell, the town where it is said that, in 1947, an alien vessel crashed and the government hushed it up. See pictures of the crash and an FBI memo. By the way, here is the real explanation: the debris that crashed was from secret experiments the Pentagon was running called Project Mogul. The purpose of these experiments was to develop technology capable of detecting Russian atomic tests (which, it was thought, were about to begin soon). When the apparatus crashed, the military covered it up by saying the debris was from weather balloons. This, of course, was a lie, which in later years served to stimulate the American UFO-cover-up-conspiracy buffs.

**Web:**

**http://www.protree.com/vjentpr/jroswell.html**

## SETI

SETI stands for the Search for Extraterrestrial Intelligence. In 1959, an organized effort began in which scientists began to look for intelligent life forms in outer space. Read about the history of SETI, some of their research and efforts, a bibliography and FAQ, and information about SETI observatories.

**Web:**

**http://www.seti-inst.edu/**

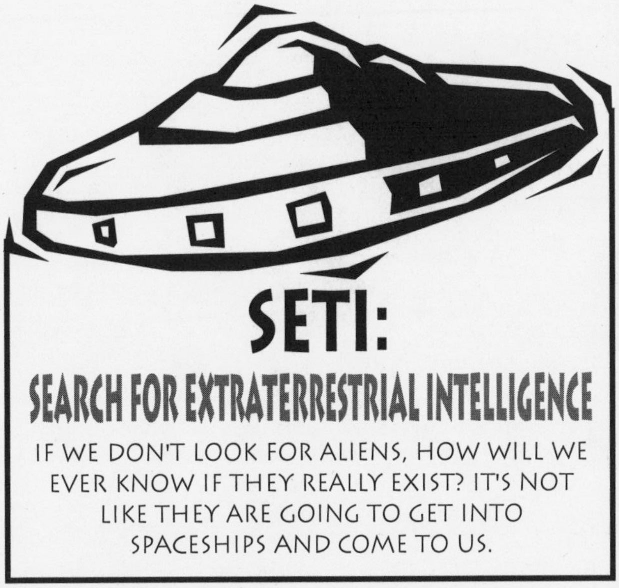
SETI:
SEARCH FOR EXTRATERRESTRIAL INTELLIGENCE
IF WE DON'T LOOK FOR ALIENS, HOW WILL WE EVER KNOW IF THEY REALLY EXIST? IT'S NOT LIKE THEY ARE GOING TO GET INTO SPACESHIPS AND COME TO US.

## UFO Chatting

When it's late at night and you are afraid of the dark, you can find some companionship on IRC. The two X-Files channels are populated by people who are fans of the X-Ffiles television show, but they also chat about aliens and UFOs. The **#ufo** channel is exclusively for talking about extraterrestrials and UFO-related subjects.

**IRC:**

**#ufo**
**#x-files**
**#xfiles**

## UFO Information Resource

These web sites have information about UFO resources, movies about UFOs, musicians who have songs about aliens, information about the Trilateral commission, organization addresses, a list of star groupings and planets that are thought to be the homes of aliens, alien crash information and more.

**Web:**

**http://ernie.bgsu.edu/~jzawodn/ufo/**
**http://www.ftech.net/~ufoinfo/**

### *Look What I Found on the Net...*

```
Newsgroup: alt.alien.visitors
Subject: Alien Visits and UFOs

There is no doubt in my mind that we will be "invaded".  But
they are not hostile.  In fact, these "aliens" are merely
Satan's angels.  Satan will soon be thrown out of the heavenly
realm, and in order to appear legitimate he will arrive as
"space aliens" and in peace.  The whole world will marvel at the
miracles that these "aliens" can perform, but do not be
deceived.  They are coming with the aid and support of the
government to bring us hell and destruction...

----------

I have seen them.  I never was a believer until last weekend.

They came to my house looking for pretzels and beer.  They had
large glossy red eyes and long scraggly beards and wore flannel
shirts and mud boots.  Their ship sort of resembled a Chevy pick
up...

It wasn't until later I realized what they really wanted: they
had really come for my body.  They wanted to impregnate me with
an alien fetus and later take over the world.  Disguised at
lumberjacks they raided the fridge...

I am writing this from their ship.... They do not know I am
here.  This is my only chance for help.  Help me please...
Oh no!  Here they come......... Ahhhhhh

----------

My husband and I were out of town for a day trip and when we
returned there was a footprint on top of our glass dining room
table.  What was strange was that the foot print only has three
toes.  If you have heard anything similar to that, please let me
know.
```

## UFO Pictures

When you need some interesting pictures for your photo album, head straight to the Net and explore these archives of UFO snapshots. You can download them and put interesting captions on them like "last year's trip to England to make crop circles" or "Uncle Marty buzzes unsuspecting American farm workers". Pictures of alleged UFOs are divided by geographic locality and year.

**Web:**

**http://ourworld.compuserve.com/homepages/AndyPage/ufopictu.htm**
**http://www.rutgers.edu/test/ufo/pictures/**

## UFO Reports

Have you seen a UFO recently and lived to tell about it? Here are some places on the Net to report it and to check to see if anyone else in your area might have seen something similar. Read about sightings from all over the world, speculate about alien visitors or just laugh at people whose reports seem unbelievable.

**Web:**

**http://www.nwlink.com/~ufocntr/**

**Usenet:**

**alt.ufo.reports**

## UFO Talk and General Discussion

Visit these Usenet groups for a cool, rational, scientific, intellectual, well-reasoned, plausible discussion about aliens visiting the Earth and swanking around like they own the place. Investigate, in person, the theory that man is really nature's last word. Just the place to spend your time when the TV is on the fritz.

**Usenet:**

**alt.alien.visitors**
**alt.paranet.abduct**
**alt.paranet.ufo**
**alt.paranormal**

## Ultimate UFO Page

When you want to hear the real talk about the virtual UFO town, this web site is the place to be. This page has all sorts of general UFO information on Roswell, abductions, alien autopsies and related topics.

**Web:**

**http://www.serve.com/tufop/**

# USENET

## Anonymous Posting

Post messages to Usenet groups anonymously. To find out how, check out the anonymous remailer collection on the Web.

**Web:**

**http://electron.rutgers.edu/~gambino/anon_servers/anon.html**

### Being Anonymous

There are many reasons why you might wish to post Usenet articles anonymously. For example, you might want to contribute personal comments to one of the sex-oriented groups. Or, you might not want your employer or system manager (or significant other) to know the nature of your postings.

In order to protect the right of anyone to say whatever they want without fear of retribution, an anonymous posting service has been set up. Once you register, you will be given a user number and all correspondence will be carried out using that number. Moreover, once you post an article anonymously, people will be able to send you mail commenting on the article, without knowing who you are.

This service is an important one and—as you can imagine—there are all sorts of self-righteous zealots who would love to shut it down. Please use your intelligence and do not abuse the system.

A B C D E F G H I J K L M N O P Q R S T U V W X Y Z

A B C D E F G H I J K L M N O P Q R S T U V W X Y Z

## Binaries from Usenet

Don't get bummed out because your site doesn't carry the **alt.binaries** Usenet groups. Go to this site which has done most of the work for you. These binaries have been uudecoded and stored as gifs on this web page so you can easily snarf all the pictures you want.

**Web:**

**http://pmwww.cs.vu.nl/usenet/.news.html**

## Cascades

Every once in a while, someone will reply to a silly one-line message with another silly one-line message. Another person will follow up with a third silly one-line message, and (let the trumpets sound) a *cascade* is born. Cascades have a life and an appeal all their own. If you are one of those lucky persons whose sense of taste is so highly developed as to make you an aficionado of cascades, then you will want to tune into this Usenet group where you can cascade till you burst.

**Usenet:**

**alt.cascade**

## Creating Alternative Usenet Discussion Groups

An alternative Usenet group is one that has been started without any special procedures, such as voting or discussion. Unlike mainstream groups—which do undergo such procedures before they can be started—alternative groups can be started by anyone who knows how to do so. The disadvantage to such groups is that they are not carried by as many news servers around the world. Alternative groups are important, however. They provide a counterpoint to the more sedate, controlled world of mainstream groups in that people are more free to create and remove alternative groups, with a minimum of fuss, as the need arises. Here is information about how alternative groups should be created. If you want to create a group, please read and follow the guidelines. They were developed by trial and error and a lot of smart thinking over a period of time. Usenet works best when people (1) think before acting, and (2) do not try to re-invent everything.

**Web:**

**http://www.cs.ubc.ca/spider/edmonds/usenet/good-newgroup.html**
**http://www.math.psu.edu/barr/alt-creation-guide.html**
**http://www4.ncsu.edu/~asdamick/www/news/create.html**

## Creating Mainstream Usenet Discussion Groups

A mainstream Usenet group is one that is created by following a specific set of procedures, involving one or more votes, serious discussion, and deliberate planning. It takes time and effort to create a mainstream group (compared to an alternative group which anyone can create if he or she knows how). The advantage of mainstream groups is that they are respected as real groups and are carried by virtually all news servers around the world. Here is an explanation of how such groups are started.

**Web:**

**http://www.fairnet.org/fnvol/training/newsgrp.html**

## Flames

A *flame* may be a complaint, a criticism of a person, or a good old-fashioned tongue-lashing reduced to bits and bytes. Join these groups and play with the people who complain for a living.

**Usenet:**

**alt.flame**
**alt.flame.abortion**
**alt.flame.airlines**
**alt.flame.canter-and-siegel**
**alt.flame.faggots**
**alt.flame.football.notre-dame**
**alt.flame.gigantic.sigs**
**alt.flame.hall-of-flame**
**alt.flame.landlord**
**alt.flame.ms-windows**
**alt.flame.mud**
**alt.flame.net-cops**
**alt.flame.parents**
**alt.flame.pascal**
**alt.flame.professor**
**alt.flame.right-wing-conservatives**
**alt.flame.roommate**
**alt.flame.rush-limbaugh**
**alt.flame.sam-donaldson**
**alt.flame.spelling**
**alt.flame.support.groups**
**alt.flame.sys-admin**

## Net Abuse

Heavy cross-posting, spamming, and annoying commercial advertising are at the top of the list of Ways to Abuse Your Net Privileges. Read about the latest sins against the laws of Net etiquette, thoughts and ideas on the concept of minding our manners, and general ranting and raving about people who rant and rave.

**Usenet:**

**alt.current-events.net-abuse**
**news.admin.net-abuse.announce**
**news.admin.net-abuse.blacklists**
**news.admin.net-abuse.forged-cancels**
**news.admin.net-abuse.mailbombing**
**news.admin.net-abuse.misc**

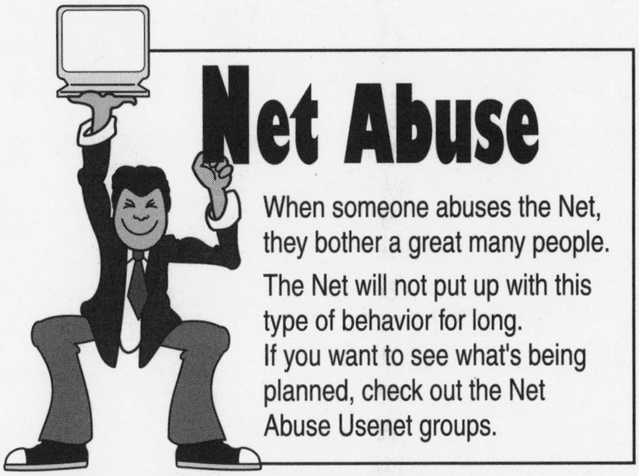
Net Abuse
When someone abuses the Net, they bother a great many people.
The Net will not put up with this type of behavior for long.
If you want to see what's being planned, check out the Net Abuse Usenet groups.

## Usenet Announcements

Stay informed on the latest new groups that are cropping up in Usenet. The **.newgroups** group is where people post when they want to propose a new group. The **.newusers** group is a place where periodic explanations about Usenet are posted for the benefit of new users.

**Usenet:**

**news.announce.conferences**
**news.announce.important**
**news.announce.newgroups**
**news.announce.newusers**

## Usenet Archiving Software

If you have been given the job of looking through certain Usenet groups to find encoded postings, you could be at the job all day. Instead, get this software, which will search through groups for encoded pictures and source codes.

**Web:**

**http://www.cs.ubc.ca/spider/phillips/grn/source**

## Usenet Culture Talk and General Discussion

Usenet has a culture all its own. Once you spend a lot of time on Usenet, you will get a feeling for its energy, its customs, its vocabulary and its importance: in other words, its culture. This is the group where you can discuss all these subjects.

**Usenet:**

**alt.culture.usenet**

## Usenet Discussion Group Administration

It's bound to happen. When you get thousands of people posting to Usenet, someone is going to decide that things need to get more organized. The **news.admin** groups are a central point for administrative topics relating to Usenet such as the dissemination of information, statement of policies, and the relating of technical details about forming and moderating Usenet groups.

**Usenet:**

**news.admin**
**news.admin.censorship**
**news.admin.hierarchies**
**news.admin.misc**
**news.admin.policy**
**news.admin.technical**

## Usenet Discussion Group Invasion

Sometimes it doesn't matter if you mind your own business. You can be happily posting away in your favorite Usenet group when it eventually erupts into chaos and disorder. And you never saw it coming. That's because the Usenet commandos planned their strategy so keenly. Their plan is to seek out groups and create a stir, cause flame wars and wreak general havoc. This is where they devise their plans.

**Usenet:**

**alt.syntax.tactical**

A B C D E F G H I J K L M N O P Q R S T U V W X Y Z

## Usenet Discussion Group Questions

Looking for a Usenet group about Armenian folk dancing or one that will tell you how to make clothes from old beer cans? If you can't find just the one you are looking for, try asking on these groups. Someone might be able to help. People will answer questions not only about specific groups, but about Usenet groups in general. It's a good source of information.

**Usenet:**

**news.groups.questions**
**news.newusers.questions**

## Usenet Filtering Service

It's going to be an all-day job if you want to check every single Usenet group for reports of Elvis sightings, so why not let someone do it for you? Subscribe to this news filtering service, and they will send you postings on any keywords or phrases that you choose. So, if you're paranoid and you could just swear people are talking about you, this will be the proof you can finally show your therapist.

**Web:**

**http://www.reference.com/**

## Usenet Hierarchies

Within the name of a Usenet group, the first part of the name indicates the hierarchy (major category) to which the group belongs. For example, when you see the names **alt.politics.usa** or **alt.sex.stories**, you can tell they are part of the **alt** (alternative) hierarchy. When you see the name **comp.infosystems.www**, you know the group is part of the **comp** (computer) hierarchy. Here are the most important hierarchies (the ones I want you to remember): **alt** (alternative), **bionet** (biology), **biz** (business), **comp** (computers), **k12** (K-12 education), **misc** miscellaneous), **news** (Usenet itself), **rec** (recreation), **sci** (science), **soc** (society) and **talk** (debate). However, there are literally hundreds of different hierarchies, most of them devoted to a particular geographical area, language or organization. This web site has a large list of Usenet hierarchies along with a brief description. If you encounter a strange name that you don't understand, look here for help.

**Web:**

**http://www.magmacom.com/~leisen/master_list.html**

### *Look What I Found on the Net...*

```
Newsgroup: alt.culture.usenet
Subject: Dejanews Archive

> I like to post a lot of articles on Usenet and I have noticed
> that the Dejanews company stores ever single post.  I really
> don't want them to keep every single thing I post, so is there
> any way I can remove all those articles from my history of
> posting on Usenet?

Oh, sure, so you'd be liking to say all manner of things on
Usenet, but you wouldn't want people to be reading after the
articles have expired and the posts are taken away.  You'd be
happy to see the things that you say vanish into the air like
the steam off a kettle of boiling water.

Well, I'm here to tell you, young friend, that there'll not be
any of that satisfaction for you, as everything you say is being
stored and preserved, and we'll have record of your every
utterance upon the Net without a blessed thing that you'll be
able to do about it.
```

## Usenet Information Center

The Usenet Information Center allows you to search for a Usenet group by keyword, or browse the groups by category. As you browse, you can get a variety of information about each group: a short description (if available), statistics, information about the FAQ (frequently asked question list), and the FAQ itself. This is a great resource.

**Web:**

**http://sunsite.unc.edu/usenet-i/**

## Usenet Junkies

If something is worth doing, it's worth doing to excess. When Usenet becomes a bit too much and you feel your sanity slipping away, check out these support groups for Usenet junkies who can't say no.

**Usenet:**

**alt.usenet.addict**
**alt.usenet.recovery**

## Usenet Kooks

It used to be safe inside your home, but not anymore. The kooks are coming off the street and straight onto the Internet. Collected at this web site are the **alt.usenet.kooks** FAQ, the net.legends archives, information on Kibology, archives of the postings of various Usenet kooks, and the all-important Kook of the Month archive. Check to see if your name is there.

**Web:**

**http://www.wetware.com/mlegare/kotm/**

**Usenet:**

**alt.usenet.kooks**



## Usenet Personalities

Just as there are people who gain notoriety in neighborhoods or in the news, there are faceless people who become equally notable in the Internet community and set tongues to wagging around the world. Read about these people and see samples of their posts and join the praise or cursing of them.

**Usenet:**

**alt.net.personalities**

## Votetaker Volunteers

The Usenet Votetaker Volunteers is a neutral third party who counts votes and keeps track of current vote status for the mainstream hierarchy groups. Read about the origins of the group and how they do the voodoo that they do.

**Web:**

**http://www.uvv.org/**

## Weird Places to Hang Out on Usenet

Among the thousands of Usenet groups, there are a few strange places to hang out where anything goes. These are groups that were started as a joke, or real groups that have been abandoned by the original settlers. Check out one of these groups and meet the squatters. Sort of the free-trade zone of Usenet commerce. (In fact, there are some groups that are so secret, I can't even tell you about them.)

**Usenet:**

**alt.0d**
**alt.1d**
**alt.alien.vampire.flonk.flonk.flonk**
**alt.alt.alt.alt.alt**
**alt.art.theft.scream.scream.scream**
**alt.basement.graveyard**
**alt.bitch.pork**
**alt.bogus.group**
**alt.cuddle**
**alt.dumpster**
**alt.non.sequitur**
**alt.religion.monica**
**alt.rmgroup**
**alt.silly-group.beable**
**alt.test.my.new.group**

## Look What I Found on the Net...

```
Newsgroup: alt.usenet.kooks
Subject: Kook of the Month Nomination: Omnipotent Philosopher

[the original posting]

> He's paranoid.  He's schizophrenic.
> He's the perfect Kook of the Month.
>
> We've heard how he couldn't get a job in world banking, but
> that he'll still do it privately for everyone at no cost, just
> 'for the fun of it'.
>
> We've seen him invent new nomenclature for philosophy,
> 'epistomology is now oncology'.
>
> We've even seen him revolutionize economics, 'set up a
> non-profit corporation and pay yourself minimum wage; just
> make sure that your company doesn't take in any money.'
>
> Can we let this kook go unrecognized?  I'd like a seconder for
> this nomination, all follow-ups directed to alt.usenet.kooks.

[here is the reply]

It looks like Xxxxxx Xxxx is slandering me again.  Could it be
he's afraid -- attempting to discredit me?  He wouldn't dare put
up a rational argument, because I would kick his butt every
time.  But then maybe he likes having his butt kicked.  Why else
would he post such a ridiculous post?

He is a known liar.  He creates problems where none exist.
He would rob you blind if he thought that was a reflection of
public opinion.

> He's paranoid.  He's schizophrenic.
> He's the perfect Kook of the Month.

You say that I am these things, but you provide no proof.
In fact, it is I who proved that you are these things because
you think that reality is created by the mind.

> We've heard how he couldn't get a job in world banking, but
> that he'll still do it privately for everyone at no cost, just
> 'for the fun of it'.

This is a complete lie.  I never, ever applied for a job at a
world bank.  I applied for a job in investment banking.  How can
anyone operate a business with no costs?  It's impossible.  And
business should be fun.  I don't view work as a chore to be
dreaded.

> We've seen him invent new nomenclature for philosophy,
> 'epistomology is now oncology'.

I've never said this.  Epistemology is the branch of philosophy
that deals with validating our understanding of reality.
Oncology is the study of tumors.  Do you see the connection
Xxxxxx Xxxx is attempting to make?

> We've even seen him revolutionize economics, 'set up a
> non-profit corporation and pay yourself minimum wage; just
> make sure that your company doesn't take in any money.'

Taken out of context, twisted and turned upside-down.  How can
you operate a business if it doesn't take in any money?

> Can we let this kook go unrecognized?  I'd like a seconder for
> this nomination, all follow-ups directed to alt.usenet.kooks.

It is Xxxxxx Xxxx who is the kook, and a lying, insane parasite.
Again he demonstrates this by attempting to assert that the
opinions of others are reality.
```

# VICES

## Chocolate

While chocolate is not one of the Seven Deadly Sins, its tastes good enough to be. If you are hooked on chocolate, check out this web site which has recipes to make lots of chocolate desserts. For the more compulsive who want chocolate information to come straight to their mailbox, try any of the mailing lists. The **choco** mailing list is a receive-only list for people who want to be sent a collection of archives collected from around the Net for the particular month. The Usenet group will give you access to chocolate chat even after all the supermarkets are closed.

**Web:**
**http://www.qrc.com/~sholubek/choco/**

**Usenet:**
**rec.food.chocolate**

**Listproc Mailing List:**
List Name: **chocolate-l**
Subscribe to: **listproc@cornell.edu**

**Listserv Mailing List:**
List Name: **chocolate**
Subscribe to: **listserv@idma.com**

**Listserv Mailing List:**
List Name: **chocolate-l**
Subscribe to: **listserv@netcom.com**

**Majordomo Mailing List:**
List Name: **choco**
Subscribe to: **majordomo@apk.net**

## Cigar Smoking

Throw away those puny cigarettes and mamby-pamby pipes and go for the real manly-man smoking pastime. Light up and meet other cigar smokers on the Net.

**Web:**
**http://www.geocities.com/TheTropics/3347/aaa.html**
**http://www.tezcat.com/~smokers/luxury.html**

**Usenet:**
**alt.smokers.cigars**

**Listserv Mailing List:**
List Name: **cigar-l**
Subscribe to: **listserv@american.edu**

## Cigarette Smoking

You run a lot of serious risks when you smoke regularly. The idea behind this web page is that, if you are going to smoke, you might as well do it well. This web site is called "Start Smoking: A Self-Help Guide". It's a somewhat tongue-in-cheek approach to cigarette smoking. Start with the dos and donts: don't start smoking until you are at least 30 years old, do get help if you are addicted to cheap American cigarettes, don't buy cigarettes in a supermarket or convenience store, don't be a habitual smoker, and so on. Then move on to enjoy cigarette reviews (with a featured cigarette of the month), and a bonus cigar page. (Personal note. Having gone to medical school and worked in hospitals, I can tell you categorically: Anyone who could see what the end-stage of cigarette smoking looks like would never smoke, even moderately. If you like to smoke, imagine yourself as an old man or woman in a hospital room, with a body ravaged by years of tobacco. Just trying to sustain enough breath to walk to the bathroom is a major achievement. Think about what looks like when a surgeon cuts into your lower jaw and pulls it open in a vain effort to remove the cancer at the back of your throat. I have seen all of this and a lot more. Take my word for it, there are a great many adjectives you can use to describe what happens to a person who smokes for years, but "cool" is not one of them.)

**Web:**
**http://www.lainet.com/magdaz/smoke.htm**

**Usenet:**
**alt.smokers**

## Drinking

After a while the same old drinks get boring. Spice up your vice with some new recipes for mixed drinks and beers. These recipes are always good to have around in case the Queen drops by for a drink.

**Web:**
**http://alpha.rollanet.org/cm3/recs/**
**http://www.inforamp.net/~mcdermot/drinks.html**

**Do a backup.**

## Gambling and Oddsmaking

When you are not sitting in a smoke-filled room taking chances with your money, fill your urges with some great gambling and oddsmaking resources on the Net. The web sites will show you hints and tips about gambling and in the Usenet groups you can talk about various gambling games.

**Web:**

**http://www.rgtonline.com/**
**http://www.vegas.com/vegascom/betbasc/bbtoc.html**

**Usenet:**

**alt.gambling**
**alt.las-vegas.gambling**
**rec.gambling**
**rec.gambling.blackjack**
**rec.gambling.craps**
**rec.gambling.misc**
**rec.gambling.other-games**
**rec.gambling.poker**

## Hangovers

It's a shame when something that can be fun causes so much misery later. But it's the same with any fun thing—sex, alcohol, excess food or roller coasters. There is always a risk of ensuing nausea or headache afterward. Don't be alone in your misery. Share stories and sure cures for hangovers. Learn from the people who never let the prospect of pain slow them down.

**Usenet:**

**alt.hangover**

## Horse Racing

And they're off! You can feel the adrenaline rush through your veins and into your fast-beating heart as your pulse quickens and you break out in little beads of perspiration. You clutch the ticket in your fist and hope like heck that your horse comes in first since you bet all of your lunch money on him. If you're addicted, or if you just like the thrill of the race, meet up with other racing fans to discuss the strategies of horse racing and handicapping. The web site contains information on handicapping, various track information and much more.

**Web:**

**http://wsnet.com/%7Esysclp/racing.html**

**Usenet:**

**alt.sport.horse-racing**
**alt.sport.horse-racing.systems**
**rec.gambling.racing**

**Listserv Mailing List:**

List Name: **hracing**
Subscribe to: **listserv@ulkyvm.louisville.edu**

## Lies

In the old days, people used to make telling lies an art form. They would call them "tall tales" or say they were "spinning windies". That made the lying okay, because everyone knew it was for fun. Besides fun, you can tell lies for profit, to get yourself out of trouble or just because you can't help yourself. Think up the biggest whopper you can and post it here. And if you get in trouble for it later you can say, "But Mom, all the other Net users were doing it..."

**Usenet:**

**alt.lies**

### *Look What I Found on the Net...*

```
(from an online gambling and oddsmaking reference)

The Kelly Criterion [for Blackjack] is a betting heuristic that
minimizes your chance of going broke while maximizing your
long-run profits.  To bet consistently with the Kelly Criterion,
you should divide your bankroll into 300-400 units and normally
bet 1-4 units on each hand.

Your optimal bet on a hand is a percentage of your CURRENT
bankroll equal to about 0.5*R/D + B, where R is the running
count, D is the number of remaining decks (so R/D is the true
count), and B is the basic strategy expectation.
```

## Lotteries

Why work all your life and feel the satisfaction of successfully making your way in the world when you can buy a lottery ticket and have the chance to win your fortune all at once? Lottery fans, get together and discuss the lotteries on Usenet, or see all the lottery resources that are on the Web, such as number generators, lottery news and helpful software.

**Web:**

**http://secure.londonmall.co.uk/drodd/links.htm**
**http://www.aksi.net/lotto/lotlink.html**

**Usenet:**

**alt.lotto.players**
**rec.gambling.lottery**

## Pipe Smoking

You know you are addicted when the sweet, rich scent of pipe tobacco makes you all goose-pimply and gives you urges to dress in velvet smoking jackets. Even if you don't like to smoke a pipe, it's fun to go in those tobacco shops with the rich wood paneling and case after case of sweet smelling leaves. Participate in pipe talk with the folks on Usenet or explore interesting pipe information at the web site.

**Web:**

**http://www.amug.org/~rbromley/ooops.html**

**Usenet:**

**alt.smokers.pipes**

## Sex Services Talk and General Discussion

Ah, the Modern Age. Overnight mail delivery, faxes, email, pizza in thirty minutes or less, home shopping networks and sex partners on demand. These are the things that make life worth living. Read about the going rates for services and where to find the various objects of your desire.

**Usenet:**

**alt.sex.erotica.marketplace**
**alt.sex.services**

## Sports Gambling

If you like to gamble on sports, you need timely and accurate information. Of course, the Net is ready to help. (However, the Net won't pay you back if you lose.) These are web sites that contain up to date information for sports gamblers. Get the odds, schedules, tips and a lot more. For discussion, you can participate in the Usenet group.

**Web:**

**http://www.covers.com/csi/covers.html**
**http://www.sportsfaxnews.com/free/**

**Usenet:**

**rec.gambling.sports**

**FAQs are cool.**

*Look What I Found on the Net...*

```
Newsgroup: alt.sex.services
Subject: Satisfy Your Sexual Desires

Satisfy Your Sexual Desires

All Real!  All Live!  Hot Internet Sex!

Live strippers, online, waiting for you RIGHT NOW!
24 hours a day.  Seven days a week.

http://www.xxxxxxxxx.com/xxxx
```

## Strip Clubs

It's nice when you go to a bar or club and you get the opportunity to see some nice scenery. And it doesn't really have to be anything special like glorious vistas that make you believe there is a God. Just something interesting will do, like a man or woman wearing nothing but strategically placed tassels as they gyrate in the vicinity of your seating area. Fans of strip clubs and exotic dancers discuss the hot clubs, dancers, and places to go when you are looking for a good time. The web site is called "The Ultimate Strip Club List". You can browse for reviews or write your own.

**Web:**

**http://www.tuscl.com/**

**Usenet:**

**alt.sex.strip-clubs**

## Virtual Slot Machine

When you can't take the time to hit the slots in Vegas, at least stop on the Web to see if you can hit the jackpot. Start off with a few coins, pull the handle and see if you can win more coins.

**Web:**

**http://www.pacificnet.net/~sonic/vslot2.html**

# VIDEO AND MULTIMEDIA

## CU-SeeMe

CU-SeeMe is a real-time, multiparty video-conferencing system for the Internet. Remember how in the future we will all be talking over video phones? Well, now you can do it on the Net. If you have a video camera connected to your computer, great: you can broadcast. If not, you can still install get the software and watch other people.

**Web:**

**http://cu-seeme.cornell.edu/**
**http://goliath.wpine.com/cu-seeme.html**
**http://magneto.csc.ncsu.edu/Multimedia/CU-SeeMe/reflect_list.html**

## Genetic Movies

Browse an interesting selection of genetic mpeg, and then take part in this interactive art piece by voicing your own opinion. After ten votes have been collected, the votes are counted and the results are used by a genetic algorithm to create new art pieces. In this way, the collection is constantly evolving and creating new movies.

**Web:**

**http://robocop.modmath.cs.cmu.edu:8001/htbin/moviegenform**

## Movie and Animation Cross-Platform Formats

This web site has information about various movie and animation formats. For each type, you can see what software is available for various operating systems. There are also comments on each program, as well as links to download sites. There is information on a variety of multimedia formats, including avi, mpeg and Quicktime.

**Web:**

**http://www.mcad.edu/Guests/EricB/xplat.movie.html**

**Someone has given you a file that contains a movie with irrefutable proof that the Pope is one of the aliens who masterminded the JFK conspiracy cover-up. However, your software cannot play that type of movie!**

**The Net can help. Go to the *Movie and Animation Cross-Platform Formats* web site and find the program you need to convert or view the file.**

**Once again (thanks to the Net), the truth will be revealed.**

A B C D E F G H I J K L M N O P Q R S T U V W X Y Z

## Mpeg Movies

When you need a break from the drab sameness of everyday life, visit one of these web sites. Here you will find a great many animated files in mpeg format. Just the thing to use up a few extra minutes of your life; minutes that will never, ever come back again. Well, at least things that move look cool on your computer...

**Web:**

**http://deathstar.rutgers.edu/people/bochkay/movies.html**
**http://esba-www.jrc.it/dvgdocs/dvg1.html**
**http://www.arc.umn.edu/GVL/Software/mpeg.html**
**http://www.cs.ucl.ac.uk/movies/**

## Mpeg Video Resources and Software

This is a site that has extensive information about the mpeg video format. The name "mpeg" (named after the Moving Picture Experts Group)" refers to a family of standards used for encoding audio-visual information in a digital compressed format. At this web site you can find an overview of mpeg, as well as news, software, a FAQ, installation guides and much more. If you need anything having to do with mpeg, this is the place to look.

**Web:**

**http://www.mpeg.org/**

## Multimedia File Formats

As an Internet user, you are going to encounter all different kinds of files. So what do you do when you find something your browser doesn't understand? Suppose you download a file named **harley.au** from the Web, but you are not sure whether you should look at it, listen to it or eat it. All the answers and more are in this wonderful, most comprehensive guide to strange but true file formats.

**Web:**

**http://ac.dal.ca/~dong/contents.htm**

## Multimedia in Education

Computing doesn't have to be complicated, dull or boring. Not with multimedia. Pictures, sounds, graphics, and animations all make computers come to life. Learn about using multimedia as a teaching tool and find out places where you can be taught to use multimedia effectively.

**Usenet:**

**misc.education.multimedia**

## Multimedia Lab

Do you feel like exploring some multimedia files? You came to the right place. Browse through this collection of movies (with and without sound), cartoons, graphics, animations, ray tracing images, and much more.

**Web:**

**http://www.acm.uiuc.edu/rml/**

## Multimedia Talk and General Discussion

This is the Usenet group for general discussion of computers and multimedia. People come here to talk about all manner of multimedia topics, including communications, user interfaces, tools, animation, and so on.

**Usenet:**

**comp.multimedia**

## PC Video Hardware

This is the Usenet group where people discuss any topic related to PC video hardware: monitors, computers, video cards, flat-panel displays, video accelerators, video capture cards and more. The web site contains the FAQ (frequently asked question list) for the group.

**Web:**

**http://www.heartlab.rri.uwo.ca/vidfaq/videofaq.html**

**Usenet:**

**comp.sys.ibm.pc.hardware.video**

## Quicktime

Quicktime equals fun time. Take a break from work (right now) and go download Quicktime for the Mac or Windows. While you are at it, you can read news and information on developers, authoring and Quicktime music.

**Web:**

**http://quicktime.apple.com/**

A B C D E F G H I J K L M N O P Q R S T U V W X Y Z

A B C D E F G H I J K L M N O P Q R S T U V W X Y Z

## VDOLive

VDOLive is a video streaming system, which allows you to watch real-time video on the Net. The software is free, and they have a gallery you can visit where you can watch videos.

**Web:**

**http://www.vdo.net/products/vdolive/**

## Video Editing

This is a wonderful site with lots of video editing resources. My favorite part of the site is the collection of articles about basic video editing. If you have an interest in video, especially if you are just starting, this is one of the places you will find useful.

**Web:**

**http://www.videonics.com/Articles.html**

## Video Glossary

The world of video, especially computer video, has a lot of specialized terminology. However, you need never feel lost. If you read or hear a word you don't understand, check the glossary at this web site. Before you know it, you will be talking like a pro. ("What do you mean the machine doesn't have a flying erase head? I need to make a telecine transfer.")

**Web:**

**http://www.actwin.com/MediaNation/DVG/Glossary/Glossary.html**

**The Net cares.**

### *Look What I Found on the Net...*

```
Newsgroup: comp.multimedia
Subject: Free Renaming Program

>>> Announcing Resequencer(tm), a FREE Windows utility to rename
>>> sequential image files.
>>>
>>> Suppose you have the files:
>>>     Image051.tga, Image052.tga...Image150.tga.
>>>
>>> With Resequencer, you can rename these files to:
>>>     Image0001.tga, Image0002.tga...Image0100.tga
>>>
>>> Resequencer is a 280 KB standalone EXE.  It requires no
>>> extra DLLs.

>> Yikes!  Does Windows really require a 280k compiled binary to
>> perform the function of a 10-line Perl script?

> No, but Visual Basic does.  Not that anyone's really asking,
> but the equivalent C program would be about 30K on Intel and
> maybe 80K on RISC processors like the Alpha.

If it required 2 MB of RAM, I would not care.  It's a utility
running on a operating system that runs on a computer that is a
tool.  It's not a religion.

Yeah, Windoze sucks.  I program in VisualBasicPro 4.0 because it
was cheap, gets the job done, and I want to spend my time
animating and creating useful utilities, not learning C.

Executable size is now a myth perpetuated as a job security
tool.  Yeah, C might run smaller and faster, but you are talking
about renaming files, not radiosity.
```

## WEATHER

### Climate Data Catalog

This is no farmer's almanac. Don't count on the ache in your knees or the singing of crickets to tell you what the weather is going to be like. Get access to oceanic datasets, surface climatologies, air-sea data, sea surface temperatures, and Navy bathymetry.

**Web:**
**http://rainbow.ldgo.columbia.edu/datacatalog.html**

### Climate Diagnostics Center

You're leaning on the fence talking to the neighbor about life and the weather when he says, "In all my born days, I reckon this is the hottest summer I can ever remember." And when you think about it, you suspect he might have a point. Don't let the mystery of his remark keep you up at night. Utilize the Climate Diagnostics Center to see exactly how the weather has been—not only for your lifetime—but for the last few centuries. Interesting climatological data is used to track persistent anomalies and see how this affects short-term weather.

**Web:**
**http://www.cdc.noaa.gov/**

### Climatic Research Unit

The Climate Monitoring and Diagnostics Laboratory is part of the National Oceanic and Atmospheric Administration in Boulder, Colorado. They have information about aerosols and radiation, ozone and water vapor, and weather observation stations.

**Web:**
**http://www.cmdl.noaa.gov/**

### Current Weather Maps and Movies

Don't risk leaving the house without knowing if you need your galoshes or not. Check out pictures and movies of the latest satellite weather images, which are updated every hour.

**Web:**
**http://rs560.cl.msu.edu/weather/**

**WHAT DO YOU DO WHEN YOU NEED TO KNOW THE CURRENT WEATHER?**

You could look outside, but wouldn't it be faster and easier to just check with the Net?

After all, you can't always trust your eyes, but you know that if you see it on the Net, it *must* be true.

### European Weather Satellite Images

Here is a current infrared satellite image of Europe, showing cloud cover and clear areas. This is the place to consult when you need to find out which parts of the Riviera are sunny, so you know where to go for the weekend.

**Web:**
**http://cspnsv.csp.it/meteo.html**

### Hurricane Forecasts

This site provides information about upcoming hurricanes for the regions around the Atlantic Ocean. Forecasting includes seasonal means and current year forecasts for the number of named storms, named storm days, hurricanes, hurricane days, major hurricanes, destruction potential, and so on. They have the archives from previous years so you can see how close they got.

**Web:**
**http://typhoon.atmos.colostate.edu/forecasts/**

### Hurricanes and Tropical Storms

If you are thinking of moving to a nice tropical place to live, consider researching the weather history of the area. This site offers access to a database containing information on past tropical storms. See pictures of the radar images, maps that track the path of the storm and important statistics.

**Web:**
**http://thunder.atms.purdue.edu/hurricane.html**

A B C D E F G H I J K L M N O P Q R S T U V W X Y Z

## Interactive Weather Browser

It's a real drag when you are the only one in the car wearing a wool suit and everyone else has on deliciously cool and lightweight cotton clothing. Next time, check out this web site for weather hints. You will always be dressed for success.

**Web:**
**http://rs560.cl.msu.edu/weather/interactive.html**

## Marine Weather Observations

When you have been working hard all day and you want to go down to the beach to snorkel, it would be a handy thing to know in advance what the water temperature is like. That way, you will know whether or not to wear your wetsuit. You can find out this information and more from this site. Just click on a coastal region to get information on water temperature, wave height and frequency, and wind conditions.

**Web:**
**http://thunder.met.fsu.edu/~nws/buoy/**

## Meteorology Resources

Weather buffs no longer have to roam the Internet looking for interesting meteorological information. At this web site you will find links to lots of meteorological resources on the Net.

**Web:**
**http://www.met.fu-berlin.de/DataSources/MetIndex.html**

## Meteorology Talk and General Discussion

It may be that no one does anything about the weather, but that doesn't stop us from talking about it. Join the discussion on Usenet about weather and all facets of meteorology.

**Usenet:**
**sci.geo.meteorology**

## Monthly Temperature Anomalies

Take control of your own weather information. This web site will allow you to create contour maps or graphs using temperature anomalies from the Global Historic Climate Network and the Monthly Climatic Data of the World. These two items are combined to give you a good overview of monthly temperature anomalies from around the world.

**Web:**
**http://www.ncdc.noaa.gov/onlineprod/ghcnmcdwmonth/form.html**

## National Center for Atmospheric Research

The National Center for Atmospheric Research (NCAR), headquartered in Boulder, Colorado, is a research center where scientists work together to solve fundamental questions that require a mix of specialties and facilities not readily available elsewhere. NCAR conducts research in many areas, including atmospheric chemistry, climate, weather, mesoscale and microscale meteorology, and the sun and upper atmosphere.

**Web:**
**http://www.ucar.edu/**

### *Look What I Found on the Net...*

```
Newsgroup: sci.geo.meteorology
Subject: Cold Nights and the Full Moon

> Is there a correlation between cold nights and the full moon?

Indirectly, but not caused by the moon.

Cloudy nights tend to be warmer (because the clouds reduce heat
loss), and clear nights tend to be cooler.  If it's very cloudy,
you won't see the moon.  So, if you can see the (full) moon, it
must not be  very cloudy and therefore it's likely to be colder.
```

## Radar and Satellite Images

The next time you attend a costume party, go as a weather forecaster. Dress up in clothing suitable for a television broadcast, set up your computer and point to this web site. It has radar images just like the ones television weather people use. Click on the map for a close-up of the area you want to forecast. Stand in front of the computer and smile and point a lot. This costume will be so convincing probably nobody will recognize you.

**Web:**

**http://www.intellicast.com/weather/usa/**

## Space Weather

It's a total drag when you are leaving Earth's gravitational influence, and you find out the weather in space is really not suitable. Next time, plan ahead. Check out today's space weather. You can see a current image of the sun, X-ray flux data, and get detailed information on solar flaring and the geomagnetic field.

**Web:**

**http://www.sel.bldrdoc.gov/today.html**

## Weather Processor

When the weather is so cold that only an inebriated polar bear would go outside, you can look at the outside from the inside by using the Net. Connect to this web page and see images and surface maps, data and observations about current weather.

**Web:**

**http://wxp.atms.purdue.edu/**

## Weather Radar

There is a lot more to the weather than licking your finger to see which way the wind is blowing. Nobody knows this better than the MIT Weather Radar Lab. They have a home page containing a gallery of radar images, a FAQ list and glossary of terms, research references, and links to other interesting web pages concerning weather radar. MIT keeps a radar data archive containing 20 years of storm system observation. While the archive is too unwieldy to access through the Net, they do list a contact person if you need information about these files.

**Web:**

**http://www-cmpo.mit.edu/Radar_Lab/Radar_Lab.html**

## Weather Reports: Canada

I grew up in Canada and you can believe me when I tell you they have a lot of weather up there. In fact, they have so much, they sometimes send some of the extra weather down to the United States. (And some people say Free Trade is bad.) If you want the official information about Canadian weather, connect to the Environment Canada web site, where you will find the latest weather forecasts, maps, satellite images, surfing forecasts, and so on.

**Web:**

**http://www.dow.on.doe.ca/text/**

**Stay connected.**

### *Look What I Found on the Net...*

```
(from the Space Weather web site)

SPACE WEATHER OUTLOOK

Solar activity is expected to be very low.

The geomagnetic field is expected to remain quiet
for the next 24 hours, with activity increasing to
quiet to unsettled on days two and three.
```

## Weather Reports: International

Here are weather reports for just about everywhere in the world. Once you have the Net access, no matter where are you or what you are planning, there is no excuse for letting the environment rain on your parade.

**Web:**

**http://www.intellicast.com/weather/intl/**
**http://www.usatoday.com/weather/basemaps/wworld1.htm**

## Weather Reports: United States

As Mark Twain once said, "Everyone talks about putting up a good old American weather server on the Net, but nobody does anything about it"—until now, that is. When Mark Twain was alive, he had to get online weather information from an old gopher text-based system that was down a lot of the time. Today you have a choice of well-maintained, attractive web sites, all ready to show you current U.S. weather information whenever you want.

**Web:**

**http://www.intellicast.com/weather/usa/**
**http://www.mit.edu/weather**
**http://www.usatoday.com/weather/wfront.htm**
**http://www.wunderground.com/**

## The Outside World

Living on the Internet is fine, but the outside world has two important advantages: (1) there is pizza, and (2) it's the only place I know of to get a computer. However, there are some significant disadvantages, and high up on the list is that the outside world has altogether too much weather. Before you actually commit yourself to going outside, use the Internet to check the weather report for your area. Why take a chance when the information is only a few keystrokes away?

## Weather World

The University of Illinois is making itself a Mecca of weather information. They provide current satellite images, weather maps and animations, as well as important meteorological information.

**Web:**

**http://www.atmos.uiuc.edu/wxworld/html/general.html**

# WEB: CREATING WEB PAGES

## Animated Gifs

A "gif" is an image that is stored using the gif format. (The name means "graphics interchange format".) An animated gif contains more than one image in the file. When your browser displays an animated gif, the series of images is displayed sequentially, providing for a primitive type of animation. These web sites contain information that explains all about animated gifs: what they are, how to make them and how to use them effectively.

**Web:**

**http://www.bendnet.com/users/brianhovis/anime.htm**
**http://www.reiworld.com/royalef/gifanim.htm**

## Beginner's Guide to HTML

HTML (Hypertext Markup Language) is the set of specifications that are used to define what a web page looks like and how it behaves. If you want to make your own web pages, you need to either (1) understand HTML, or (2) use a program that hides the details from you. You can use such a program, but you get a lot more flexibility and control if you understand HTML. Here is a document to help you get started.

**Web:**

**http://www.ncsa.uiuc.edu/General/Internet/WWW/HTMLPrimer.html**

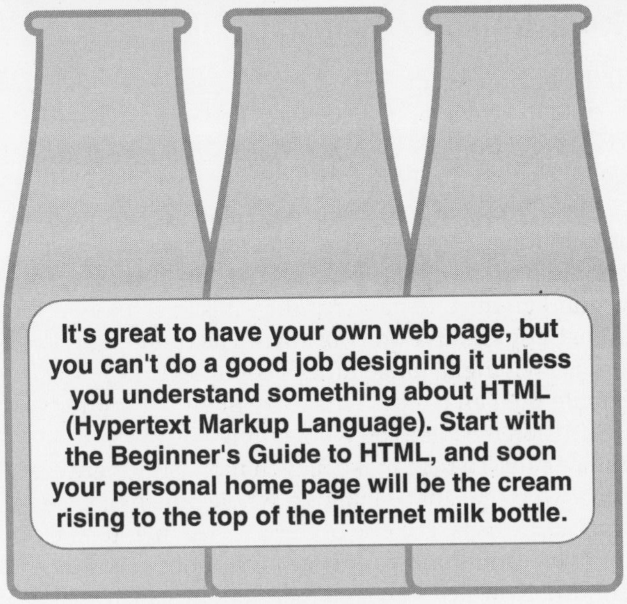
It's great to have your own web page, but you can't do a good job designing it unless you understand something about HTML (Hypertext Markup Language). Start with the Beginner's Guide to HTML, and soon your personal home page will be the cream rising to the top of the Internet milk bottle.

## Bullets, Buttons and Bars

Would you like your web page to stand out like a hyperactive elephant in a taxidermy museum? These sites can help. They are full of graphics suitable for use on web pages. Get your fill of icons, bullets, lines, backgrounds, pictures and more.

**Web:**

**http://members.aol.com/minimouze/private/ICONS.html**
**http://www.cnmnet.com/~ksdurbin/index1/graphics.html**

## CGI Scripts

CGI stands for "Common Gateway Interface", a mechanism by which a web server can process data that you enter into a form. The program that runs when you enter data is called a "CGI script". These web sites explain what CGI is and how it works. You will also find a collection of CGI scripts that you can use or modify. For discussion, you can join the Usenet group. Note: Creating CGI scripts requires programming skills.

**Web:**

**http://hoohoo.ncsa.uiuc.edu/cgi/**
**http://www.selah.net/cgi.html**

**Usenet:**

**comp.infosystems.www.authoring.cgi**

## Color Chart

No more will you have to calculate those hexadecimal numbers to figure out the color you need for the background color of your web page. This is a nice chart that shows you the colors and their corresponding codes.

**Web:**

**http://www.phoenix.net/~jacobson/rgb.html**

## Composing Good HTML

Thousands of people are going to be looking at your web page. Don't embarrass yourself with shoddy workmanship. HTML can be a work of art if it's done right. Get handy tips on how to use HTML to produce beautiful and impressive web pages. Your mama will be proud.

**Web:**

**http://union.ncsa.uiuc.edu/HyperNews/get/www/html/guides.html**
**http://www.cs.cmu.edu/~tilt/cgh/**
**http://www.quadzilla.com/**

## Frames

Frames are devices that allow you to divide a web page into independent sections. Within each frame, you can control how data is to be displayed. These web sites offer tutorials that will help you learn about frames and how to use them. Special request: Not everybody likes to use frames (and not all browsers can support them). Please take the time to ensure that your web pages work properly without frames.

**Web:**

**http://kidshealth.org/~muehlen/papers/frame/**
**http://www.newbie.net/frames/**

## Home Page Construction Kit

When it's time to make your home page and you just don't know where to start, take a look at the Home Page Construction Kit. It has information on page creation, publishing and coding. Start with this HTML template and work your way up by looking at samples of other pages.

**Web:**

**http://gnn.com/gnn/netizens/construction.html**

## HTML Editors

There are various ways to create HTML files. One way is to use a program called an HTML editor. This web site will show you various HTML editors that are available for your operating system. There is also a forum to which you can post and read messages about HTML editors. Hint: Download and evaluate more than one HTML editor. Find the one that works the way you like to work.

**Web:**

**http://union.ncsa.uiuc.edu/HyperNews/get/www/html/editors.html**

HTML Editors

It's not generally well known, but God used an HTML editor to design the universe.

(Why do you think everything lines up so well?)

## Hypertext Markup Language

You're at a party and you have your eye on a hot prospect you've been dying to talk to. You stake your claim at the onion dip, knowing at any minute she will come over, because who can resist onion dip? Finally she does and you strike up a conversation, hoping to talk about something meaningful. And she asks, "Don't you find it terribly inconvenient that, when you get the **rel** and **rev** attributes mixed up within a **<link>** tag, the relationships get all mixed up?" What are you going to do—tell her that women have trouble understanding relationships? Be prepared for situations like this by reading up on all aspects of Hypertext Markup Language *before* you go to a party.

**Web:**

**http://union.ncsa.uiuc.edu/HyperNews/get/www/html/lang.html**

**Usenet:**

**comp.infosystems.www.authoring.html**

## Icons for Fake Awards

It the beginning, the idea sort of made sense: someone would look at a lot of web pages and judge which ones were the very best. Those very best web sites could display a special icon showing that they had achieved recognition, like a "four star" restaurant that is mentioned in a guide book. What happened next should have been predictable. It's a lot easier to go around giving other awards than it is to actually do something creative on your own. The number of people willing to judge other people's work proliferated and, today, there are literally hundreds of awards on the Net. The whole thing has become rather silly. To help make it even more silly, here are some web sites that contains a whole bunch of icons for fake awards. Put one of these icons on your site, and you can thumb your nose at the entire award culture. Now *that's* an idea that deserves an award.

**Web:**

**http://www.asb.com/usr/chet/acenorth/north.htm**
**http://www.thecorporation.com/icon/icon.html**

## Image Maps

Get help trying to figure out clickable image maps. Learn what image maps are, how to make them, and how to map hot spots in your graphics. Check out the image maps tutorials for detailed advice or read the Usenet group to pick up some tips.

**Web:**

**http://www.cris.com/~automata/tutorial.shtml**
**http://www.ora.com/oracom/inet/miis/**

**Usenet:**

**comp.infosystems.www.authoring.images**

## Inlined Images

Web page designers can use this great resource for help on their color mapping and color indexing. The information on this page includes image tips and tricks and some help on problem-solving.

**Web:**

**http://www.softlab.ntua.gr/www/inline-images-faq.html**

## Learning HTML

HTML (Hypertext Markup Language) is a system used to describe the various elements that are used to create a web page. To make a web page, you create an HTML file that contains data along with special instructions (called "tags") that tell a browser how the data should be displayed and processed. You then put the HTML file where it can be accessed by a web server. Now, when someone gives the address of that file to their browser, the browser will contact your web server and request a copy of the file. When the file arrives, the browser will read the HTML and display the data appropriately. If the HTML tells the browser that your web page needs extra files (such as images or photos), the browser will request those as well and display them on the page. (This is why you often see your browser make more than one connection to a web server even though you are only looking at a single page. Each image must be retrieved separately.) HTML is complex and, to create really good web pages, you need to spend some time learning the details and experimenting. Here are two web sites to help you get started. How do you know which HTML beginner's guide to read? Look at a few and pick the one that makes the most sense to you.

**Web:**

**http://www.devry-phx.edu/webresrc/webmstry/lrntutrl.htm**

**Five Reasons**
### Why You Should Learn HTML

(1) It's fun, it's legal, and the high lasts for weeks.

(2) Making your own web page will give you a sense of freedom, independence and confidence that will mark you as a giant among men (or women).

(3) Your mother would be so proud of you.

(4) One person I know didn't learn HTML, and within a few years, his life was exposed as a hollow, meaningless sham.

(5) If all the people who know HTML were laid end to end, they would be very surprised.

**"Fun" is fun.**

## Tables

Within HTML, a "table" is a mechanism for presenting tabular information. Tables can look and work great, if they are designed properly. These web sites contain tutorials explaining tables and how to use them, along with related technical information.

**Web:**

**http://www.charm.net/~lejeune/tables.html**
**http://www.netscape.com/assist/net_sites/tables.html**

## Transparent and Interlaced GIFs

Get the low-down on transparent and interlaced gifs. Find a FAQ, links to tools by platform, and links to platform-independent web pages that will convert your gifs for you.

**Web:**

**http://dragon.jpl.nasa.gov/~adam/transparent.html**

## Web Page Counters

Why be different when you, too, can have a counter on your web page? (There are even cats on the Net who have access counters on their web pages.) Here are some resources that tell you how to put a counter on your page and offer some great samples of counter digits.

**Web:**

**http://purgatory.ecn.purdue.edu:20002/JBC/david/how.html**
**http://www.digitmania.holowww.com/**

## Web Page Creation Talk and General Discussion

This Usenet group is for a discussion of topics related to creating web pages. You can discuss HTML, design style, techniques, tips and so on.

**Usenet:**

**comp.infosystems.www.authoring.misc**

## Web Page Graphics and Icons

These days you don't have to have graphic talent (or even graphics software) to spice up your web pages. These sites have pointers and links to many different icons and graphic images you can use with HTML documents (web pages).

**Web:**

**http://www.geocities.com/Heartland/1448/**
**http://www.geocities.com/SiliconValley/6603/**
**http://www.pitt.edu/~slcst19/icon.html**

## Web Page Textures

There's nothing more tedious than a web page with a dull background. This site provides lots of different textures you can use as web page backgrounds. It also has several links to other texture-oriented web sites.

**Web:**

**http://www.meat.com/textures/**

## Web Page Validation

There are a variety of browsers used on the Net, and they don't all work exactly the same. When you create a web page, it's nice to check that your HTML will work well with various browsers. These sites contains web page validation tools that can help you ensure that the HTML you write is as portable as possible. These tools are sophisticated and provide an in-depth analysis that would be impossible to do by hand.

**Web:**

**http://www.khoral.com/staff/neilb/weblint/validation.html**
**http://www2.imagiware.com/RxHTML/**

> **Web Page Validation**
>
> **You can validate a parking receipt.**
>
> **You can validate a legal document.**
>
> **You can even validate your best friend's feelings.**
>
> **But when you put your own web page on the Net, the only thing anyone will care about is whether or not you have validated the HTML.**

## Web Style Manual

It is a good idea to learn something about good design before you create your own web page. Try reading this style manual loaded with information on document design, navigation, site structure, web page design, efficient use of the Web, design integrity and much more. There is plenty of information for both beginning or advanced users.

**Web:**

**http://info.med.yale.edu/caim/StyleManual_Top.HTML**

# WEB: SOFTWARE

## ActiveX

ActiveX is a complex system that is designed to integrate programs with interactive Internet content. In particular, web sites can use ActiveX tools to create multimedia effects, interactive objects and complex programs. With ActiveX, your browser can download programs from web sites and then execute those programs on your computer. The programs can even interact with your own software (such as your word processor, database, spreadsheet and so on). ActiveX was created by Microsoft and is being actively used by many other companies. ActiveX's main competitor is Java, developed by Sun Microsystems.

**Web:**

**http://www.microsoft.com/activex/default.htm**
**http://www.rapidramp.com/Users/kparker/**

## Browser Watch

A browser is an Internet client program that you use to access the Web. Modern browsers can also read Usenet groups, and send and receive mail. To extend the capabilities of a browser, you can use programs called "plug-ins". This web site carries news about the browser and plug-ins industry. You will find everything you need to know about upcoming browsers and plug-ins, including how to get them quickly. If you are an Internet nerd, you can feast on rumors, news and tips. There is also a big list in which you can look up any browser to see which operating systems it runs on and where to get it. If you are analytical, you can read the browser statistics and look for patterns.

**Web:**

**http://browserwatch.iworld.com/**

## Graphic Web Analysis Program

This program (**gwstat**) processes the HTML output from the **wwwstat** program and generates a set of gif graphs to illustrate the **httpd** server traffic. You can view statistics by hour, by day, by week or by the requesting country or domain. You can also plot traffic statistics for a particular URL from your server.

**Web:**

**http://dis.cs.umass.edu/stats/gwstat.html**

## Internet Explorer

This is the official home of Microsoft's flagship web browser: Internet Explorer. Come here to download the browser (for free), find out about the latest technologies, press information, demos, news and stuff for developers. You can also find all the "extra stuff" to turn your browser into a powerful, supercharged Internet cruiser. (Note: Internet Explorer requires Windows 95 or Windows NT.)

**Web:**

**http://www.microsoft.com/ie/**

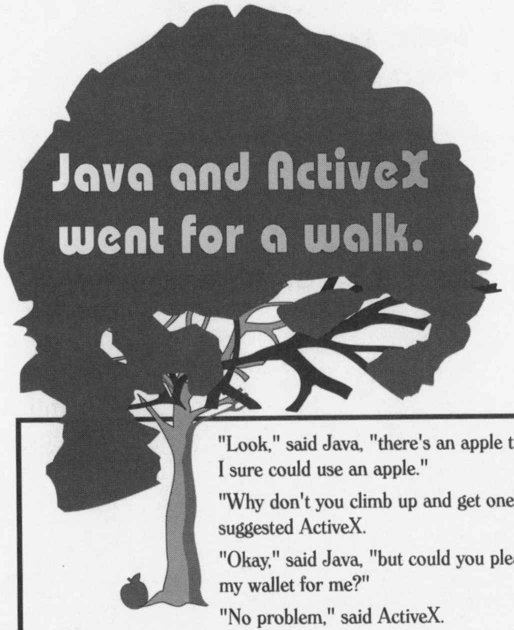
Java and ActiveX
went for a walk.

"Look," said Java, "there's an apple tree. I sure could use an apple."

"Why don't you climb up and get one?" suggested ActiveX.

"Okay," said Java, "but could you please hold my wallet for me?"

"No problem," said ActiveX.

So Java climbed the tree and picked an apple. After Java came back down, ActiveX returned the wallet.

"Wait a minute," said Java. "All the money is gone."

"Oh, that's a service charge," said ActiveX.

"A service charge?" said Java. "What for?"

"For making sure your wallet was safe while you were climbing the tree."

## Java

Java is a complex system designed to support programs that can be downloaded from the Web and run automatically. For example, when you are visiting a web site, selecting a particular link might send a program to your computer, where it will be run by your browser (which knows how to run Java programs). Why is Java important? On its own, a browser can only do so much. It can download and display data. It can also play sounds, show you pictures and images, and so on. But the capabilities of a browser are limited to what is built-in, or what is added by using plug-in or helper programs. With Java, it is possible to write a program to do just about anything, and then put that program on a web site. When someone visits the site, the program is sent to their computer where it is executed. Java is also important because it is the focus of a huge effort to build an Internet environment that can be run on various types of computers and other devices. Although Java was originally developed by Sun Microsystems, many other companies are riding along. Java's main competitor is ActiveX, developed by Microsoft.

**Web:**

**http://java.sun.com/**
**http://www-net.com/java/faq/**
**http://www.gamelan.com/**

**Usenet:**

**alt.www.hotjava**
**comp.lang.java**
**comp.lang.javascript**

## Lynx

Lynx is a text-based Web browser that runs under Unix, DOS and VMS. I like Lynx because it is fast (no graphics) and easy to use. Even if you have the most powerful graphical computer around, give Lynx a try. When you are after pure information, no browser is faster.

**Web:**

**http://www.cc.ukans.edu/about_lynx/about_lynx.html**

**FAQs are cool.**

A B C D E F G H I J K L M N O P Q R S T U V W X Y Z

## Netscape

Netscape is one of the two most popular browsers on the Web (the other browser being Microsoft's Internet Explorer). Netscape is designed to make your web experience as satisfying as possible (although you do need to supply your own food and clean up the carpet afterwards). I have included two web sites here. One is the place from which you can download the Netscape browser; the other is the main web site for the company. Although Netscape is a commercial product, people in schools and universities can use it for free, and everyone else can try it for free. You are, however, supposed to register your software and send them money once you have completed your "evaluation". (Yeah, right.)

**Web:**

**http://www.netscape.com/**
**http://www.netscape.com/comprod/products/navigator/**

## Real Audio

Real Audio is an audio streaming technology from Progressive Networks that allows you to listen to long audio files without having to wait for the entire file to download. Real Audio also makes it possible to listen to live broadcasts, such as radio stations or special events. Your browser may already come with Real Audio capability. If not, you can find the software you need here (for Windows, OS/2, Macs and Unix). You can also start here to look for some of the many places around the Net that use Real Audio to broadcast.

**Web:**

**http://www.realaudio.com/**

## Streamworks

Streamworks is a streaming audio and video player that allows you to listen to sound or look at video in real time. The Streamworks program integrates into your browser to make listening and viewing convenient and easy. Streamworks is available for Windows, Macintosh and Unix. At this web site, you can get the software, and you can find links to many of the sites around the Net that broadcast using this technology.

**Web:**

**http://www.streamworks.com/**

## VRML (Virtual Reality Markup Language)

Get to know your virtual reality from the inside out with a little Virtual Reality Markup Language, or as the cool people say: VRML. These are the places to find FAQs, programming tips, specs, mailing list archives, authoring tools, VRML browsers and more. If you want to talk about VRML, check the Usenet discussion groups.

**Web:**

**http://sdsc.edu/vrml/**
**http://vrml.wired.com/**
**http://www.intervista.com/technology/technology.html**

**Usenet:**

**alt.lang.vrml**
**comp.lang.vrml**

**With VRML, you are virtually certain to create something so realistic that no one will even recognize it.**

## Web Browser Talk and General Discussion

When you use the Web, your experience starts and ends with a browser. The browser you use very much colors your experience, so it is no surprise that people have strong opinions about what they like and what they dislike. In addition, the web browser industry is fast-moving and highly competitive, with new browsers, plug-ins, and related technology appearing all the time. All of this makes for a lot to talk about when it comes to browsers, and these Usenet groups are the places to be. (Take my browser, please.)

**Usenet:**

**comp.infosystems.www.browsers.mac**
**comp.infosystems.www.browsers.misc**
**comp.infosystems.www.browsers.ms-windows**
**comp.infosystems.www.browsers.x**

## Web Server Talk and General Discussion

When you connect to a web site, your browser requests data from a program called a web server. Web servers are complex software systems that require a fair amount of care and feeding. These are the Usenet groups in which you can discuss web servers: what is available, how they work, tips, questions, answers, and lots and lots of opinions.

**Usenet:**

**comp.infosystems.www.servers.mac**
**comp.infosystems.www.servers.misc**
**comp.infosystems.www.servers.ms-windows**
**comp.infosystems.www.servers.unix**

## Web Talk and General Discussion

The Web is one of the most important inventions in the history of mankind. These Usenet groups are used to discuss the Web and related topics. If you want to let the world know about your new web site, you can send a message to the **.announce** group.

**Usenet:**

**comp.infosystems.www.announce**
**comp.infosystems.www.misc**
**comp.infosystems.www.providers**
**comp.infosystems.www.users**

# WOMEN

## Abortion

Think you can sway someone's opinion on this issue? If you like to beat your head against a wall, join the heated discussion here about abortion.

**IRC:**

**#abortion**

If you need some quiet, non-controversial conversation to relax you, try the IRC **#abortion** channel.

## Abortion and Reproductive Rights

Whether you are pro-choice or pro-life, this web site will be of interest to you. Get information from both sides of the issue at the place with the latest news on reproductive rights around the world. You will also have access to archives of press releases and other informative files on the legal aspects of abortion.

**Web:**

**http://web.canlink.com/ocrt/abortion.htm**

## Ada Project

Sponsored by Yale University, the Ada Project acts as a clearinghouse for information and resources relating to women in computing. Find information on fellowships, grants, employment opportunities, statistics, and links to other related resources.

**Web:**

**http://www.cs.yale.edu/HTML/YALE/CS/HyPlans/tap/**

## Bibliographies of Women's Studies

For anyone doing research in Women's Studies or any topic relating to women, this list will be invaluable. The list of bibliographies is separated by topic, so you can scan the choices and select just the one you need.

**Web:**

**http://inform.umd.edu:8080/Educational_Resources/AcademicResourcesByTopic/WomensStudies/Bibliographies**

## Calls for Papers in Women's Studies

You've been slaving over that paper on feminism and family theory, plus you have the one you wrote last year on lesbian scientists. Don't let those papers just sit around gathering dust. Check here to see if anyone wants them. This list will tell you about calls for papers as well as the deadlines. This could be your big chance.

**Web:**

**http://inform.umd.edu:8080/Educational_Resources/AcademicResourcesByTopic/WomensStudies/CallsforPapers**

## Collections for Women

There are a lot of special resources on the Net just for women, and these web sites will make it easy for you to find what you want: hundreds and hundreds of women-related links are waiting for you.

**Web:**

**http://www.eskimo.com/~susan/girls.htm**
**http://www.wonet.com/**
**http://www.wwwomen.com/**

**Collections for Women**

*Some women collect souvenir spoons.*
*Other women collect dolls or teapots or motorcycles.*

*Still other women collect a large circle of friends. But on the Web, what could be more valuable than a collection of links to women-oriented resources?*

## Conferences for Women

Hit the scholarly conference scene by checking out upcoming conferences relating to Women's Studies and gender and sexuality issues. Select links to learn more about a particular conference, including an overview and dates.

**Web:**

**http://inform.umd.edu:86/Educational_Resources/AcademicResourcesByTopic/WomensStudies/Conferences**

## Cybergrrl

Cybergrrl offers lots of great resources for women, covering domestic violence, family life, health and business resources and a gigantic listing of women's web pages.

**Web:**

**http://www.cybergrrl.com/**

## Electronic Forums for Women

Figure out a way to spend even more hours on the Internet. Get this list of electronic forums relating to women. Some mailing lists are for professionals, some have a specific focus of topics, and many are of general interest to women and a nice gathering place to talk.

**Web:**

**http://sunsite.unc.edu/cheryb/women/elec-forum.html**

## Femina

Femina has been referred to as "the Yahoo of women's links". This directory has links to information and resources for both women and girls such as art and writing, business resources, computing information, culture, entertainment, feminism, health and much more.

**Web:**

**http://www.femina.com/**

## Feminism

Some people say the word with awe and pride in their voice. Some people spit the word out violently between clenched teeth and tight lips. Then there is the group who contemplates feminism and gender from a thoughtful, neutral point of view. Whatever category into which you may fall, you are welcome to join the list, but this is not a battleground to prove whether feminism is inherently good or evil. This is a place for thoughtful folk to share information on feminism, gender, women and international relations, world politics, international political economy or global politics. If you are looking for other feminism-related resources, try the nice collection at this web site.

**Web:**

**http://www.igc.apc.org/women/feminist.html**

**Listserv Mailing List:**

List Name: **femisa**
Subscribe to: **listserv@mach1.wlu.ca**

## Feminism Talk and General Discussion

If it weren't for feminists, men wouldn't have anything to grumble about except the President's Address to the Nation interrupting the football game. It's been proven through history that women are good at organizing themselves and getting things done, and they've shown it once again in Usenet. Join one or all of these groups and discuss feminism in all its forms.

**Usenet:**

**alt.feminism**
**alt.feminism.individualism**
**soc.feminism**

## Gender and Computing

For the longest time, computers have been "a guy thing". Why is that? Read articles put up by Computer Professionals for Social Responsibility that cover topics such as women in computer science, feminism, and cross-gender communication.

**Web:**

**http://www.cpsr.org/dox/program/gender/**

**The Net cares.**

### *Look What I Found on the Net...*

```
Newsgroup: soc.feminism
Subject: Clothing and the Oppression of Men

The issue is that women are allowed to wear both skirts
and pants, while men can only wear pants.  Men who wear
skirts are stigmatized by society in a way that women who wear
pants are not.

The way to gain acceptance for men's skirts is not to complain
about it or theorize on discussion groups like this.  The only
way society will change is to just go out and do it.  Look at
how women gained the right to wear pants.

Ms. Bloomer started going out in public wearing pants.  Yes, she
"caught it" from both women and men.  She was harassed and
threatened, but by making a spectacle of herself, the idea
caught on.  As more women discovered the advantages of pants,
more women began wearing them.  As more women began wearing
them, barriers slowly fell (as recent as 25 years ago, schools
forbid girls to wear pants) until now women can wear
pants with impunity.

If Ms. Bloomer merely talked to people about how nice it would
be to wear pants, or complained about male privilege, we'd
probably still be in  skirts.  But she actually went out and did
something about it.

So there's your solution, although it's not an easy one.
Men: Go out, buy or make skirts, and start wearing them.  If
you're afraid to wear them at work, wear them away from work,
socializing with friends or whatever.  Most important, wear them
in public places where other people will see them.

Yeah, some may snub you, but others will be curious and will ask
you questions.  And eventually, some other guys will start
wearing skirts.

Unfortunately, there's not much in this process that women can
do, besides being supportive of men who wear skirts.
```

## Gender and Sexuality

There's no escaping it. Gender and sexuality issues run rampant among the population, spurring arguments, thought-provoking discussion, and philosophical meanderings. Read articles and papers about gender and sexuality and explore other feminist resources available at this site.

**Web:**

**http://english-server.hss.cmu.edu/Gender.html**

## Health Concerns of Women

Woman have special health concerns—especially when it comes to illnesses like endometriosis and ovarian and breast cancer. Read information on these maladies as well as other topics, such as women and alcohol, breast implants, and AIDS.

**Web:**

**http://inform.umd.edu:86/Educational_Resources/AcademicResourcesByTopic/WomensStudies/GenderIssues/WomensHealth**

## Midwifery

You just never know when it's going to happen. You'll be stuck in an elevator or on the subway with a pregnant woman in labor. What will you do then? Plan ahead and get some information on midwifery so you will always be prepared. Articles, information on organizations, and links to other resources are a few of the things that are available.

**Web:**

**http://www.efn.org/~djz/birth/midwife.html**

## Notable Women

Everyone has heard of Susan B. Anthony. After all, her picture is on a piece of U.S. currency. Just because nobody happens to use that currency doesn't mean she's not popular. There are many other notable women who are not so famous, like Annie Jump Cannon, Blanche Ames, and Clara Adams-Ender, but they are among the many women who have done something remarkable during their lifetimes. Read these short biographies and become informed on women in history.

**Web:**

**http://mustang.coled.umn.edu/exploration/women.html**

## Sexual Assault on Campus

While this list is not exclusively for women, it does concern violence against women on college and university campuses. Learn about anti-rape activist groups and share information about assaults and methods of reducing sexual assault against women.

**Listserv Mailing List:**

List Name: **stoprape**
Subscribe to: **listserv@brownvm.brown.edu**

## Web Weavers

Come explore the wonderful world of women by visiting Web Weavers, an annotated list of web pages by women. These pages will lead you down a rabbit hole of creativity, love, and whimsy. This is not a listing of every woman's home page. They have been selected for quality, not quantity.

**Web:**

**http://www2.best.com/~tyrtle/women.html**

**Web Weavers**

**The woman who creates the Web Weaver's site has this to say about her work:**

**"I love the idea of women all over the world weaving a web of links to each other. This is my contribution to that web."**

**Can you think of anything that better captures the spirit of the Net?**

## Women in Congress

Women have been running homes for years, so they might as well run the House, too. Learn about the women in Congress by reading their online biographies.

**Web:**

**http://www.inform.umd.edu:8080/EdRes/Topic/WomensStudies/GovernmentPolitics/WomeninCongress**

## Women's Resources

The ambitious task has been undertaken: to make a women's home page and collect as much woman-stuff as possible. These are remarkable collections, not only of resources, but of writings by and about women. Topics cover professional and academic organizations, Women's Studies resources, and gender and sexuality issues.

**Web:**

**http://www.mit.edu:8001/people/sorokin/women/index.html**

**http://www.vuse.vanderbilt.edu/~suerkeck/women.html**

## Women's Studies Resources

People have been studying women for years. It's just that now they can get college credit for it. Find out about various Women's Studies programs, women's resources on the Internet, and see a special section on women and literature.

**Web:**

**http://umbc7.umbc.edu/~korenman/wmst/links.html**

## Women's Talk and General Discussion

Women: there is a place for you to go to talk with other women about anything you want. The mailing list offers a nice women's space to discuss your personal observations, interests, news, upcoming events and anything else that is relevant to your daily life. If you don't mind anyone jumping into the conversation, try the Usenet group.

**Usenet:**

**soc.women**

**Majordomo Mailing List:**

List Name: **women**
Subscribe to: **majordomo@world.std.com**

## Women's Wire

It's almost like a clubhouse on the Internet and it's just for women. This site covers topics such as women and politics, sports and fitness, women's health, women and work, and other interesting items of a more historical nature.

**Web:**

**http://www.wwire.net/**

**Wow, free software.**

*Look What I Found on the Net...*

```
Newsgroup: soc.women
Subject: Help From Men

> Women wouldn't have gotten any of their rights if men
> hadn't felt bad for them and tried to make things equal.  The
> least feminists can do is return the favor.

Okay.

I can't thank you enough for liberating us.
```

# WORLD CULTURES

## Africa

Africa is a large continent with many different cultures. Here are some resources to help to explore the art, societies, languages, literature, music and customs of Africa. To start, here is a proverb from Nigeria: "Until lions have their own historians, tales of the hunt shall always glorify the hunter."

**Web:**

**http://gwis2.circ.gwu.edu/~odn/africa.html**
**http://www.sas.upenn.edu/African_Studies/Home_Page/Country.html**

**Usenet:**

**soc.culture.african**

**Listserv Mailing List:**

List Name: **h-afrlitcine**
Subscribe to: **listserv@h-net.msu.edu**

**IRC:**

**#africa**

## Army Area Handbooks

These Army Area Handbooks, made available by the University of Missouri, St. Louis, are loaded with historical, geographical, cultural and economic information about a number of selected countries, including China, Egypt, Indonesia, Israel, Japan, the Philippines, and several other Asian, European and African countries.

**Web:**

**http://lcweb.loc.gov/homepage/country.html**



## Asia

Asia has many cultures and peoples, each with its own history, traditions and customs. There are 240 different languages that are spoken by at least one million people each. Perhaps even more incredible, there are 12 languages which are spoken by over 100 million people. (Here is the list, in order, starting from the top: Mandarin, Hindi, Spanish, English, Bengali, Arabic, Russian, Portuguese, Japanese, German, French, Malay-Indonesian.) Clearly, Asia is one of the best continents in the entire world.

**Web:**

**http://www.public.asu.edu/~timehntr/asia.html**

**Usenet:**

**soc.culture.asian**

**IRC:**

**#asian**

## Australia

This is a national web site for Australia, giving access to Australian Internet resources. It also offers a guide to Australia, an interactive map, information about networks in Australia, and much more.

**Web:**

**http://www.about-australia.com/about.htm**

**Usenet:**

**soc.culture.australia**
**soc.culture.australian**

**IRC:**

**#australia**

## Brazil

A web site about the various aspects of Brazilian culture. If you want to interact with real people, check out the Usenet group or join the Brazilian chat channel where Portuguese is often spoken and lots of Brazilians hang out.

**Web:**

**http://www.cf.ac.uk/uwcc/suon/brazil/braz-soc_2cr.html**

**Usenet:**

**soc.culture.brazil**

**IRC:**

**#brasil**

## Cajun Culture

In 1755, the British and the French were gearing up for a war in the New World and, as a preliminary courtesy, the British authorities in Acadia (at the far east of Canada) kindly asked the French colonists to either renounce their religion (Catholicism) and swear allegiance to England, or could they please remove themselves to another part of the planet. What followed was a massive, haphazard migration that ended with a large number of French Acadians settling in the southern part of Louisiana where they established small farms. (The word "Cajun" comes from the original French pronunciation of "Acadia".) Today, there is still a well-established Cajun culture—spreading through 22 of Louisiana's 64 parishes (counties)—and centered around the city of Lafayette. Cajun food has a large variety of specialties such as jambalaya, gumbo, turtle sauce piquante and crawfish bisque. What I like best is that Cajun is that only culture in which one of the traditional musical instruments is the triangle (the other instruments being the fiddle and the accordian). As you can see, when it comes to food or music, Cajun culture has something for everyone.

**Web:**

**http://http.tamu.edu:8000/~skb8721/**
**http://www.webcom.com/dpcajun/lahis.html#Cajun-Country**

**Usenet:**

**alt.culture.cajun**



## Central America

Part zine, part travel guide, this page offers information about the history, geography, and culture of Honduras, Belize, Panama, Guatemala, Nicaragua and El Salvador.

**Web:**

**http://www.greenarrow.com/welcome.htm**

**Usenet:**

**soc.culture.el-salvador**

**Listserv Mailing List:**

List Name: **centam-l**
Subscribe to: **listserv@ubvm.cc.buffalo.edu**

## Central Asia

Join in worldwide communications with other people interested in Central Asia's history, politics, demography, languages, culture, sociology, economics, religion and philosophy.

**Listserv Mailing List:**

List Name: **cenasia**
Subscribe to: **listserv@vm1.mcgill.ca**

**Majordomo Mailing List:**

List Name: **central-asia-studies-l**
Subscribe to: **majordomo@coombs.anu.edu.au**

### *Look What I Found on the Net...*

```
Newsgroup: alt.culture.cajun
Subject: Gumbo

My concept of heaven is immersion in a tub of gumbo with a
string of boudin at hand.
```

## Chile

Although it is only a little larger than Texas, the country of Chile has a coastline that is longer than the width of the continental United States. If you are interested in the culture of this unusual country, you can talk on Usenet, IRC, join the mailing list, or investigate resources on the Web.

**Web:**

**http://www.latinworld.com/countries/chile/**

**Usenet:**

**soc.culture.chile**

**Listserv Mailing List:**

List Name: **chile-l**
Subscribe to: **listserv@modlang.swt.edu**

**IRC:**

**#chile**

## China

This web page provides links to Chinese architecture resources, a Chinese calendar converter, Chinese languages, Chinese literature and music resources, and a link to a Chinese web server. The IRC channels offer discussion about China and the Chinese people.

**Web:**

**http://www.waltontech.com/ch/index.shtml**

**Usenet:**

**soc.culture.china**

**IRC:**

**#china**
**#chinese**

**Read a zine today.**

## Czech Republic

The Czech Republic has some of the most beautiful scenery and interesting culture in Eastern Europe. Take some time to browse this Internet site, and you will find a great many resources to guide you through the Czech Republic. Here is my hint for staying out of trouble: Just memorize this phrase—"To je moc drahe"—and use it as much as possible. (By the way, it is a little known fact, but some of the best typesetters in the world are of Czech descent.)

**Web:**

**http://www.muselik.com/czech/**
**soc.culture.czecho-slovak**

**Usenet:**

**soc.culture.czech**

## Egypt

Take a guided tour of Egypt without ever having to leave your seat. See pictures and learn a little of the history and culture of the land of the great pyramids. You can even download pictures of some of those great pyramids, the Temple of Osiris and the Nile, and then send them to your friends on the Net, saying, "Having a great time. Wish you were here."

**Web:**

**http://www.memphis.edu/egypt/egypt.html**

**Usenet:**

**soc.culture.egyptian**

**IRC:**

**#egypt**

## England

Spend time talking to people on the Net about England and the British. Post at your leisure in Usenet or try the IRC channels for interactive discussion about any topics relating to Great Britain or the British culture.

**Usenet:**

**soc.culture.british**

**IRC:**

**#england**
**#gb**

## Flags of the World

If you are looking for something unique and colorful with which to decorate your home, try downloading some of these flags of the world. Not only will they look nice hanging on your walls, but your visitors will be convinced that you have culture and good taste.

**Web:**

**http://www.adfa.oz.au/CS/flg/**

**Flags of the World**

Here is a good way to have fun and help humanity at the same time.

Go to the Flags of the World web site and look at all the pictures. Then make yourself a copy of each flag and hang them all outside your front door.

Pretty soon, people from all over the world will be coming to you for help in solving their problems.

## Fourth World Documentation Project

Organized by the Center for World Indigenous Studies, these documents provide researchers, tribal governments and organizations with essays, position papers, declarations, treaties, speeches and other items relating to the study of indigenous peoples.

**Web:**

**http://www.halcyon.com/FWDP/fwdp.html**

**The Net is immortal.**

## France

The French Ministry of Culture has marshalled significant resources to ensure that you can sneak a peek at France without having to suffer from jet lag. Practice your French and experience the culture of France at the same time.

**Web:**

**http://web.culture.fr/**

**Usenet:**

**soc.culture.french**

**Listserv Mailing List:**

List Name: **causerie**
Subscribe to: **listserv@inrs-urb.uquebec.ca**

**IRC:**

**#france**

## Germany

Details and information about the geography, people, economy, government, and communications of Germany. There is also a news service in German, a map of Germany, facts and statistics, and a list of all German web servers.

**Web:**

**http://www.chemie.fu-berlin.de/adressen/brd.html**

**Usenet:**

**soc.culture.german**

**IRC:**

**#germany**

## Hungary

The Hungarian web site offers an introduction to Hungary, a little of Hungary's history, its geography, and a map which provides access to Internet resources in Hungary. For Hungarian discussion, you can try Usenet, the mailing list or IRC: a real goulash.

**Web:**

**http://www.lonelyplanet.com.au/dest/eur/hun.htm**

**Usenet:**

**soc.culture.magyar**

**Majordomo Mailing List:**

List Name: **hungary-report**
Subscribe to: **majordomo@isys.hu**

**IRC:**

**#hungary**

## Immigrating to the United States

Here is a web site, maintained by a lawyer, that has a lot of information about immigrating into the United States. If your goal is to move to the Land of the Free and Home of the Brave, this site can help. It is packed with lots of great information about green cards, temporary visas, citizenship, the visa lottery and asylum. There are special sections for students, professionals, doctors and nurses, as well as job search links, news flashes and new law alerts.

**Web:**

**http://websites.earthlink.net/~visalaw/**

**This page is not under construction.**

## India

With more than 900 million people, India is the second most populous country in the world (after China). India's people represent many cultures and tradition, and speak many different languages, with Hindi and English predominating. To a foreigner, India is a mysterious place: a country divided by caste, ethnicity and custom. However, it is also the largest democracy in the world. For more information, you can use the Net to explore the cultures of this large, complex country.

**Web:**

**http://www.cnct.com/home/bhaskar/india.html**

**Usenet:**

**soc.culture.india**
**soc.culture.indian**

**IRC:**

**#india**

## *Look What I Found on the Net...*

(from the Immigration to the United States web site)

Immigration Trivia Quiz: A Governor With Illegal Roots

The Republican platform calls for a broad crackdown on illegal immigration, even endorsing an amendment to the Constitution to prevent children born in the U.S. to mothers who are not citizens or permanent residents from being considered U.S. citizens at birth.

At the Republican Convention, a prominent governor declined an opportunity to deliver a prepared speech endorsing the immigration provisions of his party's platform. He refused on the ground that "(his state) has represented hope and freedom to people from around the world and we have to continue to do that."

With admirable candor, the governor volunteered that his own uncle and grandmother had come to the U.S. illegally. His uncle was a German sailor who jumped ship while his grandmother used her sister's immigration papers when she entered the U.S. from Ireland. Both eventually became U.S. citizens.

Who is this governor and what state does he govern?

(Answer: George Pataki, governor of the state of New York)

## Indonesia

Information about Indonesian in both English and Bahasa Indonesia (the Indonesian language). View a travel guide, pages about food and recipes, music and arts, or science and technology. While you are here, check out the Indonesian comic strip.

**Web:**

**http://www.umanitoba.ca/indonesian/homepage.html**

**Usenet:**

**alt.culture.indonesia**
**soc.culture.indonesia**
**soc.culture.indonesian**

**Listproc Mailing List:**

List Name: **st-yusuf**
Subscribe to: **listproc@lists.colorado.edu**

## Ireland

Ireland has about three and a half million people in an area about the size of West Virginia. The Irish people have a well-known culture—literature, music, dance—as well as highly developed social customs. Meet, chat, and drink with Irish people on the Net, and use the Web to explore the leprechaun-loving Emerald Isle.

**Web:**

**http://celtic.stanford.edu/pmurphy/irish.html**
**http://www.paddynet.ie/island/**

**IRC:**

**#celtic**
**#eire**
**#ireland**

**Do you have a code in the head? Try "Cryptography".**

**Quick, turn the page.**

## Israel

Resources for Israel and Jewish religious, educational, and social service organizations worldwide. Includes interesting lists, articles, and information on politics, and libraries, as well as extensive information on how to make *aliyah* (go home to Israel), including housing information, military service policies, and what to expect when you get there. On IRC, you can chat with people from Israel or people who miss the Israeli homeland.

**Web:**

**http://israel.nysernet.org/**

**Usenet:**

**soc.culture.israel**

**IRC:**

**#israel**

## Italy

From ancient times, Italy has contributed mightily to world culture. Today, Italian food, fashion, language and literature are all influential outside of their native home. To find out about Italy, there are many resources on the Net you can use, as well as Usenet and IRC for discussion. (All this talk about Italy is making me hungry. I wish I had some spaghetti right now.)

**Web:**

**http://www.lainet.com/~initaly/**

**Usenet:**

**soc.culture.italian**

**IRC:**

**#italia**
**#italy**

## Japan

The Japanese information corner of the Web is available in both English and Japanese. Here you can get an audio file of the Japanese national anthem, geography facts, maps and images, details of cultures and customs, multimedia travel tours and guides, government members, Japanese laws and constitution, communication, and links to Japanese Internet sites and resources.

**Web:**

**http://www.ntt.jp/japan/**

**Usenet:**

**soc.culture.japan**

**IRC:**

**#japan**
**#nippon**

## Jerusalem

The Jerusalem One Network is an electronic Jewish library with information about the Jewish people, Jewish organizations, and Jewish art. There are also articles about fighting hate, neo-Nazis and holocaust-related articles, a Jewish calendar of events, links to Hebrew software archives, and links to other Jewish resources on the Internet.

**Web:**

**http://www.jer1.co.il/**

**The *U.S. Library of Congress* has some wonderful exhibits. Don't be misled by the fact that this is an official U.S. Government institution: there is lots of history covering various cultures from around the world. True, the exhibits are "educational" and politically correct, but it is done so well you hardly notice.**

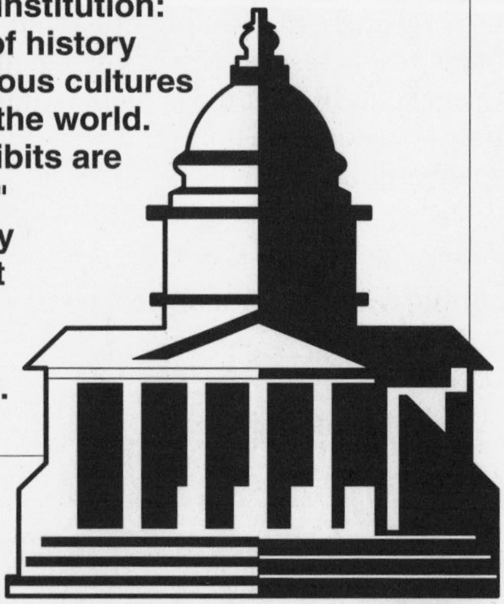

## Korea

The Korean Peninsula was first unified into a single political entity in 668 A.D. During the 19th and 20th centuries, Korea was much affected by the political and military machinations of other countries, making for an interesting and fractured history. However, during World War II, it was agreed by the major powers that, after Japan (which had invaded Korea) was defeated, the country would become an independent state. Unfortunately, at the Yalta Conference in 1945, the leaders of the United States, England and the Soviet Union agreed in secret to divide the Korean Penninsula in the middle in order to make it easier to disarm the Japanese: the U.S. would occupy the south, the Soviets would occupy the north. Well, you can guess what happened. As with other famous divisions in history—such as East and West Germany, North and South Vietnam, and North and South Dakota—one part became communist while the other developed into a Western-style something or other. Today, Koreans are a people divided: North and South Korea share the Korean Peninsula, but that is about all they share. For more information, or to discuss Korean culture, see the Net.

**Web:**

**http://www.iworld.net/Korea/**

**Usenet:**

**alt.talk.korean**
**soc.culture.korean**

**IRC:**

**#korea**

## Latin America

An index to countries, culture, economy, education and research, government, politics, and news about Latin America. This page is in both English and Spanish.

**Web:**

**http://www.latinworld.com/**

**Usenet:**

**soc.culture.latin-america**

**IRC:**

**#latinos**

## Library of Congress Cultural Exhibits

Have some fun exploring a few of the cultural exhibits that have been displayed at the Library of Congress. You'll get to see things like the Dead Sea Scrolls, displays of African-American culture and history, women journalists, photographers and broadcasters during WWII. It's a nice family outing and you don't even have to fight the traffic to get there.

**Web:**

**http://lcweb.loc.gov/homepage/exhibits.html**

## Malaysia

This IRC channel is dedicated to the discussion of the country of Malaysia. If you're planning on traveling to Malaysia, if you live there, or you're just interested, check out **#malaysia**.

**Usenet:**

**bit.listserv.berita**
**soc.culture.malaysia**

**IRC:**

**#malaysia**

## Mexico

Mexico is a large country bordered to the north by the United States and to the south by Belize and Guatemala. Mexico's indigenous population was conquered by Spain the early 16th century and regained its independence in 1822. You can read more about Mexico and its people and culture by checking out the web sites. If you want to talk with people from Mexico, you can participate in the Usenet discussion groups or chat on IRC.

**Web:**

**http://www.latinworld.com/countries/mexico/**
**http://www.mexconnect.com/MEX/FQSOCIAL.HTM**

**Usenet:**

**alt.mexico**
**soc.culture.mexican**

**IRC:**

**#mexico**

## Middle Europe

The first question one must ask when contemplating whether to join a discussion group relating to Middle Europe is: What *is* Middle Europe? It's defined as the countries lying between the Mediterranean/Adriatic and the Baltic Seas and between the German/Austrian borders and the former Soviet Union. That settled, the second question would be: What is the list about? Just about everything. The list is unmoderated, and topics cover history, culture, politics, economics, and current events.

**Listserv Mailing List:**

List Name: **mideur-l**
Subscribe to: **listserv@ubvm.cc.buffalo.edu**

## Morocco

Moonlight in Morocco. It sounds so exotic. What a great movie that would make. The first scene shows a man sitting in front of the computer looking at a web page about Morocco. He reads all about the culture, cooking and history of this country. He decides to go and while he's there he has a daring adventure, finds love, and the final scene shows him and a beautiful woman riding a camel into the sunset. This could be you. Go read about Morocco.

**Web:**

**http://maghreb.net/morocco/**

## Moscow Kremlin Online Excursion

Take a tour of the Kremlin, with this multimedia excursion. See the sights and learn the history of Red Square, the Cathedral of Vasily the Blessed, Aleksandrovsky Garden, Ivan's Square, Cathedral Square, and the Saviour Tower.

**Web:**

**http://www.moscow-guide.ru/Culture/Kremlin/Kremlin0.htm**

**The Net loves poetry.**

## Native American Mailing Lists

Whether you are Native American or simply interested their culture and way of life, here are several mailing lists that may interest you. The **native-l** and **natchat** are general discussion groups. The **nat-1492** discusses the Columbus quincentenary. The **nat-edu**, **nat-hlth**, and **nat-lang** cover the topics of Native American education, health and language.

**Listserv Mailing List:**

List Name: **nat-1492**
Subscribe to: **listserv@tamvm1.tamu.edu**

**Listserv Mailing List:**

List Name: **nat-edu**
Subscribe to: **listserv@indycms.iupui.edu**

**Listserv Mailing List:**

List Name: **nat-hlth**
Subscribe to: **listserv@tamvm1.tamu.edu**

**Listserv Mailing List:**

List Name: **nat-lang**
Subscribe to: **listserv@tamvm1.tamu.edu**

**Listserv Mailing List:**

List Name: **natchat**
Subscribe to: **listserv@tamvm1.tamu.edu**

**Listserv Mailing List:**

List Name: **native-l**
Subscribe to: **listserv@tamvm1.tamu.edu**

## Native Americans

These web sites provide information to various native tribes by name or by geographic region. Here you will find Native American literature, education links, languages, newsletters, history, literature, genealogy and other related Internet resources.

**Web:**

**http://one-web.org/oneida/**
**http://web.maxwell.syr.edu/nativeweb/**

## New Zealand

New Zealand consists of two main islands about 1500 miles east of Australia and 8200 miles southwest of Fargo, North Dakota. The two islands are called North Island and South Island, although the origin of these names is lost to antiquity. The New Zealand web site has a wonderful collection of information. You can learn about famous people from New Zealand such as Edmund Hillary (the first man to climb Mount Everest), Ernest Rutherford (who pioneered our understanding of atomic structure), and Kate Shepphard (notable women's suffragist). You can also find information about the Maori (aborginal people), New Zealand English, read a translation of Jules Verne's encounter with rampaging kiwis (large New Zealand birds), and much, much more. If you are planning a trip to New Zealand, check the Net for travel information before you leave. After all, you don't want to make a wrong turn and end up in Fargo, North Dakota.

**Web:**

**http://nz.com/NZ/**

**Usenet:**

**soc.culture.new-zealand**

## Norway

This graphical map of Norway allows you to click on the site you wish to visit. There are seven different versions of the map which categorize the sites and resources as universities and colleges, research institutes, service providers, commercial services, conferences and festivals, geographical information, or miscellaneous, allowing you to easily locate the necessary site.

**Web:**

**http://www.service.uit.no/homepage-no**

**Stay away from "X-Rated".**

## Poland

Interesting information about Poland and Polish culture, including geographical facts, maps and lists of Polish multimedia servers, Usenet groups, Warsaw Stock Exchange quotations, newspapers, journals, information on Polish satellite TV stations, and history articles.

**Web:**

**http://info.fuw.edu.pl/pl/PolandHome.html**

**Listserv Mailing List:**

List Name: **poland-l**
Subscribe to: **listserv@ubvm.cc.buffalo.edu**

**IRC:**

**#poland**
**#polska**

**Intrigue, Privacy, Secret Stuff...**

**Feel lucky? Try "Contests".**

## Portugal

A home page for Portugal, offering facts and statistics about its geography, people, economy, government, and communications, a text version of the national anthem in Portuguese, postal codes, a Portuguese news journal, list of Internet domains and public BBSs, a bibliography of Portuguese history, many photos in gif format, the song that won the Portuguese Song Contest, travel information, exchange rates, and more.

**Web:**

**http://s700.uminho.pt/Portugal/portugal.html**

**Usenet:**

**soc.culture.portuguese**

**IRC:**

**#portugal**

### *Look What I Found on the Net...*

(from the Inter-Tribal Network information site)

THE CONSTITUTION OF THE IROQUOIS NATIONS:

THE GREAT BINDING LAW, GAYANASHAGOWA

1. I am Dekanawidah and with the Five Nations' Confederate Lords I plant the Tree of Great Peace. I plant it in your territory, Adodarhoh, and the Onondaga Nation, in the territory of you who are Firekeepers.

I name the tree the Tree of the Great Long Leaves. Under the shade of this Tree of the Great Peace we spread the soft white feathery down of the globe thistle as seats for you, Adodarhoh, and your cousin Lords.

We place you upon those seats, spread soft with the feathery down of the globe thistle, there beneath the shade of the spreading branches of the Tree of Peace. There shall you sit and watch the Council Fire of the Confederacy of the Five Nations, and all the affairs of the Five Nations shall be transacted at this place before you, Adodarhoh, and your cousin Lords, by the Confederate Lords of the Five Nations...

## Russia

There's a wealth of Russian resources on the Internet. Read about the language and culture of Russia. Check out the Russian literature guide, computer-related material, glossaries and word lists, recipes, jokes, lyrics, politics, and translation information.

**Web:**

**http://www.kiae.su/www/wtr/**
**http://www.pitt.edu/~cjp/rees.html**
**http://www.serve.com/serge/rusweb/**

**Usenet:**

**soc.culture.russian**
**soc.culture.russian.moderated**
**soc.culture.soviet**

**IRC:**

**#russia**
**#russian**

## Russian and American Friendship

Join this information system developed by Russians and Americans in an effort to form a bond between the two countries. There is information on almost anything you would want to know about Russia or the relationship between Russia and America—Cyrillic alphabet, news, history, music, art, medicine, economics, travel and tourism, and culture in general.

**Web:**

**http://april.ibpm.serpukhov.su/friends/**
**http://solar.rtd.utk.edu/friends/home.html**

**Listserv Mailing List:**

List Name: **friends**
Subscribe to: **listserv@solar.rtd.utk.edu**

### Russian and American Friendship

If you are in America, you should know that this book is translated into Russian.

DEPARTMENT OF STATE
UNITED STATES OF AMERICA

If you are in Russia, you should know that this book is one of the best-selling English Internet books of all time.

Can you think of a better way to encourage friendship?

## Saudi Arabia

When the public library is closed and you have a sudden desire to read all about Saudi Arabia, fear not. This site has information about Islam, a history of Saudi Arabia, documents about the government, education, economy, health, culture and arts. The main page has current news and travel information.

**Web:**

**http://imedl.saudi.net/**

**Usenet:**

**alt.culture.saudi**

**Majordomo Mailing List:**

List Name: **islam-arabia**
Subscribe to: **majordomo@darkwing.uoregon.edu**

## Slovakia

Slovakia, a country in central Europe, was more or less under Hungarian rule until 1918, at which time it became part of Czechoslovakia. On January 1, 1993, Czechoslovakia split into Slovakia and Czech Republic. On the Net, you can find information such as maps, history, statistics, tourist information, pictures, accommodation guides, political information, transportation details, and so on. You can also use Usenet to talk about Slovakia and its culture.

**Web:**

**http://www.eunet.sk/slovakia/slovakia.html**

**Usenet:**

**soc.culture.slovak**

## Southeast Asia

This is a growing archive about Southeast Asia. Get information about the settlement of refugees and boat people, read newsletters and see pictures which illustrate a little of the Southeast Asian culture.

**Web:**

**http://www.lib.uci.edu/sea/seahome.html**

## Sweden

Sweden has a population of 8.7 million people, 85 percent of which live in the southern half of the country. Sweden is one of the oldest continuously existing countries on the entire planet, being over a thousand years old. In that thousand years, Sweden has given the world much to be thankful for: food and drink (especially vodka), automobiles, furniture, as well as a model for highly socialized democracy.

**Web:**

**http://www.webcom.com/sis/**

**IRC:**

**#sweden**

## Taiwan

Taiwan (which used to be called Formosa) is an island nation off the southeast coast of China. Taiwan was first settled by Chinese in the seventh century. It was later held by Holland, then China and then Japan. In 1945, after World War II, control of Taiwan passed back to China. However, in 1949, the Nationalists (led by Chiang Kai-Shek) were expelled from mainland China by the Communists and settled in Taiwan where they set up a government in exile. Today, Taiwan is still completely separate from China, although the two countries have significant cultural and economic ties.

**Web:**

**http://www.cybertaiwan.com/**

**IRC:**

**#taiwan**
**#tw**

**Why be ordinary, when you can read the "Bizarre" section?**

## Thailand

Thailand (once called Siam) occupies a central position in southeast Asia, both geographically and politically. The country was first established in the mid-14th century, but spent much of its history being dominated by other countries. In 1932, Thailand became a constitutional monarchy. Today, the Thai people are united in three ways: via the Buddhist religion, through their love for freedom, and by their support of the monarchy.

**Web:**

**http://www.cs.ait.ac.th/~wutt/wutt.html**

**Usenet:**

**soc.culture.thai**

**IRC:**

**#thailand**

## United Kingdom

This web site—the U.K. Guide—presents you with a number of resources, including a map of the United Kingdom and certain hot spots to investigate. You can find out information on different towns and cities, weather info, and you can also take a guided tour and learn about restaurants, pubs, hotels, museums, and more.

**Web:**

**http://www.cs.ucl.ac.uk/misc/uk/intro.html**

## United States

Here are a popular IRC channel and Usenet group, where people gather to talk about the United States. There is no doubt that American culture, inventiveness and finance all have an enormous effect on the world at large. Here are the places to discuss what America is and how it fits into the global community. Talk, argue and meet new friends, all at the same time.

**Usenet:**

**soc.culture.usa**

**IRC:**

**#usa**

## United States: Southern

The culture of the South has a rich diversity, from grand plantations to secluded hills, from the Atlantic coast to the Gulf coast. Read and discuss the history, conversational language, humor, and culture of the South, and maybe get a good recipe for barbecued ribs while you are at it.

**Web:**

**http://imp.cssc.olemiss.edu/**
**http://sunsite.unc.edu/doug_m/pages/south/south.html**

**Usenet:**

**bit.listserv.sthcult**

## Venezuela

Pictures of Venezuela, travel tips, links to Venezuelan institutions on the Net, maps, economic data, exchange rates, business practices, export descriptions, local time, and more to do with this South American country bordering the Caribbean.

**Web:**

**http://venezuela.mit.edu/**

**Usenet:**

**soc.culture.venezuela**

**IRC:**

**#venezuela**

## World Constitutions

The constitutions and basic laws for many countries around the world, including Germany, Hong Kong, the United States, Canada, China, Hungary and the Slovak Republic, as well as the texts of the English Bill of Rights, Magna Carta, John at Runnymede, and others.

**Web:**

**http://www.adi.uam.es/docencia/tex_der/constm.htm**

### Research, Net-Style

My brother Randy got his Ph.D. from Oxford University by researching and writing about Bills of Rights from British Commonweath countries. At the time, he had to do all his research in the library. Now all he would have to do is connect to the Net.

Randy had to go to England and live in continual dampness, waking up early every morning for rowing practice, and walking around in constant fear that a member of the royal family might pass by.

As a Net user, you can sit in your living room—a tall cool drink by your side, the family cat snuggling quietly in your lap—and download world constitutions with one hand tied behind your back.

## World Culture Talk and General Discussion

Usenet has many different discussion groups related to cultures. There are too many for me to list here, but all the names follow one of two patterns: either **alt.culture.***something* (for example, **alt.culture.hawaii**) or **soc.culture.***something* (for example **soc.culture.australia**).

**Usenet:**

**alt.culture.***
**soc.culture.***

## World Heritage List

A list of both cultural and natural historic sites, properties, and cities around the world as approved by UNESCO's World Heritage Committee.

**Web:**

**http://www.cco.caltech.edu/~salmon/world.heritage.html**

## Yiddish

If it wasn't for Yiddish, we wouldn't have cool words like shlemiel and schlemazel (good words useful for a variety of occasions). Even if those are the only two Yiddish words you know, you can still get enjoyment from discussing any topic that involves Yiddish, such as literature, history, news and more.

**Listserv Mailing List:**

List Name: **mendele**
Subscribe to: **listserv@yalevm.cis.yale.edu**

# WRITING

## Children's Writing

A *lot* of people want to write for children. If you are going to be successful, you must be persistent, skillful, knowledgeable, experienced, talented and lucky. Where it comes to information, the Net can help. These web sites have lots of resources for writing for children. One site contains answers to frequently asked questions, a glossary of common terms, and information about agents and submissions. The other site is maintained by an editor (not a writer), and offers information from a slightly different perspective. The Usenet group is a good place to visit. It's where real writers hang out, and if you spend some time there, you will definitely learn something.

**Web:**

**http://www.mindspring.com/~cbi/**
**http://www.users.interport.net/~hdu/**

**Usenet:**

**rec.arts.books.childrens**

## Copy Editing

Web sites and a mailing list for copy editors and other defenders of the King's English who wish to discuss editorial problems, client relations, Internet resources, dictionaries, or whatever.

**Web:**

**http://www.rt66.com/~telp/sfindex.htm**
**http://www.theslot.com/**

**Listserv Mailing List:**

List Name: **copyediting-l**
Subscribe to: **listserv@cornell.edu**

Want to converse with the people whoze job it iss to find3e mistakess? Jpin the copy editor's maleing list.

## Creative Writing Pedagogy

Are good writers born or taught? At a college and university level, creative writing is offered as part of the general curriculum. Discuss how and why creative writing is taught, the role it plays in the curriculum, the history of creative writing programs, and the atmosphere of courses and what influence it has on students' lives. This list is for teachers and students.

**Listserv Mailing List:**

List Name: **crewrt-l**
Subscribe to: **listserv@umcvmb.missouri.edu**

## Dr. Who

Who is that odd fellow bedecked in a voluminous overcoat and mile-long neck scarf? Who, that's who. Hop in your tardis and join the Dr. Who following with creative stories based on the adventures of the happy-go-unlucky doctor. (But we thought Who was on first...)

**Usenet:**

**alt.drwho.creative**

## Electronic Publishing

Here's a great idea for a rejection-notice-free writing experience. Connect to this web site and read all about electronic publishing. Gather up all your writing and then publish it on the Net. Then write yourself a nice royalty check and treat yourself to some ice cream. The Net can make dreams come true.

**Web:**

**http://www.iglou.com/hermit/epub/**

## Freelance Writing FAQ

Does the romance of uncertain work and low remuneration sound appealing to you? Perhaps you are ready to be a freelance writer. Take a look at this FAQ (frequently asked question group) all about the business of freelance writing. Learn about how to start, the best ways to submit your work, publishing terminology, and so on.

**Web:**

**http://vanbc.wimsey.com/~sdkwok/freefaq.html**

## Grammar and English Usage

When someone is reading your work, there are various demands you can make. You can ask your reader to recreate various thoughts, feelings and emotions within his or her own mind. You can expect your reader to pay attention to new words (if you explain them properly) and to follow a chain of ideas, from one point to the next. What you can't expect is for anyone to exert mental effort figuring out what you are trying to say because you didn't use the generally accepted writing conventions. Imagination is great, but not where it comes to grammar, punctuation or word usage. These web sites have a lot of information about grammar and style—information that will help you develop your writing skills. One of the web sites contains the FAQ (frequently asked question list) for the Usenet group **alt.usage.english**. This is the Usenet group in which you can discuss words, rules and how to use them.

**Web:**

**http://www.english.upenn.edu/~jlynch/grammar.html**
**http://www.stetson.edu/~hansen/writguid.html**
**http://www.webcom.com/~kcivey/engusage/**

**Usenet:**

**alt.usage.english**

## Internet Directory of Published Writers

A database of published authors and literary agents who use the Internet. You can search the database by name or category or you can just browse the list. If you are a published author, enter yourself in the database.

**Web:**

**http://www.writers.net/**

## Mystery and Crime Writing

Are you a mystery writer? Would you like to be one? These web sites have lots of useful information for mystery and crime writers. On Usenet, the **rec.arts.mystery** is the place to discuss mystery plays, books and films. The other groups are where people talk about actual and imaginary crimes. These are good places to visit when you need inspiration or information.

**Web:**

**http://www.crl.com/~mikekell/crimewriter.html**
**http://www.inkspot.com/~ohi/www/mystery.html**

**Usenet:**

**alt.crime**
**alt.true-crime**
**rec.arts.mystery**

## Online Writery

An environment for writers to explore various forms of writing resources on the Internet. This is not a list of links, but actual methods of interacting with other writers such as by email, through Usenet groups or on a MOO (a type of interactive chatting environment).

**Web:**

**http://www.missouri.edu/~wleric/writery.html**

## Prose

These bite-sized morsels of prose make the perfect afternoon brain snack. No matter what tickles your fancy, the variety of stories will have something for you. Read or share, it's up to you: just remember, if you don't use it, you'll lose it. The **.prose** Usenet groups are for stories and articles. The **.d** group is for discussion.

**Usenet:**

**alt.prose**
**alt.prose.d**
**rec.arts.prose**

## Publisher's Web Pages

Looking for information about a specific publisher? Here's a listing of publishers who have a presence on the web. They are sorted by specialty, such as children's books, mystery, non-English and reference.

**Web:**

**http://www.bookwire.com/links/publishers/publishers.html**

**Screenplays**

I have a friend who is a screenwriter, and she won't let me look at her current screenplay until it is finished.

But do I care? No, because I can go to the Net and look at as many screenplays as I want.

## Screenplays

If you are working on a screenplay, you definitely need something to do when you are not writing. The Net is always available with plenty of relevant distractions. First, you can talk to other screenwriters on Usenet or on a mailing list. The Usenet group is for the discussion of writing screenplays and other related topics. The mailing list is for writers, agents, producers and other people who are interested in screenwriting for movies and television. The web pages are great for when you need inspiration or information. One site is a huge archive of movie scripts; the other site is an ever-changing repository of news and gossip about the film industry.

**Web:**

**http://home.cdsnet.net/~nikko11/scripts.htm**
**http://www.hollywoodreporter.com/m.shtml**

**Usenet:**

**misc.writing.screenplays**

**Listserv Mailing List:**

List Name: **scripts-l**
Subscribe to: **listserv@nosferatu.cas.usf.edu**

### *Look What I Found on the Net...*

```
Newsgroup: alt.usage.english
Subject: Segue and Segway

>>> Has anyone else seen the second spelling, "segway", as valid?

>>> I thought I saw it spelled that way at two radio stations, one
>>> in New York and another in Chicago.

>> I'm a bit confused -- how can you see the spelling of anything
>> on the radio?

> Now, now.  Are we practicing a false metonymy here?

Hmm.  I don't know if he was being serious, but it does raise an
interesting issue of disambiguation.

How would one best write the sentence "I *heard* something at a
radio station" to make it absolutely clear that I was standing
next to someone speaking into a microphone at the physical plant
with a transmitter?

(And how would one best rearrange the clauses in the previous
sentence?)
```

A B C D E F G H I J K L M N O P Q R S T U V W X Y Z

## Screenwriters and Playwrights

Do you have dreams of being a successful screenwriter or playwright? Here are some resources that may help you. This is a compilation of Net resources for screenwriters and playwrights as well as some general writing resources. There are lots of good links here, so even if this page doesn't help you pay the bills, it will at least give you something to read between now and the time your electricity is shut off.

**Web:**

**http://www.teleport.com/~cdeemer/scrwriter.html**

## Speechwriting

You know, of course, that when you listen to an Important Person make a speech that he or she did not write the words. Important People have speechwriters: skilled and imaginative writers who make a living telling other, less skilled and imaginative people what to say. If writing speeches appeals to you, visit this web site for a lot of useful information. There is also a great collection of speeches along with links to other related resources on the Net.

**Web:**

**http://speeches.com/**

## Technical Writing

Technical writers create exposition: words that explain. A technical writer must be able to master a complex subject, and then describe it for a casual reader who needs to understand the relevant facts and ideas. This mailing list is for a discussion of all aspects of technical writing. The Usenet group is the same as the list, so you only need to read one of them. The web site stores archives of previous discussions.

**Web:**

**http://listserv.okstate.edu/archives/techwr-l.html**

**Usenet:**

**bit.listserv.techwr-l**

**Listserv Mailing List:**

List Name: **techwr-l**
Subscribe to: **listserv@**

## Writers Chat

This IRC channel is for writers to discuss all the aspects of writing that normal people don't understand. This channel is great for spending time blabbing when you should be writing (an important part of any writer's day). The web site is the official home for the channel. Visit the site and you can look at bios and information about the regulars. There is also information about occasional workshops that are help in IRC.

**Web:**

**http://www.erinet.com/madmax/**

**Usenet:**

**#writers**

## Writer's Resources

Holy inkwell, Batman. The Net is loaded with resources for writers. Here are some links to useful references and fun material for all types of writers.

**Web:**

**http://owl.trc.purdue.edu/resources.html**
**http://www.ceridwyn.com/motjuste/main.html**
**http://www.nashville.net/~edge/**
**http://www.vmedia.com/shannon/writing.html**

## Writers Talk and General Discussion

Being a professional writer is fun because you can sleep in and work in your pajamas all day. Professional writers or those who aspire to be writers have established a community on the Net, and share thoughts and ideas about writing, critique works in progress, and post announcements of workshops, contests, and new publications. Many of the people who have been on this list have been there for a long time, so it has a nice welcoming atmosphere. If you'd rather talk on Usenet, there is also a good writing community there. The web site is the official home of **misc.writing**.

**Web:**

**http://vanbc.wimsey.com/~sdkwok/mwrit.html**

**Usenet:**

**misc.writing**

**Listserv Mailing List:**

List Name: **writers**
Subscribe to: **listserv@mitvma.mit.edu**

## *Look What I Found on the Net...*

[things that writers talk about when they should be working...]

===============

Newsgroup: misc.writing
Subject: The Perils of Peanut Butter

I don't like raisins -- except in those big chunky chocolate squares -- what were they called? I forget! Oh, no. It's early chocolate memory loss. Help!

===============

Newsgroup: misc.writing
Subject: How Much Reading Do You Do?

How is it that two people can read a book and love it, and the same two people can read another book, and one of us loves it and the other does not?

===============

Newsgroup: misc.writing
Subject: Procrastination Tips and Tricks

When it's time to write, what do you do to procrastinate? I've done things like:

Succumb to the never-before-nor-since-experienced urge to look through the phone book for listings of old friends I haven't seen in years.

Decide I really, really, really need a haircut because my hair being too long is distracting me.

Suddenly realize I have to have a copy of Frank Zappa's "You Can't Do That On Stage Anymore, Vol. 3" -- RIGHT NOW - and make a trip to the record store.

Convince myself that writing a message to start a new thread on misc.writing will take only a couple minutes, and the sooner I do it, the sooner the discussion can begin, and then I'll get down to the real work I need to be doing. Yes, really, I will.

Ya know, I just glanced out the window, and those clouds look pretty ominous. Could be a thunderstorm brewing up, so it might be a good idea to unplug my computer...

## X-RATED RESOURCES

### Adult Site of the Day

Being an adult is lots of fun because you get to do almost anything you want. In particular, you get to look at "adult" pictures. This site canvasses the world of adult culture and, each day, presents one site that rises above the rest. Visit here every day and you will be surprised at all the interesting social and cultural horizons you can expand with just a few clicks of your mouse.

**Web:**
**http://www.aosotd.com/**

### Backside Page

Whether you are a klismaphiliac or simply curious, the Backside Page will astonish you. (Not recommended for home use.)

**Web:**
**http://www.well.com/user/cynsa/newbutt.html**

### Bondage, Discipline, Sadism and Masochism

If vanilla is too nice for you, here are a few resources that will spice up the atmosphere around your house. The web sites have lists of BDSM resources and the IRC channels are where you can meet other people into the scene.

**Web:**
**http://weber.u.washington.edu/~sfpse/ftpsite.html#bdsm**
**http://www.eden.com/~nail/bdsm.htm**

**IRC:**
**#BDSMDungeon**
**#BDSMLounge**

### Dirty Talk

Talk dirty to you? Whip me, beat me, hurt me, just don't stop talking dirty to me! It's a hot and popular channel, but you don't even have to get a word in edgewise to get a kick out of this.

**IRC:**
**#hotsex**
**#jack-off**

***Every day, in every way, you should be getting better and better.***
***(Just to help it along, it wouldn't be a bad idea to check the Adult Site of the Day.)***

### Dominant Women

Wouldn't it be a big surprise if the demure librarian you've been dating turned out to be a leather-wearing, whip-toting goddess of domination who wanted nothing more than to make you submit to doing somersaults in a vat of lime jello? On this Usenet group you can read about women who dominate and the men who love them.

**Usenet:**
**alt.sex.femdom**

### Erotic Postcards

Having access to the Net can make your day-to-day life a lot easier. For example, say you have fallen behind on writing nice letters to your family back home. Or perhaps you have not yet been able to find the time to write thank you notes for all the presents you received on your last birthday. (What? You don't write thank you notes every time someone gives you a gift? Shame on you.) Well, this web site can help. There are lots of places on the Net that will help you send an electronic postcard, but this service does it with pizzazz. Choose from a colorful collection of erotic postcards that is sure to liven up the atmosphere in just about anyone's electronic mailbox. Just make your pick, write a special message, and send that very special greeting zipping down the Net like a greased pig surfing through hot butter. Keeping in touch has never been so easy (and so effective).

**Web:**
**http://www.naked-truth.nl/porncard/**

## Erotic Resources

No bachelor party would be complete without a nice display of erotic links on your monitor. These sites will go well with any snack food you might be offering during the event except, perhaps, large slices of pizza which should be eaten using two hands. This list will take you to erotic places containing images and stories.

**Web:**

**http://shell.glo.be/~anakron/pictures/ero-am.htm**
**http://www.engr.ukans.edu/~khadjiky/links_erotic.html**
**http://www.erols.com/acer75/sexx2.htm**

**LOVE TO THINK?**

Smart, willing, intellectual women are on standby and eager to talk to you. Let us turn you on to a little Shakespeare or – for those of you into hardcore – some James Joyce. Feel free to be yourself. All that is on *our* minds is to stimulate *you* into some intellectual action. We'll talk about anything... quadratic equations, Unix, objectivism, post-modernist sculpture, the current political administration, cgi scripts, or the Big Bang theory.

Call now and fill our heads with ideas.
**Phone (900) 4-BRAINS or telnet to 127.0.0.1.**
**Only $12.95 per minute.**
Student discounts available.
Special rates for readers of
***The Internet Complete Reference.***

## Fetish Fashions

There are people who believe that nudity is highly overrated and that much of the fun in life can be had from fetish clothing like shoes, stockings and other things that you can dress the body in. Whether it's plastic, rubber, leather, silk or another material—this Usenet group is guaranteed to be interesting to people who get excited by dressing up or down.

**Usenet:**

**alt.sex.fetish.fashion**

## Kama Sutra

The Kama Sutra is perhaps the most well-known erotic self-help book. See what the ancient commentators have to teach you about mankind's oldest pastime. These teachings describe a wide variety of sex positions and techniques, including the Jewel Case, Love's Noose and the Clinging Creeper.

**Web:**

**http://entisoft.earthlink.net/kamasutr.htm**

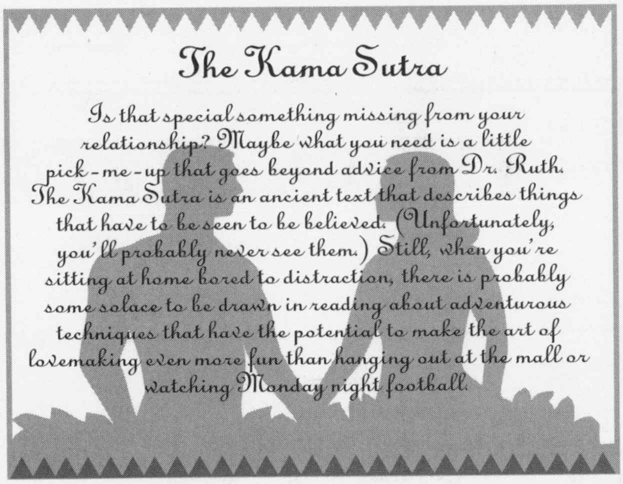
The Kama Sutra
Is that special something missing from your relationship? Maybe what you need is a little pick-me-up that goes beyond advice from Dr. Ruth. The Kama Sutra is an ancient text that describes things that have to be seen to be believed. (Unfortunately, you'll probably never see them.) Still, when you're sitting at home bored to distraction, there is probably some solace to be drawn in reading about adventurous techniques that have the potential to make the art of lovemaking even more fun than hanging out at the mall or watching Monday night football.

### *Look What I Found on the Net...*

```
(from the Kama Sutra, available on the Net)

To Enslave a Lover:

Leaves caught as they fall from trees
and powdered with peacock-bone
and fragments of a corpse's winding-sheet
will, when dusted lightly
on the love organ, bewitch any woman living.
```

## Libido Magazine

Everybody these days is talking about healthy minds, healthy bodies, healthy spirits. Well, what about a healthy libido? Take the truly holistic approach to life by reading Libido. They have pictures, erotic fiction, non-fiction articles about sex and book reviews.

**Web:**

**http://www.indra.com/libido/**

## Limericks

Probably sometime, somewhere, somebody actually did write a limerick that wasn't dirty. If so, it's not here.

**Web:**

**http://www.teleport.com/~klsmith/limerick.shtml**

**What if...?**

**:-)**

## Naughty Linx

If you are looking for something naughty, go to the people who do it for a living. This site has a great collection of adult links presented in a format that parodies Yahoo. No matter what your preference, you'll find it here somewhere.

**Web:**

**http://www.naughty.com/**

## Net Sex

You thought you'd done it everywhere. Now try it on the Net, as couples and groups indulge in verbal sex across the world. This is one of the many channels for hot chatting on IRC.

**IRC:**

**#netsex**

### *Look What I Found on the Net...*

```
                (from the list of IRC statistics)

IRC channels with over 40 people in them regularly:

   ======================
   #windows
   #os/2
   #submission
   #jack-off
   #gam - gay asian males
   #gaygifs - gay pictures
   #cybersex
   #mirc
   #sexpics
   #ircnewbies
   #c
   #windowsnt
   #hichat - home improvement chat
   #baseball
   ======================
```

## Nikkita's Outrageous Fantasies

Unlike Victoria's Secret, Nikkita's Fantasies are not secret. Top of the list has to be the I-want-to-take-my-clothes-off-in-front-of-millions-of-people fantasy. And Nikkita makes sure she indulges in her fantasy. Besides the many nude photos of Nikkita, you can read erotic stories, see adult movie reviews and read about Nikkita's wild parties.

**Web:**

**http://monkey.hooked.net/m/grinder/nikkita/**

## Oral Sex

"Do you like oral sex?" I asked her. "Oh yes," she replied, "I think everybody should talk about it." Well, on the Net everybody does talk about it. Visit these web sites to get all the information you are likely to need about oral sex. For related activities (such as begging and bragging), you are on your own.

**Web:**

**http://wso.williams.edu/peerh/sex/safesex/oralsexm.html**
**http://wso.williams.edu/peerh/sex/safesex/oralsexw.html**
**http://www.halcyon.com/elf/altsex/asfaq_cunni.html**
**http://www.halcyon.com/elf/altsex/asfaq_fella.html**

## Prostitution Around the World

This FAQ is a great guide to the world of prostitution (whatever end of the stick you happen to be on). There is a large list of many different countries. Click on the country of your choice and get the scoop on the prostitution scene there. (For convenience, there is also a link to the CIA World Factbook if you want to find out other information as well.) The presentation is complete: along with all the prostitution info, you can read about travel resources such as currency converters, foreign language guides, and so on. In addition, there are links to strip clubs, general reports about prostitution, and legal, cultural and miscellaneous articles (such as advice on how to kick the habit and prostitution limericks). Lots of good clean (free) fun. For discussion, you can try the Usenet groups.

**Web:**

**http://www.paranoia.com/faq/prostitution/**

**Usenet:**

**alt.sex.brothels**
**alt.sex.prostitution**
**alt.sex.services**

## Sex Chat

If you are looking for the popular channels for hot talkers, here is a list to get you started. Jump right in and create some action, or sit back and enjoy the show.

**IRC:**

**#sex**
**#sextalk**
**#wetsex**

## Sex Magazine Talk and General Discussion

It's important to be cultured and well-read. Not only will you win friends and influence people, but you will undoubtedly find it much easier to get a date. On the other hand, some days it's nice to give yourself a break and look at magazines that are highly prized for their picturesque qualities. Get recommendations on good magazines, where to buy them, information on trading or buying collector's editions, and general discussion about the concepts of sex magazines.

**Usenet:**

**alt.sex.magazines**

## Sex Magazines

When you are in the mood for a little culture or you want to read some informative articles, there are several big name magazines on the Net that you can browse. These magazines offer interesting excerpts of articles and columns from their print versions. For instance, while I was doing my research, I ran across an excerpt from an interview with G. Gordon Liddy in which the interviewer asked what Liddy thinks of group sex. (He likes it.) Oh, I almost forgot. These magazines have some pictures, too.

**Web:**

**http://hustler.onprod.com/**
**http://www.penthousemag.com/**
**http://www.playboy.com/**

**Stay connected.**

A B C D E F G H I J K L M N O P Q R S T U V W X Y Z

## Sex Pictures

Let's take a minute to stop and appreciate the vast resources of the Internet: all those computers, communications lines, satellites. Not to mention the tens of thousands of people working day and night to ensure that it all hangs together. All of this, just so you can download sexy...err...erotic pictures to display on your own computer. Usenet, mirroring the world at large, has a large selection of Usenet groups devoted to various aspects of visual gratification. The **.d** groups are for discussion. All the other groups are for pictures only. (Note: If you want to learn how to download pictures and what software you need, read *The Internet Complete Reference*.)

**Usenet:**

**alt.binaries.nude.celebrities**
**alt.binaries.pictures.erotica**
**alt.binaries.pictures.erotica.amateur.d**
**alt.binaries.pictures.erotica.amateur.female**
**alt.binaries.pictures.erotica.amateur.male**
**alt.binaries.pictures.erotica.anime**
**alt.binaries.pictures.erotica.art.pin-up**
**alt.binaries.pictures.erotica.black.females**
**alt.binaries.pictures.erotica.black.male**
**alt.binaries.pictures.erotica.blondes**
**alt.binaries.pictures.erotica.bondage**
**alt.binaries.pictures.erotica.breasts**
**alt.binaries.pictures.erotica.butts**
**alt.binaries.pictures.erotica.cartoons**
**alt.binaries.pictures.erotica.cheerleaders**
**alt.binaries.pictures.erotica.d**
**alt.binaries.pictures.erotica.female**
**alt.binaries.pictures.erotica.female.anal**
**alt.binaries.pictures.erotica.fetish**
**alt.binaries.pictures.erotica.fetish.feet**
**alt.binaries.pictures.erotica.furry**
**alt.binaries.pictures.erotica.gaymen**
**alt.binaries.pictures.erotica.latina**
**alt.binaries.pictures.erotica.male**
**alt.binaries.pictures.erotica.male.anal**
**alt.binaries.pictures.erotica.oral**
**alt.binaries.pictures.erotica.orientals**
**alt.binaries.pictures.erotica.pornstar**
**alt.binaries.pictures.erotica.pregnant**
**alt.binaries.pictures.erotica.redheads**
**alt.binaries.pictures.erotica.senior-citizens**
**alt.binaries.pictures.erotica.spanking**
**alt.binaries.pictures.erotica.uniform**
**alt.binaries.pictures.erotica.urine**
**alt.binaries.pictures.erotica.voyeurism**
**alt.binaries.pictures.lesbians**
**alt.binaries.pictures.nudism**
**alt.sex.pictures**
**alt.sex.pictures.d**
**alt.sex.pictures.female**
**alt.sex.pictures.male**
**alt.sex.pictures.misc**

## Sex Stories

There comes a time in everyone's life when you get tired of reading Internet books. The next time you are looking for some fresh stimulation, turn to the Usenet groups devoted to sharing erotic stories. (The **rec** group is moderated.)

**Usenet:**

**alt.sex.stories**
**rec.arts.erotica**

**Sexy Stories**

Life is so short and, one day, you will come to the realization that there are more good things to read than you will have time for. What a waste it would be if you would be if you got to the end of your life and discovered that there was a huge backlog of sexy stories floating around the Internet. Don't let your life become a meaningless charade. Start reading today.

## Sex Story Archive

Are you looking for a good bedtime story? If you have a little trouble settling down with Beowulf, try an erotic story or two instead. They might just hit the spot.

**Web:**

**http://www.nitespots.com/adult/site/erotic_pen/**

## Sex Talk and General Discussion

On Usenet, the discussion about sex ranges from serious to XXX-rated. The **alt.sex** group is for just about any topic you want. The **wizards** group is for serious questions, serious sex experts and would-be serious sex experts. (But don't let yourself get too serious.)

**Usenet:**

**alt.sex**
**alt.sex.wizards**

> Talk is not only cheap,
> on the Internet it's free.
> And what could be better than
> talking about everybody's
> favorite topic?
> Join the discussion
> on Usenet and experience
> the freedom of real talk
> about real topics.

## Tickling

Oh, the agony and the ecstasy of being tickled. Ticklers and ticklees talk about where and how they like it—on the feet, ribs, back of the knee, inner thigh or places that we can only mention between the hours of midnight and 4:00 a.m. Read stories, personal experiences and thoughts on tickling as an intimate pastime.

**Usenet:**

**alt.sex.fetish.tickling**

## Video Sex

Video conferencing is for more than stuffy business meetings. After a hard day at work, you can tune your eyeballs to a nice room with a view. Find out more on IRC.

**IRC:**

**#cuseemesex**

## X-Rated Animal Chat

Here's a channel for those folks with more than a fondness for animals. A resident sheepbot is there to keep the channel interesting with a running commentary.

**IRC:**

**#beastsex**

## X-Rated Movies

Who needs gorgeous vistas, great soundtracks and good acting when you have a few naked people gyrating around in front of the camera? Get hard and fast information on X-rated movies, actors and actresses, and FAQs from related Usenet groups.

**Web:**

**http://homepage.eznet.net/~rwilhelm/asm/dbsearch.html**

**Usenet:**

**alt.sex.movies**

**IRC:**

**#sexmovies**

## Zoophilia

There are some people who believe that if you limit yourself only to people, you are missing out on something special. Well, Mr. Ed and Flipper probably wouldn't approve, but here is an Internet site especially for the type of animal lovers who like to bring out the beast in themselves.

**Web:**

**http://www.c2.net/~valadan/frontpage.html**

### *Look What I Found on the Net...*

```
Subject: Girl Penpals
Newsgroups: alt.sex.movies

Life can be pretty hectic.

That's why I was happy to find a site where I could meet some
girl penpals.

Take a look at http://www.xxxxx.com/

The girls seem to be friendly and really looking for someone to
write to.
```

# YOUNG ADULTS

## Christian Youth

Church isn't the only place to meet with other Christian youths. Young people from around the world discuss issues that concern them: not only biblical queries, but thoughts and ideas about society. Topics include sex before marriage, how to get along with people of the same age and how to defend the Christian faith. This group is moderated.

**Usenet:**

**soc.religion.christian.youth-work**

## Cyberteens

Visit this web site if you would like to see the creative things that other teens are doing. There is a teen zine that takes submissions from teen writers and photographers, a section for young composers (some really amazing compositions), games and puzzles, a gallery of artworks and more. I really enjoyed exploring this site.

**Web:**

**http://www.cyberteens.com/**

**Cyberteens**

Young people around the world are doing some amazing things. Find out what's happening by visiting Cyberteens.

## Fishnet

Fishnet is an electronic magazine for academically gifted teens and their parents. It's packed with interesting news tidbits and has a college guide to assist a teen's move from high school to the higher education scene. Check out the collection of articles updated regularly and the teen jargon section.

**Web:**

**http://www.jayi.com/**

## Girl Stuff

This is a useful, interesting and engaging web site. Although the site is maintained by a company that makes tampons, the information is great and well worth your time. For example, you can read Tina Net, silly and embarrassing stories from a girl named Tina. You can also enjoy diary excerpts, cool tunes, hints on how to relate to guys, fashion, a question and answer column, and lots more. In addition, there is personal information for girls about changes in their bodies, menstruation, and so on. And, for everyone, there is an interactive calendar that you can use to predict when your period will start for months to come.

**Web:**

**http://www.troom.com/**

## How Money and Finance Work

One of the most valuable skills you can have is to understand money and how it works. This web site is designed to help young people understand finance. Learn about how checks are turned into cash, how to exchange money into different currencies, earning interest, contracts, stocks and so on. The examples are from the "real world" and are probably at least as interesting as most of what you hear in school.

**Web:**

**http://www.ingenius.com/product/cyberhd/youth/fred/fred.htm**

## Marijuana Facts

This site is maintained by the National Institute on Drug Abuse, a division of the United States Department of Health and Human Services. This guide has two sections, one for teens and one for parents. This is an excellent resource for people who are concerned about marijuana use and want to know more about its effects (especially the long-term effects).

**Web:**

**http://www.nida.nih.gov/MarijBroch/Marijintro.html**

## MidLink Magazine

Middle school kids do not have to feel left out. MidLink is an electronic magazine for kids ages 10 to 15. It offers an interactive space where middle school kids all over the world can see art and writings from other kids or submit their own creative works.

**Web:**

**http://longwood.cs.ucf.edu/~MidLink/**

## Scouting

Young adventure seekers will have a great time with scouting. These two web sites offer scouting information for both boys and girls. The IRC and Usenet groups give young people a chance to talk to other kids who are interested in scouting.

**Web:**

**http://www.bsa.scouting.org/**
**http://www.gsusa.org/**

**Usenet:**

**rec.scouting**

**IRC:**

**#scouting**

## Teen Chat Rooms

The great thing about working on the computer and saying it's a school project is that, when you are grounded and you can't leave the house, you can still talk to kids your own age and have fun. There are lots of special chat areas just for people your age. Pick the one that is appropriate and talk all night long (or until you have to go back to doing your homework).

**Web:**

**http://www.irsociety.com/cgi-bin/webchat_doorway.cgi?Room=Teen_13-15_Chat**
**http://www.irsociety.com/cgi-bin/webchat_doorway.cgi?Room=Teen_16-19_Chat**

**Teen Chat Rooms**

Boy, you guys are lucky.
When I was a teenager, there wasn't even an Internet, let alone chat rooms.
We had to go out in the street in order to talk (in three feet of snow).

## Teen Dating Page

Would you like to meet an interesting person to talk to by email? Visit this web site (made by teenagers) where teens have filled out forms about themselves: their favorite quote, hobbies, favorite bands, and so on. Browse through and, if you find someone you would like to know, you can get his or her email address and send them a note.

**Web:**

**http://pages.prodigy.com/Typhon/**

## Teen Driving Tips

Driving can be a lot of fun, especially when you can drive well. Here are some tips for new drivers. Read the hints for driving to school, around town and in the country. Learn about driving in bad weather, when to pass (and when not to), fatigue and buying a used car. Note: This web site was created by a teenager who is a new driver. He did a good job: the tips are great. (Hint: This is a good place to show your parents when they ask why you spend so much time on the Net.)

**Web:**

**http://www.ai.net/~ryanb/**

**Need to get the word out? Use the Net.**

## Teen Movie Critic

Here are movie reviews from a teenager's point of view. The reviews are updated weekly and use a ranking system. Read in detail why movies got good or bad reviews. This is a good place to visit before you spend your money on a new film.

**Web:**

**http://www.skypoint.com/members/magic/roger/teencritic.html**

## Teen Talk

Do you think people are not listening to you? Make yourself heard on Threads, the forum where you can post your opinions on abortion, school, relationships, recreation and philosophy.

**Web:**

**http://www.jayi.com/jayi/Threads/opent.html**

**For some cool dreams, try sleeping with this book under your pillow.**

**Over 95% of people check the "Trivia" section.**

## Teenagers

The nice thing about talking on the computer is that you don't have to worry about someone picking up the extension and listening to everything you say. Hop onto IRC and talk to teenagers around the world. They are waiting for you. (Don't forget to do your homework first.)

**IRC:**

**#teen**
**#teens**

## Trends for Teens

Read lots of good advice about how you can be trendy in the most important areas of your life: hair and clothing, hygiene products, fitness, magazines, TV shows, underwear, watches, beauty products and much more. Find out what other people think about slang, music, drugs, entertainment, movies, etc. The whole thing is one big giant list that is fascinating to read. (Hint for adults: This is a good resource if you want to buy a present for a teen and you need some ideas.)

**Web:**

**http://www.cloud9.net/~thorpy/TEEN.HTML**

### *Look What I Found on the Net...*

(from a Teen Talk forum)

Okay, I really like this guy, but he likes this other girl. I know this sounds really cut and dried, but just hear me out.

He sits right in front of me in math, and he flirts in class, and of course I flirt back. She's in my math class too, and he also flirts with her. It makes me feel really hurt when he flirts with her. His last class is right across from mine, so we talk across the hall a lot, and he seems really sweet, and we flirt, until he sees her again.

So, what should I do, give up on him, or just keep trying?

## Virtually React

For more fun than a barrel of teenaged monkeys, check out this great web site. It has an online version of React, a newspaper about teenagers. Read about teen-related news, sports features, entertainment topics, contests, jokes and lots of other stuff designed to make teenagers say, "Oh wow, Dude. That's so cool."

**Web:**

**http://www.react.com/**

**Want to get starry-eyed? Try "Romance" (or "Astronomy").**

## Young Adults Talk and General Discussion

Here are some lively places where kids and teens can post about anything they want. Traffic is high and there are lots of diverse messages, as well as some thoughtful conversation. This is a great place for young people to meet their peers.

**Usenet:**

**alt.kids-talk**
**alt.teens**

## Youth and Children Resources

Here is a great resource for kids and teens who need help or information relating to real-life problems. At this web site, kids and teens can get important toll-free numbers to hotlines and help organizations, links to resources relating to safety, child abuse, children and divorce and even some fun stuff.

**Web:**

**http://www.slip.net/~scmetro/childco.htm**

### *Look What I Found on the Net...*

```
Newsgroup: alt.teens
Subject: M&Ms Questionnaire

M&Ms Questionnaire:

What is your favorite color of M&M:

   red, green, yellow, orange,
   dark brown, light brown, any color?

As this is for a school project could you please complete a few
personal details?

   Age:
   Gender:
   State:
   Country:

Thanks for your time.
```

## ZINES

### Bad Subjects

Thinking for yourself is Bad. Thinking in ways that are not mainstream or that are radical is Bad. That's why Bad Subjects is so good. Check out the zine that promotes the questioning of old ways and tries to show how politics applies to everyday life.

**Web:**
**http://english-www.hss.cmu.edu/bs/**

**Listserv Mailing List:**
List Name: **bad**
Subscribe to: **listserv@eng.hss.cmu.edu**

> **Bad Subjects**
> Some people look at the world and ask
> **"Why?"**
> Other people look at the world and ask
> **"Why not?"**
> Bad Subjects looks at the world and asks,
> **"Why don't you figure it out for yourself?"**

### Cybermad

Cybermad is a pop culture zine with lots of craziness. Enjoy the lunchbox gallery (to show off vintage lunchboxes), Dante's pit of advice (the inferno guy giving advice to those in need), comics, weird recipes you probably never want to eat, silly science, a daily mystery site, and much more.

**Web:**
**http://www.cybermad.com/index.html**

> **There's no such thing as too much bandwidth.**

### Cyberspace Vanguard

Sometimes reading science fiction and fantasy isn't enough. Immerse yourself in the culture by getting news and reviews through Cyberspace Vanguard. This zine will fill you in on all the details of new books and movies, the latest grit from the television and movie world, and some clever opinion pieces.

**Web:**
**http://www.cybervanguard.com/**

### Ethical Spectacle

For those of you with a lack of ethical dilemmas, you can now get a zine that will give you hours of ideas to mull over. Issues include articles about genocide, sexual harassment, politics, affirmative action, and other party-pleasing topics for discussion.

**Web:**
**http://www.spectacle.org/**

### Explosive Cargo

The Internet's foremost proponent of self-deprecating humor, Michael Tucker, is in reality a mild-mannered computer trade journalist who once a week turns into a mild-mannered Internet columnist. Join the tens of thousands of Tucker's fans around the Net by subscribing to his weekly column and by exploring Explosive Cargo, his online zine devoted to wit, commentary and generally being literate.

**Web:**
**http://www.webpub.com/xcargo**

**Majordomo Mailing List:**
List Name: **explosive-cargo**
Subscribe to: **majordomo@world.std.com**

### Kingswood Kranium

It's funny, it's fresh, and it will twist your brain into amazing contortions without actually doing any permanent genetic damage to offspring you may produce in the near future. Kingswood Kranium is a great collection of silliness that you absolutely must see: witty writing, pictures with bizarre captions, contests and more.

**Web:**
**http://www.kingswood.com/**

## Kudzu

Taste some contemporary fiction, poetry and essays straight off the vine. Kudzu brings together a wonderful selection of thoughts, ideas and creativity.

**Web:**

**http://www.etext.org/Zines/Kudzu/**

## Morpo Review

There are people out on the Net who love to write and want to share their works of literary art with you for free. This bimonthly zine will offer you some great fiction, non-fiction and poetry.

**Web:**

**http://morpo.novia.net/morpo/**

## Netsurfer Digest

This is a cool zine. The fun folks at Netsurfer Digest troop around all week looking for interesting news and web sites just for you (and you, and you). I recommend you visit the site regularly, or even have the zine mailed to you, so there is always the guarantee that no matter what else happens in the chaos of day-to-day existence, at least you'll have something fun to look forward to this week. If you are new to Netsurfer Digest, check out all the back issues so you can see what you have been missing all this time.

**Web:**

**http://www.netsurf.com/nsd/**

### *Look What I Found on the Net...*

```
                    (from Kingswood Kranium)

            Great words to use in an upcoming term paper
            ============================================
                Hygrometer - Pupfish - Misguggle
                      Galago - Diadelphous

                         Soup of the Day
                         ===============
                            Ox Noodle

                   Number one reason to smile
                   ==========================
                      To air out your teeth

                 Things that make you go "ouch!"
                 ===============================
            Bumping into a disgruntled water buffalo
       Accidentally ingesting a 50 pound bag of 1/4 inch
                    galvanized roofing nails
      Getting your lower intestine caught in your zipper
      You know, you express your feelings a bit too much
```

A B C D E F G H I J K L M N O P Q R S T U V W X Y Z

## Ovi's World of the Bizarre

Do you like stories that are weird but true? You will love this zine. You can look at the Top 20, a random story, as well as the current issue of the zine. Do you need more? An archive of past issues is available. "Bangkok, Thailand: After snatching a purse from a woman, a Thai thief ran inside a building which he believed was Buddhist temple. It turned out to be a police station." (I know how he feels. I have often made the same mistake myself.)

**Web:**

**http://www.ovis.com/**

## Salon

There was a time, before television and radio, when cultured and intelligent people would gather at someone's house in order to talk. This was known as a "salon". At a salon, people would think for themselves (instead of repeating what they heard on the news and talk shows), and elegant and stimulating conversation was considered valuable. This web site seeks to capture the spirit and philosophy of the salon days, when thinkers, writers and scholars would sit in comfortable chairs and discuss ideas. You are invited to visit.

**Web:**

**http://www.salon1999.com/**

## Suck

Suck offers a running-at-the-mouth commentary about current events. The people who create Suck describe it as "an experiment in provocation, mordant deconstructionism, and buzz-saw journalism". Hmm... they should know. Should you read Suck? Only if you enjoy in-your-face diatribes that mix equal amounts of wit, research and testosterone to pick holes in everyone with more power, money and influence than the man on the virtual street.

**Web:**

**http://www.suck.com/**

## Urban Desires

If you are looking for a snazzy magazine to browse while sipping a cappuccino, you've found it. Urban Desires calls itself "an interactive magazine of metropolitan passions" and has a beautiful layout with book reviews, art, fiction, essays, regular columns and music reviews.

**Web:**

**http://desires.com/**

## Word

This frantic and entertaining web site will keep you busy, busy, busy (and coming back for more). There is no particular theme, so indulge yourself by reading humorous articles and essays, comics, quizzes and an advice column. There are a lot of articles about interesting people doing interesting things. ("The Road to Wimp Rock, or How I Became a Billy Joel Fan"; "Holy Laughter: The Story of a Bunch of Christians Who Responded to God's Presence With Fits of Hysteria and How Their Leaders Sort of Expelled Them for It"; "Head in the Clouds: The Best Orgasm Harmon Leon Ever Had Happened 10,000 Feet Over San Francisco".)

**Web:**

**http://www.word.com/**

## Worldly Web News

The Internet has its very own tabloid magazine. Full of silly Enquirer-like articles, Worldly Web News covers such burning issues as alien radio transmissions, sentient dogs on the Internet, incredible weight loss programs and alien abductions, but not necessarily in that order. Why read real news when you could read the Worldly Web News?

**Web:**

**http://www.portal.ca/~direct/satire/**

## Zine Lists

Making your own zine is the rage. In zine-land, nothing is sacred. Zines cover topics as mainstream as education, politics, and philosophy and as bizarre as hyperactive armadillos and free verse about plastic lawn ornaments.

**Web:**

**http://www.dominis.com/Zines/ByCategory/**
**http://www.mcn.net/mag.html**
**http://www.meer.net/~johnl/e-zine-list/**

## Zine Talk and General Discussion

Zines are cool whether you are in the business of making them or just reading them. Learn about the latest releases, old zines making a comeback or calls for submissions. On this Usenet group, you can also participate in the discussion of publishing or submitting, copyright issues, and the production and distribution of electronic or print zines.

**Usenet:**
alt.zines

**Zine List**
**Whatever you want, whatever you need, whatever your destiny happens to be, there is a zine waiting for you.**

# ZOOLOGY

## Entomology

Entomology is the study of insects. There are more 600,000 known insect species, representing about ninety percent of all recognized species on the planet, so if you are an entomologist, there is no shortage of material to study. This web site offers a huge collection of entomological resources on the Net. The **bugnet** mailing list is for non-professionals to send insect-related questions to professional entomologists. The **insectphysiol** mailing list is for entomologists to discuss insect physiology. The Usenet groups are for general discussion and for talk about lepidoptera (butterflies and moths).

**Web:**
**http://www.public.iastate.edu/~entomology/ResourceList.html**

**Usenet:**
**sci.bio.entomology.lepidoptera**
**sci.bio.entomology.misc**

**Listproc Mailing List:**
List Name: **bugnet**
Subscribe to: **listproc@listproc.wsu.edu**

**Listproc Mailing List:**
List Name: **insectphysiol**
Subscribe to: **listproc@msstate.edu**

## Ethology Talk and General Discussion

Ethology is the study of animal behavior. A simplistic view of animals would say that a particular type of behavior is either instinctual or learned. However, modern thought holds that much of what we observe cannot be explained so simply. We have come to realize that much depends on an interaction between an animal's genetic inheritance and its environment when it is young. I find the ethology discussions on the Net fascinating, and even if you are not a biologist, you may enjoy reading what people have to say.

**Usenet:**
**sci.bio.ethology**

**Listserv Mailing List:**
List Name: **ethology**
Subscribe to: **listserv@searn.sunet.se**

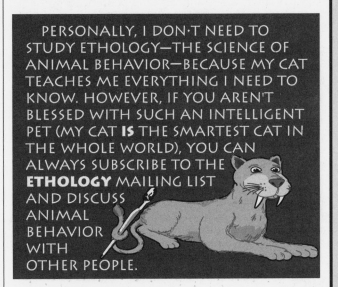

PERSONALLY, I DON'T NEED TO STUDY ETHOLOGY—THE SCIENCE OF ANIMAL BEHAVIOR—BECAUSE MY CAT TEACHES ME EVERYTHING I NEED TO KNOW. HOWEVER, IF YOU AREN'T BLESSED WITH SUCH AN INTELLIGENT PET (MY CAT **IS** THE SMARTEST CAT IN THE WHOLE WORLD), YOU CAN ALWAYS SUBSCRIBE TO THE **ETHOLOGY** MAILING LIST AND DISCUSS ANIMAL BEHAVIOR WITH OTHER PEOPLE.

## Frog Dissection Kit

Here's one of the hottest biology resources on the Net. The interactive web frog dissection kit is for use in high school biology classrooms. It uses photo images that allow you to perform a virtual dissection, including preparation, skin incisions, muscle incisions and examination of internal organs.

**Web:**
**http://george.lbl.gov/ITG.hm.pg.docs/dissect/**
**http://teach.virginia.edu/go/frog/**

## Herpetology

Herpetology is the branch of zoology that deals with reptiles and amphibians. This web site offers pictures of frogs, lizards, snakes, and other such critters. You can also find information about herpetoculture (breeding your own reptiles), and a taxonomy list showing orders/genus/species. This Usenet group is for discussing the scientific study of reptiles and amphibians. (If you like to keep these cool animals as pets, try **rec.pets.herp**.)

**Web:**

**http://gto.ncsa.uiuc.edu/pingleto/herp.html**

**Usenet:**

**sci.bio.herp**

## Mammals

Some of my favorite animals (and people) are mammals, so these two web sites are among my zoological favorites. You can find lots of information about all types of mammals, as well as a taxonomy guide to help you keep everything straight. (My philosophy is: "A name for every mammal, and a mammal for every name".)

**Web:**

**http://www.geocities.com/CapeCanaveral/3073/**
**http://www.ucmp.berkeley.edu/mammal/mammal.html**

## Marine Life

If you have a question about a marine animal, there is a good chance that the answer is at one of these web sites. One site had a fantastic database of hundreds of marine specimens. The other page will help you find marine life resources all over the Net. The Usenet groups are for discussing dolphins and whales. When you need to find out quickly how Ctenophora differ from Platyhelminthes, it's comforting to know that the Net will not let you down.

**Web:**

**http://ourworld.compuserve.com/homepages/jaap/**
**http://www.mbl.edu/html/MRC/specimens.html**

**Usenet:**

**alt.animals.dolphins**
**alt.animals.whales**
**bionet.biology.deepsea**

## Nonindigenous Aquatic Species Resources

It's nice to know that wherever you go in the world, you can look up what kind of aquatic species you might encounter. Find data on all sorts of aquatic life organized by state, hydrologic unit or species.

**Web:**

**http://www.nfrcg.gov/nas/nas.htm**

**An out-of state fish is going to visit you for the weekend, and you are embarrassed when you realize you know nothing about his particular species. Not to worry. Just use your web browser to access the Nonindigenous Aquatic Species Resources and you will be able to make even the most distant piscine guest feel as comfortable as a fish in water.**

## Ornithology

Ornithology is the study of birds. One of these web sites is a big list of bird resources on the Net. The other site provides access to the Aves database, in which you can look for books and articles about birds. Note: The database has a bias toward geese and waterfowl. (But then, don't we all?)

**Web:**

**http://www.biol.sfu.ca/wildberg/birdref.html**
**http://www.chebucto.ns.ca/Environment/NHR/bird.html**

## Primates

When you are getting down to some serious monkey business, here's the place to start. This site has information dedicated to primate biology, including discussions, a directory of primatology, newsletters, behavioral patterns, animal welfare legislation, and other items of interest.

**Web:**

**http://www.primate.wisc.edu/**

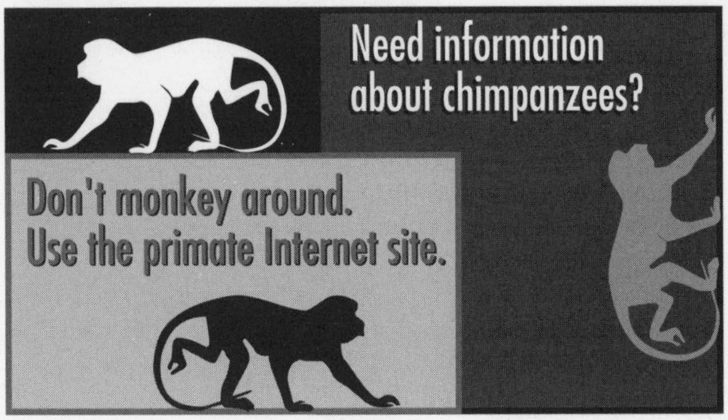
Need information about chimpanzees?
Don't monkey around.
Use the primate Internet site.

## Strange Animals

Scientists make mistakes, lots of them. This web site discusses the mistakes scientists have made in relation to animal life. Read about sea monsters, dragons, and dinosaurs, as well as forgeries and frauds perpetrated by scientists. There are also some fascinating drawings, made by scientists, that show various types of monsters.

**Web:**

**http://www.turnpike.net/~mscott/**

## Zoological Resources

Slippery, slimey, creepy, crawly, furry, or scaley, this site probably has it covered. This is a nice collection of resources such as web sites, databases, museums, databases, web servers, and image galleries related to zoology.

**Web:**

**http://www.uwyo.edu/Lib/zoo.htm**

# Index

*Main subject headings are shown in **bold***

## C

## D

## E

## I

## J

## K



## L

## M

## P

## U

## X



## Y

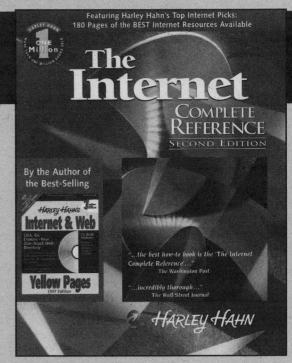

# Starting today, you can feel at home on the Internet

AT&T

## Introducing AT&T WorldNet$^{SM}$ Service

## A World of Possibilities...

With AT&T WorldNet$^{SM}$ Service, a world of possibilities awaits you. Discover new ways to stay in touch with the people, ideas, and information that are important to you at home and at work.

Make travel reservations at any time of the day or night. Access the facts you need to make key decisions. Pursue business opportunities on the AT&T Business Network. Explore new investment options. Play games. Research academic subjects. Stay abreast of current events. Participate in online newsgroups. Purchase merchandise from leading retailers. Send e-mail.

All you need is a computer with a mouse, a modem, a phone line, and the software enclosed with this mailing. We've taken care of the rest.

## If You Can Point and Click, You're There

Finding the information you want on the Internet with AT&T WorldNet Service is easier than you ever imagined it could be. That's because AT&T WorldNet Service integrates a specially customized version of the popular Netscape Navigator$^{TM}$ software with advanced Internet directories and search engines. The result is an Internet service that sets a new standard for ease of use — virtually everywhere you want to go is a point and click away.

**If you're not currently an AT&T Long Distance customer but would like to become one, please call 1 800 431-0800, ext. 21624.**

AT&T WorldNet Service's competitive pricing for 1997 can be obtained during the on-line registration process. Local, long distance, or 800 number access charges and additional access charges and/or taxes that may be imposed on subscribers or on AT&T WorldNet Service will apply to all usage.

### PC Minimum System Requirements

To run AT&T WorldNet Service, you need:

- An IBM-compatible personal computer with a 386 processor or better.
- Microsoft Windows 3.1x or Windows 95.
- 8MB RAM (16MB or more recommended).
- 11MB of free hard disk space.
- 14.4 bps (or faster) modem (28.8 bps is recommended).
- A standard phone line.

### Macintosh Minimum System Requirements

To run AT&T WorldNet Service, you need:

- Macintosh System 7.1 or higher.
- Open Transport architecture requires Version 1.1 or higher.
- 8MB of RAM (or more for better performance).
- 12MB of available hard disk space (15MB recommended).
- 14.4 bps modem connected to an outside phone line.

You will need to obtain system update software, known as the 7.5.3 revision II Patch, if your Macintosh computer:

- is a PCI PowerMac (7200,7500, 7600, 8500, 9500).
- is a 5300-based PowerBook.
- has PowerBook's Ram Doubler running or DOS - compatible software installed.

The software can be obtained from Apple by calling 1 800 293-6617 (Canada 1 800 361-6075) or via Apple's download FTP site located at: ftp://ftp.support.apple.com/pub/apple_sw_updates/US/Macintosh/System.

If your computer meets the requirements listed above, you're ready to install the AT&T WorldNet Service software in this package. It's a simple process and, of course, AT&T is ready to help you every step of the way.

## We're With You Every Step of the Way, 24 Hours a Day, 7 Days a Week

Nothing is more important to us than making sure that your Internet experience is a truly enriching and satisfying one. That's why our highly trained customer service representatives are available to answer your questions and offer assistance whenever you need it — 24 hours a day, 7 days a week. To reach AT&T WorldNet Customer Care, call **1 800 400-1447**.

## Installation Tips and Instructions

- If you have other Web browsers or online software, please consider uninstalling them according to vendor's instructions.
- At the end of installation, you may be asked to restart Windows. Don't attempt the registration process until you have done so.
- If you are experiencing modem problems trying to dial out, try different modem selections, such as Hayes Compatible. If you still have problems, please call Customer Care at **1 800 400-1447**.
- If you are installing AT&T WorldNet Service on a PC with Local Area Networking, please contact your LAN administrator for setup instructions.
- Follow the initial online prompts and/or start-up instructions given to you by the vendor product you purchased. These instructions will tell you how to start the installation of the AT&T WorldNet Service Software.
- Follow the on-screen instructions to install AT&T WorldNet Service Software on your computer.

When you have finished installing the software you may be prompted to restart your computer. Do so when prompted.

## Safeguard Your Online Purchases

By registering and continuing to charge your AT&T WorldNet Service to your AT&T Universal Card, you'll enjoy peace of mind whenever you shop the Internet. Should your account number be compromised on the Net, you won't be liable for any online transactions charged to your AT&T Universal Card by a person who is not an authorized user.*

*Today cardmembers may be liable for the first $50 of charges made by a person who is not an authorized user, which will not be imposed under this program as long as the cardmember notifies AT&T Universal Card of the loss within 24 hours and otherwise complies with the Cardmember Agreement. Refer to Cardmember Agreement for definition of authorized user.

## Setting Up Your WorldNet Account

The AT&T WorldNet Service Program group/folder will appear on your Windows desktop.

- Double-click on the AT&T WorldNet Registration icon.
- Follow the on-screen instructions and complete all the stages of registration.

After all the stages have been completed, you'll be prompted to dial into the network to complete the registration process. Make sure your modem and phone line are not in use.

## Registering With AT&T WorldNet Service

Once you have connected with the AT&T WorldNet online registration service, you will be presented with a series of screens that will confirm billing information and prompt you for additional account setup data.

The following is a list of registration tips and comments that will help you during the registration process.

I. Use registration code LISQIM631 if you are an AT&T Long Distance customer. Use registration code LISQIM632 if you use another long distance carrier.
II. We advise that you use all lowercase letters when assigning an e-mail ID and security code, since they are easier to remember.
III. Choose a special "security code" that you will use to verify who you are when you call Customer Care.
IV. If you make a mistake and exit the registration process prematurely, all you need to do is click on "Create New Account." Do not click on "Edit Existing Account."
V. When choosing your local access telephone number, you will be given several options. Please choose the one nearest to you. Please note that calling a number within your area does not guarantee that the call is free.

## Connecting to AT&T WorldNet Service

When you have finished registering with AT&T WorldNet Service, you are ready to make online connections.

- Make sure your modem and phone line are available.
- Double-click on the AT&T WorldNet Service icon.

Follow these steps whenever you wish to connect to AT&T WorldNet Service.

Explore our AT&T WorldNet Service Web site at: http://www.att.com/worldnet

AT&T

The enclosed software is not for export outside the U.S. and Canada.

# How to Use the *Harley Hahn's Internet & Web Yellow Pages* CD-ROM

The CD that accompanies this book contains a special electronic edition of *Harley Hahn's Internet & Web Yellow Pages* by Modern Age Books. Using the powerful Modern Age search engine, you can locate web sites, Usenet discussion groups, mailing lists, and other resources offline on your PC or Macintosh. You can then connect to the site of your choice using your browser.

## System Requirements

The *Harley Hahn's Internet & Web Yellow Pages* CD will run on any of the following computers: a Macintosh, Powerbook, or PowerPC Macintosh with System 7 or higher (8MB RAM); or a PC with Microsoft Windows 3.1, 3.11, or Windows 95 (8MB RAM). You can install the entire book on your hard drive for best performance or run it from the CD to conserve hard drive space.

## Installation

To use the CD, you must first install it on your system. The installation program gives you the option of installing the Modern Age Books edition of *Harley Hahn's Internet & Web Yellow Pages*, as well as AT&T WorldNet $^{SM}$ Service. (Please note that AT&T WorldNet software is operable only within the U.S.)

**If you encounter problems using the AT&T WorldNet Service, please reach AT&T WorldNet Customer Care at 1-800-400-1447. You may also call this number to obtain the Windows 95 version of the AT&T WorldNet Service software.**

To start the installation program, please choose the procedure below that is right for your system.

### Windows 3.x Users

1. Insert the CD-ROM into your CD drive.
2. From Program Manager, choose RUN from the File menu.
3. Type **d:\setup.exe** (or the appropriate drive letter) and press ENTER.
4. From the Product Selection Dialog box deselect any products you do not wish to install.
5. Click "Next" and follow the instructions on the screen.

### Windows 95 Users

1. Insert the CD-ROM into your CD drive.
2. From the Start menu choose RUN.
3. Type **d:\setup.exe** (or the appropriate drive letter) and press ENTER.
4. From the Product Selection Dialog box deselect any products you do not wish to install.
5. Click "Next" and follow the instructions on the screen.

### Macintosh Users

1. Insert the CD-ROM into your CD drive. The MA Books and AT&T Products folder will open.
2. To install the AT&T WorldNet Service, double-click on the Install AT&T WorldNet folder, then double-click on the Install AT&T WorldNet icon.
3. To install the electronic version of the book, drag and drop the Modern Age Books folder onto the hard drive icon.

## Starting the Program

Choose one of the following procedures to start your Modern Age Books electronic version of *Harley Hahn's Internet &Web Yellow Pages*:

### Windows 3.x Users

From the Program Manager, open the MAB (Modern Age Books) program group. Double-click the book icon to start the program.

### Windows 95 Users

Click the Start button, and then point to Programs. Point to Modern Age Books and click the book icon to start the program.

### Macintosh Users

Open the Modern Age Books folder and double-click on the book icon to start the program.

# Special Features

## Search Button

The Search button invokes a dialog box that allows you to search for information anywhere in the electronic book using words and phrases. An assisted search gives you additional help in finding what you are looking for.

## Direct Internet Connect Feature

Once you have located an Internet resource you can jump to it by clicking on its address with your mouse and launching your browser. This action takes you directly to the site.

- For telnet sites—once you are connected, type in the required password to logon.
- For list-server sites—type in the subscriber information requested before sending the message.

Note that once you launch your browser, you remain connected to the Internet until you Quit (Macintosh) or Exit (PC) via the browser's File menu. While the browser is active, you may return to the program at any time to search for additional resources. Clicking on a new address returns you to the browsers and to the new site you have selected.

# Electronic Books

To see more electronic books, come to the WebBook Marketplace web site:

**http://www.mabooks.com**

**WARNING: BEFORE OPENING THE DISC PACKAGE, CAREFULLY READ THE TERMS AND CONDITIONS OF THE FOLLOWING COPYRIGHT STATEMENT AND LIMITED CD-ROM WARRANTY.**

## Copyright Statement

This software is protected by both United States copyright law and international copyright treaty provision. Except as noted in the contents of the CD-ROM, you must treat this software just like a book. However, you may copy it into a computer to be used and you may make archival copies of the software for the sole purpose of backing up the software and protecting your investment from loss. By saying, "just like a book," The McGraw-Hill Companies, Inc. ("Osborne/McGraw-Hill") means, for example, that this software may be used by any number of people and may be freely moved from one computer location to another, so long as there is no possibility of its being used at one location or on one computer while it is being used at another. Just as a book cannot be read by two different people in two different places at the same time, neither can the software be used by two different people in two different places at the same time.

## Limited Warranty

Osborne/McGraw-Hill warrants the physical compact disc enclosed herein to be free of defects in materials and workmanship for a period of sixty days from the purchase date. If the CD included in your book has defects in materials or workmanship, please call McGraw-Hill at 1-800-217-0059, 9am to 5pm, Monday through Friday, Eastern Standard Time, and McGraw-Hill will replace the defective disc.

The entire and exclusive liability and remedy for breach of this Limited Warranty shall be limited to replacement of the defective disc, and shall not include or extend to any claim for or right to cover any other damages, including but not limited to, loss of profit, data, or use of the software, or special incidental, or consequential damages or other similar claims, even if Osborne/McGraw-Hill has been specifically advised of the possibility of such damages. In no event will Osborne/McGraw-Hill's liability for any damages to you or any other person ever exceed the lower of the suggested list price or actual price paid for the license to use the software, regardless of any form of the claim.

OSBORNE/McGRAW-HILL SPECIFICALLY DISCLAIMS ALL OTHER WARRANTIES, EXPRESS OR IMPLIED, INCLUDING BUT NOT LIMITED TO, ANY IMPLIED WARRANTY OF MERCHANTABILITY OR FITNESS FOR A PARTICULAR PURPOSE. Specifically, Osborne/McGraw-Hill make no representation or warranty that the software is fit for any particular purpose, and any implied warranty of merchantability is limited to the sixty-day duration of the Limited Warranty covering the physical disc only (and not the software), and is otherwise expressly and specifically disclaimed.

This limited warranty gives you specific legal rights; you may have others which may vary from state to state. Some states do not allow the exclusion of incidental or consequential damages, or the limitation on how long an implied warranty lasts, so some of the above may not apply to you.

This agreement constitutes the entire agreement between the parties relating to use of the Product. The terms of any purchase order shall have no effect on the terms of this Agreement. Failure of Osborne/McGraw-Hill to insist at any time on strict compliance with this Agreement shall not constitute a waiver of any rights under this Agreement. This Agreement shall be construed and governed in accordance with the laws of New York. If any provision of this Agreement is held to be contrary to law, that provision will be enforced to the maximum extent permissible, and the remaining provisions will remain in force and effect.

TECHNICAL SUPPORT: IF YOU HAVE A PROBLEM INSTALLING THE ELECTRONIC BOOK WHICH COMES ON THE CD-ROM, PLEASE CONTACT MODERN AGE BOOKS AT 617-440-0550. IF YOU HAVE QUESTIONS OR NEED ASSISTANCE WITH THE AT&T WORLDNET SM SERVICE SOFTWARE, PLEASE REACH AT&T WORLDNET CUSTOMER CARE AT 1-800-400-1447. AT&T WORLDNET SOFTWARE IS OPERABLE ONLY WITHIN U.S.